CANADIAN EDITION

Ecology

CONCEPTS & APPLICATIONS

Manuel C. Molles Jr.

University of New Mexico

James F. Cahill Jr.

University of Alberta

McGraw-Hill
Ryerson

Toronto • Montréal • Boston • Burr Ridge, IL • Dubuque, IA • Madison, WI • New York • San Francisco
St. Louis • Bangkok • Bogotá • Caracas • Kuala Lumpur • Lisbon • London • Madrid • Mexico City
Milan • New Delhi • Santiago • Seoul • Singapore • Sydney • Taipei

The McGraw·Hill Companies

McGraw-Hill
Ryerson

Ecology:
Concepts & Applications
Canadian Edition

Copyright © 2008 by McGraw-Hill Ryerson Limited, a Subsidiary of The McGraw-Hill Companies. Copyright © 2008, 2005, 2002, 1999 by the McGraw-Hill Companies, Inc. All rights reserved. No part of this publication may be reproduced or transmitted in any form or by any means, or stored in a data retrieval system, without the prior written permission of McGraw-Hill Ryerson Limited, or in the case of photocopying or other reprographic copying, a licence from The Canadian Copyright Licensing Agency (Access Copyright). For an Access Copyright licence, visit www.accesscopyright.ca or call toll free to 1-800-893-5777.

ISBN-13: 978-0-07-096341-2
ISBN-10: 0-07-096341-X

1 2 3 4 5 6 7 8 9 10 QPD 0 9 8

Printed and bound in the U.S.A.

Care has been taken to trace ownership of copyright material contained in this text; however, the publisher will welcome any information that enables them to rectify any reference or credit for subsequent editions.

30%
Total PCW Recycled Fibre

This book is printed on ST Generation II, which contains 30% recycled post-consumer fibre, is EcoLogo certified and manufactured using biogas energy.

EDITORIAL DIRECTOR: Joanna Cotton
EXECUTIVE SPONSORING EDITOR: Leanna MacLean
MARKETING MANAGER: Claire Morrison
MANAGING EDITOR, DEVELOPMENT: Jennifer DiDomenico
EDITORIAL ASSOCIATE: Stephanie Hess
SENIOR PRODUCTION COORDINATOR: Jennifer Hall
SENIOR SUPERVISING EDITOR: Anne Nellis
COPY EDITOR: Cat Haggert
COVER DESIGN: ArtPlus Limited
INTERIOR DESIGN: ArtPlus Limited
COVER IMAGE CREDITS: (butterfly) © Brad Perks; (fall scene) © Christine Lomas Photography;
(mountains) © Lee Canfield/SuperStock; (winter) © Lucidio Studio, Inc./SuperStock
COMPOSITION: ArtPlus Limited
PRINTER: Quebecor Printing Dubuque

Library and Archives Canada Cataloguing in Publication

Molles, Manuel C. (Manuel Carl), 1948-
    Ecology : concepts & applications / Manuel C. Molles, Jr., James F.
Cahill Jr. — Canadian ed.

Includes bibliographical references and index.
ISBN-13: 978-0-07-096341-2

    1. Ecology--Textbooks. 2. Ecology. I. Cahill, James F. II. Title.

QH541.M64 2008   577   C2007-903275-3

Dedication

To Mary Anne and Misha

M. M.

For Grayson and Liam

J. C.

Brief Contents

Contents

Manuel C. Molles Jr. is an emeritus Professor of Biology at the University of New Mexico, where he has been a member of the faculty and curator in the Museum of Southwestern Biology since 1975 and where he continues to teach ecology and advise graduate students. He received his B.S. from Humboldt State University and his Ph.D. from the Department of Ecology and Evolutionary Biology at the University of Arizona. Seeking to broaden his geographical perspective, he has taught and conducted ecological research in Latin America, the Caribbean, and Europe. He was awarded a Fulbright Research Fellowship to conduct research on river ecology in Portugal and has held visiting professor appointments in the Department of Zoology at the University of Coimbra, Portugal, in the Laboratory of Hydrology at the Polytechnic University of Madrid, Spain, and at the University of Montana's Flathead Lake Biological Station.

Originally trained as a marine ecologist and fisheries biologist, the author has worked mainly on river and riparian ecology at the University of New Mexico. His research has covered a wide range of ecological levels, including behavioural ecology, population biology, community ecology, ecosystem ecology, biogeography of stream insects, and the influence of a large-scale climate system (El Niño) on the dynamics of southwestern river and riparian ecosystems. His current research concerns the influence of climate change and climatic variability on the dynamics of populations and communities along steep gradients of temperature and moisture in the mountains of the Southwest. Throughout his career, Dr. Molles has attempted to combine research, teaching, and service, involving undergraduate as well as graduate students in his ongoing projects. Dr. Manuel Molles was named Teacher of the Year by the University of New Mexico for 1995–96 and Potter Chair in Plant Ecology in 2000.

James F. Cahill Jr. or "JC" as he is generally known, is an Associate Professor of Biology at the University of Alberta, where he has been a member of the faculty since 1999. He received his B.A. in Cultural Ecology and Biology from Trinity College (CT) in 1992 and his Ph.D. in Ecology from the University of Pennsylvania in 1997.

JC was trained as an experimental plant ecologist, originally interested primarily in the role competition for soil resources plays in structuring plant communities. Since arriving in Alberta in 1999, he has been studying a diversity of ecological questions in the surrounding native prairies. Although still interested in the causes and consequences of competition, his current research includes plant–pollinator interactions; plant–fungal interactions; insect and large mammal grazing, plant foraging, and behavioural ecology; and the evolution of ecological processes. Currently JC is also leading a project investigating the combined impacts of grazing and climate change on the sustainability of Canada's grasslands. To address these questions he maintains an active research lab including graduate students, undergraduates, and even high school students in the summers.

Teaching and service are important aspects of the job for JC. He has taught a wide variety of courses for undergraduate and graduate students at the University of Alberta, including Principles of Ecology, Fundamentals of Plant Biology, Plant Ecology, Methods in Plant Ecology, Plant-Animal Interactions, Ecology of Belowground Communities, Current Topics in Plant Ecology, and Advanced Ecology. JC also serves as an Associate Editor for the scientific journals, *The Journal of Ecology* and *Plant Ecology*.

Preface

Environmental issues are of pressing concern to Canadians. Discussions of environmental sustainability and global responsibility are common in the news and among the Canadian public. Underlying these issues is the science of ecology, and informed decisions can only be made with a clear understanding of this scientific discipline. The rapidly increasing pace of discovery, and the ever-longer list of environmental concerns, makes the teaching of ecology very challenging. However, the importance of ecology to Canada, and to the world, requires us to meet this challenge. Ideally, an introduction to ecology should include the foundations of all its major subdisciplines, yet including such breadth, and developing it to sufficient depth, is difficult. The Canadian edition of *Ecology: Concepts & Applications* provides careful organization, clear and relevant Canadian and global examples, and a conceptual approach to ease this task.

Introductory Audience

We have written this book for students taking their first undergraduate course in ecology. We have assumed that students in this one-semester course have some knowledge of basic chemistry and mathematics and that they have had a course in general biology that included introductions to physiology, biological diversity, and evolution.

Canadian Perspective

The U.S. edition of *Ecology: Concepts & Applications* is a strong book, widely used and receiving outstanding reviews from students and teachers. So, why mess with success? In my (JC) experience teaching in Canada, I have found many students simply do not believe ecology is relevant to their lives and study. At first, I was dumbfounded, as environmental issues are central to the Canadian economy (resource extraction), many Canadians holiday in natural areas, and local, national, and global environmental issues regularly receive significant media time and public debate. There are likely few countries in which ecology is more relevant to the lives of students, and yet many students leave introductory ecology courses uninspired and not understanding its relevance in the "real world." I believe part of the problem is the reliance on textbooks that predominantly draw their examples from the United States. Students learn better when they can relate to the information—places they have visited, names they recognize, issues they, too, are concerned about. My hope is that by showing students examples of ecology in Canada, they will be better able to understand the relevance of this discipline to their lives. Because of this belief, I took on the challenge of trying to make an already strong book even better for the students living and learning in Canada.

A rule I set for myself in adapting this edition was that I would not replace strong science with weaker science, just for the sake of increasing Canadian content. Fortunately, I was never faced with such a choice, as there is an amazing breadth and depth of outstanding ecological research conducted in Canada, and by researchers at Canadian universities. I have been able to keep the "foundational" examples that we are all familiar with, while adding many other examples that have been unfairly overlooked in the U.S. editions of textbooks. Without even trying, I have included an example from researchers at nearly every Canadian university, and studies that are relevant to all provinces and territories. Additionally, most existing ecology textbooks only briefly touch on the boreal forest and arctic regions. These areas are central to Canada, and are much more fully covered in this edition.

Canada also has a history of strong research in evolutionary biology, often with an ecological emphasis. In addition to adding more locally-relevant examples to all chapters, I have also greatly enhanced the evolutionary content of this book. I emphasize that ecology and evolution are inextricably linked, and many environmental issues can only be understood when evolutionary pressures are considered.

Based upon comments from reviewers, these changes have resulted in a strong general ecology textbook grounded in Canadian research and examples.

Unique Approach

In an address at the 1991 meeting of the Ecological Society of America in San Antonio, Texas, eminent ecologist Paul Risser challenged ecology instructors to focus their attention on the major concepts of the field. If we subdivide a large and dynamic subject, such as ecology, too finely, we cannot cover it in one or two academic terms. Risser proposed that by focusing on major concepts, however, we may provide students with a robust framework of the discipline upon which they can build.

This book attempts to address Risser's challenge. **Each chapter is organized around two to five major concepts, presenting the student with a manageable and meaningful synthesis of the subject.** Due to the complexity of ecology, beginning students can often absorb a few central concepts well, but then get lost in a sea of details. In this book, each concept is supported by case studies and real research results that provide evidence for the concept. This approach also introduces students to the research methods used in the various areas of ecology. Wherever possible, the original research and the scientists who did the research are presented. Allowing the scientists who created this field to emerge from the background and lead students through the discipline breathes life into the subject and helps students retain information. This approach also helps students understand that science is not just facts; instead it consists of active debates, hard work, and real people.

New to This Edition

All 23 chapters of the book have been extensively revised based upon extensive reviews by Ecology instructors in Canada. In addition to enhancing and highlighting Canadian content, the material has been updated, concepts have been added or replaced as needed, and the overall presentation has been streamlined.

All chapters now include an "Ecology In Action" box in which we highlight how the ecological principles presented in a chapter are being used in real-world situations in Canada. Examples include human-induced evolution in natural populations, fishery management and collapse, using behavioural ecology to keep elk out of the Banff townsite, and many others. These new boxes emphasize to students that ecology is not an abstract science, but instead central to solving real issues in Canada and around the world.

The presentation has been reformatted to help students orient to the flow of information. These changes are evidenced by a reordering of chapters, as well as by detailed changes within each chapter. For example, evolution is now considered foundational to the study of ecology, and has been moved to the first section of the book. This allows a much greater linkage between ecology and evolution in the subsequent chapters. The concepts in each chapter are now numbered both in the first listing of chapter concepts and at the beginning of each section in which the concepts are discussed. The concept numbers are repeated in the concept review questions that conclude each concept section. Thus, the beginning and end of each concept is clearly signalled for the student.

Statistical methods have been consolidated and expanded into a single appendix, "Building a Statistical Toolbox." Statistics are both critical to the science of ecology and often a hindrance to teaching ecology to reluctant students. The statistics appendix is now written in a friendly tone, describing the most common statistics used in ecology. For those instructors who incorporate statistics into their lectures, this appendix could be an early assigned reading. For those instructors who reduce the quantitative aspects of ecology, the appendix could serve as a resource for the students. These changes enhance the flow of information within each chapter, while also giving instructors flexibility in how they present this information to their students.

Increased linkage between ecology and evolutionary biology. Understanding many ecological concepts requires an understanding of evolutionary biology. Evolution has been given increased emphasis in nearly all chapters of the text. This refocus provides a thread that helps link the chapters together, facilitating understanding for the students.

Hundreds of study questions have been added throughout the text to help students review the major concepts. The "Concept Review" questions that conclude the presentation of each concept are designed to help students think critically about content and to encourage them to reflect on the design of research projects.

Organized Around Key Concepts

An evolutionary perspective forms the foundation of the entire textbook, as it is needed to support understanding of major concepts. The textbook begins with a brief introduction to the nature and history of the discipline of ecology, followed by Section I, which includes three chapters on natural history—life on land, life in water, and a chapter on evolution. Sections II through VI build a hierarchical perspective through the traditional subdisciplines of ecology: Section II concerns the ecology of individuals; Section III focuses on population ecology; Section IV presents the ecology of interactions; Section V summarizes community and ecosystem ecology; and finally, Section VI discusses large-scale ecology and includes chapters on landscape, geographic, and global ecology. These topics were first introduced in Section I within a natural history context. In summary, the book begins with the natural history of the planet, considers portions of the whole in the middle chapters, and ends with another perspective of the entire planet in the concluding chapter.

Significant Changes

All chapters have been extensively revised to provide more Canadian content and to update the material presented. However, the central concepts of several chapters have been significantly altered, warranting particular notice.

In **Chapter 4**, we have expanded our discussion of evolutionary biology, and have added a discussion of isolating mechanisms and speciation.

Chapter 8 is now a full chapter on behavioural ecology, rather than social relations. We provide a broad overview of central concepts in this subdiscipline. This level of treatment is unique among introductory ecology textbooks.

Chapter 9 presents life-histories and the niche, serving as a synthesis of the chapters in Section II. A focus on trade-offs helps provide a framework for understanding these multi-dimensional concepts.

Chapter 15 presents mutualism and parasitism as a continuum, rather than discrete interactions. The discussion of mutualisms has been greatly updated and given a strong theoretical framework. We have added a discussion of disease ecology and the use of host–parasite models to understand human disease.

Concept 4.1 Review

1. What is a fundamental evolutionary implication of the large amounts of genetic variation commonly found in natural populations?
2. What do the results of Tracy's experiments indicate about variation in body size among *Sauromalus* populations?
3. Can V_E be greater than V_G for a trait related to an organism's fitness? Explain.

Chapter 20 provides an in-depth and up-to-date overview of landscape ecology. We have emphasized the science and biological mechanisms involved in landscape processes, rather than pattern description. This level of treatment is not found in other introductory ecology textbooks.

Chapter 23 has been modified to highlight the importance that land-use changes have played in determining the current distribution of life on the planet. This provides a good basis from which we can emphasize the role climate change is having, and will continue to have in the future.

Features Designed with the Student in Mind

The features of this textbook are unique and were carefully planned to enhance the students' comprehension of ecology. All chapters beyond the introductory Chapter 1 are based on a distinctive learning system, featuring the following key components:

Introduction: The introduction to each chapter presents the student with the flavour of the subject and important background information. Some introductions include historical events related to the subject; others present an example of an ecological process. All attempt to engage students and draw them into the discussion that follows.

Concepts: The goal of this book is to build a foundation of ecological knowledge around key concepts. These key concepts are listed after the chapter introduction to alert the student to the major topics to follow, and to provide a place where the student can find a list of the important points of each chapter. The sections in which concepts are discussed reinforce

concepts with a focus on published studies. This case-study approach supports the concepts with evidence, and introduces students to the methods and people that have created the discipline of ecology.

Illustrations: A great deal of effort has been put into the development of illustrations, both photographs and line art. Over 250 new photographs, drawings, and graphs appear in this edition. The goal has been to create more effective pedagogical tools through skillful design and use of colour, and to rearrange the traditional presentation of information in figures and captions. Much explanatory material is located within the illustrations, providing students with key information where they need it most.

Ecology In Action Boxes: Many undergraduate students want to know how abstract ideas and general relationships can be applied to the ecological problems facing us all. They are concerned with the practical side of ecology and want to know more about the tools of science. Including applications in each chapter motivates students to learn more of the underlying principles of ecology. In addition, it seems that environmental problems are now so numerous and so pressing that they have erased a once easy distinction between general and applied ecology.

Ecological Tools: To understand the results of science requires an understanding of the methods of science. We believe it is important for students to understand that science is a process, not simply a list of facts. Therefore, in each chapter we highlight a method, or set of methods, that are used to address questions relevant to the concepts presented in that chapter. These methods are varied, including sampling designs, game theory, stable isotopes, and many others.

Ecology In Action

Impacts of Mycorrhizae on Forest Sustainability

As we have discussed, mycorrhizae have the potential to impact a plant's life positively or negatively, and the position along the mutualism–exploitation continuum depends upon the exact costs and benefits at any particular time. This issue has enormous implications for agriculture and forestry, and here we will discuss two examples in which mycorrhizal interactions may have significant consequences for forest regeneration and community composition.

Suzanne Simard, of the University of British Columbia, has studied the ecology of ectomycorrhizae and their potential impact on forest dynamics extensively. Forest dynamics are an important issue for the forest industry, and having a detailed understanding of the factors that influence regeneration can be of broad economic importance. One of the interesting aspects of mycorrhizae is that many of the fungi involved are generalists, able to colonize the roots of different species of plants. This aspect of fungal biology is not restricted to pots in a greenhouse, but also can occur in the field, where you can regularly find one individual fungus associated with the roots of many individuals of plant species—simultaneously. Simard developed an elegant design to test whether these shared connections could result in sugar moving toward or away from some plants (Simard 1997). In other words, could some plants partially parasitize others through these shared mycorrhizal connections? In her study she used three focal species, *Betula papyrifera, Pseudotsuga menziesii,* and *Thuja plicata* (fig. 15.23), all of which are important to the forestry industry of British Columbia. Simard planted young plants of these three species together in forest soil, and after some time, fed the leaves of the plants with ¹³C or ¹⁴C. Why did she use these tracers? Very simply, to follow the carbon. For example, if she fed *Betula* with ¹³C, but found ¹³C in the other plants, that would tell her the carbon moved. But does that mean it moved through hyphae? No. It is certainly possible that the carbon went from the leaves, to the roots, and then entered the soil as dead roots, or root exudate. Part of the elegance of her design is that she included *Thuja* in her study. This species does not share fungal species with *Betula* and *Pseudotsuga,* and so the amount of labelled carbon in *Thuja* would indicate

Figure 15.23 A number of tree species can be interconnected by mycorrhizal fungi in the forests of British Columbia.

how much passed through the plants to the soils, with any excess found in the other species coming through mycorrhizal connections.

Why did she use two tracers in this study? She wasn't interested in simply whether carbon moved from one plant to another (as prior studies have shown it could); instead she

Ecological Tools

Biomes of Canada and Winter Ecology

In the Ecological Tools sections of this book, we will discuss how some specific research method allows ecologists to answer ecological questions. Without the right tools, research simply can not progress. As a result, the development of new research tools often results in bursts of research activity. As natural history is a key tool for ecologists, studying ecology in Canada generally need to understand the natural history of Canada. Here we provide a brief overview of how the scientists describe the ecological landscape of Canada.

Ecozones of Canada

In this chapter we described how different regions of the planet experience difference climates, and how this is associated with the development of different natural biomes. Few countries will contain all of the biomes of the world, and instead are generally home to just a few. However, as we mentioned previously, no two communities within a single biome will be identical, and instead there can be substantial variation in species composition among locations within a single biomes. In Canada, this has been recognized, and thus the National Ecological Framework for Canada (Ecological Stratification Working Group 1996) divides Canada not into a small number of biomes, but instead into 15 terrestrial (and 5 marine) *ecozones* (fig. 2.41), which are themselves divided into more than 200 *ecoregions* (fig. 2.42), which can be further divided into *ecodistricts!* The largest level of organization used in Canada, the ecozone, is roughly analogous to the more widely used concept of biomes, with major areas classified based upon dominant vegetation and climate. Ecoregions and ecodistricts allow finer classification, which can be helpful tools for landscape planning and conservation.

In figure 2.41, you can see how using the ecozone framework allows for more specificity than the coarse tool of biomes.

For example, consider the boreal biome, which would include the boreal shield ecozone, the boreal plain ecozone, and the boreal cordillera ecozone. The boreal shield is the largest ecozone in Canada and is strongly influenced by the underlying bedrock. In contrast, the boreal plains is considered a different ecozone due to a relative lack of influence by bedrock. These both differ from the boreal cordillera, which has a large amount of mountainous terrain and is influenced by weather patterns from the Pacific Ocean. These differences have important consequences for the organisms that live within these three zones. An ecologist studying the boreal forest of Canada needs to take into account these differences in topography, soils, and vegetation to understand the ecology of a particular location. These basic differences in natural history can prove to be a critical step to understanding variations in ecological function among communities in a single biome. However, if a single country can have 15 ecozones, you can only imagine how many may be found across the globe, and thus the rough categories of biomes are critical for providing an overview of this variation. For larger-scale questions, broad divisions of biomes are helpful; for smaller-scale questions, a finer resolution is needed. A critical ecological tool is having the appropriate scale of natural history knowledge needed to answer your specific ecological question.

Regardless of whether Canada is divided into a few biomes, more ecozones, or even more ecoregions, one thing is clear. Compared to many other areas on the planet, Canada is cold and many areas receive substantial amounts of snow. As a result, one important tool of many Canadian ecologists is an understanding of the natural history of winter. Due to the importance of winter to the organisms that live in Canada, many aspects of winter ecology will be presented throughout the text. Here we provide the story of one species, the Black-Capped Chickadee.

End-of-Chapter Material:

- *Summary* The chapter summary reviews the main points of the content. The concepts around which each chapter is organized are boldfaced and redefined in the summary to reemphasize the main points of the chapter.

- *Review Questions* The review questions are designed to help students think more deeply about each concept and to reflect on alternative views. They also provide a place to fill in any remaining gaps in the information presented and take students beyond the foundation established in the main body of the chapter.

- *Suggested Readings* Each chapter ends with a list of suggested readings. Though all of the readings offer the student coverage beyond the chapter content, they have been chosen to serve a variety of purposes. Some are books that provide a broad overview; others are papers that trace the development of particular topics or controversies in ecology. We have provided a brief description and rationale for each.

End-of-Book Material:

- *Appendix* A new, student-friendly appendix, "Building a Statistical Toolbox," appears at the end of the textbook to give instructors flexibility in terms of how and when to include statistics in their course. Two additional appendices are available on the Online Learning Centre at www.mcgrawhill.ca/olc/molles: "Statistical Tables" and "Answers to Concept Review Questions."

- *Glossary*

- *References* References are an important part of any scientific work and we give credit to the researchers whose hard work made this book possible.

- *Index*

Teaching and Learning Supplements

Teaching Supplements for Instructors

Your Integrated Learning Sales Specialist is a McGraw-Hill Ryerson representative who has the experience, product knowledge, training, and support to help you assess and integrate any of our products, technology, and services into your course for optimum teaching and learning performance. Whether it's using our test bank software, helping your students improve their grades, or putting your entire course online, your *i*Learning Sales Specialist is there to help you do it. Contact your local *i*Learning Sales Specialist today to learn how to maximize all of McGraw-Hill Ryerson's resources!

We want to help bring your teaching to life using our products and services. We do this by integrating technology, events, conferences, training, and more into services surrounding the textbook. We call it *i*Services. For more information, please contact your *i*Learning Sales Specialist.

Instructor's Resource CD-ROM
(ISBN: 978-0-07-097330-5;
MHID: 0-07-097330-X)

Supplements featured on this CD-ROM include a computerized test bank, which allows instructors to search for questions by topic, format, or difficulty level, and edit existing questions or add new ones. Word files of the test bank are included for those instructors who prefer to work outside of the test-generator software. Other assets on the Instructor's Resource CD-ROM include classroom activities, PowerPoint slides, and art and photos from the textbook.

Online Learning Centre (OLC)
(www.mcgrawhill.ca/olc/molles)

This text-specific Web site offers an extensive array of teaching tools. In addition to all of the student assets available, this site includes:

- Answers to review questions
- Class activities
- PowerPoint lecture presentations
- Interactive world maps
- Digital image bank (full-colour digital files of all illustrations)

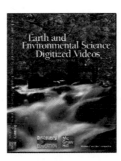

Earth and Environmental Science DVD by Discovery Channel Education
(ISBN: 978-0-07-352541-9;
MHID: 0-07-352541-3)

Begin your class with a quick peek at science in action. The exciting NEW DVD by Discovery Channel Education offers 50 short (3–5 minute) videos on topics ranging from conservation to volcanoes. Search by topic and download into your PowerPoint lecture.

McGraw-Hill's Biology Digitized Videos
(ISBN: 978-0-07-312155-0;
MHID: 0-07-312155-X)

Licensed from some of the highest quality life science video producers in the world, these brief video clips on DVD range in length from 15 seconds to two minutes and cover all areas of general biology, from cells to ecosystems. Engaging and informative, McGraw-Hill's digitized biology videos will help capture students' interest while illustrating key biological concepts, applications, and processes.

Learning Supplements for Students

Online Learning Centre (OLC)
(www.mcgrawhill.ca/olc/molles)

This text-specific Web site offers a wide variety of student resources providing many opportunities to master the core concepts in ecology. Learn more about the exciting features provided for students through the *Ecology: Concepts & Applications* Web site:

- Practice quizzing
- Hyperlinks on chapter topics
- Links to professional, educational, and governmental organizations
- Ecology/environmental science issues world map
- Periodic table
- Key term flashcards
- Appendices: "Statistical Tables" and "Answers to Concept Review Questions"

Acknowledgments

A complete list of the people who have helped me with this project would be impossibly long, and thus I can only mention a few individuals here. First, I would like to thank Manuel Molles for providing me with the opportunity to work from what I consider to be an unbelievably strong starting point. The devotion he has clearly put into this textbook has served as an example to me of what is possible if one works hard enough.

I wish to acknowledge the broad ecological research community in Canada. I have been overwhelmed by the generosity of spirit and willingness to help me complete this project. Not once was I turned away in my requests for photos, information, or reading drafts of sections. This project could not have been done without such support, and I am grateful to be part of this supportive community of scientists.

Thank you to the many reviewers of this Canadian edition, listed below, who have given much of their time and expertise to help improve this textbook. I have been consistently awed by the breadth and depth of comments received. Their comments have greatly enhanced the quality of this book, and for that, I am grateful.

Shelley Arnott, Queen's University
Robert Bailey, University of Western Ontario
Barbara L. Barnes, Lakehead University
Dawn Bazely, York University
R. Mark Brigham, University of Regina
Brian Hartwick, Simon Fraser University
Stephan Heard, University of New Brunswick
Leland J. Jackson, University of Calgary
Jeremy T. Kerr, University of Ottawa

Herbert J. Kronzucker, University of Toronto
Richard Lewis, Grant MacEwan College
Scott M. Ramsay, Wilfrid Laurier University
Shane Jan Roersma, Lethbridge Community College
Peter Ryser, Laurentian University
William M. Tonn, University of Alberta
Michael Weis, University of Windsor

During the development of this adaptation I relied quite heavily on several colleagues who freely shared their ideas and expertise, despite my constant barrage of questions, including: Lee Foote, Susan Hannon, Steve Heard, Rich Moses, Jan Murie, Heather Proctor, Bill Tonn, and Rolf Vinebrooke. Thank you to the many current and former graduate and undergraduate students in my lab who frequently gave of their time to discuss aspects of the book, and who were able to quickly adapt to my suddenly busier schedule. In particular I thank Steve Kembel, Eric Lamb, Gord McNickle, and Bryon Shore.

I also acknowledge the skilful guidance throughout the publishing process given by many individuals associated with McGraw-Hill Ryerson during this project, including: Leanna MacLean, Executive Editor; Jennifer Bastarache, Developmental Editor; Jennifer DiDomenico, Managing Editor, Development; Anne Nellis, Senior Supervising Editor; and Cat Haggert, copy editor. Particular thanks to Lindsey Carmichael, whose assistance organizing images, reading drafts, and providing general support helped me most when I thought this project was just too much.

I offer particular thanks to my friends and family who have offered unfailing support during this project. These people have been a wonderful group, and I regret not being able to list them all here. Instead, I name just a few, including: Jennifer Alabiso, the fearsome foursome: Liam and Grayson Alabiso-Cahill and Erica and Kieran St. Clair, Teena Cahill and Brooks Dyer, Jim and Ellen Cahill, Mia Cahill and Matt Sanidas, Andrew Cahill and Meaghan Shaughnessy, Benoit Rivard and Cathy Wrightson, Cam Wild and Simita Schwartzberg, and Clive Martin. Oh ... to think they thought they had seen me stressed before I started this project! Finally, I offer my thanks to Colleen St. Clair, the love of my life, for support and encouragement throughout this project. Sometimes it's true when people say they couldn't have done it without you.

James F. Cahill, Jr.

Chapter 1

Introduction:
What Is Ecology?

Outline

hat is ecology? Derived from the Greek word *oikos* (house), **ecology** can be defined as the branch of science dedicated to the study of relationships between organisms and the environment. Humans have been students of ecology as long as we have existed as a species. The earliest hunters and gatherers had to be familiar with the habits of their prey. They also had to know where to find food plants and when they would ripen. Farmers and ranchers had to be aware of how variations in weather and soils might affect their crops and livestock. Farmers also had to understand how yields would change depending upon what plants grew together, and how best to control pests and pathogens. All of this is ecology, and the needs of people to understand the natural world millennia ago continue to this day. A modern hunter, rancher, or farmer who does not understand the patterns of nature will not be successful. A society that ignores ecological changes is at risk of losing the services ecosystems provide.

Most people no longer live in rural areas surrounded by large expanses of natural areas. Instead the human population is increasingly centred in cities and urban areas. Does this mean that ecology itself is disappearing? No. Ecological interactions and processes do not end at park boundaries, and instead they occur in all systems, be they agricultural, urban, rural, or wild. Cities are not sterile areas devoid of any life other than people. Instead, cities contain an amazingly diverse set of flora and fauna, spread in a patchwork of parks, golf-courses, tree-lined boulevards, household and community gardens, and a variety of other areas. Natural selection is as strong a force in cities as in pristine natural areas, and how individual organisms interact with their local environment influences their success. This too is ecology.

Taking a step back, we see that cities are just one part of a larger landscape, made up of a mixture of land uses such as agriculture, protected wilderness, and urban areas. Organisms move in and out of these patches, corridors, and islands. Plants spread pollen and seed across vast distances, with potential movement of genes and seed across the landscape. No single area on the landscape is in complete isolation, and indeed, how land is used in one area can influence the interactions among organisms and their environment in another. This too is ecology.

Taking an even broader view of geographic regions and global patters, we see changes in temperature, varied patterns of precipitation, and altered air and water circulation. We see grasslands disappearing in the face of agricultural expansion, fisheries collapsing, and nitrogen and other chemicals falling from the sky as a consequence of industrial development. These changes to the environment will influence organisms of all types across the planet. This too is ecology.

Behind the simple definition of ecology lies a broad scientific discipline that almost defies definition. Ecologists may study individual organisms, entire grasslands or lakes, individual countries, or even the whole planet. The measurements made by ecologists include counts of individuals, rates of reproduction, spatial patterns of distribution, and rates of processes such as photosynthesis and decomposition. Ecology is an interdisciplinary science, and ecologists generally need to know as much about plant biology, animal biology, and microbiology as they do about geography, soil science, chemistry, and physics. While most people tend to think of ecologists as men and women out in the field, some of the most important advances have come from ecologists who conduct lab experiments and those who build theoretical models and computer simulations. Clearly, our simple definition of *ecology* does not communicate the great breadth of the discipline or the diversity of its practitioners.

Although ecology is broad as a scientific discipline, it does have some limits. Perhaps most importantly, ecology is a science. It is not a political philosophy, a way of life, nor does being an ecologist mean that you necessarily recycle or even enjoy eating granola. This does not mean that ecologists cannot advocate policy decisions based upon their scientific knowledge, nor does it mean that ecologists are to be excluded from political debate and environmental activism. Instead, those actions (which can be called environmental activism) may be done by ecologists, but they are not part of the science of ecology.

Similarly, ecology is not simply about knowing the names of the birds, bees, and plants that you see outside. That is natural history. As we will discuss in chapters 2 and 3, natural history serves as a foundation for much ecological research; however, in itself it is not generally considered part of the science of ecology. Ecology is about understanding the mechanisms causing the patterns that occur in the natural world. Natural history generally stops at describing the patterns.

Even within these limits, the science of ecology covers substantial intellectual terrain. To get a better idea of what ecology is, let us briefly review the scope of the discipline.

Overview of Ecology

The science of ecology addresses relationships ranging from those of individual organisms to factors influencing the state of the entire biosphere. This broad range of subjects can be arranged as levels in a hierarchy of ecological organization, such as that imbedded in the brief table of contents and sections II to VI of this book. Figure 1.1 attempts to display such a hierarchy graphically, including the relationships of the various levels to each other and to the types of problems addressed by the various subdisciplines of ecology.

Historically, the ecology of individuals, which is presented at the base of figure 1.1, has been the domain of **physiological ecology** and **behavioural ecology**. Physiological ecologists have emphasized the physiological, functional, and anatomical mechanisms by which organisms solve problems posed by physical and chemical variation in the environment. Behavioural ecologists have focused principally on the ways that plants and animals use behaviour to deal with environmental variation. However, the distinction between physiological ecology and behavioural ecology is often blurred. For instance, both behavioural ecologists and physiological ecologists study the temperature relations and the energy and nutrient relations of organisms. Both subdisciplines are strongly guided by evolutionary theory.

There is a strong conceptual linkage between studies of the ecology of individuals and population studies, particularly where they concern evolutionary processes. **Population ecology** is centred on the factors influencing population structure and process, where a population is a group of individuals of a single species inhabiting a defined area. The processes studied by population ecologists include adaptations, extinction, the distribution and abundance of species, population growth and regulation, and variation in the reproductive ecology of species. Population ecologists are particularly interested in how these processes are influenced by the environment, including nonbiological and biological components of the environment.

Bringing biological components of the environment into the picture takes us to the next level of organization studied by ecologists, the ecology of interactions such as predation, parasitism, mutualism, and competition. Some ecologists that study interactions between species emphasize the evolutionary effects of the interaction on the species involved. Others explore the effect the interaction has on the properties of ecological communities, such as species diversity.

The definition of an ecological community as an association of interacting species links **community ecology** with the ecology of interactions. Community and **ecosystem ecology** have a great deal in common, since both are concerned with the factors controlling multispecies systems. However, the objects of their study are slightly different. While community ecologists concentrate on the organisms inhabiting an area, ecosystem ecologists include the ecological community in an area plus all of the physical and chemical factors influencing the community. One goal of ecosystem ecology is to understand the controls on nutrient cycling and energy flow through ecosystems.

To simplify their studies, ecologists have long attempted to identify and study isolated communities and ecosystems. However, all communities and ecosystems on earth are open systems subject to exchanges of materials, energy, and organisms with other communities and ecosystems. The study of these exchanges, especially among ecosystems, is the intellectual territory of **landscape ecology**. However, landscapes are not isolated either but part of geographical regions subject to large-scale and long-term regional processes. These regional processes are the subjects of **geographic ecology**. Geographic ecology in turn leads us to the largest spatial scale and highest level of ecological organization—the **biosphere,** which falls within the realm of global ecology.

In addition to organizing ecology by subdisciplines and spatial extent of study, we can see there is great variation in the temporal scale of ecological research. For example, physiological ecologists might be interested in how a small sub-canopy tree can alter its rate of photosynthesis in response to a 0.3 second burst of sunlight. Alternatively, that same researcher may want to explore the lifetime consequences of these short "sunflecks" on the plant's reproductive output. These are both questions in physiological ecology, but occur at completely different temporal scales. Ecological studies can occur at even longer time scales. For example, there is currently concern that the southern edge of the boreal forest will move as a function of climate change, atmospheric nitrogen deposition, and altered fire regimes. Such "migration" may take decades or even centuries. At even deeper time scales, fossil evidence shows shifts in ecological communities over millennia. As is likely apparent, different temporal scales of ecological processes will require completely different research methods.

While this description of ecology provides a brief preview of the material covered in this book, it is by necessity a rough sketch and highly abstract. To move beyond the abstraction represented by figure 1.1, we need to connect it to the work of the scientists that have created the discipline of ecology. To do so, let's briefly review the research approaches of several ecologists working at a broad range of ecological levels and time scales.

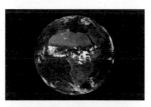

Biosphere

What role does concentration of atmospheric CO_2 play in the regulation of global temperature?

Region

How has geologic history influenced regional diversity within certain groups of organisms?

Landscape

What factors control the movement of mammals in a fragmented landscape?

Ecosystem

What factors control nutrient cycling?

Community

How does a competing species alter bison grazing behaviour?

Populations

What factors control population growth rates?

Individuals

How do plants or animals regulate their internal water balance?

Figure 1.1   Levels of ecological organization and examples of the kinds of questions asked by ecologists working at each level. These ecological levels correspond broadly to sections II to VI of this book.

The Ecology of Forest Birds: Using Field Studies to Test Theory

Robert MacArthur gazed intently through his binoculars. He was watching a small bird, called a warbler, searching for insects in the top of a spruce tree. To the casual observer it might have seemed that MacArthur was a weekend bird-watcher. Yes, he was intensely interested in the birds he was watching, but he was just as interested in testing ecological theory.

The year was 1955, and MacArthur was studying the ecology of five species of warblers that live together in the spruce forests of northeastern North America. All five warbler species, Cape May (*Dendroica tigrina*), yellow-rumped (*D. coronata*), black-throated green (*D. virens*), blackburnian (*D. fusca*), and bay-breasted (*D. castanea*), are about the same size and shape and feed on insects. Theory predicted that two species with identical ecological requirements would compete with each other and that, as a consequence, they could not live in the same environment indefinitely. However, MacArthur could observe them living together, and he wanted to understand how species with apparently similar ecological requirements could coexist.

The question of what factors allow for the coexistence of the five warbler species falls within the realm of community ecology. Additionally, MacArthur was interested in patterns that he could observe during a few years of field research, and thus he was working in a short-to-moderate time scale. MacArthur's work would prove to be a landmark study, serving as a model for future generations of ecologists. At first it may not be clear why a study of five bird species could be of such importance. However, underneath the specifics of his study was a strong research question: what factors allow, or prevent, species coexistence. How MacArthur was able to conduct a scientific study, as opposed to simply documenting natural history, will become more clear as we discuss the details of his work.

The warblers fed mainly by gleaning insects from the bark and foliage of trees. MacArthur predicted that these warblers might be able to coexist and not compete with each other if they fed on insects living in different zones within trees. To map where the warblers fed, he subdivided trees into vertical and horizontal zones. He then carefully recorded the amount of time warblers spent feeding in each.

MacArthur's prediction proved to be correct. His quantitative observations demonstrated that the five warbler species in his study area fed in different zones in spruce trees. As figure 1.2 shows, the Cape May warbler fed mainly among new needles and buds at the tops of trees. The feeding zone of the blackburnian warbler overlapped broadly with that of the Cape May warbler but extended farther down the tree. The black-throated green warbler fed toward the trees' interiors. The bay-breasted warbler concentrated its feeding in the interior of trees. Finally, the yellow-rumped warbler fed mostly on the ground and low in the trees. MacArthur's observations showed that though these warblers live in the same forest, they extract food from different parts of that forest. He concluded that feeding in different zones may reduce competition among the warblers of spruce forests. Although to a casual observer it would appear as though these five bird species were feeding on the same food (insects) in the same locations (spruce trees) at the same time, close study by MacArthur showed they subdivided their environment by having slightly different feeding behaviours. This study is a clear example

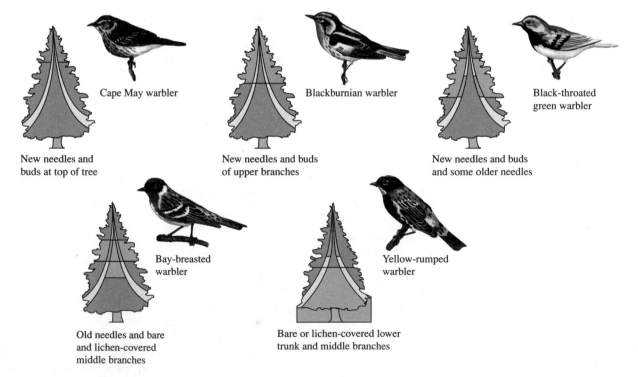

Figure 1.2   Warbler feeding zones. The several warbler species that coexist in the forests of northeastern North America feed in distinctive zones within spruce trees.

that the spatial scale of observation and study can greatly impact the results of the study. What matters here is how the birds perceive the trees (multiple microsites) rather than how people initially perceive the tree (a homogeneous unit).

MacArthur's study (1958) of foraging by warblers is a true classic in ecology. However, like most studies it raised as many questions as it answered. Scientific research is important both for what it teaches us directly about nature and for how it stimulates other studies that improve our understanding. MacArthur's work stimulated numerous studies of competition among many groups of organisms, including warblers. Some of these studies produced results that supported his work and others produced different results. All added to our knowledge of competition between species and of ecology.

One ecologist whose studies extended our knowledge of warbler ecology a great deal was Douglass Morse (1980, 1989). His research addressed several questions raised by MacArthur's work, including whether warblers use the same feeding zones in the absence of one or more of the other species. Morse studied this possibility by comparing the feeding zones of warblers living in the presence or absence of other warbler species.

Morse compared the feeding zones of warblers in spruce forests on the mainland of Maine to their feeding zones on small islands. The islands were 0.2 to 1.5 km offshore and were inhabited by one to three species of warblers. Two of the warbler species that lived on the islands, the black-throated green warbler and the yellow-rumped warbler, also lived in MacArthur's study areas. Morse found that the black-throated green warbler maintained approximately the same feeding zone whether it lived on the mainland, with many other warbler species, or on islands, with only two other warbler species. In contrast, the yellow-rumped warbler moved its feeding zone upward on islands where the black-throated green warbler was absent. This shift in feeding zone by island populations of yellow-rumped warblers is shown in figure 1.3.

Why doesn't the yellow-rumped warbler feed higher in the trees when black-throated green warblers are present? Morse found that the feeding zones of spruce-forest warblers are at least partially maintained by aggressive interactions between

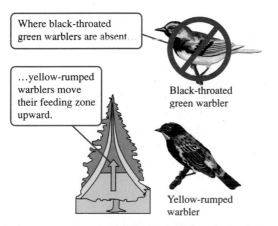

Where black-throated green warblers are absent...

...yellow-rumped warblers move their feeding zone upward.

Black-throated green warbler

Yellow-rumped warbler

Figure 1.3   The upward shift in the feeding zone of yellow-rumped warblers in the absence of black-throated warblers suggests that the typical yellow-rumped warbler feeding zone is maintained by competition.

species. He also discovered that the black-throated green warbler is socially dominant over yellow-rumped warblers. Consequently, aggression by black-throated green warblers can exclude yellow-rumped warblers from potential feeding areas. Morse proposed that aggressive interactions between warbler species help maintain differences in feeding zones of the kind described by MacArthur.

The studies of MacArthur and Morse show how field studies can be used to address ecological questions concerning competition between closely related species. Other ecologists have been concerned with the ecology of entire forests, lakes, or grasslands, which they treat as ecosystems. An **ecosystem** includes all organisms that live in an area and the physical environment with which those organisms interact. Many ecosystems studies have focused on **nutrients**, the raw materials that an organism must acquire from the environment to survive.

Ecosystem Controls: Using Large-Scale Experiments to Understand Ecosystems

The researchers we have discussed so far have focused their studies on small parts of larger systems. Although this was appropriate for the research questions they were testing, there are some questions that are not easily studied by breaking a system into individual parts. Here we present two examples of researchers who decided that if you want to understand what controls ecosystem processes, then you need to study the entire ecosystem.

In the early 1960s, scientists and politicians around the world were seeing previously clear lakes turn pea-green, a process called **eutrophication**. It was quickly realized that some nutrient was being added to these lakes, causing rapid algal growth. The question that was resisting an answer was which nutrient was to blame. In the mid 1960s, the Fisheries Research Board of Canada established the Freshwater Institute, headed by Wally Johnson. Johnson brought in Jack Vallentyne to lead the section on finding the root cause of eutrophication. The experiences of these researchers led them to believe that an answer would not be found by adding nutrients to beakers in a lab, and instead they needed to do their experiments on a much grander scale. They added nutrients to whole lakes. In 1968, the Experimental Lakes Area (ELA) was established in Ontario, and they hired David Schindler (fig. 1.4) as "Leader of Experimental Lake Investigations."

ELA consists of 17 watersheds containing 46 individual lakes. Under Schindler's research direction, the research team began to add different nutrients in different combinations to different lakes, measuring the response of each ecosystem. Adding a bit of fertilizer to a beaker in a lab is a relatively trivial exercise. Fertilizing a lake was much more complicated, involving motor boats, 200-litre barrels, and significant amounts of time.

In several landmark papers (e.g., Schindler 1974, 1977), Schindler was able to clearly show that phosphorus (P) was the nutrient responsible for eutrophication. A strong proof of this is seen in a picture of Lake 226 (fig. 1.5). For this experiment, they split the lake in half, adding nitrogen and carbon to one side and nitrogen, carbon, and P to the other. As can be seen in figure 1.5, the phosphorus addition caused a dramatic

Figure 1.4   Dave Schindler conducting field work in a lake in Jasper National Park.

Figure 1.5   Lake 226 at the Experimental Lakes Area divided in half. The eutrophied half in the background had phosphorus added, while the clear half in the foreground did not.

ecological shift in this ecosystem: eutrophication. The next question that emerged was where the P in eutrophied lakes was coming from. It quickly became apparent that the common household detergents used during that period contained significant amounts of P, and as waste water drained into lakes and streams, people were in effect fertilizing the aquatic ecosystems. Because of this ecological research, detergents containing phosphorus have been banned from many places throughout the world, substantially improving the quality of freshwater ecosystems.

It is important to know that when this work was being conducted, there were countless others around the world trying to answer the same question. Why did Schindler's approach work where others' failed? It turns out that the underlying mechanisms driving this ecological shift require the ability of the microflora and fauna to shift in species composition as nutrient levels shift, and this couldn't easily be captured in a small-scale study using beakers. Another aspect that small

scale experiments neglected was the exchange of nitrogen and carbon with the atmosphere. In windswept lakes, CO_2 from the atmosphere was able to invade the lake in enough quantity to provide the essential resource needed for photosynthesis, resulting in algal blooms. In beaker experiments, there was no such CO_2 exchange between the water and the atmosphere, and thus algal growth was often carbon limited. Lab experiments rarely ever include all species from natural areas, nor do they allow for surface-atmosphere interactions, and thus the conditions needed for eutrophication were better found in the field than the lab.

Research at ELA has continued, and Schindler has since moved to Alberta and continues whole-lake research. As time passed and questions were answered, the research focus shifted. There exist ongoing studies exploring the effect of acidification on lake communities and whether these ecosystems can recover; impacts of climate change; and consequences of introducing fish to historically fishless lakes. Using the basic experimental approach refined in the 1960s, Schindler and colleagues continue to address many of the most pressing questions in freshwater ecology (Schindler et al. 1985, 1990).

Although lakes make wonderful systems for experimental study, there is also much that can be learned about terrestrial ecosystems. In fact, just before Schindler and the group at ELA embarked on their manipulations of lakes in Ontario they were aware of an equally large-scale ecosystem manipulation happening in the forests of New Hampshire.

In the early 1960s, Gene Liken and Herbert Bormann watched work crews fell the trees covering an entire stream basin in the Hubbard Brook Experimental Forest. The felling of these trees was a key part of an experiment that Likens and Bormann had designed to study how deforestation affects the loss of nutrients, such as nitrogen, from forested lands (Bormann and Likens 1994, Likens and Bormann 1995). They had studied two small stream valleys for three years before cutting the trees in one of the valleys. The undisturbed stream valley would act as a control against which to compare the response of the deforested stream valley. Likens and Bormann combined biology with physical sciences, including geochemistry, hydrology, micrometeorology, and applied disciplines, including forestry.

The central hypothesis guiding their experiment was that organisms, especially plants, regulate the rate of nutrient loss from northern hardwood forests. Their study area, the Hubbard Brook Experimental Forest, covers approximately 3,000 ha and ranges in altitude from 200 to 1,000 m. Like much of the northeastern United States, southern Ontario, and Quebec, the Hubbard Brook valley was nearly completely deforested by 1917. Most of the present-day forest has grown up since that time. The forest is fairly representative of second-growth forests across the region and is dominated by sugar maple, beech, and yellow birch, along with some red spruce, balsam fir, and white birch.

The researchers organized their studies around small stream basins that included small tributaries of Hubbard Brook. The natural topographic boundaries of these stream basins offered the opportunity for measuring the movement of nutrients.

Before they deforested the experimental basin, Likens and Bormann inventoried the distribution of nutrients. Those measurements indicated that over 90% of the nutrients in the ecosystem were tied up in soil organic matter. Most of the rest, 9.5%, was in vegetation. They estimated the rates at which some organisms fix atmospheric nitrogen and the rates at which weathering releases nutrients from the granite bedrock of the stream basins. They also measured the input of nutrients to the forest ecosystem from precipitation and nutrient outputs with stream water. The nutrient outputs in streamflow amounted to less than 1% of the amount contained within the forest ecosystems.

After this preliminary work, they cut the trees on their experimental stream basin. They used herbicides to suppress regrowth of vegetation at their experimental site and continued to apply herbicides for three years. As figure 1.6 indicates, cutting the forest dramatically increased rates of nutrient loss from the experimental stream basin. Losses of nitrate (NO_3^-) were approximately 40 to 50 times higher. The average concentrations of other major elements in the stream draining the deforested basin increased by 177% to 1,558%. Clearly, this type of temperate forest exerts strong controls on the movement of nutrients across the landscape.

The research by Schindler, Likens, and Bormann has given ecologists new insights into the feedback between the biotic and abiotic components of ecosystems. The scale of these projects was so grand, and the outcome of the experiments so clear, that the data have been used by lawmakers throughout the world to alter environmental regulations and management practices. Despite the size of these ecosystem experiments, there are questions that occur over even larger spatial scales, and there are a group of landscape and geographic ecologists willing to tackle them.

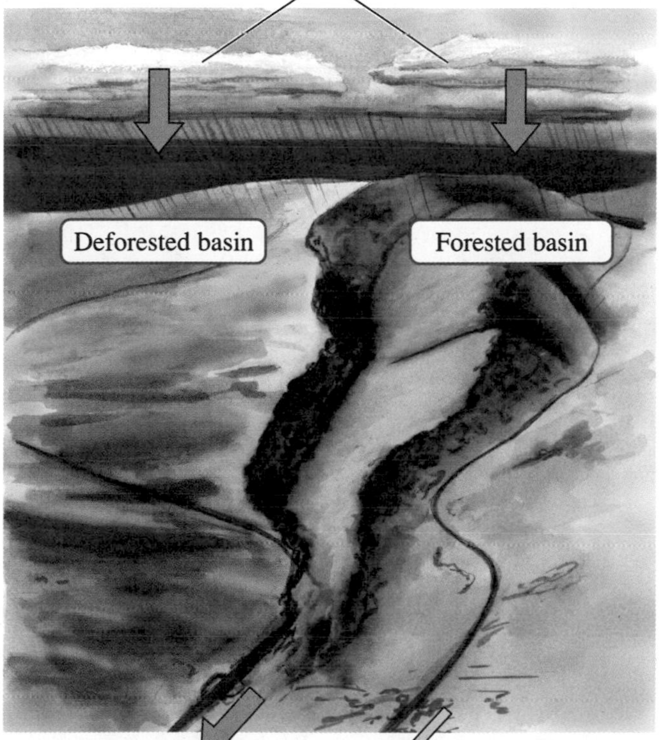

Vegetation Change: Information from Pollen Records and Modelling

The earth and its life are always changing. However, many of the most important changes occur over such a long period of time or at such large spatial scales that they are difficult to study. Two approaches that provide insights into long-term and large-scale processes are studies of pollen preserved in lake sediments and theoretical modelling.

Margaret Davis (1983, 1989) carefully searched through a sample of lake sediments for pollen. The sediments had come from a lake in the Appalachian Mountains, and the pollen they contained would help her document changes in the plants living near the lake during the past several thousands of years. Davis is a paleoecologist trained to think at very large spatial scales and about very long periods of time. She has spent much of her professional career studying changes in the distributions of plants during the Quaternary period, particularly during the most recent 20,000 years.

Some of the pollen produced by plants that live near a lake falls on the lake surface, sinks, and becomes trapped in lake sediments. As lake sediments build up over the centuries, this pollen is preserved and forms a historical record of the kinds of plants that lived nearby. As the lakeside vegetation changes, the mix of pollen preserved in the lake's sediments also changes. In the example shown in figure 1.7, the earliest appearance of pollen from spruce trees, *Picea* spp., is in the lake sediments from about 12,000 years ago and pollen from beech, *Fagus grandifolia,* first appears in the sediments from about 8,000 years ago. Chestnut pollen does not appear in the sediments until about 2,000 years ago. The pollen from all three tree species continues in the sediment record until about 1920, when chestnut blight killed most of the chestnut trees in the vicinity of the lake. Thus, the pollen preserved in the sediments of individual lakes can be used to construct a paleoecological record.

By studying many different lakes, Davis could study changes in vegetation across an entire continent. Her studies have demonstrated how forests in eastern North America changed with changing climate.

Today, the greatest diversity of deciduous trees in eastern North America is in the Appalachian Mountains. This pattern led ecologists to propose that these mountains have long been a center of diversity for deciduous trees in North America. One hypothesis proposed that deciduous trees survived the last glacial period in the southern Appalachian Mountains. However, by studying the pollen record in lakes across eastern North America, Davis showed that during the height of the

Nutrient input with precipitation

Deforested basin

Forested basin

Greater nutrient output in streamflow from deforested stream basin

Lesser nutrient output in streamflow from forested stream basin

Figure 1.6 This whole stream basin manipulation demonstrated the influence of forest trees on nutrient budgets of northeastern hardwood forests.

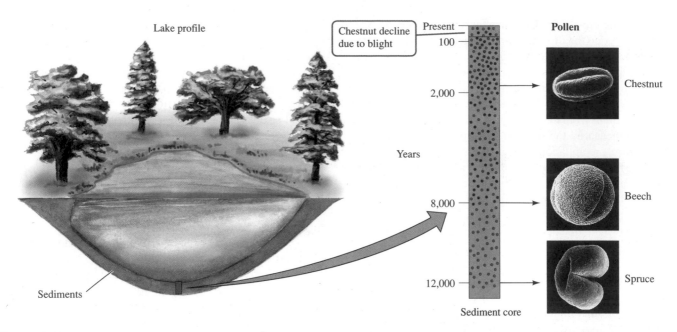

Figure 1.7   The vegetation history of landscapes can be reconstructed using the pollen contained within the sediments of nearby lakes.

last glaciation, about 18,000 years ago, the southern Appalachian Mountains were covered by coniferous trees. At that time, the nearest deciduous forests were in the lower Mississippi Valley, a pattern largely unsuspected until Davis and others studied pollen preserved in lake sediments.

In addition to using paleoecological methods, coupling empirical and theoretical studies provides insights into patterns of long-term ecological change. Essential to the success of this approach are a set of statistical methods suitable for the detection of patterns through space and time. A series of papers by Marie-Josée Fortin (fig. 1.8) and her colleagues (Fortin et al. 2000, 2005) have been exploring and expanding the tools available for the detection of ecological boundaries.

There exist a variety of types of ecological boundaries. **Ecotones** are transitions from one type of ecosystem to another, for instance the transition from an agricultural field into the surrounding forest (fig. 1.9). Boundaries can also be created through wild fires, insect outbreaks, and other large-scale disturbances (fig. 1.10). The ability to accurately identify

Figure 1.9   Boundaries within landscapes created by human activity (background) and natural environmental gradients (foreground).

Figure 1.8   Marie-Josée Fortin answers ecological questions by using advanced statistical methods on empirical data.

Figure 1.10   Detecting the edges of tree death associated with insect outbreak requires the development of advanced statistical tools.

Ecology In Action

The Scientific Method

Ecologists explore the relationships between organisms and environment using the methods of science. The series of boxes called "Ecology In Action" that are found in all the chapters of this book are discussions of various examples showing how ecologists are addressing real-world problems. Taken together, these boxes demonstrate the breadth of research conducted by ecologists. Unifying these boxes is one central idea: science can be used to answer questions of societal concern. To begin with, we present here, not an example from the field, but instead an overview of the scientific method.

Let us begin this discussion with the most basic question. What is science? The word *science* comes from a Latin word meaning "to know." Broadly speaking, science is a way of obtaining knowledge about the natural world using certain formal procedures. Those procedures, which make up what we call, "the scientific method," are outlined in figure 1.11. Despite a great diversity of approaches to doing science, sound scientific studies have many methodological characteristics in common. The most universal and critical aspects of the scientific method are: asking interesting questions and forming testable hypotheses.

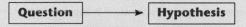

QUESTIONS AND HYPOTHESES

What do scientists do? Simply put, scientists ask and attempt to find answers to questions about the natural world. Questions are the guiding lights of the scientific process. Without them, exploration of nature lacks focus and yields little understanding of the world. Let's consider some questions asked by the ecologists discussed in this chapter. The main question asked by Robert MacArthur in his studies of warblers (pp. 4–5) was something like the following: "How can several species of insect-eating warblers live in the same forest without one species eventually excluding the others through competition?" In their studies of northern hardwood forests, Likens and Bormann asked, "What influence does forest vegetation have on the rate of nutrient loss from northern hardwood forests?" While this focus on questions may seem obvious, one of the most common questions asked of scientists at seminars and professional meetings is, "What is your question?"

If scientists are in the business of asking questions about nature, where does a hypothesis enter the process? A hypothesis is a possible answer to a question. MacArthur's main

hypothesis was: "Several warbler species are able to coexist because each species feeds on insects living in different zones within trees." The central hypothesis of the Likens and Bormann study was: "Organisms, especially plants, regulate the rate of nutrient loss from northern hardwood forests." Again, the hypothesis proposed by Likens and Bormann is a tentative answer to their underlying question.

Once a scientist or team of scientists proposes a hypothesis (or multiple alternative hypotheses), the next step in the scientific method is to determine its validity by testing predictions that follow from the hypothesis. Three fundamental ways to test hypotheses are through observation, experiments, and modelling. These approaches, which are all represented in the research presented here in chapter 1 and in figure 1.11, will be discussed in detail throughout the text.

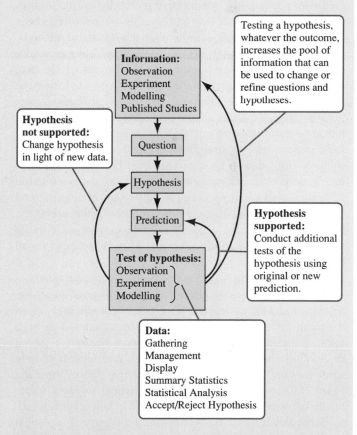

Figure 1.11   Graphic summary of the scientific method. The scientific method centres on the use of information to propose and test hypotheses through observation, experiment, and modelling.

the location of ecological boundaries has significant implications for ecologists and land managers. Historically, ecologists have ignored ecotones, instead focusing research in areas of

a "typical" forest, grassland, or other ecosystem. However, as the natural world becomes more and more fragmented through human activities and large-scale disturbances increase in frequency, the amount of transitional area in a landscape increases exponentially. There is growing appreciation that ecotones and transitional zones play important functional roles, including the exchange of nutrients and energy between the adjoining ecosystems and communities. The plant and animal species that occupy transition zones are often at their physiological limits, and may be particularly sensitive to any additional environmental change. If one is able to accurately measure the location of transition zones, then one can also measure whether these locations change over time. Such information can be a vital clue as to whether changes in regional factors (such as climate) are having broad ecological impacts. Boundary delimitation is also important for land managers and conservation groups. For example, many municipalities have strict regulations regarding land development, particularly in wetland areas. For these to be enforced requires someone to literally draw a line separating the two. Placing the line in the wrong place causes either unnecessary loss of income for the land owner or preventable ecological damage to the community. None of this work can be done without clear and accurate methods for identifying boundaries.

As you will see throughout this text, some ecological methods, particularly quantitative methods, can be used in studies of a diversity of taxa and locations. What often varies are the organisms studied, rather than the statistical methods. For example, although Fortin and colleagues have generally focused on identifying ecotones in the forests of Quebec, they have recently applied the same tools to exploring the geographic ranges and distribution limits of animals. Superficially these questions appear unrelated. However, they are linked by important conceptual issues: Where is the boundary? How wide is it? Is it straight (i.e., mostly human-made)? Is it curvy (i.e., driven by environmental factors and species interactions)? Identifying range expansion and contraction of animal and plant species has important ecological and conservation implications. Fortin and her group are at the forefront of landscape ecology, both developing new statistical methods and applying them to address issues of broad ecological concern.

As we have seen so far in this chapter, different quantitative tools are needed to address different ecological questions. Schindler and his colleagues were able to convincingly show the main impact of added P on lake eutrophication through strong experiments and clear photographs. Fortin has needed to develop complex statistical methods and models to help ecologists understand how boundaries move through time and space. Most ecologists require a statistical toolbox somewhere between these two examples, and in fact other research by Schindler and Fortin also requires a diversity of statistical approaches. Because so many of the questions in ecology are conceptually complex, it is essential that as you learn ecology you also become familiar with basic statistical approaches. We have provided you with an introduction to many statistical tests that are commonly used by ecologists, and will be discussed throughout the text (Appendix A). We encourage you to read

Appendix A before diving into the remaining 22 chapters, as that information will help guide your understanding of how ecologists actually make discoveries in ecology. We end this chapter with an overview of the nature and scope of ecology.

The Nature and Scope of Ecology

With this brief review of research approaches and topics, we return to the question asked at the beginning of the chapter: what is ecology? Ecology is indeed the study of relationships between organisms and the environment. However, as you can see from the research we have reviewed, ecologists examine those relationships over a large range of temporal and spatial scales using a wide variety of approaches. Ecology includes Fortin's studies of forests in Quebec and Davis' studies of vegetation movement across North America. Ecology also includes the observation studies of MacArthur and Morse, as well as the whole ecosystem manipulations of Schindler, Likens, and Bormann. Ecologists may study processes that take place over short periods of time over small spatial scales, or over millennia over large regions of Earth. All this is ecology.

As fun and enjoyable as it is to spend summers conducting field work in beautiful locations throughout the world, one factor that differentiates an ecologist from an eco-tourist is reliance on the scientific method. Ecologists are scientists trying to answer complex questions in natural and managed systems; we are not simply observing the landscape. If you want to predict the impacts of climate change on local species diversity, bring in an ecologist. If you want to understand how predators may alter prey densities, bring in an ecologist. If you want to determine the importance of a given patch of habitat on the migration of an endangered animal, bring in an ecologist. Critical to our ability to find answers to these questions is our ability to objectively identify and evaluate relationships in complex data sets. As a result, a strong understanding of quantitative methods and statistics is critical to the success of students of ecology.

Though it may come as a surprise to many, ecology is among the more quantitative disciplines of biology, and statistics is a critical research tool. Appendix A of this book provides a basic overview of the statistical methods that will be discussed throughout the text. We once again encourage you to read that section before moving on to chapter 2. In the remainder of this text, we will explain ecological concepts by presenting to you the details of ecological research. Understanding ecology is intimately intertwined with doing ecology.

The brief survey of ecology in this chapter has only hinted at the conceptual and methodological basis for the research described. Throughout this book we emphasize the foundations of ecology. Each chapter focuses on a few ecological concepts, and we explore some of the applications and tools associated with the concepts introduced.

We continue our exploration of ecology in section I with the natural history of life on land and in water. Natural history was the foundation upon which ecologists built modern ecology.

Section I

NATURAL HISTORY AND EVOLUTION

The science of ecology is built upon a foundation of natural history and evolutionary biology. In section I we explore some of the more common types of terrestrial and aquatic habitats found on the planet, and the dominant environmental factors that influence these habitats. We conclude section I with an overview of evolution, a set of processes intimately linked with ecological interactions.

Chapter 2

Life on Land

Outline

Natural history is the study of how organisms in a particular area are influenced by factors such as climate, soils, predators, competitors, mutualists, and evolutionary history. A solid understanding of natural history provides the foundation for modern ecology and conservation biology. One of the most dramatic restoration successes that incorporated natural history into its approach comes from Costa Rica. Daniel Janzen's goal was to restore tropical dry forest, a forest nearly as rich in species as tropical rain forest, to Guanacaste National Park, Costa Rica. As he studied the guanacaste tree, *Enterolobium cyclocarpum* (fig. 2.1), however, he realized that something was missing from the present-day forest. The guanacaste tree, a member of the pea family, produces disk-shaped fruit about 10 cm in diameter and 4 to 10 mm thick. Each year, a large tree produces up to 5,000 of these fruits, which fall to the ground when ripe. Janzen asked, Why does the guanacaste tree produce so much fruit? His answer to this question was that the fruit of the tree should promote seed dispersal by animals.

Janzen, however, knew of no native animals of the size and behaviour that would make them dependable dispersers of guanacaste seeds. Dependable dispersers would be necessary to speed restoration of tropical dry forest across Guanacaste National Park. True, some large herbivores fed on guanacaste

fruits and dispersed the seeds with their feces. But most of these dispersers were cattle and horses, which were introduced during the Spanish colonial period. Had the guanacaste tree evolved an elaborate fruit and made thousands of them each year in the absence of native dispersers? On the surface, it appeared so, but this did not seem to make sense. Without some means of dispersing their seeds, the majority of offspring would fall from the tree and remain at the base of the maternal plant. This appears to be a dangerous place for seedlings to grow, as their mother would cast shade over them and draw resources from the soils around them. Such parent-offspring conflict is often not to the benefit of either parent or offspring, and thus the lack of an obvious dispersal vector was a real puzzle.

Janzen's restoration of tropical dry forest was guided by his knowledge of natural history. Natural history eventually led Janzen to an understanding of the fruiting biology of the guanacaste tree. As he considered the long-term natural history of Central American dry forest, he found what he was looking for: a whole host of large herbivorous animals, including ground sloths, camels, and horses. The dry forest had once supported plenty of potential dispersers of guanacaste seeds. However, all these large animals became extinct about 10,000 years ago; overhunting by humans may have been a contributory factor. For thousands of years following these extinctions the guanacaste tree prepared its annual feast of fruits, but there were few large animals to consume them. Then about 500 years ago, Europeans introduced horses and cattle, which ate the fruits of the guanacaste tree and dispersed its seeds around the landscape (fig. 2.2). Janzen recognized the practical value of livestock as seed dispersers and included them in his plan for tropical dry forest restoration.

Janzen first tested the hypothesis that contemporary horses can act as effective seed dispersers for the guanacaste tree. After this test, he applied his knowledge by incorporating horses into the management plan for Guanacaste National Park. The guanacaste tree and other trees in a similar predicament would have their dispersers, and restoration of tropical dry forest would be accelerated. Janzen and others have also shown that fires are a critical part of these forests. Just as removing a native seed disperser can alter the forest, so too can fire suppression. Maintaining an ecosystem often requires understanding more than just the plants and animals.

Janzen's natural history of tropical dry forest also includes people, unlike most natural histories. He worked closely with people from all parts of Costa Rican society, from the president of the country to local schoolchildren. He realized that long-term support for Guanacaste National Park depended upon its contribution to the economic and cultural well-being of local people. It's the people in Janzen's natural history that stand guard over the Guanacaste project. Janzen calls his approach "biocultural restoration," an approach that seeks to preserve tropical dry forest for its own sake and as a place that provides a host of human benefits, ranging from drinking water to intellectual stimulation. Using natural history as their guide, Janzen and the people of Costa Rica are restoring tropical dry forest in Guanacaste National Park.

Figure 2.1   A guanacaste tree, *Enterolobium cyclocarpum*, growing in Costa Rica. Guanacaste trees, which produce large amounts of edible fruit, require large herbivores to disperse their seeds.

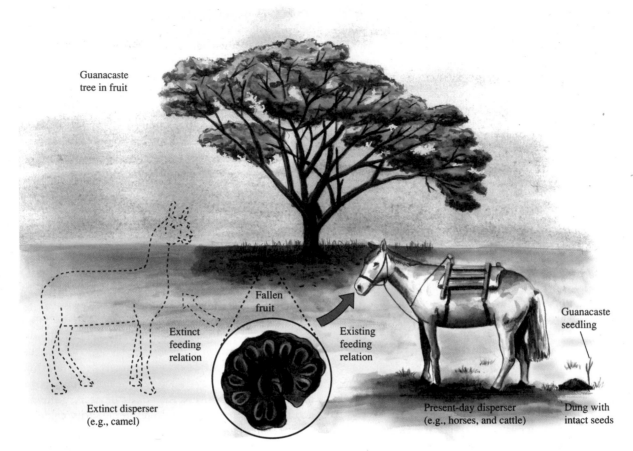

Guanacaste
tree in fruit

Fallen
fruit

Extinct
feeding
relation

Existing
feeding
relation

Guanacaste
seedling

Extinct disperser
(e.g., camel)

Present-day disperser
(e.g., horses, and cattle)

Dung with
intact seeds

Figure 2.2 Dispersers of guanacaste seeds—past and present. Most of the original dispersers of quanacaste seeds went extinct over 10,000 years ago. Now the tree depends on introduced domestic livestock for its dispersal.

Janzen's work (1981a, 1981b) shows how natural history can be used to address a practical problem. Because the science of ecology continues to rest upon a solid foundation of natural history, we devote chapters 2 and 3 to the natural history of the biosphere. In chapter 2, we examine the natural history of life on land. Before we begin that discussion, we need to introduce terrestrial biomes, the concept around which this chapter is built. We also discuss the development and ecology of soils, the living system that supports all terrestrial biomes.

Terrestrial Biomes

Chapter 2 focuses on major divisions of the terrestrial environment called **biomes.** As will become clear in chapter 18, plants make up the majority of the living biomass of most terrestrial biomes. Even casual observation out a car window as you drive along the highway makes it clear that what you see are mostly plants. It is not surprising then that biomes are distinguished primarily by the commonly observed plant species, and each is associated with a particular climate. Biomes consist of distinctive plant formations such as the tropical rain forest and the desert. Because these biomes are characterized by different types of plants and animals, and occur in regions with very different climates, their natural histories differ a great deal. The student of ecology must be aware of the major features of those differences.

The main goal of chapter 2 is to take a large-scale perspective of nature before delving, in later chapters, into finer details of structure and process. We pay particular attention to the geographic distributions of the major biomes, the climate associated with each, their soils, their salient biological relationships, and the extent of human influences. Now let's move on to the central concepts of this chapter, which concern patterns of climatic variation, soil structure and ecology, and the global distribution of the major biomes.

Concepts

2.1 **Uneven heating of the earth's spherical surface by the sun and the tilt of the earth on its axis combine to produce predictable latitudinal variation in climate.**

2.2 **Soil structure results from the long-term interaction of climate, organisms, topography, and parent mineral material.**

2.3 **The geographic distribution of terrestrial biomes corresponds closely to variation in climate, especially prevailing temperature and precipitation.**

2.1 Large-Scale Patterns of Climatic Variation

Uneven heating of the earth's spherical surface by the sun and the tilt of the earth on its axis combine to produce predictable latitudinal variation in climate. In chapter 1, ecology was defined as the study of the relationships between organisms and their environment. Consequently, identifying geographic and seasonal variations in temperature and precipitation is fundamental to understanding natural history and ecology. Several attributes of climate vary predictably over the earth. For instance, average temperatures are lower and more seasonal (varying predictably over the year) at middle and high latitudes than near the equator. Deserts, which are concentrated in a narrow band of latitudes around the globe, receive little precipitation, which generally falls unpredictably in time and space. Here we will discuss the major mechanisms that produce these and other patterns of climatic variation.

Temperature, Precipitation, and Atmospheric Circulation

Much of earth's climatic variation is caused by uneven heating of its surface by the sun. This uneven heating results from the spherical shape of the earth and the angle at which the earth rotates on its axis as it orbits the sun. Because the earth is a sphere, the sun's rays are most concentrated where the sun is directly overhead. However, the latitude at which the sun is directly overhead changes with the seasons. This seasonal change occurs because the earth's axis of rotation is not perpendicular to its plane of orbit about the sun but is tilted approximately 23.5° away from the perpendicular (fig. 2.3).

Because this tilted angle of rotation is maintained throughout earth's orbit about the sun, the amount of solar energy received by the Northern and Southern Hemispheres changes seasonally. During the northern summer the Northern Hemisphere is tilted toward the sun and receives more solar energy than the Southern Hemisphere. During the northern summer solstice on approximately June 21, the sun is directly overhead at the tropic of Cancer, at 23.5° N latitude. During the northern winter solstice, on approximately December 21, the sun is directly overhead at the tropic of Capricorn, at 23.5° S latitude. During the northern winter, the Northern Hemisphere is tilted away from the sun and the Southern Hemisphere receives more solar energy. The sun is directly overhead at the equator during the spring and autumnal equinoxes, on approximately March 21 and September 23. On those dates, the Northern and Southern Hemispheres receive approximately equal amounts of solar radiation.

This shift in the latitude at which the sun is directly overhead drives seasonality. At high latitudes, in both the Northern and Southern Hemispheres, seasonal shifts in input of solar energy produce winters with low average temperatures and shorter day lengths and summers with high average temperatures and longer day lengths. In contrast, between the tropics of Cancer and Capricorn seasonal variations in temperature and day length are slight. As we explain next, patterns in the seasonality of temperature do not necessarily correlate with the seasonality of precipitation.

Heating of the earth's surface and atmosphere drives circulation of the atmosphere and influences patterns of precipitation. As shown in figure 2.4*a*, the sun heats air at the equator, causing the air to expand and rise. This warm, moist air cools as it rises. Since cool air holds less water vapour than warm air, the water vapour carried by this rising air mass

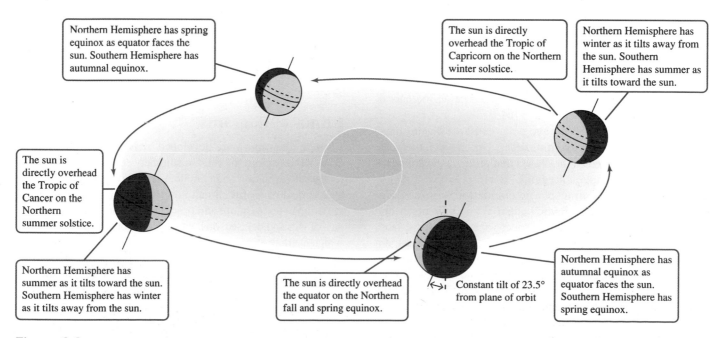

Figure 2.3 The seasons in the Northern and Southern Hemispheres.

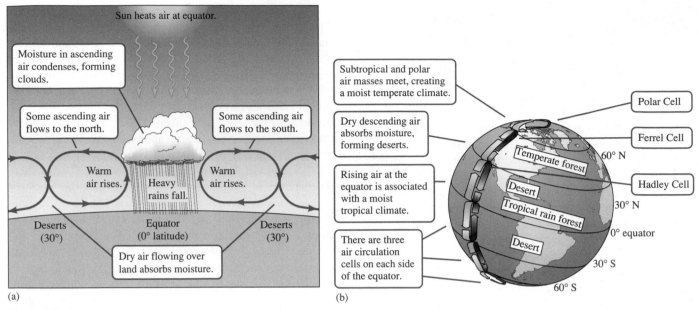

Figure 2.4   (*a*) Solar-driven air circulation. (*b*) Latitude and atmospheric circulation.

condenses and forms clouds, which produce the heavy rainfall associated with tropical environments.

Eventually, this equatorial air mass ceases to rise and spreads north and south. This high-altitude air is dry, since the moisture it once held fell as tropical rains. As this air mass moves away from the equator, it cools, which increases its density. Eventually it sinks back to the earth's surface at about 30° latitude and spreads north and south. This dry air draws moisture from the lands over which it flows, creating deserts.

Air moving from 30° latitude back to the equator completes a thermal loop, which forms the Hadley cell. As figure 2.4*b* shows, there are three atmospheric cells on either side of the equator, called the Hadley, Ferrel, and polar cells. The polar cells function in a manner similar to the Hadley cells, driven by air movement associated with warming at 60° latitude and cooling at the poles. The polar cells are primarily responsible for the weather patterns associated with most northerly and southerly areas, bringing cool weather from the poles.

The Ferrel cells occur at mid-latitudes, and are driven in part by the effects of the Hadley and polar cells. In general, the warm, moist air flowing from the Hadley cells rises as it meets cold air flowing from the polar cells. As this air mass rises, moisture picked up from desert regions at lower latitudes condenses to form the clouds that produce the abundant precipitation of temperate regions.

The patterns of atmospheric circulation shown in figure 2.4*b* suggest that air movement is directly north and south. However, this does not reflect what we observe from the earth's surface as the earth rotates from west to east. An observer at tropical latitudes observes winds that blow from the northeast in the Northern Hemisphere and from the southeast in the Southern Hemisphere (fig. 2.5). These are the *northeast* and *southeast trades.* Someone studying winds within the temperate belt between 30° and 60° latitude would observe that winds blow mainly from the west. These are the *westerlies* of temperate latitudes. At high latitudes, our

observer would find that the predominant wind direction is from the east. These are the *polar easterlies.*

Why don't winds move directly north to south? The prevailing winds do not move in a straight north–south direction because of the **Coriolis effect**. In the Northern Hemisphere, the Coriolis effect causes an apparent deflection of winds to the right of their direction of travel and to the left in the Southern Hemisphere. We say "apparent" deflection because we see this deflection only if we make our observations from the surface of the earth. To an observer in space, it would appear that winds move in approximately a straight line, while the earth rotates beneath them. However, we need to keep in mind that the perspective from the earth's surface is the ecologically relevant perspective.

Geographic variation in temperature and precipitation is very complex. How can we study and represent geographic variation in these climatic variables without being overwhelmed by a mass of numbers? This practical problem is addressed by a visual device called a climate diagram.

Climate Diagrams

Climate diagrams were developed by Heinrich Walter (1985) as a tool to explore the relationship between the distribution of terrestrial vegetation and climate. Climate diagrams summarize a great deal of useful climatic information, including seasonal variation in temperature and precipitation, the length and intensity of wet and dry seasons, and the portion of the year during which average minimum temperature is above and below 0°C.

As shown in figure 2.6, climate diagrams summarize climatic information using a standardized structure. The months of the year are plotted on the horizontal axis, beginning with January and ending with December for locations in the Northern Hemisphere and beginning with July and ending with June in the Southern Hemisphere. Temperature is plotted on the left vertical axis and precipitation on the right vertical

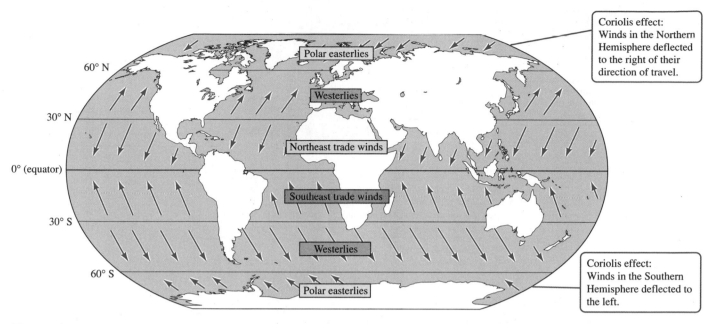

Figure 2.5 The Coriolis effect and wind direction.

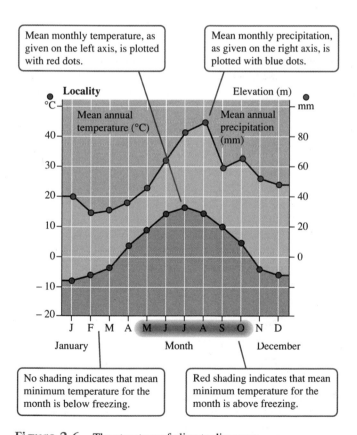

Figure 2.6 The structure of climate diagrams.

axis. Temperature and precipitation are plotted on different scales so that 10°C is equivalent to 20 mm of precipitation.

Because the temperature and precipitation scales are constructed so that 10°C equals 20 mm of precipitation, the relative positions of the temperature and precipitation lines reflect water availability. Theoretically, adequate moisture

for plant growth exists when the precipitation line lies above the temperature line. These moist periods are indicated in the figure by blue shading. When the temperature line lies above the precipitation line, potential evaporation rate exceeds precipitation. These dry periods are indicated by gold shading in the climate diagram. Notice that gold shading of the climate diagram for Yuma, Arizona (fig. 2.7*a*), indicates year-round drought, while the blue shading of the climate diagram for Kuala Lumpur (fig. 2.7*b*) indicates moist conditions year-round. Climate diagrams for wet areas such as tropical rain forest compress the precipitation scale for precipitation above 100 mm so that 10°C is equivalent to 200 mm of precipitation. With this change in scale, rainfall data from very wet climates can be fit on a graph of convenient size. This change in scale is represented by darker shading in the climate diagram for Kuala Lumpur, Malaysia (fig. 2.7*b*). Notice that the precipitation at Kuala Lumpur exceeds 100 mm during all months of the year.

The climate diagram for Dzamiin Uuded, Mongolia (fig. 2.7*c*), is much more complex than those of either the rain forest or hot desert. This complexity results from the much greater seasonal change in the cold desert climate. Dzamiin Uuded is moist from October to April. These moist periods are separated by the months of May to September, when the temperature line rises above the precipitation line, indicating drought. During October to April, the mean *minimum* temperature at Dzamiin Uuded is below freezing (0°C). The months when the mean minimum temperature is above freezing are May through September.

Climate diagrams also include the mean annual temperature, which is presented in the upper left corner (e.g., 27.5°C at Kuala Lumpur). The mean annual precipitation (e.g., 86 mm at Yuma, Arizona) is presented in the upper right corner of each climate diagram. The elevation of each site, in meters above sea level (e.g., 962 m at Dzamiin Uuded), is also presented in the upper right corner.

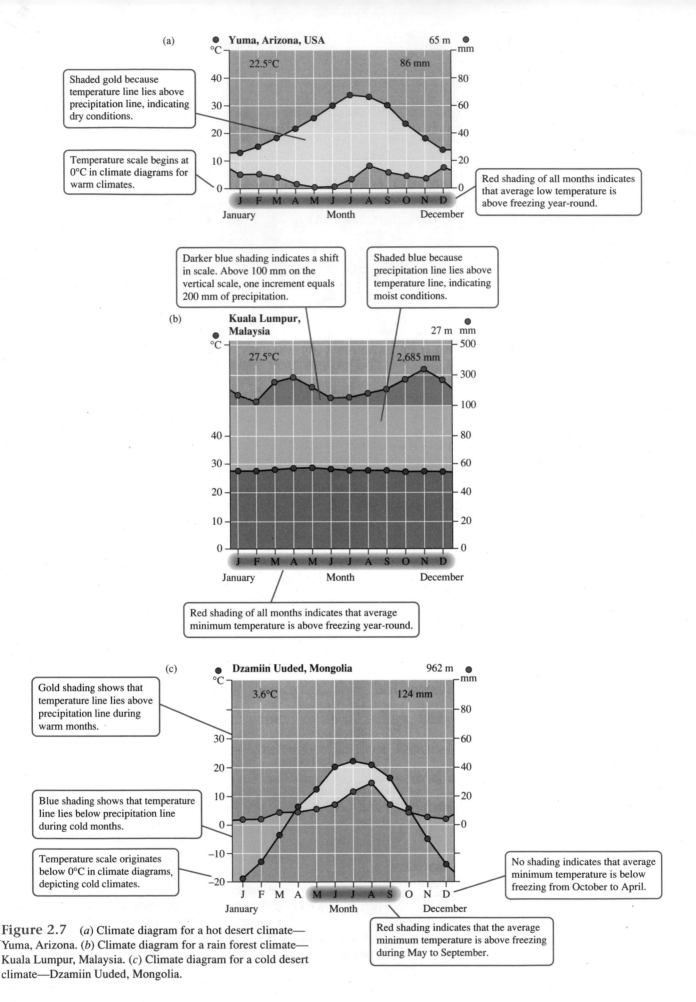

(a)

Yuma, Arizona, USA   65 m

Shaded gold because temperature line lies above precipitation line, indicating dry conditions.

Temperature scale begins at 0°C in climate diagrams for warm climates.

Red shading of all months indicates that average low temperature is above freezing year-round.

Darker blue shading indicates a shift in scale. Above 100 mm on the vertical scale, one increment equals 200 mm of precipitation.

Shaded blue because precipitation line lies above temperature line, indicating moist conditions.

(b)

Kuala Lumpur, Malaysia   27 m

Red shading of all months indicates that average minimum temperature is above freezing year-round.

(c)

Dzamiin Uuded, Mongolia   962 m

Gold shading shows that temperature line lies above precipitation line during warm months.

Blue shading shows that temperature line lies below precipitation line during cold months.

Temperature scale originates below 0°C in climate diagrams, depicting cold climates.

No shading indicates that average minimum temperature is below freezing from October to April.

Red shading indicates that the average minimum temperature is above freezing during May to September.

Figure 2.7 (a) Climate diagram for a hot desert climate—Yuma, Arizona. (b) Climate diagram for a rain forest climate—Kuala Lumpur, Malaysia. (c) Climate diagram for a cold desert climate—Dzamiin Uuded, Mongolia.

18

Ecology In Action

Natural History of Soils

In each chapter of the book, we will provide at least one example of how ecologists use their understanding of the natural world to address questions of concern to Canada. The "Ecology In Action" boxes are meant to demonstrate that the science of ecology can provide great insights into many of the pressing environmental issues that we currently face in Canada and across the globe. Some of the examples will be specific studies, while others, such as this one, will discuss a general topic or even a scientific controversy. In this first chapter on natural history, we show how ecologists are beginning to realize how little natural history may actually be known, even in our own backyards.

A fundamental goal of ecology is to understand the processes that influence the distribution and abundance of organisms. This knowledge can be then be used to address a variety of environmental issues that people face throughout the world, such as climate change, controlling the spread of invasive species, and trying to integrate agriculture, economic development, human housing, and wilderness within a limited amount of land.

However, before we are able to explain patterns of abundance, we must first know the organisms we are studying. For many groups of taxa, such as birds, mammals, and many vascular plants, there are numerous published accounts of species descriptions and natural histories, providing the foundation for strong ecological studies. Some of these groups of organisms are so well studied that researchers are unlikely to ever even know someone that has found a new species, let alone identify one themselves. Does this mean the days of natural history are over? If not, then where can more natural history make significant contributions to our ability to understand the science of ecology?

The answer will not be found as a single lat./long. reading on a GPS unit, but is instead quite literally underneath your feet. Soils are the "poor man's rainforest," home to countless numbers of fungi, bacteria, micro- and mesofauna, algae, bryophytes, and numerous other types of organisms. The diversity of these systems is simply staggering, with many more species unidentified than there are identified (fig. 2.8). The relatively small size and subterranean habitat of these organisms has greatly impeded efforts at identifying and understanding the ecology of soils. Nonetheless, although many people will go their whole lives without seeing a bear, wolf, or whale in its natural environment, we each likely walk upon dozens or hundreds of species new to science every day in the soils below us. Only recently have ecologists appreciated that our lack of knowledge of the most basic natural history of these groups of organisms may be a serious impediment to understanding how natural systems function.

We do know that the activity of these soil organisms strongly influences the rates of carbon and nutrient cycling,

soil respiration, and the transfer of nutrients to vascular plants. They also provide food and habitat for larger organisms, and are key to the development of the soil structure itself. Although our understanding of exactly how these processes emerge from the complex web of soil interactions is still limited, it is very clear that changes in composition of communities of soil organisms is likely to alter the efficiency of these processes. Such changes can have significant impacts on a variety of environmental issues of concern to people, including carbon sequestration, primary production, litter buildup, and nutrient leaching. The first step in understanding how the members of the soil community interact will be to understand what organisms are there. Although soils do not represent the world that surface dwellers like humans typically inhabit, they are homes to large numbers of small organisms that greatly affect our lives. It will be up to the next generation of natural historians and ecologists to determine how.

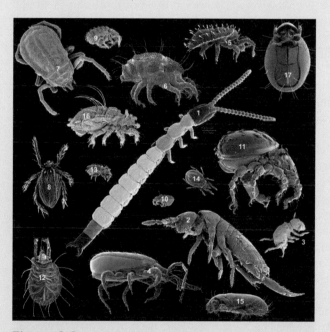

Figure 2.8 A diversity of species live within the soils, the ecology of which remains to be explored. Shown are species of arthropods from the following taxa: 1. Diplura (Japygidae), 2. Collembola (Entomobryidae), 3. Collembola (Neelidae), 4–17 Acari, 4. Mesostigmata (Ologamasidae), 5. Mesostigmata (Zerconidae), 6. Prostigmata (Stigmaeidae), 7. Prostigmata (Labidostomatidae), 8. Prostigmata (Trombiculidae), 9. Endeostigmata (Terpnacaridae), 10. Endeostigmata (Nanorchestidae), 11. Oribatida (Hermanniidae), 12. Oribatida (Phenopelopidae), 13. Oribatida (Brachychthoniidae), 14. Oribatida (Suctobelboideae), 15. Oribatida (Lohmanniidae), 16. Oribatida (Cosmochthoniidae), 17. Oribatida (Phthiracaroidea). These species include predators (1, 4, 5, 6, 7), microbivores/detritivores (2, 3, 10, 13–17), parasites (8), and fungivores (9, 11, 12).

As you can see, climate diagrams efficiently summarize important environmental variables. In the following section, we discuss another central aspect of all terrestrial biomes: soil.

Concept 2.1 Review

1. How would seasonality in temperature and precipitation be affected if the earth's rotation on its axis were perpendicular to its plane or orbit about the sun?
2. Why does the annual rainy season in regions near 23°N begin in June?

2.2 Soil: The Foundation of Terrestrial Biomes

Soil structure results from the long-term interaction of climate, organisms, topography, and parent mineral material. What is **soil**? Why should an ecologist care? It is fair to say that there are few topics that many biology students find less interesting than soil. An ecologist studies wolves, elk, caribou, and the beauty of the North, right? Yes, some ecologists study those things, and many important questions have been answered. However, none of those things would exist without soil. Soil is a complex mixture of living and nonliving material upon which most terrestrial life depends. In addition to its importance in sustaining the communities and ecosystems that we can easily see, soils themselves are complex ecological systems. The amount of organic material, living and dead, found in soil is not trivial. In fact, it is estimated that there is more organic carbon stored below ground than above ground (Schimel 1995), leading to the logical conclusion that "the terrestrial world is brown and black, not green" (Wall et al. 2005). Although most students may imagine ecology to be primarily about the study of the charismatic megafauna that you see on nature shows and hear about from environmental lobbying groups, the reality is that much of what drives the world's systems occurs below our feet. It may then come as no surprise that a growing number of ecologists are realizing that if we want to understand the ecological interactions in communities, or the movement of energy and nutrients within ecosystems, it is critical that ecologists understand what happens below ground at least as well as what happens on the surface. Here we provide an overview of the natural history of soils, including their structure, development, and biodiversity.

From the surface, many soils look quite similar: a dark base with a layer of fallen leaves and branches on top of it. However, when the soil is broken and a pit is dug, it becomes quite apparent that soils differ dramatically in colour, depth, smell, and structure from one place to another. One of the first things that is noticed is that there appear to be differently coloured layers, or horizons, which merge into one another as you dig deeper into the soil (fig. 2.9). At the surface of the soil lies the majority of the organic matter. In Canada, this organic horizon will be called either the O horizon or the LFH horizon. **O horizons** are found in soils in which the plant material

is primarily aquatic in nature (e.g. peat mosses), and **LFH horizons** are generally found in more upland sites. Regardless of the designation, at the surface of the organic horizon you will find freshly fallen organic matter, such as whole leaves, twigs, flowers, and fruits. This organic litter is the food source and home to a wide variety of organisms, and their activity results in the deeper portions of the organic horizon containing highly fragmented and partially decomposed organic matter. The size of the organic horizon varies among locations. Small organic horizons are found in areas with little litter deposition (e.g., deserts and farmland) or high decomposition rates (e.g., tropical rainforests). Deep organic horizons are found in areas with substantial litter inputs and/ or low decomposition rates (e.g., bogs and fens).

The **A horizon** contains a mixture of mineral materials, such as clay, silt, and sand, as well as organic material derived from the organic horizon above. The A horizon also supports substantial biological activity, including burrowing animals such as earthworms, which can mix organic matter from the organic horizon into the A horizon. As a result, the A horizon is generally rich in mineral nutrients, including those essential for plant growth. With rainfall, the A horizon is leached of clays, iron, aluminum, silicates, and humus (partially decomposed organic matter), all of which gradually move down through the soil profile into the B horizon.

The **B horizon** contains the materials leached from above, often resulting in a distinctive banding pattern. Below the B horizon is the **C horizon**, consisting of weathered parent material, which has been broken down through the actions of frost, water, microbial activity, and deep penetrating roots. This weathering results in the production of the sand, silt, clay, and rock fragments that we generally associate with soils. Under the C horizon we find unweathered parent material, which is often bedrock.

Although soils appear static, their structure is actually in a constant state of flux due to the interactive actions of climate, organisms, topography, parent material, and time (Jenny 1980). Plants secrete numerous **root exudates**, which, along with the living roots and plant litter, serve as substrates for numerous bacterial, fungal, and animal species. The growth and activity of these organisms provides stability to the mineral components of the soil, allowing the development and maintenance of complex canals of air spaces and cavities within the soil. Climate affects the rates of weathering of parent materials, leaching of organic and inorganic substances, erosion, and decomposition of organic matter through direct weathering effects. Climate can also alter decomposition by directly impacting the activity of soil organisms, as well as indirectly altering soil activity by influencing the type and amount of plant species which can grow in a given area.

In short, soil is a complex and dynamic entity. It forms the medium in which organisms grow, and the activities of those organisms, in turn, affect soil structure. As with many aspects of ecology, it is often difficult to separate organisms from their environment. The biome discussions that follow provide additional information on soils by including aspects of soil structure and chemistry characteristic of each biome.

LFH Organic horizon. Upper layer contains loose, fragmented plant litter.

LFH or forest floor

Ae

A Mineral soil mixed with some organic matter, clay, iron, aluminum, silicates and soluble organic matter are gradually leached from A horizon.

Bm1

B Depositional horizon. Materials leached from A horizon are deposited in B horizon. Deposits may form distinctive banding patterns.

Bm2

BC

C Weathered parent material. The C horizon may include many rock fragments. It often lies on bedrock.

Figure 2.9   Soil profile exposed in a boreal forest site, showing LFH, A, B, and C horizons.

Concept 2.2 Review

1. Desert soils and agricultural soils support greatly different amounts of plant growth, but both generally have limited organic layers. Why?
2. Can soils be developed in the absence of plants?

2.3 Natural History and Geography of Biomes

The geographic distribution of terrestrial biomes corresponds closely to variation in climate, especially prevailing temperature and precipitation.   Early in the twentieth century, many plant ecologists studied how climate and soils influence the distribution of vegetation. This discipline went out of fashion in the later part of the twentieth century. However, in the face of global change and the realization that plants not only respond to climatic change but can influence climate themselves, ecologists are once again studying climatic influences on the distribution of vegetation. International teams of ecologists, geographers, and climatologists are exploring the influences of climate on vegetation with renewed interest and with much more powerful analytical tools.

In this section, we discuss the climate, soils, and organisms of the earth's major biomes and how they have been influenced by humans. However, don't be concerned if you know of some places that don't quite fit any of the biomes discussed. Dividing the world into biomes is a subjective action. It is important to recognize that biomes are not truly distinctive entities, and instead they change gradually along environmental gradients. In addition, no two boreal forests, grasslands, or tundra locations are exactly alike. Because of this variability, not all ecologists will agree on whether there are 7, 17, or 27 biomes. Here we will present 7 biomes that capture the majority of the major regions of the world. The locations of the biomes drawn on the maps in this chapter are approximate and are drawn at a very coarse scale.

Tundra

Starting at the most northerly areas of vegetation, we find an open landscape of mosses, lichens, and dwarf willows, dotted with small ponds and laced with clear streams (fig. 2.10). This is the **tundra.** The tundra has long been the destination of adventurers, artists, and scientists. The vastness of the landscape creates a truly stunning beauty. If it is summer and surface soils have thawed, your progress will be cushioned by a spongy mat of lichens and mosses and punctuated by sinking

Figure 2.10 The tundra at the base of the Torngat mountains in Labrador consists primarily of low-growing mosses, lichens, perennial herbaceous plants, and shrubs.

into soggy accumulations of peat. The air will be filled with the cries of nesting birds that have come north to take advantage of the brief summer population explosion of their plant and animal prey. You may find the air surprisingly warm. Just as often, you will feel the bite of a midsummer snowstorm. After the long, deep winter, the midnight sun signals an annual celebration of light and life.

Geography

The arctic tundra rings the top of the globe, covering most of the lands north of the Arctic Circle (fig. 2.11). The tundra extends from northern-most Scandinavia, across northern European Russia, through northern Siberia, and right across northern Alaska and Canada. It reaches far south of the Arctic Circle in the Hudson Bay region of Canada and is also found in patches on the coast of Greenland and in northern Iceland.

Climate

The tundra climate is typically cold and dry. However, temperatures are not quite as extreme as in the boreal forest to the south; the tundra usually doesn't get quite as cold in the winter or quite as warm in the summer. A defining characteristic of the northern tundra is short summers (fig. 2.11). Precipitation on the tundra varies from less than 200 mm to a little over 600 mm. Still, because average annual temperatures are so low, precipitation exceeds evaporation. As a consequence, the short summers are soggy and the tundra landscape is alive with ponds and streams.

Soils

Soil building is slow in the cold tundra climate. Because rates of decomposition are low, organic matter accumulates in deposits of peat and humus. Surface soils thaw each summer but are often underlain by a layer of **permafrost** that may be

Figure 2.11 Tundra geography and climate.

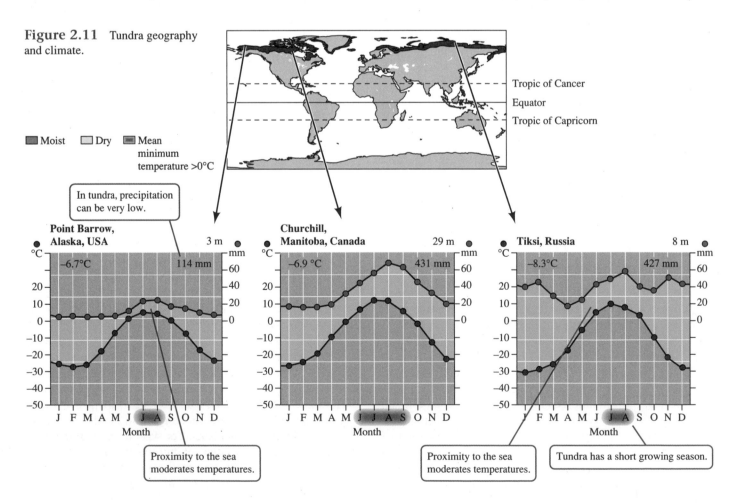

In tundra, precipitation can be very low.

Proximity to the sea moderates temperatures.

Proximity to the sea moderates temperatures.

Tundra has a short growing season.

many meters thick. Permafrost is a permanently frozen layer of soil that remains frozen even during the summer months. The annual freezing and thawing of surface soil combines with the actions of water and gravity to produce a variety of surface processes that are largely limited to the tundra. One of these processes, **solifluction,** slowly moves soils down slopes. In addition, freezing and thawing brings stones to the surface of the soil, forming a netlike, or polygonal, pattern on the surface of tundra soils (fig. 2.12).

Biology

The open tundra landscape is dominated by a richly textured patchwork of perennial herbaceous plants, especially grasses, sedges, mosses, and lichens. The lichens, associations of fungi and algae, are eagerly eaten by reindeer and caribou. The woody vegetation of the tundra consists of dwarf willows and birches along with a variety of low-growing shrubs.

The short periods of warm weather present significant challenges to the residents of the tundra. Plants are generally very slow growing, with nearly all of the living biomass below ground. Plants tend to be very short with strong stems, able to resist the often fierce winds of the north. In the most northerly reaches of the tundra, the sun will never set during the summer, and the plants are able to photosynthesize nearly continuously.

The tundra is one of the last biomes on earth that still supports substantial numbers of large native mammals, including caribou, reindeer, musk ox, bear, and wolves. Small mammals such as arctic foxes, weasels, lemmings, and ground squirrels are also abundant. Resident birds such as the ptarmigan and snowy owl are joined each summer by a host of migratory bird species. Insects, though not as diverse as in biomes farther south, are very abundant. Each summer, swarms of mosquitoes and other insects emerge from the many tundra ponds and streams.

Figure 2.12 Freezing and thawing forms netlike polygons on the surface of the tundra as seen here in an aerial photo of Alaska.

Human Influences

Until recently, human presence in the tundra was largely limited to small populations of hunters and nomadic herders. As a consequence, the tundra has been viewed as one of the last pristine areas of the planet. Recently, however, human intrusion has increased markedly. This biome has been the focus of intense oil exploration and extraction. Airborne pesticides and radionuclides, which originate in distant human population centres, have been deposited on the tundra, sometimes with devastating results. For example, radioactive cesium-137 from the Chernobyl power plant disaster of 1986 was deposited with rainfall, more than 2,000 km away, on the tundra of Norway. In some areas, cesium-137 became so concentrated as it passed through the food chain from lichens to reindeer that both the milk and meat of reindeer were rendered unfit for human consumption.

An equally pressing concern in the North is the impact of rapidly rising temperatures on the permafrost and rates of decomposition. Because of patterns of global air and ocean circulation, areas of the arctic tundra are warming at particularly alarming rates (chapter 23). Although this is a general concern to all biomes, the deep expanses of permafrost in the arctic raise a unique concern. As permafrost melts, the rich organic material it contains becomes available to soil microbes and insects for decomposition, potentially releasing enormous amounts of CO_2 into the atmosphere, amplifying the greenhouse effect and global warming. The exact extent to which this will occur is still unclear, in large part because of the difficulties in working in the North, and our general lack of understanding of the ecology of soils.

Such concerns have shattered the illusion of the tundra as an isolated biome, and the last earthly refuge from human influence. Instead, ecological study in the tundra has made it clear that all biomes are connected, and that no ecological system is truly alone.

Boreal Forest

The **boreal forest,** or **taiga,** is a world of wood and water that covers over 11% of the earth's land area. This biome extends right around the globe in a repeating pattern: forest-water, forest-water, etc. (fig. 2.13). In places, the trees stand so close together you can barely walk through them. Elsewhere, so many trees have been toppled by wind that you can walk on their piled trunks, 1 to 2 m above the ground, for many kilometers. In still other places, the forest is open and you can wander wherever you like on its soft floor of needles and duff. Here and there, where light penetrates, are berry bushes of many varieties where wildlife and humans alike pause and snack on fresh morels or an assortment of berries. A trek through a boreal forest eventually leads to the edge of a lake, river, fen, or bog, where shade and cover give way to light and space. Along the lake margins grow willows and other water- and light-loving plants. The summer forest is coloured green, gray, and brown; the autumn adds brilliant splashes of yellow and red; and the long northern winter turns the boreal forest into a land of white solitude.

Figure 2.13 Boreal forests, such as this one in Siberian Russia, are dominated by a few species of conifer trees.

Geography

Boreal comes from the Greek word for north, reflecting the fact that boreal forests are confined to the Northern Hemisphere. Boreal forests extend from Scandinavia, through European Russia, across Siberia, to central Alaska, and across all of central Canada in a band between 50° and 65° N latitude (fig. 2.14).

These forests are bounded in the south either by temperate forests or temperate grasslands and in the north by tundra. Fingers of boreal forest follow the Rocky Mountains south along the spine of North America, and patches of boreal forest reappear on the mountain slopes of south-central Europe and Asia.

Climate

The boreal forest is found where winters are usually longer than six months, and the summers too short to support temperate forest (fig. 2.14). The boreal forest zone includes some fairly moderate climates, such as that at Umeå, Sweden, where the climate is moderated by the nearby Baltic Sea. However, boreal forests are also found in some of the most variable climates on earth. For instance, the temperature at Verkhoyansk, Russia, in central Siberia, ranges from about –70°C in winter to over 30°C in summer, an annual temperature range of 100°C! Precipitation in the boreal forest is moderate, ranging from about 200 to 600 mm. Yet, because of low temperatures and long winters, evaporation rates are low, and drought is either infrequent or brief. When droughts do occur, however, forest fires can burn vast areas of boreal forest.

Soils

Boreal forest soils tend to be of low fertility, thin, and acidic. Low temperatures and low pH impede decomposition of plant litter and slow the rate of soil building. As a consequence, nutrients are largely tied up in a thick layer of plant litter that

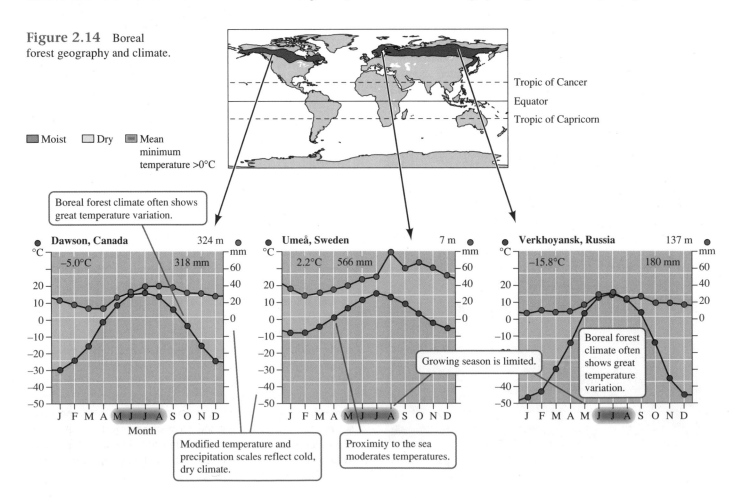

Figure 2.14 Boreal forest geography and climate.

Tropic of Cancer
Equator
Tropic of Capricorn

■ Moist   □ Dry   ■ Mean minimum temperature >0°C

Boreal forest climate often shows great temperature variation.

Dawson, Canada   324 m
–5.0°C   318 mm

Modified temperature and precipitation scales reflect cold, dry climate.

Umeå, Sweden   7 m
2.2°C   566 mm

Growing season is limited.

Proximity to the sea moderates temperatures.

Verkhoyansk, Russia   137 m
–15.8°C   180 mm

Boreal forest climate often shows great temperature variation.

carpets the forest floor. In turn, most trees in boreal forests have a dense network of shallow roots that, along with associated mycorrhizal fungi, tap directly into the nutrients bound up in this litter layer. The topsoil, which underlies the litter layer, is thin. In the more extreme boreal forest climates, the subsoil is permanently frozen in a layer of "permafrost" that may be several meters thick.

Biology

The boreal forest is generally dominated by evergreen conifers such as spruce, fir, and, in some places, pines. Larch, a deciduous conifer, dominates in the most extreme Siberian climates. Deciduous aspen and birch trees grow here and there in mature conifer forests and may dominate the boreal forest during the early stages of recovery following forest fires. Willows grow along the shores of rivers and lakes. Along the base of most trees and on the forest floor lies a lush carpet of mosses and other non-vascular plants. These plants trap much of the rainfall, and are home to a large diversity of insects and other organisms. Between the moss and canopy layers the forest is fairly open with little herbaceous vegetation under the often thick forest canopy. The plants of the boreal are adapted to cold winters and low nutrient availability. The conical shape of the trees helps reduce the risk of limbs being broken by the weight of snow, and the long-lived needles help conserve the nutrients that are of such low availability in the acidic soil.

Scattered throughout much of the boreal forests of the world are large expanses of bogs and fens dominated by a variety of moss species. These areas have waterlogged "soils," with islands of vascular plants centred around a few trees and shrubs. They are home to countless species, including many plants who feed upon the insects they capture with their leaves. The diversity and vastness of the boreal forest offers an exciting opportunity for the adventurous ecologist.

The boreal forest is home to many animals. This is the winter home of migratory caribou and reindeer and the year-round home of moose and woodland bison. The wolf is the major predator of the boreal forest. This biome is also inhabited by black bears and grizzly bears in North America and the brown bear in Eurasia. A variety of smaller mammals such as lynx, wolverine, snowshoe hare, porcupines, and red squirrels also live in boreal forests. The boreal forest is the nesting habitat for many birds that migrate from the tropics each spring and the year-round home of other birds such as crossbills and spruce grouse.

Human Influences

Ancient cave paintings in southern France and northern Spain, made during the last ice age when the climate was much colder, reveal that humans have lived off boreal forest animals, such as the migratory reindeer, for tens of thousands of years. In Eurasia, from Lapland in Scandinavia to Siberia, hunting of reindeer eventually gave way to domestication and herding. In northern Canada and Alaska, where some Native Americans still rely on wild caribou for much of their food, we find a reminder of the earliest human ways of making a

Figure 2.15   Deforestation in the boreal forest.

living in these northern lands. Northern peoples have also long harvested the berries that grow in abundance in the boreal forest. The many berry dishes of Scandinavia are living testimony to this heritage.

For most of history, human intrusion in the boreal forest was relatively light. More recently, however, harvesting of both animals and plants has become intense. Hunting and trapping impact populations of many wildlife species. Boreal forests are being rapidly cut for lumber and pulp (fig. 2.15) and oil and gas exploration is occurring in increasingly large areas. Although the impacts of each of these developments are relatively small, there is increasing awareness that the combined effects of all activities may have large impacts on the boreal forest. However, there continue to be new pressures placed on the forest, ones of tremendous potential economic gain. For example, Alberta currently has allowed oil sand mining in about 3,000 kim^2 of boreal forest. However, deeper deposits occur in over 125,000 km^2, raising the potential for extensive deforestation and development.

Temperate Forest

Old-growth **temperate forest** (fig. 2.16) contains the largest living organisms on earth, perhaps the largest that have ever lived, the sequoias of western North America and the giant *Eucalyptus* trees of southern Australia. The temperate forests of eastern North America, Europe, and Asia still harbour ancient trees that are no less impressive. Enter the subdued light of this cool, moist realm, this world of mushrooms and decaying leaves, and feel yourself shrink before the giants of the biosphere. At dusk, in the heart of old-growth forest, it is easy to understand how cultures around the earth came to make the temperate forest the haunt of diverse mythical creatures such as the nymphs and elves of European folk tales. If you can, visit one of the remaining stands of old-growth temperate forest. There, among giant and ancient trees, you may find a fresh perspective on yourself and life.

Figure 2.16 Old-growth redwood forest in western North America. Redwoods are the tallest trees in the world, with some individual trees growing to heights of over 100 m.

Geography

Temperate forest can be found between 30° and 55° latitude. However, the majority of this biome lies between 40° and 50° (fig. 2.17). In Asia, temperate forest originally covered much of Japan, eastern China, Korea, and eastern Siberia. In western Europe, temperate forests extended from southern Scandinavia to northwestern Iberia and from the British Isles through eastern Europe. North American temperate forests are found from the Atlantic sea coast to the Great Plains and reappear on the West Coast as temperate coniferous forests that extend from northern California through southeastern Alaska. In the Southern Hemisphere, temperate forests are found in southern Chile, New Zealand, and southern Australia.

Climate

Temperate forests, which may be either coniferous or deciduous, occur where temperatures are not extreme and where annual precipitation averages anywhere from about 650 mm to over 3,000 mm (fig. 2.17). These forests generally receive more winter precipitation than temperate grasslands. Deciduous trees usually dominate temperate forests, where the growing season is moist and at least four months long. In deciduous forests, winters last from three to four months. Though snowfall may be heavy, winters in deciduous forests are relatively mild. Where winters are more severe or the summers drier, conifers are more abundant than deciduous trees. The temperate coniferous forests of the Pacific Coast of North America receive most of their precipitation during fall, winter, and spring and are subject to summer drought.

Figure 2.17 Temperate forest geography and climate.

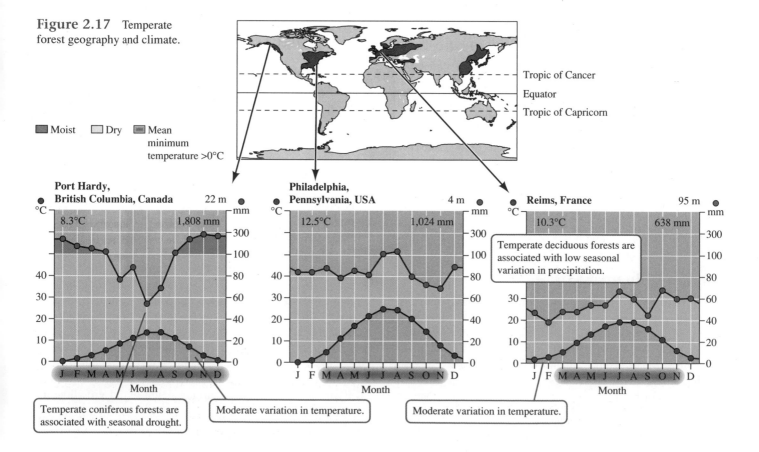

Soils

Temperate forest soils are usually fertile. The most fertile soils in this biome develop under deciduous forests, where they are generally neutral or slightly acidic and rich in both organic matter and inorganic nutrients. Rich soils may develop under coniferous forests but conifers are also able to grow on poorer, acidic soils. Nutrient movement between soil and vegetation tends to be slower and more conservative in coniferous forests; nutrient movement within deciduous forests is generally more dynamic. For example, each year, temperate deciduous forests recycle about twice the amount of nitrogen recycled by temperate coniferous forests of similar age.

Biology

While the diversity of trees found in temperate forests is lower than that of tropical forests, temperate forest biomass can be as great, or greater. Like tropical rain forests, temperate forests are vertically stratified. The lowest layer of vegetation, the herb layer, is followed by a layer of shrubs and saplings, then shade-tolerant understory trees, and finally the canopy, formed by the largest trees. The height of this canopy varies from approximately 40 m to over 100 m. Young saplings of canopy trees have no immediate hope reaching the canopy high above. Many species will have a "sapling bank," with individual plants staying under 1 m in height for decades. When an opening appears these saplings rapidly grow to fill the space. Birds, mammals, and insects make use of all layers of the forest from beneath the forest floor to above the canopy. Small arboreal mammals such as deer mice, tree squirrels, and flying squirrels use the tree canopy. Other mammals such as deer, bear, and fox make their livings on the forest floor. Bats and other animals will find homes inside cavities of large trees. Still others burrow into the rich forest soil. But the most important consumers of all are the fungi and bacteria, largely unnoticed members of entirely different kingdoms. They, along with a diversity of microscopic invertebrate animals, consume the large quantities of wood stored on the floor of old-growth temperate forest (fig. 2.18). The activities of these organisms recycle nutrients, a process upon which the function of the entire forest depends. Thus, the temperate forest, realm of the giants of the biosphere, emerges as a partnership of the great and the very small.

Human Influences

What, besides being large cities, do Tokyo, Beijing, Moscow, Warsaw, Berlin, Paris, London, New York, Washington, D.C., Boston, Toronto, Chicago, and Seattle have in common? They are all built on lands that once supported a temperate forest. Major population centres have grown up in the temperate forest regions of Europe, eastern China, Japan, and North America. The first human settlements in temperate forests were concentrated along forest margins, usually along streams and rivers. Eventually, agriculture was practiced in these forest clearings, and animals and plant products were harvested from the surrounding forest. This was the circumstance several thousand years ago, in Europe and Asia, and five centuries ago, in North America. Since those times, most of the ancient forests have fallen before ax and saw. For example, the Black Forest of central Europe, where forest still survives, has been largely replaced by tree plantations.

Few tracts of the virgin deciduous forest that once covered most of the eastern half of the continent remain, and there are fierce conflicts among disparate interests over the fate of the remaining 1%–2% of old-growth forests in western North America. Finding a way to preserve a sense of wilderness and majesty in the face of unprecedented human expansion and development will be a challenge for years to come. One encouraging sign is that many temperate deciduous forests are able to recover following years of logging and agriculture. Throughout much of eastern North America, there has actually been an increase in forest cover over the last several decades as old and unproductive agricultural fields have been abandoned.

Temperate Grassland

In their original state, **temperate grasslands** extended unbroken over vast areas (fig. 2.19). Nothing other than the open sea feels quite like standing in the middle of unobstructed prairie, under a dome of blue sky. It is no accident that early visitors from forested Europe and eastern North America often referred to the prairie in the American Midwest as a "sea of grass" and to the wagons that crossed them as "prairie schooners." Prairies were the home of the bison and pronghorn and of the nomadic cultures of Eurasia and North America.

Geography

Temperate grassland is the largest biome in North America and is even more extensive in Eurasia (fig. 2.20). In North America, the prairies of the Great Plains extend from southern Canada to the Gulf of Mexico and from the Rocky Mountains to the deciduous forests of the east. Additional grasslands are found on the Palouse prairies of Idaho and Washington and in the central valley and surrounding foothills of California. In Eurasia, the temperate grassland biome forms a virtually unbroken band from eastern Europe all the way to eastern China. In the Southern Hemisphere, temperate grassland occurs in Argentina, Uruguay, southern Brazil, New Zealand, and Australia.

Figure 2.18 Massive amounts of wood are stored on the forest floor of the virgin temperate coniferous forests of the Pacific Northwest, such as this one in southeastern Alaska.

(a)   (b)

Figure 2.19   (*a*) Pronghorn, native grazers of the temperate grasslands of North America. (*b*) Badlands region of southeastern Alberta, Canada.

Climate

Temperate grasslands receive between 300 and 1,000 mm of precipitation annually. Though wetter than deserts, temperate grasslands experience droughts that may persist for several years. The maximum precipitation usually occurs in summer during the height of the growing season. This summer peak in precipitation is clearly shown in the climate diagrams for Lethbridge, Alberta, Canada; Magnitogorsk, Russia; and Taiyuan, China (fig. 2.20).

Soils

Temperate grassland soils are derived from a wide variety of parent materials. The best temperate grassland soils are deep, basic or neutral, and fertile and contain large quantities of organic matter. The black prairie soils of North America and Eurasia, famous for their fertility, contain the greatest amount of organic matter. The brown soils of the more arid grasslands contain less organic matter.

Figure 2.20   Temperate grassland distribution and climate.

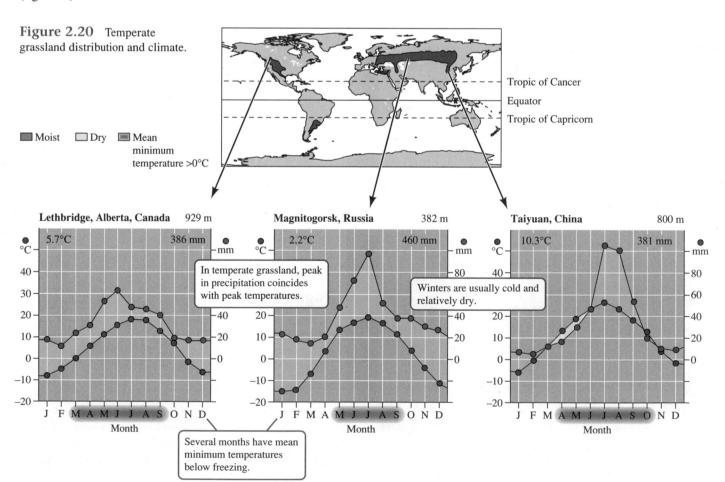

Biology

Temperate grassland is thoroughly dominated by herbaceous vegetation. A combination of fire, drought, and grazing exclude woody vegetation from temperate grasslands, where trees and shrubs are often limited to the margins of streams and rivers. These factors also result in strong pressures on plants to protect themselves from these stresses. It is not surprising to find up to 80% of the living biomass of some grasslands below ground. In addition to grasses, which make up the bulk of vegetative biomass, there can be a striking diversity of other herbaceous vegetation. Spring graces temperate grasslands with showy anemones, roses, iris, and other wild flowers; up to 70 species can bloom simultaneously on the species-rich North American prairie (fig. 2.21). The height of grassland vegetation varies from about 5 cm in dry, short-grass prairies to over 300 cm in the wetter tall-grass prairies.

Temperate grasslands once supported huge herds of roving herbivores: bison and pronghorns in North America (see fig. 2.19a); wild horses and Saiga antelope in Eurasia. As in the open sea, the herbivores of the open grassland banded together in social groups; as did their attendant predators, the steppe and prairie wolves. North American prairies are also the historical home of the grizzly bear. However, human pressures have been so great that these animals have been pushed into the mountains. The smaller animals, such as grasshoppers and mice, inconspicuous among the herbaceous vegetation, were even more numerous than the large herbivores. Grassland animals of intermediate size generally had one of two life-styles: there were the burrowing, like the badger and prairie dog, and the fleet, like the swift fox and prairie falcon. With domestication of the horse, the human cultures of temperate grasslands joined this second group.

Human Influences

The extent of agricultural development in North America and throughout the world has left grasslands among the most critically endangered biomes. The first human populations on temperate grasslands were nomadic hunters. Next came the nomadic herders. Later, with their plows, came the farmers, who broke the sod and tapped into fertile soils built up over thousands of years. Under the plow, temperate grasslands have produced some of the most fertile farmlands on earth and fed much of the world. However, much of this productivity depends on substantial additions of inorganic fertilizers. For example, prairie soils have lost as much as 35% to 40% of their organic matter in just 35 to 40 years of cultivation. In addition, the more arid grasslands, with their frequent droughts, do not appear capable of supporting farming indefinitely. The future of agriculture in temperate grasslands hinges on several unanswered questions, among them: Can the losses of organic matter and nutrients be reversed? What level of agricultural production can be sustained over the long term?

Mediterranean Woodland and Shrubland

The **Mediterranean woodland and shrubland** climate was the climate of the classical Greeks and the coastal Native American tribes of Old California. The mild temperate climate experienced by these cultures was accompanied by high biological richness (fig. 2.22). The richness of the Mediterranean woodland flora is captured by a folk song from the Mediterranean region that begins: "Spring has already arrived. All the countryside will bloom; a feast of color!" To this visual feast, Mediterranean woodlands and shrublands around the Mediterranean Sea add a chorus of bird song and the smells of aromatic plants, including rosemary, thyme, and laurel.

Figure 2.21 Large numbers of plant species can flower at once in this grassland in Kinsella, Alberta.

Figure 2.22 A Mediterranean woodland in California shown during the cool moist season, when the herbaceous vegetation is still green.

Geography

Mediterranean woodlands and shrublands occur on all the continents except Antarctica (fig. 2.23). They are most extensive around the Mediterranean Sea and in North America, where they extend from California into northern Mexico. They are also found in central Chile, southern Australia, and southern Africa. Under present climatic conditions Mediterranean woodlands and shrublands grow between about 30° and 40° latitude. This position places the majority of this biome north of the subtropical deserts in the Northern Hemisphere, and south of them in the Southern Hemisphere. The farflung geographic distribution of Mediterranean woodland and shrubland is reflected in the diversity of names for this biome. In western North America, it is called chaparral. In Spain, the most common name for Mediterranean woodland and shrubland is *matoral*. Farther east in the Mediterranean basin the biome is referred to as *garrigue*. Meanwhile in the Southern Hemisphere, South Africans call the biome *fynbos,* while Australians refer to at least one form of it as *mallee*. While the names for this biome vary widely, its climate docs not.

Climate

The Mediterranean woodland and shrubland climate is cool and moist during fall, winter, and spring. In most regions the Mediterranean woodland and shrubland summers are hot and dry. The danger of frost varies considerably from one Mediterranean woodland and shrubland region to another. When they do occur, however, frosts are usually not severe. The combination of dry summers and dense vegetation, rich in essential oils, creates ideal conditions for frequent and intense fires.

Soils

The soils of Mediterranean woodlands and shrublands are generally of low to moderate fertility and have a reputation for being fragile. Some soils, such as those of the South African fynbos, have exceptionally low fertility. Fire in the Mediterranean woodlands and shrublands of southern California can cause 40-fold increases in soil losses through erosion. Fire coupled with overgrazing has stripped the soil from some Mediterranean woodland and shrubland landscapes. Elsewhere, these landscapes, under careful stewardship, have maintained their integrity for thousands of years.

Biology

The plants and animals of Mediterranean woodlands and shrublands, like their desert neighbours, show several adaptations to drought. Trees and shrubs are typically evergreen and have small, tough leaves. This vegetation conserves both water and nutrients; many plants of Mediterranean woodlands and shrublands have well-developed mutualistic relationships with microbes that fix atmospheric nitrogen.

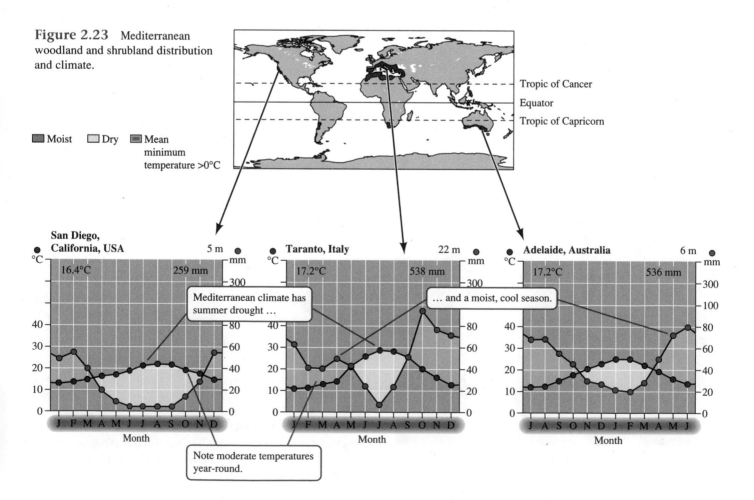

Figure 2.23 Mediterranean woodland and shrubland distribution and climate.

The process of decomposition is greatly slowed during the dry summer and then started again with the coming of fall and winter rains. Curiously, this intermittent decomposition may speed the process sufficiently so that average rates of decomposition are comparable to those in temperate forests

Fire, a common occurrence in Mediterranean woodlands and shrublands, has selected for fire-resistant plants. Many Mediterranean woodland trees have thick, tough bark that is resistant to fire (fig. 2.24). In contrast, many shrubs in Mediterranean woodlands are rich in oils and burn readily but resprout rapidly. Most herbaceous plants grow during the cool, moist season and then die back in summer, thus avoiding both drought and fire.

The animals of the Mediterranean woodlands and shrublands, both vertebrates and invertebrates, are highly diverse. In addition to resident species, many migratory birds and some migratory insects spend the winter in Mediterranean woodland and shrubland climates, as do some human populations. The plants and animals of the far-flung Mediterranean woodlands have been derived from diverse evolutionary lineages. For example, in the Mediterranean woodlands and shrublands of North America, the native browsers, herbivores that feed on the buds, twigs, and bark of woody plants, are deer. Around the Mediterranean Sea, in addition to deer, there are wild sheep and goats. In southern Africa, the native browsers are small antelope, and in Australia, they are kangaroos.

Human Influences

Human activity has had a substantial influence on the structure of landscapes in Mediterranean woodlands and shrublands.

Figure 2.24   The thick bark of the cork oak of the Mediterranean region protects the tree from fire.

For example, the open oak woodlands of southern Spain and Portugal are the product of an agricultural management system that is thousands of years old. In this system, cattle graze on grasses, pigs consume acorns produced by the oaks, and cork is harvested from cork oaks as a cash crop. Selected areas are planted in wheat once every five to six years and allowed to lie fallow the remainder of the time. This system of agriculture, which emphasizes low-intensity cultivation and long-term sustainability, may offer clues for long-term sustainable agriculture in other regions.

Whether in southern France or southern California, people generally find the Mediterranean woodland and shrubland climate agreeable. High population densities coupled with a long history of human occupation have left an indelible mark on Mediterranean woodlands and shrublands. Early human impacts included clearing of forests for agriculture, setting fires to control woody species and encourage grass, harvesting brush for fuel, and grazing and browsing by domestic livestock. Today, Mediterranean woodlands and shrublands around the world are being covered by human habitations. In Mediterranean woodlands and shrublands, as is often the case with fragile things that we hold dear, enjoyment and destruction are close kin.

Desert

In the sparse **desert** landscape, sculpted by wind and water, the ecologist grows to appreciate geology, hydrology, and climate as much as organisms (fig. 2.25). In the desert, drought and flash floods, and heat and bitter cold, often go hand in hand. Yet, the often repeated description of life in the desert as "life on the edge" betrays an outsider's view. Life in the desert is not luxuriant, but it does not follow that living conditions there are necessarily harsh. For many species, the desert is the centre of their world, not the edge. In their own way, many desert organisms flourish on meager rations of water, high temperatures, and saline soils. To understand life in the desert, the ecologist must see it from the perspective of its natural inhabitants. The ecologist who can peer out at the desert environment from under the skin of a cactus or sand viper is on the threshold of understanding.

Geography

Deserts occupy about 20% of the land surface of the earth. Two bands of deserts ring the globe, one at about 30° N latitude and one at about 30° S (fig. 2.26). These bands correspond to latitudes where dry subtropical air descends (see fig. 2.4), drying the landscape as it spreads north and south. Other deserts are found either deep in the interior of continents, for example, the Gobi of central Asia, or in the rain shadow of mountains, for example, the Great Basin Desert of North America. Few may realize that the Great Basin Desert extends into Canada (fig. 2.26). Still others are found along the cool western coasts of continents, for example, the Atacama of South America and the Namib of southwestern Africa, where air circulating across a cool ocean delivers a great deal of fog to the coast but little rain.

(a)   (b)

Figure 2.25 Deserts differ across the world. (*a*) Acacia trees between a gravel plain and sand dunes in the Namib Desert of southwestern Africa. (*b*) The landscape around the deserts of Osoyoos, British Columbia.

Climate

Environmental conditions vary considerably from one desert to another. Some, such as the Atacama and central Sahara, receive very little rainfall and fit the stereotype of deserts as extremely dry places. Other deserts, such as some parts of the Sonoran Desert of North America, may receive nearly 300 mm of rainfall annually. Whatever their mean annual rainfall, however, water loss in deserts due to evaporation and transpiration by plants exceeds precipitation during most of the year.

Figure 2.26 includes the climate diagrams of two hot deserts. Notice that drought conditions prevail during all months and that during some months average temperatures exceed 30°C at both Yuma, Arizona, and Faya Largeau, Chad. The maximum shade temperatures in any biome, greater than 56°C, were recorded in the deserts of North Africa and western North America. However, some deserts can be bitterly cold. For example, average winter temperatures at Dzamiin Uuded, Mongolia, in the Gobi Desert of central Asia sometimes

Figure 2.26 Desert distribution and climate.

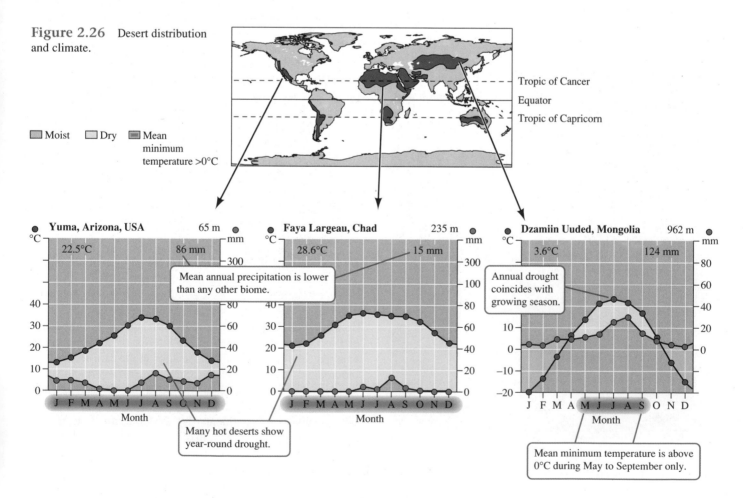

fall to –20°C. Notice that the average annual temperature at Dzamiin Uuded is only 3.6°C and the growing season, as indicated by the months shaded red on the climate diagram, lasts only five months. The relatively moist period at Dzamiin Uuded occurs during the cold season when average temperatures are below 0°C.

It is a lack of available water, rather than extremely hot temperatures that makes a desert. Even large expanses of Antartica are considered deserts.

Soils

Desert plants and animals can turn this landscape into a mosaic of diverse soils. Desert soils are generally low in organic matter, with the soils consisting primarily of sand and rock. However, the soils under desert shrubs often contain large amounts of organic matter and form islands of fertility. Desert animals can also affect soil properties. For example, in North America, kangaroo rats change the texture and elevate the nutrient content of surface soils by burrowing and hoarding seeds. In Middle Eastern deserts, porcupines and isopods strongly influence a variety of soil properties.

Desert soils, particularly those in poorly drained valleys and lowlands, may contain high concentrations of salts. Salts accumulate in these soils as water evaporates from the soil surface. Salt accumulation increases the aridity of the desert environment by making it harder for plants to extract water from the soils.

Biology

The desert landscape presents an unfamiliar face to the visitor from moist climates. Plant cover is absent from many places, exposing soils and other geological features. Where there is plant cover, it is sparse. The plants themselves look unfamiliar. Desert vegetation often cloaks the landscape in a gray-green mantle. This is because many desert plants protect their photosynthetic surfaces from intense sunlight and reduce evaporative water losses with a dense covering of plant hairs. Other plant adaptations in the desert include small leaves, producing leaves only in response to rainfall and then dropping them during intervening dry periods, or having no leaves at all (fig. 2.27). Some desert plants, such as cacti, have taken reduced leaf area to an extreme, with photosynthesis occurring in green stems while the leaves have been modified into spines (fig. 2.27). Many of the columnar cacti species further minimize the harmful effects of the strong desert sun by growing directly towards the sun. At first this seems counterintuitive, but as you can see in figure 2.27, this action exposes the minimum amount of surface area to direct sunlight, reducing transpiration and heat imbalance. Some desert plants avoid drought almost entirely by remaining dormant in the soil as seeds, which germinate and grow only during infrequent wet periods. Because these wet periods can be so short-lived, the growth rates of many desert annual plant species are among the fastest on the planet.

(a)

(b)

Figure 2.27   Similarity among desert plants: (*a*) cactus in North America, (*b*) *Euphorbia* in Africa.

In deserts, animal abundance tends to be low but diversity can be high. Most desert animals use behaviour to avoid environmental extremes. In summer, many avoid the heat of the day by being active at dusk and dawn or at night. In winter, the same species may be active during the day. Animals also use body orientation to minimize heat gain in the summer.

Human Influences

Many human cultures have arisen independently in the deserts of North America, Australia, Africa, and Asia. Desert peoples have flourished where nature is stingiest. Compared to true desert species, however, humans are profligate water users. Consequently, human populations in desert regions are concentrated around oases and river valleys, and wherever they live, desert people dream of the sound of water. That dreaming, gone awry, litters desert landscapes around the world with outrageous fountains, ancient and modern water diversions, agricultural schemes, and large urban centres complete with artificial lakes and numerous golf courses. Pushed, the desert blooms. Unfortunately, many desert landscapes have been pushed until they now grow little but salt crystals.

The desert is one biome that, because of human activity, is increasing in area. Plowing, overgrazing, and deforestation of arid regions all lead to soil erosion. Once the O horizon blows away, it is difficult for it to be re-established and desertification often occurs.

Tropical Savanna

Stand in the middle of a savanna, a tropical grassland dotted with scattered trees, and your eye will be drawn to the horizon for the approach of thunderstorms or wandering herds of wildlife (fig. 2.28). The **tropical savanna** is the kingdom of the farsighted, the stealthy, and the swift and is the birthplace of humankind. It was from here that humans eventually moved out into every biome on the face of the earth. The first naturalists, our ancient ancestors, knew the tropical savanna biome best, and the fascination continues.

Geography

Most tropical savannas occur north and south of tropical dry forests within 10° to 20° of the equator. In Africa south of the Sahara Desert, tropical savannas extend from the west to the east coasts, cut a north–south swath across the east African highlands, and reappear in south-central Africa (fig. 2.29). In South America, tropical savannas occur in south-central Brazil and cover a great deal of Venezuela and Columbia. Tropical savannas are also the natural vegetation of much of northern Australia in the region just south of the tropical dry forest. The savanna is the natural vegetation of an area in southern Asia just east of the Indus River in eastern Pakistan and northwestern India.

Figure 2.28   Tropical savanna and grazers in Kenya. The tropical savanna landscape is partially maintained by periodic fires that reduce the density of woody vegetation.

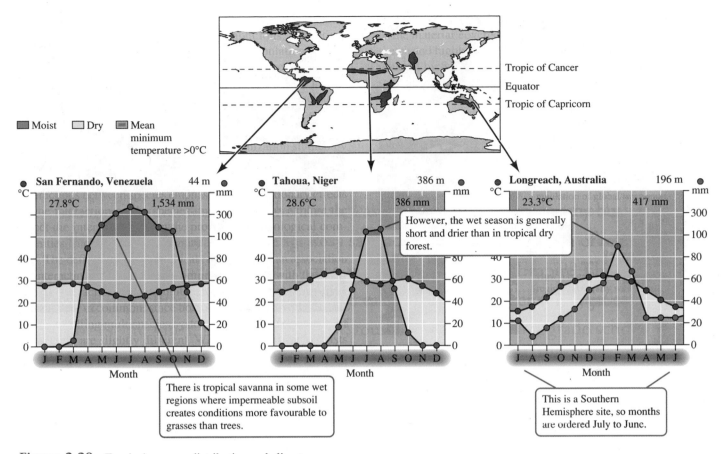

Figure 2.29 Tropical savanna distribution and climate.

Climate

Life on the savanna cycles to the rhythms of alternating dry and wet seasons (fig. 2.29). Here, however, seasonal drought combines with another important physical factor, fire. The rains come in summer and are accompanied by intense lightning. This lightning often starts fires, particularly at the beginning of the wet season when the savanna is tinder dry. These fires kill young trees while the grasses survive and quickly resprout. Consequently, fires help maintain the tropical savanna as a landscape of grassland and scattered trees.

The savanna climate is generally drier than that of tropical dry forest. The longer dry season and lower annual precipitation of most savannas are clearly shown by the climate diagrams for Tahoua, Niger, and Longreach, Australia (fig. 2.29). The mean rainfall for these two areas is within the range (300–500 mm) occurring on most savannas. However, the climate diagram for San Fernando, Venezuela (fig. 2.29) shows that some savannas receive as much rainfall as a tropical dry forest. Other savannas occur in areas that are as dry as deserts. What keeps the wet savannas near San Fernando from being replaced by forest and how can savannas persist under desertlike conditions? The answer lies deep in the savanna soils.

Soils

Soil layers with low permeability to water play a key role in maintaining many tropical savannas. For instance, because a dense, impermeable subsoil retains water near the surface, savannas occur in areas of southwest Africa that would otherwise support only desert. Impermeable soils also help savannas persist in wet areas, particularly in South America. Trees do not move onto savannas where an impermeable subsoil keeps surface soils waterlogged during the wet season. In these landscapes, scattered trees occur only where soils are well drained.

Biology

The tropical savanna is populated by wandering animals that move in response to seasonal and year-to-year variations in rainfall and food availability. The wandering consumers of the Australian savannas include kangaroos, large flocks of birds, and, for at least 40,000 years, humans. During droughts, some of these Australian species travel thousands of kilometers in search of suitable conditions. The African savanna is home to a host of well-known mobile consumers, such as elephants, wildebeest, giraffes, zebras, lions, and, again, humans (see fig. 2.28).

The parklike landscape of the savanna is maintained by a dynamic interplay of physical and biological forces. The diverse mammalian herbivores of the African savanna harvest all above ground parts of the vegetation, from low herbs to the tops of trees. As noted, fire plays a key role in maintaining the savanna landscape. Frequent fires have selected for fire resistance in the savanna flora. The few tree species on the savanna resist fire well enough to be unaffected by low-intensity

Figure 2.30   Domestic livestock, such as these cattle on an African savanna, have had a major impact on tropical savannas around the world.

fires, and some even require fire for dispersal and germination of their seed. Although tropical savannas are confined to an area between the tropics of Cancer and Capricorn, there also exist more temperate savannas throughout the world. For example, the Aspen parkland is a mosaic of Aspen stand and grasslands, extending through much of western Canada. Though parklands are often thought of simply as transition zones from the grasslands to the south and Boreal to the north, they are true savannas, native home to bison, wolves, raptors, and bear.

Human Influences

Humans are, in some measure, a product of the savanna and the savanna, in turn, has been influenced by human activity. One of the factors that forged an indelible link between us and this biome is fire. Long before the appearance of hominids, fire played a role in the ecology of the tropical savanna. Later, the savanna was the classroom where early humans observed and learned to use, control, and make fire. Eventually, humans began to purposely set fire to the savanna, which, in turn, helped to maintain and spread the savanna itself. We had entered the business of large-scale manipulation of nature.

Originally, humans subsisted on the savanna by hunting and gathering. In time, they shifted from hunting to pastoralism, replacing wild game with domestic grazers and browsers. Today, livestock ranching is the main source of livelihood in all the savanna regions. In Africa, livestock raising has coexisted with wildlife for millennia. In modern-day subsaharan Africa, however, the combination of growing human populations, high density of livestock, and drought has devastated much of the region known as the Sahel (fig. 2.30).

Tropical Dry Forest

During the dry season, the **tropical dry forest** is all earth tones; in the rainy season, it's an emerald tangle (fig. 2.31).

Figure 2.31   The same view of a tropical dry forest in Guanacaste, Costa Rice during the wet and dry seasons.

Life in the tropical dry forest responds to the rhythms of the annual solar cycle, which drives the oscillation between wet and dry seasons. During the dry season, most trees in the tropical dry forest are dormant. Then, as the rains approach, trees flower and insects appear to pollinate them. The pace of life quickens. Eventually, as the first storms of the wet season arrive, the trees produce their leaves and transform the landscape.

Geography

Tropical dry forests occupy a substantial portion of the earth's surface between about 10° and 25° latitude (fig. 2.32). In Africa, tropical dry forests are found both north and south of the central African rain forests. In the Americas, tropical dry forests are the natural vegetation of extensive areas south and north of the Amazon rain forest. Tropical dry forests also

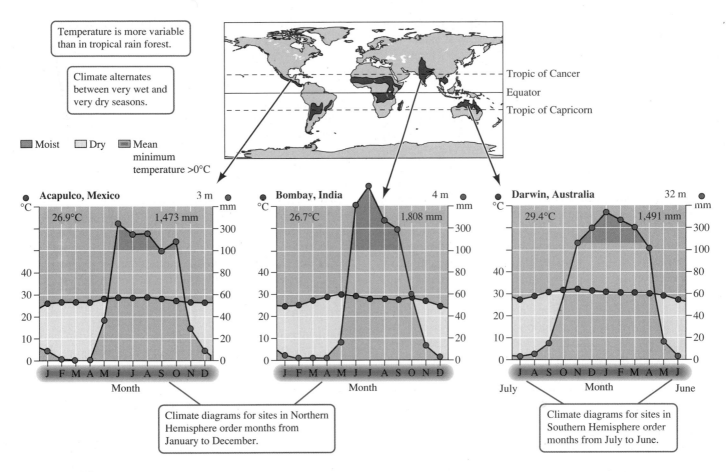

Temperature is more variable than in tropical rain forest.

Climate alternates between very wet and very dry seasons.

Tropic of Cancer
Equator
Tropic of Capricorn

Moist ▪   Dry □   Mean minimum temperature >0°C ▪

Acapulco, Mexico   3 m
°C   mm
26.9°C   1,473 mm
                       300
                       100
40   80
30   60
20   40
10   20
0   0
J F M A M J J A S O N D
Month

Bombay, India   4 m
°C   mm
26.7°C   1,808 mm
                       300
                       100
40   80
30   60
20   40
10   20
0   0
J F M A M J J A S O N D
Month

Darwin, Australia 32 m
°C   mm
29.4°C   1,491 mm
                       300
                       100
40   80
30   60
20   40
10   20
0   0
J A S O N D J F M A M J
July   Month   June

Climate diagrams for sites in Northern Hemisphere order months from January to December.

Climate diagrams for sites in Southern Hemisphere order months from July to June.

Figure 2.32 Tropical dry forest distribution and climate.

extend up the west coast of Central America and into North America along the west coast of Mexico. In Asia, tropical dry forests are the natural vegetation of most of India and the Indochina peninsula. Australian tropical dry forests form a continuous band across the northern and northeastern portions of the continent.

Climate

The climate of tropical dry forests is more seasonal than that of tropical rain forests. The three climate diagrams shown in figure 2.32, each show a dry season lasting for six to seven months, followed by a season of abundant rainfall. This wet season lasts for about five months in Acapulco, Mexico, and Bombay, India, and about six months in Darwin, Australia. Heavy rains occur during the wet season at all three sites with wet season monthly precipitation similar to that found in tropical rain forests. The climate diagrams also indicate more seasonal variation in temperature than we saw in the climate diagrams for the tropical rain forest. Notice that the seasonal rains in the tropical dry forest come during the warmer part of the year.

Soils

The soils of many tropical dry forests are of great age, particularly those in the parts of Africa, Australia, India, and Brazil that were once part of the ancient southern continent of Gondwana. The soils of tropical dry forests tend to be less

acidic than those of rain forests and are generally richer in nutrients. However, the annual pulses of torrential rain make the soils of tropical dry forest highly vulnerable to erosion, particularly when deforested and converted to agriculture.

Biology

The plants of the tropical dry forest are strongly influenced by physical factors. For example, the height of the dry forest is highly correlated with average precipitation. Trees are tallest in the wettest areas. In the driest places, where the trees are smallest and the landscape more open, the tropical dry forest can blend into areas of tropical savanna or even desert. In addition, in the driest habitats, all trees drop their leaves during the dry season; in wetter areas over 50% may be evergreen. Many plant species in the tropical dry forest produce fruits that are attractive to animals and, as in the tropical rain forest, have animal-dispersed seeds. However, wind-dispersed seeds are also common in more open tropical dry forests.

The tropical dry forest shares many animal species with the rain forest and savanna, including monkeys, parrots, and large cats such as the tiger in Asia and the jaguar in the Americas. The lives of dry forest animals, like those of its plants, are organized around alternating wet and dry seasons. Many dry forest birds, mammals, and even insects make seasonal migrations to wetter habitats along rivers or to the nearest rain forest. The discovery of these migrations has led to other questions that await study: Do dry forest species require nearby rain forests for refuge during the dry season? To what extent may some "rain forest" species depend upon intact dry forest?

Human Influences

Peter Murphy and Ariel Lugo (1986) studied the patterns of human settlement in the tropical forests of Central America. They divided the types of forests into rain forest, wet forest, moist forest, dry forest, and very dry forest. Their analysis showed a very uneven pattern of human settlement. Murphy and Lugo calculated that tropical rain forest and tropical wet forest include approximately 7% of the human population of Central America. In contrast, tropical dry forest and moist forest include about 79% of the Central American population. As figure 2.33 shows, the population density—the number of people per square kilometer—in tropical dry and moist forests is more than 10 times higher than in tropical wet and rain forests.

Heavy human settlement has devastated the tropical dry forest. While the world's attention has been focused on the plight of rain forests, intact tropical dry forests have nearly disappeared. Why have tropical dry forests been more densely settled? The relatively fertile soil of tropical dry forests has attracted agricultural development. Extensive clearing for agriculture has reduced tropical dry forests in Central America and Mexico to less than 2% of its former area. People have replaced tropical dry forests with cattle ranches, grain farms, and cotton fields. Tropical dry forests are more vulnerable to human exploitation than tropical rain forests because the dry season makes them more accessible and easier to burn. Murphy and Lugo also suggested that there may be less impact from human diseases in tropical dry forests.

Intensive settlement and agricultural development have whittled away at tropical dry forests over a period of centuries. In contrast, rain forests are disappearing in a recent push involving far fewer people but an enormous application of mechanical energy. This energy is directed at the extraction of lumber and minerals and at large-scale conversion of land from rain forest to agriculture. Though human impacts on tropical dry forests and rain forests have differed in tempo, their ecological consequences appear to be the same—massive loss of biological diversity.

The loss of the dry forest is significant because, while rain forests may support a somewhat greater number of species, many dry forest species are found nowhere else. However, out of this devastation has come Guanacaste National Park in Costa Rica, a model attempt to restore a tropical dry forest in a way that also helps serve the cultural and economic needs of local people (see the introduction to chapter 2).

Tropical Rain Forest

Tropical rain forest is nature's most extravagant garden (fig. 2.34). Beyond its tangled edge, a rain forest opens into a surprisingly spacious interior, illuminated by dim greenish

Figure 2.34 Tropical rain forest in Borneo. Within the three-dimensional framework of tropical rain forests live a higher diversity of organisms than in any other terrestrial biome.

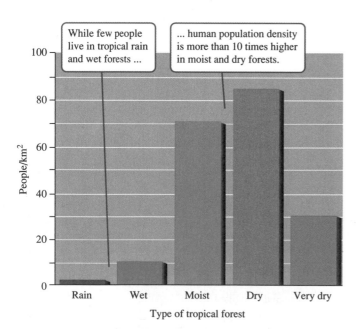

While few people live in tropical rain and wet forests ...

... human population density is more than 10 times higher in moist and dry forests.

Figure 2.33 Human population density in the tropical forests of Central America (data from Murphy and Lugo 1986, after Tosi and Voertman 1964).

light shining through a ceiling of leaves. High above towers the forest canopy, home to many rain forest species and the aerial laboratory of a few intrepid rain forest ecologists. The architecture of rain forests, with their vaulted ceilings and spires, has invited comparisons to cathedrals and mansions. However, this cathedral is alive from ceiling to sub-basement. In the rain forest, the sounds of evening and morning, the brilliant flashes of colour, and rich scents carried on moist night air speak of abundant life, in seemingly endless variety.

Geography

Tropical rain forests straddle the equator in three major regions: Southeast Asia, West Africa, and South and Central America (fig. 2.35). Most rain forest occurs within 10° of latitude north or south of the equator. Outside this equatorial band are the rain forests of Central America and Mexico, southeastern Brazil, eastern Madagascar, southern India, and northeastern Australia.

Climate

The global distribution of rain forests corresponds to areas where conditions are warm and wet year-round (fig. 2.35). Temperatures in tropical rain forests vary little from month to month and often change as much in a day as they do over the entire year. Though rain forests have a reputation for being extremely hot places, they are not. Average temperatures are about 25° to 27°C, lower than the average maximum summer temperatures in many deserts and temperate regions. Annual rainfall ranges from about 2,000 to 4,000 mm, and some rain forests receive even more precipitation. To support a tropical rain forest, rainfall must be fairly evenly distributed throughout the year. Notice that the climate diagrams for Belem, Kisangani, and Kuala Lumpur indicate moist conditions throughout the year. In summary, the tropical rain forest climate is warm, moist, and one of the least seasonal on earth.

Soils

Heavy rains gradually leach nutrients from rain forest soils and rapid decomposition in the warm, moist rain forest climate keeps the organic horizon narrow. Consequently, rain forest soils are often nutrient-poor, acidic, thin, and low in organic matter. In many areas, **lateritic soils** occur. These soils are the result of extensive weathering of the parent rocks, resulting in high concentrations of iron and aluminum, and low concentrations of essential plant nutrients. In many rain forests, more nutrients are tied up in living tissue than in soil. Rain forest plants are adept at conserving and acquiring nutrients. Large numbers of free-living fungi, bacteria, and soil animals rapidly scavenge nutrients from plant litter and animal wastes, further tightening the nutrient economy of the rain forest. It is often only a matter of minutes before insects and other organisms attack the feces left behind by the myriad animals of the rainforest.

Some rain forests, however, occur where soils are very fertile. For instance, rain forests grow on young volcanic soils that have not yet been leached of their nutrients by heavy tropical rains. Fertile rain forest soils also occur along rivers, where a fresh nutrient supply is delivered with each flood.

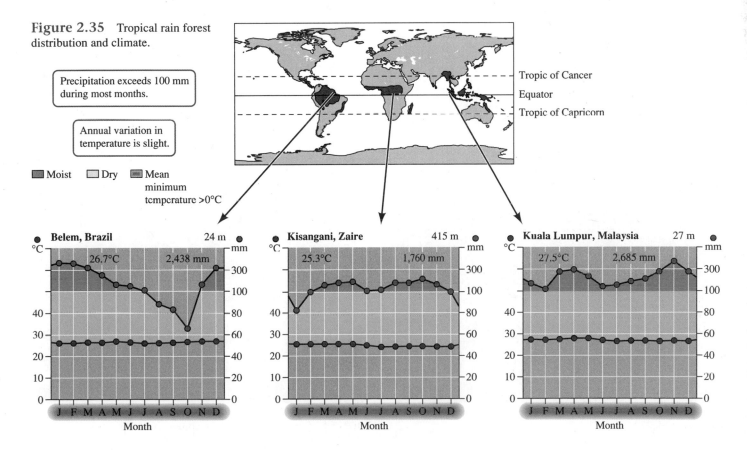

Figure 2.35   Tropical rain forest distribution and climate.

Biology

Humans live mostly in two dimensions and are most at home on the rain forest floor. In contrast, many organisms in the rain forest have evolved to use the vertical dimension provided by trees. Trees dominate the rain forest landscape and average about 40 m in height. However, some reach 50, 60, or even 80 m tall. Despite the great heights of these trees, many tropical rain forest species form very shallow root systems that grow through, over, and under the thin layer of organic matter on the forest floor. By having such shallow roots, these trees are able to absorb nutrients as soon as they are made available through the activity of the soil food web. Some plants have taken this approach to an extreme, growing roots up the stems of their neighbours. Such growth allows them to absorb the nutrients that are leached out of leaves as a consequence of the heavy rainfall. How can these giants of the rain forest grow so tall without a deep anchoring root system for structural support? Rather than anchors, many of these trees use **buttress roots**, which are equally effective in keeping them upright (fig. 2.36*a*). Buttress roots are large roots on all sides of a tree that occur above the soil surface, providing structural support rather than nutrient capture.

The diversity of rain forest trees is also impressive. One hectare (100 m × 100 m) of temperate forest may contain a few dozen tree species; 1 ha of tropical rain forest may contain up to 300 tree species.

The three-dimensional framework formed by rain forest trees is festooned with other plant growth forms. The trees are trellises for climbing vines and growing sites for **epiphytes**, plants that grow on other plants (fig. 2.36*b*). The pools of water and foliage provided by epiphytes are also home to large populations of even more species of bacteria, fungi, arthropods, algae, plants, and small vertebrates. It seems that at every turn in the tropical rain forest there are more organisms to be found.

Rain forest animals, from parrots and bats to sloths, snakes, frogs, and monkeys, are also strongly arboreal and the insects of the rain forest canopy are the most diverse of all. A single rain forest tree may support several thousand species of insects, many of which have not been described by scientists. Biologists now estimate that millions of undiscovered insect species may live in tropical rain forests, above and below ground.

The rain forest is not, however, just a warehouse for a large number of dissociated species. Intricate relationships weave these species into a living green tapestry. Most rain forest plant species depend on animals, from bats and birds to butterflies and bees, to pollinate the orchids and other flowers for which the rain forest is famous. The plants also produce a striking variety of fruit and many rely on animals to disperse

(a)

(b)

Figure 2.36   (*a*) Large buttress roots in a tropical rain forest. (*b*) A epiphytic plant growing on the branch of a tree.

their seeds. For the service of seed dispersal, the plants trade a nutritious meal. In the tropical rain forest there are plants that cannot live without particular species of ants, mites that make their homes in the flowers of plants and depend on hummingbirds to get them from flower to flower, and trees and vines that continuously compete for access to light. How did this incredible diversity of species and relationships arise? How is it maintained? Does the health of the rain forest depend on this stunning biological diversity? We hope the answers to these questions can be provided by the generations of ecologists yet to come.

Human Influences

People from all over the globe owe more to the tropics than is generally realized. Many of the world's staple foods, including maize (called corn in North America and Australia), rice, bananas, and sugarcane, and approximately 25% of all prescription drugs, were originally derived from tropical plants. Many more species, directly useful to humans, may await discovery. In addition, the tropics continue to harbour important genetic varieties of domesticated plant species. Unfortunately, tropical rain forests are fast disappearing. Without them, our understanding of the causes and maintenance of biological diversity will remain forever impoverished.

Humans have exploited tropical rain forests for thousands of years through a mixture of hunting and gathering and shifting agriculture. The hunter-gatherer cultures of rain forests, whether in Asia, Africa, or the Americas, have each used hundreds of species for everything from food and building materials to medicines. Today, we are destroying rain forest for timber, minerals, and short-lived agricultural profits. In response to demographic pressures from exploding human populations in tropical countries and economic pressures from the developed countries, traditional systems of exploitation have given way to the bulldozer and chain saw. Can modern tropical societies create a balanced contract with nature that preserves the invaluable biological resources of the rain forest and provides a decent livelihood for local people? This question will be answered by the present generation.

Mountains: Islands in the Sky

We now shift our attention to mountains, though they do not represent a specific biome. Because of the environmental changes that occur with altitude, several biomes may be found on a single mountainside. We include mountains here because they often introduce unique environmental conditions and organisms to regions around the globe.

Everywhere, mountains capture the imagination as places of geological, biological, and climatic diversity and as places with a view (fig. 2.37). You can stand with eagles and gaze on the plains below, an experience that in the days before air travel was unique to mountains. Mountains have long offered refuge for special flora and fauna and humans alike. Like oceanic islands, they offer unique insights into evolutionary and ecological processes.

Figure 2.37 Mount Logan, Yukon. Environmental conditions and organisms vary greatly from low to high elevations on mountains.

Geography

Mountains are built by geological processes, such as volcanism and movements of the earth's crust that elevate and fold the earth's surface. These processes operate with greater intensity in some places than others, and so mountains are concentrated in belts where these geological forces have been at work (fig. 2.38). In the Western Hemisphere, these forces have been particularly active on the western sides of both North and South America, where a chain of mountain ranges extends from northern Alaska across western North America to Tierra del Fuego at the tip of South America. Ancient low mountain ranges occupy the eastern sides of both continents. In Africa, the major mountain ranges are the Atlas Mountains of northwest Africa and the mountains of East Africa that run from the highlands of Ethiopia to southern Africa like beads on a string. In Australia, the flattest of the continents, mountains extend down the eastern side of the continent. Eurasian mountain ranges include the Pyrenees, the Alps, the Caucasus, and of course, the Himalayas, the highest of them all.

Climate

On mountains, climates change from low to high elevation, but the specific changes are different at different latitudes. On mountains at middle latitudes, the climate is generally cooler and wetter at higher altitudes (fig. 2.39). In contrast, there is less precipitation at the higher elevations of polar mountains and on some tropical mountains. In other tropical regions, precipitation increases up to some middle elevation and then decreases higher up the mountain. On high tropical mountains, warm days are followed by freezing nights. The organisms on these mountains experience summer temperatures every day and winter temperatures every night. The changes in climate that occur up the sides of mountains have profound influences on the distribution of mountain organisms.

Soils

Mountain soils change with elevation and have a great deal in common with the various soils we've already discussed. However, some special features are worth noting. First, because of the steeper topography, mountain soils are generally well drained and tend to be thin and vulnerable to erosion. Second, persistent winds blowing from the lowlands deposit soil particles and organic matter on mountains, materials that can make a significant contribution to local soil building. In some locations in the southern Rocky Mountains, coniferous trees draw the bulk of their nutrition from materials carried by winds from the valleys below, not from local bedrock.

Biology

Climb any mountain that is high enough and you will notice biological and climatic changes. Whatever the vegetation at the base of a mountain, that vegetation will change as you climb and the air becomes cooler. The sequence of vegetation up the side of a mountain may remind you of the biomes we encountered on our journey from the poles to the equator. In the cool highlands of desert mountains in the southwestern United States, you can hike through spruce and fir forests much like those we encountered far to the north. However, what you see on these desert mountains differs substantially from boreal forests. These mountain populations have been isolated from the main body of the boreal forest for over 10,000 years; in the interim, some populations have become extinct, some teeter on the verge of extinction, while others have evolved sufficiently to be recognized as separate species or subspecies. On these mountains, time and isolation have forged distinctive gene pools and mixes of species.

The species on high equatorial mountains are even more isolated. Think for a moment of the geography of high tropical mountains: some in Africa, some in the highlands of Asia, and

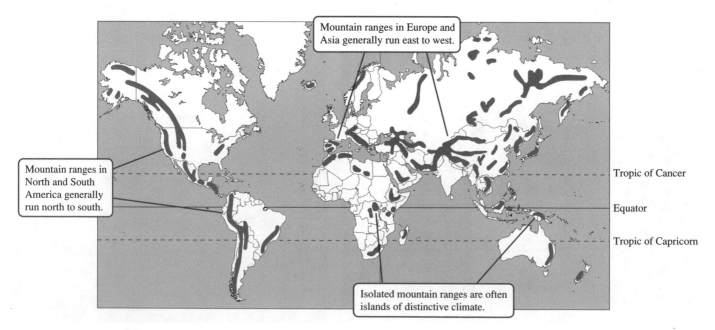

Figure 2.38   Mountain geography.

■ Moist ☐ Dry ▨ Mean minimum temperature >0°C

Niwot Ridge, Colorado, USA   3,743 m High elevation

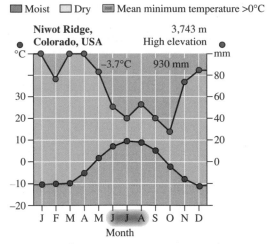

−3.7°C   930 mm

Elevation ↑   Temperature ↓   Precipitation ↑

Allenspark, Colorado   2,590 m Middle elevation

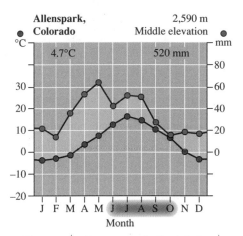

4.7°C   520 mm

Elevation ↑   Temperature ↓   Precipitation ↑

Boulder, Colorado   1,660 m Low elevation

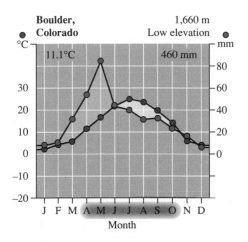

11.1°C   460 mm

Figure 2.39 Mountain climates along an elevational gradient in the Colorado Rockies. Temperatures decrease and precipitation increases from low to high elevations in these midlatitude mountains.

the Andes of South America. The high-altitude communities of Africa, South America, and Asia share very few species. On the other hand, despite differences in species composition, there are structural similarities among the organisms on these mountains (fig. 2.40). These similarities suggest there may be general rules for associating organisms with environments.

(a)

(b)

Figure 2.40 Convergence among tropical alpine plants: (*a*) *Senecio* trees on Mount Kilimanjaro, Africa; (*b*) *Espeletia* in the Andes of South America.

Human Influences

Because mountains differ in climate, geology, and biota (plants and animals) from the surrounding lowlands, they have been useful as a source of raw materials such as wood, forage for animals, medicinal plants, and minerals. Some of these uses, such as livestock grazing, are highly seasonal. In temperate regions, livestock are taken to mountain pastures during the summer and back down to the lowlands in winter. Human exploitation of mountains has produced ecological degradation in many places and surprising balance in others. Increased human pressure on mountain environments has sometimes created conflict between competing economic interests, between recreation seekers and livestock ranchers, and even between groups of scientists. Because of their com- pressed climatic gradients and biological diversity, mountains offer living laboratories for the study of ecological responses to climatic variation.

Concept 2.3 Review

1. Why do regions that contain high mountains tend to be more biologically diverse than regions without mountains?
2. Why are soils in tropical rain forest generally depleted of their nutrients more rapidly compared to soils in the boreal forest?
3. Why do biomes differ in the relative amount of plant biomass that is found below ground? Why is most bio- mass in tundra and grasslands below ground?

Ecological Tools

Biomes of Canada and Winter Ecology

In the Ecological Tools sections of this book, we will discuss how some specific research method allows ecologists to answer ecological questions. Without the right tools, research simply can not progress. As a result, the development of new research tools often results in bursts of research activity. As natural history is a key tool for ecologists, ecologists working in Canada generally need to understand the natural history of Canada. Here we provide a brief overview of how the scientists describe the ecological landscape of Canada.

Ecozones of Canada

In this chapter we described how different regions of the planet experience difference climates, and how this is asso- ciated with the development of different natural biomes. Few countries will contain all of the biomes of the world, and instead are generally home to just a few. However, as we mentioned previously, no two communities within a single biome will be identical, and instead there can be substantial variation in species composition among locations within a single biomes. In Canada, this has been recognized, and thus the National Ecological Framework for Canada (Ecological Stratification Working Group 1996) divides Canada not into a small number of biomes, but instead into 15 terrestrial (and 5 marine) *ecozones* (fig. 2.41), which are themselves divided into more than 200 *ecoregions* (fig. 2.42), which can be further divided into *ecodistricts*! The largest level of organization used in Canada, the ecozone, is roughly analogous to the more widely used concept of biomes, with major areas classified based upon dominant vegetation and climate. Ecoregions and ecodistricts allow finer classification, which can be helpful tools for landscape planning and conservation.

In figure 2.41, you can see how using the ecozone frame- work allows for more specificity than the coarse tool of biomes.

For example, consider the boreal biome, which would include the boreal shield ecozone, the boreal plain ecozone, and the boreal cordillera ecozone. The boreal shield is the largest ecozone in Canada and is strongly influenced by the underlying bedrock. In contrast, the boreal plains is consid- ered a different ecozone due to a relative lack of influence by bedrock. These both differ from the boreal cordillera, which has a large amount of mountainous terrain and is influenced by weather patterns from the Pacific Ocean. These differences have important consequences for the organisms that live within these three zones. An ecologist studying the boreal forest of Canada needs to take into account these differences in topography, soils, and vegetation to understand the ecology of a particular location. These basic differences in natural history can prove to be a critical step to under- standing variations in ecological function among communi- ties in a single biome. However, if a single country can have 15 ecozones, you can only imagine how many may be found across the globe, and thus the rough categories of biomes are critical for providing an overview of this variation. For larger-scale questions, broad divisions of biomes are helpful; for smaller-scale questions, a finer resolution is needed. A critical ecological tool is having the appropriate scale of natural history knowledge needed to answer your specific ecological question.

Regardless of whether Canada is divided into a few biomes, more ecozones, or even more ecoregions, one thing is clear. Compared to many other areas on the planet, Canada is cold and many areas receive substantial amounts of snow. As a result, one important tool of many Canadian ecologists is an understanding of the natural history of winter. Due to the importance of winter to the organisms that live in Canada, many aspects of winter ecology will be presented throughout the text. Here we provide the story of one species, the Black- Capped Chickadee.

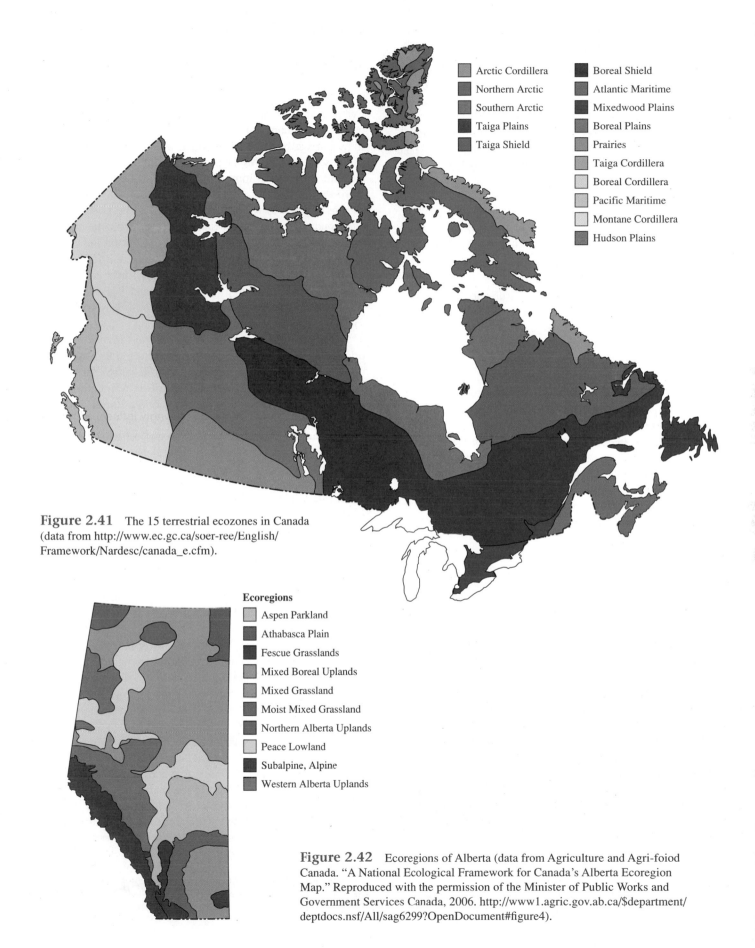

Figure 2.41 The 15 terrestrial ecozones in Canada (data from http://www.ec.gc.ca/soer-ree/English/ Framework/Nardesc/canada_e.cfm).

Ecoregions

- Aspen Parkland
- Athabasca Plain
- Fescue Grasslands
- Mixed Boreal Uplands
- Mixed Grassland
- Moist Mixed Grassland
- Northern Alberta Uplands
- Peace Lowland
- Subalpine, Alpine
- Western Alberta Uplands

Figure 2.42 Ecoregions of Alberta (data from Agriculture and Agri-foiod Canada. "A National Ecological Framework for Canada's Alberta Ecoregion Map." Reproduced with the permission of the Minister of Public Works and Government Services Canada, 2006. http://www1.agric.gov.ab.ca/$department/ deptdocs.nsf/All/sag6299?OpenDocument#figure4).

Legend (Figure 2.41):
- Arctic Cordillera
- Northern Arctic
- Southern Arctic
- Taiga Plains
- Taiga Shield
- Boreal Shield
- Atlantic Maritime
- Mixedwood Plains
- Boreal Plains
- Prairies
- Taiga Cordillera
- Boreal Cordillera
- Pacific Maritime
- Montane Cordillera
- Hudson Plains

Winter Ecology of the Black-Capped Chickadee

As I sit at home in Edmonton writing this section in early December, it is –25°C. A relentless north wind makes for an effective temperature of –39°C and Environment Canada warns that exposed flesh can freeze in just 10 minutes. My neighbours dash from house to car and mainly hunker indoors as I am doing. My kids haven't had an outdoor recess all week and it's hard to say whether it'll be the teachers or the kids who crack first. Yet even in this hostile environment, a chickadee (fig. 2.43) flits past my window, unperturbed, even cheerful. How can this be? It seems incredible that this tiny, 10-g bird can survive this temperature, let alone function. Looking closer at this amazing little animal (and doing a little reading), I can better appreciate how chickadees and other winter warriors pull this off.

The black-capped chickadee, *Poecile atricapilla*, has a very broad geographic range. It occurs throughout the temperate and deciduous biomes of North America, reaching as far north as the Yukon and the Northwest Territories in Canada. Even more amazing, the bird is a permanent resident of these areas, unlike the many snowbirds that leave Canada for Florida and Texas when winter arrives. Like many resident species, chickadees have several morphological, physiological, and behavioural adaptations (chapter 5) that make it possible to survive extremely cold temperatures, which many other animals simply avoid by migrating or hibernating. Morphologically, they dress right; their feathers can maintain a temperature differential of nearly 40°C between their skin and the air. A round body shape, which chickadees share with marine mammals, muskoxen, and polar bears, conserves heat more effectively than a long elongate body.

Physiologically, chickadees do some very unusual things. Because chickadees store no more fat on their bodies than will carry them through a single winter night, they must forage

Figure 2.43   The black-capped chickadee is a permanent resident in biomes with harsh winter conditions.

voraciously every day on a combination of animals (mainly insect larvae) and plants (mainly seeds). But they can forage only during the day, and daylight during midwinter at the northern limit of their range consists of but a few hours of twilight. Chickadees conserve energy during long winter nights by huddling in tree cavities and permitting their body temperatures to drop by as much as 10°C while regulating this descent into nightly hypothermia with bouts of shivering. Ground squirrels, chipmunks, bears, and bats hibernate to solve the problem of winter warmth and a majority of bird species migrate to warmer areas. A few other birds, like the caribou do, migrate within Canada in their seasonal quest for food. Other species dig pits and dens beneath the snow. These small spaces, combining the warm body temperatures of winter animals and insulative properties of snow, can result in surprising warmth even in the depths of winter. But no other bird is known to use regulated hypothermia as a daily adaptation to cold.

Behaviourally, chickadees make the most of their foraging opportunities (chapter 8). Like tree squirrels, mice, and a few other bird species (such as blue jays), chickadees cache food when temperatures are warm and retrieve it on colder days. They scatter these resources by depositing a single food item in each location. This strategy reduces their vulnerability to thieves, but it also destines them to an endless and challenging game of Concentration to find their stashes. Consequently, chickadees have phenomenal memories; comparable to that of a young child (unless, of course, you ask your child where he left his toque). Forgotten seeds may germinate the following spring. Edmonton has a healthy population of non-native oak trees in its river valley, "planted" there by forgetful blue jays foraging on ornamental trees. Much of the chickadee diet, particularly in winter, consists of insect larvae hidden under the bark of tree trunks and branches. For this reason, chickadees and other insectivores (chapter 7) exert significant effects on insect populations and limit the outbreaks of species like forest tent caterpillars.

As we see with the chickadees, winter places a variety of stresses on living organisms. In addition to the obvious risk of frozen tissues, there is limited food, water available only as ice, and for many, large numbers of hungry predators. Across Canada and the planet there is substantial variation in the climatic conditions that occur during winter. In some areas, only a few months have average minimum temperatures above 0°C, while in other areas, it barely freezes at all. The ecology that occurs during winter is of critical importance to the populations and communities of the many habitats. However, the world is changing and much of the north is getting warmer (chapter 23). How these changes will affect the natural history in Canada is unknown, and these discoveries await the next generation of ecologists.

Summary

Natural history is helping with the difficult task of restoring tropical dry forest in Costa Rica. Natural history also formed the foundation upon which modern ecology developed. Because ecological studies continue to be built upon a solid foundation of natural history, this chapter is devoted to the natural history of terrestrial biomes. Biomes are distinguished primarily by their predominant vegetation and are associated with particular climates.

Uneven heating of the earth's spherical surface by the sun and the tilt of the earth on its axis combine to produce predictable latitudinal variation in climate. Because the earth is a sphere, the sun's rays are most concentrated at the latitude where the sun is directly overhead. This latitude changes with the seasons because the earth's axis of rotation is not perpendicular to its plane of orbit about the sun but is tilted approximately 23.5° away from the perpendicular. The sun is directly overhead at the tropic of Cancer, at 23.5° N latitude during the northern summer solstice. During the northern winter solstice the sun is directly overhead at the tropic of Capricorn, at 23.5° S latitude. The sun is directly overhead at the equator during the spring and autumnal equinoxes. During the northern summer the Northern Hemisphere is tilted toward the sun and receives more solar energy than the Southern Hemisphere. During the northern winter, the Northern Hemisphere is tilted away from the sun and the Southern Hemisphere receives more solar energy.

Heating of the earth's surface and atmosphere drives atmospheric circulation and influences global patterns of precipitation. As the sun heats air at the equator, it expands and rises, spreading northward and southward at high altitudes. This high-altitude air cools as it spreads toward the poles, eventually sinking back to the earth's surface. Rotation of the earth on its axis breaks up atmospheric circulation into six major cells, three in the Northern Hemisphere and three in the Southern Hemisphere. These three circulation cells correspond to the trade winds north and south of the equator, the westerlies between 30° and 60° N or S latitude, and the polar easterlies above 60° latitude. These prevailing winds do not blow directly south because of the Coriolis effect.

As air rises at the tropics it cools, and the water vapour it contains condenses and forms clouds. Precipitation from these clouds produces the abundant rains of the tropics. Dry air blowing across the lands at about 30° latitude produces the great deserts that ring the globe. When warm, moist air flowing toward the poles meets cold polar air it rises and cools, forming clouds that produce the precipitation associated with temperate environments. Complicated differences in average climate can be summarized using a climate diagram.

Soil structure results from the long-term interaction of climate, organisms, topography, and parent mineral material. Terrestrial biomes are built upon a foundation of soil, a vertically stratified and complex mixture of living and nonliving material. Most terrestrial life depends on soil and much life occurs within soil. Soil structure varies continuously in time and space. Soils are generally divided into O (and LFH), A, B, and C horizons. The O and LFH horizons are made up of freshly fallen organic matter, including leaves, twigs, and other plant parts. The A horizon contains a mixture of mineral materials and organic matter derived from the O horizon. The B horizon contains clays, humus, and other materials that have been transported from the A horizon. The C horizon consists of weathered parent material.

The geographic distribution of terrestrial biomes corresponds closely to variation in climate, especially prevailing temperature and precipitation. The major terrestrial biomes and climatic regimes are: *Tundra:* Cold; low precipitation; short, soggy summers; poorly developed soils; permafrost; dominated by low vegetation and a variety of animals adapted to long, cold winters; migratory animals, especially birds, make seasonal use. *Boreal forest:* Long, severe winters; climatic extremes; moderate precipitation; infertile soils; permafrost; occasional fire; extensive forest biome, dominated by conifers. *Temperate forest:* Moderate, moist winters; warm, moist growing season; fertile soils; high productivity and biomass; dominated by deciduous trees where growing seasons are moist, winters are mild, and soils fertile; otherwise dominated by conifers. *Temperate grassland:* Hot and cold seasons; peak rainfall coincides with growing season; droughts sometimes lasting several years; fertile soils; fire important to maintaining dominance by grasses; historically inhabited by roving bands of herbivores and predators. *Mediterranean woodland and shrubland:* Cool, moist winters; hot, dry summers; low to moderate soil fertility; organisms adapted to seasonal drought and periodic fires. *Desert:* Hot or cold; dry; unpredictable precipitation; low productivity but often high diversity; organisms well-adapted to climatic extremes. *Tropical savanna:* Warm and cool seasons; pronounced dry and wet seasons; impermeable soil layers; fire important to maintaining dominance by grasses; still supports high numbers and diversity of large animals. *Tropical dry forest:* Warm and cool seasons; seasonally dry; biologically rich; as threatened as tropical rain forest. *Tropical rain forest:* Warm; moist; low seasonality; infertile soils; exceptional biological diversity and intricate biological interactions. *Mountains:* Temperature, precipitation, soils, and organisms shift with elevation; mountains are climatic and biological islands.

Review Questions

1. Daniel Janzen (1981a, 1981b) proposed that the seeds of the guanacaste tree were once dispersed by several species of large mammals that became extinct following the end of the Pleistocene about 10,000 years ago. There may have been other plant species with a similar relationship with large herbivorous mammals. How do you think the distributions of these plant species may have changed from the time of the extinctions of Pleistocene mammals until the introduction of other large herbivores such as horses? How might the introduction of horses about 500 years ago have affected the distribution of these species? How could you test your ideas?

2. Draw a soil profile for the area around your university. Indicate the principal layers, or horizons. Describe the characteristics of each layer.

3. Describe global patterns of atmospheric heating and circulation. What mechanisms produce high precipitation in the tropics? What mechanisms produce high precipitation at temperate latitudes? What mechanisms produce low precipitation in the tropics?

4. Use what you know about atmospheric circulation and seasonal changes in the sun's orientation to earth to explain the highly seasonal rainfall in the tropical dry forest and tropical savanna biomes. (Hint: Why does the rainy season in these biomes come during the warmer months?)

5. We focused much of our discussion of biomes on their latitudinal distribution. The reasonably predictable relationship between latitude and temperature and precipitation provides a link between latitude and biomes. What other geographic variable might affect the distribution of temperature and precipitation and, therefore, of biomes?

6. You probably suggested altitude in response to the previous question because of its important influence on climate. Some of the earliest studies of the geographic distribution of vegetation suggested a direct correspondence between latitudinal and altitudinal variation in climate, and our discussion in this chapter stressed the similarities in climatic changes with altitude and latitude. Now, what are some major climatic differences between high altitude at midlatitudes and high altitude at high latitudes?

7. How is the physical environment on mountains at midlatitudes similar to that in tropical alpine zones? How do these environments differ?

8. English and other European languages have terms for four seasons: spring, summer, autumn, and winter. This vocabulary summarizes much of the annual climatic variation at midlatitudes in temperate regions. Are these four seasons useful for summarizing annual climatic changes across the rest of the globe? Look back at the climate diagrams presented in this chapter. How many seasons would you propose for each of these environments? What would you call these seasons?

9. Biologists have observed much more similarity in species composition among boreal forests and among areas of tundra in Eurasia and North America than among tropical rain forests or among Mediterranean woodlands around the globe. Can you offer an explanation of this contrast based on the global distributions of these biomes?

10. To date, which biomes have been the most heavily affected by humans? Which seem to be the most lightly affected? How would you assess human impact? How might these patterns change during the coming century?

11. Draw a climate diagram for the location of your university. Climate data for Canada can be found at the Environment Canada Web page.

Suggested Readings

Attenborough, D., P. Whitfield, P. D. Moore, and B. Cox. 1989. *The Atlas of the Living World*. Boston: Houghton Mifflin.

A survey of the biosphere written for the general reader. Richly illustrated and well written.

Bardgett, R., M. Usher, and D. Hopkins. 2005. *Biological Function and Diversity in Soils*. Cambridge. Cambridge University Press.

An overview of the causes and consequences of species diversity in soil communities.

Breckle, S. W. 2002. *Walter's Vegetation of the Earth*. 4 ed. New York. Springer-Verlag.

A review of global patterns of climate and their correspondance to major classes of vegetation.

Lawrence, R. D. and M. Polak. 2005. *The Natural History of Canada*. Toronto. Key Porter Books.

An overview of the diversity of landscapes and organisms found in Canada

Wilson, E. O. 1992. The Diversity of Life. New York: W. W. Norton.

A highly acclaimed synthesis on the patterns and threats to biological diversity—an engaging and provocative discussion.

Chapter 3

Life in Water

Outline

he names that people around the world have given to our planet reveal a perspective consistent across cultures. Those names, whether in English (earth), French (*la terre*), Greek (Γεοσ, *geos*), or Chinese (地球, *di qiu*), all refer to land or soil, revealing that cultures everywhere hold a land-centred perspective. The Hawaiians, Polynesian inhabitants of the most isolated specks of land on earth, call the planet *ka honua,* an allusion to a level landing place or dirt embankment. This universal land-centred perspective may partly explain why portraits of earth transmitted from space are so stunning. Those images challenge our sense of place by portraying our planet as a shining blue ball, as a landing place in space covered not by land but mostly by water (fig. 3.1).

From our perspective as terrestrial organisms, the aquatic realm remains an alien environment governed by unfamiliar rules. In the aquatic environment, life is often most profuse where conditions appear most hostile to us: along cold, wave-swept seacoasts, in torrential mountain streams during the depths of winter, in murky waters where rivers meet the sea. The aquatic world has particular importance for Canada, and this country has been a world leader in ecological research in freshwater and marine systems. This should come as no surprise, as Canada is surrounded on three sides by oceans, is home to thousands of lakes and streams, and contains vast expanses of peatlands throughout the boreal ecozones. The goal of this chapter is to make this realm more familiar; we'll take a look at the natural history of several aquatic environments.

Figure 3.1   From space earth shows itself as a planet covered mostly by water.

Concepts

3.1 The hydrologic cycle exchanges water among reservoirs.

3.2 The biology of aquatic environments corresponds broadly to variations in physical factors such as light, temperature, and water movements and to chemical factors such as salinity and oxygen.

3.1   The Hydrologic Cycle

The hydrologic cycle exchanges water among reservoirs. Over 71% of the earth's surface is covered by water. This water is unevenly distributed among aquatic environments such as lakes, rivers, and oceans. The oceans contain over 97% of the water in the biosphere, and the polar ice caps and glaciers contain an additional 2%. Less than 1% is freshwater in rivers, lakes, and actively exchanged groundwater. The situation on earth is indeed as Samuel Coleridge's ancient mariner saw it: "Water, water, everywhere, nor any drop to drink."

Even the small amount of freshwater than exists on the planet is not evenly distributed. Nearly 20% of all freshwater on the planet is found in Canada alone. Across the earth, over 65% of freshwater is found in glaciers and ice fields, and nearly 30% is groundwater. This leaves only a very small fraction of the planet's freshwater as surface waters (lakes and streams), upon which most of human society depends. As human populations continue to grow (chapter 12), the demands on existing freshwater reserves increase, seemingly without end.

Alberta is a good example of the increasing pressures being faced by freshwater reserves. The mountains in the west of the province contain glaciers, but the glaciers in Jasper and Banff National Parks continue to retreat. Much of southern Alberta is dry-mixed prairie, and where the prairie has been converted to agricultural uses extensive irrigation networks exist (the global impacts of agriculture are discussed in chapter 23). In the north, extraction of oil from the oil sands requires large volumes of water to increase the mobility of the thick oil. On top of all of this, the oil boom is accompanied by a population boom. This growth causes increased pressures to dam the few wild rivers that remain, diverting water to support more strip malls, housing developments, and golf courses. Wetland and lake networks can slow water flows, remove pollutants, and permit groundwater recharge, but only if they persist on the landscape.

What happens within these freshwater ecosystems not only influences the ecology of these habitats, but will also have far-reaching consequences for human health, economic development, and population sustainability. But all is not lost. David Schindler (see chapter 1) is once again arguing strongly for the need to protect the freshwater reserves of Alberta. Sandra Postel from the Global Water Policy Project is working tirelessly to increase global awareness of these problems, helping governments achieve solutions before the water has run dry.

The distribution of water across the biosphere is not static. Figure 3.2 summarizes the dynamic exchanges called the **hydrologic cycle.** The various aquatic environments such as lakes, rivers, and oceans plus the atmosphere, ice, and even organisms can be considered as "reservoirs" within the hydrologic cycle, places where water is stored for some period of time. The water in these reservoirs is renewed, or turned over.

As a result of the hydrologic cycle, water is constantly entering each reservoir either as precipitation or as surface or subsurface flow and leaving each reservoir either as evaporation or as flow. The hydrologic cycle is powered by solar energy, which drives the winds and evaporates water, primarily from the surface of the oceans. Water vapour cools as it rises from the ocean's surface and condenses, forming clouds. These clouds are then blown by solar-driven winds across the planet, eventually yielding rain or snow, the majority of which falls back on the oceans and some of which falls on land. The water that falls on land has several fates. Some immediately evaporates and reenters the atmosphere; some contributes to icefields and glaciers; some is consumed by terrestrial organisms; some percolates through the soil to become groundwater; and some ends up in lakes and ponds or in streams and rivers, which may eventually find their way back to the sea.

Turnover time is the time required for the entire volume of a particular reservoir to be renewed. Because reservoir size and rates of water exchange differ, water turnover occurs at vastly different rates. The water in the atmosphere turns over about every 9 days. The renewal time for river water, 12 to 20 days, is nearly as rapid. Lake renewal times are longer, ranging anywhere from days to centuries, depending on lake depth, area, and rate of drainage. But the biggest surprise is the renewal time for the largest reservoir of all, the oceans. With a renewal time of only 3,100 years, the total volume of the oceans, over 1.3 billion km³ of water, has turned over more than 30 times in the last 100,000 years or so, since the first *Homo sapiens* gazed out on the deep blue sea.

Concept 3.1 Review

1. How will global warming affect the proportion of the earth's water that resides in the oceans?
2. How does the construction of dams for storing water affect the turnover time for water in rivers?
3. What aspects of the hydrological cycle are influenced most directly by increased human population growth?

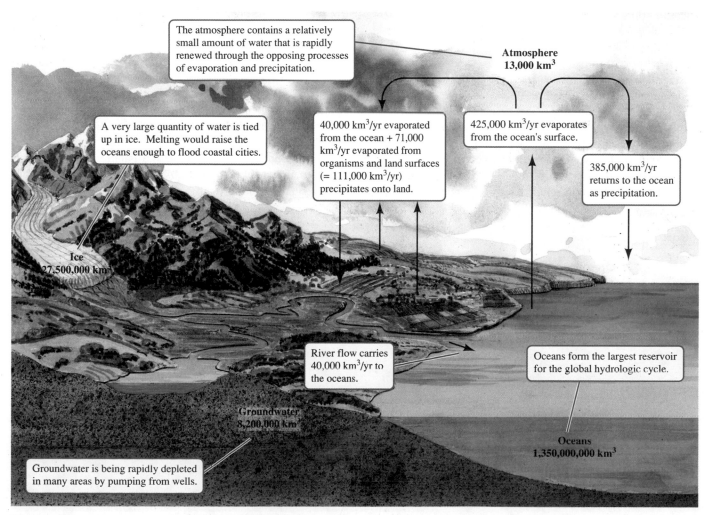

The atmosphere contains a relatively small amount of water that is rapidly renewed through the opposing processes of evaporation and precipitation.

Atmosphere 13,000 km³

A very large quantity of water is tied up in ice. Melting would raise the oceans enough to flood coastal cities.

40,000 km³/yr evaporated from the ocean + 71,000 km³/yr evaporated from organisms and land surfaces (= 111,000 km³/yr) precipitates onto land.

425,000 km³/yr evaporates from the ocean's surface.

385,000 km³/yr returns to the ocean as precipitation.

Ice 27,500,000 km³

River flow carries 40,000 km³/yr to the oceans.

Oceans form the largest reservoir for the global hydrologic cycle.

Groundwater 8,200,000 km³

Oceans 1,350,000,000 km³

Groundwater is being rapidly depleted in many areas by pumping from wells.

Figure 3.2   Major reservoirs and flows of the hydrological cycle.

3.2 The Natural History of Aquatic Environments

The biology of aquatic environments corresponds broadly to variations in physical factors such as light, temperature, and water movements and to chemical factors such as salinity and oxygen. Although the Ontario musical comedy group, The Arrogant Worms, sings about Canada being full of "Rocks and Trees," they end their chorus with the word "Water." Even in pop culture, there is recognition of how much water shapes the landscape of Canada. Our discussion of the natural history of aquatic environments begins with the natural history of the oceans, the largest aquatic environment on the planet. We continue our tour with environments found along the margins of the oceans, including kelp forests and coral reefs, the intertidal zone, and salt marshes. We then venture up rivers and streams, important avenues for exchange between terrestrial and aquatic environments. Finally, we consider the inland aquatic environments of lakes, bogs, and fens. As you will see, all but a few of these freshwater and marine systems are found in and around Canada.

The Deep Blue Sea

The blue solitude of open ocean is something palpable, a sensation you can almost taste. As we have seen, the only terrestrial biomes that evoke anything close to the feeling of this place are the "big sky" of the open prairies and the "sand sea" of deserts like the Namib. But there is a difference between these terrestrial environments and the sea. On the open ocean, all is blue—blue sea stretching to the horizon, where it meets blue sky (fig. 3.3).

Experience with terrestrial organisms cannot prepare you for what you encounter in samples taken from the deep ocean. We dream of unknown extraterrestrial beings, some friendly and some monstrous, all with strange and shocking anatomy. We parade them through science fiction literature and films,

while, unknown to most of us, creatures as odd and wonderful, some beyond imagining, live in the deep blue world beyond the continental shelves. Figure 3.4 shows one of the species found in the deep sea—a female deep-sea anglerfish with her male partner.

Geography

The world ocean covers over 360 million km^2 of earth's surface (70%) and consists of one continuous, interconnected mass of water. This water is spread among five major oceans: the Arctic, Atlantic, Indian, Pacific, and Southern oceans, each with several smaller seas along its margins (fig. 3.5). The largest of the oceans, the Pacific, has a total area of nearly 180 million km^2 and extends from the Antarctic to the Arctic Sea. In the Pacific Ocean, major seas include the Gulf of California, the Gulf of Alaska, the Bering Sea, the Sea of Okhotsk, the Sea of Japan, and the Coral Sea. The second largest basin, the Atlantic, has a total area of over 106 million km^2 and extends nearly from pole to pole. Major seas of the Atlantic include the Mediterranean, the North Sea, the Baltic Sea, the Gulf of Mexico, and the Caribbean Sea. The Indian Ocean covers 73 million km^2, and is bounded by southern Asia to the north, Africa to the west, and southeast Asia and Australia to the south. Major seas include the Red Sea, Timor Sea, Arabian Sea, and the Persian Gulf. The Southern Ocean is confined to the southern hemisphere with an area of 20 million km^2 extending from Antarctica to 60° south latitude. Major seas include the Ross Sea, Amundsen Sea, and the Weddell Sea. The smallest of the world's oceans, the Arctic Ocean, covers a total of 14 million km^2 and is confined to the Northern Hemisphere. Its major seas are the Barents Sea, Beafort Sea, Greenland Sea, Hudson Bay, and Baffin Bay. The Arctic Ocean is also the home of the seasonally open Northwest Passage connecting the Atlantic and Pacific oceans through Canada and the United States. A similar Northern Sea Route is seasonally open through Norway and Russia.

Figure 3.3   The open ocean is the most extensive biome on earth.

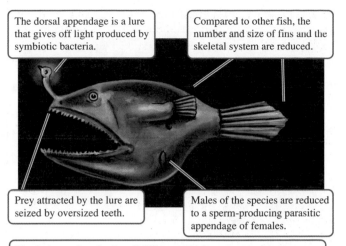

The dorsal appendage is a lure that gives off light produced by symbiotic bacteria.

Compared to other fish, the number and size of fins and the skeletal system are reduced.

Prey attracted by the lure are seized by oversized teeth.

Males of the species are reduced to a sperm-producing parasitic appendage of females.

The darkness, low food availability, and high pressures of the deep-sea environment have selected for organisms quite different from those typical of either shallow seas or the terrestrial environment. Only the females of this deep-sea anglerfish species are active predators.

Figure 3.4 Deep-sea anglerfish.

The Pacific is also the deepest ocean, with an average depth of over 4,000 m. The average depths of the Atlantic is about 3,500 m, while the average depth of the Arctic Ocean is only 1,000 m. Undersea mountains stud the floor of the deep sea, some isolated and some in long chains that run as ridges for thousands of kilometers. Undersea trenches, some of great depth and volume, rip through the seafloor. One such trench, the Marianas, in the western Pacific Ocean, is over 10,000 m deep—deep enough to engulf Mount Everest with 2 km to spare. The peak of Mauna Loa in Hawaii is a bit over 4,000 m above sea level, a modest height for a mountain. But Mauna Loa hides a secret below its sea apron. The base of Mauna Loa extends 6,000 m below sea level, making it, from base to peak, one of the tallest mountains on earth.

Structure

The oceans can be divided into several vertical and horizontal zones. The shallow shoreline under the influence of the rise and fall of the tides is called the **littoral,** or **intertidal, zone.** The **neritic zone** extends from the coast to the margin of the continental shelf, where the ocean is about 200 m deep. Beyond the continental shelf lies the **oceanic zone.** The ocean is also generally divided vertically into several depth zones. The **epipelagic zone** is the surface layer of the oceans that extends to a depth of 200 m. The **mesopelagic zone** extends from 200 to 1,000 m, and the **bathypelagic zone** extends from 1,000 to 4,000 m. The layer from 4,000 to 6,000 m is called the **abyssal zone,** and finally the deepest parts of the oceans belong to the **hadal zone.** Habitats on the bottom of the

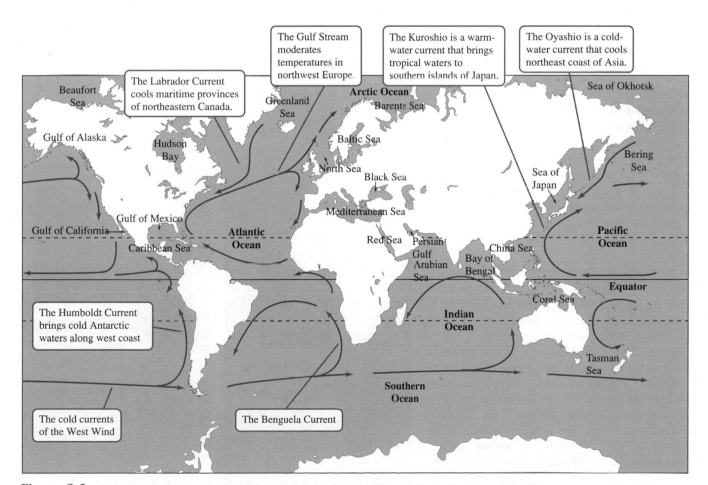

The Gulf Stream moderates temperatures in northwest Europe.

The Kuroshio is a warm-water current that brings tropical waters to southern islands of Japan.

The Oyashio is a cold-water current that cools northeast coast of Asia.

The Labrador Current cools maritime provinces of northeastern Canada.

The Humboldt Current brings cold Antarctic waters along west coast

The cold currents of the West Wind

The Benguela Current

Figure 3.5 Oceanic circulation, which is driven mainly by the prevailing winds, moderates earth's climate.

ocean, and other aquatic environments, are referred to as **benthic,** while those off the bottom, regardless of depth, are called **pelagic.** Each of these zones supports a distinctive assemblage of organisms. Figure 3.6 sketches the general structure of the oceans.

Physical Conditions

Light

Approximately 80% of the solar energy striking the ocean is absorbed in the first 10 m. Most ultraviolet and infrared light is absorbed in the first few meters. Within the visible range, red, orange, yellow, and green light are absorbed more rapidly than blue light. In the terrestrial world, chlorophyll absorbs blue (and red) light in photosynthesis, while reflecting green light, and thus plants appear green. In the open ocean algae are at low concentrations and very little of the blue light available is used in photosynthesis. Consequently, the open ocean appears blue. In the first 10 m, the marine environment is bright with all the colours of the rainbow; below 50 or 60 m it is a blue twilight. Even in the clearest oceans on the brightest days, the amount of sunlight penetrating to a depth of 600 m is approximately equal to the intensity of starlight on a clear night. That leaves, on average, about 3,400 m of deep black water in which the only light is that produced by bioluminescent fishes and invertebrates. Figure 3.7 compares the colours seen by a scuba diver in deep and shallow water to demonstrate the selective absorption of light by water.

Temperature

The sunlight absorbed by water increases the *kinetic state,* or velocity of motion, of water molecules. We detect this increased kinetic state as increased temperature. Because more rapid molecular motion decreases water density, warm water floats on cold water. As a consequence, surface water warmed by the sun floats on the colder water below. These warm and cold layers are separated by a **thermocline,** a layer of water through which temperature changes rapidly with depth. This layering of the water column by temperature, which is called *thermal stratification,* is a permanent feature of tropical seas. Temperate oceans are stratified only during the summer, and the thermocline breaks down as surface waters cool during fall and winter. At high latitudes, thermal stratification is only weakly, if ever, developed. As we shall see, these differences in thermal conditions at different latitudes have far-reaching consequences to the ecological functioning of the oceans.

At the ocean surface, average annual temperature and annual variation in temperature change with latitude but, at all latitudes, oceanic temperatures are much more stable than terrestrial temperatures. The lowest average oceanic temperature, about −1.5°C, is around the Antarctic. The highest average surface temperatures, a bit over 27°C, occur near the equator. Maximum annual variation in surface temperature, approximately 7°C to 9°C, occurs in the temperate zone above 40° N latitude. Near the equator, as in

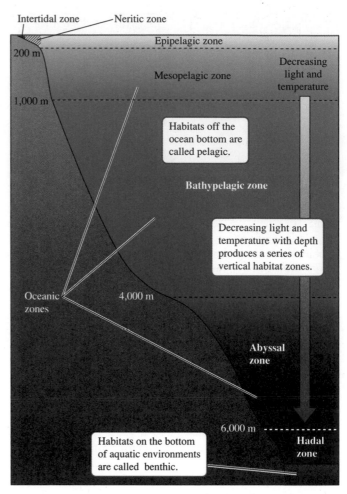

Figure 3.6   Vertical structuring of the oceans is associated with substantial variation in light and temperature with depth.

(a)   (b)

Figure 3.7   Changes in light quality with depth: (*a*) the rich colours on a shallow coral reef; (*b*) the blue of the deeper reef.

the tropical rain forest, the total annual range in temperature, about 1°C, approximately equals the daily range. The greatest stability in oceanic temperatures, however, is below the surface, where, at just 100 m depth, annual variation in temperature is often less than 1°C.

Water Movements

If you are standing on the deck of a small boat off the coast of Labrador during a spring storm, you quickly learn to appreciate the movements of the ocean. The oceans are never still. Prevailing winds drive currents that transport nutrients, oxygen, and heat, as well as organisms, across the globe. These currents moderate climates, fertilize the surface waters off the continents, stimulate photosynthesis, and promote gene flow among populations of marine organisms. For example, wind-driven surface currents sweep across vast expanses of open ocean to create great circulation systems called **gyres** that move to the right (clockwise) in the Northern Hemisphere and to the left (counterclockwise) in the Southern Hemisphere. The great oceanic gyres transport warm water from equatorial regions toward the poles, moderating climates at middle and high latitudes. A segment of one of these gyres, the Gulf Stream, moderates the climate of northwest Europe.

Even if you are standing in your boat under bright skies and on flat seas, the ocean remains in motion. In addition to surface currents, there are deepwater currents such as those produced as cooled, high-density water sinks at the Antarctic and Arctic and then moves along the ocean floor. Deep water may also be moved to the surface in a process called **upwelling.** Upwelling occurs along the west coasts of continents and around Antarctica, where winds blow surface water offshore, allowing colder water to rise to the surface. These various water movements are like undersea winds but with a difference: water is vastly more dense than air. How might this difference in density affect the anatomy, behaviour, and distributions of marine organisms?

Chemical Conditions

Salinity

The amount of salt dissolved in water is called **salinity.** Salinity varies with latitude and among the seas that fringe the oceans. In the open ocean, it varies from about 34 g of salt per kilogram of water ($^0/_{00}$ or parts per thousand) to about 36.5 $^0/_{00}$. The lowest salinities occur near the equator and above 40° N and S latitudes, where inputs of freshwater through snow and rainfall exceed evaporation, thereby diluting the salts in these oceans. The excess of precipitation over evaporation at these latitudes is clearly shown by the climate diagrams for temperate forests, boreal forests, and tundra that we examined in chapter 2 (see figs. 2.17, 2.14, and 2.11). Highest salinities occur in the subtropics at about 20° to 30° N and S latitudes, where precipitation is low and evaporation high—precisely those latitudes where we encountered deserts (see fig. 2.26). Salinity varies a great deal more in the small, enclosed basins along the margins of the major oceans. The Baltic Sea, which is surrounded by temperate and boreal forest biomes and receives large inputs of freshwater, has local salinities of 7 $^0/_{00}$ or lower. In contrast, the Red Sea, which is surrounded by deserts, has surface salinities of over 40 $^0/_{00}$.

Despite considerable variation in total salinity, the relative proportions of the major ions (e.g., sodium [Na^+], magnesium [Mg^{+2}], and chloride [Cl^-]) remain approximately constant from one part of the ocean to another. This uniform composition, which is a consequence of continuous and vigorous mixing of the entire world ocean, underscores the connections between different regions of the world's oceans.

Oxygen

Oxygen is present in far lower concentrations and varies much more in the oceans than in aerial environments. A litre of air contains about 200 ml of oxygen at sea level, while a litre of seawater contains a maximum of about 9 ml of oxygen.

Oxygen is a critical resource for all aerobic life in the oceans and on land. Oxygen is needed by plants, algae, and animals for respiration. Without a reliable source of oxygen, most organisms die very quickly. Due to diffusion, winds, and wave action, there is substantial exchange of gases between the ocean surface and the oxygen-rich atmosphere. Additionally, algal growth is generally highest near the surface, and through photosynthesis these organisms produce additional O_2 which is released into the water column. Through the combination of algal growth and atmosphere-surface interactions, the highest concentrations of oxygen in the ocean are generally found near the surface. The upper ocean (or lake) layer in which photosynthesis occurs is called the **photic zone**. Below this zone, oxygen consumption by aerobic organisms is greater than oxygen production, and oxygen concentrations rapidly decrease with increasing depth. Oxygen concentrations generally reach a minimum at around 1,000 m, but then increase, as the movement of cold, dense, and oxygen-rich water from shallow polar regions flows downwards into most ocean basins, resulting in an increase in oxygen as you approach the deep ocean floor.

Biology

A century and a quarter of research on the open ocean has revealed close correspondence between physical and chemical conditions and the diversity, composition, and abundance of oceanic organisms. For instance, because of the limited penetration of sunlight into seawater, photosynthetic organisms are limited to the brightly lit upper epipelagic zone of the ocean (see fig. 3.6). The most significant photosynthetic inhabitants of this zone are microscopic organisms called **phytoplankton** that drift with the currents in the open sea. The small animals that drift with these same currents are called **zooplankton.** While there is no ecologically significant photosynthesis below the photic zone, there is no absence of deep-sea organisms. Fishes, ranging from small bioluminescent forms to giant sharks, whales, and invertebrates from tiny crustaceans to giant squid, prowl the entire water column, from the surface of the oceans to the bottom. There is life even in the deepest trenches, below 10,000 m.

Linking the biotic and abiotic parts of the ocean ecosystem is a complex and extremely diverse set of microbial interactions.

Microbes are the unsung heroes of most ecological communities. For every undergraduate ecology student who dreams about studying bacteria and fungi, there must be hundreds who want to work on dolphins, whales, polar bears, wolves, and butterflies. However, as you will see throughout this text, personal interest does not necessarily reflect ecological importance. In the deep ocean, these small organisms fill a variety of roles in the functioning of this ecosystem. They are key players in global carbon and nutrient cycles, as well as being food for yet more organisms. The exact role of this diverse group of species is only now being discovered, with many surprises likely to emerge. Because of the enormous size of the oceans, it is very likely that ocean microbes will drive global responses to climate change.

Most deep-sea organisms are nourished—whatever their place in the food chain—by organic matter fixed by photosynthesis near the surface. It was long assumed that the rain of organic matter from above was the *only* source of food for deep-sea organisms. Then, about two decades ago the sea surprised everyone. There are entire biological communities on the seafloor that are nourished not by photosynthesis at the surface but by chemosynthesis on the ocean floor (see chapter 7). These oases of life are associated with undersea hot springs and harbour many life-forms entirely new to science. Figure 3.8 shows the great density of organisms found on the ocean floors near an undersea hydrothermal vent.

The deep ocean shines with the blue of pure water and is often called a "biological desert." This description suggests that the open ocean is an area nearly devoid of life—a wasteland, perhaps—that can be dismissed. While it is true that the average rate of photosynthesis per square meter of ocean surface is similar to that of terrestrial deserts, the oceans, because they are so vast, contribute approximately one-fourth of the total photosynthesis in the biosphere. This oceanic production constitutes a substantial contribution to the global carbon and oxygen budget. So why "desert"? Oceanic populations live at such low densities that there is little in the open ocean that can be economically harvested for direct human consumption.

J. H. Ryther (1969) estimated that the open ocean contains less than 1% of the harvestable fish stocks. Most fish are found along the coasts. We can, however, appreciate the open ocean from other perspectives.

The open ocean is home, the only home, for thousands of organisms with no counterparts on land. There are currently between 29 and 35 animal phyla that have been described—different scientists count different groups. The terrestrial environment supports 11 animal phyla, only 1 of which is endemic to the terrestrial environment—that is, found in no other environment (Onychophora; velvetworms). Fourteen phyla live in freshwater environments but none are endemic. Meanwhile the marine environment supports 28 phyla, 13 of which are endemic to the marine environment. Figure 3.9 compares the number of phyla in terrestrial, freshwater, and marine environments.

Does the greater diversity of phyla in the marine environment shown in figure 3.9 contradict our impression of high biological diversity in biomes such as the tropical rain forest? No, it does not. The terrestrial environment is extraordinarily diverse because there are many species in a few animal and plant phyla, especially arthropods and flowering plants. Still, the number of marine species may also be very high. J. F. Grassle (1991) estimated that the number of bottom-dwelling, or benthic, marine species may exceed 10 million, a level of species diversity that would rival that of the tropical rain forest. We still have not documented the full extent of species diversity in the oceans.

Human Influences

Human impact on the oceans was once less than on other parts of the biosphere. For most of our history, the vastness of the oceans has been a buffer against human intrusions. Even into the late 1800s it was argued in scientific societies that

Figure 3.8 Chemosynthesis-based community on the East Pacific Rise.

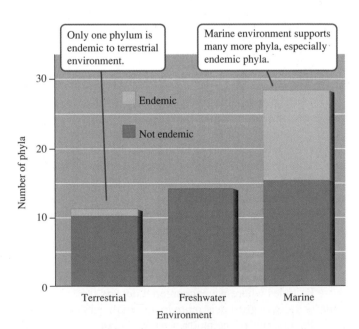

Figure 3.9 Distribution of animal phyla among terrestrial, freshwater, and marine environments (data from Grassle 1991).

the oceans were a limitless source of food, whose populations of fish could never by reduced to any biologically meaningful degree. However, times have changed and the impacts of humans have become apparent. The decline of large whale populations around Antarctica and elsewhere sounded a warning of what we can do to the open ocean system. The killing of whales has been curtailed, but there are plans to harvest the great whales' food supply, the small planktonic crustaceans known as *krill*. Although we may find them less engaging than their predators, the large whales, these zooplankton may be more important to the life of the open ocean. Whales are not the only marine populations that have collapsed. Overfishing has led to great declines in commercially important fish stocks, such as the Grand Banks cod population. Many marine fish populations, which once seemed inexhaustible, are now all but gone and fishing fleets sit idle in ports all over the world.

Another threat to marine life is the possibility of dumping wastes of all sorts, including nuclear and chemical wastes, into the deep ocean. In recent years, chemical pollution of the sea has increased substantially, and chemical pollutants are accumulating in deep-sea sediments. Assaults such as these will continue as long as the deep sea is considered by most to be a biological desert. The threats to this blue wilderness could be reduced by changes in human activities based on an appreciation of the great biological richness of the oceans and their critical importance to global carbon and oxygen budgets. Like all terrestrial systems, a balance between wildness and human needs has yet to be achieved.

Shallow Waters: Kelp Forests and Coral Gardens

The shallow waters along continents and around islands support marine communities of very high diversity and biomass.

Imagine yourself snorkeling along a marine shore, beyond the intertidal zone. If you are at temperate latitudes and over a solid bottom, you are likely to swim through groves of brown seaweed called *kelp*. Along many coasts, kelp grows so tall, over 40 m in some places, and in such densities that they resemble submarine forests (fig. 3.10).

If you snorkel in the tropics, you may come across a coral reef diverse in colour and texture. The colours on a coral reef rival that of any terrestrial biome (fig. 3.11).

Figure 3.10   A scene from a kelp forest off the west coast of North America. Like terrestrial forests, kelp forests are home to a large diversity of organisms. Shown above are several sea urchins and at least one fish (can you find it?).

Figure 3.11   Coral reefs, such as this one in Manado, Indonesia, support one of the most diverse assemblages of organisms on the planet.

What Lies Below?

In chapter 2 we argued that soils were the biggest frontier for discovery of life on land. What about the world of water? Not too surprisingly, people's tendency to study those things more readily observable is not limited to the terrestrial world. As we move from the surface of the ocean towards the sediment below, our understanding of basic natural history becomes as black as the water around us. There are obvious difficulties working in and around sediment, similar to those in soil ecology. The habitat is dark, organisms are difficult and expensive to reach, and many of the most common organisms are small and hard to see. Deep ocean studies are made even more difficult by extreme pressure differences, where simply bringing organisms up to the surface for study is often fatal to the organism. However, for those willing to take on these challenges, there is a great reward: a chance to explore a truly unknown world (fig. 3.12).

Our lack of understanding of deep waters and sediments is completely counter to their likely importance in the functioning of natural systems and global processes. Because of the expanse of the oceans coupled with abundant underwater mountain ranges that increase the surface area of the ocean floor, ocean bottoms are the single most common habitat on the planet. One researcher who has dedicated his professional life to understanding the biology of the deep sea is Paul Snelgrove of Memorial University in Newfoundland. He has written extensively on the diversity and importance of ocean sediments as reservoirs of biodiversity and as a key player in global nutrient cycling (Snelgrove 1999, 2000).

The level of diversity on the ocean floor is simply staggering, with estimates suggesting somewhere between 1 million and 1 billion species, with less than 1% of these currently described (fig. 3.13). Even excluding the practically unknown

Figure 3.12   Some of the diversity found 145 m deep along a fjord wall at Hosie Islands, Barkley Sound, British Columbia. In the photo are glass sponges (*Aphrocallistes vastus*), fish, a variety of invertebrates in the sediment, and the manipulator arm of the remote operated vehicle, ROPOS. The green is fluorescein dye that researcher squirted onto the sponges to test whether they were pumping.

diversity of bacteria, there could be millions of species yet to be discovered. Of the 13 animal phyla endemic to marine environments, all have species that live in, or on, marine sediment. Because of this diversity at deep branches in the evolutionary tree of animals, understanding of the diversity of this group of organisms can provide insights into fundamental process of animal ecology and evolution.

In a kelp forest and coral reef, chance meetings with large carnivorous sea animals seldom fade from memory. The kelp that form the canopy and understory of the temperate submarine forest are not members of the plant kingdom but are, at least in some current classifications, gigantic photosynthetic protists. The corals that form the framework of the coral garden are not plants either, but animals that secrete a stony skeleton and that depend for their survival on photosynthesis by photosynthetic protists called zooxanthellae that live in their tissues.

Geography

The nearshore marine environment and its inhabitants vary with latitude. In temperate to subpolar regions, wherever there is a solid bottom and no overgrazing there are profuse growths of kelp. As you get closer to the equator, these kelp forests are gradually replaced by coral reefs. Coral reefs are confined to middle latitudes between 30° N and S latitudes. (fig. 3.14)

Structure

Charles Darwin (1842) was the first to place coral reefs into three categories: fringing reefs, barrier reefs, and atolls. **Fringing reefs** hug the shore of a continent or island. Barrier reefs, such as the Great Barrier Reef, which stretches for nearly 2,000 km off the northeast coast of Australia, stand some distance offshore. A **barrier reef** stands between the open sea and a lagoon. Coral **atolls,** which dot the tropical Pacific and Indian Oceans, consist of coral islets that have

Taxon	Described Species	Estimated Total Species
Bacteria	500	Unknown. May be as high as 10^9
Fungi	600	2,000
Protists	3,000	30,000
Meiofauna	7,000	10^8
Macrofauna	87,000	725,000
Total	98,100	10^6–10^9

Figure 3.13 Described and estimated species diversity of organisms living in marine sediments. Meiofauna are organisms up to 1 mm in length. Macrofauna are larger than 1 mm (data from Snelgrove 1999).

When we imagine the diversity of the ocean, it is often sharks, whales, and algae that come to mind. In reality, most species that live in the ocean are at the bottom, and many of these are barely visible to the naked eye. As you can imagine, since we have such a limited understanding of the types of organisms that live in ocean sediment, we have an even worse understanding of their natural history. For example, many deep ocean species have a free-living larval stage whose basic ecology may be fundamentally different from that of the adults. At a most basic level, it is unclear how these small creatures of the deep are able to settle in suitable habitats in which they can develop into sessile adults. Scientific understanding of the natural history of larval stages is even more limited than our understanding of the benthic adults.

The realization that a large bulk of the diversity in the oceans lies on the floor results in a very simply question. Why?

It seems counter-intuitive that the bottom of the great "desert" should hold such a wealth of diversity. Ecologists have proposed several theories, none of which have yet been fully supported (Grassle 1991). One possibility is that the deep ocean has a relatively stable environment (cold, dark, constant nutrient flow drifting down from the waters above), reducing the chance of severe climatic events that are often found in other habitats (such as drought, flooding, fire, and so on). Climatic stability may allow species with relatively small populations to persist, whereas they would go extinct in areas with more climatic disturbance. A second possibility could be simply that the deep ocean is expansive, and this large contiguous area could further allow species to persist, even at low densities, due to the potential size of the habitat range that is available. Further, within this seemingly homogenous area will be periodic localized disturbances (e.g., whale carcass, animal burrows, sponge mats), which create a diversity of microhabitats upon which other species may specialize. In short, the mechanisms that generate diversity of deep oceans may be very similar to the mechanisms that generate diversity in other ecosystems. By studying areas that are poorly understood we have the ability to test broader ecological theories about the factors that govern species distributions and abundance.

Efforts to explore the ocean floor are underway, including several ambitious projects involving researchers throughout Canada and the United States. These teams of scientists are laying powered cables on the ocean floor around Vancouver Island and into the deep ocean. This research infrastructure will finally allow real-time imagery and monitoring of the local residents and environmental conditions. This is a critical step in improving the understanding of the basic natural history of the deep. Though we often think of the deep sea being a bottomless desert, it is not; all oceans have a bottom, and to many species, it is home.

built up from a submerged oceanic island and ring a lagoon. Darwin's theory of the long-term development of reefs and the structure of fringing reefs, barrier reefs, and atolls is presented in figure 3.15.

Distinctive habitats associated with coral reefs include the *reef crest*, where corals grow in the surge zone created by waves coming from the open sea. The reef crest extends to a depth of about 15 m. Below the reef crest is a *buttress zone*, where coral formations alternate with sand-bottomed canyons. Behind the reef crest lies the *lagoon*, which contains numerous small coral reefs called *patch reefs* and sea grass beds.

Beds of kelp, particularly those of giant kelp, have structural features similar to those of terrestrial forests. At the water's surface is the *canopy*, which may be more than 25 m above

the seafloor. The *stems*, or *stipes*, of kelp extend from the canopy to the bottom and are anchored with structures called *holdfasts*. On the stipes and fronds of kelp grow numerous species of epiphytic algae and sessile invertebrates. Other seaweed species of smaller stature usually grow along the bottom, forming an understory to the kelp forest (fig. 3.16).

Physical Conditions

Light

Both seaweeds and reef-building corals grow only in surface waters, where there is sufficient light to support photosynthesis. The depth of light penetration sufficient to support kelp and coral varies with local conditions from a few meters to nearly 100 m.

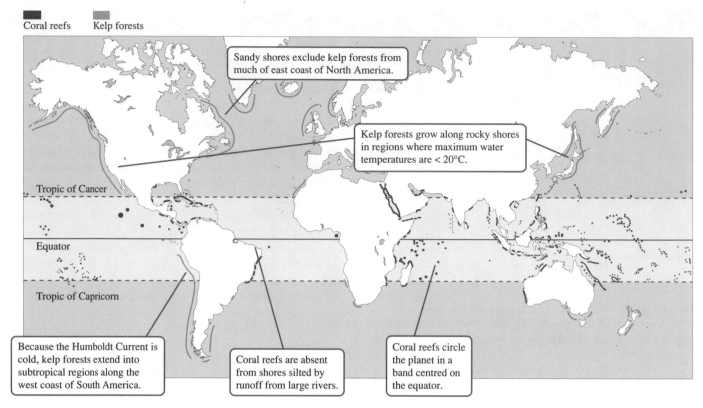

Figure 3.14   Distribution of kelp forests and coral reefs (data from Barnes and Hughes 1988, after Schumacher 1976).

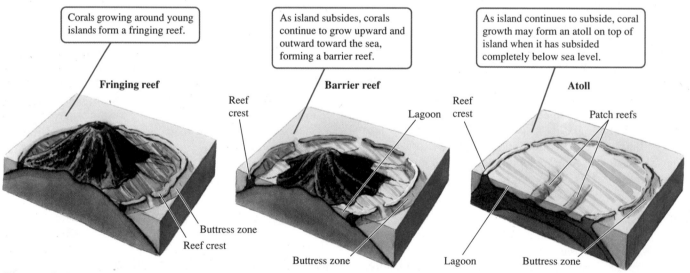

Figure 3.15   Types of coral reefs.

Temperature

Temperature limits the distribution of both kelp and coral. Most kelp are limited to temperate shores, to those regions where temperatures may fall below 10°C in winter and rise to a bit above 20°C in the summer. Corals are restricted to warm waters, to those regions where the minimum temperature does not fall below about 18° to 20°C and average temperatures usually vary from about 23° to 25°C. Reef-building corals are also sensitive to high temperatures, however, and temperatures above about 29°C are usually lethal.

Water Movements

Coral reefs and kelp beds are continuously washed by oceanic currents. These currents deliver oxygen and nutrients and remove waste products. The biological productivity of kelp beds and coral reefs may depend upon the flushing action of these currents. However, extremely strong currents and wave action, as during hurricanes, can detach entire kelp forests and flatten entire coral reefs built up over many centuries. Periodic disturbance is a characteristic of both the kelp bed and the coral reef, and both may require some abiotic disturbance for their long-term survival.

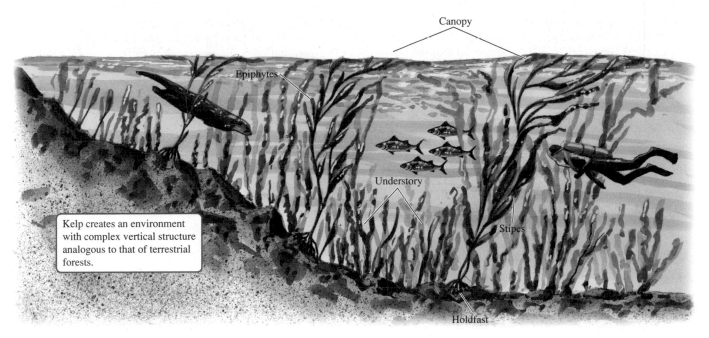

Figure 3.16 Kelp forest structure.

[Labels on figure: Canopy, Epiphytes, Understory, Stipes, Holdfast]

[Callout box: Kelp creates an environment with complex vertical structure analogous to that of terrestrial forests.]

Chemical Conditions

Salinity

Coral reefs grow only in waters with fairly stable salinity. Heavy rainfall or runoff from rivers that reduces salinity below about 27% of seawater can be lethal to corals. Kelp beds appear to be more tolerant of freshwater runoff and grow well along temperate shores, where surface salinities are substantially reduced by runoff from large rivers.

Oxygen

Coral reefs and kelp beds occur where waters are well oxygenated.

Biology

Coral reefs face intense, and sometimes complex, biological disturbance. Periodic outbreaks of the predatory crown-of-thorns sea star, *Acanthaster planci,* which eats corals, have devastated large areas of coral reef in the Indo-Pacific region. In a Caribbean coral reef community, populations of a sea star relative, the sea urchin *Diadema antillarum,* were infected by a pathogen and crashed to 1% to 5% of previous densities. It turns out that urchins, which eat both algae and corals, may benefit the corals. In the absence of urchins, algal biomass increased greatly, covering previously bare areas needed by young corals to establish themselves. Algal populations, no longer held in check by predation, compete for space with young corals. In the long run, reducing populations of urchins may reduce coral reproductive success. This is a good example of the complexity and indirect effects that characterize ecological relationships. Figure 3.17 shows one of these sea urchins on a coral reef in the Caribbean Sea.

Corals also compete vigorously among themselves. Reminiscent of rain forest trees and vines, corals engage in a ceaseless struggle for light and space. The corals, however, add a new dimension to the struggle. They actively attack and kill neighbouring corals of other clones that differ genetically from themselves.

Figure 3.17 The sea urchin *Diadema* on a coral reef. Feeding by *Diadema* appears to play a key role in the interaction between reef-building corals and benthic algae.

Coral reefs and kelp beds are among the most productive and diverse of all ecological systems in the biosphere. Robert Whittaker and Gene Likens (1973) estimated that the rate of primary production on coral reefs and algal beds exceeds that of tropical rain forests. The centre of diversity for reef-building corals is the western Pacific and eastern Indian Oceans, where there are over 600 coral species and over 2,000 species of fish. By comparison, the western Atlantic Ocean supports about 100 species of corals. Biotic diversity on reefs is also impressive on a small scale. A single coral head may support over 100 species of polychaete worms (Grassle 1973) and over 75 species of fish (Smith and Tyler 1972).

On the coral reef, the ecologist is faced with the same seeming paradox encountered in the tropical rain forest: overwhelming diversity and high primary production in an ecosystem that is nutrient-poor. For the coral reef and for the rain forest, ecologists explain that the answer lies with the organisms themselves and their biotic interactions, including mutualisms, and with rapid recycling and retention of nutrients in the biological parts of the ecosystem.

Human Influences

Coral reefs and kelp forests are increasingly exploited for a variety of purposes. Tons of kelp are harvested for use as a food additive and for fertilizer. Fortunately, most of this harvest is quickly replaced by kelp growth. Corals, however, which are intensively harvested and bleached for decorations, do not quickly replace themselves. The fish and shellfish of kelp forests and coral reefs have also been heavily exploited. Once again, it appears that coral reefs are more vulnerable. Some coral reefs have been so heavily fished, both for food and for the aquarium trade, that most of the larger fish are rare. Unfortunately, some especially destructive means of fishing are used on coral reefs, including dynamite and poison, with disastrous results. In the Philippines, over 60% of the area once covered by coral has been destroyed by these techniques during recent years. While an appreciation of the threats to rain forests grows, there is less said of the plight of the rain forest's marine cousin, the coral reef, as it is changed from marine garden to wasteland. There is some evidence that healthy coral reefs can buffer the effects of large waves as they approach shore. As a result, destruction of reefs in the water can have additional consequences inland. Again, the question is how can local people and coral reefs thrive together.

Where Waves Meet Rocks: Intertidal Zones

The rise and fall of the tides make the shore one of the most dynamic environments in the biosphere. The intertidal zone is a magnet for the curious naturalist and one of the most convenient places to study ecology. Where else in the biosphere does the structure of the landscape change several times each day? Where else does nature expose entire aquatic communities for leisurely exploration? Where else are environmental and biological gradients so compressed? It should be no surprise that here in the intertidal zone, immersed in tide pools, salt spray, and the sweet smell of kelp, ecologists have found the inspiration and circumstance for some of the most elegant experiments and most enduring generalizations of ecology. The intertidal zone, the area covered by waves at high tide and exposed to air at low tides, has proved to be an illuminating window to the world. Figure 3.18 shows the tangle of diverse life that can be observed on a rocky shore during low tide.

Geography

Countless thousands of kilometers of coastline around the world have intertidal zones. From a local perspective, it is significant to distinguish between exposed and sheltered shores. Battered by the full force of ocean waves, exposed shores support very different organisms from those found along sheltered shores on the inside of headlands or in coves and bays. A second important distinction is between rocky and sandy shores.

Structure

The intertidal zone can be divided into several vertical zones (fig. 3.19). The highest zone is called the *supratidal fringe,* or *splash zone.* The supratidal fringe is seldom covered by high tides but is often wetted by waves. Below this fringe is the intertidal zone proper. The upper intertidal zone is covered

Figure 3.18   A rocky shore at low tide, showing the great abundance that can be attained by populations of intertidal organisms.

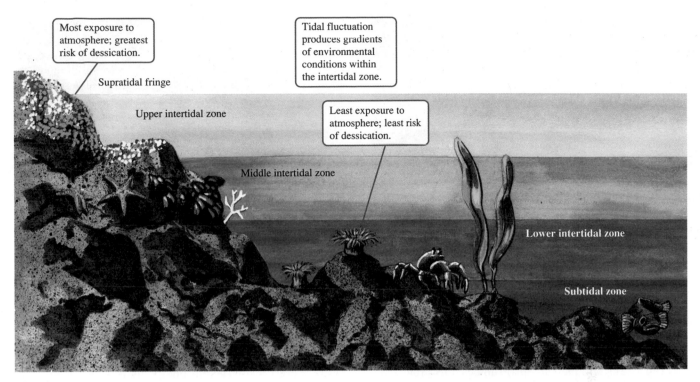

Most exposure to atmosphere; greatest risk of dessication.

Supratidal fringe

Upper intertidal zone

Tidal fluctuation produces gradients of environmental conditions within the intertidal zone.

Least exposure to atmosphere; least risk of dessication.

Middle intertidal zone

Lower intertidal zone

Subtidal zone

Figure 3.19 Intertidal zonation.

only during the highest tides, and the lower intertidal zone is uncovered only during the lowest tides. Between the upper and lower intertidal zones is the middle intertidal zone, which is covered and uncovered during average tides. Below the intertidal zone is the *subtidal zone,* which remains covered by water even during the lowest tides. As we shall see in the next two sections (Physical Conditions and Chemical Conditions), tidal fluctuation produces steep gradients of physical and chemical conditions within the intertidal zone.

Physical Conditions

Light

Intertidal organisms are exposed to wide variations in light intensity. At high tide, water turbulence reduces light intensity. At low tide, intertidal organisms are exposed to the full intensity of the sun. How might this variation in light intensity affect the distribution of photosynthetic organisms in the intertidal zone? How vulnerable are intertidal organisms to damage by sunlight, compared to organisms from other marine environments?

Temperature

Because the intertidal zone is exposed to the air once or twice each day, intertidal temperatures are always changing. At high latitudes, tide pools, small basins that retain water at low tide, can cool to freezing temperatures during low tides, while tide pools along tropical and subtropical shores can heat to temperatures in excess of 40°C. The dynamic intertidal environment contrasts sharply with the stability of most marine environments and presents substantial environmental challenges.

Water Movements

The two most important water movements affecting the distribution and abundance of intertidal organisms are the waves that break upon the shore and the tides. The tides vary in magnitude and frequency. Most tides are *semidiurnal,* that is, there are two low tides and two high tides each day. However, in seas, such as the Gulf of Mexico and the South China Sea, there are *diurnal* tides, that is, a single high and low tide each day. The total rise and fall of the tide varies from a few centimeters along some marine shores to the world's largest tide of 15 m at the Bay of Fundy between Nova Scotia and New Brunswick (fig. 3.20).

The main tide-producing forces are the gravitational pulls of the sun and moon on water. Of the two forces, the pull of the moon is greater because, although the sun is far more massive, the moon is much closer. Tidal fluctuations are greatest when the sun and moon are working together, that is, when the sun, moon, and earth are in alignment, which happens at full and new moons. These times of maximum tidal fluctuation are called **spring tides**. Tidal fluctuation is least when the gravitational effects of the sun and moon are working in opposition, that is, when the sun and moon, relative to earth, are at right angles to each other, as they are at the first and third quarters of the moon. These times of minimum tidal fluctuation are called **neap tides**. The size and geographic position of a bay, sea, or section of coastline determine whether the influences of sun and moon are amplified or damped and are responsible for the variations in tides from place to place.

Intertidal organisms have a lot to withstand—not only potential dessication from exposure to air during low tide but also the pounding of waves breaking on the seashore. The

(a)

(b)

Figure 3.20   Hopewell (flowerpot) rocks at the Bay of Fundy at: (*a*) high tide; and (*b*) low tide.

amount of wave energy to which intertidal organisms are exposed varies considerably from one section of coast to another; this variation affects the distribution and abundance of intertidal species. Exposed headlands are hit by high waves (fig. 3.21), and they are also subjected to strong currents, which are at times as strong as those of swift rivers. Coves and bays are the least exposed to waves, but even the most sheltered areas may be subjected to intense wave action during storms.

Chemical Conditions

Salinity

Salinity in the intertidal zone varies much more than in the open sea, especially within tide pools isolated at low tide. Rapid evaporation during low tide increases the salinity within tide pools along desert shores. Along rainy shores at high latitudes and in the tropics during the wet season, tide pool organisms can experience much reduced salinity.

Figure 3.21   Storm waves pounding rocky headlands such as these in Newfoundland have an important influence on the distribution and abundance of intertidal organisms.

Oxygen

Oxygen does not generally limit the distributions of intertidal organisms for two major reasons. First, intertidal species are exposed to oxygen-rich air at each low tide. Second, the water of wave-swept shores is thoroughly mixed and well oxygenated. An intertidal environment where oxygen availability may be low is in interstitial water within the sediments along sandy or muddy shores, especially in sheltered bays, where water circulation is weak.

Biology

The inhabitants of the intertidal zone are adapted to an amphibious existence, partly marine, partly terrestrial. All intertidal organisms are adapted to periodic exposure to air, but some species are better equipped than others to withstand that exposure. This fact produces one of the most noticeable intertidal features, **zonation of species.** Some species inhabit the highest levels of the intertidal zone, are exposed by almost all tides, and remain exposed the longest. Others are exposed during the lowest tides only, perhaps once or twice per month, or even less frequently. On an even finer spatial scale, microtopography influences the distribution of intertidal organisms. Tide pools support very different organisms than sections of the intertidal zone from which the water drains completely. The channels in which seawater runs, like a salty stream, during the ebb and flow of the tides offer yet another habitat.

The substratum also affects the distribution of intertidal organisms. Hard, rocky substrates support a biota different from that on sandy or muddy shores. You can see an obvious profusion of life on rocky shores because most species are attached to the surface of the substratum (see fig. 3.18). The residents of the rocky intertidal zone you will likely see are sea stars, barnacles, mussels, and seaweeds. But even here, where low tide seems to freely yield the secrets of the sea, all is not obvious. Most organisms take shelter at low tide, some among the fronds and holdfasts of kelp and others under boulders. There are even animals that burrow into and live inside rocks. As we shall see when we discuss competition in chapter 13 and predation in chapter 14, biological interactions make major contributions to the distributions of intertidal organisms.

On soft bottoms some species wander the surface of the substrate, but most are burrowers and shelter themselves within the sand or mud bottom. To study the life of sandy shores you must separate organisms from sand or mud. Perhaps this is the reason rocky shores have gotten more attention by researchers and why we know far less about the life of sandy shores. Beaches, like the open ocean, have been considered biological deserts. Careful studies, however, have shown that the intensity and diversity of life on sandy shores rivals that of any benthic aquatic community (MacLachlan 1983).

Human Influences

People have long sought out intertidal areas, first for food and later for recreation, education, and research. Shell middens, places where prehistoric people piled the remains of their seafood dinners, from Scandinavia to South Africa, are testimony to the importance of intertidal species to human populations for over 100,000 years. Today, each low tide still finds people all over the world scouring intertidal areas for mussels, oysters, clams, and other species. But the intertidal zone, which resists, and even thrives, in the face of twice daily exposure to air and pounding surf, is easily devastated by the trampling feet and probing hands of a few human visitors. Relentless exploitation has severely reduced many intertidal populations. Exploitation for food is not the only culprit, however. Collecting for education and research also takes its toll. The intertidal zone is also vulnerable to devastation by oil spills, which have damaged intertidal areas around the world.

Ocean-Land Transitions: Salt Marshes and Mangrove Forests

As we move from the ocean onto land we find ecosystems that blend aspects of the terrestrial and aquatic environments. **Salt marshes** (fig. 3.22) and **mangrove forests** (fig. 3.23) are concentrated along low-lying coasts with sandy shores. In areas

Figure 3.22 The salt marsh at La Pérouse Bay, east of Churchill, Manitoba.

Figure 3.23 The prop roots of mangroves provide a complex habitat for a high diversity of marine fish and invertebrates.

in which a river flows out into a sea we find an **estuary**, the part of the river where fresh- and saltwater merge. Salt marshes and mangroves are often associated with estuaries, but can also be found far from the nearest river. All of these areas are transitions between very different environments, and have a great deal in common physically, chemically, and biologically. Surrounded on three sides by oceans, a substantial portion of coastal Canada consists of salt marshes (fig. 3.24). Although people often associate salt marshes with warm climates, there exists substantial salt marsh habitat in the arctic regions of Canada and the world. One such marsh, La Pérouse Bay, near Churchill, Manitoba, has been the summer home for a generation of ecologists exploring the impact that grazing geese have on this community. As found for intertidal zones, herbivory in this system can have significant effects on the plants and nutrients (chapter 14).

Geography

Salt marshes, which are dominated by herbaceous vegetation, are concentrated along sandy shores from temperate to high latitudes. At tropical and subtropical latitudes the herb-dominated salt marsh is replaced by mangrove forests. Mangroves are associated with warmer climates due mainly to the sensitivity of mangroves to frost. Figure 3.24 maps the global distributions of salt marshes and mangrove forests.

Structure

Salt marshes generally include channels, called tidal creeks, that fill and empty with the tides. These meandering creeks can create a complex network of channels across a salt marsh (fig. 3.25). Fluctuating tides move water up and down these channels, or tidal creeks, once or twice each day. These daily movements of water gradually sculpt the salt marsh into a gently undulating landscape. Tidal creeks are generally bordered by natural levees. Beyond the levees are marsh flats, which may include small basins called *salt pans* that periodically collect water that eventually evaporates, leaving a layer of salt. This entire landscape is flooded during the highest tides and drains during the lowest tides. A typical cross section of a salt marsh is shown in figure 3.26.

The mangrove trees of different species are usually distributed according to height within the intertidal zone. For instance, in mangrove forests near Rio de Janeiro, Brazil, the mangroves growing nearest the water belong to the genus *Rhizophora*. At this level in the intertidal zone, *Rhizophora* is inundated by average high tides. Above *Rhizophora* grow other mangroves such as *Avicennia*, which is flooded by the average spring tides, and *Laguncularia*, which is touched only by the highest tides. Figure 3.27 shows zonation within a mangrove forest.

Physical Conditions

Light

Estuaries, salt marshes, and mangrove forests experience significant fluctuations in tidal level. Consequently, the organisms in these environments are exposed to highly variable light conditions. They may be exposed to full sunlight at low

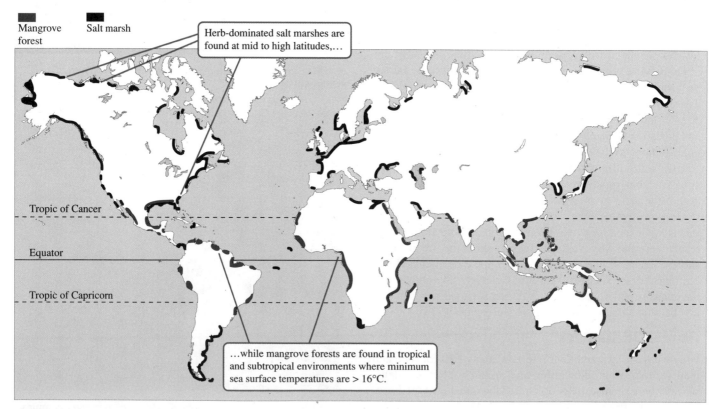

Figure 3.24 Salt marsh and mangrove forests (data from Chapman 1977, Long and Mason 1983).

Figure 3.25   Viewing a salt marsh from the air reveals great structural complexity.

tide and very little light at high tide. The waters of these areas are usually turbid because shifting currents, either from the tides or rivers, keep fine organic and inorganic materials in suspension.

Temperature

Several factors make the temperatures of estuaries, salt marshes, and mangrove forests highly variable. First, because their waters are generally shallow, particularly at low tide, water temperature varies with air temperature. Second, the temperatures of seawater and river water may be very different. If so, the temperature of an estuary may change with each high and low tide. Salt marshes at high latitudes may freeze during the winter. In contrast, mangroves grow mainly along desert and tropical coasts, where the minimum annual temperature is about 20°C. The shallows in these environments can heat up to over 40°C.

Figure 3.26   Salt marsh channels shown in cross section.

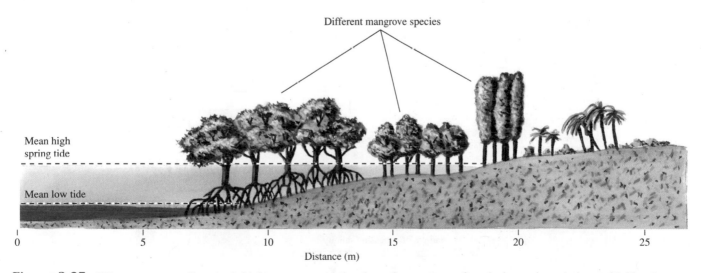

Figure 3.27   Where mangrove diversity is high, mangrove species show clear patterns of vertical zonation relative to tidal level.

Water Movements

Complex tidal currents flow in salt marshes and mangrove forests, where they are involved in ecological processes and also fragment and transport the litter produced by salt marsh and mangrove vegetation. Once or twice a day, high tides create saltwater currents that move up the estuaries of rivers and the channels within salt marshes and mangrove forests. Low tides reverse these currents and saltwater moves seaward. Tidal height may fluctuate far from where an estuary meets the sea. For example, tidal fluctuations occur over 200 km upstream from where the Hudson River flows into the sea. The vigorous mixing, in more than one direction, makes these transitional environments some of the most physically dynamic in the biosphere. Penetration of light and water movements vary over short distances and in the course of a day. This physical variability is reflected in highly variable chemical conditions.

Chemical Conditions

Salinity

The salinity of estuaries, salt marshes, and mangrove forests may fluctuate widely, particularly where river and tidal flow are substantial. In such systems, the salinity of seawater can drop to nearly that of freshwater an hour after the tide turns. Because estuaries are places where rivers meet the sea, their salinity is generally lower than that of seawater. In hot, dry climates, however, evaporation often exceeds freshwater inputs and the salinity in the upper portions of estuaries may exceed that of the open ocean.

Tidal flow is not the only factor that can influence salinity; interactions between plants, animals, and water all play an important role. A major contributing factor to increased salinity is high rates of evaporation. Within a salt marsh, evaporation rates will tend to be highest in areas exposed to sun, and lower in areas with a cover of vegetation reducing direct exposure of the water to the sun. As a result, when plants grow, they often reduce soil salinity, allowing even more plant growth. Animals can influence this through high levels of grazing, which can reduce vegetation cover, increase evaporation, and increase soil salinity.

Estuarine waters are also often stratified by salinity, with lower-salinity, low-density water floating on a layer of higher-salinity water, isolating bottom water from the atmosphere. On the incoming tide, seawater coming from the ocean and river water are flowing in opposite directions. As seawater flows up the channel, it mixes progressively with river water flowing in the opposite direction. Due to this mixing, the salinity of the surface water gradually increases down river from less than 1 ‰ to salinities approaching that of seawater at the river mouth (fig. 3.28).

Oxygen

In estuaries, salt marshes, and mangrove forests, oxygen concentration is highly variable and often reaches extreme levels. Decomposition of the large quantities of organic matter produced in these environments can deplete dissolved oxygen to very low levels, and isolation of saline bottom water from the atmosphere adds to the likelihood that oxygen will be depleted. At the same time, however, high rates of photosynthesis can increase dissolved oxygen concentrations to supersaturated levels. Again, the oxygen concentrations to which an organism is exposed can change with each turn of the tide.

Biology

The salt marshes of the world are dominated by grasses such as *Spartina* spp. and *Distichlis* spp., by pickleweed, *Salicornia* spp., and by rushes, *Juncus* spp. The mangrove forest is dominated by mangrove trees belonging to many genera. The

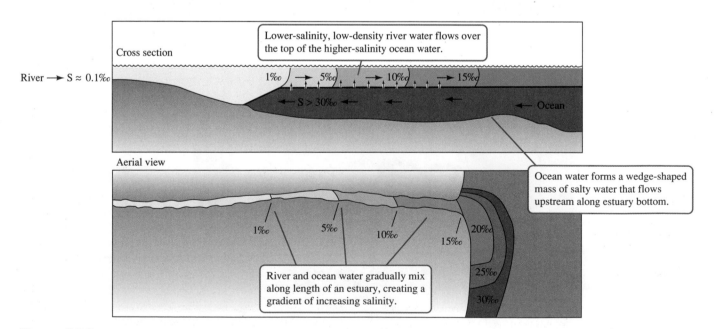

Figure 3.28   Structure of a salt wedge estuary.

species that make up the forest change from one region to another; however, within a region, there is great uniformity in species composition.

Estuaries and salt marshes don't support a great diversity of species, but their primary production is very high. These are places where some of the most productive fisheries occur and where aquatic and terrestrial species find nursery grounds for their young. Most of the fish and invertebrates living in estuaries evolved from marine ancestors, but estuaries also harbour a variety of insects of freshwater origin. Estuaries and salt marshes also attract birds, especially water birds. In the mangrove forest, birds are joined by crocodiles, alligators, and, in the Indian subcontinent, by tigers.

Human Influences

Estuaries, salt marshes, and mangrove forests are extremely vulnerable to human interference. People want to live and work at the coast, but building sites are limited. One solution to the problem of high demand for coastal property and low supply has been to fill and dredge salt marshes, replacing wildlife habitat with human habitat (fig. 3.29). Throughout human history, villages have been established in these highly productive habitats. Because cities benefit from access to the sea, many, such as Boston, San Francisco, and London, have

Figure 3.29 Dredging and filling of salt marshes, such as the operation shown in this photo, has destroyed vast areas of these highly productive biomes.

been built on estuaries. As a consequence, many estuaries have been polluted for centuries. The discharge of wastes depletes oxygen supplies, which physiologically stresses aquatic organisms. The discharge of organic wastes depletes oxygen directly as it decomposes, and the addition of nutrients such as nitrogen can lead to oxygen depletion by stimulating primary production. Heavy metals discharged into estuaries and salt marshes are incorporated into plant and animal tissues and have been, through the process of bioaccumulation, elevated to toxic levels in some food species. The assaults on estuaries and salt marshes have been chronic and intense, but the interest and concerns of people grow steadily.

Running Waters: Rivers and Streams

As we continue to head upstream and away from the brackish waters of estuaries we find ourselves in the flowing freshwater of rivers and streams. As we have previously mentioned, Canada is home to a substantial portion of the world's freshwater reserves, including large numbers of rivers and streams flowing through the countryside.

We become aware of the importance of rivers in human history and economy as we name the major ones: Nile, Danube, Tigris, Euphrates, Yukon, Indus, St. Lawrence, Mekong, Ganges, Rhine, Mississippi, Missouri, Yangtze-Kiang, Mackenzie, Amazon, Seine, Zaire, Volga, Thames, Rio Grande. The names of these rivers, and many others great and small, ring with a thousand images of history, geography, and poetry. The importance of rivers to human history, ecology, and economy is inestimable. However, river ecology has lagged behind the ecological study of lakes and oceans and is one of the youngest of the many branches of aquatic ecology.

What might rivers offer to the science of ecology? Their most notable feature is their dynamism. In art and literature, this characteristic has made rivers symbols of ceaseless change. For example, Leonardo da Vinci wrote: "In rivers the water you touch is the last of what has passed and the first of that which comes. So with time present." The ancient Greeks said simply: "You never step in the same river twice." In ecology, we call dynamic ecosystems such as rivers "nonequilibrial." **Nonequilibrial theory,** one of the newest branches of theoretical ecology, may find, as has art and literature, precisely the metaphor it needs in the rivers of the world. The meandering pattern of the river shown in figure 3.30 suggests the dynamism of river ecosystems.

Geography

Rivers drain most of the landscapes of the world. When rain falls on a landscape, a portion of it runs off, either as surface or subsurface flow. Some of this runoff water eventually collects in small channels, which join to form larger and larger water courses until they form a network of channels that drains the landscape. A river basin is that area of a continent or island that is drained by a river drainage network, such as the Mississippi River basin in North America or the Congo River basin in Africa. Rivers eventually flow out to sea or to some interior basin like the Aral Sea or the Great Salt Lake. Some

Figure 3.30   The meandering Okavango River, Botswana.

rivers, such as the Finke River in central Australia, do not flow into a lake or ocean but can dry out along the way. The Finke is one of the oldest rivers in the world and its waters naturally run dry in the Simpson Desert. River basins are separated from each other by watersheds, that is, by topographic high points. For instance, the peaks of the Rocky Mountains divide runoff from snowmelt. Water on the east side of the peaks flows to the Atlantic Ocean, while water on the west side flows to the Pacific Ocean. Figure 3.31 shows the distribution of the major rivers of the planet.

Structure

River, stream, creek, brook; you are certainly familiar with all of these words. Unfortunately, it is difficult to find agreement on the scientific differences among these terms. Part of this is because of the great complexity that is found when studying these features. Rivers and streams can be divided along three dimensions (fig. 3.32). They can be divided along their *lengths* into pools, runs, riffles, and rapids and, because of variation in flow, rivers can also be divided across their *widths* into wetted channels and active channels. In general, rivers are larger than the other groups, but much variability exists. Rather than worry about fine details of these terms, we focus here on ecologically important features. A wetted channel contains water even during low flow conditions. An active channel, which extends out from one or both sides of a wetted channel, may be dry during part of the year but is inundated annually during high flows. Outside the active channel is the **riparian zone,** a transition between the aquatic environment of the river and the upland terrestrial environment.

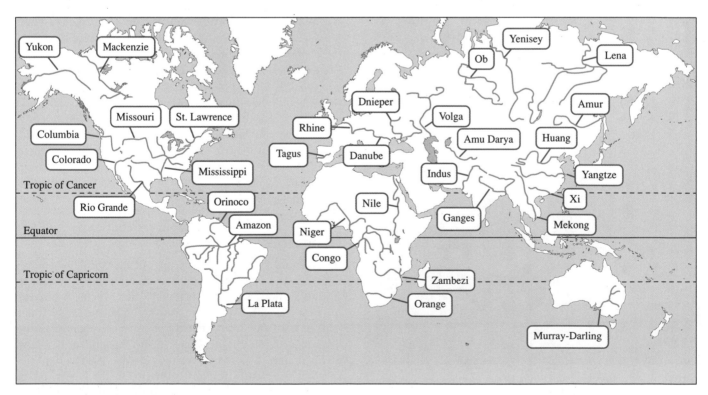

Figure 3.31   Major rivers.

Aquatic organisms live in all zones from the phreatic zone to the water column.

Water flows from river channels into groundwater and from groundwater into river channels.

Riffle

Riffle

Pool

Riparian zone

Active channel

Water column

Height of groundwater

Benthic zone

Hyporheic zone

Phreatic zone

Wetted channel

Active channel is usually flooded at least once each year.

Wetted channel contains water year-round.

Roots of trees growing in the riparian zone often draw water from groundwater.

Figure 3.32 The three dimensions of stream structure.

Rivers and streams can be divided *vertically* into the water surface, the water column, and the bottom, or benthic, zone. The benthic zone includes the surface of the bottom substrate and the interior of the substrate through depths at which substantial surface water still flows. Below the benthic zone is the **hyporheic zone,** a zone of transition between areas of surface water flow and groundwater. The area containing groundwater below the hyporheic zone is called the **phreatic zone.** Each part of a river or stream is a physically and chemically distinctive environment and each supports different organisms. Unique to stream and river environments is the constant and unidirectional flow of water. As a result, upstream processes generally have a stronger influence on downstream processes than vice versa. This asymmetry leads to a hierarchy of streams and rivers within a drainage network. Streams and rivers within a drainage network can be classified based on a system called **stream order** (fig. 3.33) developed

by Arthur Strahler (1952). In this system, headwater streams are first order, while a stream formed by the joining of two first order streams is a second order stream. A third order stream results from the joining of two second order streams and so on. In this system, a lower order stream, say a first order, joining a higher order stream, for instance, a second order stream, does not raise the order of the stream below the junction. In this case, that stream would remain a second order stream.

Physical Conditions

Light

There are two principal aspects of light to consider in relation to rivers and streams. First, how far light penetrates into the water column and second, how much light shines on the surface of a river. Streams and rivers vary considerably in water clarity. Generally, however, even the clearest streams are much more turbid than clear lakes or seas. The reduced clarity of rivers results from two main factors. First, rivers are in intimate contact with the surrounding landscape, and inorganic and organic materials continuously wash, fall, or blow into rivers. Second, river turbulence erodes bottom sediments and keeps them in suspension, particularly during floods. The headwaters of rivers are generally shaded by riparian vegetation. Shading may be so thorough along some streams that there is very little photosynthesis by aquatic primary producers. The extent of shading decreases progressively downstream as stream width increases. In desert regions, headwater streams usually receive large amounts of solar radiation and support high levels of photosynthesis. Figure 3.34 contrasts the environments of headwater streams flowing through a forest and a desert.

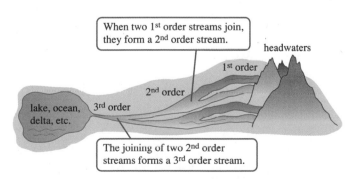

When two 1st order streams join, they form a 2nd order stream.

headwaters

1st order

2nd order

lake, ocean, delta, etc.

3rd order

The joining of two 2nd order streams forms a 3rd order stream.

Figure 3.33 A drainage network can be described based upon stream orders.

(a)

(b)

Figure 3.34 Headwater streams in: (*a*) forested Great Smoky Mountains; and (*b*) Sonoran Desert. The consumers in headwater streams draining forested lands generally depend on energy from the surrounding forest. Meanwhile desert streams are open to sunlight and support high levels of photosynthesis by stream algae, the source of most energy for desert-stream consumers.

Temperature

The temperature of rivers closely tracks air temperature but does not reach the extremes of terrestrial habitats. The coldest river temperatures, those of high altitudes and high latitudes, may drop to a minimum of 0°C. The warmest rivers are those flowing through deserts, but even desert rivers seldom exceed 30°C. The outflows of hot springs can be boiling in their upper reaches, but populations of thermophilic bacteria live in even the hottest of these.

Water Movements

What is notable about a river is the continuous movement of water. Although the river as a whole moves continuously, there will be substantial variation in flow rates among microsites within the river. Some areas will be **lotic**, where there is clearly free-flowing water. Other areas within the river will be **lentic**, with standing water. These differences are obvious to anyone who canoes the rivers throughout Canada: as you attempt to navigate the class IV rapids one minute, the next minute you look up to find your wet backpack and tent (that flew out of your canoe) sitting in a still pool at the side of the river. Currents in quiet pools may flow at only a few millimeters per second, while water in the rapids of swift rivers in a flood stage may flow at 6 m per second. Contrary to popular belief, the currents of large rivers may be as swift as those in the headwaters. These differences in flow rate can have significant effects on the species that live within the river.

The amount of water carried by rivers, which is called *river discharge,* differs a lot from one climatic regime to another. River flows are often unpredictable and "flashy" in arid and semiarid regions, where extended droughts may be followed by torrential rains. The flow in tropical rivers varies considerably. Many tropical rivers, which flow very little during the dry season, become torrents during the wet season. Some of the most constant flows are found in forested temperate regions, where, as we saw in chapter 2, precipitation is fairly evenly distributed throughout the year. Forested landscapes can damp out variation in flow by absorbing excessive rain during wet periods and acting as a reservoir for river flow during drier periods. Figure 3.35 compares the annual flows of rivers of moist temperate and semiarid climates.

It appears that the health and ecological integrity of rivers and streams depend upon keeping the natural flow regime for a region intact. Historical patterns of flooding have particularly important influences on river ecosystem processes, especially on the exchange of nutrients and energy between the river channel and the floodplain and associated wetlands. This idea, which was first proposed as the **flood pulse concept,** is supported by a growing body of evidence from research conducted on rivers on virtually every continent.

Chemical Conditions

Salinity

Water flowing across landscapes or through soils picks up dissolved materials. The amount of salt dissolved in river water reflects the history of leaching that has gone on in its basin. As we saw in chapter 2, annual rainfall is high in tropical regions. Consequently, many tropical soils have been leached of much of their soluble materials and it is in the tropics that the salinity of river water is often very low. Desert rivers generally have the highest salinities. Figure 3.36 shows that the salinity of river water from different regions may show 10- to 100-fold differences.

Oxygen

The oxygen content of river water is inversely correlated with temperature. Oxygen supplies are generally richest in cold, thoroughly mixed headwater streams and lower in the warm downstream sections of rivers. However, because the waters in streams and rivers are continuously mixed, oxygen is generally

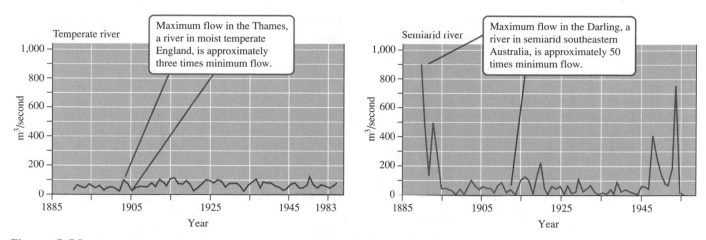

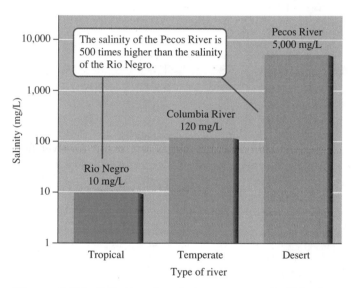

Figure 3.35 Annual flow of rivers in moist temperate and semiarid climates (data from Calow and Petts 1992).

Figure 3.36 Salinities of tropical, temperate, and arid land rivers (data from Gibbs 1970).

not limiting to the distribution of river organisms. The major exception to this generalization is in sections of streams and rivers receiving organic wastes from cities (wastes with high biochemical oxygen demand or BOD) and industry. Only organisms tolerant of low oxygen concentrations can inhabit these sections.

Biology

As in the terrestrial biomes, large numbers of species inhabit tropical rivers. The number of fish species in tropical rivers is much higher than in temperate rivers. For example, the Mississippi River basin, which supports one of the most diverse temperate fish faunas, is home to about 300 fish species. By contrast, the tropical Congo River basin contains about 669 species of fish, of which over 558 are found nowhere else. The most impressive array of freshwater fish is that of the Amazon River basin, which contains over 2,000 species.

The organisms of river systems change from headwaters to mouth. These patterns of biological variation along the courses of rivers have given rise to a variety of theories that predict downstream change in rivers and their inhabitants. One of these theories is the **river continuum concept** (Vannote et al. 1980). According to this concept, in temperate regions, leaves and other plant parts are often the major source of energy available to the stream ecosystem. Upon entering the stream, this coarse particulate organic matter (CPOM) is attacked by aquatic microbes, especially fungi. Colonization by fungi makes CPOM more nutritious for stream invertebrates. The stream invertebrates of headwater streams are usually dominated by two feeding groups: shredders (such as some caddisflies and amphipods), which feed on CPOM, and collectors (such as black fly larvae and other caddisflies), which feed on fine particulate organic matter (FPOM). The fishes in headwater streams are usually those, such as trout, that require high oxygen concentrations and cool temperatures.

The river continuum concept predicts that the major sources of energy in medium-sized streams will be FPOM washed down from the headwater streams and algae and aquatic plants. Algae and plants generally grow more profusely in medium streams because they are too wide to be entirely shaded by riparian vegetation. Because of the different food base, shredders make up a minor portion of the benthic community, which is dominated by collectors and grazers (such as snails and riffle beetles) on the abundant algae and aquatic plants. The fishes of medium streams generally tolerate somewhat higher temperatures and lower oxygen concentrations than headwater fishes.

In large rivers, the major sources of energy are FPOM and, in some rivers, phytoplankton. Consequently, the benthic invertebrates of large rivers are dominated by collectors, which make their living by filtering FPOM from the water column. In large rivers, there are also zooplankton. The fish found in large temperate rivers are those, such as carp and catfish, that are more tolerant of lower oxygen concentrations and higher water temperatures. Because of the development of a plankton community, plankton-feeding fish also live in large rivers. The major changes in temperate river systems predicted by the river continuum concept are summarized in figure 3.37.

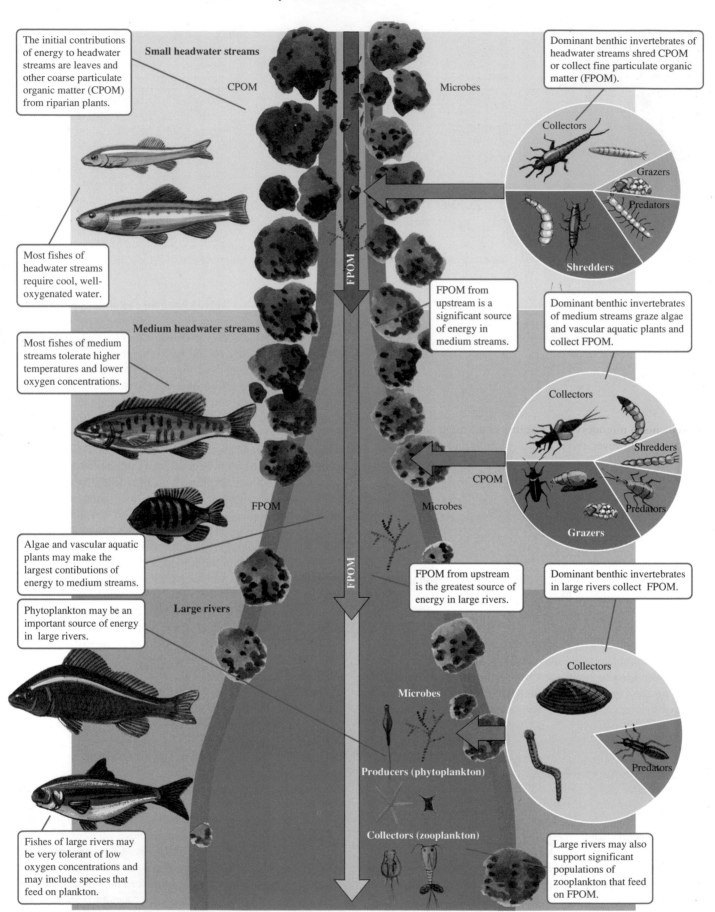

The initial contributions of energy to headwater streams are leaves and other coarse particulate organic matter (CPOM) from riparian plants.

Small headwater streams

CPOM

Microbes

Dominant benthic invertebrates of headwater streams shred CPOM or collect fine particulate organic matter (FPOM).

Collectors

Grazers

Predators

Shredders

Most fishes of headwater streams require cool, well-oxygenated water.

FPOM

FPOM from upstream is a significant source of energy in medium streams.

Dominant benthic invertebrates of medium streams graze algae and vascular aquatic plants and collect FPOM.

Medium headwater streams

Most fishes of medium streams tolerate higher temperatures and lower oxygen concentrations.

Collectors

Shredders

CPOM

Microbes

Predators

Grazers

FPOM

Algae and vascular aquatic plants may make the largest contibutions of energy to medium streams.

FPOM from upstream is the greatest source of energy in large rivers.

Dominant benthic invertebrates in large rivers collect FPOM.

Phytoplankton may be an important source of energy in large rivers.

Large rivers

Microbes

Collectors

Predators

Producers (phytoplankton)

Fishes of large rivers may be very tolerant of low oxygen concentrations and may include species that feed on plankton.

Collectors (zooplankton)

Large rivers may also support significant populations of zooplankton that feed on FPOM.

Figure 3.37   The river continuum.

Most of the invertebrates of streams and rivers live on or in the sediments; that is, most are benthic. These benthic organisms are influenced substantially by the type of bottom sediments. Stony substratum in the riffles and runs of rivers harbour fauna and flora that are different from those in sections with silt or sand bottoms mainly because of differences in the structure and stability of these bottom types. River ecologists have recently discovered that a great number and diversity of invertebrate animals live deep within the sediments of rivers in both the hyporheic and phreatic zones. These species may be pumped up with well water many kilometers from the nearest river. We know very little about the lives of these organisms. Once more, nature has yielded another surprise.

Human Influences

The influence of humans on rivers has been long and intense. Rivers have been important to human populations for commerce, transportation, energy, irrigation, and waste disposal. Because of their potential to flood, they have also been a constant threat. In the service of human populations, rivers have been channelized, poisoned, filled with sewage, dammed, filled with nonnative fish species, and dried. One of the most severe human impacts on river systems has been the building of reservoirs. Reservoirs eliminate the natural flow regime—including flood pulses—alter temperatures, and impede the movements of migratory fish. Because of the rapid turnover of their waters, however, rivers have a great capacity for recovery and renewal. The River Thames in England was severely polluted in the Middle Ages and remained so until recent times. During recent decades, great efforts have been made to reduce the amount of pollution discharged into the Thames, and the river has recovered substantially. The Thames once again supports a run of Atlantic salmon and gives hope to all the beleaguered river conservationists of the world.

Still Waters: Lakes and Ponds

In 1892, F. A. Forel defined the scientific study of lakes as the *oceanography of lakes*. On the basis of a lifetime of study, Forel concluded that lakes are much like small seas (fig. 3.38). Differences between lakes and the oceans are due, principally, to the smaller size of lakes and their relative isolation. Perhaps because they are cast on a more human scale, lakes have long captured the imagination of everyone from poets to scientists. For poets such as Henry David Thoreau (1854), they have been sources of inspiration and mirrors of inner truth. For scientists such as Stephen A. Forbes (1887), who wrote, "The lake as a microcosm," they have been mirrors of the outside world and microcosms of the ecological universe.

Geography

Lakes are simply basins in the landscape that collect water like so many rain puddles. Most lakes are found in regions worked over by the geological forces that produce these basins. These forces include shifting of the earth's crust (tectonics), volcanism, and glacial activity.

Most of the world's freshwater resides in a few large lakes. The Great Lakes of North America together cover an

Figure 3.38   Oligotrophic Lake Baikal in Siberian Russia contains 20% of all the surface freshwater on earth.

area of over 245,000 km^2 and contain 24,620 km^3 of water, approximately 20% of all the freshwater on the surface of the planet. An additional 20% of freshwater is contained in Lake Baikal, Siberia, the deepest lake on the planet (1,600 m), with a total volume of 23,000 km^3. Much of the remainder is contained within the rift lakes of East Africa. Lake Tanganyika, the second deepest lake (1,470 m), alone has a volume of 23,100 km^3, virtually identical to that of Lake Baikal. Still, the world contains tens of thousands of other smaller, shallow lakes and ponds, usually concentrated in "lake districts" such as northern Minnesota, much of Scandinavia, and vast regions across north central Canada and Siberia. Figure 3.39 shows the locations of some of the larger lakes.

Structure

Lake structure parallels that of the oceans but on a much smaller scale (fig. 3.40). The shallowest waters along the lake shore, where rooted aquatic plants may grow, is called the littoral zone. Beyond the littoral zone in the open lake is the **limnetic zone.** Lakes are generally divided vertically into three main depth zones. The **epilimnion** is the warm surface layer of lakes. Below the epilimnion is the thermocline, or **metalimnion.** The thermocline is a zone through which temperature changes substantially with depth, generally about 1°C per meter of depth. Below the thermocline are the cold dark waters of the **hypolimnion.** Each of these zones supports a distinctive assemblage of lake organisms.

Physical Conditions

Light

Lake colour ranges from the deep blue of the clearest lakes to yellow, brown, or even red. The colour, which depends on light absorption within a lake, is influenced by many factors but especially lake chemistry and biological activity. In lakes where the surrounding landscape delivers large quantities of nutrients, primary production is high and phytoplankton populations reduce light penetration. These highly productive lakes are usually a deep green. They are also often shallow and surrounded by cultivated lands or cities. Dissolved organic compounds, such as humic acids leached from forest soils,

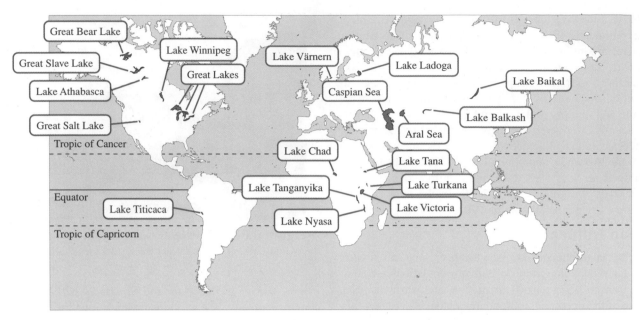

Figure 3.39 Distributions of some major lakes.

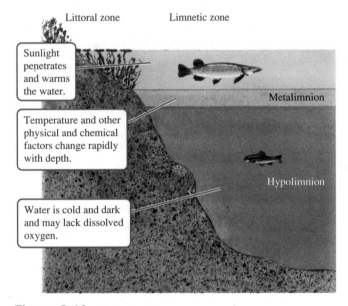

Figure 3.40 Lake structure.

increase absorption of blue and green light. Absorption in this range shifts lake colour to the yellow-brown end of the spectrum. These acid-stained lakes are generally of low productivity. In deep lakes where the landscape delivers low quantities of either nutrients or dissolved organic compounds, phytoplankton production is generally low and light penetrates to great depths. These lakes, such as Lake Baikal in Siberia, Lake Tahoe in California, and Crater Lake in Oregon, are nearly as blue as the open ocean.

Temperature

As in the oceans, lakes become thermally stratified as they heat. Consequently, during the warm season they are substantially warmer at the surface than they are below the thermocline. Temperate lakes are stratified during the summer, while low-

land tropical lakes are stratified year-round. As in temperate seas, thermal stratification breaks down in temperate lakes as they cool during the fall. Where climatic conditions cause lakes to freeze over in winter, lake area can strongly influence the severity of freezing on the organisms that live within the lake. Small lakes can freeze solid in cold winters, killing all vertebrates in a phenomenon often referred to as "fishkill." Larger lakes are more likely to just form ice on their surface, with liquid water remaining below. Where lakes freeze over in winter, the water immediately under the ice is approximately 0°C. Meanwhile, bottom water is a comparatively warm 4°C, the temperature at which the density of water is highest. In spring, once the ice has melted, temperate lakes spend a period without thermal stratification. As summer approaches, they gradually become stratified again. In high-elevation tropical lakes, a thermocline may form every day and break down every night! This dynamic situation occurs on the same tropical mountains where, as we saw in chapter 2, terrestrial organisms experience winter temperatures every night and summer temperatures every day. As in the oceans, these patterns of thermal stratification determine the frequency and extent of mixing of the water column. The seasonal dynamics of thermal stratification and mixing in temperate lakes are shown in figure 3.41.

Water Movements

Wind-driven mixing of the water column is the most ecologically important water movement in lakes. As we have just seen, temperate zone lakes are thermally stratified during the summer, a condition that limits wind-driven mixing to surface waters above the thermocline. During winter on these lakes, ice forms a surface barrier that prevents mixing. In the spring and fall, however, stratification breaks down and winds drive vertical currents that can mix temperate lakes from top to bottom. These are the times when a lake renews oxygen in bottom waters and replenishes nutrients in surface waters. Like tropical seas,

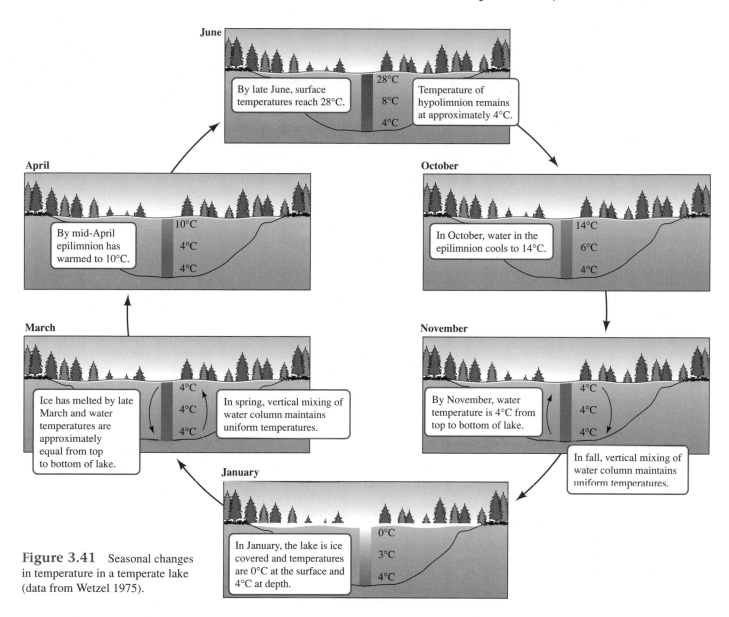

Figure 3.41 Seasonal changes in temperature in a temperate lake (data from Wetzel 1975).

tropical lakes at low elevations are permanently stratified. Of the 1,400 m of water in Lake Tanganyika, for example, only about the upper 200 m is circulated each year. Tropical lakes at high elevations heat and stratify every day and cool sufficiently to mix every night. Patterns of mixing have profound consequences to the chemistry and biology of lakes.

Chemical Conditions

Salinity

The salinity of lakes is much more variable than that of the open ocean. The world average salinity for freshwater, 120 mg per liter (approximately 0.120 ⁰/₀₀), is a tiny fraction of the salinity of the oceans. Lake salinity ranges from the extremely dilute waters of some alpine lakes to the salt brines of desert lakes. For instance, the Great Salt Lake in Utah sometimes has a salinity of over 200 ⁰/₀₀, which is much higher than oceanic salinity.

Oxygen

Mixing and biological activities have profound effects on lake chemistry. Well-mixed lakes of low biological production, which are called **oligotrophic,** are nearly always well oxygenated. Lakes of high biological production, which are called **eutrophic,** may be depleted of oxygen. Recall from chapter 1 that David Schindler and colleagues identified phosporus pollution as a major cause of human-involved eutrophication. Oxygen depletion is particularly likely during periods of thermal stratification, when decomposing organic matter accumulates below the thermocline and consumes oxygen. In eutrophic lakes, oxygen concentrations may be depleted from surface waters at night as respiration continues in the absence of photosynthesis. Oxygen is also often depleted in winter, especially under the ice of productive temperate lakes. In tropical lakes, water below the euphotic zone is often permanently depleted of dissolved oxygen.

Biology

In addition to their differences in oxygen availability, oligotrophic and eutrophic lakes also differ in factors such as availability of inorganic nutrients and temperature (fig. 3.42). Because aquatic organisms differ widely in their environmental requirements, oligotrophic and eutrophic lakes generally support distinctive biological communities. In temperate regions, oligotrophic lakes generally support the highest diversity of phytoplankton. These lakes are also usually inhabited by fish requiring high oxygen concentrations and relatively low temperatures, such as trout and whitefish. The benthic faunas of these lakes are rich in species and include the larvae of mayflies and caddisflies, small clams, and, along wave-swept shores, the larvae of stoneflies. Eutrophic temperate lakes, which tend to be warmer and, as we have seen, periodically depleted of oxygen, are inhabited by fish tolerant of high temperatures and low oxygen concentrations, such as carp and catfish, or fish that can breathe air in an emergency, such as gars and bowfins. The benthic invertebrate faunas of these lakes also tend to be tolerant of low oxygen concentrations; for example, midge larvae and tubificid worms, common in such lakes, have hemoglobin that helps them extract oxygen from oxygen-poor waters.

Much less is known about the biology of tropical lakes; however, a few generalizations are possible. Tropical lakes can be very productive. Also, their fish faunas may include a great number of species. Three East African lakes, Lake Victoria, Lake Malawi, and Lake Tanganyika, contain over 700 species of fish, approximately the number of freshwater fish species in all of the United States and Canada; all of western and central Europe and the former Soviet Union together contain only about 400 freshwater fish species. The invertebrates and algae of tropical lakes are much less studied, but it appears that the number of species may be similar to that of temperate zone lakes.

Human Influences

Human populations have had profound, and usually negative, influences on the ecology of lakes. In addition to examples of ecological degradation, however, are cases of amazing resilience and recovery—resilience in the face of fierce ecological challenge and recovery to substantial ecological integrity. Because lakes offer ready access to water for domestic and industrial uses, many human population centres have grown up around them. In both the United States and Canada, for example, large populations surround the Great Lakes. The human population around Lake Erie, one of the most altered of the Great Lakes, grew from 2.5 million in the 1880s to over 13 million in the 1980s. The primary ecological impact of these populations has been the dumping of astounding quantities of nutrients and toxic wastes into Lake Erie. By the mid-1960s, the Detroit River alone was dumping 1.5 billion gallons of waste water into Lake Erie each day. The Cuyahoga River, which flows through Cleveland before reaching the lake, was so fouled with oil in the 1960s that it would catch fire. In the face of such ecological challenges, much of Lake Erie, particularly the eastern end, was transformed from a healthy lake with a rich fish fauna to one that was, for a time, essentially an algal soup in which only the most tolerant fish species could live. With greater controls on waste disposal, the process of degradation began to reverse itself, and Lake Erie recovered much, but not all, of its former health and vitality by the 1980s.

Nutrients aren't the only things that people put into lakes, however. Fish and other species are constantly moved around, either intentionally or unintentionally. For instance, the canals that were dug to connect the Great Lakes with each other and to bypass Niagara Falls inadvertently introduced two species of fish, the sea lamprey and the alewife, that seriously disrupted the biology of the lakes. Once in the Great Lakes, sea lampreys fed mainly on lake trout, lake herring, and chubs. This predation, combined with intense fishing, devastated these commercially

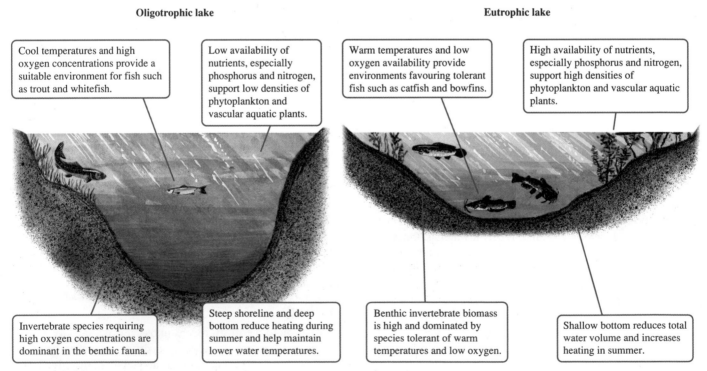

Oligotrophic lake

Cool temperatures and high oxygen concentrations provide a suitable environment for fish such as trout and whitefish.

Low availability of nutrients, especially phosphorus and nitrogen, support low densities of phytoplankton and vascular aquatic plants.

Invertebrate species requiring high oxygen concentrations are dominant in the benthic fauna.

Steep shoreline and deep bottom reduce heating during summer and help maintain lower water temperatures.

Eutrophic lake

Warm temperatures and low oxygen availability provide environments favouring tolerant fish such as catfish and bowfins.

High availability of nutrients, especially phosphorus and nitrogen, support high densities of phytoplankton and vascular aquatic plants.

Benthic invertebrate biomass is high and dominated by species tolerant of warm temperatures and low oxygen.

Shallow bottom reduces total water volume and increases heating in summer.

Figure 3.42 Oligotrophic and eutrophic lakes.

important fish populations. As these populations declined, alewife populations exploded. With exploding alewife populations came periodic and massive die-offs that littered beaches with tons of rotting fish. Massive efforts at controlling the sea lamprey by the United States and Canada have been reasonably successful.

These early introductions of fish into the Great Lakes were just a preview of future biological challenges, however. The rogues' gallery of introductions to the Great Lakes, which now includes species such as the zebra mussel, the river ruffe, and the spiny water flea, continues to grow, and there appears to be no end in sight. As figure 3.43 shows, 139 species of fish, invertebrates, plants, and algae had been introduced to the Great Lakes by 1990.

The population growth of many introduced species has been explosive and has had great ecological and economic impacts. One such introduction was that of the zebra mussel, *Dreissena polymorpha,* a bivalve mollusk native to the drainages emptying into the Aral, Caspian, and Black Seas. Zebra mussels disperse by means of pelagic larvae but spend their adult lives attached to the substrate by means of byssal threads. Their pelagic larvae allows them to disperse at a high rate. Though they spread throughout western Europe by the early 1800s, zebra mussels were not recorded in North America until the late 1980s. In 1988, they were collected in Lake Saint Clair, which connects Lake Huron and Lake Erie. In just three years, zebra mussels spread to all the Great Lakes and to most of the major rivers of eastern North America.

Locally, zebra mussels have established very dense populations within the Great Lakes. Shells from dead mussels have accumulated to depths of over 30 cm along some shores. Such dense populations threaten the native mussels of the Great Lakes with extinction. Zebra mussels are also fouling water intake structures of power plants and municipal water supplies, which may result in billions of dollars in economic impact. Biologists are working furiously to document and understand the impact of zebra mussels and other species introduced in the Great Lakes. Meanwhile, the governments of Canada and the United States are taking steps to reduce the rate of biological invasion of the Great Lakes. As a consequence of introductions of zebra mussels and other species, the Great Lakes have become a laboratory for the study of human-caused biological invasions (fig. 3.44).

Peatlands: Bogs and Fens

Throughout history, much of northern North America, western Europe, and the Siberian Lowlands have been covered in large expanses of peatlands (fig. 3.45). Words like moors, muskegs, and mires continue to be closely identified with the cultures of the British Isles. These areas have been of critical importance to early human populations as a source of fuel (peat bricks and coal) and forage (many berry-producing shrubs). The unique smell of burning peat is ingrained in the walls and whiskeys of Ireland and Scotland. But what exactly are peatlands? Wetland habitats come in two forms, those that form **peat**, and those that do not. Peat consists of partially decomposed plant material that builds up in certain poorly drained wetland habitats. We

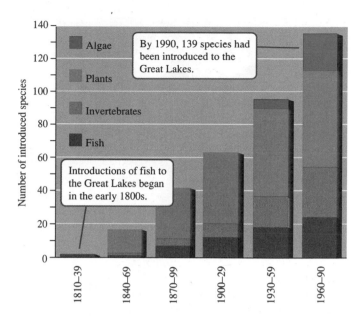

Figure 3.43 Cumulative number of species introduced to the Great Lakes (data from Mills et al. 1994).

(a)

(b)

Figure 3.44 Two invaders of the Great Lakes: (*a*) sea lamprey; and (*b*) zebra mussels. Invading species, such as these, have created ecological disasters in freshwater ecosystems around the globe.

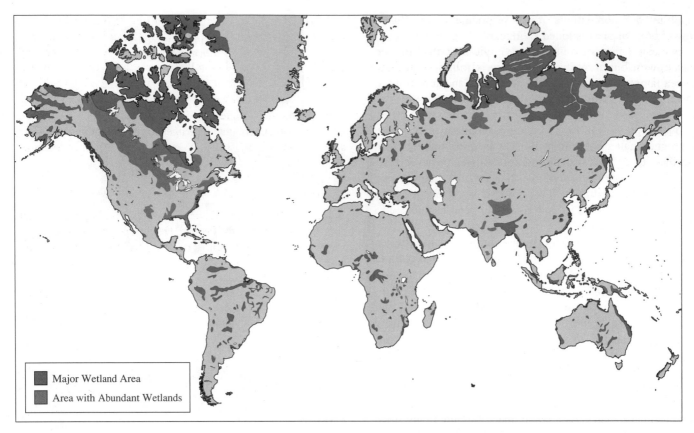

Figure 3.45   Global distribution of peatlands.

have already discussed several non-peat forming wetlands, such as coastal marshes and mangroves. Here we discus the two types of peat-forming wetlands, **bogs** and **fens** (fig. 3.46).

Geography

Peatlands occupy over 5% of the world's land base, with over 80% located in the high latitudes of the boreal and subarctic. Approximately 40% of the world's peatlands are found in North America, and over 15% of Canada's land base is peatland. Peatlands require significant water inputs, and thus will not be found in the drier regions of the world. There exist a mixture of peatland types, interspersed with non-peat forming wetlands and upland habitats. Although in chapter 2 we discussed the boreal forest as a terrestrial ecosystem, in a broader view the boreal region is a mixture of forest, bog, fen, and other wetland habitats.

Structure

The dominant feature of bogs and fens is a very well-developed layer of mosses and sedges, coupled with very low rates of decomposition. As a result, dead plant material accumulates, resulting in a buildup of peat. If water tables are stable, this process can continue for millennia, with peat deposits in some areas reaching more than 10 m in depth.

Bogs and fens differ as a function of the source of the water in the ecosystem. Bogs are found in depressions in the landscape, with precipitation being the only source of water into the system. Water levels tend to be around 50 cm below the surface. In contrast, fens are fed both through precipitation

(a)

(b)

Figure 3.46   Representative (*a*) bog and (*b*) fen communities. Notice the wave-like patterning of hummock and hollows in the bog community.

as well as by connections to ground or surface waters. Water levels tend to be at or near the surface.

Because of the high water level, fens are typically flat. Bogs, however, often exhibit patterning of raised *hummocks* and lower *hollows* (see fig. 3.46a). The upper layers of hummocks are above the water table and thus are drier than the rest of the peatlands. As a result, hummocks are aerated, allowing root growth, and thus are home to a diversity of vascular plants. Only a very shallow segment of the peatland is photosynthetically active, with the majority of the depth of this system occupied by dead plant material.

Physical Conditions

Light

Light conditions can vary widely within and among peatlands. How much light hits the moss layer is strongly influenced by the presence (or absence) of taller vascular plants, including trees. Bogs generally have a well-developed shrub layer, with only interspersed trees. Fens can be more variable, with some having few trees, and others having nearly full tree cover. In general, the drier the area within a peatland, the greater the chance for vascular plant growth and reduced light reaching the moss layer. The water surrounding the mosses is generally dark due to high concentrations of chemicals that leach from the mosses and vascular plants, as well as large amounts of suspended particulates. As a result, there is limited light penetration below the moss layer, and limited algal growth.

Temperature

Peatlands occur when rates of decomposition are lower than rates of production, and when water inputs are greater (or equal to) outputs. If either of these conditions changes, peatland development is slowed, or will even cease. Temperature can have significant effects on both of these processes. All biological reactions are temperature dependent, and increasing temperatures will increase decomposition rates. Whether the increase in temperature will have a stronger effect on decomposition than production is unknown and likely site-specific. Increased temperatures will certainly increase evaporation rates, thereby reducing water outputs from these systems. At the same time, increased temperature may also alter water outputs through changes to plant transpiration rates. Because of the large amounts of stored carbon in peatlands across the planet, understanding the potential impact of global warming on the function of these systems is an active area of ecological research.

Water Movements

Relatively still waters are a prerequisite for bog and fen formation, and peat accumulation is only possible when water levels are stable over extended periods of time. If the water table lowers, large areas of the peatlands will often dry. This is a serious issue for many of the moss species in these communities, as they are generally not adapted for desiccation and require water for reproduction. At a larger scale, when peatlands dry out they are prone to fire, as if they were a pile of leaves thousands of years old. As a result of these factors, vertical water movement can prevent peatland formation and persistence on the landscape.

Similarly, rapid horizontal water movement reduces the likelihood of fen formation, and instead is more likely to produce non-peat-forming wetlands. Rapid water movement aerates the environment, increasing microbial growth and decomposition rates. It also "flushes" the system of a variety of chemicals produced by many of the mosses and vascular plant that would otherwise reduce decomposition. Physically, rapid water movement creates challenges for plant establishment and growth, which many species common to fens cannot overcome.

Chemical Conditions

Salinity

Salinity is not a major factor influencing the organisms that reside in bogs and fens. Instead, the productivity of these systems can be strongly influenced by pH. Bogs are uniformly acidic with pH < 4.5. This acidity is due to a lack of a source of basic ions that would be carried in moving waters. Fens vary in pH, with some being as acidic as bogs, while others are neutral or even basic. The pH of fens will be strongly influenced by the chemical composition of the ground or surface waters that feed the community. In both bogs and fens, low pH greatly reduces decomposition, nutrient availability, and plant growth. Acidic fens will generally be less productive than fens with a more neutral pH.

Oxygen

A dominant feature of bogs and fens is a water-logged anaerobic environment due to the high water levels. This lack of oxygen coupled with potentially low pH results in a greatly reduced microbial activity and limited decomposition. These water-logged "soils" also limit the growth of vascular plants, as roots need oxygen for respiration and survival. Higher oxygen levels would greatly alter the biology of these systems, likely converting them to a non-peat forming wetland.

Biology

Despite the harsh chemical regime of many peatlands, they are home to a great number of plants and animals. The types of plants found vary widely across peatlands, with more productive areas dominated by trees and shrubs, and acidic areas having relatively few vascular plants. In all peatlands there will be a dominant moss layer, consisting of many bryophyte species and associated microfauna.

One of the most recognizable features of many bog habitats is that they are home to a variety of carnivorous plants (fig. 3.47). Carnivory is a great example of a novel solution to a very difficult situation. As a plant, nitrogen and other soil resources are essential for growth and reproduction (chapter 7). However, decomposition rates in bogs are extremely slow, and thus there is very little nitrogen available. It appears that there has been strong selection for unique methods of acquiring sources of nitrogen outside the soil environment. One of the more common types of carnivorous plants in bogs throughout North America is the pitcher plant. Inside the pitcher formed from modified leaves, the plants secrete a variety of enzymes that accelerate the decomposition of insects that get trapped inside. Further enhancing decomposition is a complex network of

Figure 3.47 Carnivorous plants, such as this pitcher plant (*Sarracenia purpurea*) are commonly found in bog habitats.

fungi and bacteria that live inside the pitchers. These plants are also home to a variety of spiders and other species, creating islands of diversity in a manner similar to the epiphytes that are common in tropical and temperate rain forests (chapter 2).

Animal life is not as diverse in peatlands as in other aquatic environments. The low calcium levels tend to reduce abundances of vertebrates and mollusks, though many transient species can be found passing through the area. Insect diversity and numbers are often very high in peatlands, particularly for species with aquatic larval stages.

Human Influences

The status of peatlands varies widely across the planet. Peat is mined throughout its range, with uses including that of a fuel source, construction material, and as a raw ingredient to soils used in greenhouses and gardens across the globe. The process of mining peat can result in altered hydrology, which can lead to widespread drying and loss of the habitat. Mining has occurred on a larger scale over a longer time period throughout much of Europe, with the vast expanses of peatlands in North America generally removed from direct human influence.

However, much like the seemingly remote arctic tundra, being removed from most direct human influence does not mean peatlands are not facing widespread challenges. The most pressing concern is how peatlands will respond to climate changes. Altered precipitation or temperature regimes can both cause peatlands to expand (where it becomes wetter and cooler) or contract (where it becomes drier and warmer). The loss of peatlands is of particular concern because they hold 30% of the world's soil carbon. Release of that carbon to the atmosphere through either increased decomposition rates or increased fire frequency may have significant implications for further climate change. Because of the potential for this positive feedback loop in the peatlands, they are currently a hotbed of activity for climate change researchers.

As we have seen in all of the habitats we explored in chapters 2 and 3, humans have significant influences on all areas of the planet, no matter how remote they may seem. Because of this, it is important to understand that current ecological processes occur in a world dominated by people. It is up to ecologists to determine how this influence will alter plant and animal distributions. This information will be critical for lawmakers and land managers in the development of strategies to protect the world's biological diversity.

Concept 3.2 Review

1. After years of successful reductions in phytoplankton populations, phytoplankton blooms are on the increase in parts of Lake Erie following the introduction of zebra mussels. Why?
2. Why is the prospect of global warming considered to be a serious threat to peatlands?
3. What ecological factors differ between lakes and marine habitats?

Ecological Tools

Reconstructing Lake Communities

How can we put our knowledge of the natural history of aquatic life to work? A major question ecologists often face is whether a certain environmental factor will alter an aquatic community. To answer this, we first need a clear understanding of the species composition and abundances of the focal community under current environmental conditions. In the first chapter we described the experimental approach that David Schindler and colleagues at the Experimental Lakes Area have used to test the impacts fertilization, acidification, and a variety of other factors have had on lake communities. Here we will describe a different approach used by John Smol and colleagues

at PEARL, the Paleoecological Environmental Assessment and Research Laboratory, based at Queen's University, Canada. The goal of this team of researchers is to provide the historical context to environmental change, through detailed study of the paleoenvironmental record on lakes throughout the world. This is the field of **paleolimnology**, which is broadly defined as the scientific discipline that uses the biological, chemical, and physical information archived in lake sediment profiles to track past environmental changes. By understanding the historical patterns of variation in lake communities, the researchers can generate hypotheses about how environmental factors have shaped the communities we see now, and possibly predict what we will find in the future.

How to Reconstruct Past Communities

The fundamental research subject in most paleolimnological studies is the sediment core (fig. 3.48a). Suspended in the waters of all lakes are numerous microscopic organisms. When they die, many will sink down to the bottom. Some of these will then decompose, while many will leave behind hard shells and crusts that get covered up by the continuing rain of detritus and dirt that falls from above. Sediments are continually accumulating, and the deeper you dig into them, the further back in time you move. The basic paleolimnological approach is to take a sediment core, divide it into many sections of differing depths, identify the approximate age of each depth, and identify the remains of the organisms and other paleolimnological information found at each depth. By putting this information together, a researcher can infer shifts in lake communities over long periods of time. The validity of this entire process depends upon two critical assumptions: (1) you can accurately determine the age of each depth (and that age is constant within a depth segment), and (2) the species you are measuring in the sediment cores are unbiased indicators of past lake conditions.

Age

Sediment cores are generally removed from the lake bottom and divided into numerous thin segments. Each segment is then typically subjected to radioisotopic measurement to determine the approximate age of the cores. Accurate measures of age are highly dependent upon the ability of researchers in the field to take reliable and undisturbed sediment cores. Any significant mixing of sediment during the field sampling will invalidate countless hours of work and cost thousands of dollars. It is important to remember that even studies built upon high-tech analyses and microscopic imagery can fail if the most basic of methods are conducted poorly. Though one often associates the critical point of research being the "Eureka" ideas of the scientist, in fact, those breakthroughs can never occur without accurate data collection.

Species Identification

Not all species that live in lakes will be suitable indicator species for paleolimnological studies. Good candidates will be species found in large numbers in the cores that also have hard bodies resistant to decomposition. One commonly used group of algal species are diatoms. Diatoms have hard silicate "shells" and are dominant members of the phytoplankton and periphyton (algae attached to submerged surfaces in shallow waters) in most aquatic communities). There are over 10,000 species of diatoms, and thus one can observe shifts in the abundance of different species through time, rather than just the presence or absence of diatoms as a group. The shapes and sculpturing of the silicate structures are species specific, and patterns of abundance for individual species can be followed throughout the depth of the core (fig. 3.48b). Additionally, the environmental conditions that are required for the growth of many diatom species are well studied, and

(a)

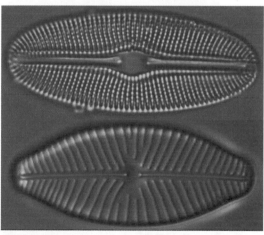

(b)

Figure 3.48 (*a*) A PEARL member collecting a sediment core while resting on the pontoon of a helicopter; (*b*) Two species of diatoms showing clearly distinct morphologies.

thus if paleolimnologists find that a given diatom species was abundant during a particular time period, they are able to infer something about the likely lake conditions (such as climate, pH, and nutrients) during that time interval.

It is through linking species identification with basic knowledge about the natural history of these species that paleolimnologists are able to reconstruct lake conditions of times past. We will now explore an example which uses these research tools to address an ecological question.

Climate-Lake Linkages

Due to patterns of global water and air circulation, and ice/snow-atmosphere feedbacks, human-induced climate change is widely believed to be particularly pronounced in polar regions (Moritz et al. 2002). What is less well known is whether warming is associated with broad ecological changes in arctic lakes (fig. 3.49). There is reason for concern, as primary production and nutrient cycling in arctic lakes are often limited by the short growth season. Increased temperatures could decrease ice cover, alter thermal stratification, and change nutrient cycling. All of these factors can influence the species composition of lakes, and thus there is reason to believe that rapid climate change in arctic areas has resulted in rapid ecological shifts.

John Smol and colleagues (Smol et al. 2005) tested the hypothesis that lakes that were believed to have experienced more climate change will also have experienced greater change in species composition than lakes which have experienced less climate change. They were able to obtain data on temperature changes over the last 50 years in the area of their study lakes, but to determine how ecosystems have changed on longer time frames, before instrumental data were available, they had to use indirect approaches. The team turned to paleolimnology for the tools needed to obtain the biological data. Sediment cores were obtained from lakes that ranged in latitude from 58° N to 82° N, with each core divided by depths, and ages and species composition of diatoms and other hard-bodied organisms were determined. Within each core, they estimated the amount of change in species composition over time, which they report as

beta-diversity. The higher the value of beta-diversity, the greater the change in species composition within the lake during the time interval represented in the sediment core. It is important to realize that species composition can change over time for reasons other than climate change. To provide a measure of the background level of change that occurs, Smol and colleagues used a group of 14 non-arctic lakes as a reference area.

Figure 3.50 shows that climate change has been most rapid at more northerly latitudes. It is also clear that beta-diversity is also higher at more northerly latitudes, suggesting that the rate of ecological change is associated with the rate of warming of a region. In fact, beta-diversity of 81% of the lakes north of the treeline was greater than that found in the reference lakes, while only 58% of the lakes south of the treeline had beta-diversity levels higher than the reference lakes.

These data are a good example of how describing a community in a rigorous scientific framework can lead to great insights into the basic ecology of systems. Although experimental approaches are useful for addressing many ecological questions, we must not forget that in many systems "natural experiments" have already occurred, with the results sitting at the bottom of a lake waiting to be collected.

Figure 3.49 Two typical high arctic lakes on Ellesmere Island, Canada. Ice can remain in the centre of some lakes year round.

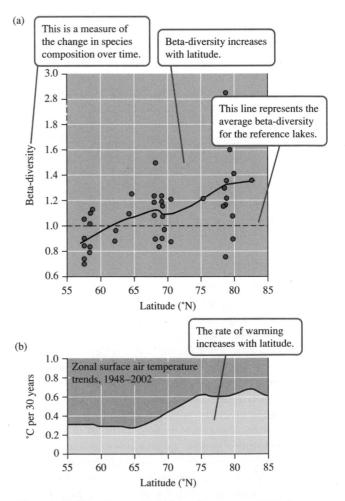

Figure 3.50 Change in (*a*) beta-diversity; and (*b*) air temperature as a function of latitude (data from Smol et al. 2005).

Summary

Humans everywhere hold a land-centred perspective of the planet. However, aquatic life is often most profuse where conditions appear most hostile to people, for example, along cold, wave-swept seacoasts, in torrential mountain streams, and in the murky waters where rivers meet the sea.

The hydrologic cycle exchanges water among reservoirs. Of the water in the biosphere, the oceans contain 97% and the polar ice caps and glaciers an additional 2%, leaving less than 1% as freshwater. The turnover of water in the various reservoirs of the hydrologic cycle ranges from only 9 days for the atmosphere to 3,100 years for the oceans.

The biology of aquatic environments corresponds broadly to variations in physical factors such as light, temperature, and water movements and to chemical factors such as salinity and oxygen.

The *oceans* form the largest continuous environment on earth. An ocean is generally divided vertically into several depth zones, each with a distinctive assemblage of marine organisms. Limited light penetration restricts photosynthetic organisms to the photic, or epipelagic, zone and leads to thermal stratification. Oceanic temperatures are much more stable than terrestrial temperatures. Tropical seas are more stable physically and chemically; temperate and high-latitude seas are more productive. Highest productivity occurs along coastlines. The open ocean supports large numbers of species and is important to global carbon and oxygen budgets.

Kelp forests are found mainly at temperate latitudes. *Coral reefs* are limited to the tropics and subtropics to latitudes between 30° N and S latitudes. Coral reefs are generally one of three types: fringing reefs, barrier reefs, and atolls. Kelp beds share several structural features with terrestrial forests. Both seaweeds and reef-building corals grow only in surface waters, where there is sufficient light to support photosynthesis. Kelp forests are generally limited to areas where temperature ranges from about 10°C to 20°C, while reef-building corals are limited to areas with temperatures of about 18°C to 29°C. The diversity and productivity of coral reefs rival that of tropical rain forests.

The *intertidal* zone lines the coastlines of the world. It can be divided into several vertical zones: the supratidal, high intertidal, middle intertidal, and low intertidal. The magnitude and timing of the tides is determined by the interaction of the gravitational effects of the sun and moon with the configuration of coastlines and basins. Tidal fluctuation produces steep gradients of physical and chemical conditions within the intertidal zone. Exposure to waves, bottom type, height in the intertidal zone, and biological interactions determine the distribution of most organisms within this zone.

Salt marshes, mangrove forests, and *estuaries* occur at the transitions between freshwater and marine environments and between marine and terrestrial environments. Salt marshes, which are dominated by herbaceous vegetation, are found mainly at temperate and high latitudes. Mangrove forests grow in the tropics and subtropics. Estuaries are extremely dynamic physically, chemically, and biologically. The diversity of species is not as high in estuaries, salt marshes, and mangrove forests as in some other aquatic environments but productivity is exceptional.

Rivers and streams are very dynamic systems and can be divided several ways into distinctive environments: longitudinally, laterally, and vertically. Periodic flooding has important influences on the structure and functioning of river and stream ecosystems. The temperature of rivers follows variation in air temperature but does not reach the extremes occurring in terrestrial habitats. The flow and chemical characteristics of rivers change with climatic regime. Current speed, distance from headwaters, and the nature of bottom sediments are principal determinants of the distributions of stream organisms.

Lakes are much like small seas. Most are found in regions worked over by tectonics, volcanism, and glacial activity, the geological forces that produce lake basins. A few lakes contain most of the freshwater in the biosphere. Lake structure parallels that of the oceans but on a much smaller scale. The salinity of lakes, which ranges from very dilute waters to over 200 %/oo, is much more variable than that of the oceans. Lake stratification and mixing vary with latitude. Lake flora and fauna largely reflect geographic location and nutrient content.

Peatlands occur primarily in northern latitudes and contain large stores of partially decomposed plant material. Bogs receive water only through precipitation, and have very low pH. Fens are fed both through precipitation as well as ground or surface waters, with pH varying among fens. In all peatlands, oxygen levels and microbial activity are low. As a result, decomposition rates are slower than production rates, allowing for the accumulation of peat. Peatlands face challenges through direct harvest, as well as indirectly through changes to global temperatures and precipitation patterns.

Paleolimnologists measure shifts in the composition of aquatic communities through time. Lake sediments are deposited continuously, and the remains of the hard-bodied organisms such as diatoms serve as a historical record of prior lake conditions. By comparing patterns in species turnover to recent records of changes in temperatures or other environmental factors, paleolimnologists are able to develop hypotheses about how lakes will respond to continued human influence in the future.

Review Questions

1. Review the distribution of water among the major reservoirs of the hydrologic cycle. What are the major sources of freshwater? Explain why according to some projections availability of freshwater may limit human populations and activity.

2. The oceans cover about 360 million km^2 and have an average depth of about 4,000 m. What proportion of this aquatic system receives sufficient light to support photosynthesis? Make the liberal assumption that the photic zone extends to a depth of 200 m.

3. Below about 600 to 1,000 m in the oceans there is no sunlight. However, many of the fish and invertebrates at these depths have eyes. In contrast, fish living in caves are often blind. What selective forces could maintain eyes in populations of deep-sea fish? (Hint: Many species of deep-sea invertebrates are bioluminescent.)

4. Darwin (1842) was the first to propose that fringing reefs, barrier reefs, and atolls are different stages in a developmental sequence that begins with a fringing reef and ends with an atoll. Outline how this process might work. How would you test your ideas?

5. How might a history of exposure to wide environmental fluctuation affect the physiological tolerances of intertidal species compared to close relatives in subtidal and oceanic environments? How might salinity tolerance vary among organisms living at different levels within the intertidal?

6. According to the river continuum model, the organisms inhabiting headwater streams in temperate forest regions depend mainly upon organic material coming into the stream from the surrounding forests. According to the model, photosynthesis within the stream is only important in the downstream reaches of these stream systems. Explain. How would you go about testing the predictions of the river continuum model?

7. How could you test the generalization that lake primary production and the composition of the biota living in lakes are strongly influenced by the availability of nutrients such as nitrogen and phosphorus? Assume that you have unlimited resources and that you have access to several lakes.

8. Biological interactions may also affect lake systems. How does the recent history of the Great Lakes suggest that the kinds of species that inhabit a lake influence the nature of the lake environment and the composition of the biological community?

9. Why are peatlands of particular interest to researchers who study climate change? What factors are likely to influence whether peatlands begin to release their vast stores of carbon into the atmosphere at a much faster rate?

10. What aspects of life in a bog may have favoured selection for carnivory in plants? Why are carnivorous plants relatively rare in all other types of communities, such as temperate forest, salt marshes, and even the tropical forest?

Suggested Readings

Barnes, R. S. K. and R. N. Hughes. 1999. *An Introduction to Marine Ecology*. 3d ed. Oxford: Blackwell Scientific Publications.

An excellent and readable introduction to marine ecology.

Cushing, C. E. and J. D. Allan. 2001. *Streams: Their Ecology and Life*. San Diego, Calif.: Academic Press.

Dodson, S. 2004. *Introduction to Limnology*. New York: McGraw-Hill.

Fraser, L. H. and P. A. Keddy. 2005. *The World's Largest Wetlands*. Cambridge University Press.

A series of papers describing the largest wetlands found across the planet.

Mills, E. L., J. H. Leach, J. T. Carlton, and C. L. Secor. 1994. Exotic species and the integrity of the Great Lakes. *BioScience* 44:666–76.

The causes and consequences of introductions of exotic species are presented in this reference.

Snelgrove, V. R. 1999. Getting to the bottom of Marine biodiversity: Sedimentary habitats. *Bioscience* 49:129–38.

A very readable review of the diversity that lies on the ocean floor.

Teal, J. and M. Teal. 1969. *Life and Death of the Salt Marsh*. Boston: Little, Brown.

A classic introduction to salt marsh natural history.

Thorne-Miller, B. and J. Catena. 1991. *The Living Ocean: Understanding and Protecting Marine Biodiversity*. Washington, D.C.: Island Press.

An exploration of marine biodiversity. Much biodiversity is left to be discovered in marine environments.

Chapter 4

Evolution and Speciation

Outline

*T*he great diversity of organisms that live on the planet, as well as the even greater diversity of organisms which have gone extinct, are the product of evolution and speciation. These organisms interact in countless ways with each other and their surroundings. These interactions can influence an individual's probability of survival and reproduction. As you will see later in this chapter, this can cause evolution. Ecology and evolution are linked, with changes in one leading to changes in the other. Evolution is in part the outcome of many ecological processes, and at the same time, there would be no ecology without the species that are produced through evolution and speciation. This linkage is widely recognized among ecologists, and evolutionary biology is integrated into the study of individuals (section II), populations (section III), interactions among species (section IV), communities (section V), and even many larger-scale questions (section VI). Because evolution is central to so many ecological studies, it is important that students of ecology have a broad understanding of evolution and speciation. We begin with a single person who fundamentally changed our understanding of the natural world.

Darwin's theory of evolution by natural selection, the unifying concept of modern biology, was crystallized by his observations in the Galápagos Islands. In mid October of 1835 under a bright equatorial sun, a small boat moved slowly from the shore of a volcanic island to a waiting ship. The boat carried a young naturalist who had just completed a month of exploring the group of islands known as the Galápagos, which lie on the equator approximately 1,000 km west of the South American mainland (fig. 4.1). As the seamen rowed into the oncoming waves, the naturalist, Charles Darwin, mused over what he had found on the island. His observations had confirmed expectations built on information gathered earlier on the other islands he had visited in the archipelago. Later Darwin recorded his thoughts in his journal, which he later published (Darwin 1839), "The distribution of the tenants of this archipelago would not be nearly so wonderful, if, for instance, one island had a mocking-thrush, and a second island some other quite distinct genus—if one island had its genus of lizard and a second island another distinct genus, or none whatever. … But it is the circumstance, that several of the islands possess their own species of the tortoise, mocking-thrush, finches, and numerous plants, these species having the same general habits, occupying analogous situations, and obviously filling the same place in the natural economy of this archipelago, that strikes me with wonder."

Darwin wondered at the sources of the differences among clearly related populations and attempted to explain the origin of these differences. He would later conclude that these populations were descended from common ancestors whose descendants had changed after reaching each of the islands. The ship to which the seamen rowed was the H.M.S. *Beagle,* halfway through a voyage around the world. The main objective of the *Beagle*'s mission, charting the coasts of southern South America, would be largely forgotten, while the thoughts of the young Charles Darwin would eventually develop into one of the most significant theories in the history of science.

Figure 4.1   On the Galápagos Islands Charles Darwin encountered many examples of readily observed plants and animal species that differed physically from one island to another island. Here a Galápagos hawk lands on a giant tortoise for which the islands are named.

Darwin's wondering, carefully organized and supported by a lifetime of observation, would become the theory of evolution by natural selection, a theory that would transform the prevailing scientific view of life on earth and rebuild the foundations of biology. The theory of natural selection coupled with a strong understanding of natural history is a foundation of the science of ecology.

Darwin left the Galápagos Islands convinced that the various populations on the islands were gradually modified from their ancestral forms. In other words, Darwin concluded that the island populations had undergone a process of **evolution,** a process that changes populations of organisms over time. Though Darwin left the Galápagos convinced that the island populations had evolved, he had no mechanism to explain the evolutionary changes that he was convinced they had undergone. However, a plausible mechanism to produce evolutionary change in populations came to Darwin almost exactly three years after his taking leave of the Galápagos Islands. In October of 1838 while reading the essay on populations by Thomas Malthus, Darwin was convinced that during competition for limited resources, such as food or space, among individuals within populations, some individuals would have a competitive advantage. He proposed that the characteristics producing that advantage would be "preserved" and the unfavourable characteristics of other individuals would be "destroyed." As a result of this selection by the environment, those individuals with favourable characteristics would have a greater chance of surviving and producing offspring than those individuals without those characteristics. Another way of saying this is that some traits will increase the **fitness** of the individual that possesses that trait. A modern definition of fitness is the relative genetic contribution of individuals to future generations, though Darwin was unaware of genetic mechanisms for his theory. Because selection can produce individuals with different fitness, populations would change over time. With this mechanism for change in hand, Darwin sketched out the first draft of his theory of natural selection in 1842. It would take him many years and many drafts before he honed the theory to its final form and amassed sufficient supporting information. The theory of **natural selection** can be summarized as follows:

1. More offspring are produced each generation than can be supported by the environment.

2. There is variation in physical, physiological, and behavioural traits among individuals in a population. Some of this variation is heritable (passed on to offspring).

3. Some traits will give some individuals an advantage over the other members of the population. These individuals will have a higher chance of surviving and reproducing than the other members of the population, increasing their fitness.

Darwin (1859) proposed that differential survival and reproduction of individuals would produce changes in species populations over time. That is, the environment acting on variation among individuals in populations would result in **adaptation** of the population to the environment. He now had a mechanism to explain the differences among populations that he had observed on the Galápagos Islands. Still, Darwin was aware of a major insufficiency in his theory. The theory of natural selection depended upon the passage of "advantageous" characteristics from one generation to the next. The problem was that the mechanisms of inheritance were unknown in Darwin's time. In addition, the prevailing idea at the time, blending inheritance, suggested that rare traits, no matter how favourable, would be blended out of a population, preventing change as a consequence.

As Darwin explored the Galápagos Islands, halfway around the world in central Europe a schoolboy named Johann Mendel was beginning an education that would eventually lead him to uncover the basic mechanisms of inheritance. Although Darwin and Mendel did not work together, their studies have been combined by later generations to form our modern understanding of evolution by natural selection (fig. 4.2).

Johann would be renamed Gregor Mendel when he joined the Augustinian order of monks that maintained a monastery near his birthplace. In a garden within the walls of the abbey, Mendel would discover what Darwin's around-the-world voyage would not reveal. The two keys to Mendel's discoveries would be excellent training in mathematics and physics, from which he derived a sense of quantitative relationships, and the power of an experimental approach to the study of the natural world.

What did Mendel discover? Briefly, he discovered what we now call "Mendelian genetics," including the very fundamental concept of particulate inheritance. That is the concept that characteristics pass from parent to offspring in the form of discrete packets of information that we now call genes. Mendel also determined that genes come in alternative forms, which we term **alleles.** For instance, Mendel worked with alleles that led to traits such as round versus wrinkled seeds and tall versus short plants. In addition, he found that some alleles prevent the expression of other alleles. We call such alleles "dominant" and the alleles that they suppress "recessive." Mendel's work also revealed the distinction between genotype and phenotype and the difference between homozygous and heterozygous genotypes. Mendel's work, which disclosed still other aspects of the laws of inheritance, laid a solid foundation for the science of genetics.

Figure 4.2   The work of Charles Darwin forms the foundation for modern evolutionary theory.

How did Mendel succeed, while so many others had failed? The sources of his success can be traced to his education and his own special genius. Mendel's education at the University of Vienna exposed him to some of the best minds working in the physical sciences and to an approach to science that emphasized experimentation. His introduction to the physical sciences included a solid foundation in mathematics, including probability and statistics. As a consequence, Mendel could quantify the results of his experimental research.

Mendel chose to work with plants which could be maintained in the abbey garden. His most famous and influential work was done on the garden pea, *Pisum sativum.* Many domestic varieties of peas, which showed a great deal of physical variation, were available to Mendel. Rather than treat the phenotype as a whole, Mendel subdivided the organism into a set of manageable characteristics such as seed form, stem length, and so forth, which it turned out were controlled by individual genes. This analytical perspective of his study organisms was probably another legacy of his training in the physical sciences. Finally, to his excellent education and genius, Mendel added a lot of hard work and perseverance.

Darwin and Mendel complemented each other perfectly and their twin visions of the natural world revolutionized biology. The synthesis of the theory of natural selection and genetics gave rise to modern evolutionary ecology, a very broad field of study. Here we examine several major concepts within that broad discipline.

Concepts

4.1 Phenotypic variation among individuals in a population results from the combined effects of genes and environment.

4.2 The Hardy-Weinberg equilibrium model helps identify evolutionary forces that can change gene frequencies in populations.

4.3 Changes in gene frequency within a population can occur through both natural selection and random processes such as genetic drift.

4.4 Physical and ecological processes interact with selection and drift to produce new species.

4.1   Variation Within Populations

Phenotypic variation among individuals in a population results from the combined effects of genes and environment. Because phenotypic variation is the substrate upon which the environment acts during the process of natural selection, determining the extent and sources of variation within populations is one of the most fundamental considerations in evolutionary studies. A critical finding has been that genes and the environment interact to co-use substantial phenotype variation.

Phenotypic Variation in a Desert Lizard

Natural selection can not occur unless there is phenotypic variation among the individuals in a population for a trait associated with fitness. However, such variation is not enough, as some of this variation must be heritable. Here we will describe several studies that have used populations of the chuckwalla, *Sauromalus ater* (formerly *Sauromalus obesus*), a large herbivorous lizard of the southwestern United States and northwestern Mexico (fig. 4.3) to explore the various causes of phenotypic variation. *Sauromalus* prefers to feed on annual forbs and grasses but will feed on the leaves of shrubs if its preferred and more nutritious foods are not available.

Figure 4.3 A chuckwalla, *Sauromalus ater*. Chuckwallas are large herbivorous lizards living in the southwestern United States and northwestern Mexico.

Though it grows most rapidly when young, the species continues growing throughout life, reaching a body length of over 220 mm (excluding the tail) and a mass of about 400 g.

Ted Case (1976) explored variation in body size among *Sauromalus* populations at twelve sites distributed across its geographic range, and found that average summer temperatures at his desert study sites ranged from 23.8°C to 35°C, while average annual rainfall varied from approximately 35 to 194 mm. Because the environments in which *Sauromalus* lives vary greatly across its range, we might expect that selection has favoured different characteristics in different parts of the species' range.

Clearly, *Sauromalus* lives in hot, dry places. Just how hot and dry some of these places are is shown by the climate graph for one of Case's study sites, Yuma, Arizona (see fig. 2.26). However, Case found considerable variation in climate over the elevational range of 4 to 1,166 m where *Sauromalus* lives. Elevation was especially well correlated with winter weather (fig. 4.4). As you can see in figure 4.4, average winter rainfall increases with elevation, from less than 20 mm at the lowest elevations to over 60 mm at the highest elevations. Winter rain is critical for growing the annual herbaceous plants that *Sauromalus* prefers to eat and the amount of winter rainfall largely determines the amount of plant growth in these desert environments.

Higher average rainfall at higher elevations translates into more food available for *Sauromalus*. However, the higher elevations inhabited by *Sauromalus* not only receive higher average rainfall, they also show less year-to-year variation in amount of rainfall. At the other end of the environmental spectrum, the *Sauromalus* at lower elevations lives in environments where much less rain falls and where there is more year-to-year variation in rainfall. What does variation in rainfall

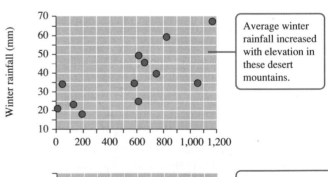

Average winter rainfall increased with elevation in these desert mountains.

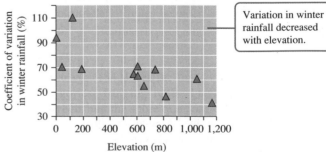

Variation in winter rainfall decreased with elevation.

Figure 4.4 Average winter rainfall and variation in rainfall among sites inhabited by *Suromalus ater* (data from Case 1976).

mean to *Sauromalus?* Variation in rainfall translates into variation in food availability. The lizards at lower elevations, on average, have access to less food and the amount available on any given year is unpredictable. Meanwhile the lizards at higher elevations live in a relatively food-rich environment where food availability is much more constant.

Case found that the lizards from the food-rich higher elevations are approximately 25% longer than those from lower elevations. This difference in body length translates into a twofold difference in body mass! What is the source of these size differences among populations? Of the many environmental variables that he measured, Case determined that the best predictor of *Sauromalus* body length across his study sites is average winter rainfall (fig. 4.5).

Case uncovered substantial variation in size among *Sauromalus* populations. How might we determine whether the differences in body size among *Sauromalus* populations Case observed are due to differences in food availability or due to genetic differences among populations? The solution would be to rear individuals from low- and high-elevation populations in a common environment. This is precisely what was done by Christopher Tracy (1999).

Tracy collected 12 to 15 juvenile *Sauromalus* from six populations in Arizona, California, and Nevada, living at elevations ranging from 200 to 890 m. He then raised these juvenile lizards under identical environmental conditions in a laboratory. By growing juvenile *Sauromalus* under identical environmental conditions, Tracy could determine the contributions of environmental versus genetic factors to size differences among *Sauromalus* populations.

Tracy set up the laboratory environment in a way that simulated late spring conditions, including 14 hours of light and 10 hours of darkness daily. These conditions provided the lizards with long periods for daily activity. He provided rocks for shelter and a heat lamp for basking. The laboratory environment maintained a temperature gradient from room temperature to 42°C under a heat lamp, which allowed the lizards the opportunity to use behaviour to maintain their body temperatures at a preferred 36°C. Tracy also made an abundance of high quality food and vitamins available at all times so that food would not limit rates of lizard growth. In addition, he took *Sauromalus* social life into account. Observations by other ecologists had shown that *Sauromalus* eats more and grows faster when living in small groups than when isolated from other *Sauromalus*. Therefore, Tracy kept his lizards in groups of 3 to 5 while he followed their growth under laboratory conditions for 462 days.

How did *Sauromalus* from different elevations respond to Tracy's laboratory conditions? Lizards from all populations grew well in the laboratory. However, they showed markedly different patterns of growth. Lizard size at the end of the laboratory experiment was highly and positively correlated with the elevation at which they had been collected as juveniles (Fig. 4.6). In the end, lizards from the higher elevations grew to a larger size, approximating in a laboratory common garden for lizards the pattern of variation in body size found in the field.

What do the results of Tracy's experiment indicate about variation in body size among *Sauromalus* populations? One important conclusion is that the differences in body size observed in the field are at least partly determined by genetic differences among populations. It appears that natural selection has favoured different sized individuals at different elevations. Tracy's study of *Sauromalus* demonstrates how morphological and laboratory studies can make significant contributions to our understanding of variation in populations. Because of the critical importance that phenotypic variation plays in allowing natural selection to occur, there are countless other studies documenting environmental and genetic causes of variation in natural populations. Phenotypic variation has been found for many traits in many taxa, including bacteria, fungi, plants, and other animal species. It is fair to say that phenotypic

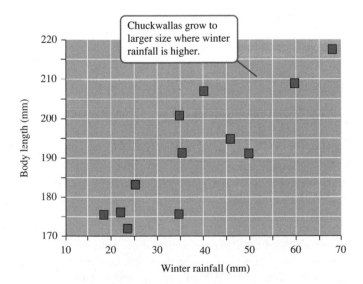

Figure 4.5 Relationship between winter rainfall and chuckwalla, *Sauromalus*, size (data from Case 1976).

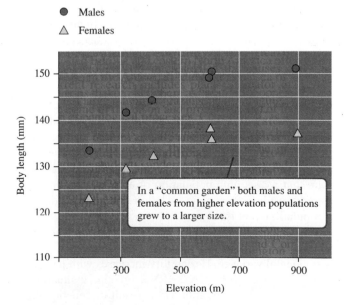

Figure 4.6 Chuckwalla body lengths at the end of a laboratory rearing experiment (data from Tracy 1999).

variation occurs broadly across the planet. However, if there is selection for a certain trait, why does variation persist in natural populations? In other words, why doesn't selection result in populations in which all individuals have the "best" genes? To answer this question, we need to understand the nature of trait heritability.

Genetic Variation and Heritability

Darwin was keenly aware that the only way natural selection can produce evolutionary change in a population is if the phenotypic traits upon which natural selection acts can be passed from generation to generation. In other words, evolution by natural selection depends upon the heritability of traits. We can define **heritability** of a trait—usually symbolized as h^2—in a broad sense as the proportion of total phenotypic variation in a trait, such as body size or pigmentation, that is attributable to genetic variance. In equation form, heritability can be expressed as:

$$h^2 = V_G/V_P$$

Here V_G represents genetic variance and V_P represents phenotypic variance. (See Appendix A for how to calculate variance.) Many different factors contribute to the amount of phenotypic variance in a population. We will subdivide phenotypic variance into only two components: variance in phenotype due to genetic effects, V_G, and variance in phenotype due to environmental effects on the phenotype, V_E. There are several additional sources that can cause phenotypic variation. One of these, the genotype x environment interaction, will be discussed in depth in chapter 8 (behavioural ecology). Subdividing V_P in the heritability equation given above produces the following:

$$h^2 = V_G/(V_G + V_E)$$

This simplified expression for heritability has important implications, so let's examine it. First, consider environmental variance, V_E. Environment has substantial effects on many aspects of the phenotype of organisms. For instance, the quality of food eaten by an animal can contribute to the growth rate of the animal and to its eventual size. Similarly, the amount of light, nutrients, temperature, and so forth, affect the growth form and size of plants. So, when we consider a population of plants or animals, some of the phenotypic variation that we might measure will be the result of environmental effects, that is, V_E. However, we are just as familiar with the influence of genes on phenotype. For example, some of the variation in stature that we see in a population of animals or plants will generally result from genetic variation among individuals in the population, that is, V_G.

What our equation says is that the heritability of a particular trait depends on the relative sizes of genetic versus environmental variance. Heritability increases with increased V_G and decreases with increased V_E. Imagine a situation in which all phenotypic variation is the result of genetic differences between individuals and none results from environmental effects. In such a situation, V_E is zero and $h^2 = V_G/(V_G + V_E)$

is equal to $h^2 = V_G/V_G$ (since $V_E = 0$), which equals 1.0. In this case since all phenotypic variation is due to genetic effects, the trait is perfectly heritable. We can also imagine the opposite circumstance in which none of the phenotypic variation that we observe is due to genetic effects. In this case, V_G is zero and so the expression $h^2 = V_G/(V_G + V_E)$ also equals zero. Because all of the phenotypic variation we observe in this population is due to environmental effects, natural selection cannot produce evolutionary change in the population. Generally, heritability of traits falls somewhere in between these extremes in the very broad region where both environment and genes contribute to the phenotypic variance shown by a population. For instance, Peter Boag and Peter Grant (1978), the latter formerly a professor at McGill University, estimated bill width in the Galápagos finch *Geospiza fortis* to have a heritability of 0.95. By comparison they estimated that bill length in the species has a heritability of 0.62. In a study of morphological variation in the water lily leaf beetle, a team of Dutch scientists (Pappers et al. 2002) found that body length and mandible width had heritabilities of between 0.53 and 0.83.

In the next section we will move from heritability of traits to change in gene frequencies across generations.

Concept 4.1 Review

1. What is a fundamental evolutionary implication of the large amounts of genetic variation commonly found in natural populations?
2. What do the results of Tracy's experiments indicate about variation in body size among *Sauromalus* populations?
3. Can V_E be greater than V_G for a trait related to an organism's fitness? Explain.

4.2 Hardy-Weinberg Equilibrium

The Hardy-Weinberg equilibrium model helps identify evolutionary forces that can change gene frequencies in populations. We defined evolution as a change in a population over time. Since evolution ultimately involves changes in the frequency of heritable traits in a population, we can define evolution more precisely as a change in gene frequencies in a population. Therefore a thorough understanding of evolution must include some knowledge of population genetics.

Calculating Gene Frequencies

Consider a population of Asian lady beetles of the species *Harmonia axyridis* (fig. 4.7). *Harmonia* populations generally include a great deal of variation in colour pattern on the wing covers, or elytra, and over 200 colour variants are known. Many colour forms are so distinctive that early taxonomists described them as different species or even different genera. Genetists in the first half of the twentieth century, especially Chia-Chen Tan (1946), Chia-Chen Tan and Ju-Chi Li (1934) and Theodosius Dobzhansky (1937), determined that the variation in colour patterns shown by *Harmonia* is due to the effects

Figure 4.7 Two colour forms of *Harmonia axyridis*, the Asian lady beetle. The genetic basis of the colour forms of *H. axyridis* is well studied, making it a useful species for studies of population genetics and natural selection.

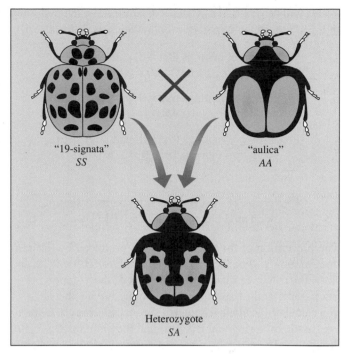

Figure 4.8 Colour patterns in the Asian lady beetle, *Harmonia axyridis* (after Dobzhansky 1937 and Tan 1946).

of more than a dozen alternative alleles for colour pattern. The phenotypic expressions of two of those alleles are shown in figure 4.8. The **homozygous** "19-signata" genotype of *Harmonia*, which we can represent as *SS*, has yellow elytra with several black spots, while the homozygous "aulica" genotype, represented here as *AA*, has elytra with prominent black borders and a large oval area of yellow or orange. Tan and Li, who did extensive breeding experiments using *Harmonia* that they collected in southwestern China, found that crosses between 19-signata and aulica genotypes produce **heterozygous** offspring, indicated here as *SA*, with a colour pattern that includes elements of both the 19-signata and the aulica parental forms (fig. 4.8). One of the convenient features of knowing so much about the colour pattern inheritance in *Harmonia* is that by observing the colour patterns of an individual you will also know its genotype at that locus.

Now suppose that you sampled the genotypes of *Harmonia* in a tract of forest in Asia and found that the frequency of beetles with genotype *SS* is 0.81 (81%), the frequency of the *SA* genotype is 0.18 (18%), and the frequency of the *AA* genotype is 0.01 (1%). What is the frequency of the *S* and *A* alleles in this population? The frequency in the *S* allele is:

$$\text{Frequency of } SS + 1/2(\text{Frequency of } SA)$$
$$= 0.81 + 1/2(0.18) = 0.81 + 0.09 = 0.90$$

The frequency of the *A* allele is:

$$\text{Frequency of } AA + 1/2(\text{Frequency of } SA)$$
$$= 0.01 + 1/2(0.18) = 0.01 + 0.09 = 0.10$$

These calculations show that the frequency of the *S* allele in this lady beetle population is 0.90, while the frequency of the *A* allele is 0.10. You will notice that in the calculation of the frequency of the S allele (and the A allele) we included the value of 1/2 (frequency of SA). This was because 1 of the 2 alleles in the heterozygote was S (and the other allele was A).

Evolutionary ecologists are interested in knowing what factors may change allele frequencies in a population such as that of our hypothetical population of *Harmonia*. Those factors, which we can consider as evolutionary forces, are revealed indirectly by the **Hardy-Weinberg principle.** The Hardy-Weinberg principle states that in a population mating at random in the absence of evolutionary forces, allele frequencies will remain constant.

George H. Hardy, a British mathematician, and Wilhelm Weinberg, a German physician, established their principle, one of the most fundamental of population genetics, in 1908. They did so to address a growing controversy surrounding the applicability of Mendelian genetics to human populations. Hardy was addressing the assertion by a contemporary biologist that a dominant allele introduced to a randomly breeding population would increase in frequency until it reached a frequency of 0.5, producing a ratio of genotypes of one homozygous dominant individual: two heterozygous individuals: one homozygous recessive individual. Because some genetically dominant human traits, such as brachydactyly (which produces short fingers), remain rare and do not occur in such simple "Mendelian" ratios, some biologists of the early 1900s claimed that Mendelian genetics does not apply to human populations. Hardy and Weinberg independently revealed the flaws in this line of reasoning and established the Hardy-Weinberg principle.

Let us review how random mating will influence gene frequencies in the *Harmonia* beetle population we just examined. Assuming equal fertility and fitness of the *SS, SA,* and *AA* genotypes, the proportion of *S* and *A* alleles in the population, 0.9 and 0.1, are also the proportions of eggs and sperm carrying the two alleles. With random mating, the probability that any two alleles will be paired in a zygote is determined by the frequency of the alleles in our hypothetical population as follows:

Proportion of matings that will pair an S sperm
with an S egg = $0.9 \times 0.9 = 0.81$ (81%),

Proportion of matings that will pair an S sperm
with an A egg = $0.9 \times 0.1 = 0.09$ (9%),

Proportion of matings that will pair an A sperm
with an S egg = $0.1 \times 0.9 = 0.09$ (9%)

and

Proportion of matings that will pair an A sperm
with an A egg = $0.1 \times 0.1 = 0.01$ (1%)

The proportion of the three genotypes produced by this random mating will be: $SS = 0.81$, $SA = 0.09 + 0.09 = 0.18$, and $AA = 0.01$. Notice that the proportions of these genotypes in the parents and offspring in the population are the same. If you calculate the **allele frequencies** from the genotype frequencies in the offspring you will find that they remain at $S = 0.90$ and $A = 0.10$, which is what the Hardy-Weinberg principle predicts when mating in a population is random. A central prediction of the Hardy-Weinberg principle is that in the absence of selection and with random mating, genetic variation will be maintained in a population.

We can represent these relationships in a more general way using some basic algebra, if we let p equal the frequency of one allele and q the frequency of the second allele. In the case of the *Harmonia* example just discussed, let p = the frequency of the S allele and q = the frequency of the A allele. Expressing these frequencies in numbers, $p = 0.90$ and $q = 0.10$. For a population in Hardy-Weinberg equilibrium in a situation where there are only two alleles at a particular locus, $p + q = 1.0$. Again referring to the *Harmonia* example, $p + q = 0.90 + 0.10 = 1.0$. Using this relationship we can calculate the frequency of genotypes in a population in Hardy-Weinberg equilibrium as:

$$(p + q)^2 = (p + q) \times (p + q) = p^2 + 2pq + q^2 = 1.0$$

The result of this calculation is:

$$(0.90)^2 + 2(0.90 \times 0.10) + (0.10)^2 = 0.81 + 0.18 + 0.01 = 1.0$$

According to this equation, the frequencies of the genotypes in our hypothetical *Harmonia* population are:

$$p^2 = (0.90)^2 = 0.81 = \text{frequency of the } SS \text{ genotype,}$$

$$2pq = 2(0.90 \times 0.10) = 0.18 = \text{frequency of the } SA \text{ genotype,}$$

and

$$q^2 = (0.10)^2 = 0.01 = \text{frequency of the } AA \text{ genotype.}$$

These calculations are equivalent to the combining of alleles that would occur if individuals in the *Harmonia* population ⌐ed at random. The mathematics of the Hardy-Weinberg ⌐re further dissected in figure 4.9.

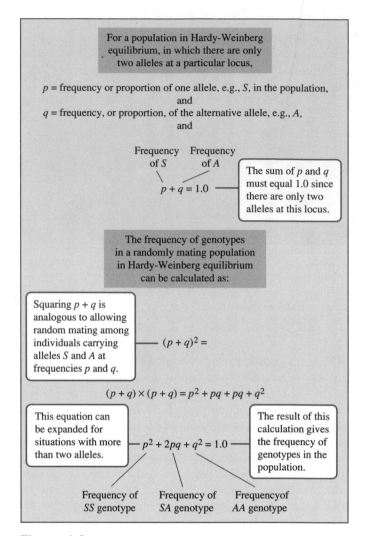

Figure 4.9 Anatomy of a Hardy-Weinberg equilibrium equation.

In the equations we just explored, random mating is sufficient to maintain constant genotype and allele frequencies. However, Hardy pointed out in his 1908 paper that in natural populations, other conditions are also required to maintain constant allele frequencies. For instance, Hardy recognized that nonrandom mating or differences in fertility among genotypes can change allele frequencies in a population. Some of the conditions necessary to maintain constant allele frequencies in a population, what is called Hardy-Weinberg equilibrium, are as follows:

1. *Random mating.* Nonrandom or preferential mating, in which the probability of pairing alleles is either greater or lower than would be expected based on their frequency in the population, can change the frequency of genotypes.

2. *No mutations.* Mutations that add new alleles to the population or change an allele from one form to another have the potential to change allele frequencies in a population and therefore disrupt Hardy-Weinberg equilibrium.

3. *Large population size.* Small population size increases the probability that allele frequencies will change from one generation to the next due to chance alone. Change

in allele frequencies due to chance or random events is called **genetic drift.** There are a variety of random events that can cause genetic drift. For example, let us assume that two alleles, *S* and *A*, have equal fitness. If by chance several individuals homozygous for one allele (*S*) did not mate one year, while all of the individuals that were homozygous for a different allele did mate (*A*) the result would be a lower frequency of *S* alleles and a higher frequency of *A* alleles among the gametes. Genetic drift reduces genetic variation in populations over time by increasing the frequency of some alleles and reducing the frequency of some alleles or eliminating others.

4. *No immigration.* Immigration can introduce new alleles into a population or, because allele frequencies are different among immigrants, alter the frequency of existing alleles. In either case immigration will disrupt Hardy-Weinberg equilibrium.

5. *All genotypes have equal fitness, where fitness is the probability of surviving and reproducing.* If different genotypes survive and reproduce at different rates, then gene and genotype frequencies will change in populations.

Hardy-Weinberg equilibrium requires that all five of these conditions be met. How likely is it that all the conditions required for Hardy-Weinberg equilibrium will be present in a natural population? In places and at times the conditions appear to be present. However, it is very likely that one or more of these conditions will not be met and allele frequencies will change over time. By carefully defining the highly restrictive conditions under which evolution is not expected, the analysis by Hardy and Weinberg leads us to conclude that the potential for evolutionary change in natural populations is often very great.

When a population is not in Hardy-Weinberg equilibrium, the principle helps us to identify the evolutionary forces that may be in play. For instance, Dobzhansky (1937) did extensive surveys of *Harmonia* across Asia and found the aulica form in many sites along with the 19-signata form (see fig. 4.8). However, he did not report the intermediate form, 19-signata crossed with aulica (see fig. 4.8). The absence of this intermediate phenotype from Dobzhansky's surveys suggests that the populations he studied were not in Hardy-Weinberg equilibrium.

Why would these intermediate types not be present in sufficient numbers for Dobzhansky to report them? One possible reason is nonrandom mating within the populations. Is there evidence of nonrandom mating by *Harmonia?* Substantial work on associations of colour variants of *Harmonia* has been done in Japan. Taku Komai and Yasushi Hosino (1951) found that *Harmonia* with different colour patterns had different habitat associations in a village landscape near Nagoya, Japan. Differences in habitat preferences among variants within a population can contribute to nonrandom mating. In addition, other Japanese researchers have more recently made direct observations of nonrandom mating in *Harmonia.* Naoya Osawa and Takayoshi Nishida (1992) observed preferential mating based on colour pattern in a population of *Harmonia* near Kyoto, Japan. In 1998, H. Ueno, Y. Sato, and K. Tsuchida

observed preferential mating in another *Harmonia* population in Japan based on size not on colour pattern.

Meanwhile, other researchers have documented changes in gene frequencies in *Harmonia* populations near Vladisvostok, Russia, that have taken place since the 1920s, when they were studied by Dobzhansky. L. Bogdanov and N. Gagal'chii (1986) collected *Harmonia* near Vladisvostok and compared the frequencies of colour variants within their collections to those found by Dobzhansky (1937) approximately one-half century earlier. What they found was a great departure from Hardy-Weinberg equilibrium. While most colour variants decreased in frequency, 19-signata increased by 30%. Meanwhile, the aulica colour variant had disappeared entirely. The work by Bogdanov and Gagal'chii clearly documents changes in genotype frequencies within these populations. In other words, though they did not document the mechanisms involved, they found evidence for evolutionary change.

In the remaining sections of chapter 4 we will discuss examples in which one or more of the conditions for Hardy-Weinberg equilibrium have not been met and where evolutionary change has occurred in populations as a consequence. We will also discuss how evolution within a population can eventually lead to speciation.

Concept 4.2 Review

1. What happens to gene frequencies if the conditions set forth in the Hardy-Weinberg principle are not met? Why?
2. Why is genetic drift likely to cause a larger shift in gene frequencies in small populations than in large populations?
3. In the equation describing the Hardy-Weinberg equilibrium, the frequency of heterozygotes is determined by $2pq$. Why is it $2pq$ and not $1pq$?

4.3 Evolution

Changes in gene frequency within a population can occur through both natural selection and random processes such as genetic drift. In the previous sections of this chapter, we have shown that phenotypic variation exists in natural populations, due to both environmental and genetic causes. We have also shown that under very stringent sets of conditions, allelic variation will be maintained, and thus evolution will not occur. However, as Darwin elegantly described in his *Theory of Natural Selection,* there is a struggle for existence among organisms that can lead to evolutionary changes. In this section, we will link our understanding of population genetics to two mechanisms of evolutionary change: natural selection and genetic drift.

The Process of Natural Selection

The basic concept of natural selection is that some heritable traits result in unequal fitness amongst individuals in a population. This results in an increase in the frequency of those favourable traits over time. Although this idea is easy enough to grasp, natural selection does not take the same form every-

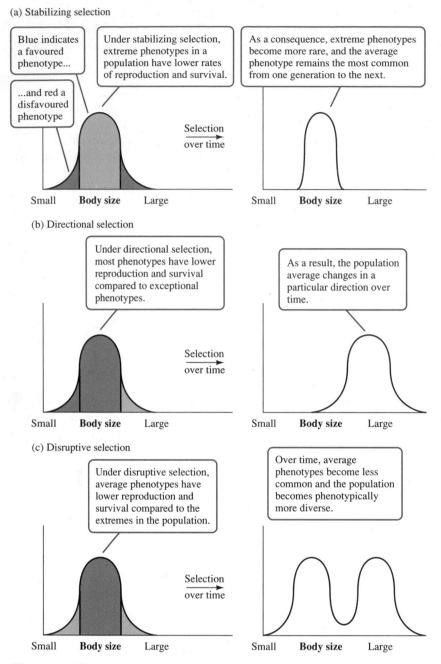

(a) Stabilizing selection

Blue indicates a favoured phenotype...

...and red a disfavoured phenotype

Under stabilizing selection, extreme phenotypes in a population have lower rates of reproduction and survival.

As a consequence, extreme phenotypes become more rare, and the average phenotype remains the most common from one generation to the next.

Selection over time

Small   **Body size**   Large   Small   **Body size**   Large

(b) Directional selection

Under directional selection, most phenotypes have lower reproduction and survival compared to exceptional phenotypes.

As a result, the population average changes in a particular direction over time.

Selection over time

Small   **Body size**   Large   Small   **Body size**   Large

(c) Disruptive selection

Under disruptive selection, average phenotypes have lower reproduction and survival compared to the extremes in the population.

Over time, average phenotypes become less common and the population becomes phenotypically more diverse.

Selection over time

Small   **Body size**   Large   Small   **Body size**   Large

Figure 4.10 Three principle forms of natural selection: (*a*) stabilizing selection, (*b*) directional selection, and (*c*) disruptive selection.

where and at all times. Natural selection can act against different segments of the population under different circumstances. Natural selection can accelerate changes in one population, and inhibit changes in another. We will begin our discussion of natural selection by describing the major forms of selection which occur in natural population, and then discuss the consequences on allelic frequencies.

Stabilizing Selection

One of the conclusions that we might draw from the discussion of the Hardy-Weinberg equilibrium model is that most ~~~ons have a high potential for evolutionary change.

However, our observations of the natural world suggest that species can remain little changed for generation after generation. If the potential for evolutionary change is high in populations, why does it not always lead to obvious evolutionary change at least on the short term? One form of natural selection, called **stabilizing selection,** can act to impede directional changes in populations.

Stabilizing selection acts against extreme phenotypes and as a consequence favours the average phenotype. Figure 4.10*a* pictures stabilizing selection, using a normal distribution of body size. Under the influence of stabilizing selection, individuals of average size have higher survival and reproductive rates, while the largest and smallest individuals in the population have lower rates of survival and reproduction. As a consequence of stabilizing selection, a population tends to sustain the same average phenotype over time while the frequency of extreme phenotypes can decrease. Stabilizing selection occurs where average individuals in a population are best adapted to a given set of conditions. If a population is well adapted to a given set of environmental circumstances, stabilizing selection may sustain the match between prevailing environmental conditions and the average phenotype within a population. However, stabilizing selection for a particular trait can be challenged by environmental change. In the face of environmental change the dominant form of selection may be directional.

Directional Selection

If we examine the fossil record or trace the history of well-studied populations over time, we can find many examples of how populations have changed in many characteristics over time. For instance, there have been remarkable changes in body size or body proportions in many evolutionary lineages. Such changes may be the result of **directional selection.**

Directional selection favours an extreme phenotype over other phenotypes in the population. Figure 4.10*b* presents an example of directional selection, again, using a normal distribution of body size. In this hypothetical situation, larger individuals in the population realize higher rates of survival and reproduction, while average and small individuals have lower rates of survival and reproduction. As a consequence of these differences in survival and reproduction, the average phenotype under directional selection changes over time. In the example shown in figure 4.10*b,* average body size increases with time. Directional selection occurs where one extreme phenotype has an advantage over all other phenotypes. However, there are circumstances in which more than one extreme phenotype may have an advantage over the average phenotype. Such a circumstance can lead to diversification within a population.

Ecology In Action

Human-Induced Evolution

When we talk about evolution and natural selection, we often think about the Galápagos Islands and Darwin's finches, or other species responding to challenges in remote areas of the world. However, this view of evolution being something that happens only in the wilderness is not reflective of reality. Instead, there is reason to believe that humans are the greatest evolutionary force in the world (Palumbi 2001). Humans live, farm, fish, hunt, and build, placing direct selection pressure on populations of many species. Industrial emissions impact global biogeochemistry (chapter 19), resulting in nitrogen and toxin deposition in even the most remote corners of the globe. These direct and indirect changes to natural populations serve as strong evolutionary forces, upon which natural selection continues to act.

Evidence for evolution by natural selection is everywhere. For example, what does it mean when you hear that some disease-causing bacterium has developed antibiotic resistance? It means that at one point in time a given species of bacteria could be killed by the application of some toxin. Obviously, this puts an enormous selective pressure on the bacterial population, such that any individuals immune to that toxin will have a much higher fitness than those that are killed. As a result, the frequency of the genes that confer resistance will increase within the population. This eventually reaches a point where the bacterial population consists primarily of individuals that can not be killed by that particular antibiotic. This is evolution by natural selection, and it is a serious concern among medical professionals. Development of antibiotic resistance is widespread and rapid. The first evidence of resistance to a new antibiotic generally occurs within 10 years of the drug first being introduced (Palumbi 2001).

The underlying force of natural selection resulting in the evolution of resistance to poisons is also strong in plant and insect populations, with very negative consequences for agriculture. The introduction of new pesticides puts strong evolutionary pressures on insect populations, with natural selection favouring those individuals with resistance. Not surprisingly, resistance to insecticides quickly follows the introduction of new pesticides. Importantly, this happens both in conventional agriculture and in plants that have been genetically-modified to produce their own pesticides. Similar evolution occurs in weed populations that are regularly sprayed with herbicides. Soon after the introduction of a new poison, natural selection favours individuals who are resistant. The medical and agricultural worlds provide very clear examples of evolution in action, with humans as the dominant selective force. Similar patterns also occur outside of these highly managed systems. Here we will present examples from populations of Atlantic cod (*Gadus morhua*) and mountain sheep (*Ovis canadensis*).

The coasts of Labrador and Newfoundland have supported a commercial cod fishery for centuries (fig. 4.11*a*). In the late 1980s and early 1990s, this fishery collapsed, leading to an offshore fishing ban (see chapter 14 for a discussion of predator-prey dynamics). An international team of researchers from Canada, Austria, and Norway asked the question of whether the long-term harvest of cod caused any evolutionary response of these fish populations (Olsen et al. 2004).

Let us begin by asking what fish traits might be affected by commercial fishing activity. The most obvious is fish size. Larger fish are more likely to be caught in a net than smaller fish, and this can cause directional selection resulting in a reduction in average body size (Handford et al. 1977). In cod, like many other species, it takes several years before an individual is sexually mature. The greater the age of maturation, the greater the risk of mortality due to harvest prior to breeding. Being captured prior to breeding has an obviously greater negative consequence on an individual's fitness than if captured after breeding. As a result, we might expect sustained fishing to select for individuals who become sexually mature at a younger age and smaller size. Olsen and colleagues pored

(a)

(b)

Figure 4.11 Continued harvest of (*a*) cod and (*b*) mountain sheep by humans has caused evolutionary changes in maturation rates and horn lengths.

over the records of over 10,000 fish that were caught and measured between 1977 and 2002 in three populations off the coasts of Newfoundland and Labrador. In the early 1980s, 50% of the fish caught were sexually mature by age 6. During the fishery collapse, age of maturity had been reduced to age 5 (fig. 4.12). Although this is suggestive of evolution, this change could also be caused by a density-dependent response. In other words, by harvesting fish, the fish that remained may have benefited from less competition for food and thus grew faster and were able to mature earlier. Olsen and his colleagues investigated the relationship between size and age of maturation. Under the density-dependent model, you would expect that the size at maturation would not change; instead the fish would simply get bigger faster. Olsen employed an elegant set of statistical analyses to suggest that it was evolution, and not density-dependence driving the reduced age at maturity. Olsen found that during the years of fishing, there was a trend towards smaller size at maturation, while following the fishing moratorium, this was actually reversed. These results suggest that fishing put strong selective pressure for maturation at younger ages and smaller size, while the relaxation of fishing has resulted in selection for a return towards maturation at larger sizes.

We now turn our attention from the Atlantic ocean of eastern Canada to the Rocky Mountains of western Canada. Bighorn sheep live throughout the Rocky Mountains, and hunters will pay thousands of dollars for a license allowing them to harvest an individual ram. Particularly desired by hunters are trophy rams; individuals which are particularly large with big horns (fig. 4.11b). David Coltman of the University of Alberta and colleagues from the Université de Sherbrooke, the Alberta Department of Sustainable Development, and the United States decided to explore the evolutionary consequences of trophy hunting in a population of bighorn sheep (Coltman et al. 2003). Coltman explored a dataset that contained the measurements of 192 harvested and unharvested rams between 1971 and 2002. This data set also contained information about the parents of all individuals, and thus patterns of paternity could be established. Both horn length and body size are heritable traits ($h^2 = 0.69, 0.41$ respectively), and larger values of both of these traits result in higher breeding values for those males. In other words, larger males with bigger horns are likely to sire more offspring than smaller males. What might happen when hunters begin to kill those males with larger breeding values? As with cod, increased risk of mortality means that an individual is less likely to produce the number of offspring that he would in the absence of harvesting. As a result, the trait that used to confer a fitness advantage (size and horn length) now provides a fitness disadvantage and should become less common in the population through natural selection. This is in fact what Coltman and his colleagues found (fig 4.13a); longevity decreased with horn-length breeding values, as did the number of paternities. Coltman also found that weight and horn length breeding values decreased through

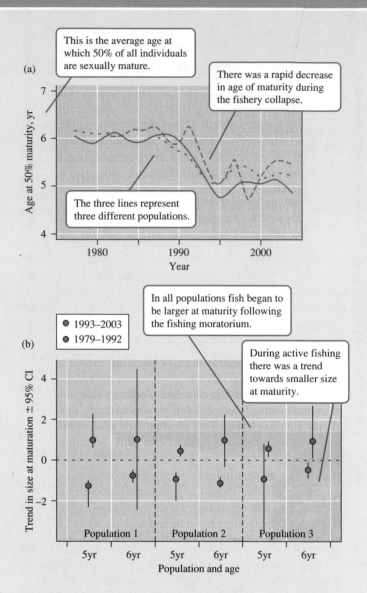

Figure 4.12   (a) Age of maturity of Atlantic cod decreased during the fishery collapse. (b) Evidence of maturation at smaller sizes during years with fishing than in the years following the moratorium (data from Olsen et al. 2004).

the course of the study (fig 4.13b). These results indicate that traits that historically conferred fitness benefits to males, such as enhanced size and larger horns, were becoming liabilities due to human-induced selection. What does this mean over the long-term? If these current trends continue, it is reasonable to expect to find this population dominated by smaller males with shorter horns. This may then decrease their attractiveness to hunters, relaxing this selection pressure. As you can see, evolution by natural selection is continuous.

All of these examples occurred through the intervention of people; however, the origin of selective pressures is irrelevant to the functioning of the mechanisms that cause evolution to occur. What influences gene frequencies is whether there is a shift in the phenotype with the highest fitness, not why that shift has occurred. People can alter the fitness associated with different phenotypes in wild populations, and evolution occurs exactly as is predicted by theory. People can not be thought of as distinct from the functioning of "natural" populations, for our actions alter the evolutionary trajectories of

countless numbers of species. In fact, by understanding the evolutionary responses of different species to our actions, we may be better able to develop sustainable practices that decrease the likelihood of negative changes to natural population such as fisheries collapses and loss of trophy rams.

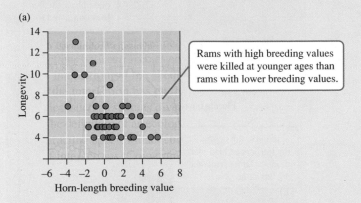

(a)

Rams with high breeding values were killed at younger ages than rams with lower breeding values.

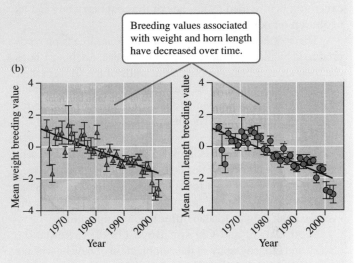

Breeding values associated with weight and horn length have decreased over time.

(b)

Figure 4.13 (*a*) Longevity decreases with increased horn-length breeding value of harvested rams. (*b*) Mean-weight and horn-length breeding values have decreased over the last 30 years of trophy hunting (data from Coltman 2003).

Disruptive Selection

There are populations that do not show a normal distribution of characteristics such as body size. In a normal distribution such as those depicted in figures 4.10*a* and 4.10*b*, there is a single peak, which coincides with the population mean. That is, the average phenotype in the population is the most common and all other phenotypes are less common. However, in some populations there may be two or more common phenotypes. In many animal species, for example, males may be of two or more discrete sizes. For example, it appears that in some animal populations small and large males have higher reproductive success than males of intermediate body size. In such populations, natural selection seems to have produced a diversity of male sizes. One way to produce such diversity is through **disruptive selection.**

Disruptive selection favours two or more extreme phenotypes over the average phenotype in a population. In figure 4.10*c*, individuals of average body size have lower rates of survival and reproduction than individuals of either larger or smaller body. As a consequence, both smaller and larger individuals increase in frequency in the population over time. The result is a distribution of body sizes among males in the population with two peaks. That is, the population has many large males and many small males but few of intermediate body size.

Figure 4.10*b* and 4.10*c* indicate change in the frequencies of phenotypes in the two hypothetical populations after a period of natural selection. This change depends on the extent to which genes determine the phenotype upon which natural selection acts.

Different types of selection (stabilizing, direction, and disruptive) can occur on different traits within a single popu-

lation, or on a single trait in multiple populations. One factor that can also vary is the rate of evolution due to natural selection. As you can imagine, not all selective pressures are equally strong. Some traits will be lethal, resulting in strong selective pressures and rapid evolution. Others will be more subtle, requiring thousands of generations before any measurable shift in gene frequency can be found (fig. 4.14).

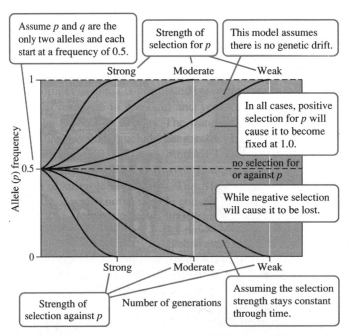

Assume p and q are the only two alleles and each start at a frequency of 0.5.

Strength of selection for p

This model assumes there is no genetic drift.

In all cases, positive selection for p will cause it to become fixed at 1.0.

no selection for or against p

While negative selection will cause it to be lost.

Strength of selection against p

Number of generations

Assuming the selection strength stays constant through time.

Figure 4.14 Variation in the rate of evolution as a function of the strength of selection.

Evidence for Selection: Rapid Adaptation by Soapberry Bugs to New Host Plants

Herbivores must overcome a wide variety of physical and chemical defenses employed by their host. As a consequence, plants theoretically exert strong selection on herbivore physiology, behaviour, and anatomy. Nonetheless, few studies have documented the process of herbivore adaptation. A notable exception is provided by studies of the soapberry bug and its evolution on new host plants.

The soapberry bug, *Jadera haematoloma,* feeds on seeds produced by plants of the family Sapindaceae. Soapberry bugs use their slender beaks to pierce the walls of the fruits of their host plants. To allow the bug to feed on the seeds within the fruit, the beak must be long enough to reach from the exterior of the fruit to the seeds. The distance from the outside of the fruit wall to the seeds varies widely among potential host species. As a result, there is likely strong selection within soapberry bug populations for beaks long enough to reach the seed of the particular species it feeds upon. If different bug populations feed upon different host plants, one would predict the average beak lengths to also differ among populations.

Scott Carroll and Christin Boyd (1992) reviewed the history and biogeography of the colonization of new host plants by soapberry bugs. Historically, soapberry bugs fed on three main host plants in the family Sapindaceae: the soapberry tree, *Sapindus saponaria* v. *drummondii,* in the southcentral region of the United States; the serjania vine, *Serjania brachycarpa,* in southern Texas; and the balloon vine, *Cardiospermum corindum,* in southern Florida. During the second half of the twentieth century three additional species of the plant family Sapindaceae were introduced to the southern United States. The round-podded golden rain tree, *Koelreuteria paniculata,* from east Asia and the flat-podded golden rain tree, *K. elegans,* from southeast Asia are both planted as ornamentals, while the subtropical heartseed vine, *Cardiospermum halicacabum,* has invaded Louisiana and Mississippi. At some point after their introduction, some soapberry bugs shifted from their native host plants and began feeding on these introduced plant species.

Carroll and Boyd reconstructed the history of the colonization of the southern United States by new species of host plants and colonization of these new plants by soapberry bugs. Extensive historical museum collections of plants and insects allowed them to assemble the history of this host shift by an herbivorous insect. They were particularly interested in determining whether the beak length had changed in soapberry bugs that shifted from native to introduced host plants.

Figure 4.15 contrasts the fruit radius of native and introduced host plants in Florida and the south central United States. In Florida the fruit of the native host plant *C. corindum* has a much larger radius than the fruit of the introduced *K. elegans* (11.92 mm versus 2.82 mm). In the south central United States soapberry bugs shifting to introduced host plants faced the opposite situation. There, the fruit of the native *S. saponaria* has a smaller radius (6.05 mm) than the fruits of the introduced *K. paniculata* (7.09 mm) and *C. halicacabum* (8.54 mm).

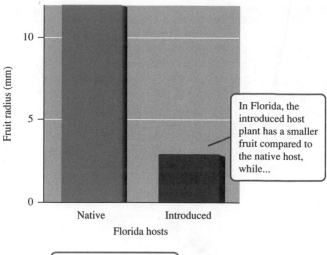

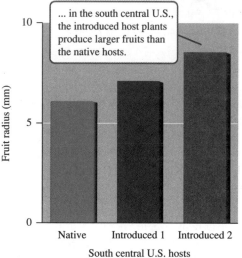

Figure 4.15   Comparison of the radius of fruits produced by native and introduced species of Sapindaceae (data from Carroll and Boyd 1992).

Carroll and Boyd reasoned that if beak length was under natural selection to match the radius of host plant fruits, bugs shifting to the introduced plants in Florida should be selected for reduced beak length, while those shifting to introduced hosts in the south central United States should be selected for longer beaks. Figure 4.16 shows the relationship between soapberry beak length and the radius of fruits of their host plants. As you can see, there is a close correlation between fruit radius and beak length.

At this point we should ask whether the differences in beak length observed by Carroll and Boyd might be developmental responses to the different host plants. In other words, are the differences in beak length due to genetic differences among populations of soapberry bugs or were they induced by the different host plants? Fortunately, Carroll reared juvenile bugs from the various populations on alternative host plants so we can answer this question. As it turns out, the differences in beak length observed in the field among bugs feeding on the various native and introduced host plants were retained in bugs that developed on alternative hosts. Here we have evidence for a genetic basis for interpopulational differences among soapberry bugs. Consequently, we can conclude that

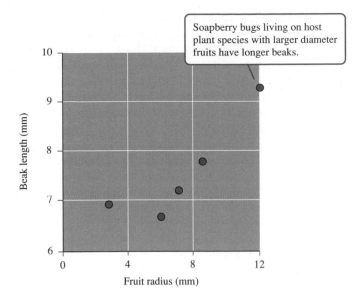

Figure 4.16 Relationship between fruit radius and beak length in populations of native and introduced species of soapberry bugs (data from Carroll and Boyd 1992).

the differences in beak length documented by Carroll and Boyd were likely the result of natural selection for increased or decreased beak length.

Scott Carroll, Stephen Klassen, and Hugh Dingle (1997, 1998) have done extensive additional studies of soapberry bugs that document substantial genetic differences between populations living on native versus introduced plants in the family Sapindaceac. Significantly, from the perspective of natural selection, the differences between these populations of soapberry bugs are great enough that both show reduced reproduction and survival when forced to live on the alternative host plants. That is, when soapberry bugs that normally live on native host plants are moved to introduced plants, their survival and reproductive rates decrease. However, when soapberry bugs that now live on introduced plants are moved to native plants, which their ancestors fed on only 30 to 100 years ago, their reproductive and survival rates also decrease. These additional studies of the genetic differences between soapberry bug populations provide additional evidence that populations of these bugs living on different host plants have undergone natural selection for traits that favour their survival and reproduction on their plant hosts.

Evolution Through Genetic Drift

While we may often think of evolutionary change as a consequence of predictable forces such as natural selection which favour particular genotypes over others, allele frequencies can also change as a consequence of random processes such as genetic drift. In fact, genetic drift occurs in all sexually reproducing populations at all times. However, the strength of drift and the resulting evolutionary change is much greater in small populations than in large ones. Here we will first discuss what exactly genetic drift is, and then provide an example of how drift caused evolution in a real-world population.

How Does Genetic Drift Occur?

Consider an individual that is heterozygous at a given locus (Aa). In the absence of any selection at this locus, one-half of the gametes produced will contain 'A', and the other one-half will contain 'a'. Now suppose this individual mates with another heterozygous individual, who also produces A:a gametes in a 1:1 ratio. It is easy to see that if these two individuals produce an infinite number of offspring; this will result in genotypic frequencies of:

$$AA = 0.5 \, (A) \times 0.5 \, (A) = 0.25$$
$$Aa = 0.5 \, (A) \times 0.5 \, (a) + 0.5 \, (a) \times 0.5 \, (A) = 0.50$$
$$aa = 0.5 \, (a) \times 0.5 \, (a) = 0.25$$

Following the Hardy-Weinberg principles, the frequencies of A and a will not change from one generation to the next. However, what happens if these individuals only produce three offspring? It should be immediately obvious that there is a problem. It is not possible to produce 25% AA offspring, 50% Aa, and 25% aa when only three offspring are produced. As a result, the frequencies of the genotypes and alleles in the offspring will not be exactly identical to the frequencies of the parents. This issue can be scaled up and extended to an entire population. Imagine that both 'A' and 'a' are present with a frequency of 0.5. With all individuals producing an infinite number of offspring, gene frequencies will not change from generation to generation. However, with a finite number of individuals producing a finite number of offspring, gene frequencies will change. This is evolution by genetic drift, and this is just as real a mechanism for evolution as is natural selection. In fact, genetic drift occurs on all loci within a genome, not only those upon which selection acts. The dominant factor that influences the rate of evolution due to genetic drift is population size, with drift causing more rapid evolutionary change in smaller populations (fig. 4.17). As we will discuss below, loss of genetic variation through drift is a significant concern for small populations, such as those often found in endangered species and on isolated habitats such as mountain tops and islands.

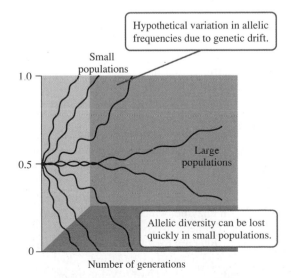

Figure 4.17 Random events cause allelic frequencies to change over time in a process called genetic drift.

Evidence of Genetic Drift in Chihuahua Spruce

One of the greatest concerns associated with fragmentation of natural ecosystems due to human land use is that reducing habitat availability will decrease the size of animal and plant populations to the point where genetic drift will reduce the genetic diversity within natural populations.

Many natural populations have undergone fragmentation as a consequence of changing climates and natural habitat fragmentation. One of those is the Chihuahua spruce, *Picea chihuahuana*, which is now restricted to the peaks of the Sierra Madre Occidental in northern Mexico. During the Pleistocene glacial period when the global climate was much cooler, spruce were found much farther south in Mexico and in more extensive populations. However, following the end of the Pleistocene and the onset of the warmer recent, or Holocene period, spruce populations moved northward and to higher elevations. Today, all spruce populations in Mexico are restricted to small, highly fragmented areas of subalpine environment in the mountains of states of Chihuahua and Durango. On these high mountains, Chihuahua spruce lives in an 800 km long band along the crest of the Sierra Madre Occidental at elevations between 2,200 and 2,700 m. On a local scale, the species is mainly found on cooler north-facing slopes along well-watered stream corridors, which are the microclimates where you would expect to find the descendants of an ice age relictual population. In these mountain refuges, Chihuahua spruce persists as far south as 23°30′ N latitude, just south of the Tropic of Cancer.

While the spruce of Durango have not been censused yet, all the Chihuahua spruce in the State of Chihuahua have been located and counted. Local populations of the species range in size from 15 to 2,441 individuals. This situation presents itself as a natural experiment on the effects of population size and habitat fragmentation on genetic diversity in populations. The opportunity for such studies was pursued by a joint team of U.S. and Mexican scientists (Ledig et al. 1997). F. Thomas Ledig and Paul D. Hodgskiss from the USDA Forest Service and Virginia Jacob-Cervantes and Teobaldo Eguiluz-Piedra of the Universidad Autonoma of Chapingo, Mexico, combined efforts to determine whether Chihuahua spruce has lost genetic diversity as a consequence of reduced population size following climatic warming after the end of the last ice age. They were also interested in whether reduced genetic diversity may be contributing to continuing decline of the species and its potential for extinction.

Ledig and his colleagues were particularly interested in the relationship between genetic diversity and population size. They used a technique called starch gel electrophoresis to determine the number of alleles present for 16 enzyme systems. Enzymes are of course gene products, and greater numbers of the various forms of an enzyme, which are called **allozymes,** indicate higher levels of genetic diversity in a population. The team assayed allozyme diversity for 24 genes, or **loci,** in seven populations ranging in size from 17 to 2,441 individuals.

As you might predict from the Hardy-Weinberg principle, Ledig and his colleagues found a significant positive correlation between population size and genetic diversity of their study populations. Figure 4.18 indicates that the smallest populations of Chihuahua spruce have much lower levels of genetic diversity than the largest populations. These results are consistent with the Hardy-Weinberg principle, which predicts that genetic drift will be most important in small populations.

How might drift occur in populations of spruce living on isolated mountain peaks in western Mexico and how might genetic drift reduce genetic variation in spruce populations? Imagine a population of 15 Chihuahua spruce on a mountain peak in the Sierra Madre Occidental at the beginning of July when the summer rains begin. The forest is dry after a long spring drought and as the lightning produced by a thunderstorm begins to strike the mountain, one bolt hits one of the spruce trees. The tree explodes as its interior water is turned into superheated steam, sending showers of splintered wood 50 m in all directions. The spruce tree then catches fire and the flames engulf two neighbouring spruce trees before the ensuing torrential rains put out the fire. The result is a small spot fire that has killed three trees. The deaths of three trees would make very little difference in a population of several thousand. However, in a population of just 15, three trees represent 20% of the individuals. When individuals are removed from very small populations their removal often reduces the frequency of some alleles; such events will eventually eliminate some alleles entirely from a small population.

It seems clear that drift is causing evolution and reducing genetic diversity in these populations of spruce. Many other researchers have shown similar patterns for other species of plants, as well as numerous species of animals. The loss of genetic diversity is an interesting issue on its own merits, but can also result in significant concern among ecologists and conservation biologists. Next we will discuss a study that was able to draw a connection between genetic diversity within a population and the probability of extinction.

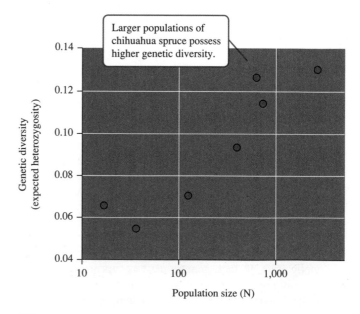

Figure 4.18 Relationship between population size and genetic diversity of chihuahua spruce, *Picea chihuahuana*, populations (data from Ledig et al. 1997).

Genetic Diversity and Butterfly Extinctions

The landscape of Åland in southwestern Finland is a patchwork of lakes, wetlands, cultivated fields, pastures, meadows, and forest (see fig. 21.12). Here and there in this well-watered landscape you can find dry meadows that support populations of plants, *Plantago lanceolata* and *Veronica spicata*, that act as hosts for the Glanville fritillary butterfly, *Melitaea cinxia* (fig. 4.19). As we will discuss in chapter 21, the meadows where *Melitaea* lives vary greatly in size, and *Melitaea* population size increases directly with the size of meadows (see fig. 21.13). Careful studies of these populations by Ilkka Hanski, Mikko Kuussaari, and Marko Nieminen (1994) showed that small populations of *Melitaea* living in small meadows were most likely to go extinct.

Several factors likely influence the greater vulnerability of small populations to extinction. However, what role might genetic factors, especially reduced genetic variation, play in the vulnerability of small populations to extinction? Richard Frankham and Katherine Ralls (1998) point out that one of the contributors to higher extinction rates in small populations may be **inbreeding.** Inbreeding, which is mating between close relatives, is more likely in small populations. Combining already low genetic variation in small populations with a high rate of inbreeding has several negative impacts on populations, including reduced fecundity, lower juvenile survival, shortened life span and it further accelerates the loss of genetic diversity.

Ilik Saccheri and colleagues (1998) reported one of the first studies giving direct evidence that inbreeding contributes to extinctions in wild populations. Saccheri and his colleagues studied 1,600 dry meadows and found *Melitaea* in 524, 401, 384, and 320 of the meadows in 1993, 1994, 1995, and 1996, respectively. Over this period they documented an average of 200 extinctions and 114 colonizations of meadows annually. In order to determine the extent that genetic factors, especially inbreeding, may contribute to these local extinctions, Saccheri

and his colleagues conducted genetic studies on populations of *Melitaea* in 42 of the meadows. They estimated heterozygosity, an indicator of genetic variability, with respect to seven enzyme systems and one locus of nuclear **microsatellite DNA.** Microsatellites are short repeating units in DNA that can be used identity relatedness among individuals. The researchers used the level of heterozygosity within each meadow population as an indicator of inbreeding, with low heterozygosity indicating high levels of inbreeding.

The results of the study indicated that influence of inbreeding on the probability of extinction was very significant. It turned out that the populations with the highest levels of inbreeding (lowest heterozygosity) had the highest probabilities of extinction. Saccheri and his colleagues found a connection between heterozygosity and extinction through effects on larval survival, adult longevity, and egg hatching. Females with low levels of heterozygosity produced smaller larvae, fewer of which survived to the winter dormancy period. Pupae of mothers with low heterozygosity also spent more time in the pupal stage, exposing them to greater attack by parasites. In addition adult females with low heterozygosity had lower survival and laid eggs with a 24% to 46% lower rate of hatching. These effects have the potential to reduce the viability of local populations of *Melitaea,* which are made up of individuals of low heterozygosity (low genetic variation), and increase their risk of local extinction.

We have seen how the small population size and isolation can influence the genetic structure of populations of many kinds of organisms, including the Chihuahua spruce isolated in cool moist microenvironments in the mountains of Mexico and the Glanville fritillary, *Melitaea* in the dry meadow environments of southwestern Finland. In situations like these, chance plays a significant role in determining the genetic structure of populations.

Concept 4.3 Review

1. If you observe no changes in gene frequencies in a population over several generations, can you conclude that the population is not subject to natural selection?
2. Why is rapid, human-induced environmental change a potential threat to some, but not other, species?
3. Can a trait with no heritability ($h^2=0$) evolve? Explain your answer.
4. What must have been true for beak length in soapberry bug populations before new species of soapberry plants were introduced into the United States?

4.4 Speciation

Physical and ecological processes interact with selection and drift to produce new species. Natural selection and genetic drift are two mechanisms that can cause dramatic changes in gene frequencies within a population. Such evolutionary changes have obvious implications for interactions among individuals within the larger ecological community.

Figure 4.19 Long-term studies of the Glanville fritillary butterfly, *Melitaea cinxia,* have provided exceptional insights into the relationship between population size and genetic diversity.

For example, selection toward larger body size in a predator may alter the intensity of predation experienced by the prey. What we have not yet discussed is what happens over even longer time scales, where these changes in gene frequencies can result in the evolution of a new species. Species are the raw material for all ecological interactions, and thus any process that can alter the rate of speciation will have significant ecological consequences. In this section we will discuss a variety of mechanisms which can cause speciation. However, before we can discuss how species evolve, we must first have an understanding of what we mean by species.

What Is a Species?

This at first may seem like a trivial question, but in fact, this issue is at the heart of substantial disagreement among researchers. Originally, groups of individuals that shared similar morphologies were grouped together as members of a single species. This approach was championed by Carolus Linnaeus (later known as Carl von Linné), who is responsible for the Linnaean classification system that is currently used in biology. At the essence of this approach lies the concept of Platonic idealism in which there is a single truth that is unchanging. By extension, under the Linnaean system, species were discrete units that were constant through time.

Although this morphological approach is still widely used, and is the principle form of species identification for amateur naturalists everywhere, it is not the definition of species most used by ecologists and evolutionary biologists. Instead, the most widely used definition of species is the **biological species concept**, and this was presented by Ernst Mayr in 1942. Mayr defined species as "groups of actually or potentially interbreeding populations, which are reproductively isolated from other such groups" (Mayr 1942). This definition of species is not based upon arbitrary descriptions of morphology nor based upon patterns of occurrence. Instead, this is based upon a real (and measurable) ecological concept: reproductive isolation.

Although this is the most widely used definition of species, and the one we will use here, it is important to note that this definition is not particularly useful for a large number of the "species" that exist on the planet. Many bacteria, fungi, and even plants rarely interbreed, even within individuals from the same species. Instead, reproduction is often asexual, through a number of mechanisms. Additionally, many species occasionally form viable hybrids with individuals of other species. In these situations, the biological species concept breaks down. If a particular species of fungi consists of many genotypes, none of which ever interbreed, does this mean that each genotype is its own species? If individuals of different species are able to produce a viable offspring just once, is that enough to rule they are not actually different species? There are no clear answers. As an alternative, there are a variety of species concepts that are independent of reproduction, and instead are based upon phylogenetic similarity and patterns of descent, a full discussion of which is beyond the scope of this book. Instead, we will follow the biological species concept, as this is the one most people are familiar with. We begin our discussion of speciation by talking about sex.

What Is Reproductive Isolation?

As you see from Mayr's definition of species, a critical requirement is reproductive isolation between populations. What is not clear, however, is how you go from having a single population of interbreeding individuals of a single species to two populations of reproductively isolated individuals, and thus two species. To answer this, we need to identify the mechanisms which can cause reproductive isolation.

Isolating mechanisms can be roughly categorized into two groups, pre- and postzygotic isolating mechanisms (fig. 4.20). Prezygotic isolating mechanisms are processes which prevent two individuals from forming a zygote. Postzygotic isolating mechanisms are equally efficient at maintaining species integrity, but they occur after a zygote has been formed.

How do two individuals actually produce a zygote? Though this is the sort of question discussed in fourth-grade health class, it is equally relevant to university-level ecology. Two individuals need to find each other, they both need to be sexually receptive at the same time, they need to engage in certain behaviours that allow for mating, their reproductive organs need to be compatible, and the sperm and egg need to be able to fuse. Things can go wrong at any of these steps, and thus there are a variety of possible prezygotic isolating mechanisms. Ecological isolation occurs when two individuals are physically separated, such that they are unable to encounter each other. This could be as extreme as being isolated on different continents, or more subtle such as being restricted to different heights within a single forest canopy. Temporal isolation occurs when individuals are fertile at different times, such that even if they do encounter each other, they are not both producing viable gametes. Behavioural isolation is found in many animal species which require specific behaviours by one or both partners prior to mating (see chapter 9). Even if both individuals are fertile and appear in the same location, they may not mate if the proper behavioural cues have not been received by one or both individuals. Mechanical isolation can be as obvious as the two individuals having reproductive plumbing that simply does not fit together; you can't get a square peg into a round hole. Mechanical isolation can also be more subtle, such as an inability of one plant's pollen tube to grow through the style of another, or if plants use different pollen vectors (chapter 15).

Essential steps to producing offspring

	Step	Isolating Mechanism
Prezygotic	Find a mate	Ecological
	Both be fertile	Temporal
	Give & receive mating cue	Behavioural
	Mate & form zygote	Mechanical
Postzygotic	Zygote & embryonic development	Hybrid inviability
	Production of grandchildren	Hybrid sterility

Figure 4.20 Reproductive isolation can occur from a diversity of pre- and postzygotic isolating mechanisms.

Suppose two individuals have made it through all of these potential isolating mechanisms and formed a zygote. There exist a variety of postzygotic isolating mechanisms which can be equally effective at preventing the production of a viable offspring. Hybrid inviability results if zygotic development is abnormal and the developing hybrid dies prior to sexual maturity. Hybrid sterility occurs if the hybrid develops normally, but is unable to produce viable gametes.

Figure 4.20 summarizes the steps that must occur for the production of a viable offspring. Evolution can cause changes anywhere along this pathway, and if these changes are of a sufficient magnitude, reproductive isolation can occur and lead to speciation. What factors influence the evolution of the isolating mechanisms?

What Causes Speciation?

The Hardy-Weinberg principle shows that under a certain set of restrictive assumptions, gene frequencies will not change over time. However, in real-world populations, both genetic drift and natural selection can cause significant shifts in gene frequencies. If this occurs for a trait that influences reproduction, reproductive isolation can occur. We generally divide speciation into three forms, allopatric, parapatric, and sympatric.

Allopatric, or *geographic*, **speciation** occurs when a single population becomes spatially subdivided into multiple subpopulations (fig. 4.21). How does a population become spatially subdivided? The most obvious example would be if a mountain range divides a previously contiguous area, and if it is impossible for individuals of a species to cross that divide. The appearance of a mountain or river may seem unlikely to occur in ecological timescales, but these events do occur in the deeper scales of geological and evolutionary time. Faster processes of geographic isolation are also possible, such as the formation of a new river, island, or lake. A second form of speciation, **parapatric speciation**, occurs when a population expands into a new habitat within the pre-existing range of the parent species. For example individuals of a forest-dwelling species may possess mutations that allow them to live within the grassland areas on the landscape. If these subpopulations do not interbreed, reproduction isolation may evolve, leading to speciation.

In both allopatric and parapatric speciation, the evolution of reproductive isolation could occur through drift or natural selection. Since genetic drift is random, fluctuations in allele frequencies in subpopulations will be independent, and thus loss of genetic diversity through drift could lead to reproductive isolation. Alternatively, many geographic barriers may alter the local environment; or many new habitats within a landscape may contain a new microclimate. In such cases, there could be differential selective pressures on the subpopulations, and genetic differentiation could occur. If this influences a trait related to the production of a viable offspring, reproductive isolation and speciation can occur.

Sympatric speciation has historically been more controversial among ecologists and evolutionary biologists, with many believing it does not occur. In sympatric speciation, a single parent population forms genetically distinct subpopulations without any geographic barrier or spatial isolation (fig. 4.21).

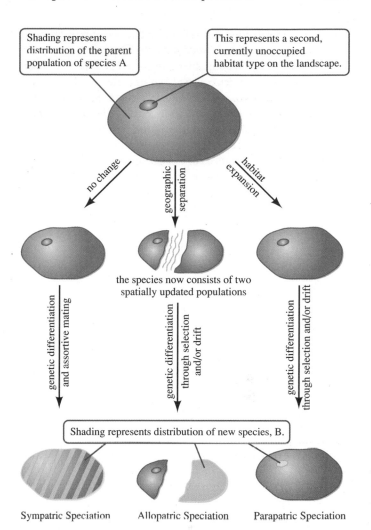

Figure 4.21 Speciation can be sympatric, allopatric, or parapatric. In all three cases reproductive isolation among subpopulations needs to occur; however, the mechanisms that cause this isolation will differ.

It is unlikely that genetic drift is important in sympatric speciation, and instead it is natural selection that drives this process. The most common model for sympatric speciation is that there exists disruptive selection for some trait (fig. 4.10), resulting in groups of individuals that differ greatly in phenotype even within a single population. If this is coupled with **assortative mating**, genetic differentiation can occur, leading to the evolution of reproductive isolation. What is assortative mating? One of the critical assumptions of the Hardy-Weinberg principle is that mate selection is random. If this is violated, you will get a shift in gene frequencies, as certain phenotypes will be favoured over others. In assortative mating, individuals may choose as mates individuals that are similar to themselves (positive assortative mating), or individuals that are different (negative assortative mating). It is positive assortative mating that is likely to lead to sympatric speciation. For example, if an insect chooses to mate only with individuals that feed upon the same host plant, there is the potential for genetic differentiation within the insect population based upon host plant selection (see chapter 14 for a discussion of host-race formation).

In recent years, there has been renewed interest among evolutionary ecologists in understanding speciation and testing these models of speciation. This interest has been sparked in part because the development of readily available and inexpensive genetic tools has allowed the collection of data previously unavailable (see the Ecological Tools section). In addition, there is widespread interest in the fate of the world's biodiversity, and understanding the causes of speciation is just as important as understanding the causes of extinction. Next we will discuss two studies that are examples of current efforts in understanding whether ecological divergence can lead to reproductive isolation and speciation.

Reproductive Isolation and Ecological Divergence

Allopatric speciation through genetic drift is fairly easy to understand, and does not even require any ecology for it to occur! Instead, it simply requires a population to be split and random events can then cause reproductive isolation. In this section, we discuss issues more relevant to this book: how does ecology influence speciation?

Central to many models of speciation we have discussed is the idea that a diversity of habitats within the range of a species can lead to reproductive isolation. As subpopulations diverge ecologically, reproductive isolation and speciation may occur. This can be reworded into a testable prediction: Increased ecological divergence will be associated with increased reproductive isolation (fig 4.22). Dan Funk and colleagues (Funk et al. 2006) decided to conduct a broad test of this prediction. They wanted to examine the widest number of species possible, and so dug through a variety of previously published data sets. Each data set contained pairs of closely related species, whose degree of pre- and postzygotic reproductive isolation was identified. Funk and colleagues then went through hundreds of additional studies and gathered information on the habitat that each species was generally found in, such as altitude, vegetation type, and moisture. The research team used a variety of statistical approaches to determine the average difference in habitats (divergence) between two species, and was able to conduct a series of regression analyses to determine whether habitat divergence was associated with reproductive isolation. In total, the data sets used contained over 500 species pairs, including plants, insects, birds, fish, and frogs. Using both parametric and nonparametric tests for correlations (Appendix A), they found that the more different the habitats were, the more reproductively isolated the pairs of related species were (fig. 4.22). This study lends support to a central prediction of several theories that suggest ecological interactions influence speciation by natural selection. Additional support for the role of natural selection in causing speciation comes from a team of researchers from Canada, Japan, and the United States (McKinnon et al 2004).

One of the particularly strong examples of natural selection at work is the process of **parallel evolution**, in which species in similar habitats, but geographically isolated, evolve similar traits. Genetic drift is a random process, and so it is

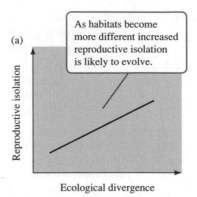

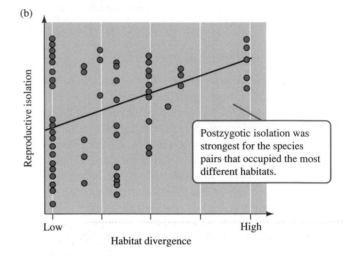

Figure 4.22 (*a*) Theory predicts that the strength of reproductive isolation should increase with increasing habitat divergence between closely related species. (*b*) This pattern was found for most groups of organisms by Funk et al. (2006), with the results from angiosperm plants presented here.

unlikely to produce similar changes in isolated populations. Parallel speciation is a logical extension of this concept, in which the traits that result in reproductive isolation evolve similarly in populations subjected to similar conditions and selective pressures. Dolph Schluter and his lab at the University of British Columbia have conducted extensive research on this issue, focusing their efforts on small fish called sticklebacks (fig. 4.23; *Gasterosteus* spp.). There currently exists a diversity of *Gasterosteus* species, which occupy marine and freshwater habitats, with the freshwater species derived from the andadromous threespine stickleback (*Gasterosteus aculeatus*). Andadromous fish are those that migrate from the ocean into rivers, breeding in freshwater. This stickleback species is particularly interesting for study, as it has marine and stream populations throughout the world, often co-occurring. McKinnon and colleagues (2004) wanted to know to what extent ecological divergence plays in the early stages of speciation. To do this, they collected fish from marine and stream populations in Alaska, British Columbia, Iceland, Scotland, Norway, and Japan. They brought these fish back to the lab and placed them in experimental aquaria. There were particularly interested in knowing which combinations of individuals would, or would not, mate. Their experimental factors included

Figure 4.23 The threespine stickleback (*Gasterosteus aculeatus*) has been used as a model organism for the study of evolutionary ecology.

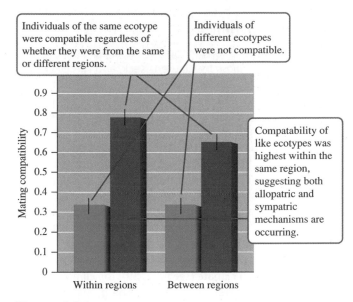

Individuals of the same ecotype were compatible regardless of whether they were from the same or different regions.

Individuals of different ecotypes were not compatible.

Compatability of like ecotypes was highest within the same region, suggesting both allopatric and sympatric mechanisms are occurring.

Figure 4.24 Mating compatibility between different ecotypes collected from populations located throughout the world (data from McKinnon et al. 2004).

ecotype (andadromous or stream) and location (same or different region). They found a much greater level of mating compatibility between individuals of the same ecotype, regardless of whether they were from the same area or from areas separated by thousands of kilometres (fig. 4.24). In other words, reproductive isolation occurred based upon ecological differentiation, and not primarily geographic isolation.

What trait likely caused this result? It appears there has been divergent selection between habitats, resulting in the stream ecotypes being much smaller than the andadromous ecotypes. Additionally, there was strong evidence for size-assortative mating in which females were less likely to mate with males of very different sizes. As we discussed previously, divergent selection coupled with assortative mating are expected to be preconditions for sympatric speciation. Overall, this study provides strong evidence that changes in the ecology of an organism can lead to reproductive isolation of sympatric populations. Additionally, because stream ecotypes were smaller than the andadromous ecotypes in numerous geographic regions, it suggests that similar habitats can apply similar evolutionary pressures, allowing for parallel evolution to occur.

These studies by Funk and McKinnon have shown that many of the assumptions and predictions made by current models of speciation through natural selection are supported by ecological data. We are a long way from understanding all of the conditions necessary for speciation to occur, leaving much opportunity for the next generation of ecologists. At the core of understanding speciation is the need to understand and identify genotypic and phenotypic variations within and across species. In the next section, we discuss many of the ecological tools that allow scientist to explore the genetic basis of variation.

Concept 4.4 Review

1. Reproductive isolation effectively eliminates many individuals as possible mates for each other. Is this likely to influence the fitness of the isolated individuals? Explain.
2. Allopatric, sympatric, and parapatric speciation can all occur in the same location at the same time. How?
3. What ecological processes are likely to speed up, or slow down, the rate of speciation?

Ecological Tools

Estimating Genetic Variation in Populations

In chapter 4 we have focused considerable attention on genetic variation in populations. Here we return to genetic variation to review some historical and recent methods used to measure this aspect of population structure. The earlier research used transplant experiments to detect genetic differences among populations. Later research on genetic variation in Chihuahua spruce (Ledig et al. 1997) and in the Glanville fritillary butterfly (Saccheri et al. 1998) used techniques developed in molecular biology. Though the number of molecular-based studies of genetic variation is growing at a tremendous rate, transplant experiments remain a useful tool for studying genetic differences among populations.

Transplant Experiments

A classic study of variation among individual plants of the species *Potentilla glandulosa* by Clausen, Keck, and Hiesey (1940) provides a model for the design and interpretation of transplant, or common garden, studies. Figure 4.25 shows photos of the transplant gardens used by Clausen and his colleagues at Stanford (lowland elevation 30 m), Mather (mid-elevation 1,400 m), and Timberline (alpine 3,050 m). Because these photos show the local natural vegetation in the background, they give a visual impression of the biomes in which the gardens were established. The natural vegetation at the sites were temperate woodland at the lowland elevation site, temperate coniferous forest at the mid-elevation site, and subalpine forest grading into alpine meadow at the alpine site.

As you would predict from our earlier review of the influence of elevation on climate (see fig. 2.39), the climates at the three study sites differed substantially. The growing seasons were 12 months at the lowland elevation site, 5 1/2 months at the mid-elevation site, and approximately 2 months at the alpine site. Minimum monthly temperatures ranged from –2°C at the lowland elevation site and –10°C at the mid-elevation site down to –22°C at the alpine site. Maximum monthly temperatures ranged from 35°C at the lowland and mid-elevation sites to 25°C at the alpine site. While there was no snow at the lowland site, snow cover at the mid-elevation site generally persisted from October to April. Meanwhile, at the alpine site snows began in September and continued to approximately the first of July. This range of conditions certainly offers the potential for local adaptation and genetic variation among local populations of *P. glandulosa*. Clausen and his colleagues designed their transplant experiments to reveal those differences if they existed.

Figure 4.26 summarizes the details of the *P. glandulosa* transplant experiments. The upper panel of figure 4.26 sketches how plants from each study area were transplanted to the other garden sites where they were grown beside the local plants. How did Clausen, Keck, and Hiesey's transplant experiment indicate genetic differences among local populations of *P. glandulosa*? To understand how their results showed genetic differences we need to consider how the results would have looked if there were no genetic differences among local populations. This hypothetical situation is presented as a null hypothesis in the middle panel of figure 4.26. If there were no genetic differences among populations, all plants would have shown the same characteristics at each site. Contrast these uniform responses, expected if the null hypothesis were true, with the representation of the actual results in the lower panel. Each population showed unique growth responses at each of the transplant gardens. On the basis of differences in growth, flower number (fig. 4.27), survival, and several other characteristics, Clausen and his coauthors concluded that the study populations of *P. glandulosa* differed genetically.

The continued utility of transplant experiments is shown by the results of Tracy's (1999) study of variation among chuckwalla lizard, *Sauromalus,* populations (see fig. 4.6). In that

a)

b)

c)

Figure 4.25   Photos of gardens used by Clausen, Keck, and Hiesey (1940) in transplant experiments with *Potentilla glandulosa*. The photos show (*a*) the Timberline (3,050 m), (*b*) Mather (1,400 m), and (*c*) Stanford (30 m) sites.

study Tracy transplanted lizards from different regions into a controlled laboratory environment. Since modern molecular methods allow us to look directly at genetic differences among

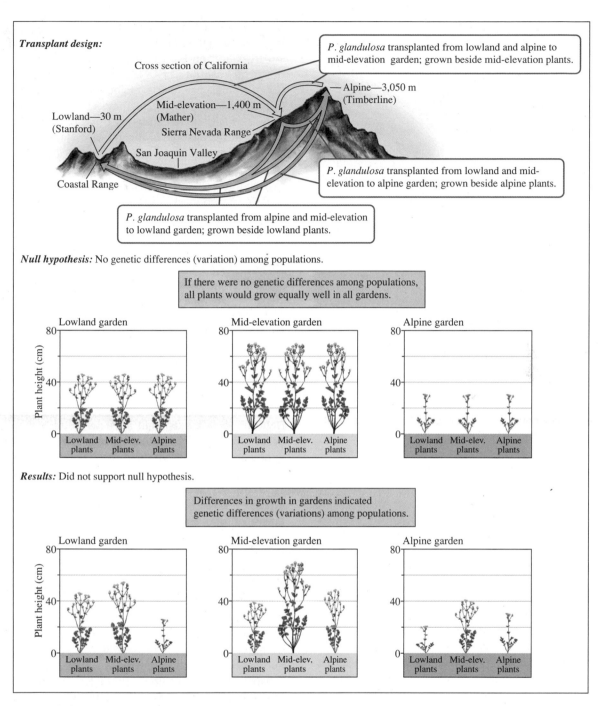

Figure 4.26 A common garden approach to studying genetic variation among populations of *Potentilla glandulosa* (data from Clausen, Keck, and Hiesey 1940).

populations, why would some biologists continue to use transplant experiments? One advantage of transplant experiments is that they are simple and require little investment in technology. What are some of the disadvantages of transplant experiments? They often require more time and labour to carry out and they can be applied to a limited number of organisms. While transplant experiments continue to be useful, modern molecular techniques are allowing evolutionary ecologists to explore details of genetic variation within and among populations that were previously impossible to study.

Molecular Approaches to Genetic Variation

The tools of molecular biology can be used to determine the genotypes of individuals either by looking at products of genes, such as enzymes, or by analyzing DNA directly. Ledig and his coauthors (1997) estimated genetic variation in populations of Chihuahua spruce by measuring variation in the allozymes of 16 different enzyme systems (see fig. 4.18). Because allozymes of the same enzyme are the products of different alleles of the same gene locus, the number of allozymes produced by a population can be used as an indicator of genetic variation within

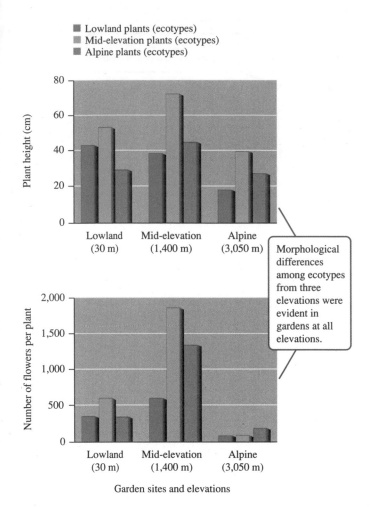

Morphological differences among ecotypes from three elevations were evident in gardens at all elevations.

Figure 4.27 Growth responses by *Potentilla glandulosa* grown at three elevations (data from Clausen, Keck, and Hiesey 1940).

the population. Many studies of enzymes examine all **isozymes,** which are all enzymes with the same biochemical function. Different isozymes may be produced by the same or different loci. Though enzyme studies remain a useful and powerful tool in evolutionary studies, genetic variation is increasingly assessed by looking directly at DNA. For instance, Saccheri and his colleagues (1998) used a combination of enzyme and direct DNA studies to characterize the genetic structure of populations of the Glanville fritillary butterfly. A detailed review of molecular methods used to study genetic variation is well beyond the scope of this discussion. However, reviewing at least the basics of some of the common molecular methods used to study genetic variation will offer an entry to this powerful set of modern tools.

In enzyme studies the tissues of organisms are generally mechanically homogenized and the resulting homogenate analyzed for the presence and kinds of enzymes. Generally, larger tissue samples are required for enzyme studies than for studies of DNA. Since DNA studies may be performed on very small samples, biologists may sample populations without damaging them. Noninvasive sampling is especially important in the study of endangered species or in any study following known individuals over long periods of time. For instance, the

grizzly bears of Glacier National Park are being counted and mapped using the DNA in hair that the bears leave on scratching trees and on baited hair traps (USGS 2000). To obtain sufficient quantities of DNA for analysis, such as that contained within a hair follicle, biologists generally use one of two techniques to amplify the quantity of DNA present in a sample. DNA is usually cloned either by using bacteria and recombinant DNA technology, or it can be amplified by a procedure called polymerase chain reaction or PCR (Hillis et al. 1996). During the PCR process, short, single-stranded DNA is used as primers for DNA synthesis. Each primer is highly specific for a given nucleotide sequence and can be used to amplify a specific locus or gene.

Once a sufficient quantity of DNA has been obtained, the sample may be analyzed in several ways. One commonly applied method uses **restriction enzymes,** enzymes produced naturally by bacteria to cut up foreign DNA. Restriction enzymes cut DNA molecules at particular places called **restriction sites**. The locations of restriction sites along a DNA molecule are determined by the locations of specific nucleotide sequences. **Nucleotides** are the basic building blocks of nucleic acids and are made up of a five-carbon sugar (deoxyribose or ribose), a phosphate group, and a nitrogenous base (guanine, cytosine, adenine, or thymine). The nucleotide sequences determining restriction sites along the length of a DNA molecule are different for different restriction enzymes. Because restriction sites are determined by a specific sequence of base pairs on the DNA molecule, differences in number and location of restriction sites reflect differences in DNA structure. When exposed to a particular restriction enzyme, a given DNA molecule will be broken up into a series of DNA fragments of precise number and lengths. The number and lengths of DNA fragments, called **restriction fragments,** are determined by the number and location of restriction sites for a particular restriction enzyme. Therefore, if DNA samples from different organisms exposed to the same restriction enzyme yield different numbers and lengths of DNA fragments, we can conclude that those organisms differ genetically.

The number and sizes of restriction fragments resulting from treating a DNA molecule with restriction enzymes or the number of isozymes present in the homogenized tissues of an organism may be analyzed using a technique called **electrophoresis.** Electrophoresis uses the rate at which enzymes, DNA fragments, or other macromolecules move in an electrical field as a means of identifying the molecules (fig. 4.28). When placed in an electrical field, a molecule will move either toward the positive or negative end of the field. Negatively charged molecules will move toward the positive end, while positively charged molecules will move toward the negative pole. Smaller molecules move more rapidly than larger molecules. Due to the influences of molecule size and charge on rates of movement, isozymes or DNA restriction fragments of different structure will migrate at different rates during electrophoresis. Consequently, during a given time interval, molecules of different sizes will migrate different distances from the point where they are initially placed in the electrical field.

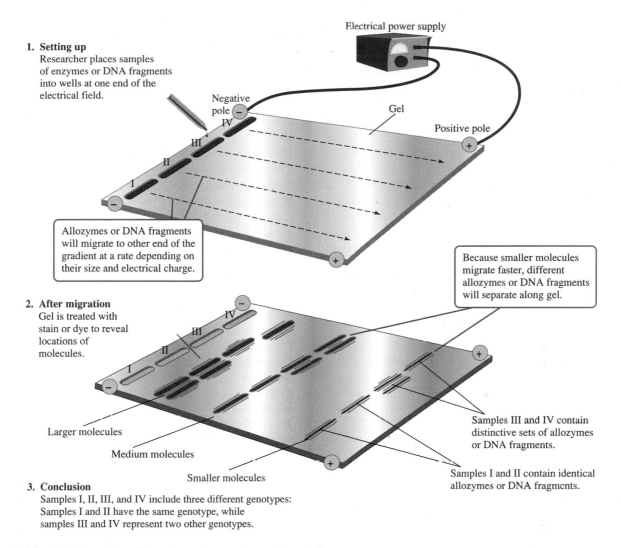

1. Setting up
Researcher places samples of enzymes or DNA fragments into wells at one end of the electrical field.

Electrical power supply

Negative pole

Gel

Positive pole

Allozymes or DNA fragments will migrate to other end of the gradient at a rate depending on their size and electrical charge.

2. After migration
Gel is treated with stain or dye to reveal locations of molecules.

Because smaller molecules migrate faster, different allozymes or DNA fragments will separate along gel.

Larger molecules

Medium molecules

Smaller molecules

Samples III and IV contain distinctive sets of allozymes or DNA fragments.

Samples I and II contain identical allozymes or DNA fragments.

3. Conclusion
Samples I, II, III, and IV include three different genotypes: Samples I and II have the same genotype, while samples III and IV represent two other genotypes.

Figure 4.28 Gel electrophoresis can be used to study genetic variation.

Electrophoresis is generally referred to as gel electrophoresis because migration of molecules generally takes place in one of several possible types of gels. Various stains and other techniques have been developed to detect the locations of DNA fragments or of specific enzymes within the gel after an electrophoresis run. The result is a pattern of banding in a gel that generally allows the biologist to identify genetic differences among individuals. By sampling many individuals from a population researchers can characterize the genetic structure of the population and determine if populations differ genetically.

What do the banding patterns, such as those shown in figure 4.28, reveal about the genetics of individuals and populations? We can say that the sample of four hypothetical individuals depicted in figure 4.28 includes three different genotypes. Individuals I and II have the same genotype, while individuals III and IV are of two other genotypes. By sampling many individuals and many enzyme systems or genetic loci in a population, the biologist will be able to estimate the genetic variation and genetic composition of a population. After characterizing several populations, we can test questions such as

whether population size influences genetic variation in species such as the Chihuahua spruce (see fig. 4.18).

An approach that gives a very high resolution picture of the genetic makeup of individuals and populations and that is receiving increasing attention is **DNA sequencing**. Because sequencing reveals the sequence of nucleic acids along DNA molecules, this tool gives the ultimate genetic information. The number of DNA sequences described is increasing rapidly and our ability to interpret and compare DNA sequence data is also increasing at an impressive rate (Hillis et al. 1996). While the human genome project has assumed centre stage (DOE 2000), the genomes of many other species are completely described or will be soon.

David Hillis and his coauthors (1996) suggest that DNA sequencing can be used as a powerful tool for studying genetic variation within and among populations. Some of the areas where sequencing might be applied include geographic variation among populations and gene flow among populations. However, Hillis and his team point out that there are trade-offs. Obtaining and interpreting the highly detailed information provided by sequencing for one or two loci necessarily limits the number of loci that the biologist can study. Where the emphasis is on studying larger numbers of loci, isozyme studies or restriction fragment analyses allow the researcher to study larger numbers of loci. At this point in time, the biologist's choice of methods is governed by these trade-offs.

One place that molecular methods may strongly influence ecological research is with the ability to quickly and reliably identify species. Paul Hebert, of the University of Guelph, is spearheading efforts to create "DNA barcodes" (Hebert et al. 2003). The basic idea is that each species contains sequences of DNA that are unique to it, and no other species on the planet. In the barcode of life, Hebert and colleagues are working to rapidly find such sequences for large numbers of species. There are a variety of reasons that such a project is urgently needed. First, accurate ecological studies often require species identification, and it simply is not practical to think each ecologist will also be an expert in species identification. This is particularly an issue for researchers of diverse groups, such as insects, bacteria, and fungi. In theory, the DNA barcode system would allow an ecologist to extract a DNA sequence for a specimen collected in the field, compare it to sequences in a large database, and find its species name. Such a database would be a significant help to ecological field studies. A second need for DNA barcodes comes as the result of one of the great tragedies of modern scientific funding: a nearly world-wide decline in taxonomic expertise in universities and museums. Because of this, fewer and fewer people are able to accurately identify specimens collected in the field. If DNA barcodes exist for many taxonomic groups, there would be reduced demand for taxonomic experts. However, DNA barcodes are likely to be most effective when combined with continued support for taxonomy. For example, the barcode database is only as good as the data it contains. Taxonomists are needed to add new species, to verify existing records, and to provide guidance when molecular methods provide ambiguous results. Hebert's DNA barcodes are a great example of how continually developing molecular methods may fundamentally alter ecological research.

Future technological advances in sequencing and analysis will very likely improve the potential for comparing large numbers of loci using sequence data. The field of molecular ecology is rapidly evolving, providing better, less expensive methods at a rapid rate. Regardless of future development, ecologists now have many powerful tools for assessing the extent of genetic variation in populations. These tools will be invaluable as this generation of ecologists works to understand the causes and consequences of interactions between species and their environment.

Summary

Although they did not work together, the twin visions of Darwin and Mendel revolutionized biology. The synthesis of the theory of natural selection and genetics gave rise to modern evolutionary ecology. Here we examine four major concepts within the area of population genetics and natural selection.

Phenotypic variation among individuals in a population results from the combined effects of genes and environment. The first biologists to conduct thorough studies of phenotypic and genotypic variation and to incorporate experiments in their studies focused on plants. Clausen, Keck, and Hiesey explored the extent and sources of morphological variation in plant populations, including both the influences of environment and genetics. Case determined that the best predictor of chuckwalla, *Sauromalus*, body length was average winter rainfall. Tracy's laboratory growth experiments indicated that variation in body size among chuckwalla populations is at least partly determined by genetic differences among populations.

The Hardy-Weinberg equilibrium model helps identify evolutionary forces that can change gene frequencies in populations. Because evolution involves changes in gene frequencies in a population, a thorough understanding of evolution must include the area of genetics known as population genetics. One of the most fundamental concepts in population genetics, the Hardy-Weinberg principle, states that in a population mating at random in the absence of evolutionary forces, allele frequencies will remain constant. For a population in Hardy-Weinberg equilibrium in a situation where there are only two alleles at a particular locus, $p + q = 1.0$. The frequency of genotypes in a population in Hardy-Weinberg equilibrium can be calculated as $(p + q)^2 = (p + q) \times (p + q) = p^2 + 2pq + q^2 = 1.0$. The conditions necessary to maintain constant allele frequencies in a population are: (1) random mating, (2) no mutations, (3) large population size, (4) no immigration, and (5) equal survival and reproductive rates for all genotypes. When a population is not in Hardy-Weinberg equilibrium, the Hardy-Weinberg principle helps us to identify the evolutionary forces that may be in play.

Changes in gene frequency within a population can occur through both natural selection and random processes such as genetic drift. Natural selection can lead to changes in gene frequencies within populations (directional and disruptive selection), or can be a conservative force impeding change (stabilizing selection). These three forms of selection differ as a function of which phenotypes are favoured. In directional selection one extreme is favoured, in stabilizing selection the average phenotypes is favoured, and in disruptive selection, both extremes are favoured. In all types of selection, the rate of evolution increases with the strength of the selective force. There is abundant evidence from a variety of species showing that natural selection is a continuous process, occurring in extant species. Natural selection can cause shifts in feeding morphology associated with colonization of a new habitat as found in the studies of soapbugs. Evolution also occurs by the random process of genetic drift. Although drift occurs continuously in all populations, it is a greater evolutionary force in small populations, where chance events can impact a greater proportion of the individuals of the population. In populations of Chihuahua spruce, small populations were associated with lower levels of genetic diversity, attributed to loss through drift. A lack of genetic diversity is also associated with increased risk of local extinctions, as was found for populations of the Glanville fritillary butterfly.

Physical and ecological processes interact with selection and drift to produce new species. Both natural selection and genetic drift can cause reproductive isolation to occur between populations of a single species. Reproductive isolation can occur at both Prezygotic and postzygotic stages, through changes in location, timing, behaviour, morphology and physiology, and development pathways. Reproductive isolation is a necessary condition for speciation. Speciation can occur within a single location (sympatric speciation), when a population is geographically separated (allopatric speciation), or when a species extends into a new habitat (parapatric speciation). Increased habitat divergence is positively correlated with increased reproductive isolation, suggesting the current ecology of organisms can influence the likelihood of speciation. Ecological similarity can cause parallel evolution in geographically distinct populations, and assortative mating can lead to sympatric speciation.

Early research on adaptation of populations to local environmental conditions used transplant experiments to detect genetic differences among populations. More recent studies combine this approach with a variety of techniques developed by molecular biologists. The combination of classical and molecular tools has allowed ecologists to address questions with a level of experimental sophistication not previously possible. Continued advances in the development of DNA barcodes may also provide rapid and reliable means of species identification.

Review Questions

1. Contrast the approaches of Charles Darwin and Gregor Mendel to the study of populations. What were Darwin's main discoveries? What were Mendel's main discoveries? How did the studies of Darwin and Mendel prepare the way for the later studies reviewed in chapter 4?
2. What environmental variable did Ted Case determine to be the best predictor of variation in body size among populations of chuckwallas? Did Case's studies of chuckwallas demonstrate genetic differences among his study populations? What did the more recent studies by Christopher Tracy add to our understanding of variation among chuckwalla populations?
3. What is the Hardy-Weinberg principle? What is Hardy-Weinberg equilibrium? What conditions are required for Hardy-Weinberg equilibrium?
4. Review the Hardy-Weinberg equilibrium equation. What parts of the equation represent gene frequencies? What elements represent genotype frequencies and phenotype frequencies? Are genotype and phenotype frequencies always the same? Use a hypothetical population to specify alleles and allelic frequencies as you develop your presentation.
5. What is genetic drift? Under what circumstances do you expect genetic drift to occur? Under what circumstances is genetic drift unlikely to be important? Does genetic drift increase or decrease genetic variation in populations?
6. Suppose you are a director of a captive breeding program for a rare species of animal, such as Siberian tigers, that are found in many zoos around the world but are increasingly rare in the wild. Design a breeding program that will reduce the possibility of genetic drift in captive populations.
7. How did the studies of Scott Carroll and his colleagues demonstrate rapid evolutionary adaptation to introduced soapberry plants? What advantages do a group of organisms, such as soapberry bugs, offer to researchers studying natural selection compared to larger organisms such as Chihuahua pines and chuckwalla lizards?
8. How do classical approaches to genetic studies, such as common garden experiments, and modern molecular techniques, such as DNA sequencing, complement each other? What are the advantages and disadvantages of each?
9. Suppose you are in charge of constructing the harvesting rules for a large fishery. How could you use information on changes in body size and age of maturity as potential indicators of the effects of harvesting on the population? Would you expect to see different impacts of harvesting on these traits if you only harvest post-reproductive individuals?
10. Much like Santa Claus, some people do not believe in sympatric speciation. What ecological conditions would make sympatric speciation more likely to occur? What evidence could an ecologist collect that would support, or refute, a claim that a particular species is the result of sympatric speciation?

Suggested Readings

Carroll, S. P. and C. Boyd. 1992. Host race radiation in the soapberry bug: natural history with the history. *Evolution* 46:1052–69.

Carroll, S. P., S. P. Klassen, and H. Dingle. 1998. Rapidly evolving adaptations to host ecology and nutrition in the soapberry bug. *Evolutionary Ecology* 12:955–68.

This pair of papers traces the fascinating story of some of the research that has revealed one of the best documented cases of natural selection of herbivorous insect populations for living as specialists on particular plant species. These papers showcase well designed and carefully executed studies of evolutionary ecology.

Case, T. J. 1976. Body size differences between populations of the chuckwalla, *Sauromalus obesus*. Ecology 57:313–23.

Coyne, J. A. and H. A. Orr. 2004. *Speciation*. Sinaur Associates, New York.

A recent overview of the mechanisms of speciation.

Tracy, C. R. 1999. Differences in body size among chuckwalla (*Sauromalus obesus*) populations. *Ecology* 80:259–71.

Separated by over 20 years, these companion papers explore the relationship between climate, variation in morphology, and local adaptation by chuckwallas—careful work on an interesting animal.

Ehrlich, P. R. and I. Hanski. 2004. On the Wings of Checkerspots: *A Model System for Population Biology*. Oxford: Oxford University Press.

Inspiring and readable book, summarizing decades of research on checkerspot butterflies on two continents.

Reznick, D. N. and C. K. Ghalambor. 2005. Selection in nature: experimental manipulations of natural populations. *Integrative and Comparative Biology 45:456–62.*

Excellent and concise summary of the foremost field experiments on natural selection.

Darwin, C. 1859. *The Origin of the Species by Means of Natural Selection, or the Preservation of Favored Races in the Struggle for Life*. New York: Modern Library.

Mayr, E. 1942. *Systematics and the Origin of Species*. Columbia University Press, NY.

Two required readings for all students interested in ecology and evolution.

Section II

INDIVIDUALS

In section II we discuss how individual organisms interact with their local surroundings. As a foundation for these discussions, we present the concepts of allocation and ecological tradeoffs. Three dominant stressors that influence the survival and fitness of individuals are temperature, water (chapters 5 and 6), and the need for energy and nutrients (chapter 7). An organism's behavioural strategies (chapter 8) can influence its ability to cope with its environment and its neighbours. Individuals do not face these challenges one at a time, but instead simultaneously encounter numerous biotic and abiotic stressors. The total set of strategies, abilities, and limitations of an individual species is described as its life history (chapter 9).

Chapter *5*

Temperature Relations

Outline

any organisms regulate the temperature of their bodies or the temperature of parts of their anatomy. At least one plant of the arctic tundra regulates the temperature of its reproductive structures. Peter Kevan, of the University of Guelph, had come to Ellesmere Island to study sun-tracking behaviour by arctic flowers. It was summer, there was little wind, and at 82°N latitude, the sun stayed above the horizon 24 hours each day. As the sun's position in the arctic sky changed, one of the common tundra flowers, *Dryas integrifolia* (fig. 5.1), like the sunflowers of lower latitudes, followed.

Kevan found that the sun-tracking behaviour of *Dryas* increased the temperature of its flowers. Though the air temperature hovered around 15°C, the temperature of the *Dryas* flowers was nearly 25°C. Kevan discovered that the flowers act like small solar reflectors; their parabolic shape reflects and concentrates solar energy on the reproductive structures. He also observed that many species of small insects, attracted by their warmth, basked in the sun-tracking *Dryas* flowers, elevating their body temperatures as a consequence (fig. 5.1). *Dryas* depends on these insects to pollinate its flowers.

How do *Dryas* and its insect visitors benefit from their basking behaviours? How does cloud cover affect the temperature and sun-tracking behaviour of *Dryas* flowers? These are the kinds of questions addressed by Kevan (1975) and other ecologists who study the ecology of temperature relations, one of the most fundamental aspects of ecology. In their quest for answers to questions like these, ecologists learn how the world works.

The thermometer was one of the first quantitative instruments to appear in the scientific tool kit, and we have been measuring and reporting temperatures ever since. Why is *Homo sapiens* so concerned with temperature? For us and all other species, the impact of extreme temperatures can range from discomfort, at a minimum, to extinction. Long-term changes in temperature have set entire floras and faunas marching across

continents, some species thriving, some holding on in small refuges, and others becoming extinct. Areas now supporting temperate species were at times tropical and at other times the frigid homes of reindeer and woolly mammoths. These global changes in climate continue (chapter 23), with dramatic implications for individuals of nearly all species.

Concepts

5.1 **Macroclimate interacts with the local landscape to produce microclimatic variation in temperature.**

5.2 **Most species perform best in a fairly narrow range of temperatures.**

5.3 **Many organisms have evolved ways to compensate for variations in environmental temperature by regulating body temperature.**

5.4 **Organisms exhibit a diversity of mechanisms to cope with extreme temperatures.**

5.1   Microclimates

Macroclimate interacts with the local landscape to produce microclimatic variation in temperature. As we saw in chapter 2, temperatures are extremely variable across the planet in both space and time. For instance, which is warmer, Regina, Saskatchewan, or Tofino, British Columbia? These areas are different biomes (grassland vs. temperature forest), does that give us the answer? No. The answer is going to depend first upon the question of "when"? Tofino is generally warmer than Regina in the winter, but cooler in the summer. This answer is also going to depend upon the answer of "where"? Are you standing on the open coastline of Tofino but under an aspen stand in Regina? As you will see in this section, the actual temperatures an individual encounters will be strongly influenced by the fine details of the local environment, and by the behaviour of the individual.

Microclimate is a fundamental aspect of environmental variation. What do we mean by macroclimate and microclimate? **Macroclimate** is what weather stations report and what we represented with climate diagrams in chapter 2. Macroclimate is determined by the global patterns of air and water circulation, and other forces, also described in chapters 2 and 3. **Microclimate** is climatic variation on a scale of a few kilometers, meters, or even centimeters, usually measured over short periods of time. You acknowledge microclimate when you choose to stand in the shade on a summer's day or in the sun on a winter's day. Macroclimate and microclimate are usually substantially different. Many organisms live out their lives in very small areas during periods of time ranging from days to a few months. For these organisms macroclimate may be less important than microclimate. Microclimate is influenced by landscape features such as altitude, aspect, vegetation, colour of the ground, and presence of boulders and burrows. The physical nature of water reduces temperature variation in aquatic environments.

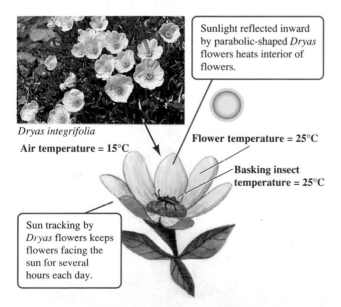

Dryas integrifolia
Air temperature = 15°C

Sunlight reflected inward by parabolic-shaped *Dryas* flowers heats interior of flowers.

Flower temperature = 25°C

Basking insect temperature = 25°C

Sun tracking by *Dryas* flowers keeps flowers facing the sun for several hours each day.

Figure 5.1 Sun-tracking behaviour of the arctic plant, *Dryas integrifolia*, heats the reproductive parts of its flowers, making them attractive to pollinating insects. This species is found in many Canadian Arctic and Alpine habitats.

Altitude and Aspect

As we saw in chapter 2 (see fig. 2.39), temperatures are generally lower at high elevations. Along the elevational gradient presented in figure 2.39, average annual temperature is 11.1°C at 1,660 m compared to –3.7°C at 3,743 m. Lower average temperatures at higher elevations are a consequence of several factors. First, because atmospheric pressure decreases with elevation, air rising up the side of a mountain expands. The energy of motion (kinetic energy) required to sustain the greater movement of air molecules in the expanding air mass is drawn from the surroundings, which cool as a result. A second reason that temperatures are generally lower at higher elevations is that there is less atmosphere to trap and radiate heat back to the ground.

Topographic features such as hills, mountains, and valleys create microclimates that would not occur in a flat landscape. Mountains and hillsides create these microclimates by shading parts of the land. In the Northern Hemisphere, the shaded areas are on the north-facing sides, or *northern aspects*, of hills, mountains, and valleys, which face away from the equator. In the Southern Hemisphere, the *southern aspect* faces away from the equator.

You can see the effect of aspect, in miniature, around buildings. If you want to warm yourself on a sunny winter's day in the Northern Hemisphere, you go to the south side of a building, to its southern aspect, which faces the equator. In the Southern Hemisphere, you would generally find the warmest spot on the north side of a building. Similarly, the northern and southern aspects of mountains and valleys offer organisms contrasting microclimates. The microclimates of north- and south-facing aspects of hillsides may support very different types of vegetation (fig. 5.2).

The greater density of oaks and shrubs on the north-facing slope shown in figure 5.2 is paralleled in miniature on north- and south-facing dune slopes in the Negev Desert, where north-facing slopes support a higher density of crust-forming mosses. G. Kidron, E. Barzilay, and E. Sachs, earth scientists from Hebrew University Jerusalem, documented a possible physical basis for the differences in moss cover (Kidron, Barzilay, and Sachs 2000). They found that north-facing dune slopes are cooler: 7.8° to 9.2°C cooler at midday in winter and 1.8° to 2.5°C cooler at midday in summer. These scientists also found

Figure 5.2   The north-facing slope at this site supports a Mediterranean woodland, while the vegetation on the south-facing slope is mainly grassland.

north-facing slopes remain moist approximately 2.5 times longer than south-facing slopes following rainfall. They suggested that lower evaporation rates on north-facing slopes are at least partly responsible. Detailed physical studies such as this one by Kidron, Barzilay, and Sachs provide for a basic understanding of the distribution of organisms, especially vegetation.

Vegetation and Ground Colour

Because they also shade the landscape, plants both create and respond to microclimates. For instance, trees, shrubs, and plant litter (fallen leaves, twigs, and branches) produce ecologically important microclimates in deserts. The desert landscape, which often consists of a mosaic of vegetation and bare ground, is also a patchwork of sharply contrasting thermal environments. Such a patchwork is apparent near Kemmerer, Wyoming, a cold desert much like the Gobi in Mongolia. Kemmerer can be bitterly cold in winter and blistering hot in summer. One summer's day Robert Parmenter and his colleagues (1989) measured the temperatures in various parts of the Kemmerer landscape. Parmenter found that while the temperature on bare soil soared to 48°C, a few meters away in plant litter under a tall shrub the temperature was 21°C (fig. 5.3). Meanwhile, temperatures under low

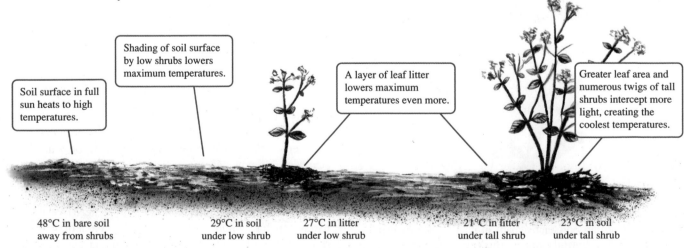

Soil surface in full sun heats to high temperatures.

Shading of soil surface by low shrubs lowers maximum temperatures.

A layer of leaf litter lowers maximum temperatures even more.

Greater leaf area and numerous twigs of tall shrubs intercept more light, creating the coolest temperatures.

48°C in bare soil away from shrubs

29°C in soil under low shrub

27°C in litter under low shrub

21°C in litter under tall shrub

23°C in soil under tall shrub

Figure 5.3   Desert shrubs create distinctive thermal microclimates in the desert landscape (data from Parmenter, Parmenter, and Cheney 1989).

(a)

(b)

(c)

Figure 5.4 Ground cover and colour such as shown here in (*a*) white sand, (*b*) black sand, and (*c*) snow in Nunavut, alter the local albedo, causing altered microclimates. High albedos are found in white snow or white sand, with low albedos found on dark sand or other dark soils.

shrubs with less leaf area were a bit warmer but still not as hot as soil in the open. A small organism in this landscape could choose microclimates differing in temperature by 27°C!

Two additional factors that can affect temperature are the colour of the ground, and the presence of any covering, such as vegetation or snow (fig. 5.4). Cover and colour influence microclimates through their effects on the local **albedo**, the reflectivity of the landscape. As you may recall from other course work, objects that appear white reflect all visible colours and have a high albedo. Objects that appear black absorb all visible colours, reflecting little, and have a low albedo. Vegetation is generally green, which means it absorbs some colours and reflects others, resulting in an albedo between white and black.

Albedos are not fixed properties of landscapes, and instead will change as local conditions change, resulting in potentially large changes in the local temperature. For example, snow cover reflects large amounts of light, resulting in a cooling effect (fig. 5.5). When snow melts, the underlying soil will generally have a lower albedo, and absorb more light energy, causing local warming. As a result, any change in snow cover can have cascading effects on local temperatures. Over larger areas, decreased snow cover across much of the landscape, potentially associated with global climate change, has the potential to further enhance the warming that is currently occurring (chapter 23). Small-scale human-induced changes, such as deforestation, also alter albedo, with potentially cascading impacts on local temperatures.

Presence of Boulders and Burrows

Many children soon discover that the undersides of stones harbour a host of organisms seldom seen in the open. This is partly because the stones create distinctive microclimates. E. B. Edney's classic studies (1953) of the seashore isopod *Ligia oceanica* documented the effect of stones on microclimate. Edney found that over the space of a few centimeters, *Ligia* could choose air temperatures ranging from 20°C in the open

to 30°C in the air spaces under stones, which heated to between 34° and 38°C. This small-scale variation in temperature is summarized in figure 5.6.

Animal burrows also have their own microclimates, in which temperatures are usually more moderate than outside ambient conditions. For example, the Eurasian badger, *Meles meles*, constructs extensive burrows, called *setts*. In a study of temperatures inside and outside of several setts on farmland, Moore and Roper (2003) found that setts generally had average temperature fluctuations of less than 1°C each day, while surface temperatures generally varied by 9°C daily. Over an entire year, there was only a 10°C variation within setts, while more than 20°C variation outside. Moore and Roper also found that setts occupied by a badger were on average 2.5°C warmer than unoccupied setts, highlighting the fact that organisms themselves can alter their own microclimates.

Figure 5.5 By reflecting most visible light, snow creates a much cooler microclimate than nearby bare ground.

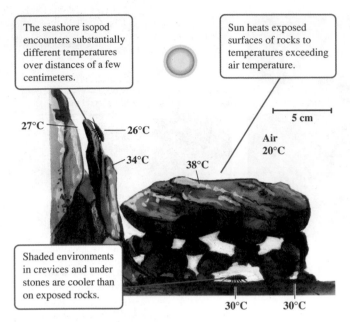

The seashore isopod encounters substantially different temperatures over distances of a few centimeters.

Sun heats exposed surfaces of rocks to temperatures exceeding air temperature.

5 cm

Air 20°C

27°C 26°C

34°C 38°C

Shaded environments in crevices and under stones are cooler than on exposed rocks.

30°C 30°C

Figure 5.6 Stones create distinctive microclimates (data from Edney 1953).

Aquatic Temperatures

As we saw in chapter 2, air temperature generally fluctuates more than water temperature. The thermal stability of the aquatic environment derives partly from the high capacity of water to absorb heat energy without changing temperature (a capacity called *specific heat*). This capacity is about 3,000 times higher for water than for an equal volume of air. It takes approximately 1 calorie of energy to heat 1 cm^3 of water 1°C. For an equal volume of air, this temperature rise requires only about 0.0003 calories.

A second cause of the thermal stability of aquatic environments is the large amount of heat absorbed by water as it evaporates (which is called the *latent heat of vaporization*). This amounts to about 584 calories per gram of water at 22°C

and 580 calories per gram of water at 35°C. So, 1 g of water evaporating from the surface of a desert stream, a lake, or a tide pool at 35°C draws 580 calories of heat from its surroundings. From the definition of a calorie, this is enough energy to cool 580 g of water 1°C. What makes evaporative coolers, whether mechanical or biological, so effective? The answer is that you need to evaporate relatively little water to cool a great deal of either air or living matter.

A third cause of the greater thermal stability of aquatic environments is the heat energy that water gives up to its environment as it freezes (the *latent heat of fusion*). Water gives up approximately 80 calories as 1 g of water freezes because the energy of motion of water molecules decreases as they leave the liquid state and become incorporated into the crystalline latticework of ice. So, as 1 g of pond water freezes, it gives off sufficient energy to heat 80 g of water 1°C, thus retarding further cooling.

The aquatic environments with greatest thermal stability are generally large ones, such as the open sea. These are environments that store large quantities of heat energy and where daily fluctuations are often less than 1°C. Even the temperatures of small streams, however, usually fluctuate less than the temperatures of nearby terrestrial habitats. Figure 5.7 summarizes the daily range in air temperature with that in the Coal River in Tasmania. While air temperature ranged from 2.5°C to 28°C, daily surface temperatures in the river ranged from 7°C to 20°C. In other words, the range in air temperature was nearly twice that of water temperature. Meanwhile, the temperature 60 cm below the surface of the Coal River ranged from 10°C to 14°C, a fraction of the daily variation in air temperature.

There are, of course, limits to the thermal stability of aquatic systems. One of the most obvious examples is what you feel if you dive deep into a lake or ocean. Water temperatures generally decrease with depth, due in large part to reduced penetration of solar radiation (chapter 3). Other factors besides the physics of water can affect the temperature of

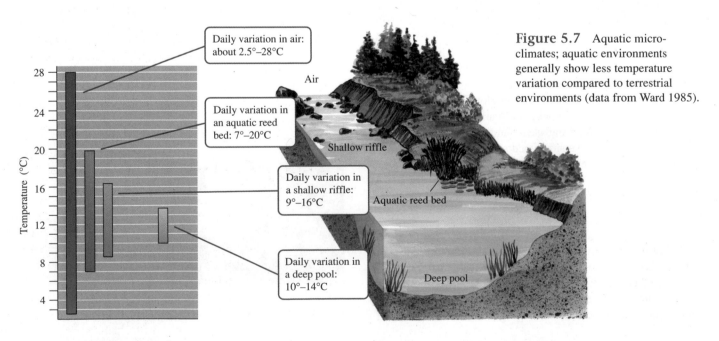

Daily variation in air: about 2.5°–28°C

Air

Daily variation in an aquatic reed bed: 7°–20°C

Daily variation in a shallow riffle: 9°–16°C

Shallow riffle

Aquatic reed bed

Daily variation in a deep pool: 10°–14°C

Deep pool

Figure 5.7 Aquatic microclimates; aquatic environments generally show less temperature variation compared to terrestrial environments (data from Ward 1985).

Temperature (°C)

28
24
20
16
12
8
4

aquatic environments. **Riparian vegetation,** that is, vegetation that grows along rivers and streams, influences the temperature in streams in the same way that vegetation modifies the temperature of desert soils—by providing shade. Shading by riparian vegetation reduces temperature fluctuations by insulating the stream environment.

Concept 5.1 Review

1. What advantages might the warm microenvironments of *Dryas* flowers offer to the insects attracted to them?
2. Contrast the microclimates of the leaves and roots of a tree in the boreal forest in summer.
3. Why is thermal stability greater in large, rather than small, bodies of water?

 ## Temperature and Performance of Organisms

Most species perform best in a fairly narrow range of temperatures. Ecologists concerned with the ecology of individual organisms study how environmental factors, such as temperature, water, and light, affect the physiology and behaviour of organisms: how fast they grow; how many offspring they produce; how fast they run, fly, or swim; how well they avoid predators; and so on. We can group these phenomena and say that ecologists study how environment affects the "performance" of organisms.

The performance of organisms generally varies as a function of differences in temperature, moisture, light, nutrient availability, or other environmental conditions. At extreme levels of any of these factors, many species are unable to survive. At severe levels, species may survive, but not thrive. At more moderate levels, growth and reproduction may be highest. In other words, the performance of most species is greatest in a fairly narrow range of environmental conditions (fig. 5.8). The entire range of conditions (e.g., temperature) over which a species is able to survive in is called its **range of tolerance**. What do you imagine will be the evolutionary consequences for individuals living just on the edge of their range of tolerance? Before that question is answered, we must first understand why temperature can impact individual performance and fitness. In this section, we discuss the influence of temperature on animal performance, on photosynthesis by plants, and on microbial activity. You will see in the examples that although these processes are able to occur in a wide range of temperatures, optimum conditions are often similar to those found in the species' natural habitat.

Temperature and Animal Performance

Let's begin our discussion of temperature and animal performance by reviewing the influence of temperature on enzyme function. The influence of temperature on the performance of organisms begins at the level of biomolecules, which often perform their functions by balancing opposing tendencies. Consider

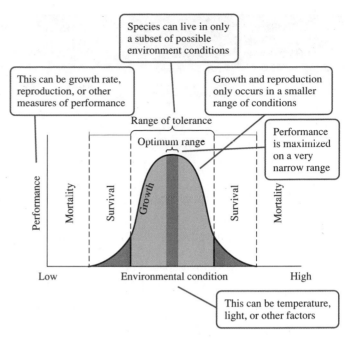

Figure 5.8 An individual's performance can be limited by environmental conditions, such as temperature.

enzymes. Because they must match the shape of the substrate upon which they act, enzymes must assume a specific shape for proper function. Most enzymes have a rigid, predictable shape at low temperatures, but rates of chemical reactions tend to be low at these low temperatures. Also, rigidity does not help an enzyme perform its function. Their functioning often depends upon flexibility, the ability to assume another shape after binding with the substrate. Enzymes have greater flexibility at higher temperatures, but excessively high temperatures destroy their shape. Temperatures at either extreme thus impair the functioning of enzymes.

Enzymes usually work fastest in some intermediate range of temperatures, where they retain both proper shape and sufficient flexibility. In other words, there is usually some optimal range of temperatures for most enzymes. How might you determine the optimal temperature for an enzyme? One way is to determine the minimum concentration of substrate required for an enzyme to work at a particular rate. If this concentration is low, the enzyme is performing well, that is, the enzyme has a high affinity for the substrate. The affinity of an enzyme for its substrate is one measure of its performance.

John Baldwin and P. W. Hochachka (1970) studied the influence of temperature on the activity of acetylcholinesterase, an enzyme produced at the synapse between neurons. This enzyme promotes the breakdown of the neurotransmitter acetylcholine to acetic acid and choline and so turns off neurons, a process critical for proper neural function. The researchers found that rainbow trout, *Oncorhynchus mykiss,* produce two forms of acetylcholinesterase. One form has highest affinity for acetylcholine at 2°C, that is, at winter temperatures. However, the affinity of this enzyme for acetylcholine declines rapidly above 10°C. The second form of acetylcholinesterase shows highest affinity for acetylcholine at 17°C, at summer

Impacts of Stream Temperature on Salmon Recruitment

The family Salmonidae consists of both trout and fish we generally refer to as "salmon." In this box, we will discuss how changes to the spawning grounds of salmon alter the thermal environment, with potentially significant impacts on the health of individual salmon species, as well as commercial and recreational fishing.

Canada is home to many species of wild salmon, living in both the Atlantic and Pacific oceans (though some lakes also are home to salmon). Most species and populations of wild salmon are **anadromous**, meaning the adults live primarily in the ocean, and then move into freshwaters to spawn. After the eggs hatch, the developing fry will initially feed and grow in the streams, eventually making a migration to the ocean. Adults have the tendency to return to their own birthing grounds to spawn, a fact that is both part of the mythology of salmon, as well as a potential threat to their populations as industrial development grows around a number of previously isolated spawning grounds.

Salmon are important in Canada for a number of reasons. Culturally, the vision of these fish swimming in a clear coastal river, surrounded by a large and intact forest is an image etched into the minds of generations of Canadians (fig. 5.9). Recreationally, salmon are valued by anglers, to the extent that many areas are regularly stocked with salmon with the desire by some to establish new populations, or at least provide anglers with more fish to catch. Finally, the harvest of wild salmon results in significant economic gains for British Columbia. For example, in 2004 the value of the harvest of all wild salmon species in BC was estimated at just over $52,000,000, making this group of species the most valuable fishery in BC

Figure 5.9   Many salmon spawning grounds, such as the Little Qualicum river in British Columbia, consist of water surrounded by forest.

(excluding aquaculture and farmed salmon). Because of these reasons, and others, there has been extensive research conducted on the factors that influence the health of wild salmon populations. One fact that has emerged is that a variety of human activities cause significant changes to the thermal environment of the spawning streams, with negative consequences for many populations.

Like all organisms, salmon have upper lethal temperatures, above which, mortality occurs. These lethal upper temperatures vary among species and life-stage. However, the mature ocean-living stage is likely at limited risk from changes in temperature. Why? As you recall from earlier in this chapter, the thermal properties of water reduce temperature variation relative to terrestrial habitats, and large bodies of water (oceans) will exhibit less variation than small bodies of water (streams).

temperatures. However, the affinity of this second form of acetylcholinesterase falls off rapidly at both higher and lower temperatures. In other words, the optimal temperatures for the two forms of acetylcholinesterase are 2° and 17°C (fig. 5.10).

This influence of temperature on the performance of acetylcholinesterase makes sense if you consider the temperatures of the rainbow trout's native environment. Rainbow trout are native to the cool, clear streams and rivers of western North America. During winter, the temperatures of these streams hover between 0° and 4°C, while summer temperatures approach 20°C. These environmental temperatures are similar to the temperatures at which the acetylcholinesterase of rainbow trout performs optimally.

Today, rainbow trout have been introduced around the world but are still largely confined to cold waters that don't

get much warmer than about 20°C, even at the height of summer. Now you have a biochemical mechanism to explain these distributional limits. At temperatures above 20°C, what happens to the performance of the acetylcholinesterase produced by rainbow trout? Some signs of thermal stress in fish are loss of equilibrium, swimming on their sides, and swimming in spirals. Can you explain these responses using what you now know about the influence of temperature on the performance of the acetylcholinesterase?

Studies of reptiles, especially lizards and snakes, are offering additional valuable insights into the influence of temperature on animal performance. Widely distributed species often offer the opportunity for studies of local variation in ecological relationships, including the influence of temperature on performance. For example, the eastern fence lizard, *Sceloporus*

As a result, although the ocean-living stage of salmon may suffer other sources of increased mortality (e.g., fishing), its physiological ecology with respect to temperature is not a concern. In contrast, it is the egg and juvenile stages of salmon that appear to be most at risk due to human activity, both of which are found in streams. The issue here is not just one of survival, but also one of reproduction. As we saw earlier in the chapter, there is generally a unimodal relationship between temperature and performance, with reproduction happening only in a narrow range of temperatures, even though survival can occur in a larger range. For example, Chinook Salmon have an upper lethal temperature of around 25°C, have zero growth above 19°C, an upper spawning threshold of 16°C, and exhibit maximum growth at around 15°C (McCullough 1999). In other words, increases in temperature do not have to kill a fish to put its population at risk, and even minor changes to stream temperatures can reduce, or prevent, reproduction. As we saw in chapter 3, not all streams are equal, and they can vary greatly in size. Spawning grounds located in the smallest streams in the headwaters will be most sensitive to change.

One factor that can influence stream temperature is logging activity. In small streams, trees often overhang the water, reducing light penetration to the water surface. If the vegetation is completely removed, there is a clear and immediate increase in stream temperature. For example, Steve MacDonald of the Canadian Department of Fisheries of Oceans, and his colleagues at Simon Fraser University found that in a sub-boreal forest in British Columbia, stream temperatures can be raised by 4°C–6°C, even five years after logging (MacDonald et al. 2003). The temperature changes can be in part mitigated by logging management practices, such as maintaining an unharvested buffer zone along the stream edge, however MacDonald shows that trees in these buffers are very susceptible to wind damage,

reducing their effectiveness over time. In this particular study, even the elevated temperatures following logging were below the lethal temperatures for salmonids, however, in shallower or more exposed streams this will not necessarily be the case.

Humans influence stream temperatures in a variety of other ways, including the construction of dams. Dams used to generate electrical power generally result in varied stream flows, depending upon the electrical needs at any point in time. As a result, there will be substantial variation in stream depths and temperatures, as a function of how much water is being released through a dam. At a scale even greater than individual dams and streams, changes to climate associated with global warming may be increasing stress for Atlantic Salmon populations.

In Newfoundland, salmon rivers are closed to anglers on days in which river flow is low and river temperatures are high, out of concern that angling will further decrease the sustainability of Atlantic Salmon populations. Brian Dempson and his colleagues at the Department of Fisheries and Oceans found that the frequency of stream closures due to these "environmental" reasons has increased over the last decade (Dempson et al 2001), suggesting an increase the in the frequency of warm waters that could put these fish populations at risk.

Salmon are but one example of a group of species whose abundance can be influenced by changes in temperature. The ideas of upper and lower lethal temperatures are not abstract ecological concepts, but instead are critical pieces of information needed to understand how species will respond to continued human-mediated changes. Indirect effects of human activity have significant consequences for a diverse set of species, and it is the role of many ecologists to understand why, and to work with government and industry to develop solutions to reduce the risk to natural populations.

undulatus, is found across approximately two-thirds of the United States, living in a broad diversity of climatic zones. Taking advantage of this wide range of environmental conditions, Michael Angilletta (2001) studied the temperature relations of *S. undulatus* over a portion of its range. In one of his studies, Angilletta determined how temperature influences metabolizable energy intake or MEI. He measured MEI as the amount of energy consumed (C) minus energy lost in feces (F) and uric acid (U), which is the nitrogen waste product produced by lizards. We can summarize MEI in equation form as:

$$MEI = C - F - U$$

Angilletta studied two populations from New Jersey and South Carolina, regions with substantially different climates. He collected a sample of lizards from both populations and

maintained portions of his samples from both populations at 30°, 33°, and 36°C. Angilletta kept his study lizards in separate enclosures and provided them with crickets that he had weighed as food. Since he had determined the energy content of an average cricket, Angilletta was able to determine the energy intake by each lizard by counting the number of crickets they ate and calculating the energy content of that number. He determined the energy lost as feces (F) and uric acid (U) by collecting all the feces and uric acid produced by each lizard and then drying and weighing this material. He estimated the average energy content of feces and uric acid using a bomb calorimeter.

The results of Angilletta's experiment, which are shown in figure 5.11, show clearly that MEI is highest in both populations of lizards at the intermediate temperature of 33°C.

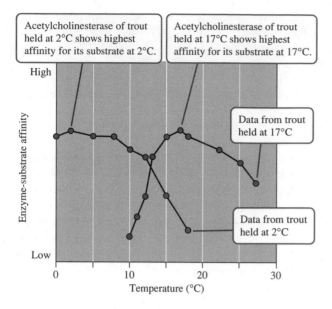

Figure 5.10 Enzyme activity is affected substantially by temperature (data from Baldwin and Hochachka 1970).

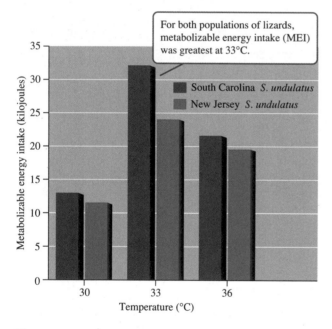

Figure 5.11 The rate of metabolizable energy intake by two populations of the eastern fence lizard, *Sceloporus undulatus*, peaks at the same temperature (data from Angilletta 2001).

Note that the differences in performance indicated by this experiment were observed over a relatively small range of temperatures: from 30° to 36°C. This result is consistent with the concept that most species perform best in a fairly narrow range of temperatures. Analogous influences of temperature on performance have also been well documented in plants.

Extreme Temperatures and Photosynthesis

One of the most fundamental characteristics of plants is their ability to photosynthesize. **Photosynthesis,** the conversion of light energy to the chemical energy of organic molecules, is the basis of the life of plants—their growth, reproduction, and so on—and the ultimate source of energy for most heterotrophic organisms.

Photosynthesis can be summarized by the following equation:

$$6\ CO_2 + 12\ H_2O \xrightarrow[\text{Chlorophyll}]{\text{Light}} C_6H_{12}O_6 + 6\ O_2 + 6\ H_2O$$

This equation indicates that as light interacts with chlorophyll, carbon dioxide and water combine to produce sugar and oxygen.

Extreme temperatures generally reduce the rate of photosynthesis by plants. Figure 5.12 shows the influence of temperature on rate of photosynthesis by a moss from the boreal forest, *Pleurozium schreberi,* and a desert shrub, *Atriplex lentiformis.* The moss and the desert shrub both photosynthesize at a maximum rate over some narrow range of temperatures. Both plants photosynthesize at lower rates at temperatures above and below this range. How do the responses of the boreal moss and desert shrub to temperature differ? The major difference is that their rates of photosynthesis peak at different temperatures. The moss photosynthesizes at a maximum rate at about 15°C, while the desert shrub photosynthesizes at a maximum rate at 44°C.

The results shown in figure 5.12 demonstrate that the moss and the shrub have substantially different optimal temperatures for photosynthesis. At 15°C, where the moss photosynthesizes at a maximum rate, the desert shrub photosynthesizes at about 25% of its maximum. At 44°C, where the desert shrub is photosynthesizing at its maximum rate, the moss would probably die. These physiological differences clearly reflect differences in the environments where these species live and seem to say something about their evolutionary histories. While the moss lives in the cool boreal forests of Finland, the

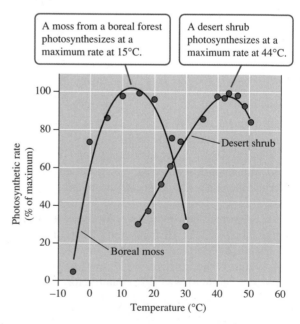

Figure 5.12 The optimal temperatures for photosynthesis by a boreal forest moss and a desert shrub differ substantially (data from Kallio and Kärenlampi 1975, Pearcy and Harrison 1974).

study population of the desert shrub, *A. lentiformis,* lives near Thermal, California, in one of the hottest deserts on earth.

The pattern of photosynthetic response to temperature by these two species is remarkably similar to the response of acetylcholinesterase to temperature (see fig. 5.10). Why might this be? (Hint: What roles do enzymes play in the process of photosynthesis?)

Plant responses to temperature, as well as those of animals, can also reflect the short-term physiological adjustments called **acclimation.** Acclimation involves physiological, not genetic, changes in response to temperature; acclimation is generally reversible with changes in environmental conditions. Studies of *A. lentiformis* by Robert Pearcy (1977) clearly demonstrate the effect of acclimation on photosynthesis. Pearcy located a population of this desert shrub in Death Valley and grew plants for his experiments from cuttings. By propagating plants from cuttings, he was able to conduct his experiments on genetically identical clones. The clones from the Death Valley plants were grown under two temperature regimes: one set in "hot" conditions of 43°C during the day and 30°C at night; the other set under cool conditions of 23°C during the day and 18°C at night.

Pearcy then measured the photosynthetic rates of the two sets of plants. The plants grown in a cool environment photosynthesized at a maximum rate at about 32°C. Those grown in a hot environment photosynthesized at a maximum rate at 40°C, a difference in the optimum temperature for photosynthesis of 8°C. Figure 5.13 summarizes the results of Pearcy's experiment. How can we be sure that the different responses to temperature shown by *A. lentiformis* grown under cool and hot conditions were due to physiological adjustments to their growing conditions and not to genetic differences between the

plants? Remember that the experimental plants were clones grown from cuttings. Pearcy used clones so he could control for the effects of genes and uncover the effects of physiological adjustment through acclimation.

The physiological adjustments made by *A. lentiformis* correspond to what these plants do during an annual cycle. The plant is evergreen and photosynthesizes throughout the year, in the cool of winter and in the heat of summer. The physiological adjustments suggest that acclimation by *A. lentiformis* may shift its optimal temperature for photosynthesis to match seasonal changes in environmental temperature. Plants from cooler areas also acclimate in response to changing temperatures. These changes allow many boreal species to photosynthesize later into fall than could occur without acclimation. Cold-acclimation appears more complex than warm-acclimation, and includes altering lipid membrane saturation to maintain fluidity even in cold temperatures.

Temperature and Microbial Activity

Although often overlooked, microbes often control the flow of energy and nutrients in terrestrial and aquatic ecosystems. As we will see throughout the book (chapters 7, 19, 20) changes in microbial activity can have significant consequences for the other organisms that live alongside these organisms. Additionally, changes in microbial activity can influence nutrient availability, which in turn alters a variety of ecosystem properties such as productivity and nutrient retention. It may come as no surprise that microbes can be extremely sensitive to changes in temperature.

Microbes appear to have adapted to all temperatures at which there is liquid water, from the frigid waters around the Antarctic to boiling hot springs. However, while each of these environments harbours one or more species of microbes, no known species thrives in all these conditions. All microbes that have been studied perform best over a fairly narrow range of temperatures. Let's look at two microbes that live in environments at opposite extremes of the aquatic temperature spectrum.

In chapter 3, we saw that most of the oceanic environment, the largest continuous environment on the earth, lies below the well-lighted surface waters. The organisms that live in the deep oceans live in darkness. Their environment is also cold, generally below 5°C. This cold-water environment extends to the surface in the Arctic and Antarctic. A wide variety of organisms live in these cold waters. How do you think the performance of these organisms is affected by temperature?

Richard Morita (1975) studied the effect of temperature on population growth among cold-loving, or **psychrophilic,** marine bacteria that live in the waters around Antarctica. He isolated and cultured one of those bacteria, *Vibrio* sp., in a temperature-gradient incubator. During the experiment, the temperature gradient within the incubator ranged from about –2°C to just over 9°C. The results of the experiment show that this *Vibrio* sp. grows fastest at about 4°C. At temperatures above and below this, its population growth rate decreases. As figure 5.14 shows, Morita recorded some growth in the *Vibrio* population at temperatures approaching –2°C, however, populations did not grow at temperatures above 9°C.

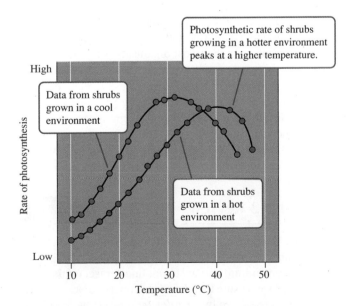

High

Photosynthetic rate of shrubs growing in a hotter environment peaks at a higher temperature.

Data from shrubs grown in a cool environment

Rate of photosynthesis

Data from shrubs grown in a hot environment

Low

10   20   30   40   50

Temperature (°C)

Figure 5.13 Growing the same species of shrub in cool versus hot environments altered their optimal temperature for photosynthesis. This change was a short-term physiological adjustment due to acclimation (data from Berry and Björkman 1980, after Pearcy 1977).

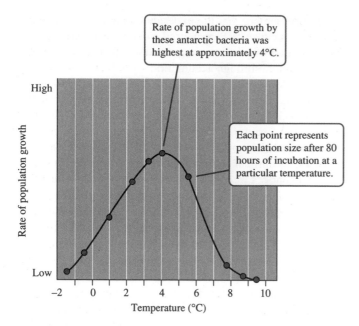

Figure 5.14 Antarctic bacteria have a very low optimal temperature for population growth (data from Morita 1975).

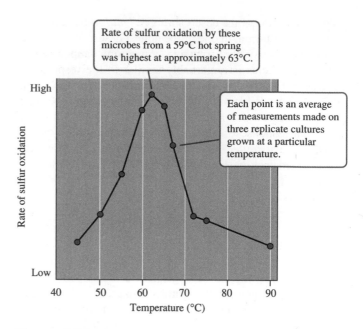

Figure 5.15 Hot spring microbes have a very high optimal temperature for population growth (data from Mosser, Mosser, and Brock 1974).

Morita has recorded population growth among some cold-loving bacteria at temperatures as low as –5.5°C.

Some microbes can live at very high temperatures. Microbes have been found living in all of the hot springs that have been studied. Some of these heat-loving, or **thermophilic,** microbes grow at temperatures above 40°C in a variety of environments. The most heat-loving microbes are the hyperthermophiles, which have temperature optima above 80°C. Some hyperthermophiles grow best at 110°C! Some of the most intensive studies of thermophilic and hyperthermophilic microbes have been carried out in Yellowstone National Park by Thomas Brock (1978) and his students and colleagues. One of the genera they have studied is *Sulfolobus,* a member of the microbial Domain Archaea, which obtains energy by oxidizing elemental sulfur. Jerry Mosser and colleagues (1974) used the rate at which *Sulfolobus* oxidizes sulfur as an index of its metabolic activity. They studied the microbes from a series of hot springs in Yellowstone National Park that ranged in temperature from 63°C to 92°C. The temperature optimum for the *Sulfolobus* populations ranged from 63°C to 80°C and was related to the temperature of the particular spring from which the microbes came. For instance, one strain isolated from a 59°C spring oxidized sulfur at a maximum rate at 63°C. This *Sulfolobus* population oxidizes sulfur at a high rate within a temperature range of about 10°C (fig. 5.15). Outside of this temperature range, its rate of sulfur oxidation is much lower.

New research tools are creating a new frontier in ecology, the ecology of microbes. Tools developed in molecular biology and in phylogenetics, the study of evolutionary relationships among organisms, are helping microbial ecologists explore the diversity of microbes and develop approaches to studying their ecology. For instance, Anna-Louise Reysenbach, Marissa

Ehringer, and Karen Hershberger (2000) used some of these modern tools to uncover the existence of previously unknown microbial lineages within the well-studied hot springs of Yellowstone National Park. Meanwhile, other researchers (e.g., Ishii and Marumo 2002) are using these modern tools to probe the microbial diversity of seafloor hydrothermal systems. Wherever these researchers apply their modern approaches, however, it remains correct to say that temperature plays a key role in determining the distribution of individual species and the composition of communities.

We have reviewed how temperature can affect microbial activity, plant photosynthesis, and animal performance. These examples demonstrate that most organisms perform best over a fairly narrow range of temperatures. Consider the effects of temperature on the performance of organisms relative to our discussion of how temperatures can vary greatly over small distances. In addition, the climate diagrams presented in chapter 2 showed us that temporal variation in temperature can also be substantial. In the next section, we review how some organisms respond to variation in environmental temperatures.

Concept 5.2 Review

1. Signs of thermal stress in fish include swimming on their sides and swimming in spirals. Using what you know about temperature and acetylcholinesterase, explain.
2. How can we be sure that the two distinctive responses to temperature shown by *Atriplex lentiformis* were due to acclimation and not the result of genetic differences?
3. Will all species within a single habitat have similar temperature optima for a given ecological process, such as photosynthesis? Explain.

5.3   Regulating Body Temperature

Many organisms have evolved ways to compensate for variations in environmental temperature by regulating body temperature.   So, how do organisms respond to the juxtaposition of thermal heterogeneity in the environment and their own fairly narrow thermal requirements? Do they sit passively and let environmental temperatures affect them as they will, or do they take a more active approach? Many organisms have evolved ways to regulate body temperatures.

Balancing Heat Gain Against Heat Loss

Organisms regulate body temperature by manipulating heat gain and loss. An equation, used by K. Schmidt-Nielsen (1983), can help us understand the components of heat that may be manipulated:

$$H_s = H_m \pm H_{cd} \pm H_{cv} \pm H_r - H_e$$

Here, H_s, the total heat stored in the body of an organism, is made up of H_m, heat gained from metabolism; H_{cd}, heat gained or lost through conduction; H_{cv}, heat lost or gained by convection; H_r, heat gained or lost through electromagnetic radiation; and H_e, heat lost through evaporation. These heat components represent ways that heat is transferred between an organism and its environment. **Metabolic heat,** H_m, is the energy released within an organism during the process of cellular respiration. **Conduction** is the movement of heat between objects in physical contact, as occurs when you sit on a stone bench on a cold winter's day; **convection** is the process of heat flow between a solid body and a moving fluid, such as wind or flowing water. During the process of conduction or convection, H_{cd} and H_{cv}, the direction of heat flow is always from the warmer region to the colder.

Heat may also be transferred through electromagnetic radiation. This transfer of heat, H_r, is often called simply **radiation.** All objects above absolute zero, (–273°C), give off electromagnetic radiation, but the most obvious source in our environment is the sun. Curiously, we are blind to most of this heat flux, because at sea level over half of the energy content of sunlight falls outside our visible range. Much of this radiation that we cannot see is in the infrared part of the spectrum. The electromagnetic radiation emitted by most objects in our environment, including our own bodies, is also infrared light. Infrared light is responsible for most of the warmth you feel when standing in front of a fire or that you feel radiating from the sunny side of a building on a winter's day. The chilling effect of standing outdoors under a clear, cold night sky with no wind is also mainly due to radiative heat flux, in this case from your body to the surroundings, including the night sky.

Heat, H_e, may be lost by an organism through **evaporation.** In general, we need only consider the heat lost as water evaporates from the surface of an organism. The ability of water to absorb a large amount of heat as it evaporates makes cooling systems based on the evaporation of water very effective. Figure 5.16 summarizes the potential pathways by which heat can be transferred between an organism and the environment.

So how do these factors interact to determine body temperature, and how can organisms maintain a constant internal temperature? First of all, not all species have constant body temperatures. These species, called **poikilotherms**, have body temperatures that vary in response to changes in the external environment. In contrast, **homeotherms** maintain relatively constant internal temperatures even in the face of changing external temperatures. There are a variety of physiological challenges that are unique to each of these conditions. As we have discussed, individual enzymes generally have specific temperature optima. For homeotherms, stabilizing selection will favour enzymes with optima generally near the constant internal environment of the organism (and selection will favour a body temperature near enzyme optima!). For poikilotherms, internal temperatures are variable and thus stabilizing selection is unlikely to be operating. Instead, many poikilotherms have redundant enzyme systems for critical functions, each with different temperature optima. Can you imagine any energetic cost associated with maintaining redundant systems? If so, why aren't all species homeotherms?

The answer is that homeothermy also has costs associated with the mechanisms that organisms use to maintain constant body temperatures. Some organisms, such as humans, are called **endotherms**. Endotherms rely heavily on internally derived metabolic heat energy, H_m, to elevate internal temperatures over external temperatures. Endothermic birds and mammals use metabolic energy to heat most of their bodies, while some endothermic fish and insects selectively heat critical organs. For endotherms, lowering the body temperature is generally more difficult than raising the body temperature, though it can be achieved through mechanisms such as panting, sweating, and altered body hair and feather positioning (increasing energetic losses through convection, conduction,

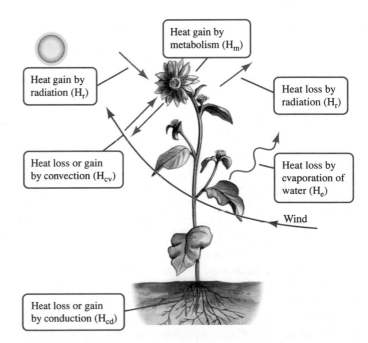

Figure 5.16   There are multiple pathways for heat exchange between organisms and the environment.

evaporation, and radiation). As a result of the limited effectiveness of the cooling mechanisms relative to the warming mechanism, most endotherms are able to survive at ambient temperatures well below their set body temperatures while at only a limited range of temperatures above their set body temperature. In other words, endotherms tend to live closer to the upper end of their range of tolerance than the lower end.

Ectotherms are able to control their body temperatures through the use of external sources of energy, manipulating H_c, H_r, and H_e. Ectotherms will often use behaviour to control their internal temperatures. For example, many reptiles can be found laying still on roads, rocks, and other exposed objects early in the morning. Why? This behaviour exposes their body to the sun, resulting in an elevated temperature. Later in the day, these same animals will often be found in crevices, cracks, or underground, preventing their body temperature from reaching a lethal point. Clearly, being an ectotherm will "cost" less energy than being an endotherm. Why then are not all species ectotherms? One answer may come to you if you consider how rarely you actually see snakes, lizards, and other terrestrial ectotherms being active.

There is a great natural diversity in temperature relations between organisms and their environments. It is because of this diversity of nature that the old terms of *cold-blooded* and *warm-blooded* are frustratingly inaccurate. For example, the behavioural changes of many ectotherms are so effective that they are actually homeotherms, at least for part of the day. Ectotherms of the deep ocean are also homeotherms, as the lack of change in the external temperatures results in a lack of change in body temperatures. Some endotherms, such as many hummingbirds, maintain constant body temperatures during the day, and then are poikilothermic during the night. Let's now take a closer look at how plants and animals thermoregulate.

Temperature regulation presents both plants and ectothermic animals with a similar problem. Both groups of organisms rely primarily on external sources of energy. Despite the much greater mobility of most ectothermic animals, the ways in which plants and ectothermic animals solve these problems are similar.

Temperature Regulation by Plants

What sorts of environments are best for studying temperature regulation by plants? Plant ecologists have typically concentrated their studies in extreme environments, such as the tundra and desert, where the challenges of the physical environment are great and where ecologists believed they would find the most dramatic adaptations.

Arctic and Alpine Plants

Cold environments present a variety of unique challenges to plants: freezing can destroy their vascular systems, enzymatic reactions are slower under cold conditions, and staying warm has significant consequences for plant fitness. How do plants meet these challenges? They, like plants from other environments, use morphology, physiology, and behaviour to alter heat exchange with the environment. Plants engage in a number of behaviours—the sunflower orienting its flowers towards

the sun being amongst the best known—they just tend to do things more slowly than animals. So how do plants thermoregulate in cold conditions?

We can ignore H_m, metabolic energy, as most plants produce only a small quantity of heat by metabolism. Evaporative cooling (H_e) is not relevant as plants in these locations are faced with challenges for warming, not cooling. We thus start with the equation:

$$H_s = H_{cd} \pm H_{cv} \pm H_r$$

To stay warm, arctic and alpine plants have two main options: increase their rate of radiative heating, H_r, and/or decrease their rate of convective cooling, H_{cv}. It appears that many have evolved to do both and, as a result, can heat up to temperatures far above air temperature. Natural selection has favoured arctic and alpine plants with dark pigments that absorb light. These dark pigments increase radiative heat gain, H_r. Arctic and alpine plants, such as the *Dryas integrifolia* (see fig. 5.1), also increase their H_r gain by orienting their leaves and flowers perpendicular to the sun's rays. In addition, many plants increase their H_r gain from the surroundings by assuming a "cushion" growth form that "hugs" the ground. The ground often warms to temperatures exceeding that of the overlying air and radiates infrared light, which can be absorbed by cushion plants. Cushion plants can also gain heat from warm substrate through conduction, H_{cd}.

The cushion growth form also reduces convective heat loss, H_{cv}, in two main ways. First, growing close to the ground gives them some shelter from the wind. Second, the compact, hemispherical growth form of cushion plants reduces the ratio of surface area to volume, which slows the movement of air through the interior of the plant. Reduced surface area also reduces the rate of radiative heat loss.

Figure 5.17 summarizes the processes involved in thermal regulation by a cushion plant. As a consequence of these processes, cushion plants are often warmer than the surrounding air and than plants with other growth forms. Y. Gauslaa (1984), who studied the heat budgets of a variety of Scandinavian plants, documented the thermal consequences of the cushion growth form. He found that while the temperature of plants with an open growth form closely matches air temperature, the temperature of cushion plants can be over 10°C higher than air temperature. The results of one of Gauslaa's comparisons is shown in figure 5.18. Though these plants were measured in Scandinavia, many of the species occur throughout the Canadian arctic.

Desert Plants

The desert environment challenges plants to avoid overheating; that is, plants are challenged to reduce their heat storage, H_s. How do desert plants meet this challenge? For the most part they do everything opposite to what we saw in arctic and alpine locations. Additionally, evaporative cooling of leaves, which would increase heat loss, H_e, is not a workable option because desert plants usually have inadequate supplies of water. So, for a plant in a hot desert environment, our equation for heat balance reduces to:

$$H_s = H_{cd} \pm H_{cv} \pm H_r$$

Darkly pigmented leaves reduce reflection and increase heat gain by radiation (H_r).

Arctic and alpine plants also increase H_r by orienting their leaves perpendicular to sunlight.

Compact, hemispherical growth form decreases exposure of plant surfaces to wind.

Low convective heat loss to wind

Ground-hugging growth form increases heat gain from solar-heated surroundings through:

Wind

Radiation H_r and Conduction (H_{cd}).

Figure 5.17 Arctic and alpine cushion plant form and orientation increases heat gain from sunlight and the surrounding landscape and conserves any heat gained.

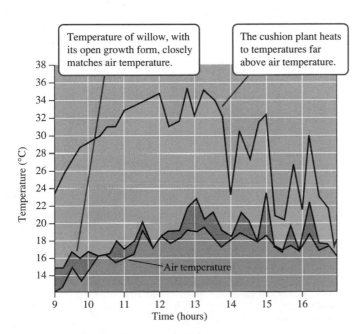

Temperature of willow, with its open growth form, closely matches air temperature.

The cushion plant heats to temperatures far above air temperature.

Air temperature

Figure 5.18 An arctic cushion plant (*Loiseleuria procumbens*) maintains significantly higher temperatures compared to plants with a more open growth form, such a willow (*Salix glauca*) (data from Fitter and Hay 1987, after Gauslaa 1984).

To avoid heating, plants in hot deserts have three main options: decreasing heating by conduction, H_{cd}, increasing rates of convective cooling, H_{cv}, and reducing rates of radiative heating, H_r. Many desert plants place their foliage far enough above the ground to reduce heat gain by conduction. Many desert plants have also evolved very small leaves and an open growth form, adaptations that give high rates of convective cooling because they increase the ratio of leaf surface area to volume and the movement of air around the plant's stems and foliage. Some desert plants have low rates of radiative heat gain, H_r, because they have evolved reflective surfaces. As we observed in chapter 2, many desert plants cover their leaves with a dense coating of white plant hairs. These hairs reduce H_r gain by reflecting visible light, which constitutes nearly half the energy content of sunlight.

We can see how natural selection has adapted plants to different temperature regimes by comparing species in the genus *Encelia,* which are distributed along a temperature and moisture gradient from the coast of California to Death Valley. James Ehleringer (1980) showed that the leaves of the coastal species, *Encelia californica,* lack hairs entirely and reflect only about 15% of visible light. He also found that two other species that grow part way between the cool coast regions

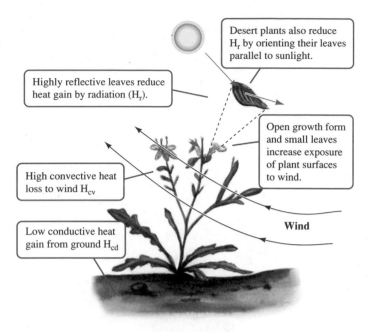

Figure 5.19 The form and orientation of desert plants reduces heat gain from the environment and facilitates cooling.

and Death Valley produce leaves that are somewhat pubescent and reflect about 26% of visible light. The desert species, *Encelia farinosa,* produces two sets of leaves, one set in the summer and another when it's cooler. The summer leaves are highly pubescent (hairy) and reflect more than 40% of solar radiation. What do you think the cool season leaves are like? If you predict that they are much less pubescent than summer leaves you are correct. Why is that? We know the benefits of leaf pubescence. What might be some costs? (Hint: What do plants do with visible light other than heat up?)

Plants can also modify radiative heat gain, H_r, by changing the orientation of leaves and stems. Many desert plants reduce heating by orienting their leaves parallel to the rays of the sun or by folding them at midday, when sunlight is most intense. Figure 5.19 portrays the main processes involved in heat balance in desert plants.

Temperature Regulation by Ectothermic Animals

Like plants, the vast majority of animals, including fish, amphibians, reptiles, and invertebrates of all sorts, use external sources of energy to regulate body temperature. These ectothermic animals use means analogous to those used by plants, including variations in body size, shape, and pigmentation. The obvious difference between plants and ectothermic animals is that the animals have more options for using behaviour to thermoregulate. Yet, as we shall see, the difference between the behaviour of these animals and that of plants is more a matter of degree than of kind.

Can thermoregulation by ectotherms be either effective or precise? Let's allow an ectotherm from a rigorous environment to answer our question.

Liolaemus Lizards

Oliver Pearson (1954) studied *Liolaemus multiformis,* an unusual lizard because it thrives in a cold environment. This lizard lives in the high Andes Mountains of South America at altitudes over 4,800 m. In these mountains, it is cold year-round, with morning temperatures falling as low as −5°C. The lizard spends the night in burrows, where its rate of cooling is lower than it would be in the open. However, Pearson found that during the night, its body temperature may still fall to as low as 2.5°C. Even at these temperatures, the lizard emerges from its burrows early each morning and immediately begins to bask, usually on a mat of plant material. By perching on plant material and avoiding contact with stones, it reduces its rate of heat loss by conduction to the ground.

While basking, *Liolaemus* orients its back toward the sun, which increases radiative heat gain. It also presses itself flat against the substrate, which reduces its exposure to the wind and heat losses by convection. In addition, Pearson observed that cold lizards emerging from their burrows are dark. He proposed that this dark pigmentation increases the rate of radiative heat gain by basking lizards.

Pearson demonstrated that these behaviours produce a rapid rise in body temperature. After an hour of basking, as air temperature rises to about 1.5°C, the body temperature of *Liolaemus* rises to about 33°C, over 30°C above that of the surrounding air! As the day progresses, and air temperature continues to rise, the lizard maintains a more or less constant body temperature of 35°C. Figure 5.20 summarizes this basking behaviour. We asked whether thermoregulation by an ectotherm can be either effective or precise. Pearson's studies suggest that thermoregulation by ectotherms can be both.

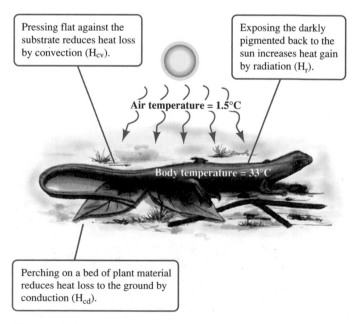

Figure 5.20 The high-elevation lizard, *Liolaemus multiformis,* uses a combination of behaviour and dark pigmentation to increase solar heat gain and elevate its body temperature (data from Pearson 1954).

While the early studies of Oliver Pearson show that thermoregulation by ectotherms can be both effective and precise, we are left with many important biological questions. For instance, what relationships are there between temperature regulation, temperature preference, and optimal performance by a particular species? Insights into these relationships have come from studies of the eastern fence lizard, *Sceloporus undulatus*. Research by Michael Angilletta showed that the rate of metabolizable energy intake is maximized at a temperature of 33°C (fig. 5.11). Now, what relationship does this optimal temperature bear to the preferred temperature of *S. undulatus*? Angilletta (2001) explored this relationship by placing *S. undulatus* from New Jersey and South Carolina in a temperature gradient that ranged from 26°C at one end to 38°C at the other end. He determined preferred temperature early each morning by quickly measuring the body temperature of each lizard. Body temperature would indicate where each lizard had been in the temperature gradient, that is, its "preferred" temperature. Angilletta examined thermoregulation by measuring the body temperatures of active individuals in the field.

The results of Angilletta's study provide strong evidence for a correspondence between preferred temperature, thermoregulation, and optimal temperatures in *S. undulatus* (fig. 5.21). Lizards from New Jersey and South Carolina had virtually identical preferred temperatures: 32.8°C versus 32.9°C respectively. The body temperatures found by Angilletta in the field were also very similar. The body temperatures of *S. undulatus* measured in the field in New Jersey averaged 34.0°C, while the body temperatures of *S. undulatus* taken in South Carolina averaged 33.1°C. As shown in figure 5.21, both preferred temperatures determined in the laboratory and the body temperatures of *S. undulatus* measured in the field are very close to the temperature that maximizes metabolizable energy intake by these lizards. The following example shows that effective thermoregulation by ectotherms is not limited to lizards.

Grasshoppers: Some Like It Hot

Many grasshoppers also bask in the sun, elevating their body temperature to 40°C or even higher. R. I. Carruthers and his colleagues (1992) described how some species of grasshoppers even adjust their capacity for radiative heating, H_r, by varying the intensity of their pigmentation during development. When reared at low temperatures, these species appear to compensate by developing dark pigmentation; while at higher developmental temperatures, they produce less pigmentation (fig. 5.22). How would changing pigmentation in response to developmental temperatures affect thermoregulation by these grasshoppers? Because grasshoppers reared at low temperatures develop darker pigmentation, they increase their potential for H_r gain. Because those reared at high temperatures develop lighter pigmentation, they reduce their potential for H_r gain.

The clear-winged grasshopper, *Camnula pellucida,* inhabits subalpine grasslands in the White Mountains of eastern Arizona, where the cool mornings warm up quickly under the mountain sun. During early morning, *Camnula*, like *Liolaemus,* orients its body perpendicular to the sun's rays and quickly heats to 30°C to 40°C. Given the opportunity, young *Camnula*

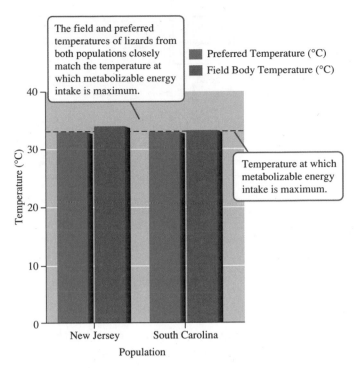

Figure 5.21   Two populations of the eastern fence lizard, *Sceloporus undulatus*, both regulate their body temperatures to match closely the temperature of maximum metabolizable energy intake (data from Angilletta 2001).

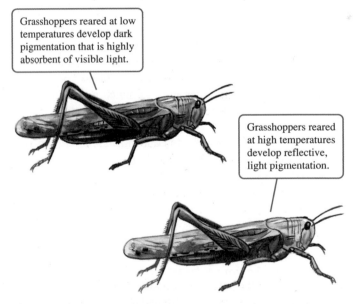

Figure 5.22   Rearing temperatures influence the pigmentation of the clear-winged grasshopper.

will maintain a body temperature around 38°C to 40°C, very close to its optimal temperature for development. In the laboratory, *Camnula* is able to elevate its body temperature to 12°C above air temperature and maintain it within a very narrow range (± 2°C) for many hours.

Carruthers and his colleagues divided a sample of *Camnula* into two groups, which were kept at an air temperature of about 18°C. One of the groups also had access to light,

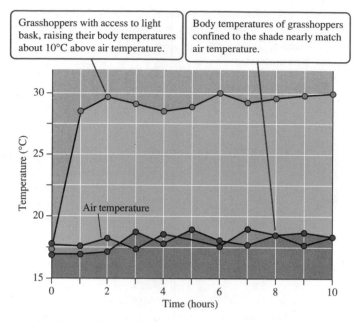

Figure 5.23 Basking allows the clear-winged grasshopper to elevate its body temperature significantly (data from Carruthers et al. 1992).

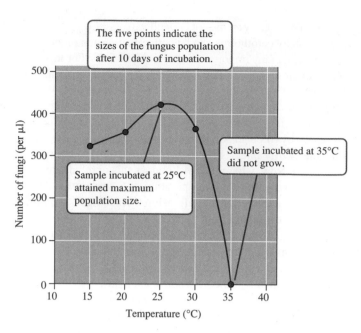

Figure 5.24 High temperatures inhibit growth by *Entomophaga grylli* (data from Carruthers et al. 1992).

while the other was restricted to the shade. The grasshoppers that had access to light basked and elevated their body temperatures about 10°C above air temperature. Meanwhile, the body temperatures of the grasshoppers kept in the shade remained close to air temperature (fig. 5.23).

Why does *Camnula* bask and maintain a body temperature above air temperature? The researchers estimated that by basking in the sun the grasshopper develops faster than it would if it allowed its body temperature to match air temperature. What other benefits might *Camnula* gain by maintaining a high body temperature? The grasshopper may raise its body temperature to 38°C to 40°C to control *Entomophaga grylli*, a fungus that infects and kills grasshoppers.

The idea that high temperatures could control *Entomophaga* was tested by growing the fungus in artificial media at 15°C, 20°C, 25°C, 30°C, 35°C, and 45°C. The populations grew fastest at 25°C; above and below 25°C the fungus populations grew at a slower rate; they did not grow at 35°C and were killed at 45°C (fig. 5.24).

What are the limitations of the experiment summarized in figure 5.24? This experiment was conducted on fungus populations growing on artificial media. Therefore, we should be cautious about predicting how temperature may affect *Entomophaga* growing inside of living grasshoppers. After studying the growth of the fungus in artificial media, the researchers studied how temperature influences mortality among grasshoppers infected with the fungus. They found that exposure to 40°C temperatures for as few as 4 hours each day significantly reduced the numbers of grasshoppers dying of *Entomophaga* infections. The results of these experiments support the hypothesis that by maintaining body temperatures of 38°C to 40°C, clear-winged grasshoppers create an environment unsuitable for one of their most serious pathogens.

How does the effect of temperature on population growth by *Entomophaga* compare to the effect of temperature on population growth by bacteria as shown in figures 5.14 and 5.15?

Temperature Regulation by Endothermic Animals

Do endothermic animals thermoregulate differently than the other organisms we've discussed? Endotherms use all the anatomical and behavioural tricks used by other organisms to manipulate heat exchange with the environment. So, our basic equation for temperature regulation, $H_s = H_m \pm H_{cd} \pm H_{cv} \pm H_r - H_e$, still applies but with some changes in the relative importance of the terms. Most significantly, endotherms rely a great deal more on metabolic heat, H_m, to maintain constant body temperature.

Environmental Temperature and Metabolic Rates

P. F. Scholander and his colleagues (1950) studied thermoregulation in several endothermic species by monitoring metabolic rate while exposing them to a range of temperatures. The range of environmental temperatures over which the metabolic rate of a homeothermic animal does not change is called its **thermal neutral zone** (Figure 5.25). When environmental temperatures are within the thermal neutral zone of an endothermic animal, its metabolic rate stays steady at resting metabolism. An endotherm's metabolic rate will rapidly increase to two or even three times resting metabolism if the environmental temperature falls below or rises above the thermal neutral zone.

What causes metabolic rates to rise when environmental temperatures are outside the thermal neutral zone? We can use

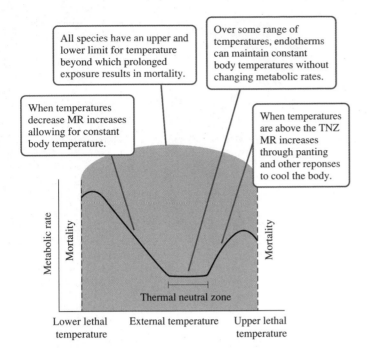

All species have an upper and lower limit for temperature beyond which prolonged exposure results in mortality.

Over some range of temperatures, endotherms can maintain constant body temperatures without changing metabolic rates.

When temperatures decrease MR increases allowing for constant body temperature.

When temperatures are above the TNZ MR increases through panting and other reponses to cool the body.

Metabolic rate

Mortality

Mortality

Thermal neutral zone

Lower lethal temperature

External temperature

Upper lethal temperature

Figure 5.25 In response to changing external temperatures, endotherms vary metabolic rates to maintain a constant body temperature.

humans as a model for the responses of endotherms generally. At low temperatures, we start shivering, which generates heat by muscle contractions. We also release hormones that increase our metabolic rate, the rate at which we metabolize our energy stores, which are mainly fats. Increasing metabolic rate increases the rate at which we generate metabolic heat, H_m. At high temperatures, heart rate and blood flow to the skin increase. This increased blood flow transports heat from the body core to the skin, where an evaporative cooling system based on sweating accelerates unloading of heat to the external environment. Many large endotherms, such as horses and camels, also cool by sweating. Other endotherms do not sweat but evaporatively cool by other means: dogs and birds pant and marsupials and rodents moisten their body surfaces by salivating and licking.

The breadth of the thermal neutral zone varies a great deal among endothermic species. Scholander and his colleagues suggested that differences in the width of the thermal neutral zone defines two groups of organisms: tropical species, with narrow thermal neutral zones, and arctic species, with broad thermal neutral zones. The researchers pointed out that the narrow thermal neutral zone of *Homo sapiens* is similar to that of several species of rain forest mammals and birds. Meanwhile, arctic species, such as the arctic fox, have impressively broad thermal neutral zones.

Since the normal body temperature of most endotherms varies from about 35°C to 40°C, it is no surprise that this range of temperatures falls within the thermal neutral zone of both tropical and arctic species. What distinguishes tropical and arctic species is the great tolerance that arctic species have for cold. For instance, the arctic fox can tolerate environmental temperatures down to at least –40°C without showing any increase in metabolic rate. Meanwhile the metabolic rate of some tropical species begins to increase when air temperature falls below 29°C. Figure 5.26 contrasts the thermal neutral zones of some arctic and tropical species.

Is this classification of thermal responses consistent with what we learned about the relative temperature variation in tropical versus high-latitude environments? Yes, it is. Compare the climate diagrams for the tropical rain forest and tropical savanna with those for the boreal forest and tundra—Does *H. sapiens* somehow violate this classification? We live virtually everywhere on the planet yet our thermal neutral zone suggests that we are tropical. How can you explain this?

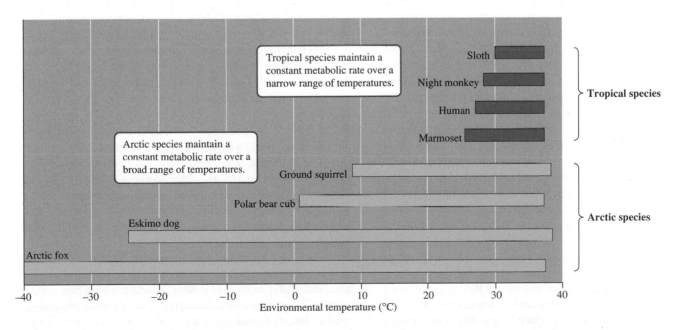

Figure 5.26 Temperature and the thermal neutral zone of arctic and tropical mammals. Bars indicate range of temperatures over which metabolic rate does not change for each species (data from Scholander et al. 1950).

While humans live virtually everywhere on earth, we do so by virtue of our ability to manipulate the environment. We spend a great deal of time and energy compensating for variation in temperature, using devices as simple as clothing or as complex as houses fitted with mechanical systems for heating and cooling. We put on extra clothing when it's cold and wear less when it's warm. When it's hot, we decrease radiative heating by wearing a straw hat. When it's cold, we decrease radiative cooling by wearing a toque. Our ability to create large, temperature-controlled environments in the interiors of schools, office buildings, sports stadiums, and theatres is unique in the biosphere. Yet these controlled environments, like our narrow thermal neutral zone, suggest a tropical heritage. Can you imagine the temperature controls within a shopping mall designed by arctic foxes?

From an ecological perspective, the important point of this discussion is that thermoregulation outside the thermal neutral zone costs energy that could be otherwise directed toward reproduction. How might such energetic costs affect the distribution and abundance of organisms in nature? This is one of the central questions of ecology.

Aquatic Birds and Mammals

Now let's turn to thermoregulation by aquatic endotherms, where the aquatic environment limits the possible ways organisms can regulate their body temperatures. Why is that? First, as we have seen, the capacity of water to absorb heat energy without changing temperature is about 3,000 times that of air. Second, conductive and convective heat losses to water are much more rapid than to air, over 20 times faster in still water and up to 100 times faster in moving water. Thus, the aquatic organism is surrounded by a vast heat sink. The potential for heat loss to this heat sink is very great, particularly for gill-breathing species that must expose a large respiratory surface in order to extract sufficient oxygen from water. In the face of these environmental difficulties, only a few aquatic species are truly endothermic.

Aquatic birds and mammals, such as penguins, seals, and whales, can be endothermic in an aquatic environment for two major reasons: First, they are all air breathers and do not expose a large respiratory surface to the surrounding water. Second, many endothermic aquatic animals, including penguins, seals, and whales, are well insulated from the heat-sapping external environment by a thick layer of fat, while others, such as the sea otter, are insulated by a layer of fur that traps air. The parts of these animals that are not well insulated, principally appendages, are outfitted with *countercurrent heat exchangers,* vascular structures that reduce the rate of heat loss to the surrounding aquatic environment. Figure 5.27 diagrams the structure and functioning of a countercurrent heat exchanger in the flipper of a dolphin.

Heat exchangers are so efficient at conserving heat that some species of fish are able to maintain a significant thermal gradient between some of their muscles and the external environment. While not capable of regulating the temperature of their body core, as aquatic birds and mammals do, these fish can selectively heat certain muscle groups and perhaps increase their swimming performance over a larger range of temperatures as a consequence.

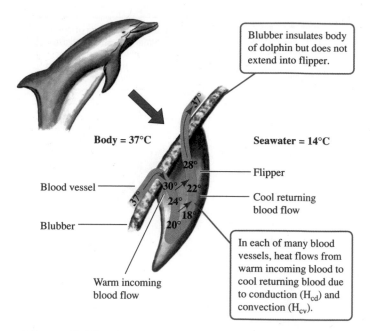

Figure 5.27   Countercurrent heat exchange in dolphin flippers promotes conservation of body heat.

Warming the Swimming Muscles of Large Marine Fish

Francis Carey (1973) was fascinated to learn that some fishes, such as tuna and mackerel sharks, have body temperatures *above* that of the surrounding water, a fact that seemed to contradict the physics of heat exchange. Consequently, Carey and his colleagues at the Woods Hole Oceanographic Institution set out to determine how this could be. As a consequence of their research program, we now know a great deal more about the temperature relations of large endothermic fishes.

The lateral swimming muscles of endothermic fish, such as tunas and mackerel sharks, are well supplied with blood vessels that function as countercurrent heat exchangers. These heat exchangers heat cool arterial blood as it carries oxygen to the lateral swimming muscles, and by the time this blood delivers its supply of oxygen and nutrients it has been heated to the same temperature as the active muscles. On the return trip the heat in this warm blood is used to heat the newly arriving blood and so, when blood exits the swimming muscles, it is again approximately the same temperature as the surrounding water. The countercurrent heat exchangers of tuna are efficient enough at conserving heat that these fish can elevate the temperature of their swimming muscles up to 14°C above the temperature of the surrounding water. The anatomy of the countercurrent heat exchange in bluefin tuna muscle is presented in figure 5.28.

Carey and his colleagues implanted devices that would measure and transmit the temperature of the muscles of bluefin tuna and of the surrounding water. Their tracking boat could usually follow a released fish carrying a temperature-sensing implant for a few hours, which provided enough time to collect data that revealed a great deal about their temperature relations. As one of the monitored fish swam through water varying in

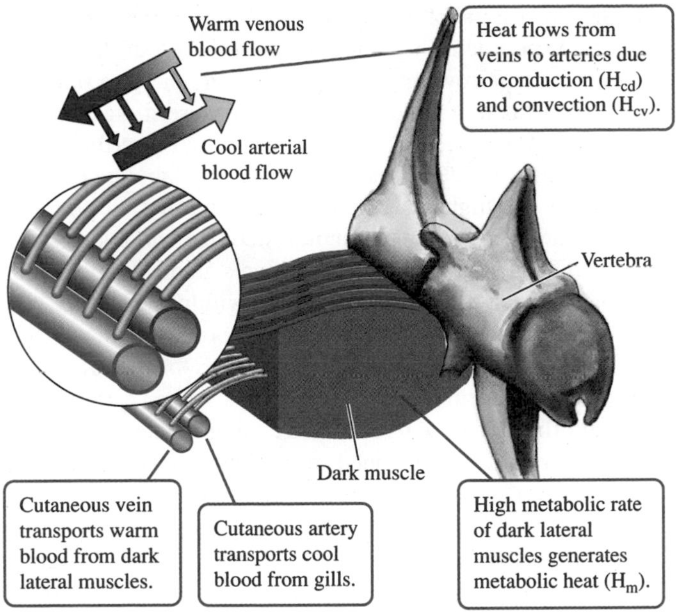

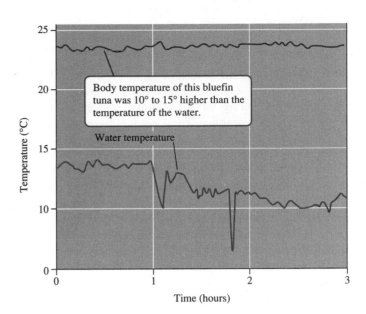

Figure 5.28 Countercurrent heat exchange in the lateral muscles of bluefin tuna.

Figure 5.29 The muscle temperature of an actively swimming bluefin tuna is elevated above that of the surrounding ocean water (data from Carey 1973).

temperature from 7°C to 14°C, the temperature of its swimming muscles remained a constant 24°C. These results, shown in figure 5.29, demonstrate that a bluefin tuna can maintain a remarkably constant muscle temperature even in the face of substantial variation in water temperature. More recent work has shown that other organs, such as the stomach, of bluefin tuna vary in temperature much more than do the swimming muscles (Stevens, Kanwisher, and Carey 2000).

Now, let's move from the sea and the giant bluefin tuna, which can reach up to 1,000 kg, to land, where we find some of the smallest endotherms. Many terrestrial insects have evolved the capacity to heat their flight muscles.

Warming Insect Flight Muscles

Have you ever gone outside on a cool fall or spring morning when few insects were active and yet met with bumblebees visiting flowers? Were you surprised? While you may have taken the meeting for granted, these early morning forays by bumblebees require some impressive physiology. Most insects use external sources of energy to heat their bodies, but there are some notable exceptions. Bumblebees maintain the temperature of their thoraxes, which house the flight muscles, at 30°C to 37°C regardless of air temperature (Heinrich 1979). Because they can warm their flight muscles, bumblebees can fly when environmental temperatures are as low as 0°C. A number of other insects use metabolic heat, H_m, to warm their flight muscles, including large nocturnal moths, which were the subject of some of the earliest studies of endothermic insects.

Bernd Heinrich (1993) has spent a great deal of his professional life studying thermoregulation by insects. Some of the inspiration that launched this work came to him when he was a graduate student recording the body temperatures of moths in the highlands of New Guinea. Heinrich relates how as he captured moths flying to a sheet illuminated by a lantern, air tem-

peratures were about 9°C. Despite these low temperatures, some of the larger moths captured had thoracic temperatures of 46°C, 9°C higher than Heinrich's own body temperature. It was at this point that he became convinced that some insects can thermoregulate by endothermic means. However, you don't have to travel to the highlands of New Guinea to meet endothermic insects. Some of Heinrich's most elegant studies of thermoregulation have been done on moths from temperate latitudes.

Studies of temperature regulation by moths began in the early 1800s. Many of these studies were focused on moths of the family Sphingidae, the sphinx moths. Sphinx moths are convenient insects for study because many reach impressive sizes, large enough to be mistaken for hummingbirds. Heinrich's dissertation focused on thermoregulation by the sphinx moth *Manduca sexta,* whose large green caterpillars feed on a wide variety of plants including tobacco and tomato plants. *M. sexta* is among the larger sphinx moths and weighs 2 to 3 g —which is heavier than some hummingbirds and shrews, the smallest of the birds and mammals.

Since the nineteenth century, researchers have been aware that active sphinx moths have elevated thoracic temperatures. These early researchers also knew that temperature increases within the thorax were due to activity of the flight muscles contained within the thorax that vibrated the wings. Later researchers discovered that during flight, the muscles responsible for the upstroke of the wings and those responsible for the downstroke contracted sequentially. However, during preflight warm-up, the upstroke and downstroke muscles contracted nearly simultaneously. Consequently, the wings of a moth warming its flight muscles only vibrated. Once warmed up and actively flying, sphinx moths maintained a relatively constant thoracic temperature over a broad range of environmental temperatures. This was evidence that sphinx moths thermoregulate.

You can see that a lot was known before Heinrich began his dissertation research. However, a significant problem remained. No one knew how sphinx moths accomplished thermoregulation. Phillip Adams and James Heath (1964) proposed that the moths thermoregulate by changing their metabolic rate in response to changing environmental temperatures. In terms of our equation for thermoregulation, Adams and Heath proposed that the moths increased H_m when environmental temperatures fell and decreased H_m when environmental temperatures rose.

Several observations led Heinrich to propose an alternative hypothesis, however. He proposed that active sphinx moths have a fairly constant metabolic rate and so generate metabolic heat, H_m, at a constant rate. Heinrich also proposed that sphinx moths thermoregulate by changing their rates of heat loss to the environment. In terms of our equation for thermoregulation, the moths *decrease* their rate of cooling by convection and conduction when environmental temperatures fall and when temperatures rise, sphinx moths *increase* their cooling rates.

Heinrich tested his hypothesis with a series of pioneering experiments that demonstrated *M. sexta* cools its thorax by using its circulatory system to transport heat to the abdomen.

In other words, the blood of these moths acts as a coolant. In his first experiment, he immobilized a moth and heated its thorax with a narrow beam of light while monitoring the temperature of the thorax and abdomen. Because it was narrow, the light beam increased radiative heat gain, H_r, of the thorax only. Heinrich used the beam to simulate metabolic heat production by the flight muscles. He observed that the thoracic temperature of these heated moths stabilized at about 44°C. Meanwhile, their abdominal temperatures gradually increased.

These results indicated that heat within the thorax was transferred to the abdomen. Heinrich proposed that blood flowing from the thorax to the abdomen was the means of heat transfer. To confirm this, he conducted a second experiment. He tied off blood flow to the thorax using a fine human hair. With this blood flow stopped, flying moths overheated and stopped flying. Instead of stabilizing at 44°C, the thoracic temperatures approached the lethal limit of 46°C. An interesting debate between two groups of researchers with competing hypotheses was decided by two decisive experiments, which are summarized by figure 5.30.

Endothermic insects were a surprise to many biologists. The existence of endothermic plants was even more surprising.

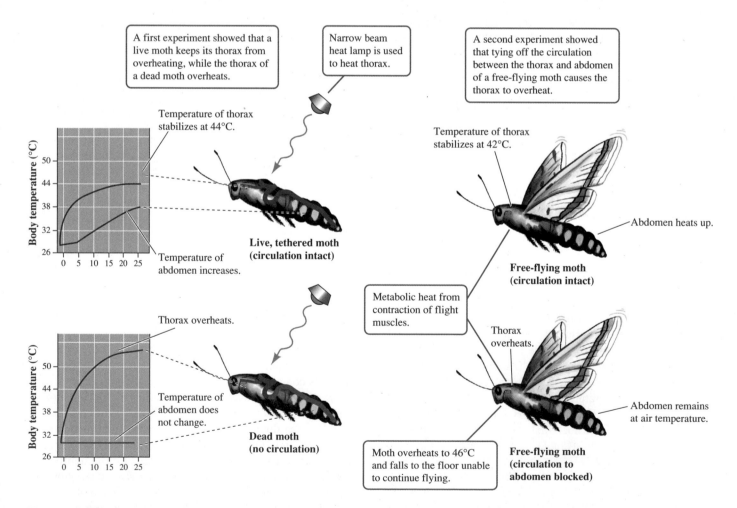

Figure 5.30   The circulatory system plays a central role in thermoregulation by the moth, *Manduca sexta* (data from Heinrich 1993).

Temperature Regulation by Thermogenic Plants

Roger Knutson (1974, 1979) visited a marsh on a cold February day in northeast Iowa. There he saw eastern skunk cabbage, *Symplocarpus foetidus,* emerging from the frozen landscape. Each plant was surrounded by a melted circle in the snow. It appeared as though the skunk cabbage had generated enough heat to melt its way through the snow. Knutson returned the next day with a thermometer and so began a research project that produced some surprising observations of thermoregulation by plants.

Almost all plants are poikilothermic ectotherms. However, plants in the family Araceae have the unusual habit of using metabolic energy to heat their flowers. Some of the temperate species in this mostly tropical family use this ability to protect their inflorescences from freezing and to attract pollinators. One of the most studied of these temperate species is the eastern skunk cabbage, which lives in the deciduous forests of eastern North America including much of eastern Canada. This skunk cabbage blooms from February to March, when air temperatures vary between −15°C to 15°C. During this period, the inflorescence of the plant, which weighs from 2 to 9 g, maintains a temperature 15°C to 35°C above air temperature. As Knutson observed, this temperature is warm enough so that *S. foetidus* can melt its way through snow. The plant's inflorescences can maintain these elevated temperatures for up to 14 days. During this period, it functions as an endothermic organism.

How does the skunk cabbage fuel the heating of its inflorescence? It has a large root in which it stores large quantities of starch. Some of this starch is translocated to the inflorescence, where it is metabolized at a high rate, generating large quantities of heat in the process. This heat, besides keeping the inflorescence from freezing, may help attract pollinators. Various pollinators are attracted to both the warmth and the sweetish scent given off by the plant. Some of the biology of this interesting plant is summarized in figure 5.31.

The inflorescence of the skunk cabbage maintains a high respiratory rate, equivalent to that of a small mammal of similar size. However, its metabolic rate is not constant. The plant adjusts its metabolic rate to changes in environmental temperatures. The metabolic rate increases with decreasing temperature, which increases the rate of metabolic heat production. By adjusting its metabolic rate, the plant can maintain its inflorescence at a similar temperature despite substantial variation in environmental temperature (fig. 5.32).

In this section, we have considered how various organisms regulate their body temperatures by using external sources of energy, internal sources of energy, or both. Thermoregulation is possible where organisms face temperatures within their range of tolerance. However, organisms do not always respond to variation in environmental temperatures by thermoregulating. In many circumstances, they use various means to survive extreme environmental temperatures, as we shall discuss next.

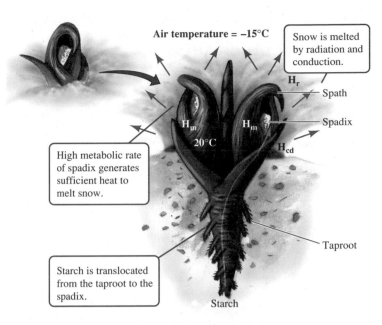

Air temperature = −15°C

Snow is melted by radiation and conduction.

H_r

Spath

Spadix

H_m H_m

20°C

H_{cd}

High metabolic rate of spadix generates sufficient heat to melt snow.

Taproot

Starch is translocated from the taproot to the spadix.

Starch

Figure 5.31   Eastern skunk cabbage, an endothermic plant, can melt its way up through spring snow cover (data from Knutson 1974).

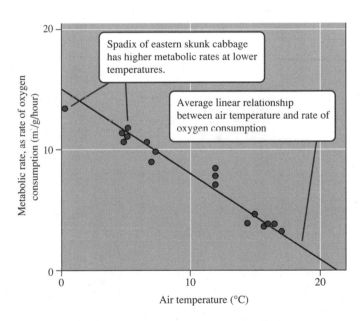

Spadix of eastern skunk cabbage has higher metabolic rates at lower temperatures.

Average linear relationship between air temperature and rate of oxygen consumption

Metabolic rate, as rate of oxygen consumption (m³/g/hour)

Air temperature (°C)

Figure 5.32   Air temperature has a clear influence on the metabolic rate of eastern skunk cabbage (data from Knutson 1974).

Concept 5.3 Review

1. Why would selection likely act against the production of light pigmentation and white hairs on the leaf surface of arctic plants?
2. Can behavioural thermoregulation be precise? What evidence supports your answer?
3. Why are all endothermic fish relatively large?

5.4   Surviving Extreme Temperatures

Organisms exhibit a diversity of mechanisms to cope with extreme temperatures.   Think of an environment that is either very cold or very hot, perhaps a −40°C winter day in the boreal forest. For certain, you are likely to notice less obvious biological activity on that day than you will in the same location in the middle of the summer. However, even that cold winter day is not devoid of life. In this section we will discuss strategies that have evolved allowing species to survive extreme temperatures. When we use the term extreme, it is necessary to understand that this is a relative term, and what is extreme to one species may in fact be quite comfortable to another. We use the term to indicate temperatures well beyond the range of tolerance for most species. For example, although many species of spruce trees are able to survive at temperatures as low as −80°C, most reasonable scientists would agree that that is an extreme temperature. Extreme conditions can last for a day, a week, or months, with different strategies existing for all of these scenarios. One thing that is common in response to extreme temperatures is that relatively simple solutions such as panting, increasing hair cover, or other minor behavioural and physiological changes can help, but individually are likely not quite enough. Instead, dramatic environmental conditions have resulted in the evolution of equally dramatic ecological responses. Here we examine some of the more common responses to extreme temperatures, particularly responses to extreme cold (fig. 5.33).

Figure 5.33   Plants and animals exhibit a variety of adaptations to surviving extreme winter conditions.

Death

You may not consider death to be a particularly adaptive response to extreme conditions, but in fact it is a common strategy used by many organisms. Why? To answer this we must first introduce the idea of **energy budgets**, a topic we will discuss in most subsequent chapters in the text. All organisms have a certain amount of energy based upon what they eat (or photosynthesize). This can be represented in a pie diagram, with the size of the pie representing the total amount of available energy to the organism (fig. 5.34). For a given organism at a given point in time, the size of the pie is fixed, and energy spent on one biological process can not also be spent on another process. The main types of energy expenditure for all organisms (plants, animals, microbes, etc.) can be broken down into four general groups: growth, maintenance, activity, and reproduction (fig. 5.34). Growth consists of all the energy needed to build new tissues and organs; maintenance represents the basal metabolic costs of simply staying alive; reproduction costs include the production of reproductive organs (e.g., flowers), mechanisms of mate attraction (e.g., nectar, showy plumage), and the development of offspring; and activity costs include the extra energy required to move, eat, defend territories, and most anything else that organisms do when they are not asleep or dormant. The relative size of each of these slices of pie will differ among species. For example, endotherms will have much larger maintenance costs than will ectotherms.

How does this relate to extreme environments? One strategy for surviving harsh conditions can be increased energy expenditures for maintenance (e.g., increasing metabolic rate, construction of freeze resistant tissues, etc.), resulting in less energy available for other activities, such as reproduction. For many other organisms, natural selection has favoured a solution that involves minimal investment in maintenance and maximal investment in reproduction (see chapter 9). What types of organisms do this? "Annual" plants and many insects are among the more common examples. What does being "annual"

actually mean for plants? It means that an individual completes its life cycle within a single year. As it turns out, the adult life-stage generally dies just prior to the more extreme temperatures, which would be winter for most parts of Canada. A reasonable question to ask is if extreme conditions kill the adults of a particular species, how is it possible to find that same species in the same location the following year? The solution to this problem lies in the realization that many species or organisms have different life-stages that have inherently different morphologies and ranges of tolerance. For example, each seed of a flowering plant is a living, breathing organism (with its own very small energy pie); it is not an inert piece of the soil. Pause to consider this for a minute. How many lives are you killing when you grind wheat to make a loaf of bread? How about when you eat a single strawberry, with all of those seeds exposed on the outer surface of the fruit? Although most seeds are unable to withstand the grinding abilities of grain mills or your teeth, many seeds do have seed coats and other protective tissues that allow them to withstand environmental conditions that would kill them as adults. As a result, when spring arrives, these seeds are able to germinate, grow, and reproduce, until the arrival of winter again causes their death as well. Protective structures and coatings are also found in the eggs and early instars of many insects, spores of many fungi, and cell walls of many bacteria.

Migration

The boreal forest comes alive in the spring and summer with the arrival of countless bird species that winter in the more temperate climates to the south. There are over 300 bird species in the boreal forest and it is estimated that over 90% of these migrate south as winter approaches. These species result in an estimated 3 billion breeding adults, and 5 billion migrating individuals (adults and offspring) each year. Needless to say, migration is a common method of coping with extreme temperatures! Small animals, with large surface area:volume ratios are at particular risk from extreme temperatures, and thus it is not surprising that many small songbirds fly south each winter.

Extreme shifts in temperature drive the migration of many other species as well, including the Monarch butterfly, which summers in southern Canada and throughout the United States, wintering in the mountains of Mexico. Migration will be discussed in more depth in later chapters in relation to feeding (chapters 9 and 14) and landscape ecology (chapter 20). Here, it is important to remember that the impressive display of the movement of large numbers of organisms each fall and spring is very often a direct consequence of their physiological ecology. A question to consider: why don't these birds and butterflies stay in their "winter" homes all year long?

Resistance

The third general strategy for coping with extreme weather conditions is possession of traits which allow the individual to tolerate extreme temperatures. Individuals that find themselves in harsh temperatures and do not posses specialized traits (or either of the two strategies described above), are

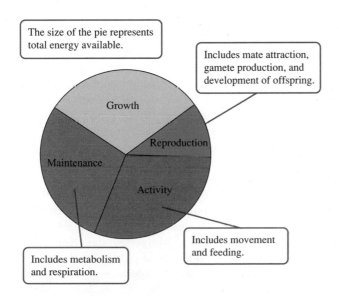

Figure 5.34 Pie diagrams can be used to represent energy budgets for organisms.

destined to become evolutionary losers—producing fewer and lower-quality offspring than their neighbours that are adapted to life under extreme conditions. Across plant and animal species, there exists substantial variation in an organism's ability to survive and thrive under low temperature conditions. Many tropical plant species die when temperatures reach a relatively warm 5°C, while white spruce is able to survive temperatures as low as –80°C! Because of this variation, the minimum temperature that is reached during the winter months (chapter 2) sets the northern limit of the range of many species (chapter 10). What do you think might happen to the ranges of such temperature-limited species under global warming? Books can (and have!) be written about the specialized traits that allow some species to thrive where others die. Here are a few of the more common adaptations to extreme temperatures.

Fur, Fat, and Feathers

Here is the problem. Imagine you are a homeothermic endotherm living in the arctic, and you will stay active during the winter. As the air temperature decreases, you will need to increase you basal metabolic rate to maintain your body temperature. However, this process uses substantial energy reserves, leaving less energy available for other activities. What do you do? One effective strategy is to increase the insulative properties of your body, which has the result of decreasing your energy lost by radiation. Many mammals do this by depositing a subcutaneous layer of fat at the onset of winter, as well as increased production of body hair (fur). The fat often serves two roles. First, it provides increased stored energy that can be used to pay for the increased metabolic rates often associated with winter. Second, increased fat decreases heat loss through radiation while also decreasing the rate at which the body cools down. Fur, and feathers in birds, also enhance the thermal properties of the organism by trapping warm air near the body.

Acclimation

Early in the chapter we described the idea of acclimation, and that exposure to mild cold (or heat) causes physiological changes in many species. Acclimation is a critical adaptation for many species that live in extreme environments. This may best be shown by the numerous studies conducted by C.J. Weiser and the laboratory of cold hardiness at the University of Minnesota. It was Weiser and his colleagues who identified the importance of winter temperatures to setting the northern limit of many plant species (Sakai and Weiser 1973). Weiser also found that for many species, the lower lethal temperature (i.e., killing temperature) decreases as winter approaches (Weiser 1970). For example, *Cornus stolonifera*, red-osier dogwood, will die if exposed to temperatures near freezing in July or August. However, that same species can withstand temperatures below –30°C in November (Weiser 1970). Clearly, acclimation to cold plays an important role in allowing species to live in extreme environments.

Inactivity and Avoidance

A simple way to avoid extreme environmental temperatures is to seek shelter during the hottest or coldest times of the day. We have already seen one example of this behaviour. During the cold nights of the tropical alpine zone, *Liolaemus* lizards take shelter in burrows, where temperatures are several degrees warmer than on the surface. This form of behavioural response is common among many organisms, including reptiles, amphibians, and many insects, and it is equally effective in avoiding cold as well as excessive heat. As we have seen with badger stetts, being belowground is an effective way of hiding from potential extreme surface temperatures.

Going underground is not always an option in cold climates, where the ground itself is frozen solid. Instead, many species take relief from the cold air by forming burrows within the snow. Fresh snow is an extremely good insulator, even better than the glass wool used in the walls of many modern homes (Marchand 1996)! As the snow ages, and becomes more compact, it also becomes a poorer insulator. This process is very similar to what we see for fur and feathers. These are great insulators for animals when they are full of air, but if the fur becomes matted down and compressed, its insulative properties also are reduced. With a deep enough snow pack (generally more than 20 cm), ground temperatures can hover near zero, even if air temperatures are well below that value. This warm refuge serves as a critical way that many small mammals, unable to add substantial fat or fur, are able to survive in the north. The insulative properties of snow are also of great importance to people that live and travel in extreme temperatures.

Not all species will, or can, move to warmer microclimates, and instead their bodies will be exposed to subzero temperatures for at least some part of the winter. Having ice inside of one's body is not a particularly attractive notion, as ice crystals can rip apart cells and tissues, destroying critical organs in the process. However, freezing is not inevitable, even when temperatures are below zero. Why? Because the freezing point of water can be modified by changes in pressure and solute concentration. Organisms have little control over atmospheric pressure, but they can exert significant control over the solute concentration of the intra- and extracellular fluids, in effect manipulating them to become anti-freeze agents. As a result, many plant, insect, and polar marine fish are able to avoid having critical tissues destroyed by ice formation, even when temperatures are below zero.

A more extreme solution is found in a variety of ectotherms of northern areas: freeze tolerance. A number of species of turtles, snakes, and frogs are able to survive extreme temperatures because they allow their bodies to freeze, rather than spending substantial amounts of energy on the avoidance-of-freezing strategy dominant among endotherms. One of the best known examples is the wood frog, *Rana sylvatica*. The wood frog is found in forests over a broad geographic range, from above the Arctic Circle down into the Appalachian Mountains. It is found as far east as the Maritime provinces and west into Alaska. In a review of freezing tolerance in ecothermic vertebrates, Kenneth and Janet Storey of Carleton University describe many of the freezing features of this remarkable animal (1992). Wood frogs can survive more than 10 days, frozen, with body temperatures of –6°C. During this time, over 60% of the body fluids can be frozen solid (fig. 5.35). There is evidence of

Figure 5.35 Wood frogs can survive freezing during cold winter months.

acclimation for freezing, with frogs in the fall having higher freezing-survival than do frogs of the spring. During the freezing, heart beat slows to around 4 beats/min, and then stops once the frog has frozen. The heart starts again within an hour of the body temperature reaching more than 3°C.

Why can these frogs do this? Freeze tolerance requires several critical adaptations. One of the most important is the presence of ice-nucleating compounds. These can be proteins, minerals, or microbes that initiate and control extracellular ice-formation, the opposite effect we found for the anti-freeze agents found with the freeze-avoidance strategy, above. Without these nucleating compounds, ice formation would either be non-existent or, worse, would occur in a haphazard manner within the body, causing serious tissue damage. A second critical adaptation is the presence of high levels of cryoprotectants, such as glucose. Rapid synthesis of glucose in the liver by wood frogs occurs immediately following ice crystal-

lization on the body surface. The glucose is distributed to cells throughout the body where it reduces cell damage. The exact mechanisms involved remain unclear. A third critical adaptation in wood frogs is that prior to freezing much of the extracellular fluids are removed from critical organs and stored in the lymphatic system and coelom. Even a few jagged ice crystals in the lymph system or coelom are unlikely to cause significant damage.

Reducing Metabolic Rate

The last group of physiological adaptations to extreme temperatures are likely the most familiar to you, and all involve reducing an organism's metabolic rate. One of the great difficulties for many organisms that live in areas of extreme temperatures is that even if they are able to survive exposure to the conditions, there is little available food. As a result, their maintenance costs (e.g., metabolism) will be greater than their entire energy budget, and thus substantial weight loss and/or mortality may ensue. There is nothing an animal can do about whether its food items are available or not; however, the maintenance cost of the organism can be controlled. Many organisms enter periods in which they reduce their metabolic rates, thereby reducing their energy demands.

Hummingbirds depend upon a diet of nectar and insects to maintain a high metabolic rate and a body temperature of about 39°C. When food is abundant, they maintain these high rates throughout the day and night. However, when food is scarce and night temperatures are cold, they may enter a state of torpor (fig. 5.36). **Torpor** is a state of self-induced hypothermia that generally lasts for only a few hours. In torpor, metabolic rates are reduced and core body temperatures are lowered, saving energy. During torpor, the hummingbird's body temperature may drop to between 12°C–17°C. F. L. Carpenter and colleagues (1993) estimated that rufus hummingbirds that maintain full body temperature all night metabolized 0.24g of fat. In torpor, these birds used only 0.02g of fat, an energy savings of over 90%.

Day

The amount of nectar available to a broad-tailed hummingbird determines whether it goes into torpor during the night.

Night

If nectar is scarce, torpor

A hummingbird in torpor has a low metabolic rate and so uses little energy.

If nectar is adequate, no torpor

To meet its energy demands, a hummingbird that does not go into torpor must consume large quantities of nectar just before roosting.

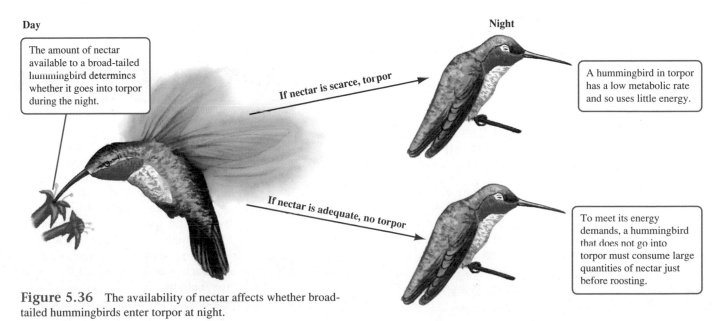

Figure 5.36 The availability of nectar affects whether broad-tailed hummingbirds enter torpor at night.

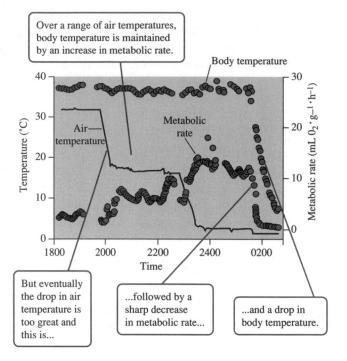

Over a range of air temperatures, body temperature is maintained by an increase in metabolic rate.

But eventually the drop in air temperature is too great and this is...

...followed by a sharp decrease in metabolic rate...

...and a drop in body temperature.

Figure 5.37   Some mammals, such as the big brown bat, can enter torpor. The graph describes the metabolic recording in one evening for one nonreproductive big brown bat (*Eptesicus fuscus*). Metabolic rate is measured as net O_2 consumption, V_{O_2} (data from Willis et al. 2005).

Torpor can also be found among a diverse set of mammal species. Mark Brigham, of the University of Regina, has been investigating the use of torpor by a diversity of organisms over the last several decades. He and colleagues (Willis et al. 2005) have shown that big brown bats, *Eptesicus fuscus*, can experience substantial drops in body temperature (fig. 5.37). They found that the bats generally entered torpor as soon as the ambient temperature went below the lower limit of the thermal neutral zone. As a result, although these bats are

mammals, there was only a very narrow range of temperatures in which they maintained constant body temperatures.

Torpor generally only lasts for a few hours. Prolonged states of reduced metabolic activity are common in many other species. If this occurs mainly in winter, it is called **hibernation**, if in summer it is called **estivation**. During hibernation, the body temperature of arctic ground squirrels may drop to 2°C. The metabolic rates of hibernating marmots may fall to 3% of the levels seen during active periods. During estivation, the metabolic rates of long-neck turtles may fall to 28% of their normal metabolic rate. Such reductions in metabolism allow individuals to survive long arctic and alpine winters, or hot and dry periods in the desert, during which they must rely entirely on stored energy reserves. Without this reduction in metabolism, metabolic costs would be too great for their energy budget and mortality would occur.

Temperature relations are a significant factor influencing the ecology of a diversity of species across the globe. This branch of ecology is attracting increased attention within the scientific community, fuelled by concerns about the ecological consequences of global warming, a topic we discuss in depth in chapter 23. In the Ecological Tools section, we look at how studies of temperature relations and climatic warming are helping to explain the local extinction of a species.

Concept 5.4 Review

1. How can death be considered an evolutionarily successful strategy for coping with extreme temperatures?
2. Do plants and animals have similar or completely different mechanisms for dealing with extreme temperatures? Explain.
3. Why don't hummingbirds save energy by going into torpor at night even when food supplies are abundant? In other words, what would be a possible disadvantage of routine, nightly torpor?

Ecological Tools

Climatic Warming and the Local Extinction of a Land Snail

Between 1906 and 1908, a Ph.D. candidate named G. Bollinger (1909) studied land snails in the vicinity of Basel, Switzerland. Eighty-five years later, Bruno Baur and Anette Baur (1993) carefully resurveyed Bollinger's study sites near Basel for the presence of land snails. In the process, they found that at least one snail species, *Arianta arbustorum*, had disappeared from several of the sites. This discovery led the Baurs to explore the mechanisms that may have produced extinction of these local populations.

A. arbustorum is a common land snail in meadows, forests, and other moist, vegetated habitats in northwestern and central Europe. The species lives at altitudes up to 2,700 m in the Alps. The Baurs report that the snail is sexually mature at 2 to 4 years and may live up to 14 years. Adult snails have shell diameters of 16 to 20 mm. The species is hermaphroditic. Though individuals generally mate with other *A. arbustorum*, they can fertilize their own eggs. Adults produce one to three batches of 20 to 80 eggs each year. They deposit their eggs in moss, under plant litter, or in the soil. Eggs generally hatch in 2 to 4 weeks, depending upon temperature. The egg is an especially sensitive stage in the life cycle of land snails. *A. arbustorum* often lives alongside *Cepea nemoralis*, a land snail with a broader geographic distribution that extends from southern Scandinavia to the Iberian peninsula.

How did the Baurs document local extinctions of *A. arbustorum*? If you think about it a bit, you will probably realize that it is usually easier to determine the presence of a species than its absence. If you do not encounter a species during a survey, it may be that you just didn't look hard enough. Fortunately, the Baurs had over 13 years of experience doing field work on *A. arbustorum* and knew its natural history well. For instance, they knew that it is best to search for the snails after rainstorms, when up to 70% of the adult population is active. Consequently, the Baurs searched Bollinger's study sites after heavy rains. They concluded that the snail was absent at a site only after two 2-hour surveys failed to turn up either a living individual or an empty shell of the species.

The Baurs found *A. arbustorum* still living at 13 of the 29 sites surveyed by Bollinger near Basel. Eleven of these remaining populations lived in deciduous forests and the other two lived on grassy riverbanks. However, the Baurs could not find the snail at 16 sites. Eight of these sites had been urbanized, which made the habitat unsuitable for any land snails because natural vegetation had been removed. Between 1900 and 1990 the urbanized area of Basel had increased by 500%. However, the eight other sites where *A. arbustorum* had disappeared were still covered by vegetation that appeared suitable. Four of these sites were covered by deciduous forest, three were on riverbanks, and one was on a railway embankment. These vegetated sites also supported populations of five other land snail species, including *C. nemoralis*.

What caused the extinction of *A. arbustorum* at sites that still supported other snails? The Baurs compared the characteristics of these sites with those of the sites where *A. arbustorum* had persisted. They found no difference between these two groups of sites in regard to slope, percent plant cover, height of vegetation, distance from water, or number of other land snail species present. The first major difference the Baurs uncovered was in altitude. The sites where *A. arbustorum* was extinct have an average altitude of 274 m. The places where it survived have an average altitude of 420 m. The places where the snail had survived were also cooler.

A thermal image of the landscape taken from a satellite showed that surface temperatures in summer around Basel ranged from about 17°C to 32.5°C. Surface temperatures where *A. arbustorum* had survived averaged approximately 22°C, while the sites where the species had gone extinct had surface temperatures that averaged approximately 25°C. The sites where the snail was extinct were also much closer to very hot areas with temperatures greater than 29°C. Figure 5.38 is based on the Baurs' thermal image of the area around Basel and shows where the snail was extinct and where it persisted.

The Baurs attributed the higher temperatures at the eight sites where the snail is extinct to heating by thermal radiation from the urbanized areas of the city. Buildings and pavement store more heat than vegetation. In addition, the cooling effect of evaporation from vegetation is lost when an area is built over. Increased heat storage and reduced cooling make urbanized landscapes thermal islands. Heat energy stored in urban centres is transferred to the surrounding landscape through thermal radiation, H_r.

The Baurs documented higher temperatures at the sites near Basel where *A. arbustorum* is extinct and identified a well-studied mechanism that could produce the higher temperatures of these sites. However, are the temperature differences they observed sufficient to exclude *A. arbustorum* from the warmer sites? The researchers compared the temperature relations of *A. arbustorum* and *C. nemoralis* to find some clues. They concentrated their studies on the influence of temperature on reproduction by these two snail species.

The eggs of each species were incubated at four temperatures—19°C, 22°C, 25°C, and 29°C. Notice that these temperatures fall within the range measured by the satellite image (fig. 5.38). The eggs of both species hatched at a high rate at 19°C. However, at higher temperatures, their eggs hatched at significantly different rates. At 22°C, less than 50% of *A. arbustorum* eggs hatched, while the eggs of *C. nemoralis* continued to hatch at a high rate. At 25°C, no *A. arbustorum* eggs hatched, while approximately 50% of the *C. nemoralis* eggs

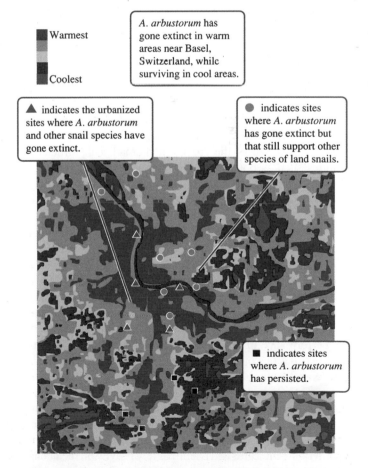

Figure 5.38 Relative surface temperatures and patterns of extinction and persistence by the snail *Arianta arbustorum* around Basel, Switzerland (data from Baur and Baur 1993).

hatched. At 29°C, the hatching of *C. nemoralis* eggs was also greatly reduced. Figure 5.39 summarizes the results of this hatching experiment.

The results of this study show that the eggs of *A. arbustorum* are more sensitive to higher temperatures than are the eggs of *C. nemoralis*. This greater thermal sensitivity can explain why *A. arbustorum* is extinct at some sites, while *C. nemoralis* survived. These results also suggest that climatic warming can lead to the local extinction of species. As we face the prospect of warming on a global scale, studies of temperature relations will assume greater importance. In chapter 6, we look at a related topic, water relations.

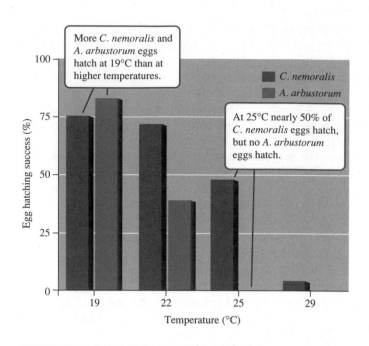

Figure 5.39 Temperature and hatching success of two snail species; the eggs of *Arianta arbustorum* are sensitive to high temperatures (data from Baur and Baur 1993).

Summary

Macroclimate interacts with the local landscape to produce microclimatic variation in temperature. The sun's uneven heating of the earth's surface and earth's permanent tilt on its axis produce macroclimate. Macroclimate interacts with the local landscape—mainly albedo, altitude, aspect, vegetation, colour of the ground, and small-scale structural features such as boulders and burrows—to produce microclimates. For the individual organism, macroclimate may be less significant than microclimate. The physical nature of water limits temperature variation in aquatic environments.

Most species perform best in a fairly narrow range of temperatures. The influence of temperature on the performance of organisms begins at the molecular level, where extreme temperatures impair the functioning of enzymes. Rates of photosynthesis and microbial activity generally peak in a narrow range of temperatures and are much lower outside of this optimal temperature range. How temperature affects the performance of organisms often corresponds to the current distributions of species and their evolutionary histories.

Many organisms have evolved ways to compensate for variations in environmental temperature by regulating body temperature. Temperature regulation balances heat gain against heat loss. Plants and ectothermic animals use morphology and behaviour to modify rates of heat exchange with the environment. Birds and mammals rely heavily on metabolic energy to regulate body temperature. The physical nature of the aquatic environment reduces the possibilities for temperature regulation by aquatic organisms. Most endothermic aquatic species are air breathers. Some organisms, mainly flying insects and some large marine fish, improve performance by selectively heating parts of their anatomy. The energetic requirements of thermoregulation may influence the geographic distribution of species.

Organisms exhibit a diversity of mechanisms to cope with extreme temperatures. Many species are unable to live in extreme temperatures, restricting their range. For some species, the adult stages of many organisms will die during extreme events, while an alternative life-stage, such as seeds, persist during these periods. Other species avoid extreme temperatures through regular migrations to more moderate climates. For species that stay year-round in extreme environments, maintaining positive energy budgets are a real challenge. Energy budgets can be described by pie diagrams, with tradeoffs in allocation between growth, maintenance, reproduction, and activity. Increasing insulative properties of the organism through fur, fat, and feathers reduces heat loss through radiation. Moderate microclimates can often be found underground or beneath deep snow pack, reducing the need for elevated metabolic rates. Many animals enter a state of torpor, reducing metabolic rates during periods of inactivity. Periods of reduced metabolic rates can also persist for several months. If this occurs mainly in winter, it is called hibernation. In summer, it is called estivation. Energy savings from reducing metabolic rates allow organisms to live in environments even when resources are periodically scarce and temperatures are extreme.

Long-term studies of populations of land snails around Basel, Switzerland, have documented local extinctions of these land snails. These extinctions are attributable to habitat destruction and climatic warming. The results of these studies suggest that climatic warming can lead to the local extinction of species. As we face the prospect of climatic warming at a global scale, studies of temperature relations will assume greater importance.

Review Questions

1. Many species of plants and animals that are associated with boreal forests also occur on mountains far to the south of the boreal forests. Using what you have learned about microclimates, predict how aspect and elevation would influence their distributions on these southern mountains.

2. Imagine a desert beetle that uses behaviour to regulate its body temperature above 35°C. How might this beetle's use of microclimates created by shrubs, burrows, and bare ground change with the season?

3. Figure 5.10 shows how temperature influences the activity of acetylcholinesterase in rainbow trout. Assuming that the other enzymes of rainbow trout show similar responses to temperature, how would trout swimming speed change as environmental temperature increases above 20°C?

4. The Ecological Tools section reviews how the studies of Bruno Baur and Anette Baur (1993) have documented the local extinction of the land snail *Arianta arbustorum*. Their research also shows that these extinctions may be due to reduced egg hatching at higher temperatures. Do these results show conclusively that the direct effect of higher temperatures on hatching success is responsible for the local extinctions of *A. arbustorum*? Propose and justify alternative hypotheses. Be sure you take into account all of the observations of the Baurs.

5. Butterflies, which are ectothermic and diurnal, are found from the tropical rain forest to the Arctic. They can elevate their body temperatures by basking in sunlight. How would the percentage of time butterflies spend basking versus flying change with latitude? Would the amount of time butterflies spend basking change with daily changes in temperature?

6. Some plants and grasshoppers in hot environments have reflective body surfaces, which make their radiative heat gain, H_r, less than it would be otherwise. If you were to design a beetle that could best cope with thermal challenges associated with living on snow, what colour would it be? If these beetles were white, what would that tell us about the relative roles of thermoregulation and predation pressure in determining beetle colour? What does this example imply about the ability of natural selection to "optimize" the characteristics of organisms?

7. In most of the examples discussed in chapter 5, we saw a close match between the characteristics of organisms and their environment. However, natural selection does not always produce an optimal, or even a good, fit of organisms to their environments. To verify this you need only reflect on the fact that most of the species that have existed are now extinct. What are some of the reasons for a mismatch between organisms and environments? Develop your explanation using the environment, the characteristics of organisms, and the nature of natural selection.

8. Why do species exhibit different strategies for coping with extreme temperatures? Why hasn't evolution resulted in all species doing the "right" thing under these conditions?

9. Draw energy budgets using pie diagrams for a typical endotherm and ectotherm. What aspects of these budgets likely represent the largest energy expenditure? Which type of organism likely has more food intake and a larger overall energy budget?

10. Many animals huddle together in extreme cold. What is the possible energetic benefit of this behaviour? Under what climatic conditions is huddling likely to be disadvantageous?

Suggested Readings

Angilletta, M. J., Jr. 2001. Thermal and physiological constraints on energy assimilation in a widespread lizard (*Sceloporus undulatus*). Ecology 82:3044–56.

Angilleta, M. J., Jr., T. Hill, and M. A. Robson. 2002. Is physiological performance optimized by thermoregulatory behavior?: A case study of the eastern fence lizard, *Sceloporus undulatus*. *Journal of Thermal Biology* 27:199–204.

Exemplary studies of the temperature relations of an ectotherm, with clear explanations of study design.

Heinrich, B. 1996. *The Thermal Warriors: Strategies of Insect Survival.* Cambridge, Mass.: Harvard University Press.

Heinrich combines the knowledge of a scientist with the skills of artist and poet to make the technical details of insect thermal ecology accessible and interesting to general readers. Valuable for readers at any level of biological knowledge.

Jensen, M. N. 2004. Climate warming shakes up species. *Bio Science* 54:722–29.

Compelling account of how climate warming is affecting the timing of critical events in the lives of organisms.

Marchand, P.J. 1996. *Life in the Cold.* 3rd Ed. University Press of New England. Hanover, NH.

Jones, N. G. 2001. *Snow Ecology: An interdisciplinary examination of snow-covered ecosystems.* Cambridge University Press, Cambridge.

Two well-written books that provide a broad overview of the unique challenges faced by the plants and animals that live in cold regions of the world.

Staley, J. T. and A.-L. Reysenbach. 2002. *Biodiversity of Microbial Life: Foundation of Earth's Biosphere.* New York: Wiley.

Reference that provides a window to the world of the prokaryotes found in extreme thermal environments.

ater plays a central role in the lives of all organisms in all habitats. However, water acquisition and conservation is particularly critical for desert organisms. As a consequence, many ecologists studying the water relations of organisms have focused their attention on desert species. The steady buzzing of the Sonoran Desert cicada, *Diceroprocta apache,* seemed to amplify the withering heat. Air temperature in the shade hovered around 46°C, and the ground surface temperature was over 70°C. All other animals had taken refuge from the desert heat. Nothing else called, and nothing moved, except a lone biologist with an insect net who stalked in the direction of the calling cicada.

The biologist was Eric Toolson. Toolson was well acquainted with the calls of the cicadas in the region and he knew their natural history. Toolson associated the call of *Diceroprocta* with the hottest hours of the day, when air temperatures often exceeded the lethal limit for the species. His goal was to understand the ecology of this extraordinary cicada.

Questions raced through Toolson's mind as he made his way through the shimmering desert air toward the cicada. How could this species be active in apparently lethal air temperatures? We might ask the same question of Toolson himself. How did he maintain a body temperature of approximately 37°C in this desert heat? Humans evaporatively cool by sweating. To keep from becoming dehydrated, Toolson took frequent drinks from the water bottle at his side. This enabled him to maintain sufficient internal water and continue to evaporatively cool by sweating.

During his pauses to drink, more questions came. Did the cicada keep cool by using small, shady microclimates in the mesquite tree from which it called? Did the cicada somehow manage to evaporatively cool? This seemed unlikely, since biologists had long assumed that insects were too small and vulnerable to water loss to do so. If *Diceroprocta* did evaporatively cool, how did it avoid desiccating in the desert heat? It did not, like Toolson, have a water bottle strapped to its waist.

As Toolson stalked the cicada, he pursued an even greater prize: an understanding of how *Diceroprocta* can regulate the temperature and water content of its body while living in such an extreme environment. This second pursuit would lead Toolson to discover an unsuspected physiological process in these desert insects. Toolson and his students, Stacy Kaser and Jon Hastings, would be the first to comprehend a bit of nature that had escaped the notice of all researchers before them. Few scientists make such a fundamental discovery and those that do never forget the thrill. Figure 6.1 summarizes the physical conditions under which *Diceroprocta* lives that inspired Toolson and his colleagues to study its ecology (Toolson 1987, Toolson and Hadley 1987).

Before we discuss the ecology of these desert cicadas, we need to introduce some background information. Water and life on earth are closely linked. The high water content of most organisms, which ranges from about 50% to 90%, reflects life's aquatic origins. Life on earth originated in salty aquatic environments and is built around biochemistry within an aquatic medium. To survive and reproduce, organisms must maintain

Air temperature of 46°C is higher than lethal maximum for the cicada.

Falling to the ground, with a temperature of 70°C, would be certain death for the cicada.

How does the cicada remain active when environmental temperatures exceed its lethal maximum?

Figure 6.1   An ecological puzzle: the cicada, *Diceroprocta apache*, is active when air temperatures would appear to be lethal for the species.

appropriate internal concentrations of water and dissolved substances. To maintain these internal concentrations organisms must balance water losses to the environment with water intake. How organisms maintain this water balance is called their water relations, which is the subject of chapter 6.

In some environments, organisms face the problem of water loss. Elsewhere, water streams in from the environment. The problem of maintaining proper water balance is especially strong for those organisms, such as *Diceroprocta*, that live in arid terrestrial environments. A parallel challenge faces organisms that live in aquatic environments with a high salinity. In these extreme environments, the water relations of organisms stand out in bold relief. However, most organisms must expend energy to maintain their internal pool of water. In the study of relationships between organisms and the environment, which we call ecology, the study of water relations is fundamental.

Concepts

6.1 The movement of water down concentration gradients in terrestrial and aquatic environments determines the availability of water to organisms.

6.2 Terrestrial plants and animals regulate their internal water by balancing water acquisition against water loss.

6.3 Marine and freshwater organisms use complementary mechanisms for water and salt regulation.

6.1 Water Availability

The movement of water down concentration gradients in terrestrial and aquatic environments determines the availability of water to organisms. The tendency of water to move down concentration gradients and the magnitude of those gradients from an organism to its environment determine whether an organism tends to lose or gain water from the environment. In chapter 1 we pointed out that ecologists may study purely physical aspects of the environment to understand the ecology of organisms. To understand the water relations of organisms, we must understand the basic physical behaviour of water in terrestrial and aquatic environments.

In chapter 2, we saw that water availability on land varies tremendously, from the tropical rain forest with abundant moisture throughout the year, to hot deserts with year-round drought. In chapter 3, we reviewed the considerable variation in salinity among aquatic environments, ranging from the dilute waters of tropical rivers to hypersaline lakes. The majority of aquatic environments, including the sea, fall somewhere between these extremes. Salinity, as we shall see, reflects the relative "aridity" of aquatic environments.

In snow-covered areas such as the arctic tundra and boreal forests, water availability can vary widely across the globe, as well as within a single year. As we saw in chapter 2, tundra habitats can be dry, with less than 200 mm precipitation a year, or relatively moist, with over 500 mm/yr. Such variability also occurs in the boreal forest. One unique feature of these colder habitats is that the precipitation is frozen for much of the year, making it unusable by the resident organisms until snowmelt. Even within Canada, there is substantial geographic variation in both the average duration and average maximum snow depth (fig. 6.2). Notice that in the far north there are relatively few snow-free days each year. As a consequence, liquid water is available to support plant growth for only short periods of each year. Throughout most of Canada, snowmelt generally results in moist soils in the spring, and water is not generally limiting to spring and early summer plant growth. Water may

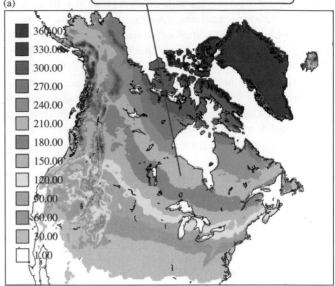

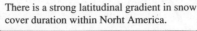
There is a strong latitudinal gradient in snow cover duration within Norht America.

(a)

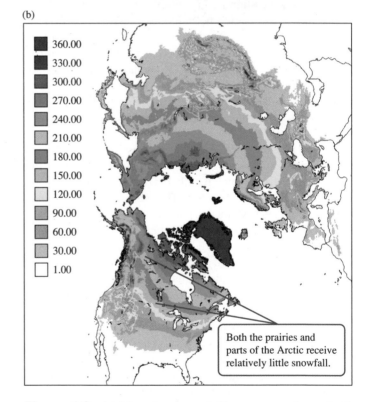

(b)

Both the prairies and parts of the Arctic receive relatively little snowfall.

Figure 6.2 (*a*) Mean duration and (*b*) average maximum depth (mm) of snow cover throughout Canada.

become more limiting during the summer, depending upon the amount of rainfall that is received.

These preliminary descriptions in chapters 2 and 3 do not include the situations faced by individual organisms within their microclimates—microclimates such as those experienced by a desert animal that lives at an oasis, where it has access to abundant moisture, or a rain forest plant that lives in the forest canopy, where it is exposed to full tropical sun and drying winds. As with temperature, to understand the water relations of an organism we must consider its microclimate. For instance, consider the microclimates available to the seashore isopod, *Ligia oceanica* (see fig. 5.6). In addition to temperature, those microclimates vary considerably in relative humidity, a measure of the relative water content of air. The relative humidity of air within crevices is usually close to 100%, while in the open it can be as low as 70%. Such differences in relative humidity can significantly affect rates of water loss by organisms. To fully understand a comparison of microclimates such as this one, we turn now to the measurement of water.

Water Content of Air

As we saw when we reviewed the hydrologic cycle in chapter 3, water vapour is continuously added to air as water evaporates from the surfaces of oceans, lakes, and rivers. On land, evaporation also accounts for much of the water lost by organisms. The potential for such evaporative water loss depends upon the temperature and water content of the air around the organisms. As the amount of water vapour in the surrounding air increases, the water concentration gradient from organisms to the air is reduced and the rate at which organisms lose water to the atmosphere decreases.

We know how temperature is measured, but how is the water content of air measured? The quantity of water vapor in the air can be expressed in relative terms. Since air rarely contains all the water vapour it can hold, we can use its degree of saturation with water vapour as a relative measure of water content. The most familiar measure of the water content of air relative to its content at saturation is **relative humidity,** defined as:

$$\text{Relative humidity} = \frac{\text{Water vapour density}}{\text{Saturation water vapour density}} \times 100$$

The actual amount of water in air is measured directly as the mass of water vapour per unit volume of air. This quantity, the *water vapour density,* is the numerator in the relative humidity equation and is given either as milligrams of water per litre of air (mg H_2O/L) or as grams of water per cubic meter of air (g H_2O/m³). The quantity of water vapour that air potentially can hold is its *saturation water vapour density,* the denominator in the relative humidity equation. Saturation water vapour density changes with temperature and, as you can see from the red curve in figure 6.3, warm air can hold more water vapour than cold air.

A visual demonstration of this difference in water holding capacity of air as a function of temperature is seen each winter. Why exactly can you see your breath on a cool winter morning? As an endotherm, your breath will be a fairly consistent temperature of approximately 37°C. Additionally, the function of gas exchange in our lungs is dependent upon the alveoli being saturated with water. As a result, our breath is generally at 100% relative humidity, which at body temperature results in over 40 g/m³ of water leaving our bodies upon exhalation. What happens when that wet, hot air leaves your body? If the humidity of the air is less than 100%, some of the water in your breath will be absorbed by the surrounding air. However,

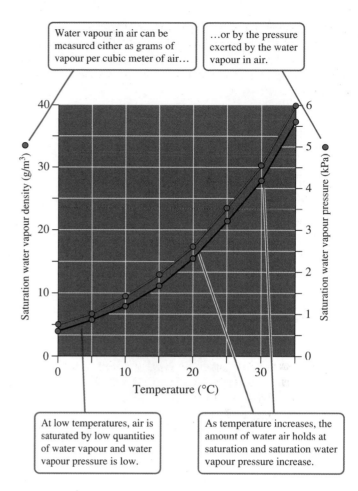

Water vapour in air can be measured either as grams of vapour per cubic meter of air...

...or by the pressure exerted by the water vapour in air.

At low temperatures, air is saturated by low quantities of water vapour and water vapour pressure is low.

As temperature increases, the amount of water air holds at saturation and saturation water vapour pressure increase.

Figure 6.3 The relationship between air temperature and two measures of water vapour saturation of air.

if the air temperature is low, such as 0°C, it will hold substantially less water (5 g/m³ at 0°C). This means the remaining 35 g/m³ can not enter the air, and instead condenses into a cloud. And you see your breath.

One of the most useful ways of expressing the quantity of water in air is in terms of the pressure it exerts. If we express the water content of air in terms of pressure, we can use similar units to consider the water relations of organisms in air, soil, and water. We usually think in terms of *total atmospheric pressure,* the pressure exerted by all the gases in air, but you can also calculate the partial pressures due to individual atmospheric gases such as oxygen, nitrogen, or water vapour. We call this last quantity **water vapour pressure.** At sea level, atmospheric pressure averages approximately 760 mm of mercury, the height of a column of mercury supported by the combined force (pressure) of all the gas molecules in the atmosphere. The international convention for representing water vapour pressure, however, is in terms of the pascal (Pa), where 1 Pa is 1 newton of force per square meter. Using this convention, 760 mm of mercury, or one atmosphere of pressure, equals approximately 101,300 Pa, 101.3 kilopascals (kPa), or .101 megapascals (MPa = 10⁶ Pa).

The pressure exerted by the water vapour in air that is saturated with water is called **saturation water vapour pressure.**

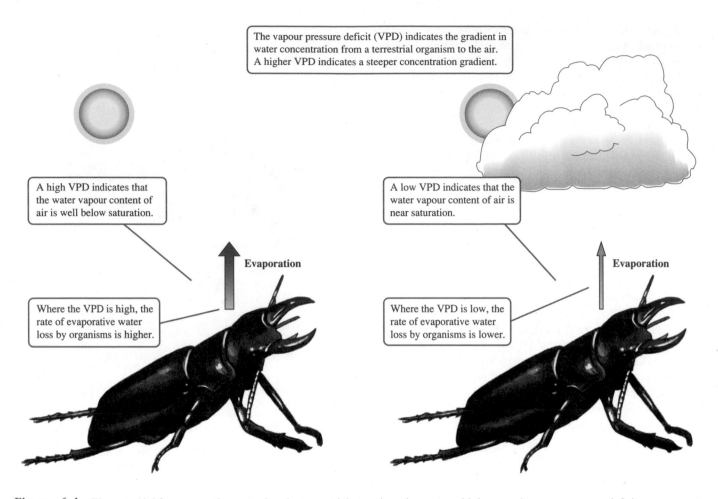

The vapour pressure deficit (VPD) indicates the gradient in water concentration from a terrestrial organism to the air. A higher VPD indicates a steeper concentration gradient.

A high VPD indicates that the water vapour content of air is well below saturation.

A low VPD indicates that the water vapour content of air is near saturation.

Evaporation

Evaporation

Where the VPD is high, the rate of evaporative water loss by organisms is higher.

Where the VPD is low, the rate of evaporative water loss by organisms is lower.

Figure 6.4   The potential for evaporative water loss by terrestrial organisms increases with increased vapour pressure deficit.

As the black curve in figure 6.3 shows, this pressure increases with temperature and closely parallels the increase in saturation water vapour density shown by the red curve. Why are the two curves so similar? They are similar because the amount of pressure exerted by a gas, in this case water vapour, is directly proportional to its density.

We can also use water vapour pressure to represent the *relative* saturation of air with water. You calculate this measure, called the **vapour pressure deficit (VPD),** as the difference between the actual water vapour pressure and the saturation water vapour pressure at a particular temperature. In warm moist environments, air is near saturation and VPD is low. In warm dry environments, relative humidity will be lower and VPD is higher. In terrestrial environments, water flows from organisms to the atmosphere at a rate influenced by the vapour pressure deficit of the air surrounding the organism. Figure 6.4 shows the relative rates of water loss by an organism exposed to air with a low versus high vapour pressure deficit. Again, one of the most useful features of vapour pressure deficit is that it is expressed in units of pressure, generally kilopascals.

Water Movement in Aquatic Environments

In aquatic environments, water moves down its concentration gradient. It may sound silly to speak of the amount of water in an aquatic environment but, as we saw in chapter 2,

all aquatic environments contain dissolved substances. These dissolved substances dilute the water. While oceanographers and limnologists (those who study bodies of freshwater) generally focus on salt content, or salinity, we take the opposite point of view in order to build a consistent perspective for considering water relations in air, water, and soil. From this perspective, pure H_2O is the most concentrated. Slightly less concentrated will be freshwater which is itself more concentrated than the oceans. The oceans, in turn, contain more water per liter than do saline lakes such as the Dead Sea or the Great Salt Lake. The relative concentration of water in each of these environments strongly influences the biology of the organisms that live in them.

The body fluids of all organisms contain water and solutes, including inorganic ions and amino acids. We can think of aquatic organisms and the environment that surrounds them as two aqueous solutions separated by a selectively permeable membrane. If the internal environment of the organism and the external environment differ in concentrations of water and salts, these substances will tend to move down their concentration gradients. This movement of solutes is called **diffusion.** We give the movement of water across a semipermeable membrane a special name, however: **osmosis,** where water moves from areas of high water concentration to low water concentration.

In the aquatic environment, water moving down its concentration gradient produces osmotic pressure. Osmotic pressure, like vapour pressure, can be expressed in pascals. The strength of the osmotic pressure across a semipermeable membrane, such as the gills of a fish, depends upon the difference in water concentration across the membrane. Larger differences, between organism and environment, generate higher osmotic pressures.

Aquatic organisms generally live in one of three environmental circumstances. Organisms with body fluids containing the same concentration of water as the external environment are **isosmotic.** Organisms with body fluids with a higher concentration of water (lower solute concentration) than the external medium are **hypoosmotic** and tend to lose water to the environment. Those with body fluids with a lower concentration of water (higher solute concentration) than the external medium are **hyperosmotic** and are subject to water flooding inward from the environment. In the face of these osmotic pressures, aquatic organisms must expend energy to maintain a proper internal environment. How much energy the organism must expend depends upon the magnitude of the osmotic pressure between them and the environment and the permeability of their body surfaces. Figure 6.5 summarizes the movement of water and salts into and out of isosmotic, hyperosmotic, and hypoosmotic organisms.

Water Movement Between Soils and Plants

On land, water flows from the organism to the atmosphere at a rate influenced by the vapour pressure deficit of the air surrounding the organism. In the aquatic environment, water may flow either to or from the organism, depending on the relative concentrations of water and solutes in body fluids and the surrounding medium. But here too, water flows down its concentration gradient. As shown in figure 6.6, water moving from the soil through a plant and into the atmosphere flows down a gradient of **water potential.** Water in soils and plants moves through the small pore spaces within soils and within the small water-conducting cells of plants. Therefore, water potential in soils and plants is determined by the concentration gradient of water plus other factors related to the movement of water through these small spaces. Understanding water potential takes some patience, but that patience will be paid off by a significant improvement in understanding the water relations of terrestrial plants.

Plants play a critical role in the global hydrological cycle (chapter 3), principally through taking up liquid water from the soil and releasing it as water vapour through transpiration. On a global scale, it is estimated that 10% of the water vapour in the atmosphere is there due to transpiration. Any change in transpiration rates could have significant consequences for cloud cover and groundwater reserves. For example, Nicola Gedney and colleagues (2006) explored the possible reasons why freshwater runoff has increased by approximately 3% throughout the twentieth century. Using a series of simulation models, they found the largest contributor is likely decreased transpiration of plants due to increased atmospheric CO_2 concentrations. This reduction in transpiration is thought to have increased annual global runoff by 2,000 km^3, with many

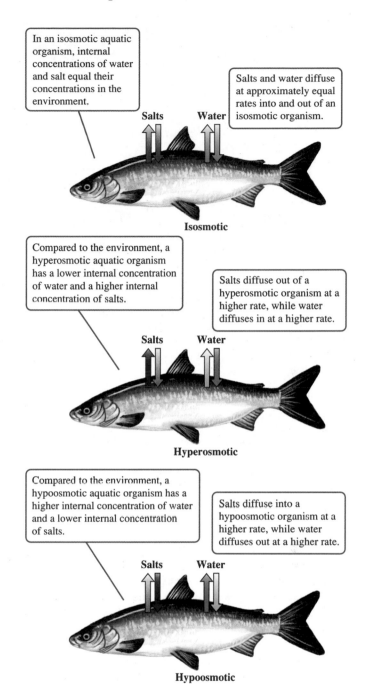

Figure 6.5   Water and salt regulation by isosmotic, hyperosmotic, and hypoosmotic aquatic organisms.

potential ecological and societal consequences. We will discuss the links between CO_2 and transpiration in chapter 7, but first we must better understand transpiration itself.

We can conceptualize water potential as the capacity of water to do work. Flowing water has the capacity to do work such as turning the water wheel of a water mill or the turbines of a hydroelectric plant. The capacity of water to do work depends upon its free energy content. Water flows from positions of higher to lower free energy. Under the influence of gravity, water flows downhill from a position of higher free energy, at the top of the hill, to a position of lower free energy, at the bottom of the hill.

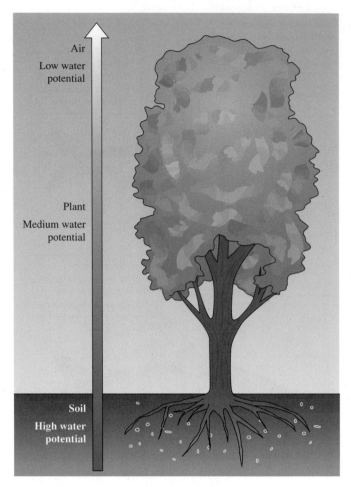

Figure 6.6   A gradient of water potential: water potential generally decreases from soil to plant to air.

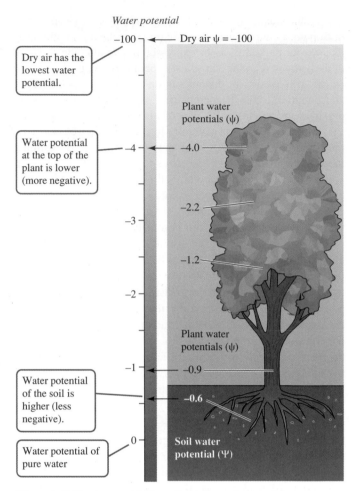

Figure 6.7   A quantified gradient of water potential: water potentials become more negative from soil to plant to air (data from Wiebe et al. 1970).

In the section "Water Movement in Aquatic Environments," we saw that water flows down its concentration gradient, from locations of higher water concentration (hypoosmotic) to locations of lower water concentration (hyperosmotic). The measurable "osmotic pressure" generated by water flowing down these concentration gradients shows that water flowing in response to osmotic gradients has the capacity to do work. Which has a higher free energy content, pure water or seawater? Since osmotic flow would be from pure water to seawater and water flows from high to low free energy, pure water must have a higher free energy content than seawater. We measure water potential, like vapour pressure deficit and osmotic pressure, in pascals, usually megapascals (MPa = Pa × 10⁶). By convention, water potential is represented by the symbol Ψ (Psi) and the water potential of pure water is set at 0. If the water potential of pure water is 0, then the water potential of a solution, such as seawater, must be negative (i.e., < 0).

In nature, water potentials are generally negative. Why is that? This must be so since all water in nature, even rainwater, contains some solute or occupies spaces where matric forces (see following) are significant. So, gradients of water potential in nature are generally from less negative to more negative water potential. This convention takes a bit of getting used to!

Once familiar, however, the convention is useful for representing and thinking about the water relations of plants. Figure 6.7, a quantified version of the gradient of water potential we saw in figure 6.6, shows that water is flowing down a gradient of water potential that goes from a slightly negative water potential in the soil through the moderately negative water potentials of the plant to the highly negative water potential of dry air.

Now let's look at some of the mechanisms involved in producing a gradient of water potential such as that shown in figure 6.7. We can express the water potential of a solution as:

$$\Psi = \Psi_{solutes}$$

$\Psi_{solutes}$ is the *reduction* in water potential due to dissolved substances, which is a negative number.

Within small spaces, such as the interior of a plant cell or the pore spaces within soil, other forces, called **matric forces,** are also at work. Matric forces are a consequence of water's tendency to adhere to the walls of containers such as cell walls or the soil particles lining a soil pore. Matric forces lower water potential. The water potential for fluids within plant cells is approximately:

$$\Psi_{plant} = \Psi_{solutes} + \Psi_{matric}$$

In this expression, Ψ_{matric} is the *reduction* in water potential due to matric forces within plant cells. At the level of the whole plant, another force is generated as water evaporates from the surfaces of leaves into the atmosphere. Evaporation of water from the surfaces of leaves generates a negative pressure, or tension, on the column of water that extends from the leaf surface through the plant all the way down to its roots. This negative pressure reduces the water potential of plant fluids still further.

So, the water potential of plant fluids is affected by solutes, matric forces, and the negative pressures exerted by evaporation. Consequently, we can represent the water potential of plant fluids as:

$$\Psi_{plant} = \Psi_{solutes} + \Psi_{matric} + \Psi_{pressure}$$

Here again, $\Psi_{pressure}$ is the *reduction* in water potential due to negative pressure created by water evaporating from leaves.

Meanwhile, the solute content of soil water is often so low that soil matric forces account for most of soil water potential:

$$\Psi_{soil} \cong \Psi_{matric}$$

Matric forces vary considerably from one soil to another, depending primarily upon soil texture and pore size. Coarser soils, such as sands and loams, with larger pore sizes exert lower matric forces, while fine clay soils, with smaller pore sizes, exert higher matric forces. So, while clay soils can hold a higher quantity of water compared to sandy soils, the higher matric forces within clay soils bind that water more tightly. As long as the water potential of plant tissues is less than the water potential of the soil, $\Psi_{plant} < \Psi_{soil}$, water flows from the soil to the plant.

The higher water potential of soil water compared to the water potential of roots induces water to flow from the soil into plant roots. As water enters roots from the surrounding soil, it joins a column of water that extends from the roots through the water-conducting cells, or xylem, of the stem to the leaves. Hydrogen bonds between adjacent water molecules bind the water molecules in this water column together. Consequently, as water molecules at the upper end of this column evaporate into the air at the surfaces of leaves, they exert a tension, or negative pressure, on the entire water column. This negative pressure further reduces the water potential of plant fluids and helps power uptake of water by terrestrial plants. Figure 6.8 summarizes the mechanisms underlying the flow of water from soil to plants.

As plants draw water from the soil, they soon deplete the water held in the larger soil pore spaces, leaving only water held in the smaller pores. Within these smaller soil pores matric forces are greater than in the larger pores. Consequently, as soil dries, soil water potential becomes more and more negative and the remaining water becomes harder and harder to extract.

This section has given us a basis for considering the availability of water to organisms living in terrestrial and aquatic environments. Let's use the foundation we have built here to explore the water relations of organisms on land and in water. To survive and reproduce, organisms must maintain appropriate internal concentrations of water and dissolved substances. As a consequence, in the face of variation in water availability, organisms have been selected to regulate their internal water.

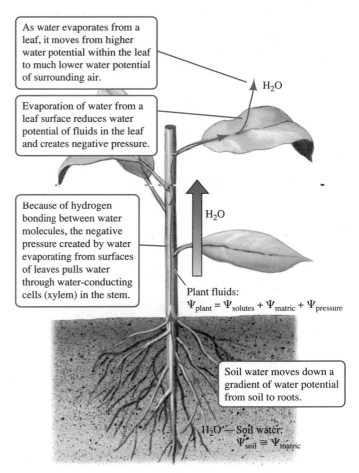

As water evaporates from a leaf, it moves from higher water potential within the leaf to much lower water potential of surrounding air.

Evaporation of water from a leaf surface reduces water potential of fluids in the leaf and creates negative pressure.

H_2O

Because of hydrogen bonding between water molecules, the negative pressure created by water evaporating from surfaces of leaves pulls water through water-conducting cells (xylem) in the stem.

H_2O

Plant fluids:
$\Psi_{plant} = \Psi_{solutes} + \Psi_{matric} + \Psi_{pressure}$

Soil water moves down a gradient of water potential from soil to roots.

H_2O — Soil water:
$\Psi_{soil} \cong \Psi_{matric}$

Figure 6.8 Mechanisms of water movement from soil through plants to the atmosphere.

Concept 6.1 Review

1. Why are the two curves shown in figure 6.3 so similar?
2. Which has a higher free energy content, pure water or seawater?
3. Why are water potentials in nature generally negative?

6.2 Water Regulation on Land

Terrestrial plants and animals regulate their internal water by balancing water acquisition against water loss. When organisms moved into the terrestrial environment, they faced two major environmental challenges: potentially massive losses of water to the environment through evaporation, and reduced access to replacement water. Many adaptations helped terrestrial organisms meet these challenges and acquire the capacity to regulate their internal water content. We can summarize water regulation by terrestrial animals as:

$$W_i = W_d + W_f + W_a - W_e - W_s$$

This says simply that the internal water of an animal (W_i) results from a balance between water acquisition and water loss. The major sources of water are:

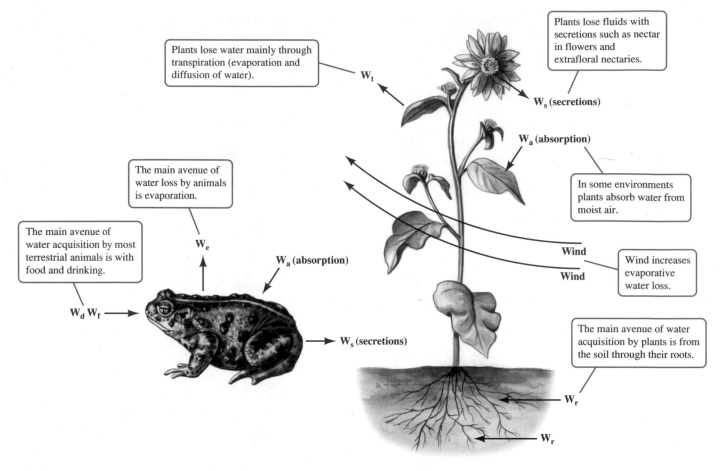

Figure 6.9   Terrestrial plants and animals can be characterized by analogous pathways for water gain and loss.

W_d = water taken by drinking

W_f = water taken in with food

W_a = water absorbed from the air

The avenues of water loss are:

W_e = water lost by evaporation

W_s = water lost with various secretions and excretions including urine, mucus, and feces

We can summarize water regulation by terrestrial plants in a similar way:

$$W_i = W_r + W_a - W_t - W_s$$

The internal water concentration of a plant (W_i) results from a balance between gains and losses, where the major sources of water for plants are:

W_r = water taken from soil by roots

W_a = water absorbed from the air

The major ways that plants lose water are:

W_t = water lost by transpiration

W_s = water lost with various secretions including nectar, and tissue loss including fruit, seeds, and senescent leaves and roots

The main avenues of water gain and loss by terrestrial plants and animals are summarized in figure 6.9. The figure presents a generalized picture of the water relations of terrestrial organisms. However, organisms in different environments face different environmental challenges and they have evolved a wide variety of solutions to those problems. Let's now look at the diverse ways in which terrestrial plants and animals regulate their internal water.

Water Acquisition by Animals

Many small terrestrial animals can absorb water from the air. Most terrestrial animals, however, satisfy their need for water either by drinking or by taking in water with food. In moist climates, there is generally plenty of water, and, if water becomes scarce, the mobility of most animals allows them to go to sources of water to drink. In deserts, animals that need abundant water must live near oases. Those that live out in the desert itself, away from oases, have evolved adaptations for living in arid environments.

Some desert animals acquire water in unusual ways. Coastal deserts such as the Namib Desert of southwest Africa receive very little rain but are bathed in fog. This aerial moisture is the water source for some animals in the Namib. One of these, a beetle in the genus *Lepidochora* of the family Tenebrionidae, takes an engineering approach to water acquisition. These beetles dig trenches on the face of sand

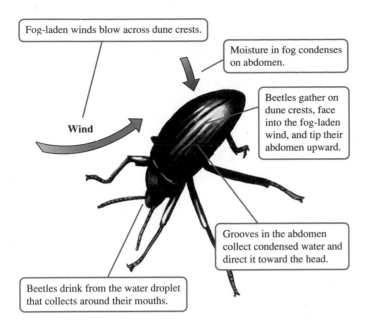

Figure 6.10 Some beetles of the Namib Desert can harvest sufficient moisture from fog to meet their needs for water.

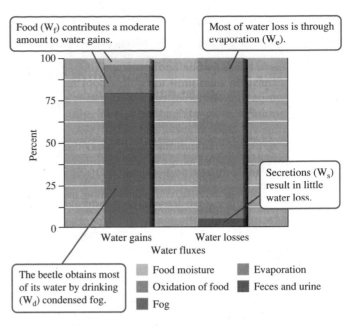

Figure 6.11 Water budget of the desert beetle, *Onymacris unguicularis* (data from Cooper 1982).

dunes to condense and concentrate fog. The moisture collected by these trenches runs down to the lower end, where the beetle waits for a drink. Another tenebrionid beetle, *Onymacris unguicularis,* collects moisture by orienting its abdomen upward. Fog condensing on this beetle's body flows to its mouth. Figure 6.10 shows this beetle's unique means of obtaining drinking water. *Onymacris* also takes in water with its food. Some of this water is absorbed within the tissues of the food. The remaining water is produced when the beetle metabolizes the carbohydrates, proteins, and fats contained in its food. We can see the source of this "metabolic water" if we look at an equation for oxidation of glucose:

$$C_6H_{12}O_6 + 6\,O_2 \rightarrow 6\,CO_2 + \mathbf{6\,H_2O}$$

As you can see, cellular respiration liberates the water that combined with carbon dioxide during the process of photosynthesis (see chapter 5). The water released during cellular respiration is called **metabolic water.**

Paul Cooper (1982) estimated the water budget for free-ranging *Onymacris* from the Namib Desert near Gobabeb. He estimated the rate of water intake by this beetle at 49.9 mg of H_2O per gram of body weight per day. Of this total, 39.8 mg came from fog, 1.7 mg came from moisture contained within food, and 8.4 mg came from metabolic water. The rate of water loss by these beetles, 41.3 mg of H_2O per gram per day, was slightly less than water intake. Of this total, 2.3 mg were lost with feces and urine, and 39 mg by evaporation. The water budget of the beetle studied by Cooper is shown in figure 6.11.

While *Onymacris* gets most of its water from fog, other small desert animals get most of their water from their food. Kangaroo rats of the genus *Dipodomys* in the family Heteromyidae don't have to drink at all and can survive entirely on metabolic water. Knut Schmidt-Nielsen (1964) showed that the approximately 60 ml of water gained from 100 g of barley

makes up for the water a Merriam's kangaroo rat, *D. merriami,* loses in feces, urine, and evaporation while metabolizing the 100 g of grain. The 100 g of barley contains only 6 ml of absorbed water, that is, water that can be driven off by drying. The remaining 54 ml of water is released as the animal metabolizes the carbohydrates, fats, and proteins in the grain. The importance of metabolic water in the water budget of Merriam's kangaroo rat is pictured in figure 6.12.

While animals generally obtain most of their water by drinking or with their food, these options are not available to plants. Though many plants can absorb some water from the air, most get the bulk of their water from the soil through their roots.

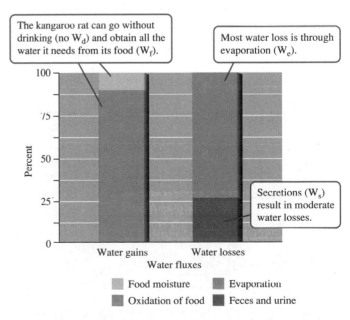

Figure 6.12 Water budget of Merriam's kangaroo rat *Dipodomys merriami* (data from Schmidt-Nielsen 1964).

Water Acquisition by Plants

The extent of root development by plants is affected by many factors including water availability. Plants in dry climates generally grow relatively more roots than do plants in moist climates. In dry climates, plant roots tend to grow deeper in the soil and to constitute a greater proportion of plant biomass. The tap roots of some desert shrubs can extend 9 or even 30 m down into the soil, giving them access to deep groundwater. Roots may account for up to 90% of total plant biomass in deserts, grasslands and tundra. In coniferous forests, roots constitute only about 25% of total plant biomass.

You don't have to compare forests and deserts, however, to observe differences in root development. R. Coupland and R. Johnson (1965) compared the rooting characteristics of plants growing in the dry mixed grasslands of western Canada. During their study, they carefully excavated the roots of over 850 individual plants, digging over 3 m deep to trace some roots. The level of care and attention to detail required to collect these data are really unimaginable. They found that many species have lower root biomass and higher aboveground biomass in moist microclimates within the temperate grassland biome. For instance, the roots of *Artemesia frigida* penetrate over 120 cm into the soil on dry sites; on moist sites, its roots grow only to a depth of about 60 cm (fig. 6.13). This contrast in root development is only one of many uncovered by the work of Coupland and Johnson.

Deeper roots often help plants from dry environments extract water from deep within the soil profile. This generalization is supported by studies of two common grasses that grow in Japan, *Digitaria adscendens* and *Eleusine indica*. The grasses overlap broadly in their distributions in Japan, however, only *Digitaria* grows on coastal sand dunes, which are among the most drought-prone habitats in Japan.

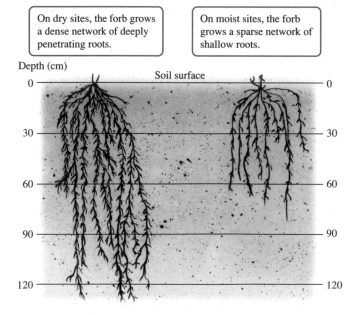

> On dry sites, the forb grows a dense network of deeply penetrating roots.

> On moist sites, the forb grows a sparse network of shallow roots.

Figure 6.13 Soil moisture influences the extent of root development by this desert forb (data from Coupland and Johnson 1965).

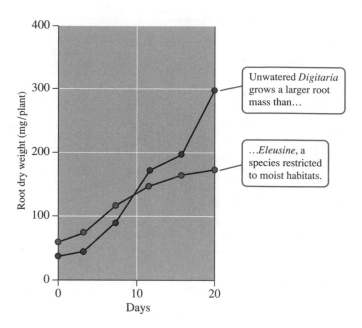

> Unwatered *Digitaria* grows a larger root mass than…

> …*Eleusine*, a species restricted to moist habitats.

Figure 6.14 A grass from a dry habitat responded to a simulated drought by greater root growth compared to a grass from a moist habitat (data from Park 1990).

Y.-M. Park (1990) was interested in understanding the mechanisms allowing *Digitaria* to grow on coastal dunes where *Eleusine* could not. Because of the potential for drought in coastal dunes, Park studied the responses of the two grasses to water stress. He grew both species from seeds collected at the Botanical Gardens at the University of Tokyo. Seeds were germinated in moist sand and the seedlings were later transplanted into 10 cm by 90 cm PVC tubes filled with sand from a coastal dune. Park planted two seedlings of *Digitaria* in each of 36 tubes and two of *Eleusine* in 36 other tubes. He watered all 72 tubes with a nutrient solution every 10 days for 40 days. At the end of the 40 days, Park divided the 36 tubes of each species into two groups of 18. One group of each species was kept well watered for the next 19 days, while the other group remained unwatered.

Unwatered *Digitaria* and *Eleusine* responded differently. The root mass of *Digitaria* increased almost sevenfold over the 19 days of no watering, while the root mass of *Eleusine* increased about threefold. In addition, the roots of *Digitaria* were still growing at the end of the experiment, while those of *Eleusine* stopped growing about 4 days before the end of the experiment. Figure 6.14 summarizes these results.

Park found that the differences in root growth were greatest in the deeper soil layers. Below 60 cm in the growing tubes, the unwatered group of *Eleusine* showed suppressed root growth, while *Digitaria* did not. With its greater mass of more deeply penetrating roots, *Digitaria* maintained high leaf water potential throughout the 19 days of no watering. During this same period, *Eleusine* showed a substantial decline in leaf water potential. The leaf water potentials of *Digitaria* and *Eleusine* over the 19 days are shown in figure 6.15.

Park's results suggest that *Digitaria* can be successful in the drier dune habitat because it grows longer roots, which

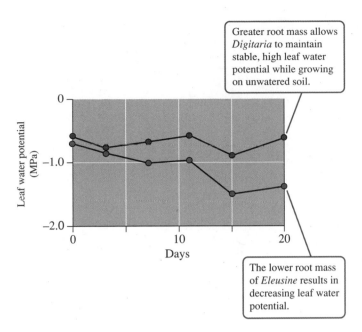

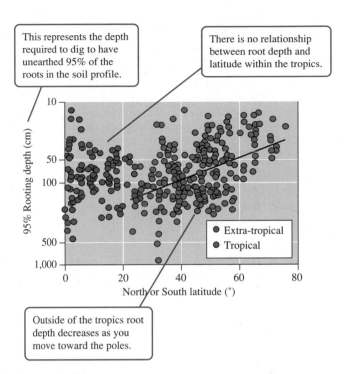

Figure 6.15   A grass from a dry habitat maintained a higher water potential during a simulated drought compared to a grass from a moist habitat (data from Park 1990).

Figure 6.16   Rooting depth varies across a broad geographical gradient (data from Schenk and Jackson 2002).

exploit deeper soil moisture. With these deeper roots, *Digitaria* can keep the water potential of its tissues high even in relatively dry soils, where *Eleusine* suffers lowered water potential. In other words, *Digitaria* maintains higher leaf water potentials because its greater root development maintains a higher rate of water intake—higher W_r.

The examples we've just reviewed concern rooting by individual plant species either in the field or under experimental conditions. An important question that we might ask is whether there have been enough root studies to make tentative generalizations about the rooting biology of plants. Jochen Schenk and Robert Jackson (2002) conducted an analysis of 475 root profile (see fig. 6.13) studies from 209 geographic localities from around the world. In over 90% of the 475 root profiles at least 50% of roots were in the top 0.3 m of the soil and at least 95% of roots were in the upper 2 m (figure 6.16). However, they also found pronounced geographic differences in rooting depth. Rooting depth increased from 80° to 30° latitude, that is from arctic tundra to Mediterranean woodlands and shrublands and deserts (chapter 2). However, there were no clear trends in rooting depth in the tropics. Consistent with our present discussion, Schenk and Jackson found that deeper rooting depths occur mainly in water-limited ecosystems.

Water Conservation by Plants and Animals

Another way to balance a water budget is by reducing water losses. One of the most obvious ways to cut down on water losses is by waterproofing to reduce evaporation. Many terrestrial plants and animals cover themselves with a fairly waterproof "hide" impregnated with a variety of waterproofing waxes.

However, some organisms are more waterproof than others, and rates of evaporative water loss vary greatly from one animal or plant species to another.

Why do the water loss rates of organisms differ? One reason is that species have evolved in environments that differ greatly in water availability. As a consequence, selection for water conservation has been more intense in some environments than others. Species that evolved in warm deserts are generally much more resistant to desiccation than relatives that evolved in moist tropical or temperate habitats. In general, populations that evolved in drier environments lose water at a slower rate. For instance, turtles from wet and moist habitats lose water at a much higher rate than do desert tortoises (fig. 6.17). As the following example shows, however, the water loss rates of even closely related species can differ substantially.

Neil Hadley and Thomas Schultz (1987) studied two species of tiger beetles in Arizona that occupy different microclimates. *Cicindela oregona* lives along the moist shoreline of streams and is active in fall and spring. In contrast, *Cicindela obsoleta* lives in the semiarid grasslands of central and southeastern Arizona and is active in summer. The researchers suspected that these differences in microclimate select for differences in waterproofing of the two tiger beetles.

Hadley and Schultz studied the waterproofing of the tiger beetles by comparing the amount of water each species lost while held in an experimental chamber. They pumped dry air through the chamber at a constant rate and maintained its temperature at 30°C. They weighed each beetle at the beginning of an experiment and then again after 3 hours in the chamber. The difference between initial and final weights gave them an estimate of the water loss rate of each beetle.

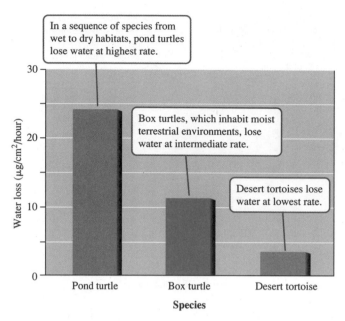

Figure 6.17 Rates of water loss by two turtles and a tortoise indicate an inverse relationship between the dryness of the habitat and water loss rates (data from Schmidt-Nielsen 1969).

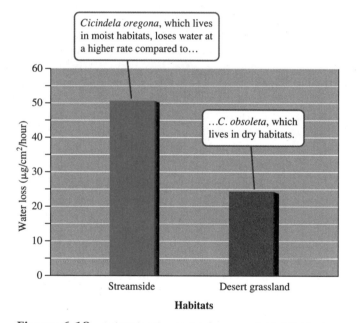

Figure 6.18 A tiger beetle species from a moist habitat lost water at a higher rate than one from a dry habitat (data from Hadley and Schultz 1987).

By determining water loss for several individuals of each species, they estimated the average water loss rates for *C. oregona* and *C. obsoleta*. Hadley and Schultz found that *C. oregona* loses water two times as fast as *C. obsoleta* (fig. 6.18). In other words, the species from the drier microclimate, *C. obsoleta* appears to be more waterproofed.

Waterproofing of the cuticles of terrestrial insects is usually provided by hydrocarbons. Hydrocarbons include organic compounds such as lipids and waxes. Because of their influences on waterproofing, Hadley and Schultz analyzed the cuticles of the two species of tiger beetles for their hydrocarbon

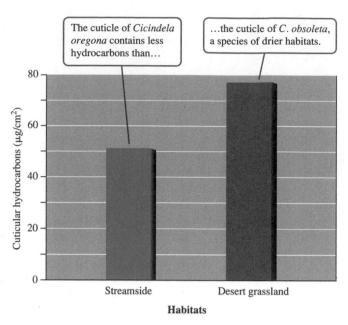

Figure 6.19 The cuticles of tiger beetles from dry habitats tend to contain a higher concentration of waterproofing hydrocarbons compared to tiger beetles from moist habitats (data from Hadley and Schultz 1987).

content. They found that the concentration of hydrocarbons in the cuticle of *C. obsoleta* is 50% higher than in the cuticle of *C. oregona* (fig. 6.19). In addition, the two species differ in the percentages of cuticular hydrocarbons that are saturated with hydrogen. Fully saturated hydrocarbons are much more effective at waterproofing. One hundred percent of the hydrocarbons in the cuticle of *C. obsoleta* are saturated. In contrast, only 50% of the cuticular hydrocarbons of *C. oregona* are saturated. These results support the hypothesis that *C. obsoleta* loses water at a lower rate because its cuticle contains a higher concentration of waterproofing hydrocarbons.

Merriam's kangaroo rats conserve water sufficiently that they can live entirely on the moisture contained within their food and on "metabolic water" (see fig. 6.12). This capacity is assumed to be an adaptation to desert living. Over long periods of time as the American Southwest became increasingly arid, the ancestors of today's Merriam's kangaroo rats were subject to natural selection that favoured a range of adaptations to dry environments, including water conservation. However, Merriam's kangaroo rat is a widespread species that lives from 21° N latitude in Mexico to 42° N latitude in northern Nevada. Over this large geographic range, Merriam's kangaroo rat populations are exposed to a very broad range of environmental conditions.

Intrigued by their large geographic range and exceptional adaptation to desert living, Richard Tracy and Glenn Walsberg studied three populations of Merriam's kangaroo rats across a climatic gradient. Their main objective was to determine if different populations of Merriam's kangaroo rat vary in their degree of adaptation to living in dry environments (Tracy and Walsberg 2000, 2001, 2002). The three populations studied by Tracy and Walsberg live in southwest Arizona near Yuma, central Arizona, and north-central Arizona, at elevations of 150 m,

Kangaroo rats from the driest site showed much lower rates of water loss.

Figure 6.20 Water loss rates by Merriam's kangaroo rats from across a moisture gradient suggest adaptation to local climate by each of the populations (data from Tracy and Walsberg 2001).

(a)

(b)

Figure 6.21 Changing leaf area: (*a*) following rainfall ocotillo plants of the Sonoran Desert develop leaves and flower; (*b*) during dry periods they lose their leaves and blossoms.

400 m, and 1200 m respectively. Mean annual maximum temperatures at the study sites are 31.5°C, 29.1°C, and 23.5°C and mean annual precipitation at the three sites is 10.6 cm, 33.6 cm, and 43.6 cm. The differences in climates at the three study sites are reflected in the vegetation. The habitat at the driest site consists of sand dunes with scattered shrubs; the intermediate site is a desert shrubland; and the vegetation at the moist site consists of a pinyon-juniper woodland.

One of the main questions asked by Tracy and Walsberg was whether rates of evaporative water loss would differ among the Merriam's kangaroo rats at dry, intermediate, and moist sites. The results of this study showed clear differences among the study populations. The mean rate of evaporative water loss at the dry site was 0.69 mg of water per g per hour, compared to 1 mg H_2O/g/h and 1.08 mg H_2O/g/h at the intermediate and moist sites respectively (fig. 6.20). Tracy and Walsberg expressed the rate of water loss by the kangaroo rats on a per gram basis because the kangaroo rats from the three sites differ significantly in size. The average mass of individuals from the moist site was approximately 33% greater than the mass of rats from the dry site. In additional studies, Tracy and Walsberg found that acclimating animals to laboratory conditions did not eliminate the differences in water conservation among populations. In other words, even after being kept in the laboratory under controlled conditions, Merriam's kangaroo rats from the driest study site continued to lose water at a lower rate. The evidence from these studies supports the conclusion that these three populations differ in their degree of adaptation to desert living.

Animals adapted to dry conditions have many other water conservation mechanisms besides waterproofing. These mechanisms include producing concentrated urine or feces with low water content, condensing and reclaiming the water vapour in breath, and restricting activity to times and places that decrease water loss.

Plants have also evolved a wide variety of means for conserving water, which result in different water use efficiencies (WUE). WUE is defined as the biomass of plant tissue produced per gram of water used, and this value will vary among species. The WUE of a plant depends in part on its leaf area relative to its root area or length. Plants with more leaf surface per length of root lose more water. Compared to plants from moist climates, arid land plants generally have less leaf area per unit area of root and higher WUE. Many plants reduce leaf area over the short term by dropping leaves in response to drought. Some desert plants produce leaves only in response to soaking rains and then shed them when the desert dries out again. These plants reduce leaf area to zero in times of drought. Figure 6.21 shows one of these plants, the ocotillo of the Sonoran Desert of North America.

Dams, Flows, and Cottonwoods

The western prairies of North America are often viewed as flat and dry expanses of unending fields of grasses. However, cutting through these areas are a variety of rivers and streams, generally flowing out from the Rocky Mountains. Along these rivers we find a completely different type of habitat, a wetter riparian area often dominated by trees (fig. 6.22). Standing on the bank of a river in the prairies, you will find yourself in floodplain forests dominated by a few species of Cottonwoods (*Populus* spp.). When you walk just a few hundred metres away, these species are nowhere to be found. Floodplain forests are oases in the prairie for many native animals as well as livestock. They are home to species of plants, insects, fungi, and other organisms not found in the drier regions of the prairie landscape. In short, these habitats are critical to both maintenance of biodiversity and to the economic health of the dry prairies of western North America. However, over the last several decades many researchers have noticed a decline in Cottonwood abundances throughout the west, raising great concerns. To try to understand why this decline has occurred, and to see if the pattern can be reversed, we turn to the work of Stewart Rood of the University of Lethbridge.

We begin by trying to understand why Cottonwoods are restricted to riparian habitats, rather than being distributed broadly throughout the prairie itself. Cottonwoods tend to be early colonizers of bare riparian areas, providing a critical service of stream-bank stabilization (Rood et al. 2003). Isotopic analyses (see the Ecological Tools section later in this chapter) indicate that Cottonwoods predominantly use **alluvial groundwater** (water that comes from a surface stream) rather than deeper ground water, at least during dry periods of the summer (Rood et al. 2003). As a result of this reliance on surface waters, these plants are very sensitive to drought. The trees respond very quickly to reduced water availability through altered hormonal levels, stomatal closures (to reduce evaporation), and decreased photosynthesis (Rood et al 2003). Over longer periods, drought leads to reduced growth and

(a)

(b)

(c)

Figure 6.22   (*a*) Cottonwood forests along the Old Man River in southern Alberta; (*b*) a flood on the Old Man River; (*c*) bands of Cottonwood trees of different ages, each establishing during different river floods.

Other plant adaptations that conserve water include thick leaves, which have less transpiring leaf surface area per unit volume of photosynthesizing tissue than thin leaves do; few stomata on leaves rather than many; structures on the stomata that impede the movement of water; dormancy during times when moisture is unavailable; and alternative, water-conserving pathways for photosynthesis. (We discuss these alternative pathways for photosynthesis in chapter 7.)

We should remember that plants and animals in terrestrial environments other than deserts also show evidence of selection for water conservation. For instance, Nona Chiariello and her colleagues (1987) discovered an intriguing example of adjusting leaf area in the moist tropics. *Piper auritum*, a large-leafed, umbrella-shaped plant, grows in clearings of the rain forest. Because it grows in clearings, the plant often faces drying conditions during midday. However, it reduces the leaf area it exposes

increased plant mortality. One of the unique aspects of Cottonwood water relations is that they are particularly prone to **cavitation**. In cavitation, air bubbles form in the xylem, effectively breaking the chain of water from roots to leaves. Once cavitation occurs in the xylem, those cells no longer have the ability to move water, and thus cavitation can render large parts of the vascular tissue useless for these trees. In summary, Cottonwoods colonize bare riparian soil, use predominately shallow waters, and are uniquely sensitive to drought. These factors can explain why we don't find Cottonwoods in the driest parts of the prairies. However, what would explain why they are declining from areas that are traditionally the wettest parts of the landscape?

To answer this, we begin with a look at long-term trends in river flows heading east and west from the Rocky Mountains (Rood et al. 2005a). Rood and his colleagues collected data from a variety of existing long-term data sets of flows through 31 river reaches, with data collected upstream of any dams (we will get to dams shortly!). After adjusting for global climatic cycles (chapter 23), they found significant flow declines in 15 of the 31 river reaches. On average, rivers had a 0.22%/year flow reduction, with some Albertan rivers showing a recent decline as high at 0.5%/year. As we discussed in chapter 5, decreased water levels result in increased stream temperatures, with a variety of potential consequences for fish and other animals that live within the streams. Based upon what we know about Cottonwoods, their reliance on surface waters means reduced stream flows also puts them at increased risk of mortality and reduced growth. These changes in stream flows occurred upstream of dams, and thus are likely caused by large-scale climatic changes (e.g., global warming). However, direct human activity is putting additional pressures on these forest floodplain habitats.

Some activities, such as clearing forest for housing or agricultural development or harvesting trees for fuel and money, cause obvious negative consequences for riparian habitats that don't take any scientific understanding to understand. Instead we will discuss a more subtle and widespread challenge to these systems: dams. By design, dams modify stream flows, often with the intent of reducing flooding events and protecting property and infrastructure. Interestingly, even if dams provide a constant rate of river flow, Cottonwood forests seem to decline. In other words, there is more than just water relations driving the loss of these forests. Rood and colleagues have explored the impacts of dams on riparian forests, and have found ways to work with dam operators to help restore these challenged riparian areas (Root et al. 2005b).

As you may recall, Cottonwoods colonize bare and wet ground. Where is that bare ground found on the landscape? It is found along rivers after floods. Floods can rip out existing trees, cause severe erosion to stream beds, and leave large deposits of organic material on large expanses of the prairie. Over timescales of decades and centuries, floods are common to the rivers of the west, and are most frequent during the early summer months. Cottonwood reproduction is suited to this fairly regular occurrence, with seed dispersal and seedling establishment following the summer floods. If a dam prevents flooding, it can also prevent successful establishment of Cottonwoods. But how can you reconcile flood prevention with cottonwood preservation? Rood has been part of many restoration projects where he works with dam operators to help allow for flood events without putting human infrastructure at risk. These projects have resulted in dramatic recruitment of Cottonwoods along both the Old Man and St. Mary rivers in Alberta (fig. 6.22).

The work of Rood and his colleagues is a wonderful example of how knowledge about the ecology of an organism, coupled with an understanding of the abiotic environment, can be used to address issues of societal concern. Without knowing why Cottonwoods require water, it would be difficult to understand how to prevent further population declines. Rood has shown that ecologists can directly impact environmental decisions, in this case by helping to develop a new method of flow management from dams. However, floodplain forests still face the challenge of reduced flows even upstream of the dams, likely due to changes in global climate. It will be up to the next generation of ecologists to help solve this issue.

---

to the midday sun by wilting. Wilting at midday reduces leaf area exposed to direct solar radiation by about 55% and leaf temperature by up to 4°C to 5°C. These reductions decrease the rate of transpiration by 30% to 50%, which is a substantial water savings. The behaviour of this tropical rain forest plant reminds us that even the rain forest has its relatively dry microclimates, such as the forest clearings where *P. auritum* grows. The rapidity of *P. auritum*'s wilting response is shown in figure 6.23.

Organisms balance their water budgets in numerous ways. Some rely mainly on water conservation. Others depend upon water acquisition. However, every biologist who studies organisms in their natural environment knows that nature is marked by diversity and contrast. To sample nature's variety, let's review the variety of approaches to desert living.

As in the example with *P. auritum*, plants have developed adaptations to cope with periodic water stress; however, these

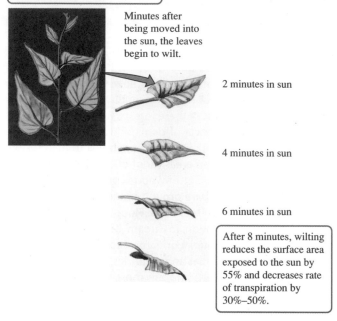

In a shaded portion of a greenhouse, the leaves of the rain forest plant are unwilted and fully exposed to incoming light.

Minutes after being moved into the sun, the leaves begin to wilt.

2 minutes in sun

4 minutes in sun

6 minutes in sun

After 8 minutes, wilting reduces the surface area exposed to the sun by 55% and decreases rate of transpiration by 30%–50%.

Figure 6.23   Temporary wilting by this rain forest plant decreases rates of water loss (data from Chiariello, Field, and Mooney 1987).

adaptations are often at odds with human needs. For example, although closing stomata reduces water loss and is likely to be a favoured strategy over evolutionary time, closing stomata also ceases photosynthesis (for most plants; chapter 7), which is bad news for a farmer trying to grow a crop. Because of this evolutionary solution to short-term water stress, many agricultural fields are irrigated through the dry summer months, particularly in the southern prairies. As we saw from Steward Rood's work, changes in stream flow—for whatever purpose—will influence other habitats within the broader prairie landscape. How plants deal with water stress, and how humans rely on plants for survival, has changed the face of the prairies over the last century. This struggle continues as human consumption of water continues to rise, and climate change increases rates of evaporation and alters precipitation patterns.

Dissimilar Organisms with Similar Approaches to Desert Life

On the surface, camels and saguaro cactus appear entirely different (fig. 6.24). If you look deeper into their biology, however, you find that they take very similar approaches to balancing their water budgets. Both the camel and the saguaro cactus acquire massive amounts of water when water is available, store water, and conserve water.

The camel can go for long periods in intense desert heat without drinking, up to 6 to 8 days in conditions that would kill a person within a day. During this time, the animal survives on the water stored in its tissues and can withstand water losses of up to 20% of its body weight without harm. For humans, a loss

(a)

(b)

Figure 6.24   Two desert dwellers, (*a*) saguaro cactus, and (*b*) camel; as different as they are, they seem to show parallel adaptations to desert environments.

of about 10% to 12% is near the fatal limit. When the camel has the opportunity, it can drink and store prodigious quantities of water, up to one-third of its body weight at a time. Such consumptions of water by humans is generally also fatal.

Between opportunities to drink, the camel is a master of water conservation. One way it conserves body water is by

The saguaro reduces heat gain by exposing only tops of its trunk and branches to the midday sun.

The trunk and branch tips are shaded and insulated with a high density of spines, which reduces heat gain.

The camel does not store water in its hump but fat, which is a source of metabolic water.

The camel reduces heat gain by facing into the sun.

The camel is covered with dense hair, which reduces heat gain.

Water is stored in the massive trunk and arms.

The saguaro reduces water loss by transpiration by keeping stomates closed and allowing its temperature to rise.

When water is available, both the saguaro and camel take in massive quantities.

The camel reduces evaporative water loss by not sweating and allowing body temperature to rise.

Figure 6.25 Dissimilar organisms with similar approaches to desert living.

reducing its rate of heat gain. Like overheating tiger beetles (see chapter 5), the camel faces into the sun, reducing the body surface it exposes to direct sunlight. In addition, its thick hair insulates it from the intense desert sun, and rather than sweating sufficiently to keep its body temperature down, the camel allows its body temperature to rise by up to 7°C. This reduces the temperature difference between the camel and the environment and so decreases the rate of additional heating. Reduced heating translates into reduced water loss by evaporation.

The saguaro cactus takes a similar approach. The trunk and arms of the plant act as organs in which the cactus can store large quantities of water. During droughts, the saguaro draws on these stored reserves and so can endure long periods without water. When it rains, the saguaro, like a camel at an oasis, can ingest great quantities of water, but instead of drinking, the saguaro gets its water through its dense network of shallow roots. These roots extend out in a roughly circular pattern to a distance approximately equal to the height of the cactus. For a 15 m tall saguaro this means a root coverage of over 700 m² of soil.

The saguaro also reduces its rate of evaporative water loss in several ways. First, like other cacti, it keeps its stomata closed during the day when transpiration losses would be highest. In the absence of transpiration, in full sun, the internal

temperature of the saguaro rises to over 50°C, which is among the highest temperatures recorded in plants. However, as we noted for the camel, higher body temperature can be an advantage because it reduces the rate of additional heating. The saguaro's rate of heating is also reduced by the shape and orientation of its trunk and arms. At midday, when the potential for heating is greatest, the saguaro exposes mainly the tips of its arms and trunk to direct sunlight. However, the tips of the saguaro's arms and trunk are insulated by a layer of plant hairs and a thick tangle of spines, which reflect sunlight and shade the growing tips of the cactus.

The parallel approaches to desert living seen in saguaro cactuses and camels are outlined in figure 6.25. Now let's examine two organisms that live in the same desert but have very different water relations.

Two Arthropods with Opposite Approaches to Desert Life

Though both are arthropods and may live within a few meters of each other, cicadas and scorpions take sharply contrasting approaches to living in the desert. The scorpion's approach is to slow down, conserve, and stay out of the sun. Scorpions are relatively large and long-lived arthropods with very low

While Sonoran Desert cicada sings from the branches of a mesquite tree during a midsummer's afternoon…

…the scorpion spends the day in its burrow near the base of the tree.

Scorpions emerge from their burrows at night, when temperatures are lower.

The low temperature and high humidity of the burrow reduces water loss.

Waterproofed cuticle also reduces evaporative water loss.

A low metabolic rate reduces respiration and further decreases water loss.

Figure 6.26 These two desert arthropods, a scorpion and a cicada, have evolved very different approaches to living in the desert.

metabolic rates. A low rate of metabolism means that they can subsist on low rations of food and lose little water during respiration. In addition, scorpions conserve water by spending most of their time in their burrows, where the humidity is higher than at the surface. They come out to feed and find mates only at night, when it's cooler. In addition, desert scorpions are well waterproofed; hydrocarbons in their cuticles seal in moisture. With this combination of water-conserving characteristics, scorpions can easily satisfy their need for water by consuming the moisture contained in the bodies of their arthropod prey. Figure 6.26 summarizes the habits of desert scorpions.

In comparison to desert scorpions, the cicada's approach to desert living may seem out of place. As we saw in the

introduction to chapter 6, the Sonoran Desert cicada, *Diceroprocta apache,* is active on the hottest days, when air temperature is near its lethal limit. How can *Diceroprocta* do this and not die? The solution to this puzzle begins with a study by James Heath and Peter Wilkin (1970). These researchers observed that just before sunrise *Diceroprocta* perches on large branches of mesquite trees, *Prosopis juliflora,* where it feeds on the fluids in the tree's xylem. As the sun rises, the cicadas move from their feeding sites to leaves and twigs exposed to full sun. They remain motionless on these perches until midmorning, when the temperature rises above 35°C. At this high temperature, birds and wasps, the main predators of the cicadas, seek shelter from the heat.

As their predators retire to the shade, the cicadas reach their peak of activity. When body temperature reaches 39°C, they shift their position to the shade of large mesquite branches, where the males sing. If the temperature does not rise above 40°C, they sing throughout midday. However, when air temperature reaches 48°C, *Diceroprocta* will sit quietly from about 1:00 to 3:00 P.M. and then resume singing.

Heath and Wilkin found that singing *Diceroprocta* have a body temperature considerably below the temperature of the surrounding air. They also found that the temperature close to the surface of the branches where the cicadas perch is cooler than other potential perches. Heath and Wilkin concluded that the cicadas keep cool by remaining in these small patches of cool air on the shady sides of large branches. They suggested that these cool microclimates are too small to be exploited by birds, the chief predators of *Diceroprocta.*

Are cool microclimates the only means of thermoregulation used by *Diceroprocta?* A study of another cicada by two graduate students suggested that *Diceroprocta* might evaporatively cool. Stacy Kaser and Jon Hastings (1981) found evidence of evaporative cooling by *Tibicen duryi,* which lives in the same region as *Diceroprocta* but at higher elevations, where it feeds on the xylem fluids of pinyon pine trees, *Pinus edulis.* Kaser and Hastings found that the abdominal temperature of *Tibicen* remained lower than air temperature when air temperature rose above 36°C. The cicadas were able to maintain these reduced abdominal temperatures as long as they had access to xylem fluids. However, when Kaser and Hastings denied their access to water, their abdominal temperatures rose. Though never observed before, these results suggested that *Tibicen* is capable of evaporative cooling.

These observations led to a series of investigations and papers by Eric Toolson and Neil Hadley which showed conclusively that cicadas, including *Diceroprocta,* are capable of evaporative cooling. In one of these studies, Eric Toolson (1987) collected *Diceroprocta* from a mesquite tree and placed them in an environmental chamber. The chamber temperature was kept at 45.5°C; however, *Diceroprocta* was able to maintain its body temperature at least 2.9°C lower. Since the cicadas within the chamber did not have access to any cool microclimates, Toolson concluded that they must be evaporatively cooling. To verify this hypothesis, he placed cicadas in the environmental chamber and then raised the relative humidity to 100%. At 100% relative humidity, the body temperatures of

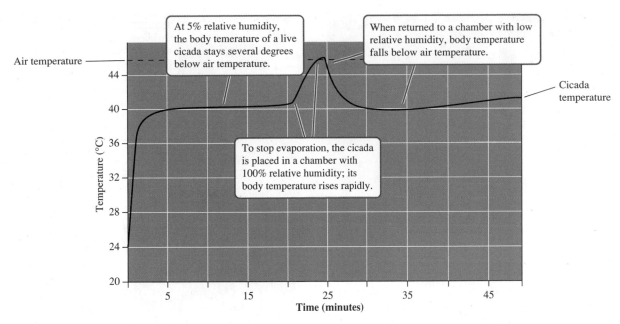

Figure 6.27 A laboratory experiment verified evaporative cooling by the cicada, *Diceroprocta apache* (data from Toolson 1987).

the cicadas quickly increased to the temperature of the environmental chamber. When Toolson reduced relative humidity to 0%, the cicadas cooled approximately 4°C within minutes. The results of this experiment are outlined in figure 6.27.

How do the results of Toolson's experiment support the hypothesis of evaporative cooling? Remember that air with a relative humidity of 100% contains all the water vapour it can hold (see p. 149). Consequently, by raising the humidity of the air surrounding the cicadas to 100%, Toolson shut off any evaporative cooling that might be taking place. When he reintroduced dry air, he created a gradient of water concentration from the cicada to the air and evaporative cooling resumed.

Toolson's results are consistent with the hypothesis that *Diceroprocta* evaporatively cools but does not demonstrate that capacity directly. Consequently, Toolson and Hadley (1987) conducted observations to make a direct demonstration. First, they placed a live *Diceroprocta* in an environmental chamber with a humidity sensor just above its cuticle. If *Diceroprocta* evaporatively cools, then this sensor would detect higher humidity as the temperature of the environment was increased. This is exactly what occurred. As the temperature was increased from 30°C to 43°C, the rate of water movement across the cicada's cuticle increased in three steps. When Toolson and Hadley increased the temperature from 37°C to 39°C, water loss increased from 5.7 to 9.4 mg H_2O per square centimeter per hour. At 41°C, water loss increased from 9.4 to 36.1 mg H_2O per square centimeter per hour and at 43°C water loss increased from 36.1 to 61.4 mg H_2O per square centimeter per hour. These results are graphed in figure 6.28.

The rate of water loss by *Diceroprocta* is among the highest ever reported for a terrestrial insect. How does water cross the cuticle of this cicada at such a high rate? Toolson and Hadley searched the cuticle of *Diceroprocta* for avenues of water movement. They found three areas on the dorsal surface with large pores that might be involved in evaporative cooling (fig. 6.29).

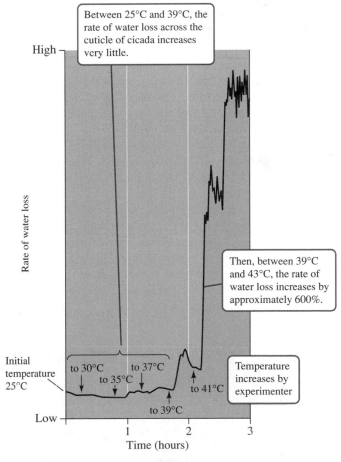

Figure 6.28 High temperatures induce massive rates of water loss by the cicada, *Diceroprocta apache* (data from Toolson and Hadley 1987).

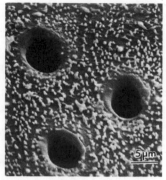

5 μm

Figure 6.29 (*a*) Magnified view of *D. apache* outlining three areas with high densities of small pores; (*b*) dorsal pores under high magnification.

When they plugged these pores *Diceroprocta* could no longer cool itself. In summary, Toolson and Hadley verified a previously unknown phenomenon, evaporative cooling by cicadas, and carefully demonstrated the underlying mechanisms.

So, it turns out that these cicadas can sing in the hottest hours of the desert day because they sweat! *Diceroprocta* is able to maintain this seemingly impossible lifestyle because it has tapped into a rich supply of water. Cicadas are members of the order Homoptera and distant relatives of the aphids. Like aphids, cicadas feed on plant fluids. So, though the cicada lives in the same macroclimate as the scorpion, it has tapped into a totally different microclimate. The cicada's scope for water acquisition is extended up to 30 m deep into the soil by the tap roots of its mesquite host plant, *P. juliflora*. *Diceroprocta* can sustain high rates of water loss through evaporation, high W_e, because it is able to balance these losses with a high rate of water acquisition, high W_d. Figure 6.30 illustrates how *Diceroprocta* uses mesquite trees to get access to deep soil moisture.

Sometimes, similar organisms employ radically different approaches to balancing their water budgets. Sometimes, organisms of very different evolutionary lineages employ functionally similar approaches. In short, the means by which terrestrial organisms balance water acquisition against water loss are almost as varied as the organisms themselves. Similar variation occurs among aquatic organisms.

Concept 6.2 Review

1. The tiger beetle *Cicindela oregona* has a distribution that extends from Arizona through the temperate rain forests of Alaska. Why should the amounts of cuticular hydrocarbons vary geographically among populations of *C. oregona*?
2. During severe droughts, some of the branches of shrubs and trees die, while others survive. How might losing some branches increase the probability that an individual plant will survive a drought?
3. How are water and temperature regulation related in many terrestrial organisms?

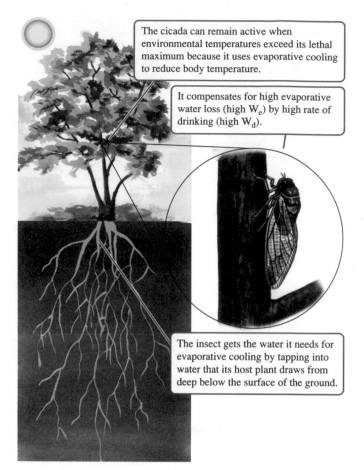

The cicada can remain active when environmental temperatures exceed its lethal maximum because it uses evaporative cooling to reduce body temperature.

It compensates for high evaporative water loss (high W_e) by high rate of drinking (high W_d).

The insect gets the water it needs for evaporative cooling by tapping into water that its host plant draws from deep below the surface of the ground.

Figure 6.30 An ecological puzzle solved.

6.3   Water and Salt Balance in Aquatic Environments

Marine and freshwater organisms use complementary mechanisms for water and salt regulation. Aquatic organisms, like their terrestrial kin, regulate internal water, W_i, by balancing water gain against water loss. We can represent water regulation in aquatic environments by modifying our equation for terrestrial water balance to:

$$W_i = W_d - W_s \pm W_o$$

Drinking, W_d, is a ready source of water for aquatic organisms. Secretion of water with urine, W_s, is an avenue of water loss. By osmosis, W_o, an aquatic organism may either gain or lose water, depending on the organism and the environment.

Marine Fish and Invertebrates

Most marine invertebrates maintain an internal concentration of solutes equivalent to that in the seawater around them. What does the animal gain by remaining isosmotic with the external environment? The isosmotic animal does not have to expend energy overcoming an osmotic gradient. This strategy is not without costs, however. Though the total concentration of solutes is the same inside and outside the animal, there are still differences in the concentrations of some individual solutes.

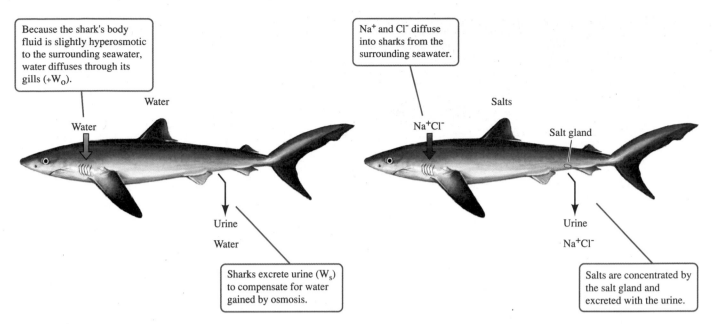

Because the shark's body fluid is slightly hyperosmotic to the surrounding seawater, water diffuses through its gills ($+W_o$).

Water

Water

Urine

Water

Sharks excrete urine (W_s) to compensate for water gained by osmosis.

Na^+ and Cl^- diffuse into sharks from the surrounding seawater.

Salts

Na^+Cl^-

Salt gland

Urine

Na^+Cl^-

Salts are concentrated by the salt gland and excreted with the urine.

Figure 6.31   Osmoregulation by sharks.

These concentration differentials can only be maintained by active transport, which consumes some energy.

Sharks, skates, and rays generally elevate the concentration of solutes in their blood to levels slightly hyperosmotic to seawater. However, inorganic ions constitute only about one-third of the solute in shark's blood; the remainder consists of the organic molecules urea and trimethylamine oxide (TMAO). As a consequence of being slightly hyperosmotic, sharks slowly gain water through osmosis, that is, W_o is slightly positive. The water that diffuses into the shark, mainly across the gills, is pumped out by the kidneys and exits as urine. Sodium, because it is maintained at approximately two-thirds its concentration in seawater, diffuses into sharks from seawater across the gill membranes and some sodium enters with food. Sharks excrete excess sodium mainly through a specialized gland associated with the rectum called the salt gland. The main point here is that sharks and their relatives reduce the costs of osmoregulation by decreasing the osmotic gradient between themselves and the external environment (fig. 6.31).

In contrast to most marine invertebrates and sharks, marine bony fish have body fluids that are strongly hypoosmotic to the surrounding medium. As a consequence, they lose water to the surrounding seawater, mostly across their gills. Marine bony fish make up these water losses by drinking seawater. However, drinking adds to salt influxes through their gills. The fish rid themselves of excess salts in two ways. Specialized "chloride" cells at the base of their gills secrete sodium and chloride directly to the surrounding seawater, while the kidneys excrete magnesium and sulfate. These ions exit with the urine. The urine, because it is hypoosmotic to the body fluids of the fish, represents a loss of water. However, the loss of water through the kidneys is low because the quantity of urine is low.

The larvae of some mosquitoes in the genus *Aedes* live in saltwater. These larvae meet the challenge of a high-salinity environment in ways analogous to those used by marine bony fish. Like marine bony fish, saltwater mosquitoes are hypoosmotic to the surrounding environment, to which they lose water. Saltwater mosquitoes also make up this water loss by drinking large amounts of seawater, up to 130% to 240% of body volume per day. This would even impress a camel! While this prodigious drinking solves the problem of water loss, it imports another: large quantities of salts that must be eliminated. Saltwater mosquitoes secrete these salts into the urine using specialized cells that line the posterior rectum. Here, saltwater mosquitoes do something that marine bony fish cannot. They excrete a urine that is hyperosmotic to their body fluids, which reduces water loss through the urine. The parallels in water and salt regulation by marine bony fish and saltwater mosquitoes are outlined in figure 6.32.

Freshwater Fish and Invertebrates

Freshwater bony fish face an environmental challenge opposite to that faced by marine bony fish. Freshwater fish are hyperosmotic; they have body fluids that contain more salt and less water than the surrounding medium. As a consequence, water floods inward and salts diffuse outward across their gills. Freshwater fish excrete excess internal water as large quantities of dilute urine. They replace the salts they lose to the external environment in two ways. Chloride cells at the base of the gill filaments absorb sodium and chloride from the water, while other salts are ingested with food.

Like freshwater fish, freshwater invertebrates are hyperosmotic to the surrounding environment. Freshwater invertebrates must expend energy to pump out the water that floods their tissues. They also expend energy by actively absorbing salts from the external environment. However, the concentration of solutes in the body fluids of freshwater invertebrates ranges from between about one-half and one-tenth that of their marine relatives. This lower internal concentration of

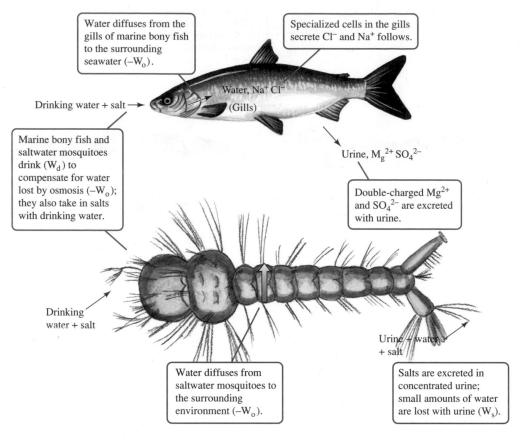

Water diffuses from the gills of marine bony fish to the surrounding seawater ($-W_o$).

Specialized cells in the gills secrete Cl^- and Na^+ follows.

Drinking water + salt

Water, Na^+ Cl^- (Gills)

Marine bony fish and saltwater mosquitoes drink (W_d) to compensate for water lost by osmosis ($-W_o$); they also take in salts with drinking water.

Urine, Mg^{2+} SO_4^{2-}

Double-charged Mg^{2+} and SO_4^{2-} are excreted with urine.

Drinking water + salt

Urine + water + salt

Water diffuses from saltwater mosquitoes to the surrounding environment ($-W_o$).

Salts are excreted in concentrated urine; small amounts of water are lost with urine (W_s).

Figure 6.32   Osmoregulation by marine fish and saltwater mosquitoes.

solutes reduces the osmotic gradient between freshwater and the outside environment and so reduces the energy freshwater invertebrates must expend to osmoregulate.

Freshwater mosquito larvae are a good model for osmoregulation by freshwater invertebrates. The larvae of approximately 95% of mosquito species live in freshwater, where they face osmotic challenges very similar to those faced by freshwater fish. Like freshwater fish, mosquito larvae must solve the twin problems of water gain and ion loss. In response, they drink very little water. They conserve ions taken with the diet by absorbing them with cells that line the midgut and rectum, and they secrete a dilute urine. Freshwater mosquito larvae replace the ions lost with urine by actively absorbing Na^+ and Cl^- from the water with cells in their anal papillae. Freshwater mosquitoes and fish use totally different structures to meet nearly identical environmental challenges. Figure 6.33 compares water and salt regulation by freshwater fish and mosquitoes.

In chapter 6, we have reviewed the water relations of individual organisms. The relationship between individual organisms and the environment is a fundamental aspect of ecology. However, ecologists are also concerned with levels of organization above the individual, such as the ecology of populations or of entire biomes. The following example in the Ecological Tools section shows how an understanding of the water relations of individual organisms is helping ecologists study the distribution of biomes across a continent.

Concept 6.3 Review

1. Why do isosmotic marine invertebrates expend less energy for osmoregulation compared to hypoosmotic marine fish?
2. The body fluids of many freshwater invertebrate species have very low internal salt concentrations. What is the benefit of such dilute internal fluids?

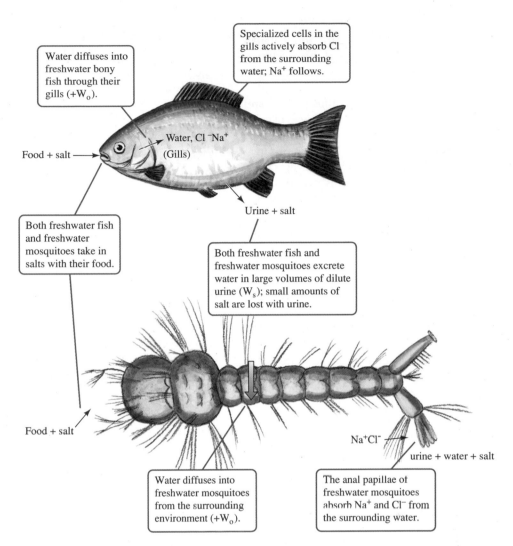

Water diffuses into freshwater bony fish through their gills ($+W_o$).

Specialized cells in the gills actively absorb Cl from the surrounding water; Na^+ follows.

Water, Cl^- Na^+ (Gills)

Food + salt

Urine + salt

Both freshwater fish and freshwater mosquitoes take in salts with their food.

Both freshwater fish and freshwater mosquitoes excrete water in large volumes of dilute urine (W_s); small amounts of salt are lost with urine.

Food + salt

Na^+Cl^-

urine + water + salt

Water diffuses into freshwater mosquitoes from the surrounding environment ($+W_o$).

The anal papillae of freshwater mosquitoes absorb Na^+ and Cl^- from the surrounding water.

Figure 6.33   Osmoregulation by freshwater fish and mosquitoes.

Ecological Tools

Using Stable Isotopes to Study Water Uptake by Plants

To fully understand the ecology of an individual plant or the dynamics of an entire landscape, ecologists need information about what happens below the earth's surface as well as about surface structure and processes. However, ecologists have produced much more information about the surface realm than about the subsurface, the domain of soil microbes, burrowing animals, and of roots. As we discussed in chapter 2, many ecologists have worked very hard to fill this gap in our knowledge. A major contributor to recent progress in below ground ecology has been the development of new tools. One of the most important of those is **stable isotope analysis,** which involves the analysis of the relative concentrations of stable isotopes, such as the stable isotopes of carbon ^{13}C and ^{12}C, in materials. Stable isotope analysis is increasingly used in ecol-

ogy to study the flow of energy and materials through ecosystems (Dawson et al. 2002). For instance, stable isotope analysis has proved a very powerful tool in studies of water uptake by plants. To understand the applications of this analytical tool, we need to know a little about the isotopes themselves and about their behaviour in ecosystems.

Stable Isotope Analysis

Most chemical elements include several stable isotopes, which occur in different concentrations in different environments or differ in concentration from one organism to another. Stable isotopes of hydrogen include ^1H and ^2H, which is generally designated as D, an abbreviation of deuterium. Stable isotopes of carbon, for example, include ^{13}C and ^{12}C; stable isotopes of nitrogen include ^{15}N and ^{14}N; and stable isotopes of sulfur include ^{34}S and ^{32}S. The relative concentrations of these stable isotopes can be used to study the flow of energy and materials through ecosystems because different parts of the ecosystem often contain different concentrations of the light and heavy isotopes of these elements.

Different organisms contain different ratios of light and heavy stable isotopes because they use different sources of these elements, because they preferentially use (fractionate) different stable isotopes, or because they use different sources *and* fractionate. For instance, the lighter isotope of nitrogen, ^{14}N, is more likely to be excreted than is ^{15}N by organisms during protein synthesis. As a consequence of this preferential excretion of ^{14}N, an organism becomes relatively enriched in ^{15}N compared to its food. Therefore, as materials pass from one trophic level to the next, tissues become richer in ^{15}N. The highest trophic levels within an ecosystem contain the highest relative concentrations of ^{15}N, while the lowest trophic levels contain the lowest concentrations. Stable isotope analysis can also measure the relative contribution of C_3 and C_4 plants to a species' diet. This is possible because C_4 plants are richer in ^{13}C than are C_3 plants. Other processes affect the relative concentrations of stable isotopes of sulfur. Because different sources of water often have different ratios of D to ^1H, for example, shallow soil moisture versus deep soil moisture, hydrogen isotope analyses have been valuable aids to identifying where plants acquire their water.

The concentrations of stable isotopes are generally expressed as differences in the concentration of the heavier isotope relative to some standard. The units of measurement are differences (±) in parts per thousand (± $^0/_{00}$). These differences are calculated as:

$$\delta X = \left[\left(\frac{R_{sample}}{R_{standard}}\right) - 1\right] \times 10$$

where:

$\delta = \pm$

X = the relative concentration of the heavier isotope, for example, D, ^{13}C, ^{15}N, or ^{34}S in $^0/_{00}$

R_{sample} = the isotopic ratio in the sample, for example, D:^1H, ^{13}C:^{12}C, or ^{15}N:^{14}N

$R_{standard}$ = the isotopic ratio in the standard, for example, D:^1H, ^{13}C:^{12}C, or ^{15}N:^{14}N

The reference materials used as standards in the isotopic analyses of hydrogen, nitrogen, carbon, and sulfur are the D:^1H ratio in Standard Mean Ocean Water, the ^{15}N:^{14}N ratio in atmospheric nitrogen, the ^{13}C:^{12}C ratio in PeeDee limestone, and the ^{34}S:^{32}S in the Canyon Diablo meteorite.

The ecologist measures the ratio of stable isotopes in a sample and then expresses that ratio as a difference relative to some standard. If $\delta X = 0$, then the ratios of the isotopes in the sample and the standard are the same; if $\delta X = -X$ $^0/_{00}$, the concentration of the heavier isotope is lower (e.g., ^{15}N) in the sample compared to the standard, and if $\delta X = +X$ $^0/_{00}$, the concentration of the heavier isotope is higher in the sample compared to the standard. The important point here is that

these isotopic ratios are generally different in different parts of ecosystems. Therefore, ecologists can use isotopic ratios to study the structure and processes in ecosystems. Here is an example of how hydrogen isotope ratios have been used to study the uptake of water by plants in a natural ecosystem. We will discuss other uses of stable isotopic analyses in later chapters.

Using Stable Isotopes to Identify Plant Water Sources

The laboratory of James Ehleringer has taken a leadership role in the development of stable isotope analysis as a tool for assessing water relations among plants and within ecosystems (e.g., Ehleringer, Roden, and Dawson 2000). In an early study Ehleringer and several colleagues (Ehleringer et al. 1991) used deuterium:hydrogen (D:^1H) ratios, or δD, to explore the use of summer versus winter rainfall by various plant growth forms in the deserts of southern Utah. They could use δD to determine the relative utilization of these two water sources since summer rains are relatively enriched with D and winter rains are relatively depleted of D. The δD of summer and winter rains in southern Utah at the time of Ehleringer's study were -25 $^0/_{00}$ and -90 $^0/_{00}$ respectively (fig. 6.34).

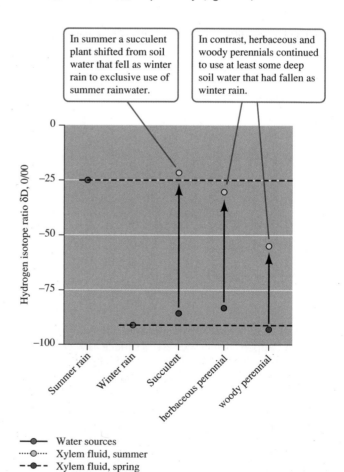

Figure 6.34 Stable isotope analysis identified the water sources used by three groups of desert plants during the spring and summer (data from Ehleringer et al. 1991).

Ehleringer measured δD in the xylem fluid of several plant growth forms during spring, when soil moisture at all rooting depths would be predominantly from winter precipitation and summer, when summer precipitation would be present as moisture in surface soils and winter precipitation would predominate at deeper soil layers. Ehleringer and his research team found that a succulent, several herbaceous perennials, and several woody perennials used winter moisture in the spring (fig. 6.34). However, when summer rains fell the succulent species shifted entirely to using soil moisture from summer rains that were stored mainly at shallow soil depths. Meanwhile herbaceous and woody perennials continued to use significant amounts of deeper soil moisture that fell the previous winter. So, stable isotope analysis opens a window to the water relations of plants that would not be accessible without this innovative tool.

Summary

The movement of water down concentration gradients in terrestrial and aquatic environments determines the availability of water to organisms. The most familiar relative measure of the water content of air is relative humidity, defined as water vapour density divided by saturation water vapour density multiplied by 100. On land, the tendency of water to move from organisms to the atmosphere can be approximated by the vapour pressure deficit of the air. Vapour pressure deficit is calculated as the difference between the actual water vapour pressure and the saturation water vapour pressure.

In the aquatic environment, water moves down its concentration gradient, from solutions of higher water concentration and lower salt content (hypoosmotic) to solutions of lower water concentration and higher salt content (hyperosmotic). This movement of water creates osmotic pressure. Larger osmotic differences, between organism and environment, generate higher osmotic pressures.

In the soil-plant system water flows from areas of higher water potential to areas of lower water potential. The water potential of pure water, which by convention is set at zero, is reduced by adding solute and by matric forces, the tendency of water to cling to soil particles and to plant cell walls. Typically, the water potential of plant fluids is determined by a combination of solute concentrations and matric forces, while the water potential of soils is determined mainly by matric forces. In saline soils, solutes may also influence soil water potential. Water potential, osmotic pressure, and vapour pressure deficit can all be measured in pascals (newtons/m^2), a common currency for considering the water relations of diverse organisms in very different environments.

Terrestrial plants and animals regulate their internal water by balancing water acquisition against water loss. Water regulation by terrestrial animals is summarized by $W_i = W_d + W_f + W_a - W_e - W_s$, where W_d = drinking, W_f = taken in with food, W_a = absorption from the air, W_e = evaporation, and W_s = secretions and excretions. Water regulation by terrestrial plants is summarized by $W_i = W_r + W_a - W_t - W_s$, where W_r = uptake by roots, W_a = absorption from the air, W_t = transpiration, and W_s = secretions and reproductive structures. Some very different terrestrial plants and animals, such as the camel and saguaro cactus, use similar mechanisms to survive in arid climates. Some organisms, such as scorpions and cicadas, use radically different mechanisms. Comparisons such as these suggest that natural selection is opportunistic.

Marine and freshwater organisms use complementary mechanisms for water and salt regulation. Marine and freshwater organisms face exactly opposite osmotic challenges. Water regulation in aquatic environments is summarized by: $W_i = W_d - W_s \pm W_o$, where W_d = drinking, W_s = secretions and excretions, W_o = osmosis. An aquatic organism may either gain or lose water through osmosis, depending on the organism and the environment. Many marine invertebrates reduce their water regulation problems by being isosmotic with seawater. Some freshwater invertebrates also reduce the osmotic gradient between themselves and their environment. Sharks, skates, and rays elevate the urea and TMAO content of their body fluids to the point where they are slightly hyperosmotic to seawater. Marine bony fish and saltwater mosquito larvae are hypoosmotic relative to their environments, while freshwater bony fish and freshwater mosquito larvae are hyperosmotic.

While the strength of environmental challenge varies from one environment to another, and the details of water regulation vary from one organism to another, all organisms in all environments expend energy to maintain their internal pool of water and dissolved substances.

Stable isotope analysis, an important new tool in ecology, involves the analysis of the relative concentrations of stable isotopes in materials. Examples of stable isotopes include the stable isotopes of hydrogen ^2H (which is usually symbolized by D, referring to deuterium) and ^1H, and the stable isotopes of carbon, ^{13}C and ^{12}C. Stable isotope analysis has proved a very powerful tool in studies of water uptake by plants. For example deuterium:hydrogen (D:^1H) ratios, or δD, has been used to quantify the relative use of summer versus winter rainfall by various plant growth forms in the deserts of southern Utah.

Review Questions

1. Turn back to chapter 5 and examine figure 5.6. Notice that the body temperature of the isopod *Ligia oceanica* is 30°C under stones but 26°C on the surface, where it is exposed to full sun. Edney (1953) proposed that the isopods in the open had lower body temperatures because they evaporatively cooled in the open air. Explain why evaporative cooling would be effective in the open air but nearly impossible under stones.

2. Distinguish between vapour pressure deficit, osmotic pressure, and water potential. How can all three phenomena be expressed in the same units of measure: pascals?

3. Leaf water potential is typically highest just before dawn and then decreases progressively through midday. Should lower leaf water potentials at midday increase or decrease the rate of water movement from soil to a plant? Assume soil water potential is approximately the same in early morning and midday. Are the water needs of the plant greater in early morning or at midday?

4. Compare the water budgets of the tenebrionid beetle, *Onymacris,* and the kangaroo rat, *Dipodomys,* shown in figures 6.11 and 6.12. Which of these two species obtains most of its water from metabolic water? Which relies most on condensation of fog as a water source? In which species do you see greater losses of water through the urine?

5. In the Sonoran Desert, the only insects known to evaporatively cool are cicadas. Explain how cicadas can employ evaporative cooling while hundreds of other insect species in the same environment cannot.

6. Many desert species are well waterproofed. Evolution cannot, however, eliminate all evaporative water loss. Why not? (Hint: Think of the kinds of exchanges that an organism must maintain with its environment.)

7. While we have concentrated in chapter 6 on regulation of water and salts, most marine invertebrates are isosmotic with their external environment. What is a potential benefit of being isosmotic?

8. Review water and salt regulation by marine and freshwater bony fish. Which of the two is hypoosmotic relative to its environment? Which of the two is hyperosmotic relative to its environment? Some sharks live in freshwater. How should the kidneys of marine and freshwater sharks function?

9. Some plants in the tropics use wilting as a mechanism to decrease internal water potentials and thus increase water uptake. However, many plants in temperate and boreal regions also wilt on hot summer days. Does wilting have a similar physiological effect on these plants from different regions, or are different mechanisms of water uptake operating in different parts of the world?

10. Jochen Schenk and Robert Jackson (2002) have shown that outside of the tropics, rooting depth decreases as you move towards the poles. Use what you have learned in other chapters about the biomes in each region of the globe to provide a potential explanation for this pattern.

Suggested Readings

Dawson, T. E., S. Mambelli, A. H. Plamboeck, P. H. Templer, and K. P. Tu. 2002. Stable isotopes in plant ecology. *Annual Review of Ecology and Systematics* 33:507–99.

Ehleringer, J. R., J. Roden, and T. E. Dawson. 2000. Assessing ecosystem-level water relations through stable isotope ratio analyses. In O. E. Sala, R. B. Jackson, H. A. Mooney, and R. W. Howarth. eds. *Methods in Ecosystem Science.* New York: Springer.

Overview and introduction to stable isotope analysis in ecology.

Dong, X. J. and X. S. Zhang. 2001. Some observations of the adaptations of sandy shrubs to the arid environment of the Mu Us Sandland: leaf water relations and anatomic features. *Journal of Arid Environments* 48:41–48.

Ohte, N., K. Koba, K. Yoshikawa, A. Sugimoto, N. Matsuo, N. Kabeya, and L. H. Wang. 2003. Water utilization of natural and planted trees in the semiarid desert of Inner Mongolia, China. *Ecological Applications* 13:337–51.

Introduction to some of the plants and application of stable isotope analysis to understanding one of the great deserts of the world.

Duncan, F. D. and M. J. Byrne. 2005. The role of the mesothoracic spiracles in respiration in flighted and flightless dung beetles. *The Journal of Experimental Biology* 208:907–14.

Fascinating recent discoveries of water conservation mechanisms in closely related beetles species that live along a gradient of aridity in southern Africa.

Schenk, H. J. and R. B. Jackson. 2002. The global biogeography of roots. *Ecological Monographs* 72:311–28.

Intriguing analysis of a massive set of 475 root profiles from 209 localities from around the earth.

Tracy, R. L. and G. E. Walsberg. 2000. Prevalence of cutaneous evaporation in Merriam's kangaroo rat and its adaptive variation at the subspecific level. *Journal of Experimental Biology* 203:773–81.

Tracy, R. L. and G. E. Walsberg. 2001. Intraspecific variation in water loss in a desert rodent, *Dipodomys merriami. Ecology* 82:1130–37.

Tracy, R. L. and G. E. Walsberg. 2002. Kangaroo rats revisited: re-evaluating a classic case of desert survival. *Oecologia* 133:449–57.

Studies revealing adaptation to local climates by a desert rodent long studied by physiological ecologists.

Chapter *7*

Energy and Nutrient Relations

Outline

*E*vidence of nutrient and energy acquisition by animals and plants can be seen everywhere in nature. A scorpion fish lies half buried in the sand near the edge of a coral reef; the only clues to its presence are the telltale movements of its gill covers. Its head looks so much like an algae-covered stone that several tiny shrimp gather over it and swim lazily in the current. A small fish on the nearby reef sees the shrimp and darts over to feed on them. The scorpion fish opens its mouth and swallows the small fish in a lightning-quick movement. However, before the scorpion fish can settle back into the sand, a green moray eel, nearly 2 m long, darts from the reef, grabs the scorpion fish with its razor-sharp teeth, and swallows it (fig. 7.1).

An herbaceous plant with broad leaves and slender stems grows in the half light of the rain forest floor. It is difficult to understand how it can live in such dim light. However, as you watch, a small shaft of intense sunlight pierces an unseen hole in the rain forest canopy and shines on one of the plant's leaves. The photosynthetic machinery of the plant takes advantage of the situation, and for a few minutes the plant uses the energy of the tiny sun fleck. Nearby is the buttressed trunk of a gigantic tree that has grown tall enough to emerge from the forest canopy and count itself among the rain forest giants, seemingly a more secure position than that of the understory herb. However, a small vine has begun to grow up the side of the tree. It will grow quickly upward, winding its way toward the sun and exploiting the woody support of the tree. Soon the vine will overwhelm and kill the tree, which will be reduced to a trellis for the vine.

Whether on coral reef, rain forest, or abandoned urban lot, organisms engage in an active search for energy and nutrients. For most organisms, life boils down to converting energy and nutrients into descendants. The energy used by different organisms comes in the form of light, organic molecules, or inorganic molecules. Nutrients are the raw materials an organism must acquire from the environment to live. Because organisms acquire energy and nutrients in diverse ways, we need to organize our discussion under the umbrella of major concepts. In chapter 7, we focus on three.

Concepts

7.1 **Organisms use one of three main sources of energy: light, organic molecules, or inorganic molecules.**

7.2 **The rate at which organisms can take in energy is limited.**

7.3 **Optimal foraging theory attempts to model how organisms feed as an optimizing process.**

7.1   Energy Sources

Organisms use one of three main sources of energy: light, organic molecules, or inorganic molecules.   Undergraduate students are often taught about biological diversity by grouping organisms on the basis of shared evolutionary histories.

Figure 7.1   The moray eel meets its energy and nutrient needs by being an effective predator.

This evolutionary approach allows for focused lectures on specific taxa such as vertebrate animals, insects, coniferous trees, and orchids. Such an approach is a useful way to understand the diversity of life but there are alternative approaches that may be more helpful in understanding functional similarities among species. One approach ecologists often use is to classify organisms by how they obtain energy—that is, by their **trophic (feeding) biology.** Organisms that use inorganic sources of both carbon and energy are called **autotrophs** ("self-feeders") and are of two types, **photosynthetic** and **chemosynthetic.** Photosynthetic autotrophs use carbon dioxide (CO_2) as a source of carbon and light as a source of energy. This group includes the plants, photosynthetic protists, and photosynthetic bacteria. These taxa have independent evolutionary histories, but share a key aspect of their ecology; the means by which they acquire energy. Chemosynthetic autotrophs use inorganic molecules as a source of carbon and energy. These are made up of a highly diverse group of chemosynthetic bacteria. **Heterotrophs** ("other-feeders") are organisms that use organic molecules both as a source of carbon and as a source of energy. The heterotrophs include bacteria, fungi, protists, animals, and parasitic plants.

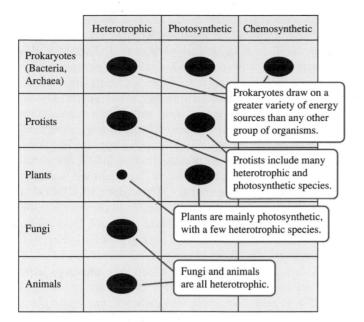

	Heterotrophic	Photosynthetic	Chemosynthetic
Prokaryotes (Bacteria, Archaea)	⬤	⬤	⬤
Protists	⬤	⬤	
Plants	•	⬤	
Fungi	⬤		
Animals	⬤		

Prokaryotes draw on a greater variety of energy sources than any other group of organisms.

Protists include many heterotrophic and photosynthetic species.

Plants are mainly photosynthetic, with a few heterotrophic species.

Fungi and animals are all heterotrophic.

Figure 7.2   A plot of trophic diversity across the major groups of organisms shows highest trophic diversity among the prokaryotic bacteria and archaea.

Prokaryotes show more trophic diversity than the other biological kingdoms (fig. 7.2). Prokaryotes, which have cells with no membrane-bound nucleus or organelles, include the bacteria and the **archaea.** The archaea are prokaryotes distinguished from bacteria on the basis of structural, physiological, and other biological features. Though first discovered in association with extreme environments, the archaea are now known to be widely spread in the biosphere, particularly in the oceans. The protists are either photosynthetic or heterotrophic, most plants are photosynthetic, and all fungi and animals are heterotrophic. In contrast, the prokaryotes include photosynthetic, chemosynthetic, and heterotrophic species, making them, as a group, the most trophically diverse organisms in the biosphere.

Some of the most ecologically significant discoveries of prokaryotic trophic diversity have come from studies of marine prokaryotes. For instance, Oded Béjà and Edward Delong and their research team discovered a new type of energy production from light, involving bacterial **rhodopsin** (Béjà et al. 2000). Rhodopsins are light-absorbing pigments found in animal eyes and in the bacteria and archaea. The rhodopsin in bacteria and archaea performs a variety of functions, including that of a proton pump involved in ATP synthesis, that is, in the production of energy. Further study by Béjà, Delong, and their research team (Béjà et al. 2001) has shown that bacterial rhodopsin is widespread through the oceans. In one particularly intriguing aspect of their study, they found that the light sensitivity of bacterial rhodopsin appears adapted to local variations in light quality. For instance, bacterial rhodopsin from deep clear waters absorbs light most strongly within the blue range of the visible spectrum, while that from shallow coastal waters absorbs most strongly in the green range (chapter 3). Discoveries such as these and others (e.g., Kolber et al. 2000, Béjà et al. 2002) are rapidly revolutionizing our understanding of how the biosphere works.

Photosynthesis

Because photosynthetic organisms use light as a source of energy, we need to learn about light. We also need to understand how photosynthetic organisms use CO_2. These are topics we investigate next.

The Solar-Powered Biosphere

As we saw in chapters 2 and 3, solar energy powers the winds and ocean currents, and annual variation in sunlight intensity drives the seasons. In chapter 5, we also discussed how organisms use sunlight to regulate body temperature. Here, building on those discussions, we look at light as a source of energy for photosynthesis.

Light propagates through space as a wave, with all the properties of waves such as frequency and wavelength. When light interacts with matter, however, it acts not as a wave but as a particle. Particles of light, called *photons,* bear a finite quantity of energy. Longer wavelengths, such as *infrared light,* carry less energy than shorter wavelengths, such as *visible* and *ultraviolet light.*

Infrared light, as we saw in chapter 5 (see fig. 5.16), is very important for temperature regulation by organisms. This is because the main effect of infrared light on matter is to increase the motion of whole molecules, which we measure as increased temperature. However, infrared light does not carry enough energy to drive photosynthesis. At the other end of the solar spectrum, ultraviolet light carries so much energy that it breaks the covalent bonds of many organic molecules. Because it can break down organic molecules, ultraviolet light can destroy the complex biochemical machinery of photosynthesis. Between these extremes is the light we can see, so-called visible light, which is also called **photosynthetically active radiation,** or **PAR.** PAR, with wavelengths between about 400 and 700 nm, carries sufficient energy to drive the light-dependent reactions of photosynthesis but not so much as to destroy organic molecules. PAR makes up about 45% of the total energy content of the solar spectrum at sea level, while infrared light accounts for about 53% and ultraviolet light for the remainder.

Measuring PAR

Ecologists quantify PAR as photon flux density. **Photon flux density** is the number of photons striking a square meter surface each second. The number of photons is expressed as micromoles (μmol), where 1 mole is Avagadro's number of photons, 6.023×10^{23}. To give you a point of reference, a photon flux density of about 4.6 μmol per square meter per second equals a light intensity of about 1 watt per square meter. Measuring light as photosynthetic photon flux density makes sense ecologically because chlorophyll absorbs light as photons.

Light changes in quantity and quality with latitude, with the seasons, with the weather, and with the time of day. In addition, landscapes, water, and even organisms themselves change the amount and quality of light. For example, in aquatic environments (see chapter 3), only the superficial euphotic zone receives sufficient light to support photosynthetic organisms. In addition, light changes in quality, as well as quantity, within the euphotic zone, which ranges in depth from a few meters to about 100 m.

As in the sea, sunlight changes as it shines through the canopy of a forest. A mature temperate or boreal forest can reduce the total quantity of light reaching the forest floor to about 1% to 2% of the amount shining on the forest canopy (fig. 7.3). However, forests also change the quality of sunlight. Within the range of photosynthetically active radiation, leaves absorb mainly blue and red light and transmit mostly green light with a wavelength of about 550 nm. As in the deep sea, the organisms on the forest floor live in a kind of twilight. Only here, the twilight is green. We will discuss how plants respond to altered light quality in chapter 13, Competition.

Alternative Photosynthetic Pathways

During photosynthesis, the photosynthetic pigments of plants, algae, or bacteria absorb light and transfer their energy to electrons. Subsequently, the energy carried by these electrons is used to synthesize ATP and NADPH. This process generally requires complex photosystems and only occurs in the light. Perhaps it comes as no surprise that these reactions are generally referred to as "light reactions." These molecules, in turn, serve as donors of electrons and energy for the synthesis of sugars. This second stage can generally occur in the light or in the dark, and these are referred to as the "dark reactions" of photosynthesis. In this way, photosynthetic organisms convert the electromagnetic energy of sunlight into energy-rich organic molecules, the fuel that feeds most of the biosphere. Within photosynthetic organisms, specific biochemical pathways carry out this energy conversion; three different biochemical pathways are known: C_3 photosynthesis, C_4 photosynthesis, and CAM photosynthesis.

Biologists often speak of photosynthesis as "carbon fixation," which refers to the reactions in which CO_2 becomes incorporated into a carbon-containing acid. In the photosynthetic pathway used by most plants and all algae, the CO_2 first combines with a five-carbon compound called *ribulose bisphosphate*,

or *RuBP*. The product of this initial reaction, which is catalyzed by the enzyme RuBP carboxylase (RUBISCO), is *phosphoglyceric acid,* or *PGA,* a three-carbon acid. Therefore, this photosynthetic pathway is usually called C_3 **photosynthesis** and the plants that employ it are called C_3 plants (fig. 7.4).

To fix carbon, plants must open their stomata to let CO_2 into their leaves, but as CO_2 enters, water exits. Water vapour flows out faster than CO_2 flows in. The movement of water is more rapid because the gradient in water concentration from the leaf to the atmosphere is much steeper than the gradient in CO_2 concentration from the atmosphere to the leaf. In C_3 plants, there is another factor that contributes to a low rate of CO_2 uptake: RUBISCO has a low affinity for CO_2. Relatively high rates of water loss are generally not a problem for plants that live in cool, moist conditions but in hot, dry climates, high rates of water loss can close the stomata and shut down photosynthesis (see chapter 6).

In arid environments, two alternative photosynthetic pathways have repeatedly evolved. Both pathways fix and store CO_2 in acids containing four carbon atoms. Light plays no part in carbon fixation, but the reactions that follow depend on light. Both alternative pathways separate the initial fixation of carbon from the light-dependent reactions.

One of these alternative pathways, C_4 **photosynthesis,** separates carbon fixation and the light-dependent reactions of photosynthesis into separate cells (fig. 7.5). C_4 plants fix CO_2 in mesophyll cells by combining it with *phosphoenol pyruvate,* or *PEP,* to produce an acid. This initial reaction, which is catalyzed by PEP carboxylase, concentrates CO_2. Because PEP carboxylase has a high affinity for CO_2, C_4 plants can reduce their internal CO_2 concentrations to very low levels. Low internal concentration of CO_2 increases the gradient of CO_2 from atmosphere to leaf, which in turn increases the rate of diffusion of CO_2 inward. Consequently, compared to C_3 plants, C_4 plants need to open fewer stomata to deliver sufficient CO_2 to photosynthesizing cells. By having fewer stomata open, C_4 plants conserve water.

In C_4 plants, the acids produced during carbon fixation diffuse to specialized cells surrounding a structure called the **bundle sheath.** There, deeper in the leaf, the four-carbon acids are broken down to a three-carbon acid and CO_2. C_4 photosynthesis also benefits plants by reducing, or even eliminating, **photorespiration**. Although RUBISCO is a carboxylase (it binds CO_2 to RuBP), it can also serve as an oxygenase, binding O_2 to RuBP. When this happens, RuBP is partly broken down and a CO_2 molecule is released from the plant, a process known as photorespiration. Needless to say, release of CO_2 from a plant is counter to the needs of photosynthesis, resulting in reduced energetic efficiency and increased water loss associated with needing to keep stomata open longer. One of the major factors influencing the rate of photorespiration is the concentration of O_2 relative to that of CO_2, with increased photorespiration in a relatively oxygen-rich and carbon dioxide-poor atmosphere. If RUBISCO is both an oxygenase and a carboxylase, why don't C_4 plants, which still contain RUBISCO, photorespire? Quite simply, their unique morphology segregates RUBISCO into the bundle sheath cells. By doing this, plants put this enzyme in an area of high CO_2 concentration (remember, it is transported out of the mesophyll cells), and low O_2 concentrations. Why are the bundle sheath cells of lower O_2

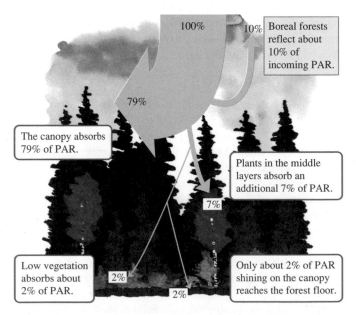

100% 10% — Boreal forests reflect about 10% of incoming PAR.

79%

The canopy absorbs 79% of PAR.

Plants in the middle layers absorb an additional 7% of PAR.

7%

Low vegetation absorbs about 2% of PAR.

2%

2%

Only about 2% of PAR shining on the canopy reaches the forest floor.

Figure 7.3 Photosynthetically active radiation (PAR) diminishes substantially with passage through the canopy of a boreal forest (data from Larcher 1995, after Kairiukstis 1967).

concentration than the mesophyll? Because the O_2 generated by the light reactions of photosynthesis occurs in the mesophyll and not the bundle sheath cells. The impacts of atmospheric oxygen and carbon dioxide levels will have strong selective forces on plant photosynthesis and evolution, something we will discuss more in the Ecology In Action section of this chapter. It is interesting to notice that C_4 plants appear to have evolved primarily during periods of low atmospheric CO_2 (Sage 2004). Review C_3 and C_4 photosynthesis (figs. 7.4 and 7.5) before considering the third major photosynthetic pathway.

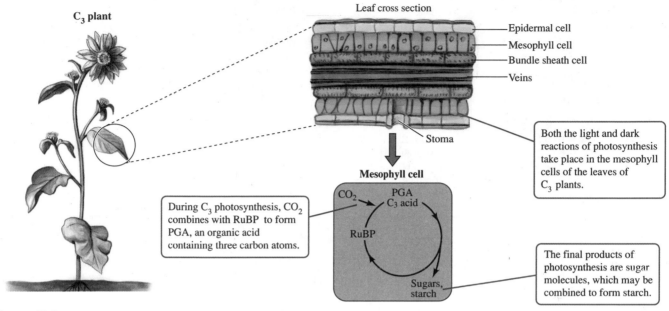

Figure 7.4 C_3 photosynthesis.

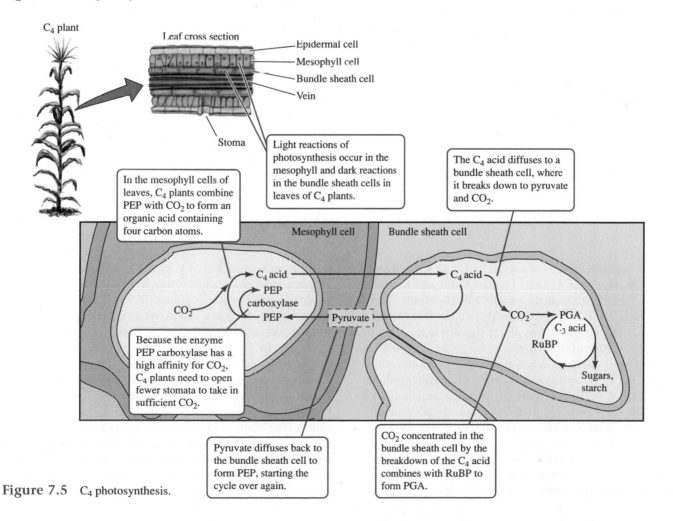

Figure 7.5 C_4 photosynthesis.

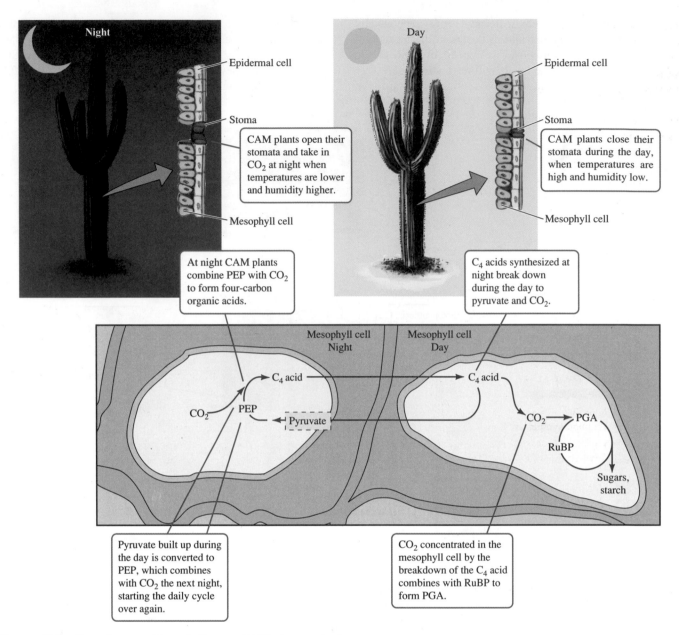

Figure 7.6 Crassulacean acid metabolism, or CAM, photosynthesis.

CAM (crassulacean acid metabolism) **photosynthesis** is largely limited to succulent plants in arid and semiarid environments. In this pathway, carbon fixation takes place at night, when lower temperatures reduce the rate of water loss during CO_2 uptake. CAM plants fix carbon by combining CO_2 with PEP to form four-carbon acids. These acids are stored until daylight, when they are broken down into pyruvate and CO_2, which then enters the C_3 photosynthetic pathway (fig. 7.6). In CAM plants, all these reactions take place in the same cells. While CAM plants do not normally show very high rates of photosynthesis, their water use efficiency, as estimated by the mass of CO_2 fixed per kilogram of water used, is higher than that of either C_3 or C_4 plants.

Separating initial carbon fixation from the other reactions reduces water losses during photosynthesis: C_3 plants lose from about 380 to 900 g of water for every gram (dry weight) of tissue produced. C_4 plants lose from about 250 to 350 g of water per gram of tissue produced, while CAM plants lose approximately 50 g of water per gram of new tissue. The differences in these numbers give us one of the reasons C_4 and CAM plants do well in hot, dry environments.

Whether the pathway of carbon fixation is CAM, C_3, or C_4, plants and photosynthetic algae and bacteria capture energy from sunlight and carbon from CO_2. These photosynthesizers package this energy and carbon in organic molecules. The photosynthesizers and other autotrophs opened the way for the evolution of organisms that could get their energy and carbon from organic molecules. And this new trophic level did indeed evolve.

Heterotrophs

Heterotrophic organisms use organic molecules both as a source of carbon and as an energy source. They depend, ultimately, on the carbon and energy fixed by autotrophs. Heterotrophs have evolved numerous ways of feeding. This trophic variety has stimulated ecologists to invent numerous terms to describe the ways heterotrophs feed, including browsers, grazers, detritivores, and omnivores. A full list of the trophic categories proposed by ecologists would be impossibly long and not especially useful to this discussion. So, we will concentrate on three major categories of consumers: **herbivores,** organisms that eat living plants; **carnivores,** organisms that mainly eat living animals; and **detritivores,** organisms that feed on nonliving organic matter. Herbivores, carnivores, and detritivores must solve fundamentally different problems to obtain adequate supplies of energy and nutrients.

Chemical Composition and Nutrient Requirements

We can get some idea of the nutrient requirements of organisms by examining their chemical composition. Biologists have found that the chemical composition of organisms is very similar. Just five elements (carbon [C], oxygen [O], hydrogen [H], nitrogen [N], and phosphorus [P]) make up 93% to 97% of the biomass of plants, animals, fungi, and bacteria. Of these four groups, plants are the most distinctive chemically. Plant tissues generally contain lower concentrations of phosphorus and nitrogen. The nitrogen content of plant tissues averages about 2%, while in fungi, animals, and bacteria it averages about 5% to 10%. Ecologists often express the relative nitrogen content of whole organisms or tissues as the ratio of carbon to nitrogen (C:N ratios). A high C:N ratio indicates low nitrogen content. The C:N ratio of plants averages about 25:1, which is substantially higher than the C:N ratios of animals, fungi, and bacteria, which average approximately 5:1 to 10:1 (fig. 7.7). Differences in C:N ratios among tissues or among organisms significantly influence what organisms eat, how rapidly consumers reproduce, and how rapidly organisms decompose. You may begin to recognize an ecological puzzle. How can an herbivore create a C:N ratio of 10:1 if it only eats food that has a 25:1 ratio?

If carbon, oxygen, hydrogen, nitrogen, and phosphorus make up 93% to 97% living biomass, then what accounts for the remainder? Dozens of other elements occur in the tissues of organisms. Essential plant nutrients include potassium (K), calcium (Ca), magnesium (Mg), sulfur (S), chlorine (Cl), iron (Fe), manganese (Mn), boron (B), zinc (Zn), copper (Cu), and molybdenum (Mo). Most of these nutrients are also essential for other organisms. Some organisms require additional nutrients. For instance, animals also require sodium (Na) and iodine (I).

Plants obtain carbon from the air through their stomata. They obtain other essential nutrients from the soil through their roots. For the most part, consumers obtain both the energy they require and essential nutrients with their food. Let's now turn to the energy and nutrient relations of detritivorous, herbivorous, and carnivorous organisms.

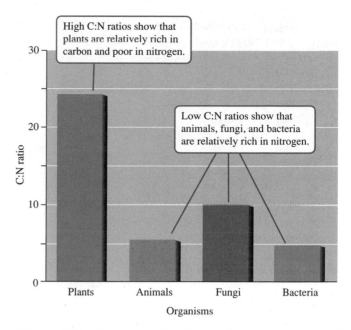

Figure 7.7 On average, the ratio of carbon to nitrogen is much higher in terrestrial plants than in other major groups of organisms (data from Spector 1956).

Detritivores

Often the first images related to the consumption of organic matter that come to mind will be something like a pack of wolves on the hunt, or even a herd of elk grazing in the mountains. As beautiful as these images may be, they do not reflect the reality: that most consumption is done by small-bodied insects, fungi, and bacteria. Most biomass produced on this planet is consumed after it dies, not while it is alive. As a result, detritivores control the movement of energy and nutrients in most ecosystems, a topic we will discuss in more depth in chapters 19 and 20. Here we will discuss some of the common constraints facing this exceptionally diverse group of species. It is important in this context to understand that in terms of biomass, animals are rare on this planet, with the majority of biomass found in plants, bacteria, and fungi (this too will be discussed in chapter 19). As a result, one of the most dominant food sources for detritivores will be dead plants and plant parts.

A central problem faced by detritivores is that dead plants are rich in carbon and energy but very poor in nitrogen. In other words, dead logs are great for the campfire, but not for serving as dinner. Dead plant litter is in fact of lower "quality" (where quality refers to N content) than living plants (fig. 7.8), which are themselves low in N relative to the organisms that feed upon them (fig. 7.7). Why might dead leaves contain less N than living leaves, even before detritivores have attacked these leaves? Nitrogen, unlike light energy, is reusable by plants. It also is often the most limiting nutrient for plant growth in natural systems. As a result there has often been strong selection acting on plants to increase their **nitrogen use efficiency (NUE)**. NUE is similar to water use efficiency discussed in chapter 6, and represents how much plants are able to grow per unit of nitrogen. One mechanism to improve NUE is to reabsorb nitrogen contained in plant organs, such as leaves,

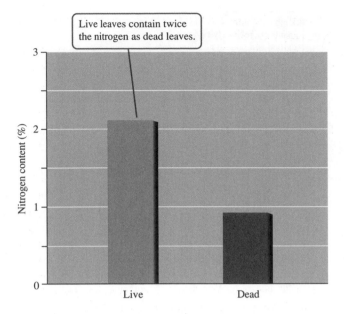

Figure 7.8 Nitrogen content of live and dead leaves (data from Killingbeck and Whitford 1996).

before the leaves are dropped from the plant, leaving a very nitrogen-poor substrate for the detritivores.

The main problems that detritivores face can be roughly summarized as search, handling, and quality. Individual organ-

isms, be they a snail, mite, or fungus, first need to find a potential food item. Once found, that item then needs to be captured, consumed, and digested. Upon digestion, the quality of the food impacts an organism's need to continue foraging, or to allocate time for a different activity. For detritivores, body size influences both the microhabitat in which they are able to live as well as a species' ability to find and handle food. Across species, detritivore body sizes range from less than one micrometer for some bacteria to over two meters for some giant earthworms. Because of the importance size plays in influencing the feeding ecology of these species, terrestrial detritivores are often classified by their size, and not solely their taxonomic affiliation (fig. 7.9). The smallest of the detritivorous animals (microfauna) live primarily within the film of water that adheres to soil particles. The slightly larger mesofauna tend to be found in larger pore spaces within the soil, while the macrofauna such as earthworms are able to create habitat through their movement. In addition to creating pore spaces in the soil, these larger classes of detritivores are also active in converting large fragments of litter (e.g., dead leaves) into small fragments, facilitating the feeding of the smaller detritivores.

Due to the relatively high abundance of plants in most communities (at least relative to animals), input of dead material is not usually limiting to the fitness of detritivorous species. Instead, the abiotic environment and chemical composition of the dead material have more direct impacts. In particular,

Figure 7.9 Detritivores are often classified according to their body size (data from Swift et al. 1979).

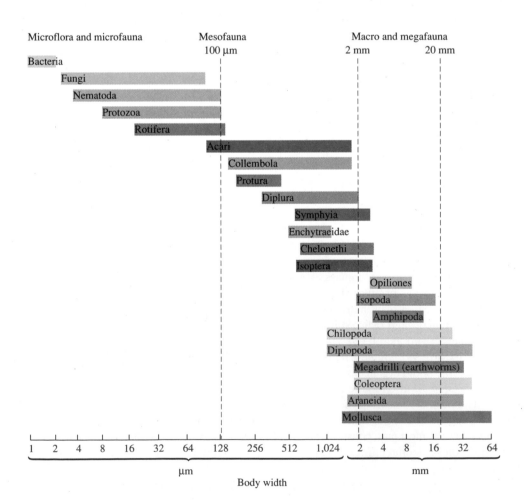

limited soil moisture greatly reduces the activity and growth of the smaller detritivores, particularly the microfauna that live within water films. As for most ectotherms, increased soil temperatures will increase body temperatures and enzymatic activity of detritivores; however, if this is coupled with reduced soil moisture many species will become dormant or will move to cooler and moister areas within the soil (i.e., shaded, deeper, etc.). Finally, tissues with lower C:N ratios will result in increased detritivore growth and activity relative to tissues with high C:N ratios. Like all other organisms, detritivores have preferred food sources, which not surprisingly will tend to be leaves, fruits, dead animals, and other sources of relatively high concentrations of nitrogen. As we described in chapter 2, ecologists have only begun to address the ecology of soils. As less than 10% of the species are likely yet identified, it is not too surprising that we have little information about the ecology of individuals in these systems.

Herbivores

While a herd of elk grazing in the foothills of Alberta or a sea turtle munching on sea grass in a tropical lagoon may suggest a life of ease, this image does not accurately represent the life of an herbivore. To only a slightly less severe extent than detritivores, herbivores face substantial problems related to nutritional chemistry. Most plant tissues contain a great deal of carbon but low concentrations of nitrogen (fig. 7.7). Additionally, herbivores are often faced with a variety of physical and chemical defenses that make the plants more difficult to eat, less nutritious, and potentially lethal. We will explore the details of plant defense strategies in chapter 14. Here we focus on the nutritional challenges that herbivores face in consuming plants: a low quality and potentially toxic food source.

As with detritivores, herbivores come in a variety of shapes and sizes (fig. 7.10). The type of food (size of litter fragment) that a detritivore eats is often strongly related to its size. This relationship does not hold up for herbivores, where individuals of greatly different sizes may all eat the same parts of the plants. For example, when you commit the herbivorous act of biting into an apple, you are likely aware of the chance that a smaller herbivore, the larvae of the codling moth (*Carpocapsa*), may itself already be consuming that fruit. You may be less aware that on the surface of that fruit a variety of mites, aphids, and other insects may have been, or still are, consuming the same apple. In other words, a single part of a plant can be a food for animals of dramatically different sizes, ranging from aphids to humans in this example. If you were instead to consume a different part of a plant, like putting plant leaves into a salad, you once again will likely be consuming a diversity of animals along with the plant tissue. Many of these animals were likely themselves busily eating away before you ruthlessly put them and their host plant into your salad bowl. These herbivores may include other species of aphids, leafhoppers, caterpillars, beetles, mites, and ants. Aside from the small herbivores that were hoping to share your lunch, there may also have been deer and hare snacking in your garden before you arrived. We can learn many things from these examples. First, the idea that a person could be a vegetarian and never consume living animals is, well, not biologically plausible. Second, the differences in the species composition of the herbivores found on different plant tissues are not just random events. Instead,

Figure 7.10 Herbivores of greatly different sizes can feed upon the same plant tissues.

different plant tissues are structurally and chemically dissimilar, even within a single plant. Because of these differences, you will find adaptations among herbivores as a function of what they eat, even if they differ greatly is size.

Herbivores must overcome a variety of chemical and physical defenses presented by plants before they are able to derive nutrition from their vegetarian diet. For example, the use of cellulose and lignin to strengthen plant tissues increases the C:N ratios of these tissues (fig. 7.11), decreasing their value to herbivores as a food source—or even preventing small mouthparts of many insects from penetrating the plant tissue. Even if the lignin and cellulose are ingested, most animal species do not possess the enzymes needed to fully digest these compounds. As a result, the time and energy spent feeding upon these plant tissues returns reduced energetic gains due to the relative unsuitability of the food source, even for herbivores. One of the central difficulties with a vegetarian diet is the high C:N ratio of plant tissues. This has likely contributed to there being relatively few species that specialize on feeding on the least nutritious of plant parts—bark, roots, and stem tissues—at least in comparison to the diversity of species that feed on leaves, fruits, and seeds (fig. 7.10), a pattern roughly analogous to the relatively low diversity of species we find in environments with harsh environmental conditions (chapter 22). Nonetheless, many species do survive eating only (well, at least primarily!) plant tissues. How do animals overcome the problem of consuming food with high C:N ratios?

One way of looking at a vegetarian diet is as a search for relatively rare essential nutrients, such as nitrogen, hidden within a sea of carbon. For animals that eat whole tissues (as opposed to fluid feeders like aphids), an essential first step will be in the physical disintegration of the ingested food. This can be a bird crushing a seed in its beak, or repeated bouts of chewing by large ungulates. This process increases

the surface area exposed to digestive enzymes and liberates nutrients from the confines of the plant cell walls. Animals that eat relatively hard plants will tend to have stronger mouthparts than those that eat softer plant tissues. Different herbivores possess different physiological mechanisms to detoxify the potentially harmful chemicals found within their food, once it reaches their guts. This could be as simple as having an alkaline pH to neutralize some compounds, to more elaborate adaptations such as mixed function oxidases (MFOs), which catalyze oxidizing reactions to detoxify a variety of compounds. The gut of many herbivores is also home to a diverse collection of **microbial symbiants**. These bacteria, fungi, and protozoa are able to digest cellulose and other complex plant compounds, converting them into new microbes. The host, in turn, digests the dead microbes, which can be the source of over 50% of the available N absorbed by ungulates. Many herbivores also make behavioural choices that allow them to eat better food, either through increased nutrient content or reduced toxicity. Some of these examples will be discussed in chapter 8 (Behavioural Ecology) and chapter 14 (Herbivory and Predation).

Despite the diversity of adaptations found among herbivores for coping with a high C:N ratio food source, plants remain a relatively poor food for most animals. As a result, individual animals generally need to consume large amounts of material, with only a small proportion of the ingested food being fully digested. For example, feces and urine of domestic cattle generally represent over 80% of the weight of their ingested food. In other words, most of what a large herbivore puts into its mouth simply comes out at the other end. There is a reason why your parents tell you that roughage will help clean you out!

As you might imagine, being eaten by an herbivore is not generally a beneficial event for an individual plant, and should act as a strong selective force. In fact, chemists have identified thousands of toxins from a diversity of plant species widely implicated in deterring herbivory. In Chapter 14, we will explore the evolutionary implications of this form of plant-animal interactions, and will discuss a variety of aspects of an ever-escalating arms race.

Carnivores

In contrast to detritivores and herbivores, carnivores consume prey that are nutritionally rich. However, just as selection has favoured plant defenses against herbivory, so too has selection favoured prey defenses against predators. In chapter 14 we will discuss a variety of specific adaptations that are common to prey species and help reduce predation. Here we focus on the predator. Just like the detritivores and herbivores, carnivores vary greatly in size. Carnivores can include predatory nematodes, mites, beetles, birds, and mammals (fig. 7.12).

In contrast to the wildly variable C:N ratios within the tissues of an individual plant (fig. 7.11), there is very little variation in C:N ratios across different animal species. As a result, different prey species available to a single carnivore are fairly similar in nutrient content, and thus changes in diet composition have relatively minor nutritional impacts on

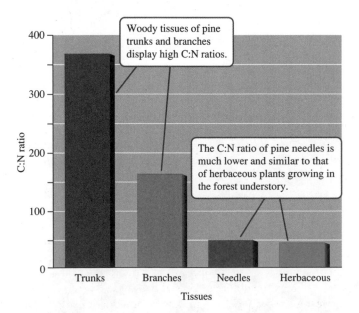

Figure 7.11 C:N ratios differ a great deal among the tissues of pines and between the woody tissues of pines and those of herbaceous plants on the forest floor (data from Klemmedson 1975).

Figure 7.12   Predators come in a diversity of shapes and sizes.

carnivores. Consequently, there can be substantial variation in the diets of individual carnivores within a single population of carnivores, as well as variation among populations across the entire range a particular species occupies. Erin Urton and Keith Hobson of the University of Saskatchewan used stable isotopic analyses to determine the likely dietary composition of wolves and other mammals in a study area centred around Prince Albert National Park (PANP) in central Saskatchewan (Urton and Hobson 2005). You may recall from chapter 6 that different biological processes discriminate among the different isotopes of common elements, such as carbon and nitrogen. As a result, different sources of water (chapter 6) or other aspects of plant physiology result in different isotopic signatures for different plant species. Because of this, the herbivores that eat these plants also can end up with unique isotopic signatures due to their food source and their own

unique physiological processes that may themselves discriminate among stable isotopes.

Urton and Hobson collected hair samples for 18 mammal species, and subjected them to isotopic analysis. As you can see in figure 7.13a, these species differ greatly in their isotopic signatures, even though they all were collected from a single (though large) study site in central Saskatchewan. You may even notice that most of the carnivore species are relatively enriched in ^{15}N and ^{13}C compared to the herbivorous species. Perhaps more surprising is that they found substantial variation in the isotopic signatures of individual wolves, both within and among different areas of the study site (fig. 7.13b). Wolves are pack hunters, and thus the assumption would be they have similar diets and thus little variation in isotopic signatures among individuals. Instead, Urton and Hobson found that the variation among individual wolves was similar

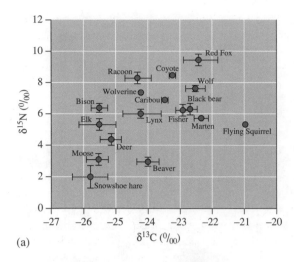

(a)

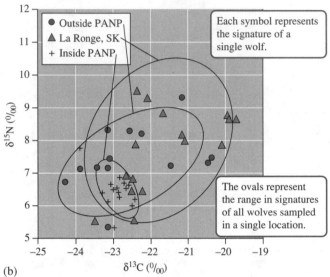

(b)

Figure 7.13 (*a*) Mammal species from central Saskatchewan differ greatly in their isotopic signatures. (*b*) There is substantial variation in isotopic signatures among individuals wolves, even within single locations in and around Prince Albert National Park and La Ronge, Saskatchewan (data from Urton and Hobson 2005).

to that found in other generalist carnivores, such as coyotes and bears. One potential explanation is that the boreal forest and aspen parkland, where this study was conducted, has a relatively rich diversity of potential prey sources, and thus there is substantial opportunity for choice in dietary composition among individuals. Despite the broad taxonomic diversity of the prey that makes up the diets of these wolves, they are all fairly similar in terms of their carbon, nitrogen, and phosphorus content. As a result, selection on carnivores often acts not on the nutritional rewards given by a particular prey, but instead on the ability and efficiencies of carnivores to catch and consume different prey.

Because predators must catch and subdue their prey, they often select prey by size, a behaviour that ecologists call **size-selective predation**. Because of this, prey size is often correlated with predator size, especially among solitary predators. One such predator, the puma, or mountain lion, *Felis concolor*, ranges from the Canadian Yukon to the tip of South America. Puma size changes substantially along this latitudinal gradient.

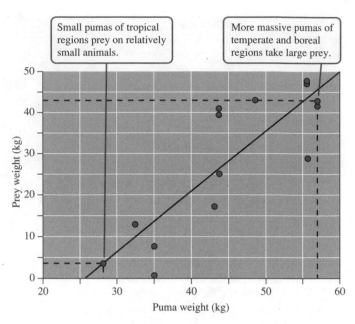

Figure 7.14 The size of pumas and their prey change with latitude (data from Iriarte et al. 1990).

Mammals make up over 90% of the puma's diet, and large mammals, especially deer, are its main prey in the northern part of its range in North America. However, Augustin Iriarte and his colleagues (1990) found that as pumas decrease in size southward, the average size of their prey also decreases (fig. 7.14). In the tropics, pumas feeds mainly on medium and small prey, especially rodents. Then, as pumas again increase in size south of the equator, large mammals form an increasing portion of their diet. Why should different-sized pumas feed on different-sized prey? One reason is that large prey may be difficult to subdue and may even injure the predator, while very small prey may be difficult to find or catch. As we shall see later in this chapter, size-selective predation may also have an energetic basis.

Now let's turn from typical heterotrophs such as wolves and pumas to organisms that obtain their energy from inorganic molecules. These are the chemosynthetic autotrophs. Though less familiar to most of us, chemosynthesis may be one of the world's oldest professions.

Using Inorganic Molecules

In 1977, a routine dive by a small submersible carried scientists exploring the Galápagos rift to a grand discovery. Their discovery changed our view of how a biosphere can be structured. Ecologists had long assumed that photosynthesis provides the energy for nearly all life in the sea. However, these unsuspecting scientists came across a world based upon an entirely different energy source, energy captured by chemosynthesis. The world they discovered was inhabited by giant worms up to 4 m long with no digestive tracts, by filter-feeding clams, and by carnivorous crabs tumbling over each other in tangled abundance (chapter 3). These organisms lived on nutrients discharged by deep-sea volcanic activity through an oceanic rift, a crack in the seafloor. Interconnected systems of rifts extend tens of thousands of kilometers along the seafloor. Subsequent explorations have confirmed that chemosynthetic communities exist at many points of volcanic discharge along the seafloor.

The autotrophs upon which these submarine oases depend are chemosynthetic bacteria. Some of the most common are sulfur oxidizers, bacteria that use CO_2 as a source of carbon and get their energy by oxidizing elemental sulfur, hydrogen sulfide, or thiosulfite. The submarine volcanic vents with which these organisms are associated discharge large quantities of sulfide-rich warm water. The sulfur-oxidizing bacteria that exploit this resource around the vents are of two types: free-living forms and those that live within the tissues of a variety of invertebrate animals, including the giant tube worms (fig. 7.15). Other communities dependent upon sulfur-oxidizing bacteria have been discovered in thermal vents in deep freshwater lakes, in surface hot springs, and in caves.

Other chemosynthetic bacteria oxidize ammonium (NH_4^+), nitrite (NO_2^-), iron (Fe^{2+}), hydrogen (H_2), or carbon monoxide (CO). Of these, the nitrifying bacteria, which oxidize ammonium to nitrite and nitrite to nitrate, are undoubtedly among the most ecologically important organisms in the biosphere. Figure 7.16 summarizes one of the energy-yielding reactions exploited by nitrifying bacteria. The importance of these

bacteria is due to their role in cycling nitrogen. As we saw earlier in this chapter, nitrogen is a key element in the chemical makeup of individual organisms. It also plays a central role in the economy of the entire biosphere. In the Ecological Tools section of this chapter, we will see how bacteria can be used to remediate polluted areas.

Mixotrophy and Omnivory

In this chapter we have presented species as if each has only a single way of capturing energy. Though this will be true for many species, others are able to exploit more than one source of carbon. One group of organisms that you are likely familiar with are the **omnivores**. These are species that are able to gain energy from, and regularly consume, both plant and animal matter. Humans are well known examples of omnivores, with teeth suited both for biting (incisors) and grinding (molars). Grizzly bears are another example, and are able to include berries, roots, small mammals, and fish in their diets.

A similar group of organisms, though less well known and studied, are the **mixotrophs**. These species are able to gain energy both from photosynthesis and from consuming organic or inorganic compounds. A variety of algae, bacteria, and protist

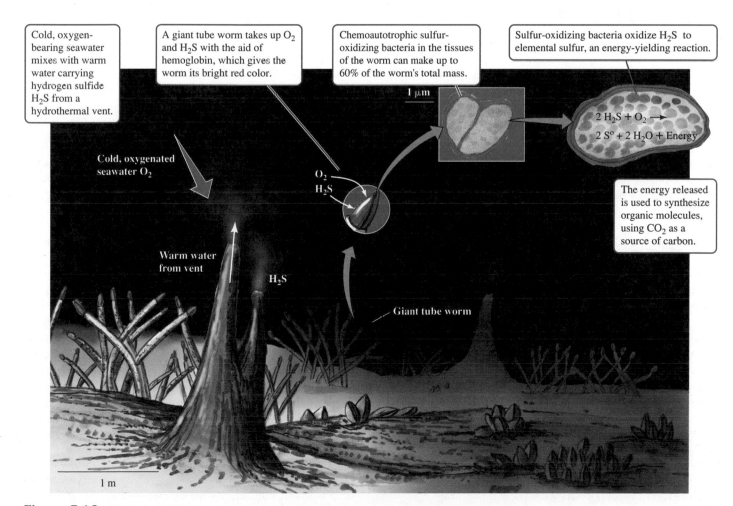

Figure 7.15 Hydrogen sulfide as an energy source for chemoautotrophic bacteria in the deep sea.

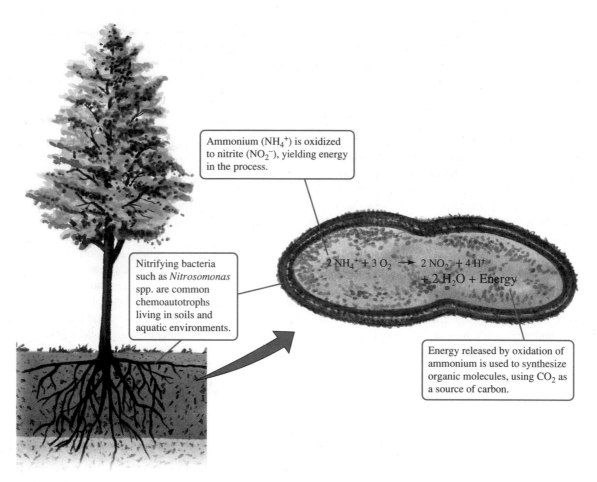

Figure 7.16   Ammonium as an energy source for chemoautotrophic bacteria in soil.

species are mixotrophs. For example, a variety of dinoflagellates are able to photosynthesize and can consume prey. There is likely a very large number of very small organisms that are mixotrophs, though like the small species found in the soil, this remains a black hole of ecological research.

As you can see, the trophic diversity among organisms is great. However, at least one ecological characteristic is shared by all organisms, regardless of the trophic group to which they belong—all organisms take in energy at a limited rate.

Concept 7.1 Review

1. What are the principle similarities between how photosynthetic, chemoautotrophic, and heterotrophic organisms capture energy from their "food" sources?
2. Why can many different sizes of herbivores consume a single leaf when it is alive, while there is strong size-bias in which detritivores can consume that same leaf when it dies?
3. How can stable isotopes be used to infer variation in diet composition of carnivores?

7.2   Energy Limitation

The rate at which organisms can take in energy is limited. Imagine that at the start of tomorrow's lecture, your professor enters the room with an enormous bag of loonies: in fact, this is a magical bag that is able to generate an unlimited supply of money. One by one your professor calls students up to the bag, and you are given 10 minutes to take as many loonies as you can. How many will you take? The answer will vary among students, but assuming you didn't try to steal the bag itself, it will always be less than infinity. In other words, even when presented with the opportunity for unlimited intake (loonie acquisition), your actual rate of intake is limited. You can only move your hands so quickly and you can only hold so many loonies before they begin to spill out of your hands and pockets. Such physical and physiological limitations on consumption are common to all species, even in the presence of an unlimited supply of resources (light, prey, etc.). Limits on the potential rate of energy intake by animals have been demonstrated by studying how feeding rate increases as the availability of food increases. Limits on rates of energy intake by plants have been demonstrated by studying how photosynthetic rate responds to photon flux density.

Photon Flux and Photosynthetic Response Curves

Plant physiologists generally test the photosynthetic potential of plants in environments that are ideal for the particular species being studied. These environments have abundant nutrients and water, normal concentrations of oxygen and carbon dioxide, ideal temperatures, and high humidity. If you gradually increase the intensity of light shining on plants growing under these conditions, that is, if you increase the photon flux density, the plants' rates of photosynthesis gradually increase and then level off. At low light intensities, photosynthesis increases linearly with photon flux density. At intermediate light intensities, photosynthetic rate rises more slowly. Finally, at high light intensity, but well below that of full sunlight, photosynthesis levels off. Organisms that show this type of photosynthetic response curve include terrestrial plants, lichens, planktonic algae, and benthic algae.

The photosynthetic response curves of different plant species generally level off at different maximum rates of photosynthesis. This rate in figure 7.17 is indicated as P_{max}. A second difference among photosynthetic response curves is the photon flux density, or **irradiance,** required to produce the maximum rate of photosynthesis. The irradiance required to saturate photosynthesis is shown in figure 7.17 as I_{sat}. A third difference among photosynthetic response curves is the **light compensation point,** or LCP. As you can see in figure 7.17, the light response curve does not pass through the origin of the graph, and instead there will be a positive x-intercept

and negative y-intercept. What do these values represent? The x-intercept is the LCP, and indicates the amount of light necessary for the plant to have a zero net production of O_2. Remember that plants, like all eukaryotic organisms, undergo oxidative respiration, and thus are continually consuming oxygen. The LCP represents the amount of light necessary for the rate of photosynthesis to equal the rate of respiration. If more light is available, the plant is producing more sugars than it consumes. If less light is available, the plant is in trouble, as it is spending more sugars than it is producing.

Differences in photosynthetic response curves have been used to divide plants into "sun" and "shade" species. The response curves of plants from shady habitats suggest selection for efficiency at low light intensities. The photosynthetic rate of shade plants levels off at lower light intensities, and they are often damaged by intense light. However, at very low light intensities, shade plants usually have higher photosynthetic rates than sun plants.

The ability of seedlings to tolerate shade has important consequences for regenerating forests following the death of canopy trees. Victor Lieffers, of the University of Alberta, has been investigating the physiological ecology of the trees of the boreal forest for several decades. In one study, Lieffers and a colleague (Landhausser and Lieffers 2001) grew seedlings of six species of common boreal forest trees in either the natural forest understory (shade) or in an adjacent sunny site (open). They then measured the light response curves of all the plants over two years (fig. 7.18). For nearly all species, the plants grown under open conditions had higher rates of maximum photosynthesis (P_{max}), saturated photosynthesis at higher levels of irradiance (I_{max}), and higher light compensation points (LCP) than the same species grown in the shade (fig. 7.19). This result should indicate a few things. First this is a clear example of *acclimation*, as discussed in chapter 5. For most species, growth under high light conditions allowed them to more efficiently exploit that resource than did growth under low light conditions. Second, this is also an example of **phenotypic plasticity**, where a single individual has the potential to express a variety of alternative phenotypes (e.g., high or low LCP) depending upon its local environment. Finally, you may also notice that there is a physiological trade-off occurring. Increasing P_{max} is generally associated with an increase in the plant's LCP. In other words, plants that adapted to use high light levels are poorly suited to growing under low light levels. Landhausser and Lieffers have shown that such tradeoffs can exist among species from a single habitat. Even more extreme differences can occur from species from different habitats. Do you imagine plants from high light environments such as the desert or arctic tundra will have high or low P_{max}? How about LCP?

Whether a shade or sun plant, photosynthetic response curves eventually level off. In other words, the rate at which photosynthetic organisms can take in energy is limited. As we shall now see, animals also take in energy at a limited rate.

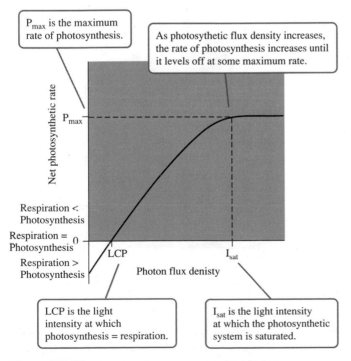

Figure 7.17 A theoretical photosynthetic response curve.

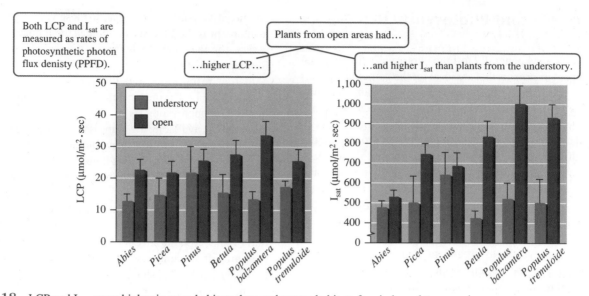

Figure 7.18 LCP and I_{max} were higher in open habitats than understory habitats for six boreal tree species (data from Landhausser and Lieffers 2001).

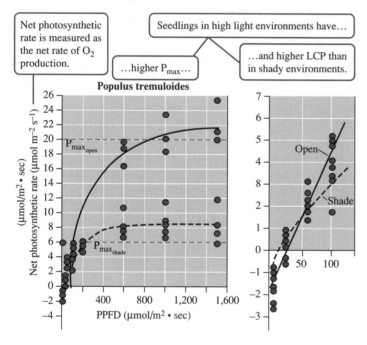

Figure 7.19 Light response curve for one tree of the boreal forest (data from Landhaussser and Lieffers 2001). Orange dot correspond to shade plants and blue to plants in the open.

Food Density and Animal Functional Response

If you gradually increase the amount of food available to a hungry animal, its rate of feeding increases and then levels off. This relationship is called the **functional response.** Ecologists use graphs to describe functional responses. C. S. Holling (1959) described three types of functional responses, all of which level off at a maximum feeding rate (fig. 7.20).

Type 1 functional responses are those in which feeding rate increases linearly (as a straight line) as food density increases and then levels off abruptly at some maximum feeding rate. The

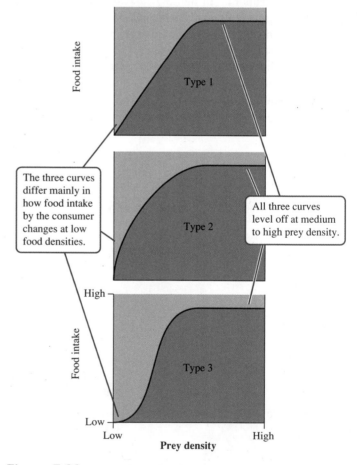

Figure 7.20 Three theoretical functional response curves.

only animals that have type 1 functional responses are consumers that require little or no time to process their food; for example, some filter-feeding aquatic animals that feed on small prey.

In a type 2 functional response, feeding rate at first rises linearly at low food density, rises more slowly at intermediate food density, and then levels off at high densities. At low food densities, feeding rate appears limited by how long it takes the animal to find food. At intermediate food densities, the animal's feeding rate is partly limited by the time spent searching for food and partly by the time spent handling food. "Handling" refers to such activities as cracking the shells of nuts or snails, removing distasteful scent glands from prey, and chasing down elusive prey. At high food density an animal does not have to search for food at all and feeding rate is determined almost entirely by how fast the animal can handle its food. At these very high densities, the animal, in effect, has "all the food it can handle."

The type 3 functional response is S-shaped. What mechanisms may be responsible for the more complicated shape of the type 3 functional response? Why does feeding rate increase slowly at low densities? At low density, food organisms may be better protected from predators because they occupy relatively protected habitats, or "safe sites." In addition, animals often ignore uncommon foods. Many animals seem to focus most of their attention on more abundant foods, switching to less common food only when it exceeds some threshold density. Animals may also require some learning to exploit food at a maximum rate. At low food densities they do not have sufficient exposure to a particular food item to fully develop their searching and handling skills. Holling's research provided a theoretical basis for later empirical studies of animal functional response.

Of the hundreds, perhaps thousands, of functional response curves described by ecologists, the most common is the type 2 functional response. Here are some examples. John Gross and several colleagues (1993) conducted a well-controlled study of the functional responses of 13 mammalian herbivore species. The researchers manipulated food density by offering each herbivore various densities of fresh alfalfa, *Medicago sativa*. The rate of food intake was measured as the difference between the amount of alfalfa offered to an animal at the beginning of a trial and how much was left over at the end. Gross and his colleagues ran 36 to 125 feeding trials for each herbivore species for a total of over 900 trials. Every species of herbivore examined, from moose to lemmings to prairie dogs, showed a type 2 functional response. Figure 7.21 shows the type 2 functional response shown by moose, *Alces alces*.

Gross and his colleagues worked in a controlled experimental environment. Do consumers in natural environments also show a type 2 functional response? To answer this question, let's examine the functional response of wolves, *Canis lupus*, feeding on moose. François Messier of the University of Saskatchewan (1994) examined the interactions between moose and wolves in North America. He focused on areas where moose are the dominant large prey species eaten by wolves. When moose density in various regions was plotted against the rate at which they are killed by wolves, the result was a clear type 2 functional response (fig. 7.22), similar to what we saw for moose feeding on plants. While these examples of functional response emphasize visual feeders, functional response should occur regardless of the sense used by consumers to detect their food. Evidence for such a functional response among nonvisual feeders was found by a team of marine ecologists, working at the Hatfield Marine Science Center in Newport, Oregon (Ryer et al. 2002). The team, headed

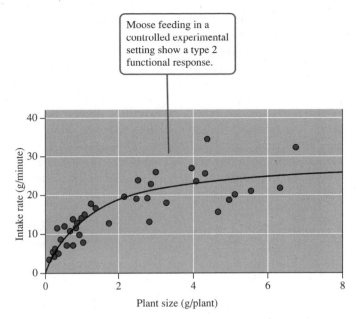

Figure 7.21 A functional response by moose (data from Gross et al. 1993).

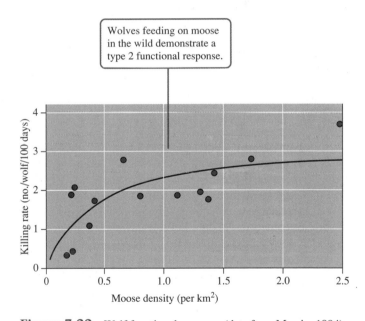

Figure 7.22 Wolf functional response (data from Messier 1994).

by Clifford Ryer, studied the feeding behaviour of juveniles of two fish species, walleye pollock, *Theragra chalcogramma*, and sablefish, *Anoplopoma fimbria*. The research team studied the functional response in the light and in the dark. In darkness, these fish detect their prey using their lateral line system, which has sensory cells that respond to water movements. Though both fish species consumed plankton at a lower rate in the dark than in the light, their rates of consumption increased in the dark with increases in prey density. The increase in feeding rate in walleye pollock followed a type 1 functional response, while that of sablefish followed a type 2 functional response. Studies such as this one provide evidence for the generality of functional responses among a diversity of consumer organisms.

Type 2 functional responses are remarkably similar to the photosynthetic response curves shown by plants (see fig. 7.17) and have the same implications. Even if you provide an animal with unlimited food, its energy intake eventually levels off at some maximum rate. This is the rate at which energy intake is limited by internal rather than external constraints. What conclusions can we draw from this parallel between plants and animals? We can conclude that even under ideal conditions, organisms as different as wolves, moose, and the plants eaten by moose take in energy at a limited rate. As we shall now see, limited energy intake is a fundamental assumption of optimal foraging theory.

Concept 7.2 Review

1. In type 3 functional response, what mechanisms may be responsible for low rates of food intake—compared to type 1 and type 2 functional response—at low food densities?
2. Why are plants such as mosses living in the understory of a dense forest, which show higher rates of photosynthesis at low irradiance, unable to live in environments where they are exposed to full sun for long periods of time?
3. What conclusion can we draw from the parallel between photosynthetic response curves in plants and functional response curves of animals?

7.3   Optimal Foraging Theory

Optimal foraging theory attempts to model how organisms feed as an optimizing process.   Evolutionary ecologists predict that if organisms have limited access to energy and if energy limits fitness, then natural selection is likely to favour individuals within a population that are more effective at acquiring energy. This prediction spawned an area of ecological inquiry called **optimal foraging theory.** Optimal foraging theory assumes that if energy supplies are limited, organisms cannot simultaneously maximize all of life's functions; for example, allocation of energy to one function, such as growth or reproduction, reduces the amount of energy available to other functions, such as defense. As a consequence, there must be compromises between competing demands. This seemingly inevitable conflict between energy allocations has been called the **principle of allocation** and this is the basis for the energy budgets presented in fig. 5.34.

Optimal foraging theory attempts to model how organisms feed as an optimizing process, a process that maximizes or minimizes some quantity. In some situations, the environment may favour individuals that assimilate energy or nutrients at a high rate (e.g., some filter-feeding zooplankton and short-lived weedy annual plants growing in disturbed habitats). In other situations, selection for minimum water loss appears much stronger (e.g., cactus and scorpions in the desert). Optimal foraging theory attempts to predict what consumers will eat, and when and where they will feed. Early work in this area concentrated on animal

behaviour. More recently the acquisition of energy and nutrients by plants has been modelled, using ideas borrowed from economic theory.

Testing Optimal Foraging Theory

How can you test optimal foraging theory? Unfortunately, you cannot test this theory, or any other complex theory, directly in one grand experiment. Consequently, researchers chip away at the problem by testing specific predictions of the theory. One of the most productive avenues of research has been to use optimal foraging theory to predict the composition of animal diets.

When ecologists consider potential prey for a consumer, they try to identify the prey attributes that may affect the rate of energy intake by the predator. One of the most important factors is the abundance of a potential food item. All things being equal, a more abundant prey item yields a larger energy return than an uncommon prey. In optimal foraging studies, prey abundance is generally expressed as the number of the prey encountered by the predator per unit of time, N_e. Another prey attribute is the amount of energy, or costs, expended by the predator while searching for prey, C_s. A third characteristic of potential prey that could affect the energy return to the predator is the time spent processing prey in activities such as cracking shells, fighting, removing noxious scent glands, and so forth. Time spent in activities such as these are summarized as handling time, H. Ecologists ask, given the searching and handling capabilities of an animal and a certain array of available prey, do animals select their diet in a way that yields the maximum rate of energy intake? We can rephrase this question mathematically by incorporating the terms for prey encounter rate, N_e, searching costs, C_s, and handling time, H, into a model.

A Model for Diet Breadth

One of the most basic questions that we might ask about feeding by a predator concerns the number of prey items that should be included in its diet. Put another way, what mix of prey will maximize energy intake by a predator feeding under a particular set of circumstances? Early theoretical work on this question was published by MacArthur and Pianka (1966) and Charnov (1973) and several others. We can represent the rate of energy intake of a predator as E/T, where E is energy and T is time. Earl Werner and Gary Mittelbach (1981) modelled the rate of energy intake for a predator feeding on a single prey species as follows:

$$\frac{E}{T} = \frac{N_{e1}E_1 - C_s}{1 + N_{e1}H_1}$$

In this equation, N_{e1} is the number of prey 1 encountered per unit of time. E_1 is the energy gained by feeding on an individual of prey 1 minus the costs of handling. C_s is the cost of searching for the prey. H_1 is the time required for "handling" an individual of prey 1. Once again, this equation expresses the net rate at which a predator takes in energy when it feeds on a particular prey species.

What would be the rate of energy intake if the predator fed on two types of prey? The rate is calculated as follows:

$$\frac{E}{T} = \frac{(N_{e1}E_1 - C_s) + (N_{e2}E_2 - C_s)}{1 + N_{e1}H_1 + N_{e2}H_2}$$

This is an extension of the first equation. Here, we've added encounter rates for prey 2, N_{e2}, the energetic return from feeding on prey 2, E_2, and the handling time for prey 2, H_2. The searching costs, C_s, are assumed to be the same for prey 1 and prey 2.

The rate of energy intake by a predator feeding on several prey can be represented as:

$$\frac{E}{T} = \frac{\displaystyle\sum_{i=1}^{n} N_{ei}E_i - C_s}{1 + \displaystyle\sum_{i=1}^{n} N_{ei}H_i}$$

Here, Σ means "the sum of" and i equals 1, 2, 3, etc., to n, where n is the total number of prey. Remember that this equation gives an estimate of the rate of energy intake. The question that optimal foraging theory asks is whether organisms feed in a way that maximizes the rate of energy intake, E/T.

Optimal foraging theory predicts that a predator will feed exclusively on prey 1, ignoring other available prey, when:

$$\frac{N_{e1}E_1 - C_s}{1 + N_{e1}H_1} > \frac{(N_{e1}E_1 - C_s) + (N_{e2}E_2 - C_s)}{1 + N_{e1}H_1 + N_{e2}H_2}$$

This expression says that the rate of energy intake is greater if the predator feeds only on prey 1. If the predator feeds on both prey species, the rate will be lower.

Optimal foraging theory predicts that predators will include a second prey species in their diet when:

$$\frac{(N_{e1}E_1 - C_s) + (N_{e2}E_2 - C_s)}{1 + N_{e1}H_1 + N_{e2}H_2} > \frac{N_{e1}E_1 - C_s}{1 + N_{e1}H_1}$$

In this case, feeding on two prey species gives the predator a higher rate of energy intake than if it feeds on one. The general prediction is that predators will continue to add different types of prey to their diet until the rate of energy intake reaches a maximum. This is called **optimization.**

Now let's get back to our basic question: Do animals select food in a way that maximizes their rate of energy intake? Testing such a prediction requires a great deal of information. Fortunately, mathematical models such as this one help focus experiments and observations on a few key variables.

Foraging by Bluegill Sunfish

Some of the most thorough tests of optimal foraging theory have been conducted on the bluegill sunfish, *Lepomis macrochirus*. The bluegill is a medium-sized fish native to eastern and central North America, where it inhabits a wide range of freshwater habitats, from small streams to the shorelines of small and large lakes. Bluegills feed mainly on benthic and planktonic crustaceans and aquatic insects, prey that differ in size and habitat and in ease of capture and handling. Bluegills

often choose prey by size, feeding on organisms of certain sizes and ignoring others. This behaviour is convenient because it gives the ecologist a relatively simple measure to describe the composition of the available prey and the composition of the theoretically optimal diet.

Werner and Mittelbach used published studies to estimate the amount of energy expended by bluegills while they search for (C_s) and handle prey. They used laboratory experiments to estimate handling times (H) and encounter rates (N_e) for various prey. For these laboratory experiments, they constructed approximations of the places where bluegills forage in nature—open water, sediments, and vegetation. These model habitats were constructed in large aquaria and stocked with some of the important prey of bluegills: damselfly larvae, midge larvae, and *Daphnia*. These experiments showed that encounter rates increase as fish size, prey size, and prey density increase and that handling time depends on the relative sizes of predator and prey. Small bluegills require a relatively long time to handle large prey, while large bluegills expend little time handling small prey.

The energy content of prey was calculated by measuring the lengths of prey available in lakes and ponds; prey length was converted to mass, and then mass was converted to energy content using published values. With this information, Werner and Mittelbach characterized the prey available in Lawrence Lake, Michigan, and then estimated the diet that would maximize the rate of energy intake. They then sampled the bluegills of Lawrence Lake and examined their stomach contents to see how closely their diet approximated the diet predicted by optimal foraging theory.

The upper graph in figure 7.23 shows the size distribution of potential prey in vegetation in Lawrence Lake. The middle graph shows the composition of the optimal diet as predicted by the optimal foraging model just presented. Finally, the bottom graph shows the actual composition of the diets of bluegills from Lawrence Lake. Bluegills feeding in vegetation selected prey that were uncommon and larger than average. The match between the optimal diet and the prey that bluegills in Lawrence Lake actually ate seems uncanny. A similar match was obtained for bluegills feeding on zooplankton in open water.

Werner and Mittelbach found that optimal foraging theory provides reasonable predictions of prey selection by natural populations of bluegills. Ecologists studying plants have developed an analogous predictive framework for foraging by plants.

Optimal Foraging by Plants

Do plants forage? When we think of foraging, it is the fish, elk, wolves, and squirrels that often come to mind. But in its most basic sense, foraging is simply the search for and acquisition of resources, something that all organisms do, including plants. The more interesting question then is not whether plants forage (they do), but instead are plants able to exhibit some form of optimality, similar to what we saw with the sunfish? At first, this idea may seem absurd; complex neurological pathways are an essential component of optimal foraging, right? No. First, the argument that natural selection favours effective resource capture due to the constraints of the principle

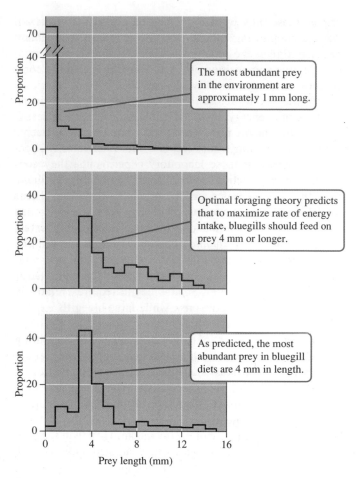

Figure 7.23 Optimal foraging theory predicts composition of bluegill sunfish diets (data from Werner and Mittelbach 1981).

of allocation are valid for all organisms whose fitness is limited by energy. Evolution should favour phenotypes that are most efficient in resource capture, and select against those that are less efficient. Second, we think of behaviour in a certain way, in large part because we are mammals and have only a single frame of reference. However, there is more than one way to express behaviour related to foraging, and not all of them require neurons, muscles, and movement. We will look here at foraging decisions made by vascular plants.

How do plants forage? Quite simply, they need to put their resource-capturing organs (leaves and roots) in the locations that have the resources. Selection should favour plants that put those organs in areas of high resource availability and not in areas of low resource availability. This would be very similar to selection favouring a squirrel that feeds in areas of high acorn abundance, while selecting against those that only forage in areas where there is no food to be had! The critical difference between the plant and animal example is that many animals are mobile, and can move their whole self from one research patch to another. Plants (and some animals) are sessile, and thus they forage not by moving the individual, but instead by either growing different organs, or placing their organs in different locations.

We will start our investigation at the whole plant level. We can simplify plants by dividing them into two parts, (1) shoots, which acquire light, and (2) roots, which acquire mineral resources and water. Using economic theory, Arnold Bloom and colleagues (Bloom et al. 1985) suggested that plants will adjust their allocation of energy to growth in such a way that all resources are equally limited. This idea is itself related to Liebig's law of the minimum, in which Justus von Liebig postulated that plant growth will be limited by the scarcest essential resource, rather than the total amount of resources available to a plant. Therefore, Bloom reasoned that if light limits plant growth, plants would invest more energy in growth of shoots and less in roots. If instead soil resources are more limiting than light, plants would be expected to increase root growth relative to shoot growth. There have been numerous experimental tests of these predictions. Most experiments generally consist of growing a certain species of plant under high and low nutrient conditions. After a given period of time, the plant would be harvested and root and shoot biomass would be weighed. In one meta-analysis, Heather Reynolds and Carla D'Antonio (1996) found that in 75% of the 206 cases they surveyed, plants had relatively less root growth under high nitrogen conditions than under low nitrogen conditions. This result was further supported by an experiment by Nichole Levang-Brilz and Mario Biondini (2002) in which they found root:shoot ratios of 62% of the 55 species they tested decreased when nitrogen was added to the soil. These studies show that across a large number of species plants do alter their relative production of roots and shoots in response to the relative abundance of mineral resources, in a manner consistent with optimal foraging theory. In chapter 13, we will also provide an example of how plants alter shoot growth in response to reduced light availability. Although altering root:shoot ratios themselves are one means by which plants can adjust their foraging strategy to the match local conditions, it is not a particularly precise one. Instead, you could imagine that within the soil surrounding an individual plant, there will be some patches of soil that are enriched in nutrients relative to the rest of the area, perhaps due to urination by a local herbivore. These enriched patches are likely short lived, either washed away in the rain or exploited by the surrounding plants. If these patches are common in natural systems, selection may have favoured mechanisms for their exploitation—something more elegant than the blunt hammer approach of altered root:shoot ratio.

M.C. Drew, of Letcombe Laboratory in England, conducted the first of what would lead to many studies on the ability of plants to alter their root growth in response to small-scale variation in nutrient distributions (Drew 1975). Drew grew barley plants in pots filled with sand, through which he continuously irrigated a nutrient solution. In a very clever experimental design, Drew divided the pots into three vertical compartments, and was able to give different parts of the root system different levels of nutrients (fig. 7.24). What he found was striking. Plants grew roots relatively uniformly in response to a uniform distribution of nutrients, while they proliferated roots in zones of high nutrients compared to zones of low nutrients (fig. 7.24). In other words, plants were able to alter the distribution of their foraging organs in response to differences in the distribution of resources! This is a form of optimal foraging.

Since Drew's study, ecologists have been working furiously to determine how widespread this phenomenon is, and whether it has any general ecological consequences. A critical step in this process has been the documentation that most natural communities are inherently heterogeneous in soil nutrient distributions, a finding summarized by Martin Lechowicz and Graham Bell of McGill University (Lechowicz and Bell 1991). They show that in many natural communities, nutrient levels can vary by orders of magnitude within the rooting zone of an individual plant. This indicates that the potential for evolution of foraging in plants exists, as the selective environment favouring precise root placement is likely widespread. At the same time, there have been countless numbers of experiments using a large number of plant species replicating Drew's basic design, though generally varying nutrients horizontally, rather than vertically. In a recent paper by one of this book's authors and a graduate student, Steve Kembel, we attempted to summarize this literature (Kembel and Cahill, 2005). We compiled data available for over 125 plant species and subjected them to a meta-analysis. On average, plants placed approximately twice as many roots in areas of high nutrient availability than in areas of low nutrient availability. Additionally, most species were significantly larger when grown in heterogeneous soil than when grown under uniform conditions. In short, most plants can forage, and when given the opportunity to do so, they perform better than under uniform conditions.

One interesting result from this study was that monocots, such as grasses, are generally less precise foragers than are dicots, such as sunflowers. Why might this be? Work by Scott Wilson and colleagues at the University of Regina provides one possible answer. They found that root densities are higher and distributed more uniformly in grasslands than in forested areas (Partel and Wilson 2002). They speculated that this results in more uniform resource distribution in grasslands than in forests. It is possible then, that any selective advantage of "optimal foraging" among grasses is reduced, as in their natural habitat they do not experience a particularly patchy world. However, these findings are all very new, and much more work needs to be conducted. The study of plant behaviour and foraging ecology is a rapidly growing field, and much of this work is being conducted in Canada.

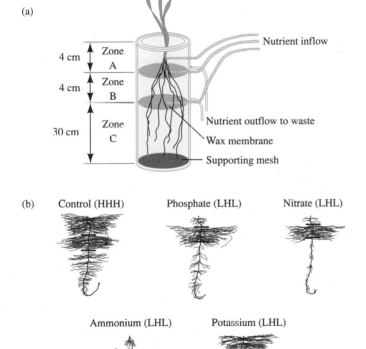

Figure 7.24 Drew (1975) manipulated nutrient levels in different zones of soil. Plants responded by non-uniform root growth.

Concept 7.3 Review

1. According to optimal foraging theory, under what conditions should a predator add a new prey species to its diet?
2. Do patterns of feeding by bluegills include any evidence that these consumers ignore certain potential prey?
3. What ecological conditions likely favour the evolution of optimal foraging in plants?

Using Ecological Knowledge to Predict C₄ Plant Distributions in a Changing World

C₃ and C₄ plants possess different photosynthetic pathways (figs. 7.4 and 7.5), and as a result perform differently under different temperature and moisture conditions. This interaction between plant physiology and abiotic conditions has profound implications for population growth and the geographic distribution of plants. For example, there currently exists a clear latitudinal gradient in the distribution of C₄ plants, with C₄ plants representing an increasing proportion of the local flora as you move from the poles and towards the equator (fig. 7.25). But the world is changing. Local and global climates are being rapidly modified through a variety of human

activities; causing changes to temperatures, precipitation, and evapotranspiration in the soil (see chapter 23 for more discussion about climate change). A shift in local climate can exert selective pressures on the species that reside within the local community. For a plant, a debate over the causes of climate change is irrelevant to the potential selective forces associated with increased atmospheric temperatures and altered precipitation. Here we will show how a strong understanding of physiological ecology can provide insights into questions of global concern. Specifically, we will address how increased temperatures may impact global distributions of C₄ plants.

Rowan Sage at the University of Toronto is a world leader in understanding the ecology of C₄ plants. Sage has blended a variety of disciplines in his work, including evolution, physiol-

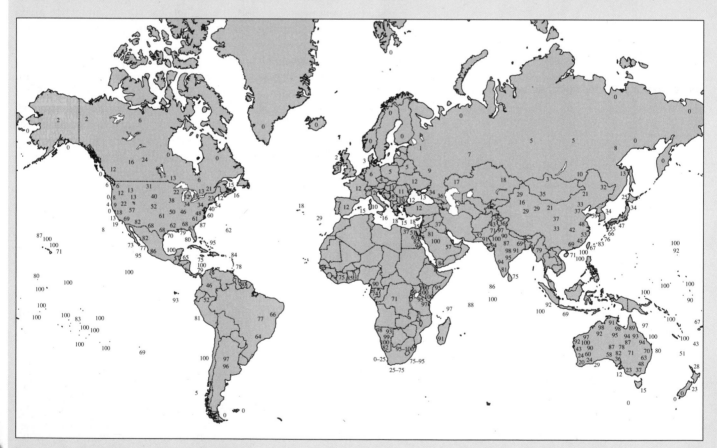

Figure 7.25   Percentage representation of C₄ grasses in grass flora from different regions of the world (data from Sage).

ogy, chemistry, ecology, and atmospheric sciences. By having such a diverse set of tools, Sage is able to address the question of how climate change may impact C_3 and C_4 plants from a more holistic perspective than could specialists in any of these individual disciplines. C_4 plants represent a relatively small fraction of the world's diversity, only 7,500 of the estimated 250,000 species of land plants (Sage 1999), with the vast majority being grasses and sedges. However, in many warm climates, C_4 plants are dominant, while decreasing in abundance as you move towards the poles or up in elevation. C_4 plants are responsible for approximately 25% of all plant growth on the planet (Sage 2003), and include species of critical agronomic importance such as corn. We have already discussed explanations for why C_4 plants can outperform C_3 plants in bright warm conditions, but what is less clear is why they get outperformed in cooler environments. In other words, what is the cost of C_4 photosynthesis? Recent work by Sage and colleagues (Kubien et al. 2003) suggest that the architecture of C_4 leaves has resulted in reduced RUBISCO concentrations. Under hot conditions, this is not an issue, as high levels of RUBISCO in C_3 plants also result in high levels of photorespiration, reducing C_3 efficiency. However, photorespiration is reduced under cooler conditions, and the reduced levels of RUBISCO appear to limit rates of photosynthesis in C_4 plants. In other words, there appears to be a fundamental tradeoff where the photosynthetic machinery is either optimized for warm or for cool conditions. What then happens when the world becomes hotter?

In analyzing current C_4 distributions, mid-summer temperature is a strong correlate of C_4 plant abundance in North America, where C_4 plants are unlikely to occur if mid-summer temperatures go below 10°C (fig. 7.26), or if average mid-summer temperatures are below 13°C (Sage and Kubien 2003). From all of this information, it is obvious then that an increase in temperatures will result in a range expansion of C_4 plants, right? Not necessarily. It is here that we must step back and realize that an increase in global temperature is relatively meaningless to an individual plant, or even a particular species. What matters much more is what degree of change is found in a given locality, and during what time of year this change occurs. Sage and Kubien (2003) summarize current warming trends, and point out that many of the predictions regarding climate change suggest the greatest changes will occur in the

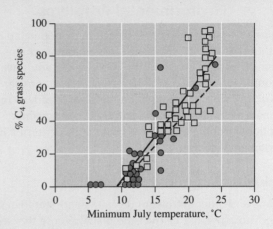

Figure 7.26   Relationship between mid-summer temperature and the relative abundance of C_4 plants in North America (data from Wan and Sage 2001).

winter, rather than the summer. This would actually result in an extended cool-growing season, favouring C_3, not C_4 plants! Even if warming does occur in the summer, if this is coupled with increased aridity, that could effectively shut down summer growth, leaving only spring and fall (the cooler seasons) for growth, again favouring C_3 plants. However, if precipitation also increases during the warmer summers, then this should increase C_4 growth at the expense of C_3 plants. In short, without detailed information about the exact climatic conditions a particular location is likely to experience, it will be difficult to predict the likely impact on plant distributions. This is even without considering there are other factors at play, including fire frequency, light, CO_2 levels, and many more.

It is clear that Sage and others are not yet able to conclusively say what will happen to plants with climate change, but you should be able to see that scientists are actively working on these questions. Questions of global patterns are particularly difficult to answer, as they require integrating many disciplines, as well as numerous interacting variables (e.g., temperature, water, etc.). Work by Sage, and others, provides examples that the most effective ecologists will possess a deep understanding the basic biology of the organisms they study. Global questions are not answered solely by describing patterns, but instead they require an understanding of the functional mechanisms that generate the patterns.

Ecological Tools

Bioremediation—Using the Trophic Diversity of Bacteria to Solve Environmental Problems

Imagine yourself in the centre of a densely populated region with thousands of leaky gasoline tanks or complex mine wastes contaminating the groundwater. How would you solve these environmental problems? Where would you turn for help? Increasingly, we are turning to nature's own cleanup crew, the bacteria. Environmental managers are taking advantage of the exceptional trophic diversity of bacteria to perform a host of environmental chores.

Leaking Underground Storage Tanks

Gasoline and other petroleum derivatives are stored in underground storage tanks all over the planet. Those that leak are a serious source of pollution. Maribeth Watwood and Cliff Dahm (1992) explored the possibility of using bacteria to clean up soils and aquifers contaminated by leaking storage tanks. The first step in their work was to determine if there are naturally occurring populations of bacteria that can break down complex petroleum derivatives such as benzene.

Watwood and Dahm collected sediments from a shallow aquifer that contained approximately 8.5×10^8 bacterial cells per gram of wet sediment. Of these, 6.55×10^4 bacterial cells per milliliter were capable of living on benzene as their only source of carbon and energy. By exposing sediments from the aquifer to benzene for six months, the researchers increased the populations of benzene-degrading bacteria approximately 100 times.

How rapidly can these bacteria break down benzene? Watwood and Dahm found that with no prior exposure, bacterial populations could break down 90% of the benzene in their test flasks within 40 days (fig. 7.27). Exposing sediments to benzene prior to their tests increased the rate of breakdown.

Briefly, this study demonstrated that naturally occurring populations of bacteria can rapidly break down benzene leaking from underground storage tanks. This study suggests that these bacteria will eventually clean up the organic contaminants from leaking gasoline storage tanks without manipulation of the environment. However, in the next example, environmental managers found that they had to manipulate the environment to stimulate the desired bacterial cleanup of a contaminant.

Cyanide and Nitrates in Mine Spoils

Many gold mines were abandoned when they could not be mined profitably with the mining technology of the nineteenth and early twentieth centuries. Then, in the 1970s, techniques were developed to economically extract gold from low-grade ores. One of the main extraction techniques was to leach ore with cyanide (CN). Dissolved CN forms chemical complexes

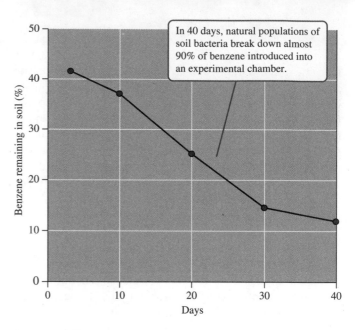

Figure 7.27 showing: "In 40 days, natural populations of soil bacteria break down almost 90% of benzene introduced into an experimental chamber." (axis: Benzene remaining in soil (%) vs Days)

Figure 7.27   Benzene breakdown by soil bacteria (data from Watwood and Dahm 1992).

with gold and other metals. The solution containing gold-bearing CN can be collected and the gold and CN removed by filtering the solution with activated charcoal.

This new method of mining solved a technical problem but contaminated soils and groundwater. When the leaching process is finished, the leached ore is stored in piles; however, much CN remains. Several kinds of bacteria can break down CN and produce NH_3. This NH_3 can, in turn, be used by nitrifying bacteria as an energy source, producing NO_3 (see "The Nitrogen Cycle" in chapter 19). Thus, leaching gold-bearing ores and subsequent microbial activity can contaminate soil and groundwater with CN, a deadly poison, and with nitrate, another contaminant.

Carleton White and James Markwiese (1994) studied a gold mine that had been worked with the CN leaching process. The leached ores from the mine were gradually releasing CN and NO_3 into the environment. The researchers looked to bacteria to solve this environmental problem. They first documented the presence of CN degraders by looking for bacterial growth in a diagnostic medium. This medium contained CN as the only source of carbon and nitrogen. Using this growth medium, White and Markwiese estimated that each gram of ore contained approximately 10^3 to 10^5 cells of organisms capable of growing on, and breaking down, CN.

The leached ores presented bacteria with a rich source of nitrogen in the form of CN and NO_3 but the ores contained little organic carbon. White and Markwiese predicted that adding a source of carbon to the residual ores would increase the rate at which bacteria break down CN and reduce the concentration of NO_3 in the environment. Why should adding

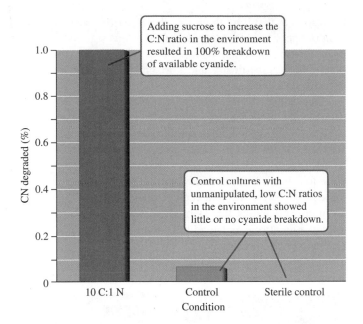

Figure 7.28 Manipulating C:N ratios to stimulate breakdown of cyanide (CN) (data from White and Markwiese 1994).

organic molecules rich in carbon increase bacterial use of nitrogen in the environment? Look back at figure 7.7, which shows that bacteria have a carbon:nitrogen ratio of about 5:1. In other words, growth and reproduction by bacteria require about five carbon atoms for each nitrogen atom.

White and Markwiese tested their ideas in the laboratory. In one experiment, they added enough sucrose to produce a C:N ratio of 10:1 within leached ores. This experiment included two controls, both of which contained leached ores without sucrose. One of the controls was sterilized to kill any bacteria. The other control was left unsterilized.

Bacteria in the treatments containing sucrose broke down all the CN within the leached ore in 13 days. Meanwhile, only a small amount of CN was broken down in the unsterilized control and no CN was broken down in the sterilized control (fig. 7.28). Why did the researchers include a sterilized control? The sterilized control demonstrated that nonbiological processes were not responsible for the observed breakdown of CN.

Figure 7.28 shows that adding sucrose to the residual ore stimulates the breakdown of CN. However, remember that this process ultimately leads to the production of NO_3. Does adding sucrose to eliminate CN lead to the buildup of NO_3, trading one pollution problem for another? No, it does not. In another experiment White and Markwiese (1994) showed that adding sucrose also stimulates uptake of NO_3 by heterotrophic bacteria and fungi. These organisms use organic molecules, in this case sucrose, as a source of energy and carbon and NO_3 as a source of nitrogen. The nitrogen taken up by bacteria and fungi becomes incorporated in biomass as complex organic molecules. Nitrogen in this form is recycled within the microbial community and is not a source of environmental pollution.

White and Markwiese recommended that sucrose be added to leached gold-mining ores to stimulate breakdown of CN and uptake of NO_3 by bacteria. This environmental cleanup project was successful because the researchers were thoroughly familiar with the energy and nutrient relations of bacteria and fungi. Another key to the project's success was the great trophic diversity of bacteria. Bacteria will likely continue to play a great role as we address some of our most vexing environmental problems.

Summary

Organisms use one of three main sources of energy: light, organic molecules, or inorganic molecules. Photosynthetic plants and algae use CO_2 as a source of carbon and light, of wavelengths between 400 and 700 nm, as a source of energy. Light within this band, which is called photosynthetically active radiation, or PAR, accounts for about 45% of the total energy content of the solar spectrum at sea level. PAR can be quantified as photosynthetic photon flux density, generally reported as μmol per square meter per second. Among plants, there are three major alternative photosynthetic pathways, C_3, C_4, and CAM. C_4 and CAM plants are more efficient in their use of water than are C_3 plants and have reduced rates of photorespiration. Heterotrophs use organic molecules both as a source of carbon and as a source of energy. Herbivores, carnivores, and detritivores face fundamentally different trophic problems. Herbivores feed on plant tissues, which often contain a great deal of carbon but little nitrogen. Herbivores must also overcome the physical and chemical defenses of plants. Detritivores feed on dead plant material, which is even lower in nitrogen than living plant tissues. Carnivores consume prey that are nutritionally rich but may be hard to capture. Chemosynthetic autotrophs, which consist of a highly diverse group of chemosynthetic bacteria, use inorganic molecules as a source of energy. Bacteria are the most trophically diverse organisms in the biosphere.

The rate at which organisms can take in energy is limited, either by external or internal constraints. The relationship between photon flux density and plant photosynthetic rate is called photosynthetic response. Plants from sunny habitats have high maximum photosynthetic rates that level off at high irradiance and high light compensation points. The lowest maximum rates of photosynthesis and LCP occur among plants from shady environments. The relationship between food density and animal feeding rate is called the functional response. The shape of the functional response is generally one of three types. The forms of photosynthetic response curves and type 2 animal functional responses are remarkably similar. Energy limitation is a fundamental assumption of optimal foraging theory.

Optimal foraging theory attempts to model how organisms feed as an optimizing process. Evolutionary ecologists predict that if organisms have limited access to energy, natural selection is likely to favour individuals that are more effective at acquiring energy and nutrients. Many animals select food in a way that appears to maximize the rate at which they capture energy. Plants allocate energy to roots versus shoots in a way that increases their rate of intake of the resources that limit their growth. In environments rich in light but poor in nutrients, plants tend to invest more energy in the growth of roots. Within a root system, root distributions will vary vertically and horizontally as a function of resource distributions.

The trophic diversity of bacteria, which is critical to the health of the biosphere, can also be used as a tool to address some of our most challenging waste disposal problems. Bacteria can be used to clean up soils and aquifers polluted by petroleum products such as benzene, and eliminate the pollution caused by some kinds of mine waste. The success of these projects requires that ecologists understand the energy and nutrient relations of bacteria. Bacteria will likely continue to play a great role as we address some of our most vexing environmental problems.

Review Questions

1. Why don't plants use highly energetic ultraviolet light for photosynthesis? Would it be impossible to evolve a photosynthetic system that uses ultraviolet light? Does the fact that many insects see ultraviolet light change your mind? Would it be possible to use infrared light for photosynthesis? (Photosynthetic bacteria tap into the near infrared range.)

2. In what kinds of environments would you expect to find the greatest predominance of C_3, C_4, or CAM plants? How can you explain the co-occurrence of two, or even all three, of these types of plants in one area? (Think about the variations in microclimate that we considered in chapters 5 and 6.)

3. What are the relative advantages and disadvantages of being an herbivore, detritivore, or carnivore? What kinds of organisms were left out of our discussions of herbivores, detritivores, and carnivores? Where do parasites fit? Where does *Homo sapiens* fit?

4. Design a planetary ecosystem based entirely on chemosynthesis. You might choose an undiscovered planet of some distant star or one of the planets in our own solar system, either today or at some distant time in the past or future.

5. What kinds of animals would you expect to have type 1, 2, or 3 functional responses? How should natural selection for better prey defense affect the height of functional response curves? How should natural selection for more effective predators affect the height of the curves? What net effect should natural selection on predator and prey populations have on the height of the curves?

6. The rivers of central Portugal have been invaded, and densely populated, by the Louisiana crayfish, *Procambarus clarki,* which looks like a freshwater lobster about 12 to 14 cm long. The otters of these rivers can easily catch and subdue these crayfish. Using the model for prey choice:

$$\frac{E}{T} = \frac{\sum_{i=1}^{n} N_{ei}E_i - C_s}{1 + \sum_{i=1}^{n} N_{ei}H_i}$$

explain why the diets of the otters of central Portugal would shift from a highly diverse menu, which includes fish, frogs, water snakes, birds, and insects, to a diet dominated by crayfish. For the crayfish, assume low handling time, very high encounter rates, and high energy content.

7. The data of Iriarte and colleagues (1990) suggest that prey size may favour a particular body size among pumas. However, this variation in body size also correlates well with latitude; the larger pumas live at high latitudes. Consequently, this variation in body size has been interpreted as the result of selection for efficient temperature regulation. Homeothermic animals are often larger at high latitudes, a pattern called Bergmann's rule. Larger animals, with lower surface area relative to their mass, would be theoretically better at conserving heat. Smaller animals, with higher surface area relative to their mass, would be theoretically better at keeping cool. So what determines predator size? Is predator size determined by climate, predator-prey interactions, or both? Design a study of the influence of the environment on the size of homeothermic predators.

8. How is plant allocation to roots versus shoots similar to plant regulation of temperature and water? (We discussed these topics in chapters 5 and 6.) Consider discussing these processes under the more general heading of homeostasis. (Homeostasis is the maintenance of a relatively constant internal environment.)

9. If herbivores are able to optimally forage, why do they not more efficiently extract resources from their food? Why has natural selection allowed for the majority of the biomass ingested by herbivores to be passed through the digestive system without being fully digested?

10. Is a plant putting roots in a resource rich patch, but not in a low resource patch the same as a predator foraging in an area of high prey density but not in an area of low prey density? Is intelligence necessary for behaviour? Why or why not?

Suggested Readings

Béjà, O., L. Aravind, E. V. Koonin, M. T. Suzuki, A. Hadd, L. P. Nguyen, S. B. Jovanovich, C. M. Gates, R. A. Feldman, J. L. Spudich, E. N. Spudich, and E. F. Delong. 2000. Bacterial rhodopsin: evidence for a new type of phototrophy in the sea. *Science* 289:1902–6.

Béjà, O., M. T. Suzuki, J. F. Heidelberg, W. C. Nelson, C. M. Preston, T. Hamada, J. A. Eisen, C. M. Fraser, and E. F. Delong. 2002. Unsuspected diversity among marine aerobic anoxygenic phototrophs. *Nature* 415:630–33.

Kolber, Z. S., C. L. Van Dover, R. A. Niederman, and P. G. Falkowski. 2000. Bacterial photosynthesis in surface waters of the open ocean. *Nature* 407:177–79.

Three papers that give insights into one of the exciting frontiers of modern ecology, microbial ecology.

Reynolds, H. L. and C. D'Antonio. 1996. The ecological significance of plasticity in root weight ratio in response to nitrogen: Opinion. *Plant and Soil* 185:75–97.

Kembel, S. K. and J. F. Cahill, Jr. 2005. Plant phenotypic plasticity belowground: a phylogenetic perspective on root foraging tradeoffs. *American Naturalist* 166:216–30.

These two papers provide an introduction to a frontier in ecology: plant foraging ecology.

Fortin, D., J. M. Fryxell, L. O'Brodovich, and D. Frandsen. 2003. Foraging ecology of bison at the landscape and plant community levels: the applicability of energy maximization principles. *Oecologia* 134:219–27.

Iason, G. R., T. Manso, D. A. Sim, and F. G. Hartley. 2002. The functional response does not predict the local distribution of European Rabbits (*Oryctolagus cuniculus*) on grass swards: experimental evidence. *Functional Ecology* 16:394–402.

Plath, K. and M. Boersma. 2001. Mineral limitation of zooplankton: stoichiometric constraints and optimal foraging. *Ecology* 82:1260–69.

Three studies of animal foraging that show the complexity of foraging decisions made by animals feeding in complex environments.

McCulley, R. L., E. G. Jobbágy, W. T. Pockman, and R. B. Jackson. 2004. Nutrient uptake as a contributing explanation for deep rooting in arid and semi-arid ecosystems. *Oecologia* 141: 620–28.

The researchers offer evidence that water shortage is not the only factor influencing the growth of very deep roots among arid land plants; nutrient relations may also play a role.

Sage, R. F. and D. S. Kubien. 2003. *Quo vadis* C_4? An ecophysiological perspective on global change and the future of C_4 plants. *Photosynthesis Research* 77:209–25.

Sage, R. F. and R. K. Monson. 1999. C_4 *Plant Biology*. Academic Press, San Diego.

This paper and book provide an in-depth analysis of the present and future of C_4 plant distributions.

Chapter 8

Behavioural Ecology

Outline

owhere are the social interactions and other behaviours of vertebrate animals easier to observe than on tropical reefs. In early evening as the sun's rays shine obliquely through the clear waters over a coral reef, the activity of some of its inhabitants quickens. As if activated by some remote switch, a vast school of fish that had remained in the lagoon all day begins to move steadily toward an opening in the reef. The school is leaving the lagoon's protection and going out to the open sea for a night of feeding. Living in a school appears to have favoured uniformity among its members. Approached underwater, the edge of the school looks like a giant translucent curtain stamped with the silhouettes of thousands of identical fish. Their coloration, countershaded dark above and silvery below, their similar size, highly coordinated movements, and great numbers give the fish within the school some protection from predators. Though seabirds and predaceous fish ambush the school as it makes its way, the schooling fish are so numerous and their individual movements so difficult to follow that only a small proportion of them are eaten. Gradually the school, moving like a gigantic, shape-shifting organism, passes through the channel connecting the lagoon to the open sea. The school of fish will be back by daybreak only to repeat its seaward journey next evening in a cycle of comings and goings that helps mark the rhythm of life on the reef.

Meanwhile along the reef, damselfish are distributed singly on territories. The damselfish retain exclusive possession of their territorial patches of coral rubble, living coral, and sand by patrolling the boundaries and driving off any fish attempting to intrude, especially other damselfish that would take their territory or other fish that would prey on eggs or consume food within the territory. Each day at this time, however, some territory-holding males are joined by females. For the space of time that they court and deposit eggs and sperm on the nest site prepared by the male, the territory contains two fish. Once mating is complete, however, the male is again alone on the territory, guarding the food and shelter contained within its boundaries as well as the newly deposited eggs that he fertilized minutes before.

Higher along the reef face a male bluehead wrasse mates with a member of the harem of females that live within his territory (fig. 8.1). In contrast to the male with his blue head, black bars, and green body, the female is mostly yellow with a large black spot on her dorsal fin. As the male bluehead extrudes sperm to fertilize the eggs laid by the female, small males, similar in colour to the female, streak by the mating pair, discharging a cloud of sperm as they do. Some of the female's eggs will be fertilized by the large territorial bluehead male while others will be fertilized by the sperm discharged by the smaller yellow streakers. In addition to differences in colour and courtship behaviour, bluehead and yellow males have distinctive histories. While the yellow males began their lives as males, the bluehead male began life as a female and only transformed to a male when the local bluehead male was eaten by a predator or met some other end. At that point, because she was the largest yellow phase among the local females and males, she was in line to become the dominant local male and so changed from the yellow to the bluehead form of the species. Within a week the former

Figure 8.1   Bluehead wrasse males with yellow females of the species. If the bluehead male is removed from a territory, the largest female in the territory can change to a fully functional bluehead male within days.

female was producing sperm and fertilizing the eggs produced by the females in the territory.

While male bluehead wrasses patrol their individual mating territories and male damselfish fight with each other at the boundaries of theirs, elsewhere on the reef groups of snapping shrimp live cooperatively in colonies that may contain over 300 individuals. Most of the individuals in the colonies are juveniles or males and each contains a single reproductive female. The female snapping shrimp, which plays a role much like the queen ant in an ant colony, breeds continuously and so is easily identified by her ripe ovaries or by the eggs she carries. Meanwhile the males of the colony, most of which will probably never mate, vigorously defend the nest site, with its "queen" shrimp and numerous juveniles, against intruders. In this shrimp society most males serve the colony and its queen by protecting her offspring and the sponge where they live. While the queen reproduces profusely, the chance to reproduce is probably rare for an individual male. The colony thrives but reproduction is restricted to a few individuals in the population.

During a short swim over a coral reef you can observe great variation in social interactions among individuals belonging to the same species. Analogous variation can be found in terrestrial environments. In chapters 5, 6, and 7 of section II, we considered the relations of organisms to physical and chemical aspects of the environment, including temperature, water, energy, and nutrients. However, to an individual organism, other members of its own species are a part of the environment as significant to it as temperature, food, or the quantity and quality of available water. In chapter 8 we will consider some of the interrelations among individuals.

The study of social relations is the territory of behavioural ecology, which concentrates on relationships between organisms and environment that are mediated by behaviour (fig. 8.2). We have already discussed many aspects of behavioural ecology in the preceding chapters, such as optimal foraging and movements associated with temperature and water regulation. In this chapter we will expand this discussion to include

Figure 8.2   Organisms exhibit a diversity of behaviours, which include foraging, heat regulation, herding, and mate selection.

aspects of the underlying theory of behavioural ecology, as well as an in-depth discussion of social interactions between organisms. Social relations, from dominance relationships and reproductive interactions to cooperative behaviours, are important since they often directly and obviously impact the reproductive contribution of individuals to future generations, a key component of Darwinian or evolutionary fitness, usually referred to simply as *fitness*. We defined fitness in chapter 4 as the number of offspring, or genes, contributed by an individual to future generations. Fitness can be substantially influenced by behaviour and social relations within a population.

One of the most fundamental social interactions between individuals takes place during sexual reproduction. The timing of those interactions and their nature is strongly influenced by the reproductive system of a species. The behavioural ecologist considers several factors. Does the population engage in sexual reproduction? Are the sexes separate? How are the sexes distributed among individuals? Are there several forms of one sex or the other? Questions such as these have drawn the attention of biologists since Darwin (1862) who wrote, "We do not even in the least know the final cause of sexuality; why new beings should be produced by the union of the two sexual elements, instead of by a process of parthenogenesis [production of offspring from unfertilized eggs] . . . The whole subject is as yet hidden in darkness." As you will see, behavioural and evolutionary ecologists have learned a great deal about the evolution and ecology of reproduction in the nearly one and a half centuries since Darwin published this statement. However, much remains to be discovered.

In this chapter we will explore the theoretical underpinning of behavioural ecology. We will then study issues associated with group living, and how natural selection can, sometimes, favour cooperation rather than competition. We will then discuss sex, combining evolutionary, ecological, and behavioural information to study a process called sexual selection. It is important to remember that behavioural ecology consists of many more topics than can be presented here, and issues of behaviour will be woven throughout our later chapters on species interactions such as competition, predation, and disease. Here we present three central concepts to this fascinating field of ecology, which in combination form the framework of chapter 8.

Concepts

8.1 **Natural selection favours those behaviours that increase the inclusive fitness of individuals.**

8.2 **The evolution of sociality is generally accompanied by cooperative feeding, defense of the social group, and restricted reproductive opportunities.**

8.3 **Mate choice by one sex and/or competition for mates among individuals of the same sex can result in selection for particular traits, a process called sexual selection.**

8.1 Evolution and Behaviour

Natural selection favours those behaviours that increase the inclusive fitness of individuals.   In chapter 4 we presented the central aspects of Darwin's Theory of Natural Selection, which included that a given trait had a heritable component and that alternative expressions of that trait resulted in differential fitness. A critical aspect of this theory is that selection acts upon *individuals*, which can cause evolution within *populations*.

When we think of natural selection, we often imagine traits such as beak size, seed number, and body size being associated with fitness and serving as the raw materials upon which selection can act. We don't usually think of behaviour. However, there is substantial evidence that a variety of commonly observed behaviours have genetic bases. One of the clearest examples of this comes from collaboration by researchers at the University of Toronto, University of Illinois at Urbana-Champaign, and the Université de Bourgogne (Ben-Shahar et al. 2002). The team of researchers was interested in the genetic control of foraging in honey bees. In honey bee colonies, worker bees work in the hive when they are young (e.g., brood care), and forage when they are older (two to three weeks later). This represents a fundamental shift in behaviour of individuals over the course of their life. Even more interesting, the timing of this switch is not fixed, but can be influenced by local needs within and external to the hive. How does this switch occur? The researchers focused on a single gene, *for*, which codes for a specific protein kinase, PKG. They found that mRNA expression was significantly higher in foraging bees than bees that remained at work in the hive. When the researchers experimentally increased PKG levels, the bees switched to foraging behaviour sooner than untreated bees! There are numerous other examples of genetic control of behaviour, including foraging decisions of zebra finches (Lemon 1993), anti-predator movement patterns in daphnia (Demeester 1993), and even anti-competitor growth in tobacco plants (Schmitt et al. 1995). In total, these studies provide clear examples that even complex behaviours can have a genetic basis, and that cognitive "choice" is not the sole determinant of how an organism behaves.

What is the evolutionary basis for this variation in behaviour as a function of bee age? It is unknown, however there

is reason to believe that certain behaviours are more *adaptive* under some circumstances than others. For example, It would make little sense for bees to be active foragers before the hive is constructed, or before plants are producing nectar. Thus foraging and hive building behaviours are both adaptive behaviours; however, their value is dependent upon local conditions. One of the great findings in behavioural ecology over the last 50 years has been that the adaptive value of a given trait is often contingent upon the specific environmental conditions that an organism faces. The idea that *either* nature *or* nurture causes individuals to act a certain way is great for sales in the media, but is sadly out of date amongst ecologists and evolutionary biologists. In other words, a squirrel exposing itself to predation risk by a hawk for a food reward makes more sense as (1) the value of the reward increases, (2) the hunger level of the squirrel increases, and (3) the probability of predation decreases. So, if we see a squirrel run after some nuts when hawks are visible, it is not fair to say that the "nature" of the squirrel is to be inherently risky; instead the squirrel possesses the ability to *either* run after the food *or* not. Evolution may fine tune this process by setting the threshold for risk taking higher or lower depending upon local conditions, creating *intraspecific* variation in behaviours. You may recall from chapter 4 that if these variations in behaviour are related to mating, they could serve as effective isolating mechanisms leading to speciation.

At a larger level, we can see *interspecific* differences in behaviour. For example, Laurence Packer, of York University, has studied the evolution of sociality and nest architecture among several species of closely related bees (Halictidae; Packer 1991). These species are known to vary greatly in behaviour, with social bee species forming large colonies each year, some species being completely solitary, and others forming a perennial colony. What was unknown was whether these interspecific differences were the result of multiple (and random) evolutionary events, or if instead there was a general pattern to the evolution of the behaviours. After constructing a phylogeny for his eight study species, Packer mapped the known behaviours against it. The results were striking: in this group social behaviour was an ancestral trait, with solitary behaviour recently derived. Packer's work was among the first to show that some interspecific variation in behaviour is likely the result of evolution, and like the more commonly studied physical traits such as beak size, behaviour can be passed on to daughter species.

There is certainly evidence that species and individuals vary in behaviour. We also know that individuals will alter their behaviour depending upon local conditions (do you always order the same food from every restaurant?). Such variation can rapidly overwhelm us, and it is helpful to have a broader theoretical framework on which we can base our discussion of behavioural ecology.

Inclusive Fitness and Types of Behaviour

Before we go any further in our discussion of behaviour, it is going to be necessary for us to recognize a broader understanding of fitness, called **inclusive fitness**. The concept of inclusive fitness was developed by William D. Hamilton (1964), and proposes that an individual's inclusive, or overall, fitness is

		Fitness Consequences to Recipient	
		+	−
Fitness Consequences to Donor	+	Cooperation	Selfishness
	−	Altruism	Spite

Figure 8.3 Hamilton (1964) proposed that social interactions can be classified into four groups based upon the potential fitness consequences for the donor and recipient of any given interaction.

determined by its own survival and reproduction plus the survival and reproduction of individuals with whom the individual shares genes. Under some conditions individuals can increase their inclusive fitness by helping increase the survival and reproduction of genetic relatives that are not offspring. Because this help is given to relatives, or kin, the evolutionary force favouring such behaviour is called **kin selection**. Using the concept of inclusive fitness, Hamilton explored the potential evolutionary consequences of different forms of social interactions. He classified all social interactions into four main classes, and argued that natural selection will favour certain types of behaviour, and select against others (fig. 8.3) Specifically, Hamilton views social relations as an interaction between a "donor" and a "recipient." A donor performs a given action, such as sings a song, removes parasites from another, or displays a threat. The recipient is the individual who recognizes the given behaviour. In this classification, Hamilton classified all behaviours as having a potential negative or positive effect on the fitness of the two participants. Using this model, we see that two sets of behaviours, *altruism* and *spitefulness*, have negative fitness consequences for the donor, and as a result, natural selection should select against these behaviours. In contrast, *cooperation* and *selfishness* have positive fitness consequences for the donor, and should be favoured by natural selection.

Although it may be tempting to argue that all observed behaviours are inherently advantageous, this approach is negatively referred to as *adaptationist*. Adaptationist stories in ecology are roughly similar to Kipling's *Just So Stories*, such as "How the Camel Got His Hump." In these stories, Kipling provided fanciful "mechanisms" that generated the patterns we observe in nature, such as hump-backed camels. Modern behavioural ecologists are well aware of the adaptationist trap, and they recognize that many behaviours are evolutionarily neutral, neither selected for or against. As a result, behavioural ecologists are not content to simply suggest an evolutionary consequence of one behaviour over another, but instead actively work to test whether such selective differences actually occur. A related issue is that for natural selection to occur there needs to be a large heritable component to a given behaviour. This in no way suggests that all behaviours need to have a genetic component, instead, only those behaviours that could be influenced by natural selection must have a genetic basis.

A second concern is that according to Hamilton's classification, some behaviours, like altruism, should not persist, as they would be selected against. However, we can go out into a variety of systems and see animals exhibiting behaviours which put themselves in immediate bodily harm, yet appear to prevent harm in others. This behaviour can be shown repeatedly within a species, strongly suggesting a genetic basis. In other words, we can see altruism, and we believe it can have a genetic basis. How can this be reconciled with Hamilton's ideas that altruism should be selected against?

Altruism and Natural Selection

Using Hamilton's classifications, an altruistic act is one that benefits the recipient but harms the donor. Examples are plentiful, such as the bird that raises the young of another species or the prairie dog that makes an alarm in response to a predator. How can behavioural ecologists explain these phenomena?

One of the earliest sets of explanations for altruism came from V. C. Wynne-Edwards (1962) who argued in favour of group selection as a means to explain many observed phenomenon. In Wynne-Edwards' presentation of **group selection**, he argued that individuals may act counter to their own personal interests for the betterment of the group. For instance, an organism may reduce its reproductive rate to prevent a population from exhausting its resources. This line of thinking was rapidly attacked by many scientists (Williams 1966, Smith and Wynne-Edwards 1964) as being inherently adaptationist without any consistency with current evolutionary understanding. They were very effective in moving discussions of altruism toward a gene-centred, rather than group-centred level. However, over the last 40 years, there is clear evidence that group selection can occur in some special circumstances (Wade 1977). It has been rebranded under the term "*multilevel selection*," and its role in the evolution of altruism is still debated. Perhaps more importantly than whether group selection can exist is that ecologists have uncovered a number of other causes of altruism: manipulation, kin selection, and reciprocal altruism.

The Brown-headed Cowbird (*Molothrus ater*) has a rather interesting mechanism for incubating its eggs and rearing its young. It is an obligate **brood parasite**, meaning that a female must lay its eggs in the nests of birds of other species. The host birds then keep the parasitic bird's eggs warm and feed the hatchling until it can fledge from the nest. Based on the principle

(a) Placed in Robin nests

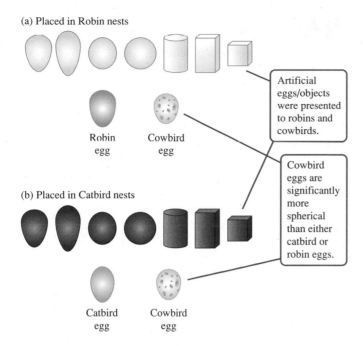

Robin egg   Cowbird egg

Artificial eggs/objects were presented to robins and cowbirds.

(b) Placed in Catbird nests

Catbird egg   Cowbird egg

Cowbird eggs are significantly more spherical than either catbird or robin eggs.

Figure 8.4 Differently shaped objects were placed in the nests of robins and catbirds (Underwood and Sealy 2006).

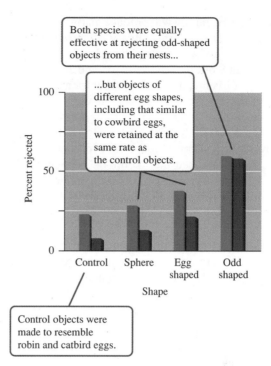

Both species were equally effective at rejecting odd-shaped objects from their nests...

...but objects of different egg shapes, including that similar to cowbird eggs, were retained at the same rate as the control objects.

Control objects were made to resemble robin and catbird eggs.

Figure 8.5 Catbirds and Robins reject objects shaped similarly to cowbird eggs no more frequently than objects shaped similarly to their own eggs (data from Underwood and Sealy 2006).

of allocation we discussed in chapters 5 and 7, you can see an obvious problem. If the host bird gives food and thermal energy to this parasitic bird, less will be available for its own offspring, reducing its own fitness. In other words, why would these host birds perform this altruistic act? The short answer to this question is that this is an example of *manipulation*, where the song sparrow doesn't appear to posses any obvious means to prevent this from occurring. In a study at Delta Marsh, the field station associated with the University of Manitoba, Todd Underwood and Spencer Sealy added artificial objects of different shapes to nests of American robins and Gray catbirds (Underwood and Sealy 2006), two species that are commonly parasitized by Brown-headed Cowbirds (fig. 8.4). The researchers found that although cowbirds eggs are significantly more spherical than their host eggs, spherical test "eggs" were only slightly more likely to be rejected by host birds than the control "eggs" (fig. 8.5). In other words, although the researchers could measure a significant difference in shape between cowbird and host eggs, the host birds apparently could not and thus cowbirds induce altruism through manipulation of the reproductive biology of their hosts. James Smith and Peter Arcese (1994), from the University of British Columbia, have measured the potential fitness consequences of cowbird parasitism on a song sparrow population on an island off the coast of British Columbia. In a 16-year study, they found the presence of a cowbird egg in a sparrow nest reduced the number of sparrows that fledged from the nest by 79%, though this was reduced to 27% when food was experimentally added. Sparrows were also more likely to fledge no sparrows from nests when parasitized than when they were not parasitized. In short, having a cowbird egg in your nest is bad news to your fitness, though obviously you are doing the cowbird a nice favour. This form of altruism persists because the host cannot do anything about it.

We now turn our attention to the idea that kin selection can promote altruism. We know that we each received 50% of our genes from each of our two biological parents. From a parental point of view, this means that each offspring they have is equivalent to approximately 50% of their own genetic material. The **coefficient of relationship** can be determined for any two individuals. It will be 25% between grandparent and grandchildren, 12.5% between great-grandparents and great-grandchildren, 50% between full siblings, and 25% between half-siblings. Have you figured out the pattern? There is a reduction of 50% in the coefficient in relationship for every additional connection between any two related individuals. So what? From an inclusive fitness point of view, if a sister had the choice to save the lives of her two siblings at the expense of her own life, her fitness would be equal regardless of what behaviour she chose. However, selection would favour her heroic act of self-sacrifice if she were able to save three siblings, or two siblings and a cousin, or any other combination of relatives whose coefficients of relationship sum to more than 1. However, most behaviours do not result in certain death for the donor, nor certain survival for the recipient, and so the costs and benefits of an action to one's fitness is generally less than one. Hamilton (1964) formalized the situation under which a particular behaviour would be advantageous as:

$$\frac{\text{Cost}}{\text{Benefit}} < \text{Coefficient of Relationship}$$

In this model, selection would favour a given behaviour only if the inclusive fitness gains exceed the inclusive fitness costs. The obvious question to ask is whether this really happens. Some of the best examples that kin selection can be important in altruistic behaviours come from studies of prairie dogs and ground squirrels. A variety of species of the small rodents of the Sciuridae family will produce alarm calls when a predator is visible. These alarm calls are often loud noises associated with the individual taking an upright and aggressive posture. Recent work by David Wilson and James Hare of the University of Manitoba also shows that for at least one species, the Richardson's ground squirrel, the vigilant animal can use an ultrasonic call to alert others to impending threat (Wilson and Hare 2004)! In a classic study of Belding's ground squirrels, Paul Sherman found that individuals displaying alarm calls increased the likelihood of themselves being attacked, but also increased the ability of others to escape predation (Sherman 1977). Importantly, the probability of an individual making an alarm call was higher when close relatives were nearby than when less closely related (or unrelated) individuals were nearby. The mechanisms of how individuals recognize kin remain an active area of research for Jim Hare and others. Through studies of numerous species of ground squirrels, it appears that some do not recognize kin per se, but instead recognize litter mates (which, without a researcher moving them around in an experiment, would most certainly be kin!). Other species, however, are able to recognize kin regardless of whether they are moved from one location to another. This fascinating area of research holds much opportunity for continued research, with clear implications for issues of sociality among a variety of species.

We will provide one final explanation for altruism, which is **reciprocal altruism**. Under this model individuals do not have to be related to each other for altruism to be evolutionarily stable. Instead, this model is based upon recognition and experience, and is also called *tit-for-tat*. We will discuss this idea in depth in the Ecological Tools section at the end of this chapter. In brief, this idea says that natural selection will favour altruistic behaviours to unrelated individuals if that individual will repay in kind. The reciprocal act does not need to be immediate (that would be cooperation, not altruism), but it does need to occur with a high degree of certainty.

In this section we have provided you with a general background into how natural selection can influence behaviour. We find that initially counterintuitive actions such as altruism can also be the result of natural selection, as long as we allow ourselves to think more broadly about who benefits, why, when, and whether there is even any choice. We will now continue this chapter with more examples of how selection can influence behaviour, with a focus on group living.

Concept 8.1 Review

1. If a researcher is interested in understanding the evolution of a behaviour, why does it matter if that behaviour has a genetic basis? Does a genetic basis of a behaviour necessarily mean the behaviour will always be expressed?
2. What is the difference between inclusive fitness as discussed in this chapter, and fitness, as defined in chapter 4?
3. What conditions are likely necessary for the evolution of altruistic behaviours in a species?

8.2   Sociality

The evolution of sociality is generally accompanied by cooperative feeding, defense of the social group, and restricted reproductive opportunities.   Chapters 5 through 7 focused on the ecology of individual organisms, mainly on how individuals solve environmental problems. Some of the problems we considered were how animals maintain a particular range of body temperatures in the face of much greater variation in environmental temperatures, or how plants sustain high rates of photosynthesis while avoiding excessive water loss. However, a fundamental change in relationships among individuals within a population takes place when individuals begin living in groups, such as colonies, herds, or schools. Cooperation generally involves exchanges of resources between individuals or various forms of assistance, such as defense of the group against predators, such as altruism among ground squirrels. Group living and cooperation signal the beginnings of **sociality**. The degree of sociality in a species ranges from acts as simple as mutual grooming or group protection of young to highly complex, stratified societies such as those found in colonies of ants or termites. This more complex level of social behaviour is called **eusociality.** Eusociality is generally thought to include three major characteristics: (1) Individuals of more than one generation living together, (2) cooperative care of young, and (3) division of individuals into sterile, or nonreproductive, and reproductive castes.

Because individuals in social species often appear to have fewer opportunities to reproduce compared to individuals in nonsocial species, the evolution of sociality has drawn a great deal of attention from behavioural ecologists. The apparent restriction of reproductive opportunities that comes with sociality appears to challenge the idea that the fitness of an individual is determined by the number of offspring it produces. How does sociality challenge this concept of fitness? The challenge emerges from the observation that in many situations, individuals in social species do not reproduce themselves, while helping others in the population to reproduce. How can we explain such behaviour that on first glance appears to be self-sacrificing? It can be argued that such behaviour should be quickly eliminated from populations. However, since eusocial species such as bees and ants have survived for millions of years, behavioural ecologists have assumed that in some circumstances, the benefits of sociality must outweigh the costs.

Behavioural ecologists have assumed that the key to understanding the evolution of sociality will result from careful assessment of its costs and benefits. However, in our quest for such understanding, where should we begin the accounting of costs and benefits? David Ligon (1999) pointed the way when he wrote, "Most, if not all, of the important issues relevant to cooperative breeding systems are . . . related to the costs and benefits of sociality." Following Ligon's suggestion, the case histories begin with cooperative breeders.

Cooperative Breeders

Species that live in groups often cooperate or help during the process of producing offspring. Help may include defending the territory or the young, preparing and maintaining a nest or den, or feeding young. Since the young that receive the care are not the offspring of the helpers, one of the most basic questions that we can ask about these breeding systems is why do helpers help? In other words, what benefits do helpers gain from their cooperation? It should be clear to you by now that one potential gain for these helpers would be an increase in their own inclusive fitness. For instance, although the young being helped are not their own young, this does not necessarily mean they are completely unrelated.

A second reason offered to explain the evolution of cooperative breeding is that helping may improve the helper's own probability of successful reproduction. Because helping gives the helper experience in raising young, helping may increase the helper's chances of successfully raising young of its own and recruiting helpers of its own. In addition, where suitable breeding habitat is limited, helpers may have a better chance of inheriting the breeding territory from the reproductive individuals they help. Again, they are improving their chances of eventually raising their own young.

What sorts of species engage in cooperative breeding? Approximately 100 species of birds are cooperative breeders. In addition, several species of mammals such as wolves, wild dogs, and African lions engage in cooperative breeding. Let's review one intensely studied species where several benefits of cooperative breeding have been demonstrated.

African Lions

Craig Packer and Anne E. Pusey have studied cooperation among African lions in the Serengeti (Packer and Pusey 1982, 1983, 1997, Packer et al. 1991). Their studies have revealed a great deal of complexity in lion societies. Female lions live in groups of related individuals called prides (fig. 8.6). Prides of female lions generally include 3 to 6 adults but may contain as many as 18 or as few as 1. In addition to adult females, prides also include their dependent offspring and a coalition of adult males. Male coalitions may be made up of closely related individuals or of unrelated individuals.

Within lion society one can observe many forms of cooperation. Female lions nurse each other's cubs. They also cooperate when hunting large, difficult-to-kill game such as zebra and buffalo. In addition, females cooperatively defend their territory against encroaching females. However, the most critical form of cooperation among females is their group defense of the young against infanticidal males. These attacks on the young generally take place as a male coalition is displaced by another invading coalition. While a single female lion has little chance in a fight against a male lion, which are nearly 50% larger, cooperating females are often successful at repelling attacking males. Males, in turn, cooperate in defending the territory against invading males, which threaten the young they have sired, and against threats from other predators such as hyenas. The challenge for the behavioural ecologist has been to determine whether these various forms of cooperation can be reconciled with evolutionary theory.

Since the females in lion prides are always close relatives, their cooperative behaviour can be readily explained within the conceptual framework of kin selection. As females cooperate in nursing or defending young against males, they contribute to the growth and survival of their own offspring or to those of close kin. Cooperative hunting and sharing the kill also contribute to the welfare of offspring and close relatives. All these contributions add to the inclusive fitness of individual females.

Figure 8.6   African lions are highly social predators.

Human–Wildlife Conflict

It is easy to understand how one could be drawn into the world of behavioural ecology. The blend of ecology, evolution, and physiology presents a continuous intellectual challenge. Even more, many of the behaviours one observes in the wild are mirrored by members of our own species. Just imagine the stories you could tell at the pub! But there is another more practical benefit of this line of research: helping develop strategies to reduce human–wildlife conflict.

Each year, tens of thousands of conflicts occur between people and wildlife throughout Canada. The "problem wildlife" involved in these interactions are often later killed, resulting in the deaths of thousands of animals annually. At the same time, some of these conflicts also kill or injure people. Sources of human–wildlife conflict are diverse and range from traffic collisions and crop damage by ungulates to home invasions by bears. These issues are increasing in severity as humans continue to expand population centres and industrial activity into formerly remote areas. Many of these problems concern hyper-abundant and human-habituated animals in urban areas. Habituated animals have little fear of people and congregate in urban areas because they can avoid wary predators and feed on the rich resources provided by human garbage and horticultural practices. Everyone is familiar with the pirating gulls (*Larus* species) of the fast food restaurant parking lot, but most do not consider this behaviour to be a problematic source of conflict. However, that perception changes for large species. For example, over each of the last 14 years in British Columbia, there has been an average of over 9,500 complaints about grizzly and black bears near humans. Over this time period there has also been an average of about eight people killed or injured per year by bears, 900 of the complaint bears killed per year, and another 175 bears captured and relocated each year (BC Ministry of Environment, pers. comm.). The magnitude of complaints received each year clearly indicates that people are quite concerned about having these large animals near where they live and work. As these numbers also clearly indicate, these concerns traditionally result in a very large number of animal deaths. Can ecologists use their knowledge to reduce human–wildlife conflict, finding solutions that both maintain the physical safety of people while also allowing animals to be wild? Here we discuss one innovative approach that is proving successful for reducing human–wildlife conflicts in Banff National Park.

Elk (*Cervus elaphus*) are prone to habituation in mountainous urban areas like Jackson Hole, Wyoming, and Banff, Alberta. Their large size and aggressive behaviour creates opportunity for injury and Banff reported an average of seven contact charges between elk and humans each year in the 1990s (G. Peers, Warden, Banff National Park, pers. comm.). Most of these occurred in or near the townsite of Banff, which is situated in the highly productive Bow Valley in the heart of the spectacular rocks and ice that make up most of the park. Solving the problem of habituated elk in Banff and elsewhere is difficult. Translocated animals typically return to their capture sites or die in their new locations. Killing habituated animals is unpalatable, even outside of protected areas, and disrupts the social structure of the animal populations. Approaching the problem by focusing on the habituated behaviour appears to offer some promise for a lasting solution. This approach was used in Banff National Park by Elsabé Kloppers, an M.Sc. student studying with Colleen Cassady St. Clair at the University of Alberta. Working in conjunction with Banff Park biologists and wardens, the research team sought to reduce conflicts by teaching habituated elk to be more wary of people.

To achieve this, they designed an experiment that used 24 radio-collared elk and daily monitoring of movement and behaviour (fig. 8.7). Sixteen animals were assigned to one of two "predator-resembling chase treatments." Eight other elk were designated as control animals, and were captured, handled, and monitored, but not chased. In both chase treatments, the researchers used repeated (up to 10 times) chase sequences during the winter, each of which lasted 15 minutes. One chase treatment used researchers and wardens wielding guns with cracker and screamer shells to chase elk away from the town core (ecologists have the coolest jobs!). The second chase treatment included the use of a professional dog handler to get border collies to emulate wolf hunting behaviour as they herded the elk out of town. Realistic predator simulation appeared to be important; a pilot study indicated that the silent hunting style of the collies initiated a flight responses by the elk, while hunting associated with barking by New Zealand huntaways resulted in charges by the elk! Both types of chases provided what psychologists would term **aversive conditioning**, a form of operant learning. Operant learning may be positive or negative and occurs whenever an animal learns to associate an unconditioned stimulus (e.g., noisy cracker shells and chasing) with a conditioned stimulus (e.g., the appearance of a human on foot). The principle of allocation (chapter 7) should favour learning that minimizes energetic costs and maximizes foraging gains.

After conditioning, the treated elk fled from approaching humans when they were at greater distances, tended to spend more time being vigilant, and foraged farther from the town perimeter relative to the control elk (fig. 8.8; Kloppers et al. 2005). Interestingly, some aspects of the strength of the conditioning effects were strongest when wolves were not very active and less effective when they were present.

(a)

(b)

(c)

Figure 8.7 (*a*) Elk relaxing in Banff; (*b*) human-based conditioning treatment; (*c*) dog-based conditioning treatment (Kloppers et al. 2005).

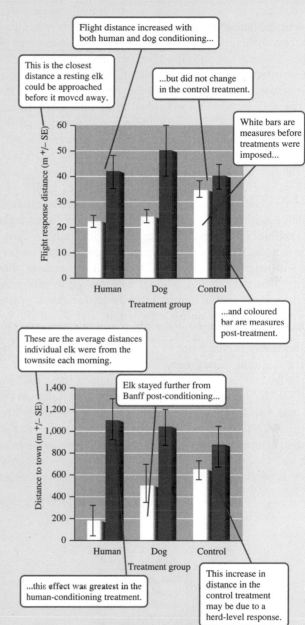

Figure 8.8 Flight response and elk location were influenced by avoidance conditioning in Banff townsite (data from Kloppers et al. 2005).

Overall, aversive conditioning appears to work as a means of reducing elk–human conflict; elk are much less common now in the townsite and there has been only one contact charge in the four years since it was implemented. Both dogs and humans are still used, but the guns (which were offensive to tourists) have been replaced with equally-effective hockey sticks (yes, hockey sticks!).

This study is a strong example that the concepts of behavioural ecology can have clear and direct conservation and management benefits. Through conditioning, the research team demonstrated that animals can learn to avoid humans, even without receiving an actual physical deterrent or being captured and translocated. The field of conservation behavioural ecology is relatively new, and it holds great promise for using research to address real-world problems. As examples, Colleen St Clair and her colleagues are using aversive conditioning to discourage waterbirds from landing on tarsand tailings ponds, to dissuade bears from consuming garbage at mountain resorts, and to encourage habituated elk to reinstate traditional migratory routes.

In contrast, because male coalitions are sometimes made up of close relatives and sometimes not, cooperation within coalitions has represented a greater challenge to evolutionary theory. However, on close consideration Packer and colleagues (Packer et al. 1991) discovered that the rules associated with the formation and behaviour of coalitions are consistent with predictions of evolutionary theory. Single males have virtually no chance of claiming and defending a pride of female lions. Therefore they must form coalitions with other males. This represents a type of ecological constraint on viable choices open to males. If males form a coalition with brothers and cousins, cooperative behaviour that increases the production and survival of offspring of the coalition will increase an individual male's inclusive fitness. However, theoretically, a male within a coalition with unrelated males must produce some offspring of his own or he is merely increasing the fitness of others at the expense of his own fitness.

The first question we should ask is, do all males within a coalition have an equal opportunity to reproduce? If all males within a coalition have an equal probability of reproducing, then forming coalitions with unrelated males is easier to reconcile with evolutionary theory. However, if there is significant variation in reproductive opportunities within coalitions, then cooperating with unrelated males is more difficult to reconcile with theories predicting that individuals will attempt to maximize their inclusive fitness. It turns out that the probability of a male siring young depends on his rank within a coalition and on coalition size. As shown in figure 8.9, males in coalitions of two sire a relatively similar proportion of the young produced by the pride. In addition, these proportions are close to the proportions sired by the two top ranked males in coalitions of three and four. However, the third ranked males in coalitions of three and the third and fourth ranked in coalitions of four sire almost no young lions. Packer and his team concluded from these data that variation in reproductive success is much higher in coalitions of three and four than in coalitions of two. In other words, the chance of reproducing is less evenly distributed among males in coalitions of three and four than in coalitions of two.

What implications do the results of Packer's studies have to the formation of coalitions containing unrelated individuals? One of the implications is that an unrelated male in a coalition of three or more runs the risk of investing time and energy in helping maintain a pride without an opportunity to reproduce himself and without improving his inclusive fitness since the other coalition members are not relatives. This result suggests that males should avoid joining larger coalitions of unrelated males, and this is just what Packer and his colleagues found (fig. 8.10). Figure 8.10 shows the percentage of males with unrelated partners in coalitions of different sizes. These patterns show clearly that males that team up with unrelated individuals mostly do so in coalitions of two or three. Larger coalitions of four to nine individuals are almost entirely made up of relatives. What are the implications of these data? They suggest that males avoid joining larger coalitions unless the coalition consists of relatives. Such a strategy avoids the risk of helping without gaining in inclusive fitness.

In summary, cooperation among African lions appears to be a response to environmental conditions that require cooperation for success. Packer and Pusey (1997) captured the situation facing African lions in a fascinating article titled, "Divided We Fall: Cooperation Among Lions." To survive, reproduce, and successfully raise offspring to maturity, African lions must work in cooperative groups. The lone lion has no chance of meeting the ecological challenges presented by living on the Serengeti in lion society with its aggressive prides and invasive and infanticidal male coalitions. However, as we have seen, within the constraints set by their environments. African lions appear to behave in a way that contributes positively to their overall fitness.

While the complexities of African lion societies have taken decades to uncover, they pale beside the intricacies of life among eusocial species such as bees, termites, and ants. Let's explore eusociality in some animal populations to get some insights into the evolution of these complex social systems.

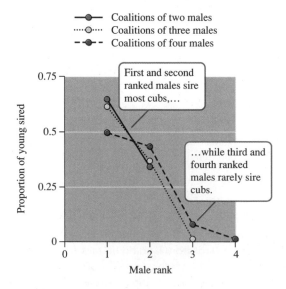

Figure 8.9 Male lion rank and proportion of cubs sired in male coalitions of different sizes (data from Packer et al. 1991).

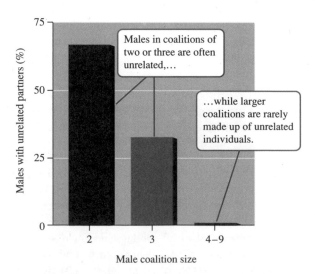

Figure 8.10 Relatedness and size of male coalitions among African lions (data from Packer et al. 1991).

Eusocial Species

Probably the most thoroughly studied of eusocial species are the ants. Ants and their complex behaviours have attracted the attention of people from the earliest times and appear in the oldest writings such as the Bible and the classical writings of ancient Greece. Such written records were likely predated by older folktales. Bert Hölldobler and Edward O. Wilson (1990) pointed out that many of the earliest accounts of ants focused on ant species that make their living by harvesting seeds. These seed-harvesting species were serious agricultural pests around the Mediterranean Sea and their dependence on grains paralleled remarkably the economy of the human populations of the region.

In the intervening centuries since these earliest writings, we have learned much more about ants. Taxonomists have described nearly 9,000 species of ants, all belonging to the family Formicidae, which, along with their relatives the wasps and bees, are members of the insect order Hymenoptera. Hölldobler and Wilson (1990) wrote a monumental summary of what was known about ants near the end of the twentieth century in a book titled simply *The Ants*. However, despite that book and the hundreds of studies done on ants since its publication, much is left to learn about this group of insects that Hölldobler and Wilson referred to as the "culmination of insect evolution."

One of the most socially complex groups of ants are the leafcutters (fig. 8.11). The 39 described species of leafcutter ants, which belong to two genera, are found only in the Americas, from the southern United States to Argentina. Leafcutter ants make their living by cutting and transporting leaf fragments to their nest, where the leaf material is fragmented and used as a substrate upon which to grow fungi. The fungi provide the primary food source for leafcutter ants.

Among the various species of leafcutter ants, some of the most thoroughly studied are species belonging to the genus *Atta*. *Atta* species live mainly in tropical Central and South America. However, at least two species reach as far north as Arizona and Louisiana in the United States. Leafcutter ants are important consumers in the tropical ecosystems, where they move large amounts of soil and process large quantities of leaf material in their nests. The nests of leafcutter ants can attain great size. For instance, the nests of *A. sexdens* can include over 1,000 entrance holes and nearly 2,000 occupied and abandoned chambers. In one excavation of an *A. sexdens* nest (cited in Hölldobler and Wilson 1990), researchers estimated that the ants had moved more than 22 m³ of soil, which weighed over 40,000 kg. Within this nest, the occupants had stored nearly 6,000 kg of leaves. Mature nests of *A. sexdens* contain a queen, various numbers of winged males and females, which disperse to mate and found colonies elsewhere, and up to 5 to 8 million workers.

Though involving far fewer individuals, there are striking analogies between the organization of ant colonies and colonies of naked mole rats, *Heterocephalus glaber,* one of the few species of eusocial mammals (fig. 8.12). Despite their common name, naked mole rats are not completely naked and they are neither moles nor rats. Like moles, naked mole rats live underground but they are rodents, not moles. However, the family of rodents to which they belong is more closely related to porcupines and chinchillas than to rats.

Naked mole rats live in underground colonies in the arid regions of Kenya, Somalia, and Ethiopia. Colonies often include 70 to 80 individuals but can sometimes contain as many as 250 individuals. The burrow system of a single colony of naked mole rats is extensive and can cover up to approximately 100,000 m², or about 20 football fields. Most of the digging required to maintain their large burrow systems is done with the naked mole rats' teeth and massive jaws. It turns out that the jaw muscles of naked mole rats make up about 25% of their entire muscle mass. This would be approximately equivalent to having muscles the size of those in your legs powering your jaws!

Both naked mole rats and leafcutter ants live in social groups in which individuals are divided among **castes** that engage in very different activities. We can define a caste as a group of physically distinctive individuals that engage in specialized behaviour within the colony. E. O. Wilson (1980) studied how labour is divided among castes of ants in a laboratory colony of *A. sexdens* that he established and studied

Figure 8.11 Leafcutter ants carrying leaf fragments back to the nest where they will be processed to create a substrate for growing the fungi that the ants eat. Smaller ants riding on leaf fragments offer protection from aerial attack by parasitoid flies.

Figure 8.12 Naked mole rats live in colonies of closely related individuals ruled by a single dominant female, or queen, shown here resting on top of members of her colony.

over a period of eight years. During this period, Wilson carefully cataloged the behaviours of individual colony members. Because the colony lived in a closed series of clear plastic containers, their behaviour could be studied easily. In addition to recording behaviours, Wilson also estimated the sizes of individuals engaging in each behaviour by measuring their head widths to the nearest 0.2 mm. He made his estimates visually by comparing an ant to a standard array of preserved *A. sexdens* specimens of known size.

When Wilson compared the leafcutter ant *A. sexdens* with three non-leafcutter ant species, he found that the leafcutter ants included a larger number of castes and engaged in a wider variety of behaviours (fig. 8.13). Wilson identified a total of 29 distinctive tasks performed by the leafcutter ants compared to an average of 17.7 tasks performed by the three other species. He found that the division of labour within the *A. sexdens* colony was mainly based on size. Possibly because

of the large number of specialized tasks that need to be performed by leafcutter ants, they have one of the most complex social structures and one of the greatest size ranges found among the ants. Within *A. sexdens* colonies, the head width of the largest individuals (5.2 mm) is nearly nine times the head width of the smallest individuals (0.6 mm). On the basis of size, Wilson identified four castes within his leafcutter colony. However, because the tasks performed by some of the size classes change as they age, Wilson discovered three additional temporal or developmental castes for a total of seven castes within the colony, compared to an average of three castes in the non-leafcutter ant species he studied.

As a consequence of this great variation, someone watching a trail of leafcutter ants bring freshly cut leaf fragments back to their nest is treated to a rich display of size and behavioural diversity. While medium-sized ants carry the leaf fragments above their heads, the largest ants line the trail like sentries, guarding against ground attacks on the column of ants carrying leaf fragments. Very small ants ride on many of the leaf fragments, protecting the ant carrying a leaf fragment from aerial attacks by parasitic flies. Meanwhile, other size classes of leafcutters performing behaviours associated with processing leaves, tending larvae, and maintaining fungal gardens remain hidden in the nest. It was the activity of these smaller individuals that Wilson's laboratory colony was able to reveal so clearly.

Careful study has revealed some remarkable parallels in the structures of naked mole rat and leafcutter ant societies. The social behaviour of naked mole rats was first reported by Jennifer Jarvis, professor at the University of Cape Town, South Africa, in a paper in the journal *Science* (Jarvis 1981). Her published study was based on more than six years of observation and experimentation with colonies of naked mole rats that she had established in the laboratory. Jarvis dug up a number of colonies and relocated them to a laboratory habitat analogous to that used by Wilson in his study of leafcutter ants. She waited approximately a year after bringing the naked mole rats to the laboratory before attempting to quantify their behaviours. Once this period of acclimation was over, Jarvis spent approximately 100 hours detailing how the members of her laboratory population of naked mole rats spent their time.

The picture of naked mole rat society that emerged from Jarvis' study was immediately intriguing to behavioural ecologists. The social organization of the colony appeared more similar to an ant colony than to any other mammal population known. Jarvis' paper in *Science* stimulated dozens of studies of naked mole rats and of related species. The results provide interesting insights into the evolution of social behaviour. Within a colony of naked mole rats, one female and only a few males breed. This group of reproductive individuals functions basically as a queen and her mates, while all of the rest of the colony is nonreproductive. Behavioural ecologists have found that life in a naked mole rat colony centres on the queen and her offspring, and the queen's behaviour appears to maintain this focus. She is the most active member of the colony and literally pushes her way around the colony. By physically pushing individuals she appears to call them to action when there is work to be done or when the colony is threatened and needs defending.

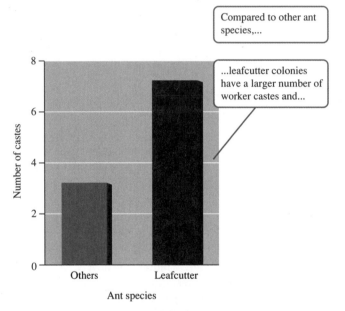

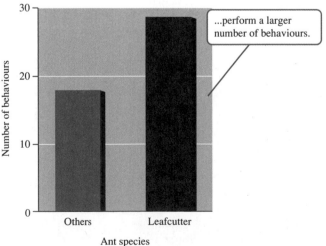

Figure 8.13 Comparison of the number of castes and number of behaviours in a colony of leafcutter ants, *Atta sexdens*, and in colonies of three other ant species (data from Wilson 1980).

The aggressiveness of the queen also appears to maintain her dominance over other females in the colony and to prevent them from coming into breeding condition. If the queen dies or is removed from the colony, one of the other females in the colony will assume the role of queen. If two or more females compete for the position of queen, they may fight to the death during the process of establishing the new social hierarchy.

In contrast to leafcutter ant colonies, where all workers are females, both males and females work in naked mole rat colonies. Jarvis found that work is divided among colony members, as in leafcutter ant colonies, according to size. However, in contrast to leafcutter ants, colonies of naked mole rats include only two worker size classes, small and large. Small workers are the most active. Small workers excavate tunnels, build the nest, which is deeper than most of the passage ways, and line the nest with plant materials for bedding. In addition, small workers also harvest food, mainly roots and tubers, and deliver it to other colony members, including the queen, for feeding. Since they spend most of their time sleeping, the role of large nonbreeders was unclear for some time. However, eventually researchers working in the field were able to observe these large nonbreeders in action. It turns out that the large workers, as in ant colonies, are a caste specializing in defense. If the tunnel system is breached by members of another colony, the large nonbreeders move out quickly from their resting places to defend the colony from the invaders, literally throwing themselves into the breach. Eventually the large nonbreeders push up enough soil to wall off the intruders. However, they may be most important in defending against snakes, the most dangerous predators of naked mole rats. When confronted with a snake, the large nonbreeders will try to kill the snake or spray it with soil until it is driven off or buried.

Evolution of Eusociality

Despite their distinctive evolutionary histories and other biological differences, the studies of Wilson and Jarvis suggest interesting parallels in the organizations of leafcutter ant and naked mole rat colonies (fig. 8.14). Similarities include division of labour within colonies based on size, with smaller

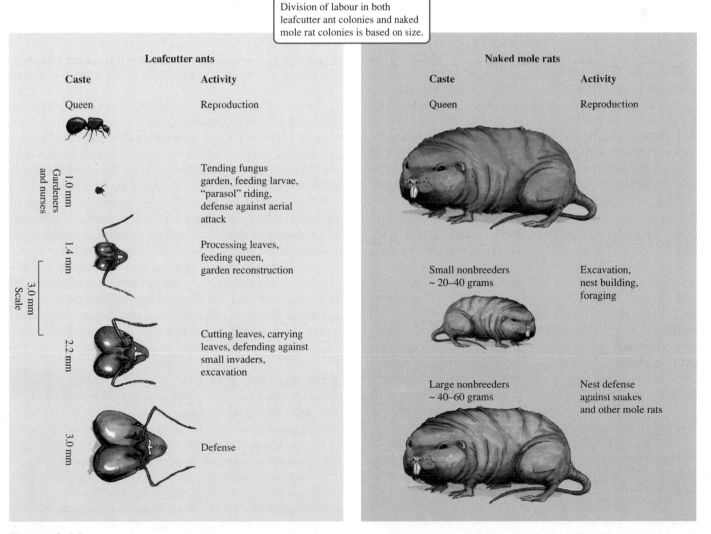

Figure 8.14 Division of labour among castes of leafcutter ants, *Atta sexdens*, and naked mole rats, *Heterocephalus glaber*. Ant sizes are head widths of workers typically engaged in each activity (data from Wilson 1980, Jarvis 1981, and Sherman, Jarvis, and Braude 1992).

workers specializing in foraging, nest maintenance, and excavation of extensive burrow systems. Meanwhile, larger workers in both species specialize in defense. In addition, reproduction in both species is limited to a single queen and her mates. These areas of convergence in social organization between such different organisms may help shed light on the forces responsible for the evolution of eusociality. Such comparisons form the basis of the comparative method.

What factors may have been important in the evolution and maintenance of naked mole rat and leafcutter ant sociality? Kin selection may play a role. Leafcutter ants, along with other Hymenoptera, such as bees and wasps, have an inheritance system called **haplodiploidy.** The term haplodiploid refers to the number of chromosome sets possessed by males and females. In haplodiploid systems males develop from unfertilized eggs and are haploid, while females develop from fertilized eggs and so are diploid. One of the consequences of haplodiploidy is that worker ants within a colony can be very similar genetically. In an ant colony where there is a single queen that mated with a single male, the workers will be more related to each other than they would be to their own offspring. W. D. Hamilton (1964) was the first to point out that under these conditions the average genetic similarity among workers would be 75%, while their relationship with any offspring they might produce would be 50% (fig. 8.15).

What is the source of this high degree of relatedness? The queen mates only during her mating flight and stores the sperm she receives to fertilize all the eggs she lays to produce daughters. If she mates with a single male, since he is haploid, all her daughters will receive the same genetic information from their male parent. As a consequence, the 50% of the genetic makeup that workers receive from their male parent will be identical. In addition, workers will share an average of 25% of their genes through those that they receive from the queen, yielding an average genetic relatedness of 50% + 25% = 75%. The important point here is that the activity of workers promotes the production of closely related individuals, their sisters, an activity that should be favoured by kin selection.

Because naked mole rat colonies are relatively closed to outsiders, the individuals within each colony, like the workers within leafcutter ant colonies, are also very similar genetically. Paul Sherman, Jennifer Jarvis, and Stanton Braude (1992) reported that approximately 85% of matings within a colony of naked mole rats are between parents and offspring or between siblings. As a consequence of these matings between close relatives, the relatedness between individuals within a colony is about 81%, suggesting that kin selection may be involved in the maintenance of nonreproductive helpers in colonies of naked mole rats.

What factors other than kin selection may have contributed to the evolution of eusociality? Many factors have been implicated. While researchers working on ants and other social Hymenoptera have emphasized the potential importance of kin selection, studies of cooperative-breeding vertebrate species have emphasized ecological constraints. What sorts of ecological common constraints are faced by leafcutter ants and naked mole rats? One of the most obvious is the work associ-

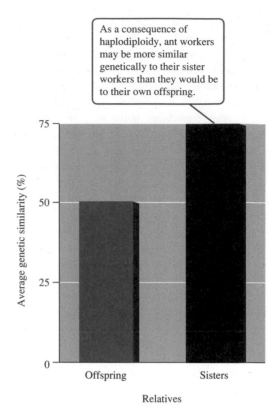

Figure 8.15 Average genetic similarity between ant workers and sisters (other workers) versus their offspring if they reproduced.

ated with the creation, maintenance, and defense of extensive burrow systems. The more social organisms are studied, the less likely it has become that one or a few simple mechanisms will be adequate to explain their evolution. However, the results of studies such as those of Wilson and Jarvis should encourage continued careful comparative studies as a means for eventual understanding of the evolution of sociality. In the application of the comparative method, species such as the leafcutter ant *A. sexdens* and naked mole rats function as invaluable tools.

We have only discussed a few aspects of sociality, completely ignoring equally important and interesting studies related to herding and other behaviours. Many of these topics will be presented in chapter 14. Others, unfortunately, are beyond the scope of this text. Here, we now turn our attention to sex.

Concept 8.2 Review

1. What are the evolutionary implications of the fact that larger coalitions of male lions consist almost entirely of close relatives?
2. Among the ants and other eusocial hymenoptera, why would kin selection favour workers that helped rear sister workers rather than their own offspring?
3. What are the two major ecological challenges favouring colony living shared by leafcutter ants and naked mole rats?

8.3 Mate Choice

Mate choice by one sex and/or competition for mates among individuals of the same sex can result in selection for particular traits, a process called sexual selection. From a human perspective, sexual reproduction appears to be the norm. However, asexual reproduction is common among many groups of organisms such as bacteria, fungi, protozoans, plants, and even some vertebrates. However, most described species of plants and animals include male and female functions, even if these same individuals are also able to reproduce asexually. The male and female functions can be distributed among individuals in a variety of ways, or *sex types*. The most obvious to us is the relatively boring condition of each individual being a single sex (male or female). The **females** are the sex that produces larger, more energetically expensive gametes (eggs or ova), and the **males** produce smaller, less costly gametes (sperm or pollen). Other species have more complicated sex types, which can include **hermaphrodites,** in which an individual is able to perform both male and female reproductive functions. Hermaphroditism is found in over 75% of all flowering plant species, and also occurs in a variety of fish species. Individuals can be instantaneous hermaphrodites, in which they perform male and female function at the same time, or sequential hermaphrodites, in which the individual changes sex over the course of its life. In plants, individual flowers within a single plant can be hermaphrodites, or the different sexes can occur on different flowers on the same plant. In short, nature produces a diversity of sex types much richer than the simple male and female combinations found in the human species.

Not surprisingly, the complexity of nature was the basis for research into the evolution of sex for a variety of scientists. Eric Charnov, J. Maynard Smith, and James Bull (1976) addressed this question in a classic paper titled "Why Be a Hermaphrodite?" These authors identified three conditions that should favour a hermaphroditic population over one with separate sexes: (1) low mobility, which limits the opportunities for male to male competition, (2) low overlap in resource demands by female and male structures and functions, such as in plants where pollen production often occurs much earlier than seed and fruit maturation, and (3) sharing of costs for male and female function, for instance in insect-pollinated plants where attractive flowers promote both male and female reproductive success.

In this section we will explore several evolutionary and behavioural patterns associated with sex in a diversity of species. As is often the case, we begin with Darwin (1871), who proposed that the social environment, particularly the mating environment, could exert significant influence on the characteristics of organisms. He was particularly intrigued by the existence of what he called "secondary sexual characteristics," the origins of which he could not explain except by the advantages they gave to individuals during competition for mates. Darwin used the term *secondary sexual characteristics* to mean characteristics of males or females not directly involved in the process of reproduction. Some of the traits that Darwin had in mind were "gaudy colors and various ornaments . . . the power of song and other such characters." How do we explain the existence of characteristics such as the antlers of male deer, the bright peacock's tail, or the gigantic size and large nose of the male elephant seal? In order to explain the existence of such secondary sexual characteristics, Darwin proposed a process that he called **sexual selection.** Sexual selection results from differences in reproductive rates among individuals as a result of differences in their mating success.

Sexual selection is thought to be important under two circumstances. The first is where individuals of one sex compete among themselves for mates, which results in a process called **intrasexual selection.** For instance, when male mountain sheep or elephant seals fight among themselves for dominance or mating territories, the largest and strongest generally win such contests. In such situations the result is often selection for larger body size and more effective weapons such as horns or teeth. Since this selection is the result of contests within one sex, it is called intrasexual selection.

Sexual selection can also occur when members of one sex consistently choose mates from among members of the opposite sex on the basis of some particular trait. Because two sexes are involved, this form is called **intersexual selection.** Examples of traits used for mate selection include female birds choosing among potential male mates based on the brightness of their feather colours or on the quality of their songs. Darwin proposed that once individuals of one sex begin to choose mates on the basis of some anatomical or behavioural trait, sexual selection would favour elaboration of the trait. For instance, the plumage of male birds' colour might become brighter over time or their songs more elaborate or both.

However, how much can sexual selection elaborate a trait before males in the population begin to suffer higher mortality due to other sources of natural selection, such as that exerted by predators? Darwin proposed that sexual selection will continue to elaborate a trait until balanced by other sources of natural selection, such as predation. Since Darwin's early work on the subject, research has revealed a great deal about how organisms choose mates and the basis of sexual selection. An excellent model for such studies is the guppy, *Poecilia reticulata.*

Mate Choice and Sexual Selection in Guppies

It would be difficult for experimental ecologists interested in mate choice and sexual selection to design a better experimental animal than the guppy (fig. 8.16). Guppies are native to the streams and rivers of Trinidad and Tobago, islands in the southeastern Caribbean, and in the rivers draining nearby parts of the South American mainland. The waters inhabited by guppies range from small clear mountain streams to murky lowland rivers. Along this gradient of physical conditions, guppies also encounter a broad range of biological situations. In the headwaters of streams above waterfalls, guppies live in the absence of predaceous fish or with the killifish *Rivulus hartii*, which preys mainly on juveniles and is not a very effective predator on adult guppies. In contrast, guppies in lowland rivers live with a wide variety of predaceous fish, including the pike cichlid, *Crenicichla alta,* a very effective visual predator of adult guppies.

Figure 8.16   A colourful male guppy courting a female guppy: What are the influences of mate selection by female guppies and natural selection by predators?

Male guppies show a broad range of colouration both within and among populations. What factors may produce this range of variation? It turns out that female guppies, if given a choice, will mate with more brightly coloured males. However, brightly coloured males are attacked more frequently by visual predators. This trade-off between higher mating success by bright males but greater vulnerability to predators provides a mechanistic explanation for variation in male colouration among different habitats. The most brightly coloured male guppies are found in populations exposed to few predators, while those exposed to predators, such as the pike cichlid, are much less brightly coloured (Endler 1995). Thus the colouration of male guppies in local populations may be determined by a dynamic interplay between natural selection exerted by predators and by female mate choice.

While field observations are consistent with a trade-off between sexual selection due to mate choice and natural selection due to predation, the evidence would be more convincing with an experimental test. John Endler (1980) performed such a test in an exemplary study of natural selection for colour pattern in guppies. This work has proven to be a classic study of experimental ecology, showing evolutionary shifts over short periods of time.

Experimental Tests

Endler performed two experiments, one in artificial ponds in a greenhouse at Princeton University (fig. 8.17) and one at field sites (fig. 8.18). For the greenhouse experiments, Endler constructed 10 ponds designed to approximate pools in the streams of the Northern Range in Trinidad. Four of the ponds were of a size (2.4 m × 1.2 m × 40 cm) typical of the pools inhabited by a single pike cichlid in smaller streams. During the final phase of the experiment, Endler placed a

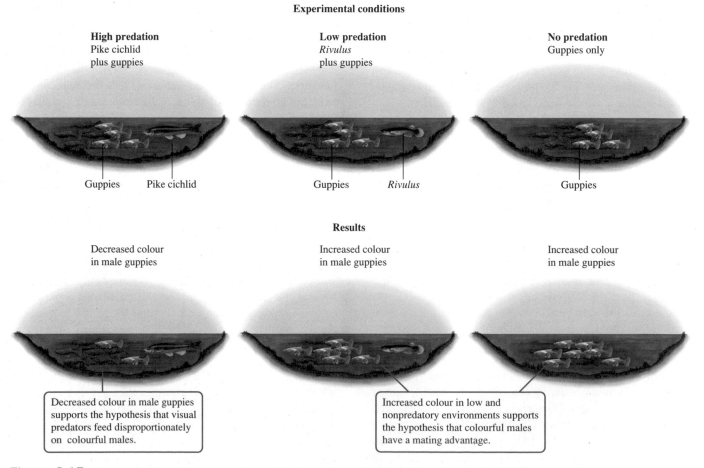

Figure 8.17   Summary of greenhouse experimental design and results (information from Endler 1980).

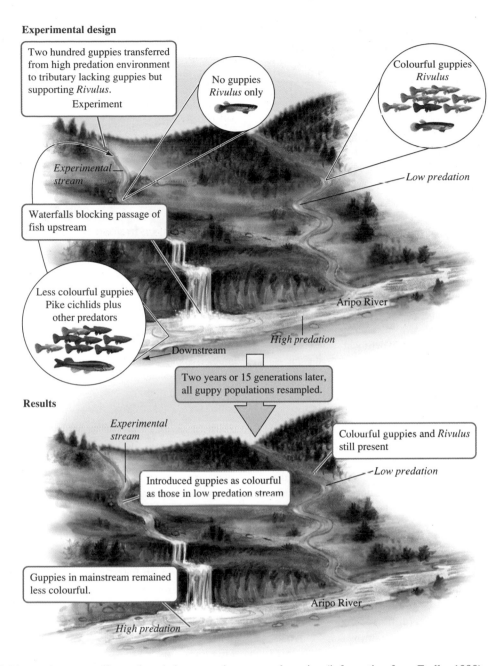

Experimental design

Two hundred guppies transferred from high predation environment to tributary lacking guppies but supporting *Rivulus*.
Experiment

No guppies
Rivulus only

Colourful guppies
Rivulus

Experimental stream

Low predation

Waterfalls blocking passage of fish upstream

Less colourful guppies
Pike cichlids plus other predators

Aripo River

High predation

Downstream

Two years or 15 generations later, all guppy populations resampled.

Results

Experimental stream

Colourful guppies and *Rivulus* still present

Introduced guppies as colourful as those in low predation stream

Low predation

Guppies in mainstream remained less colourful.

Aripo River

High predation

Figure 8.18   Field experiment on effects of predation on male guppy colouration (information from Endler 1980).

single pike cichlid in each of these ponds. The six other ponds were similar in size (2.4 m × 1.2 m × 15 cm) to stream pools in the headwaters which contain approximately 6 *Rivulus*. Endler eventually placed 6 *Rivulus* in four of these ponds and maintained the other two ponds with no predators as controls. What did Endler create with this series of pools and predator combinations? These three groups of ponds represented three levels of predation: high predation (pike cichlid), low predation (*Rivulus*), and no predation.

However, before introducing predators, Endler established similar physical environments in the pools and stocked them with carefully chosen guppies. He lined all ponds with commercially available dyed gravel, taking care to put the same proportions of gravel colours in each of the ponds. The gravel he used in all ponds was 31.4% black, 34.2 % white, 25.7 % green, plus 2.9%

each of blue, red, and yellow. Why did Endler take great care to put the same colours of gravel in the same proportions into all of his ponds? One of the most critical elements of the experiment was to standardize the background colours across all of the ponds. The influence of prey colour on vulnerability to predators depends on the background against which the prey is viewed by visual predators. As a consequence, controlling background colour was of critical importance to Endler's experiments.

Endler stocked the experimental pond with 200 guppies, which were descended from 18 different populations in Trinidad and Venezuela. By drawing guppies from so many populations, Endler ensured that the experimental populations would include a substantial amount of colour variation. As we saw in chapter 4, genetic variation is an essential requirement for evolutionary change in populations.

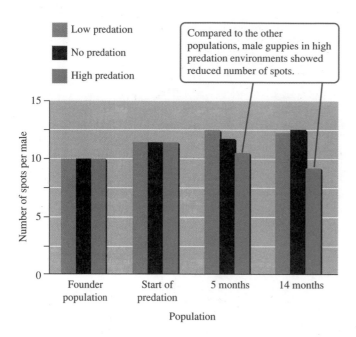

Figure 8.19   Results of greenhouse experiment, which exposed populations of guppies to no predation, low predation (killifish), and high predation (pike cichlid) environments (data from Endler 1980).

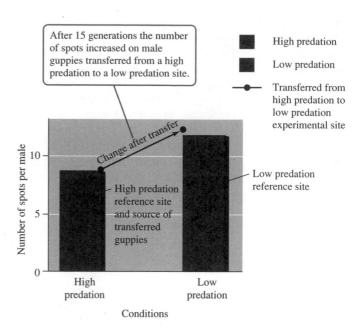

Figure 8.20   Results of field experiment involving transfer of guppies from high predation site to site with killifish, a fairly ineffective predator (data from Endler 1980).

Endler's second experiment was conducted in the field within the drainage network of the Aripo River (fig 8.18), where he encountered three distinctive situations within a few kilometers. Within the mainstream of the Aripo River, guppies coexisted with a wide variety of predators, including pike cichlids, which provided a "high predation" site. Upstream from the high predation site, Endler discovered a small tributary that flowed over a series of waterfalls near its junction with the mainstream. Because the waterfalls prevented most fish from swimming upstream, this tributary was entirely free of guppies but supported a population of the ineffective predator *Rivulus*. This potential "low predation" site provided an ideal situation for following the evolution of male colour. The third site, which was a bit farther upstream, was a small tributary that supported guppies along with *Rivulus*. This third site gave Endler a low predation reference site for his study. Endler captured 200 guppies in the high predation environment, measured the colouration of these guppies, and then introduced them to the site lacking guppies. Six months later the introduced guppies and their offspring had spread throughout the previously guppy-free tributary. Finally, two years or about 15 guppy generations after the introduction, Endler returned and sampled the guppies at all three study sites.

The results of the greenhouse and field experiments supported each other. As shown in figure 8.19, the number of coloured spots on male guppies increased in the greenhouse ponds with no predators and with *Rivulus* but decreased in the high predation ponds containing pike cichlids. Figure 8.20, which summarizes the results of Endler's field experiment, compares the number of spots on males in high predation and low predation stream environments with guppies transferred from the high predation environment to a low predation envi-

ronment. Notice that the transplanted population converged with the males at the low predation reference site during the experiment. In other words, when freed from predation, the average number of spots on male guppies increased substantially. This result, along with the results of the greenhouse experiment, supports the hypothesis that predation reduces male showiness in guppy populations.

Research by many other researchers supports the impact of predators on male ornamentation. However, the observation that male colourfulness increased in the absence of predators or in the presence of weak predation both in the field and the laboratory invites explanation. Why did male colour increase rather that just remain static? The observed changes imply that colourful males enjoy some selective advantage. That advantage appears to result from how female guppies choose their mates.

Mate Choice by Female Guppies

What cues do female guppies use to choose their mates? Anne Houde (1997), who summarized the findings of numerous studies, found that several male traits were associated with greater mating success. The weight of the evidence supports the conclusion that male colouration contributes significantly to male mating success. Colour characteristics that have been shown to confer a male mating advantage include "brightness," number of red spots, number of blue spots, iridescent area, total pigmented area, and carotenoid or orange area. These results appear to account for the increase in male colourfulness observed by Endler in the absence of predation or in the presence of low predation pressure. That is, female preference for more colourful males gave them greater fitness in the absence of strong predation. As a consequence, male colourfulness increased in the study populations in low predation or no predation environments. Male behaviour, especially their rate of making courtship displays, has also been found associated with increased male mating success.

There have been fewer studies of how competition among males, that is, intrasexual selection, may influence male mating success. Let's look at one of the few studies that does. Astrid Kodric-Brown (1993) studied whether competitive interactions among males contribute to variation in male mating success. She obtained guppies for her behavioural experiments from stock John Endler had originally collected from the Aripo and Paria Rivers in Trinidad. Males and females used in the behavioural experiments were reared separately. Males were kept in 95-liter aquaria in populations consisting of 10 males and 20 females. Meanwhile virgin females were reared in all-female groups of sisters until they were six months old. During this period they had no visual contact with males. Both males and females were fed a standardized diet and maintained at the same temperatures and exposed to the same numbers of hours of dark and light.

From her stock populations, Kodric-Brown chose 59 pairs of males with contrasting colours and 59 females. To test female preference she placed a single female into the central chamber of a test tank and each member of a male pair in the side chambers flanking the central chamber. Screens covering glass partitions prevented visual contact between males and females initially. After 10 minutes of acclimation by the guppies, Kodric-Brown removed the screens. Once the screens were removed males would usually begin courtship displays and the female would inspect the males through the glass partition. Kodric-Brown recorded the behaviour of males and females in the display tank for 10 minutes, recording the time and the rates at which males displayed, and the amount of time the female spent within 5 cm of the glass partition of each male. She designated the male that the female spent the most time with as the preferred or attractive male and the male with which the female spent less time as the nonpreferred or unattractive male.

After this initial 10-minute period during which females indicated their preferences, Kodric-Brown removed the glass partitions separating the guppies, allowing interactions among the males and the female. Kodric-Brown observed that males engaged in agonistic interactions, such as chasing and nipping, in over 94% of mating trials, which gave her a basis for determining which males were behaviourally dominant and which were subordinate. Kodric-Brown recorded the interactions between the two males and between the males and the female until 5 minutes after a copulation. After a mating trial the female was moved to a rearing tank where she eventually gave birth. The offspring from each female were raised separately. In order to establish paternity, male offspring were raised to maturity, when they expressed their full colouration, which is inherited from their fathers.

The results of Kodric-Brown's experiments indicate that reproductive success was determined by a combination of male attractiveness and male dominance status. Female mate

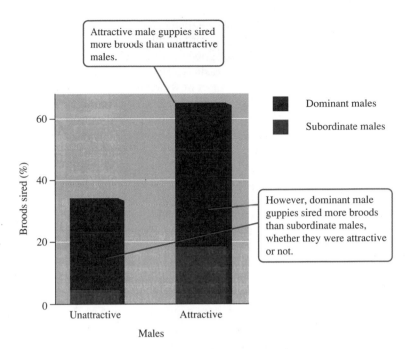

Figure 8.21   Relative reproductive success by attractive versus unattractive and dominant versus subordinate male guppies (data from Kodric-Brown 1993).

preference, which was determined when the guppies had visual contact only, was highly correlated with subsequent male mating success (fig. 8.21). The males that attracted females when viewed through the glass partition subsequently sired a greater percentage of broods than did unattractive males. Approximately 67% of the broods were sired by attractive males compared to 33% that were sired by unattractive males. However, it appears that male dominance status also contributes to male reproductive success. Among unattractive males that sired broods, 87.5% were dominant. The conclusion that reproductive success is determined by a combination of competition between males and female choice is reinforced by the low reproductive success by males that were neither attractive nor dominant. These males, which lacked the apparent advantages associated with either dominance or attractiveness, sired only 4% of the broods. The result indicates that reproductive opportunities are highly restricted for these males.

The characteristics associated with male mating success among guppies are often correlated. Kodric-Brown observed that attractive males tended to be dominant, court more, and have more and brighter orange and iridescent spots. These characteristics are closely associated with a male's anatomy and physiology. Let's look now at a mating system where male and females are engaged in significant sexual conflict.

Sexual Conflict Among Water Striders

Sex isn't free. Although one can immediately recognize the potential reproductive benefits of sex, there are a variety of potential costs. One of the most obvious is the risk of sexually transmitted diseases, which can cause significant damage to the genitalia and reproductive machinery of plant and animal species. Needless to say, being castrated by a fungus that was acquired through sex (either through direct contact of the genitalia or through the inclusion of a third member to the sex act, such as a pollinating bee) is not good for one's fitness (well, except for the fitness of the parasite!). There are, however, much more subtle costs of sex, most of which return us to the principle of allocation we discussed in chapters 5 and 7. Mating takes time, and depending upon the details of the particular species involved, it can also require expenditure of significant amounts of energy. During mating, an individual is unable to perform other tasks, such as foraging, defending, or even finding an alternative (more suitable) mate. In some cases, these costs are shared equally by both males and females. In other cases, there is *sexual conflict*, in which there is asymmetry between the sexes in the potential evolutionary costs and benefits of any particular mating event. Locke Rowe, of the University of Toronto, along with a diverse group of colleagues, has conducted extensive theoretical and empirical studies of sexual conflict, with particular emphasis on water striders.

Water striders (Heteroptera) are commonly found on the surfaces of slow flowing bodies of fresh water (fig. 8.22) throughout North America. Their graceful appearance moving across the water surface is in sharp contrast to their mating system. Conflict between the sexes at mating is visually apparent, with males chasing and grasping females in an attempt to mate. More often than not, the female escapes from the male, and mating does not occur. However, if the male grabs hold, there is a vicious struggle in which significant energy is spent and both sexes are at a greatly increased risk of predation. Only occasionally does the male maintain hold, and mating occurs (Rowe et al. 1994). The classic explanation for such conflict has been that in water striders, females are able to retain viable sperm for about 10 days, and thus repeated mating is unnecessary to achieve full fertilization for the female. In contrast, males are more likely to sire more offspring if they are the last male to mate with a female rather

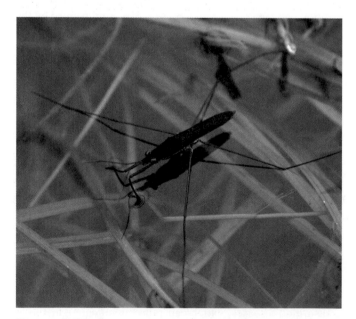

Figure 8.22 Water striders serve as a model organism for the study of sexual conflict between males and females.

than the first, and thus selection should favour male promiscuity. However, Rowe and colleagues have pointed out that this classic explanation is lacking an explanation for the female behaviour, in that these mating events are not neutral for the females, but instead are actually detrimental to their fitness. This physical conflict also results in evolutionary conflict between the sexes.

In a review of the literature, Rowe and colleagues suggest two key costs of mating for the female: (1) reduced female skating speed while carrying a male reduces foraging efficiency, and (2) mating females are at increased predation risk due to slower speed. As might be expected, sexual selection appears to have resulted in the evolution of a variety of physical and behavioural adaptations that mitigate the level of resistance in females. At the heart of this is the realization that both resisting and submitting to mating pose energetic and fitness costs to the female. As a result, evolution should favour strategies in females that minimize the costs of these two detrimental options. As you might expect, the "solution" to this problem will be dependent upon the local environmental conditions around a particular female and her population. For example, females of some species tend to spend more time hiding in vegetation when males are present than when they are absent. Though this decreases her ability to forage, this cost is likely less than she would incur during a mating struggle.

Over longer periods, sexual conflict can have significant evolutionary consequences. In a study combining comparative and experimental approaches, Goran Arnqvist and Locke Rowe (2002) have found evidence that sexual conflict has caused the **coevolution** of male and female armaments (clasping and anti-clasping appendages) in water striders. Female armaments increase the efficacy of resistance and male armaments increase the ability of males to overcome this resistance. Coevolution can be defined as a reciprocal evolutionary interaction between two or more species (or evolving groups, such as males and females). In coevolution, genetic change in one group results in genetic change in another, with this process repeating over time. Arnqvist and Rowe studied 15 species of water striders, paying particular attention to the unique morphologies of the males and females that allow them to clasp (males), or prevent clasping (females). Males and females of all species were subjected to a barrage of morphological measurements, from which the researchers were able to measure the degree of armaments of each sex of each species. They used ordination procedures (see appendix 1) to collapse these measures into fewer dimensions to facilitate interpretation. They coupled the morphological measures with behavioural observation, whereby they placed males and females of a particular species in an artificial pond and observed mating behaviours. They reasoned that it's not the total amount of armaments of the males and females that will influence the duration and outcome of mating attempts by the males, but instead it will be the relative difference in armaments between the sexes that drives mating (or escape) success. This is exactly what their data showed. The outcome of mating attempts was not related to the absolute amount of arms found in a species, but instead was determined by the relative differences between the sexes. When males were more heavily armed, mating occurred most frequently. When females were more heavily armed, mating was rarer. It is not difficult to see how sexual selection will then favour the evolution of increased armaments in the sex that is at a relative disadvantage.

We now turn our attention to plants. Though many undergraduates are surprised even to learn that plants have sex, the behavioural ecology of mating by plants is even more complex than that found among animals.

Nonrandom Mating Among Wild Radish

Wild radish grows as an annual weed in California where it can be commonly seen along roadways and in abandoned fields (fig. 8.23). The seeds of wild radish germinate in response to the first winter rains of California's Mediterranean climate (chapter 2) and the plants flower by January. Flowering may continue to late spring or early summer, depending on the length of the wet season. During their flowering season, wild radishes are pollinated by a wide variety of insects, including honeybees, syrphid flies, and butterflies. Wild radish flowers have both male (**stamens**) and female (**pistils**) parts and produce both pollen and ovules. However, a wild radish plant cannot pollinate itself, a condition called **self-incompatibility.** Because they must mate with other plants, a researcher working on wild radish can more easily control matings between plants.

Figure 8.23 The wild radish, *Raphanus sativus*, has become a model for studying the mating behavior of plants.

Diane Marshall has used the many advantages offered by wild radish, such as its rapid growth to maturity and self-incompatibility, to explore the topic of mate selection in plants. Marshall and Michael Folsom (1992) listed a number of other characteristics of wild radish that make it convenient for study. For instance, its fruits contain several seeds which allows the possibility of multiple paternity of offspring. However, the seeds are not so numerous that the researcher is overwhelmed by a vast number of seeds. In addition, each plant produces numerous flowers allowing the possibility of several kinds of matings per plant and several replications of each mating experiment on the same plant. The seeds, which weigh about 10 mg, are also a convenient size for handling and weighing. Finally, there is sufficient genetic variation among individual radish plants to identify the male parent of each seed using electrophoresis of isozymes (see Ecological Tools in chapter 4).

The insects that pollinate wild radish generally arrive at flowers carrying pollen from several different plants, and as a consequence a wild radish plant typically has about seven mates. Under these circumstances of multiple mates, Marshall asked whether siring of offspring is a random process. In other words, do the seven mates of a typical wild radish plant have an equal probability of fertilizing the available ovules? The alternative, nonrandom mating, would suggest the potential for mate choice and sexual selection. What mechanisms might produce nonrandom mating among wild radish? Nonrandom mating could result from maternal control over the fertilization process, competition among pollen, or a combination of the two processes. If it does occur in plants, nonrandom mating establishes the conditions necessary for sexual selection in plants. However, as Marshall and Folsom (1991) pointed out, though sexual selection is well documented in animals, its occurrence among plants was a controversial and open question.

While the existence of sexual selection in plants was controversial, nonrandom mating was well documented. Marshall and her colleagues have repeatedly demonstrated nonrandom mating in wild radish. For instance, Marshall (1990) carried out greenhouse experiments that showed nonrandom mating among three maternal plants and six pollen donors. In this experiment Marshall mated three seed parents or maternal plants with six pollen donors, the plants that would act as sources of pollen to pollinate the flowers of the seed plants.

Marshall used the 6 pollen donors to make 63 kinds of crosses, 6 single donor crosses plus 57 mixed donor crosses, on each maternal plant. Her crosses included all possible mixtures of pollen from 1 to 6 donors. Plants were pollinated in the greenhouse by hand. All pollinations were performed on freshly opened flowers in the morning when the temperature was cool enough for researchers to work comfortably. Pollen was collected by tapping flowers lightly on the bottom of small petri dishes from an equal number of flowers of each pollen donor. Pollen was then mixed and applied to the stigmas of flowers on the maternal plant using forceps wrapped in tissue. Sufficient pollen was applied to cover each stigma. Because each cross was replicated from 2 to 20 times depending on the type of cross, the total number of pollinations performed on each plant was 300. This is a good example of the unique opportunities for experimental work offered by plants.

One of the ways that Marshall assessed the possibility of nonrandom mating was through performance of pollen donors. She estimated pollen donor performance in three ways: (1) number of seeds sired in mixed pollinations, (2) positions of seeds sired, and (3) weight of seeds sired. The results of this analysis are shown in figure 8.24. What would you expect to see in figure 8.24 if performance was equal across pollen donors? If performance was equal, the heights of the bars would be approximately equal for all pollen donors. However they are not, and figure 8.24 indicates clearly that pollen donors vary widely in their performance. In other words, mating in this experiment was nonrandom.

Because Marshall conducted her 1990 study under greenhouse conditions, we might ask whether nonrandom mating

also occurs under field conditions. In other words, could the nonrandom mating she documented have been an artifact of greenhouse conditions? Marshall and Ollar Fuller (Marshall and Fuller 1994) designed a study to address this question. Why might nonrandom mating be limited to the greenhouse environment? Marshall and Fuller point out that the harsh and variable environments to which plants are exposed in nature might mean that the condition of the maternal plant may be of overwhelming importance in determining the amount of seed produced, the weight of seeds, and so forth. Under such conditions nonrandom pollination, which produces differences in seed weight in the greenhouse, might be undetectable and biologically insignificant.

Marshall and Fuller chose four maternal plants and grew their offspring in a field setting. Three other maternal lineages, (A, B, and C) were chosen to act as pollen donors. In the field, the maternal plants were covered with fine mesh nylon bags until the experimental pollinations were completed. Using the forceps and tissue method described earlier, Marshall and Fuller performed several kinds of hand-pollinations, including mixed pollinations using pollen from all three pollen donors. Once the hand pollinations were completed the nylon mesh bags were removed from the flowers.

The result of this experiment provided clear support for nonrandom mating in the field population. Figure 8.25 shows that during the mixed pollen donor pollinations, pollen donor C1 (56.5%) sired a much greater proportion of seeds compared to pollen donors A1 (24.8%) and B1 (18.7%). This finding suggests that the nonrandom matings observed in prior greenhouse pollination studies were not an artifact of greenhouse conditions.

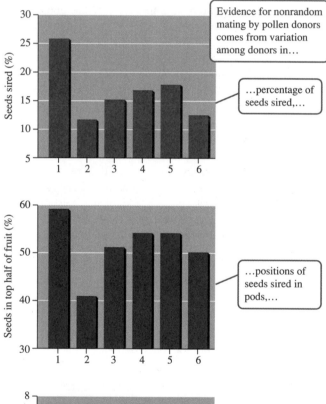

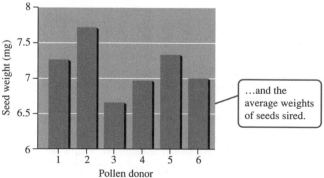

Figure 8.24 Evidence for unequal mating success among wild radish pollen donors in a greenhouse environment (data from Marshall 1990).

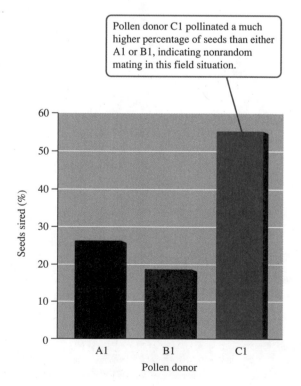

Figure 8.25 Variation in wild radish pollen donor mating success in a field environment (data from Marshall and Fuller 1994).

Additional work by Marshall and her colleagues (Marshall et al. 1996) suggests that competition between pollen grains may contribute to nonrandom mating in wild radish populations. They used three maternal plants in these crosses, which they crossed with seven pollen donors (A, B, C, D, E, F, Z). The maternal plants were pollinated with pollen from single donors and from pairs of donors. The paired pollinations (A+B, C+D, etc.) were done in two ways. In one set of experiments, the pollen from the two donors was mixed as in the previous experiments described earlier. Because the two pollen types were in physical contact with each other in these "mixed" pollinations, this method of pollinating increased the opportunity for interaction between pollen types. In the second set of experiments, the pollen of the two donors used was not mixed. Each was applied to adjacent halves of the stigma, the tip of the pistil that acts as a pollen-receptive area. Since the two pollen types did not contact each other in these "adjacent" pollinations, there was a reduced chance that they would interact. Pollen response to these conditions was measured as the percentage of pollen that germinated within 90 minutes of pollination. Reduced percentage of germination would indicate lower pollen responsiveness and the possibility of inhibition of pollen response, either through pollen to pollen interactions or through maternal tissue effects expressed through the stigma.

Some of the results of this experiment are shown in figure 8.26. The percentage of pollen that germinated after 90 minutes was essentially the same in the single donor and adjacent pollinations. Meanwhile, the rate of germination when pollen from the two donors was mixed was much reduced. This reduced germination, where pollen grains of different pollen donors were in contact with each other, indicates that interactions between pollen inhibited pollen germination. These results suggest **interference competition** among pollen grains, which usually involves some form of aggressive or inhibitory interactions between individuals.

Experiments such as this one are revealing the details of plant ecology. While ecological interactions between plants are often much less obvious than those of animals, careful and ingenious experiments such as those of Marshall and her colleagues are proving that they are every bit as rich and

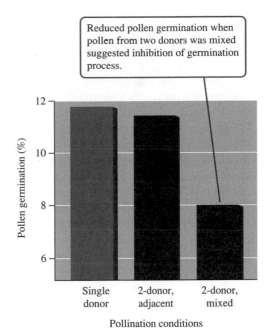

Figure 8.26 Competition between pollen from different donors (data from Marshall et al. 1996).

fascinating. Additionally, because sexual reproduction is the foundation of agriculture, understanding these basic ecological issues is of critical economic and societal importance.

Concept 8.3 Review

1. Why did John Endler take great care to put the same colours of gravel in the same proportions into all of his greenhouse ponds?
2. In Endler's field experiment, why did male colourfulness increase in the absence of effective predators and not just remain static?
3. What would you expect to see in figure 8.24 if performance was equal across pollen donors?

Ecological Tools

Using Game Theory to Understand Behaviour

Behavioural ecologists can take a variety of approaches to their research. They can use observation to document behaviours, trying to discern whether some behaviours are more frequently exhibited under some conditions than under other conditions. They can conduct manipulative experiments, in which they modify the environment, testing whether certain factors directly influence behaviour. They can also measure the fitness costs and benefits of a variety of behavioural choices, such as movement, breeding, and predator alarm calls. Linking all of these branches of behavioural ecology is

theory. It is in theory that ecologists are able to imagine alternative worlds and behaviours, testing what responses are optimum under which set of conditions. From theory can come focused experiments to test the resulting hypotheses. Behavioural ecology, however, poses a particular challenge. Individuals are able to exhibit alternative behaviours based upon the *choices* that other individuals make. For example, ground squirrels are less likely to make alarm calls in response to seeing a predator if another individual has already made a call. This makes evolutionary sense, as there is likely little benefit of alerting a predator to your presence if your kin are already aware that a predator is in the area. Understanding the relative fitness of different behaviours gets very complicated when their value is contingent upon the choices of others. This sounds an awful lot like a game. When playing *Risk*, it may make sense to capture one country to complete your occupancy of an entire continent, but only if this doesn't leave you exposed to attack and facing the potential loss of more valuable territories. It may come at no surprise that behavioural ecologists have adapted the methods of **game theory**, a branch of mathematics devoted to the study of strategy in which the players seek to maximize their individual returns.

Game theory was initially developed for use in economics, where it still forms the basis for much economic theory. Many aspects of economics, sociology, and ecology overlap (organizations = populations and communities; returns = fitness; etc.), and thus it is not surprising that there is substantial overlap in the theoretical tools used by researchers in these seemingly distinct disciplines. It was John Maynard Smith (1982) who emphasized the potential benefits of game theory to understanding behavioural ecology, and its use has grown since then. Game theory even finds outlets in popular culture. For example, Matthew Broderick's character in the movie *WarGames* learned of its use in war planning (where it is still used), and many reality-based TV shows, such as *Survivor*, create situations similar to those used by game theorists. Here we will discuss one form of a classic "game" from game theory, and show how it has been used to provide a theoretical foundation for behavioural ecology.

Evolutionary Stable Strategies

In most ecological "games," the theorist uses changes in fitness as a measure of the potential costs and benefits of different strategic decisions. Under some combinations of behaviours, fitness may increase, while under other combinations, fitness may decrease. Using game theory, researchers are able to explore if one behaviour is resistant to invasion by another behaviour. In other words, if one behaviour results in a fitness of "X," but a new behaviour results in a fitness of "X+1," natural selection will favour the second behaviour, displacing the first. One goal of game theory is to determine which behaviour (or sets of behaviours) is (are) the **evolutionary stable strategy**, often abbreviated ESS. ESS represents the

behavioural decision that is resistant to invasion and most likely to be maintained by natural selection. ESS is a critical aspect of game theory as applied to ecology, and will be discussed throughout the following examples.

Hawk–Dove

John Maynard Smith introduced many behavioural ecologists to game theory in his book entitled *Evolution and the Theory of Games* (Maynard Smith 1982). One of the games described in the book is the Hawk–Dove game. There are many variations of the game, and we will discuss one possible form. Imagine a scenario in which two individuals interact over a contested resource. Individuals within a population can exhibit one of two behaviours: (1) they can always attack the other individual, taking the resource (R) when they win (Hawk). However, if a Hawk encounters another Hawk, it will win only one-half the time, and when it loses, will suffer an injury cost (C). The alternative strategy in our game is to (2) present a threat display, but never actually engage in a fight (Dove). Doves will take the resource 1/2 the time against another Dove (the other one backs down first), but will always lose the resource to a Hawk. However, because the Doves are not engaging in a fight, they suffer no injury costs. An important rule to the game is that individuals can not switch behaviours over time; once a Dove, always a Dove. These behaviours are roughly similar to the selfishness (Hawk) and cooperation (Dove) classifications of Hamilton that we discussed earlier in this chapter. The basic question to the game is whether the Hawk or Dove strategy is evolutionarily stable.

To answer this question, we can devise a payoff matrix that describes the four possible situations that could occur. In our matrix, R represents the value of the resource and C represents the cost of injury:

The next step is to determine which strategy is an ESS. Because the payoffs to an attacker are dependent upon the behaviour of its opponent, we need to introduce another term, *p*, which represents the proportion of individuals that are Hawks in the population (and thus 1−*p* represents the proportion of Doves in the population). Using these proportions, we can now calculate the average payoff (= fitness) for Hawks and Doves.

		Behaviour of Opponent	
		Hawk	**Dove**
Behaviour of Attacker	**Hawk**	Each Hawk wins ½ the time and gets hurt ½ the time Hawk (attacker)=0.5·R−0.5·C	Hawk always wins and never gets hurt Hawk=R
	Dove	Dove always retreats and never gets hurt Dove=0	Each Dove wins ½ the time and never gets hurt Dove (attacker)=0.5·R

Hawks will encounter other Hawks with a frequency of p, and thus the return for this scenario is $p(0.5 \cdot R - 0.5 \cdot C)$. Hawks will encounter Doves at a frequency of $1-p$, and their return will be $(1-p) \cdot R$. Putting these together, the payoff for the Hawk strategy is:

$$\text{Hawk} = p(0.5 \cdot R - 0.5 \cdot C) + (1-p) \cdot R$$

Doves will encounter Hawks at a frequency of p with a payoff of $p \cdot 0$, and they will encounter other Doves with a frequency of $(1-p)$ and a payoff of $(1-p) \cdot (0.5 \cdot R)$. Putting these together, the payoff for the Dove strategy is:

$$\text{Dove} = p \cdot 0 + (1-p) \cdot (0.5 \cdot R)$$

So which strategy is an ESS for this game? Well, we can start by imagining a population that consists solely of Doves ($p=0$). In this world the fitness of a Dove would be $0.5 \cdot R$. Now we can imagine a world of only Hawks ($p=1$). The fitness of the Hawk would be $0.5 \cdot R - 0.5 \cdot C$. Clearly the fitness of Doves in a Dove world is higher than the fitness of Hawks in a Hawk world ($0.5 \cdot R$ must be greater than $0.5(R-C)$), and thus the Dove strategy is the ESS, right? No. Let's imagine we live in the world of Doves, and a single Hawk enters the population. What would its fitness be? Because it is so rare, we can still let $p=0$, and it will only encounter other Doves. In such a scenario, the Hawk's fitness will be R, exactly twice as high as that Dove's fitness ($0.5 \cdot R$)! The will result in strong selection for the Hawk behaviour, and the Doves will quickly be displaced. That means then that the Hawk is the ESS, right? Not necessarily.

What happens if we live in a Hawk world, and a single Dove enters? That Dove will always encounter Hawks, resulting in a Dove fitness of 0. Whether or not Hawk is an ESS depends on whether $0.5 \cdot R - 0.5 \cdot C$ is greater, or less than 0, the fitness of the Dove. Rearranging this equation we see that the Hawk strategy in our game will be an ESS if $R>C$. In other words, a Hawk-only population will be stable if, and only if, the value of the resource is greater than the potential cost of injury. If instead injury is more costly than the resource, then neither the Hawk nor Dove population is an ESS! Instead, the ESS population will consist of individuals of both behaviours. Game theory can actually predict the frequency of Hawks and Doves that will occur in a stable population.

What does it mean for Hawks and Doves to both persist? It simply means that the fitness of the Hawk strategy is equal to the fitness of the Dove strategy, and thus selection would not favour one over the other. But how is this possible, given that the rewards and costs are fixed (at least within a population)? The variable that can change is p, the frequency of Hawks. We can thus use the two equations:

$$\text{Hawk} = p(0.5 \cdot R - 0.5 \cdot C) + (1-p) \cdot R$$
$$\text{Dove} = p \cdot 0 + (1-p) \cdot (0.5 \cdot R)$$

We can then set Hawk = Dove:

$$p(0.5 \cdot R - 0.5 \cdot C) + (1-p) \cdot R = p \cdot 0 + (1-p) \cdot (0.5 \cdot R)$$

And solve for p:

$$p = R/C$$

What does this mean? We already know that if rewards are greater than costs ($R>C$), the ESS will be a Hawk-only world, and $p = 1$. If instead rewards are less than costs, then p will be less than one. For example, if R = 50 and C = 100, then the mixed ESS solution will be Hawks at a frequency of $50/100 = 0.5$. In other words, in this game, with those values for R and C, the ESS is a population that consists of equal numbers of Hawks and Doves. If R and C were 50 and 75, respectively, then the mixed ESS solution would be 50/75 Hawks = $p = 2/3$.

Our Hawk–Dove example shows that determining the relative fitness of individual actions will be dependent upon the frequency of other behaviours in the population, as well as the costs and rewards of a given action. A population consisting of only Doves results in the highest average fitness of individuals, but it is the least stable in this game—susceptible to invasion by Hawks regardless of the values of the reward and costs of fighting. Remember from chapter 4 that selection does not act on the absolute fitness of individuals, but instead on the relative differences in fitness among individuals within a population. Natural selection does not work towards a goal of maximizing fitness in a population; instead it simply favours those with the highest relative fitness.

These games can be expanded in a variety of ways, including adding costs of display for the Doves, costs of fighting for Hawks (independent of injury), and can include additional behaviours. Next we discuss a few examples of how researchers are using game theory to address real ecological questions.

Game Theory in Modern Ecology

In a collaboration between researchers at the University of Otago and the Université du Québec à Montréal (Poulin and Vickery 1995), game theory was used to explore cleaning symbioses. Many organisms engage in cooperative behaviours regarding the removal of dead tissue and parasites. These interactions include birds removing ticks from the backs of large ungulates, and wrasses removing parasites from other fish on coral reefs. Many of these interactions are spectacular to watch, such as wrasses that move in and out of the jaws of much larger fish, without any apparent risk of predation. However, there is ample opportunity for cheating by both parties. The cleaners could easily feed upon living tissue and blood of the host, while the host itself could feed upon the cleaners. Poulin and Vickery explored the conditions under which cheating may become favoured. A major influence for both cleaners and clients was the relative fitness value of being cleaned (or eating parasites) versus eating the cleaner (or the client). In other words, if the value of R is high, relative to the alternative food source, honesty is an ESS. You may recognize this has some similarities to our discussion of optimal foraging in chapter 7.

Dubois and Giraldeau (2005), also from the Université du Québec à Montréal, discuss the strengths and weaknesses of using the Hawk–Dove game to model the defense of resources by animals. They explain that the classic game theory model says that when the cost of defense is low, there should be increased aggression and defense of resources. However, they are able to expand this original model and show that aggression is itself going to be dependent upon the spatial distribution of resources, predation risk, the density of individuals in a population, and the value of the resources themselves. They demonstrate that animal behaviour extends well beyond simple interactions between two individuals, and to truly understand how individuals will interact it is essential to also understand the landscape in which they will compete. In other words, behaviour is displayed by individuals, but is done in response to a diversity of simultaneously interacting factors. These ideas will be more fully explored in chapter 21, Landscape Ecology.

It may surprise you that the conditional behavioural strategies that can be modelled by game theory can also apply to plants. Recall from chapter 7 that plants are very flexible in where they put their roots in response to varied nutrient levels in the soil. Not surprisingly, one of the determinants of root placement is the *choices* made by other plants, as we will explore in chapter 13. Mordechi Gersani (2001) and his colleagues explored the ESS of the "choice" faced by plants: do you put your roots near other plants to try and take all of their resources, or do you put your roots away from plants, "sharing" resources among all? Their model produced an outcome similar to the traditional Hawk–Dove model, where the ESS appears to be increased root allocation when neighbours are present, causing an increase in competition and a reduction in the absolute number of seeds (fitness) produced. Although there is currently much controversy surrounding experimental work testing these ideas (Schenk 2006), the study by Gersani and colleagues shows that the usefulness of game theory extends well beyond the realm of animals.

Summary

The behaviour of organisms and their social relations can frequently directly impact the reproductive contribution of individuals to future generations, a key component of fitness. The field of behavioural ecology blends understanding of physiology, evolution, and ecology. Many patterns observed in nature are difficult to understand without a firm grounding in behavioural ecology.

Natural selection favours those behaviours that increase the inclusive fitness of individuals. Many behaviours have a genetic basis, and are thus at least partially heritable. As a result, there is the potential for natural selection to influence not only phenotype, but also social relations. Critical to understanding the adaptive value of different behaviours is the concept of inclusive fitness, which accounts for the similarity in genetic composition of closely related individuals. By using this broader view of fitness, seemingly maladaptive behaviours such as altruism can be favoured through natural selection, through a process called kin selection. In kin selection, individuals are more likely to perform a given behaviour if the potential benefit to their inclusive fitness is greater than the cost. Not all behaviours among individuals are altruistic, and instead selection can also favour selfishness. For example, brood parasites such as the cowbird often are successful in inducing altruistic acts from their host by manipulating pre-existing behaviours and limitations. Natural selection does not necessarily favour the "nicest" behaviours, only the most effective. Cooperation can occur among individuals when there is a *tit-for-tat* arrangement in which each individual is assured of cooperation from the other. In this scenario, altruism can occur even among unrelated individuals and without manipulation.

The evolution of sociality is generally accompanied by cooperative feeding, defense of the social group, and restricted reproductive opportunities. The degree of sociality in a social species ranges from acts as simple as mutual grooming or group protection of young to highly complex, stratified societies such as those found in colonies of ants or termites. This more complex level of social behaviour, which is considered to be the pinnacle of social evolution, is called eusociality. Eusociality is generally thought to include three major characteristics: (1) individuals of more than one generation living together, (2) cooperative care of young, and (3) division of individuals into sterile, or nonreproductive, and reproductive castes. Cooperation among African lions appears to be a response to environmental conditions that require cooperation for success. To survive, reproduce, and successfully raise offspring to maturity, African lions must work in cooperative groups of females, which are called prides, and of males, which are called coalitions.

Mate choice by one sex and/or competition for mates among individuals of the same sex can result in selection for particular traits, a process called sexual selection. Species vary greatly in the combination of sex types that they contain, ranging from hermaphrodites to single sexes, with nearly all possible alternatives found somewhere in nature. Sexual selection results from differences in reproductive rates among individuals as a result of differences in their mating success. Sexual selection is thought to work either through intrasexual selection, where individuals of one sex compete with each other for mates, or intersexual selection, when members of one sex consistently choose mates from among members of the opposite sex on the basis of some particular trait.

In some species, such as the water striders, the immediate fitness consequences of mating will differ between males and females, resulting in sexual conflict. Repeated mating is not inherently beneficial for female striders, as it can increase predation risk, reduce foraging time, and is redundant if they already contain enough sperm for fertilization of their eggs. However, male striders gain benefit from being the last to mate with a given female. As a result, natural selection has resulted in an escalating arms race in morphologies that allow the male to clasp the females, and allow the females to escape. The relative difference in armaments between the sexes greatly influences the outcome of mating attempts.

Experimental evidence supports the hypothesis that the colouration of male guppies in local populations is determined by a dynamic interplay between natural selection exerted by predators, under which less-colourful males have higher survival, and by female mate choice, which results in higher mating success by more colourful males. Studies of mating in the wild radish indicate nonrandom mating and suggest interference competition among pollen from different pollen donors.

Game theory is an essential theoretical tool for behavioural ecologists. Understanding the relative fitness of behaviours is often difficult because their values are dependent upon the actions of others. By imagining behavioural interactions as a game, it is possible to determine which behaviour is evolutionary stable, and resistant to invasion by alternative behaviours. In the Hawk–Dove game, a world of Doves results in the highest absolute fitness, but is easily invaded by a Hawk. The ESS will be a mixture of Hawks and Doves, with the frequency of each being a function of the costs and benefits of each strategy. Game theory has been applied to a variety of situation in behavioural ecology, including defense of resources among both plants and animals, as well as cleaner–client relationships.

Review Questions

1. The introduction to chapter 8 included sketches of the behaviour and social systems of several fish species. Using the concepts that you have learned in the chapter, revisit those examples and predict the forms of sexual selection occurring in each species.

2. One of the basic assumptions of the material presented in chapter 8 is that the form of reproduction will exert substantial influence on social interactions within a species. How might interactions differ in populations that reproduce asexually versus ones that engage in sexual reproduction? How might having separate sexes versus hermaphrodites affect the types of social interactions within a population? How should having several forms of one sex, for example, large and small males, influence the diversity of behavioural interactions within the population?

3. Is altruism likely to become a common trait within a species if there is no fitness benefit (in either short- or long-term) to the individual performing the altruistic act? Why?

4. Endler (1980) pointed out that though field observations are consistent with the hypothesis that predators may exert natural selection on guppy colouration, some other factors in the environment could be affecting variation in male colour patterns among guppy populations. What other factors, especially physical and chemical factors, might affect male colours and should each influence male colour?

5. Examine figure 8.21. While most of the male guppies that successfully mated were dominant, a substantial proportion of attractive males that sired broods were subordinate. How might we interpret this reproductive success by attractive but subordinate males? What might these results indicate about the potential influence of female choice on mating success among male guppies?

6. Locke Rowe and colleagues have explored sexual conflict between male and female water striders. What ecological and environmental conditions are likely to result in sexual conflict in other species?

7. The results of numerous studies indicate nonrandom mating among plants at least under some conditions. These results lead to questions concerning the biological mechanisms that produce these nonrandom matings. How might the maternal plant control or at least influence the paternity of her seeds? What role might competition between pollen determine in the nonrandom patterns observed?

8. The details of experimental design are critical for determining the success or failure of both field and laboratory experiments. Results often depend on some small details. For instance, why did Jennifer Jarvis wait one year after establishing her laboratory colony of naked mole rats before attempting to quantify the behaviour of the laboratory population? What might have been the consequence of beginning to quantify the behaviour of the colony soon after it was established?

9. Behavioural interactions are often difficult to study because an individual's behaviour can be dependent upon the behavioural responses of other individuals of the same and different species. How does this differ from the physiological responses of organisms to their abiotic environment? How does game theory allow behavioural ecologists to develop theory to understand these social interactions?

10. Choose a problem in the behavioural ecology of social relations, formulate a hypothesis, and design a study to test your hypothesis. Take two approaches. In one approach use field and laboratory experiments to test your ideas. In the second design develop a study that will employ the comparative method.

Suggested Readings

Gamble, S., A. K. Lindholm, J. A. Endler, and R. Brooks. 2003. Environmental variation and the maintenance of polymorphism: the effect of ambient light spectrum on mating behaviour and sexual selection in guppies. *Ecology Letters* 6:463–72.

Godin, J. G. J. and H. E. McDonough. 2003. Predator preference for brightly colored males in the guppy: a viability cost for a sexually selected trait. *Behavioral Ecology* 14:194–200.

These papers gives a thorough update of research on mate selection in guppies.

Choe, J. C. and B. J. Crespi. 1997. *The Evolution of Social Behavior in Insects and Arachnids.* Cambridge: Cambridge University Press.

Excellent compendium of social behaviour among a wide variety of species.

Clutton-Brock, T. 2002. Breeding together: kin selection and mutualism in cooperative vertebrates. *Science* 296:69–72.

A broad overview of cooperative behaviour among vertebrate animals.

Marshall, D. L. and P. K. Diggle. 2001. Mechanisms of differential pollen donor performance in wild radish, *Raphanus sativus* (Brassicaceae). *American Journal of Botany* 88:242–57.

Skogsmyr, I. and A. Lankinen. 2000. Potential selection for female choice in *Viola tricolor. Evolutionary Ecology Research* 2:965–79.

Detailed studies of mating ecology of two species of plants.

Packer, C. and A. E. Pusey. 1997. Divided we fall: cooperation among lions. *Scientific American* 276(5):52–59.

Very interesting summary of Packer and Pusey's long-term studies of African lions.

Wilson, E.O. and B. Hölldobler. 2005. Eusociality: origin and consequences. *Proceedings of the National Academy of Sciences of the USA* 102: 13367–13371.

Provocative challenge to the long-held theory that kin selection has been a primary driver in the evolution of eusociality.

Nowak, M. A. and K. Sigmund. 2004. Evolutionary dynamics of biological games. *Science* 303:793–99.

An interesting overview of current uses of game theory to understand evolutionary processes.

Blumstein, D. T. and E. Fernández-Jurcic. 2004. The emergence of conservation behavior. *Conservation Biology.* 18:1175–77.

A brief introduction to the emerging field of conservation behaviour.

Chapter 9

Life Histories and the Niche

Outline

*D*ifferent species, often living side-by-side, reproduce at vastly different rates over lifetimes that may differ by several orders of magnitude. On a rare sunny day in a temperate rain forest, a redwood tree, *Sequoia sempervirens,* shades a nearby stream. Bathed in fog all summer, soaked by rain during fall, winter, and spring, the redwood has lived through 2,000 annual cycles. The tree was well established when Rome invaded Britain and had produced seeds for 500 years when William the Conqueror invaded the island from across the English Channel. It was 1,800 years old when rag tag colonials wrenched an American territorial prize from William's heirs, claiming it as their own country.

On this summer morning other life was stirring in the nearby stream. A female mayfly along with thousands of others of her species were shedding their larval exoskeletons as they transformed from their robust crawling aquatic stage to graceful flying adults (fig. 9.1). As a larva the mayfly had lived in the stream for a year, but her adult stage would last just this one day, during which she would mate, deposit her eggs in the stream, and then die. She had just this one chance to successfully complete her life cycle. For an adult mayfly, there is no tomorrow—one chance and no more. As the mayflies swarmed, some would be eaten by birds nesting in alder trees that grew along the stream, and some would be caught by bats that found roosting sites on the giant redwood. Some of the mayflies would be eaten by fish that they had successfully eluded for a year of larval life, and still others would be snared by spiders that spun their webs in azalea shrubs that grew between the alders and the redwood. However, this particular mayfly escaped all predators, mated, and laid her eggs.

Spent by the effort of depositing her eggs, the mayfly was caught by the current and washed downstream. Fifty meters from where she emerged that morning, the mayfly was taken from the surface by a trout as she floated past an old redwood log where the trout sheltered. The small splash of the feeding trout caught the attention of a man and a woman who had been studying the stream. They knew the stream well and knew the pool where the big trout lived and they knew the trout, which they had tried to catch many times.

Redwood, mayfly, fish, and humans, lives intertwined in a web of ecological relationships but vastly different in scale and timing. All four are players in an ecological and evolutionary drama stretching into a vast past and into an unknown future.

Figure 9.1   Adult mayflies generally live one day only.

Made of the same elements and with their genetic inheritance encoded by DNA of the same basic structure, the four species have inherited vastly different lives. While the redwood has produced seeds numbering in the millions over a lifetime that has stretched for millennia, the mayfly spends a year in the stream and then emerges to lay eggs that will number in the hundreds. The trout's spawn has numbered in the thousands, deposited during the several years of her life. Meanwhile the man and woman have produced two children during their lifetime, investing time and energy into them over a period of decades.

The story we have just told is rich in natural history, and leads to many critical ecological concepts. In the previous chapters of this section, we have focused on how organisms deal with isolated environmental and social conditions. However, individuals never encounter these factors in isolation, and instead natural selection acts upon all of these factors simultaneously. Because of limited amounts of energy, resources, and genetic variation, not all organisms are able to live everywhere, and instead we find that species are limited in the multivariate sets of conditions they can tolerate. We call this the **niche.** However, even when species have roughly similar niches, as in our story here, how they cope with the local conditions can vary greatly, and again we find evolution constrained by limited energy and resources. Some organisms will produce many small offspring, while others will produce few large offspring. These sorts of questions fall within the domain of those who study **life histories.** Chapter 9 presents several concepts from these two central aspects of ecology.

Concepts

9.1 **The fundamental niche reflects the environmental requirements of species, while the realized niche also includes interactions with other species.**

9.2 **Because all organisms have access to limited energy and other resources, there are fundamental trade-offs in how these can be allocated between survival, offspring number, and offspring size.**

9.3 **The great diversity of life histories observed in nature can be classified on the basis of a few common characteristics.**

9.1   Fundamental and Realized Niches

The fundamental niche reflects the environmental requirements of species, while the realized niche also includes interactions with other species.   In chapters 5–8 we discussed how individual factors such as temperature, water availability, and food resources can have significant implications for the evolution and ecology of organisms. Although species vary greatly in their adaptations to these environmental factors, one commonality is that most adaptations require energy—be it to feed microbial symbionts that digest cellulose, to maintain constant body temperatures, or to excrete excess salts from the body. A common theme through the chapters of section II has been the *principle of allocation*, in which allocation of energy to one aspect of the energy budget (fig. 5.34) means there is less energy to allocate for other uses. This idea is a unifying theme of ecology, and is never more apparent than in discussions of life-histories and the niche.

The word *niche* has been in use a long time. Its earliest and most basic meaning was that of a recessed place in a wall where one could set or display items. For about the last century, however, ecologists have given a broader meaning to the word. To the ecologist, the niche summarizes the environmental factors that influence the growth, survival, and reproduction of a species. In other words, a species' niche consists of all the factors necessary for its existence. If conditions in a given location fall outside of the conditions of even a single dimension of the niche, the species will be unable to persist.

The niche concept was developed independently by Joseph Grinnell (1917, 1924) and Charles Elton (1927), who use the term *niche* in slightly different ways. In his early writings, Grinnell's idea of the niche centred around the influences of the physical environment, while Elton's earliest concept included both biological interactions and abiotic factors. However their thinking and emphasis may have differed, it is clear that the views of these two researchers had much in common and that our present concept of the niche rests squarely on their pioneering work.

It was G. Evelyn Hutchinson (1957) who crystallized the niche concept, stimulating the work of an entire generation of ecologists. In his seminal paper entitled simply, "Concluding Remarks," Hutchinson defined the niche as an *n-dimensional hypervolume*, where *n* equals the number of environmental factors important to the survival and reproduction of a species. Hutchinson called this hypervolume, which specifies the values of the *n* environmental factors permitting a species to survive and reproduce, as the **fundamental niche** of the species (fig. 9.2). The fundamental niche defines the physical conditions under which a species might live, in the absence of interactions with other species. This should sound vaguely familiar, as this is simply a multivariate extension of the range of tolerance that was discussed in chapter 5. In chapter 5, we discussed how all organisms will have a range of environmental conditions (e.g., temperature) in which they perform well, poorly, or not at all. Each axis of the *Hutchinsonion* niche is made of different environmental parameters, each with its own range of tolerance. The niche itself consists of the hypervolume which is produced by overlapping tolerance zones of each axis (Fig. 9.2). Importantly, the niche is *not* a physical location, but instead it's an abstract representation of the environmental conditions necessary for a species to potentially survive. In this regard, the ecological use of the word *niche* has moved away from its original meaning as a hole in a wall.

Hutchinson's contribution to the niche concept extends beyond the fundamental (i.e., Hutchinsonian) niche. Hutchinson recognized that interactions among species, such as competition, may restrict the environments in which a species actually can persist, and he referred to these more restricted conditions as the **realized niche**. This too makes sense given

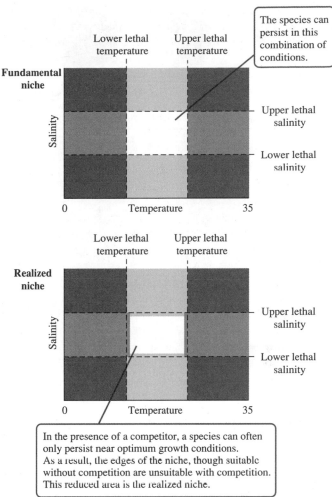

Figure 9.2 Two dimensions of a (*a*) fundamental, and (*b*) realized niche of a hypothetical species.

our discussion of the range-of-tolerance concept in chapter 5. Although species may be able to survive across a broad range of temperatures (or another environmental factor), its performance is likely greatest only in a narrow subset of this range. It is here where it can compete most effectively, while at the edge of its thermal range, it is more likely to be displaced. As a result, the fundamental niche represents the maximal niche size of an organism, while the realized niche will be smaller. This issue will be discussed in more detail in chapter 13.

Do you think it's possible to completely measure Hutchinson's *n*-dimensional hypervolume niche for any species? Probably not, since there are so many environmental factors that potentially influence fitness. Fortunately, it appears that niches are determined mostly by a few environmental factors, and so ecologists are able to apply a simplified version of Hutchinson's comprehensive concept.

The Feeding Niches of Galápagos Finches

As we saw in chapter 7, availability of suitable food significantly affects the evolution, survival, and reproduction of Galápagos finches. In other words, food has a major influence

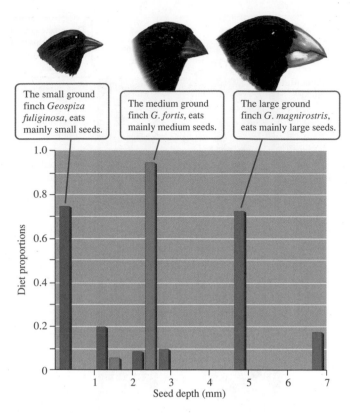

Figure 9.3   Relationship between body size and seed size in Galápagos finch species (data from Grant 1986).

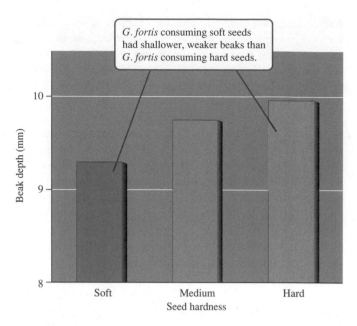

Figure 9.4   Relationship between the hardness of seeds eaten by medium ground finches, *Geospiza fortis*, and beak depth (data from Boag and Grant 1984b).

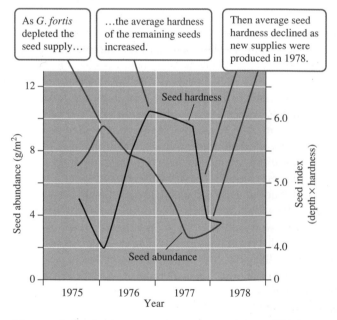

Figure 9.5   Seed depletion by the medium ground finch, *Geospiza fortis*, and average seed hardness (data from Grant 1986).

on the niches of Galápagos finches. Because the kinds of food used by birds is largely reflected by the form of their beaks, Peter Grant (1986) and his colleagues were able to represent the feeding niches of Galápagos finches by measuring their beak morphology. For instance, differences in beak size among small, medium, and large ground finches translate directly into differences in diet. The large ground finch, *Geospiza magnirostris*, eats larger seeds; the medium ground finch, *G. fortis*, eats medium-sized seeds; while the small ground finch, *G. fuliginosa*, eats small seeds (fig. 9.3).

The size of seeds that can be eaten by Galápagos finches can be estimated by simply measuring the depths of their beaks. Studies of seed use by *G. fortis* on Daphne Major showed clearly that even within species, beak size affects the composition of the diet. Within this population, individuals with the deepest beaks fed on the hardest seeds, while individuals with the smallest beaks fed on the softest seeds (fig. 9.4).

The importance of beak size to seed use was also demonstrated by the effects of a 1977 drought on the *G. fortis* population of Daphne Major. During the drought, mortality did not fall equally on all segments of the population. As seeds were depleted, the birds ate the smallest and softest seeds first, leaving the largest and toughest seeds (fig. 9.5). In other words, following the drought not only were seeds in short supply, the remaining seeds were also tougher to crack. Because they could not crack the remaining seeds, mortality fell most heavily on smaller birds with smaller beaks. Consequently, at the end of the drought, the *G. fortis* population on Daphne Major was

dominated by larger individuals that had survived by feeding on hard seeds (fig. 9.6).

These studies show that beak size provides significant insights into the feeding biology of Galápagos ground finches. Since food is the major determinant of survival and reproduction among these birds, beak morphology gives us a very good picture of their niches. However, the niches of other kinds of organisms are determined by entirely different environmental factors. Let's consider the niche of a dominant species in salt marshes.

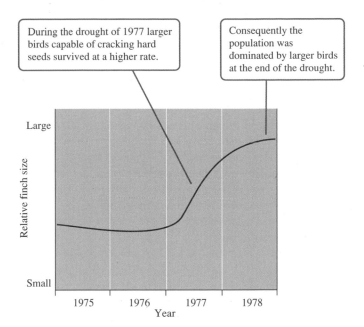

During the drought of 1977 larger birds capable of cracking hard seeds survived at a higher rate.

Consequently the population was dominated by larger birds at the end of the drought.

Figure 9.6   Selection for larger size among medium ground finches, *Geospiza fortis*, during a drought on the island of Daphne Major (data from Grant 1986).

The Habitat Niche of a Salt Marsh Grass

Biologists discovered *Spartina anglica* approximately one century ago, as a new species produced by **allopolyploidy** (fig. 9.7). Allopolyploidy is a process of speciation initiated by hybridization of two different species. *S. anglica* arose initially as a cross between *S. maritima,* a European species, and *S. alterniflora*, a North American species. At least one of these hybrid plants later doubled its chromosome number, making it capable of sexual reproduction, and produced a new species: *S. anglica*. From its centre of origin in Lymington, Hampshire, England, *S. anglica* spread northward along the coasts of the British Isles. During this same period, it colonized the coast of France and was widely planted elsewhere in northwest Europe as well as along the coasts of New Zealand, Australia, and China. The Chinese population of this salt marsh grass, established from only 21 plants in 1963, grew to cover 36,000 ha by 1980. *S. anglica* is extensively planted for stabilizing mudflats because it is more tolerant of periodic inundation and water-saturated soils than most other salt marsh plants. This environmental tolerance is reflected in the distribution of the plant in northwestern Europe, where it generally inhabits the most seaward zone of any of the salt marsh plants.

The local distribution of *S. anglica* in the British Isles is well predicted by a few physical variables related to the duration and frequency of inundation by tides and waves. The lower and upper intertidal limits of the grass are mainly determined by the magnitude of tidal fluctuations during spring tides. Where tidal fluctuations are greater, both the lower and upper limits are higher up on the shore. However, throughout its British range, the grass generally occupies the intertidal zone between mean high-water *spring tides* and mean high-water *neap tides* (fig. 9.8). Spring tides occur during new and full moons, when the tidal fluctuations are greatest. Neap tides

Figure 9.7   The salt marsh grass *Spartina anglica* originated on the coast of England as a hybrid of European and North American species of salt marsh grasses and has since spread to salt marshes in many parts of the world.

occur during the first and third quarter phases of the moon and result in the smallest amount of tidal variation (see chapter 3). A second factor that determines the local distribution of *S. anglica* is the **fetch** of the estuary. The fetch of a body of water is the longest distance over which wind can blow and is directly related to the maximum size of waves that can be generated by wind. All other factors being equal, larger waves occur on estuaries with greater fetch. The larger the fetch the higher *S. anglica* must live in an estuary to avoid disturbance by waves.

The upper limit of *S. anglica's* distribution within the intertidal zone is also negatively correlated with latitude. In northerly locations within the British Isles, the grass does not occur quite as high in the intertidal zone as it does in the south. What factors might restrict the distribution at northern sites? One factor we should consider is that *S. anglica* is a C_4 plant. Remember from chapter 7 that C_4 grasses generally do better in warm environments. In northerly locations, *S. anglica* is replaced in the upper intertidal zone by C_3 plants. Could it be that competition with these C_3 plants at northern sites excludes *S. anglica* from the upper intertidal zone? We'll

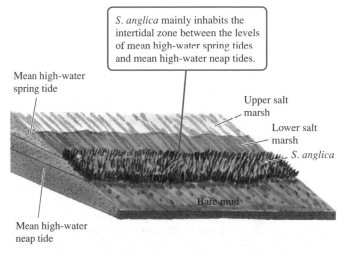

S. anglica mainly inhabits the intertidal zone between the levels of mean high-water spring tides and mean high-water neap tides.

Mean high-water spring tide

Upper salt marsh

Lower salt marsh

S. anglica

Mean high-water neap tide

Bare mud

Figure 9.8   The niche of *Spartina anglica* is related to tidal fluctuations.

take up this question later in chapter 13 when we discuss experimental approaches to the study of competition.

Next in this chapter we continue with our discussion of how trade-offs can influence the ecology of a species, focusing on trade-offs between survival and reproduction.

Concept 9.1 Review

1. Why can't the realized niche be larger than a species' fundamental niche?
2. If niches do not represent actual locations on a map, and instead represent a set of conditions necessary for survival, how could an ecologist measure the niche of a species?

9.2   Trade-offs

Because all organisms have access to limited energy and other resources, there are fundamental trade-offs in how these can be allocated between survival, offspring number, and offspring size.   In 1976 Stephen Stearns was a young graduate student at the University of British Columbia. During the process of deciding what project he wanted to tackle for his Ph.D. thesis, he wrote a paper entitled "Life-History Tactics: A Review of the Ideas," published in the *Quarterly Review of Biology*. This paper was the first synthesis of the ideas in life history, and by itself, created a field of research that would shape the careers of many researchers yet to come. As a sign of how influential Stearns was, and continues to be, this single paper has been cited over 1,800 times by other scientists. To put this in perspective, if a single paper is cited 100 times, it is generally considered an influential paper. There are not many people who create a field of research; even fewer do it while still a graduate student. Much of what we will talk about in this section comes a result of the pioneering work of Stearns, whose raised questions that were tackled by ecologists around the world.

So far, we have primarily discussed how trade-offs can affect an organism's ability to allocate energy to deal with competing abiotic conditions, such as water availability and temperature. However, the principle of allocation is just as important in influencing how an organism allocates energy within a given segment of its energy budget, such as reproduction. For example, producing large offspring simply costs more energy than an equal number of small offspring. As a result, if the amount of energy an organism has available to allocate to reproduction is limited, then there is a trade-off between offspring number and offspring size. We can imagine a second example, where the amount of energy allocated to reproduction is variable. However, if allocation to reproduction increases, that energy can't come from nowhere, it must come at the cost of reduced allocation to some other life function. As a result of this energetic reality, there is commonly observed a trade-off between the probability of adult survival and energetic allocation to reproduction. In this section, we will explore the offspring size vs. offspring number and adult survival vs. reproductive allocation trade-offs across species.

Egg Size and Number in Fish

Because of their great diversity (more than 20,000 existing species) and the wide variety of environments in which they live, fish offer many opportunities for studies of life history. Kirk Winemiller (1995) pointed out that fish show more variation in many life history traits than any other group of animals. For instance, the number of offspring they produce per brood ranges from the one or two large live young produced by mako sharks to the 600,000,000 eggs per clutch laid by the ocean sunfish! However, many variables other than offspring number and size change from sharks to sunfish. Therefore, more robust patterns of variation can be obtained by analyzing relationships within closely related species, such as within families or genera.

In a study of gene flow among populations of darters, small freshwater fish in the perch family, or Percidae, Tom Turner and Joel Trexler tried to determine the extent to which life history differences among species might influence gene flow between populations. Turner and Trexler (1998) pointed out that in such a study, it is best to focus on a group of relatively closely related organisms with a shared evolutionary history. They were particularly interested in determining the relationship between egg size and egg number, or **fecundity,** and the extent of gene flow among populations. Fecundity is simply the number of eggs or seeds produced by an organism. Turner and Trexler proposed that gene flow would be higher among populations producing more numerous smaller eggs, that is, among populations with higher fecundity.

Turner and Trexler chose the darters for their studies because they are an ideal study group. Darters are small, streamlined benthic fishes that live in rivers and streams throughout eastern and central North America. Male darters are usually strikingly coloured during the breeding season (fig. 9.9). The darters consist of 174 species in three genera within the family Percidae, which makes them one of the most species-rich groups of vertebrates in North America. Darters include at least one species, *Percina copelandi* (Channel darter) that is listed as "at risk" (chapter 10) in Ontario and Québec. The most diverse genus of darters, *Etheostoma,* includes approximately 135 species. However, despite the fact that the darters as a whole live in similar habitats and have similar anatomy, they

Figure 9.9   Darters such as this male orangethroat darter form a diverse and distinctive subfamily of fishes within the perch family. They live only in North America.

vary widely in their life histories. The genera most similar to the ancestors of the darters, *Crystallaria* (one species) and *Percina* (38 species), are larger and produce more eggs than species in the genus *Etheostoma*. However, *Etheostoma* species also vary substantially in their life histories.

Turner and Trexler sampled 64 locations on streams and rivers in the Ohio, Ozark, and Ouachita Highlands regions of Ohio, Arkansas, and Missouri, the heart of freshwater fish diversity in North America, which supports one of the most diverse temperate freshwater fish faunas on earth. Of the darters they collected at these locations, they chose 15 species, 5 in the genus *Percina* and 10 *Etheostoma* species, for detailed study. Turner and Trexler chose darter species that included a wide range of variation in life history traits, especially variation in body size, number of eggs laid, and egg size.

The species in the study ranged in length from 44 to 127 mm and the number of mature eggs that they produced ranged from 49 to 397. Meanwhile, the size of eggs produced by the study species varied from 0.9 to 2.3 mm in diameter. As they expected, Turner and Trexler found that larger darter species produce larger numbers of eggs (fig. 9.10). Their results also support the generalization that there is a trade-off between offspring size and number. On average, darters that produce larger eggs produce fewer eggs (fig. 9.11).

Turner and Trexler characterized the genetic structure of darter populations using electrophoresis of allozymes produced by 21 different loci (see chapter 4). They chose 21 loci out of 40 that they examined because they were polymorphic. A **polymorphic locus** is one for which more than one allele can be detected. In this case each allele synthesizes a different allozyme.

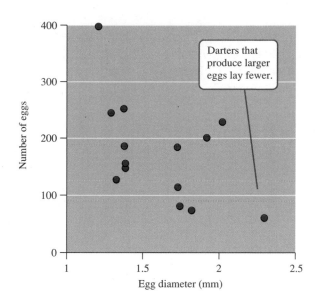

Figure 9.11   Relationship between the size of eggs laid by darters and the number of eggs laid (data from Turner and Trexler 1998).

Turner and Trexler assessed genetic structure using allelic frequencies. Allelic frequencies were measured as the frequencies of allozymes across the 21 different study loci. Populations with similar allelic frequencies were taken as genetically similar, while those that differed in allelic frequencies were concluded to be different genetically. Gene flow was estimated by the degree of similarity in allelic frequencies between populations.

How can the number and kinds of allozymes synthesized by a series of populations be used to determine the extent of gene flow among populations? Turner and Trexler assumed that the populations differing in allelic frequencies have lower gene flow between them than populations that have similar allelic frequencies. In other words, they assumed that genetic similarity between populations is maintained by gene flow, while genetic differences arise in the absence or restriction of gene flow.

What relationship is there between egg size and number and gene flow between populations? Turner and Trexler found a negative relationship between egg size and gene flow but a strong positive relationship of gene flow with the number of eggs produced by females (fig. 9.12). That is, populations of darter species that produce many small eggs showed less difference in allelic frequencies across the study region than did populations that produce fewer larger eggs.

How do differences in egg size and number translate into differences in gene flow among populations? It turns out that the larvae of darters that hatch from larger eggs are larger when they hatch. These larger larvae begin feeding on prey that live on the streambed at an earlier age, and spend less time drifting with the water current. Consequently, larvae hatching from larger eggs disperse shorter distances and therefore carry their genes shorter distances. As a result, populations of species producing fewer larger eggs will be more isolated genetically from other populations. Because of their greater isolation, such populations will differentiate genetically more rapidly compared to populations of species that produce many smaller larvae that disperse longer distances.

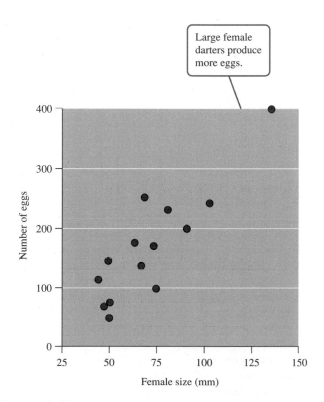

Figure 9.10   Relationship between female darter size and number of eggs (data from Turner and Trexler 1998).

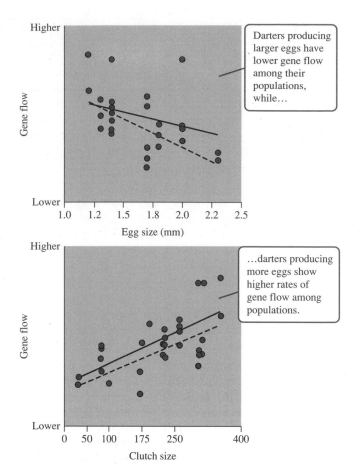

Figure 9.12 Egg size, egg number, and gene flow among darter populations (data from Turner and Trexler 1998).

Figure 9.13 A small sample of the great diversity of seed sizes and shapes.

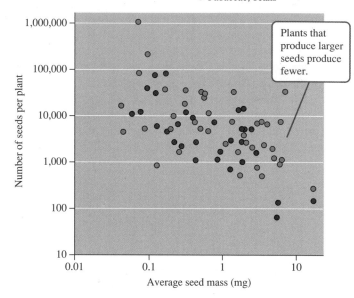

Figure 9.14 Relationship between seed mass and seed number (data from Stevens 1932).

Turner and Trexler's study not only provides a case history consistent with the generalization that there is a trade-off between offspring size and number, it also reveals some of the evolutionary consequences of that trade-off. For example, because larger offspring will travel shorter distances before feeding than smaller offspring, populations of species that produce large offspring will be more genetically distinct than the species with small offspring. Genetic differentiation is a necessary precursor to speciation events (chapter 4), and thus this most basic of life-history trade-offs: offspring size and number, has the potential to influence macro evolutionary processes, such as variation in speciation rates. It is important to recognize that although these evolutionary effects occur in some species, such as darters, they may not occur in other taxa. For example, aspects of social structure, such as parental care, can greatly impact dispersal of offspring.

Trade-offs between offspring number and size have been found in populations of many kinds of organisms. For instance, ecologists have found parallel relationships among terrestrial plants, involving seed number and size.

Seed Size and Number in Plants

Like fish, plants vary widely in the number of offspring they produce, ranging from those that produce many small seeds to those that produce a few large seeds (fig. 9.13). The sizes

of seeds produced by plants range over 10 orders of magnitude, from the tiny seeds of orchids that weigh 0.000002 g to the giant double coconut palm with seeds that weigh up to 27,000 g. While some orchids are known to produce billions of seeds, coconut palms produce small numbers of huge seeds. At this scale it is clear that there is a trade-off between seed size and seed number and while there are complexities that must be accounted for (Harper, Lovell, and Moore 1970), botanists long ago described a negative relationship between seed size and seed number (Stevens 1932). Figure 9.14 shows the relationship between average seed mass and the number of seeds per plant among species in four families of plants, daisies (Asteraceae), grasses (Poaceae), mustards (Brassicaceae), and beans (Fabaceae). In all four families, species producing larger numbers of seeds on average produce fewer seeds.

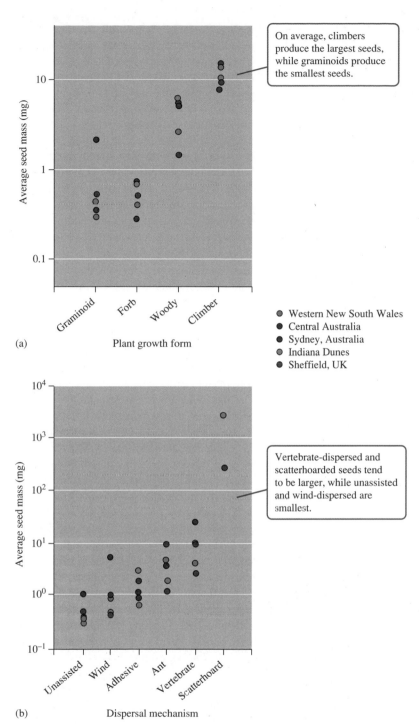

On average, climbers produce the largest seeds, while graminoids produce the smallest seeds.

Western New South Wales
Central Australia
Sydney, Australia
Indiana Dunes
Sheffield, UK

(a)   Plant growth form

Vertebrate-dispersed and scatterhoarded seeds tend to be larger, while unassisted and wind-dispersed are smallest.

(b)   Dispersal mechanism

Figure 9.15 Plant growth form and dispersal mechanism and seed mass (data from Westoby, Leishman, and Lord 1996).

orchids and coconut palms, which mixes data from a species having the growth form of an epiphyte (the orchid) and another with the growth form of a tree (the palm), may not be a valid comparison. Such a comparison may not be valid since growth form may itself influence the number and size of seeds produced by plants.

What other aspects of plant biology might influence seed size? As we will discuss in chapter 11, dispersal is an important facet of the population biology of all organisms, including plants. Since long-distance dispersal by plants is mainly by means of seeds, we might ask whether there is a relationship between seed characteristics and mode of dispersal.

Aware of the potential influence of growth form and dispersal mode on seed characteristics, Mark Westoby, Michelle Leishman, and Janice Lord (1996), studied the relationship between plant growth form and seed size. Their study included the seeds of 196 to 641 species of plants from five different regions. Three of their study regions were in Australia: New South Wales, central Australia, and Sydney; one was in Europe: Sheffield, United Kingdom; and one was in North America: Indiana Dunes National Lakeshore. Why did Westoby, Leishman, and Lord include five floras on three continents in their study? By including the plants on three different continents, Westoby, Leishman, and Lord increased their chances of discovering patterns of general importance. If they had worked within a single region, they could not be sure that the patterns they uncovered would hold in other regions.

Westoby, Leishman, and Lord recognized four plant growth forms. Grasses and grasslike plants, such as sedges and rushes, were classified as **graminoids.** Herbaceous plants other than graminoids were assigned to a **forb** category. Species with woody thickening of their tissues were considered as woody plants. Finally, climbing plants and vines were classified as climbers. The results showed a clear association between seed size and plant growth form (fig. 9.15*a*). In most of the floras analyzed by Westoby and his colleagues, the smallest seeds were produced by graminoid plants, followed by the seeds produced by forbs. In all five study regions, woody plants produce seeds that are far larger than those produced by either graminoids or forbs. However, the largest seeds in all regions are produced by vines. The researchers found that the seeds produced by woody plants and vines in the five floras were on average approximately 10 times the mass of seeds produced by either graminoid plants or forbs.

Westoby and his coauthors recognized six dispersal strategies. They classified seeds with no specialized structures for dispersal as unassisted dispersers. If seeds had hooks, spines, or barbs, they were classified as **adhesion-adapted.** Meanwhile, seeds with wings, hairs, or other structures that provide air resistance were assigned to a wind-dispersed category.

Having documented a trade-off between seed size and number, plant ecologists searched for the mechanisms favouring many small seeds in some environments and few larger seeds in others. However, when venturing into the world of plants, the ecologist should be aware of the subtleties of plant biology, much of which can be inferred from their morphology. For instance, many characteristics of plants correlate with their **growth form** or **life-form**, which itself constitutes an aspect of life history. Therefore, comparing seed production of

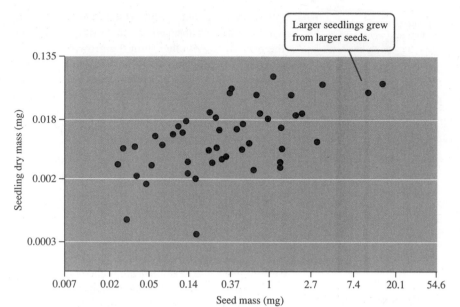

Figure 9.16 Seed mass and seedling mass among grassland plants in Sweden (data from Jakobsson and Eriksson 2000).

Animal-dispersed seeds in the study included ant-dispersed, vertebrate-dispersed, and scatterhoarded. Westoby, Leishman, and Lord classified seeds with an **elaiosome,** a structure on the surface of some seeds generally containing oils attractive to ants, as ant-dispersed. Seeds with flesh or with an **aril,** a fleshy covering of some seeds that attracts birds and other vertebrates, were classified as vertebrate-dispersed. Finally they classified as **scatterhoarded** those seeds known to be gathered by mammals and stored in scattered caches or hoards.

Westoby, Leishman, and Lord also found that plants that disperse their seeds in different ways tend to produce seeds of different sizes (fig. 9.15b). Plants that they had classified as unassisted dispersers produced the smallest seeds, while wind-dispersed seeds were slightly larger. Adhesion-adapted seeds were of intermediate size, while animal-dispersed seeds were largest. Ant-dispersed seeds were the next largest, verte-brate-dispersed seeds were somewhat larger, and scatter-hoarded were the largest by far. Westoby and his team point out that between 21% and 47% of the variation in seed size in the five floras included in their study is accounted for by a combination of growth form and mode of dispersal.

The analyses by Westoby and his colleagues show that both plant growth form and dispersal mode are associated with differences in seed size among plants. Impressively, the rela-tionships between seed size and both growth form and dispersal mode were consistent across widely separated geographic regions. However, Westoby, Leishman, and Lord pointed out that their analysis uncovered wide variation in seed size among plants in all regions. What are the factors that maintain variation in seed size? To maintain such variation, there must be advan-tages and disadvantages of producing either large or small seeds. What are those advantages and disadvantages? Plants that pro-duce small seeds can produce greater numbers of seeds. Such plants seem to have an advantage where disturbance rates are

high and where plants with the capacity to colonize newly opened space appear to thrive. Though plants that produce large seeds are constrained to produce fewer, large seeds pro-duce seedlings that survive at a higher rate in the face of environmental hazards. Those haz-ards include competition from established plants, shade, defoliation, nutrient shortage, deep burial in soil or litter, and drought.

Anna Jakobsson and Ove Eriksson (2000) studied the relationships between seed size, seedling size, and seedling recruitment among herbs and grasses living in seminatural grass-lands in southeastern Sweden. To estimate the influence of seed size and seedling size, Jako-bsson and Eriksson germinated seeds in pots containing a standardized soil mix. The pots were maintained in a greenhouse under stan-dardized conditions and seedlings were har-vested and weighed 3 weeks after **germination.** Germination is the process by which seeds begin to grow or develop, producing the small plant called a seedling in the pro-cess. Why did Jakobsson and Eriksson conduct this experiment in a greenhouse? The main reason was that their ability to control environmental conditions such as soil type, moisture availability, and temperature in the greenhouse ensured that differences in seedling size would be due mainly to differences in seed size and not due to differences in the environments in which the seeds germinated. The results of this portion of the study showed clearly that larger seeds produced larger seedlings (fig. 9.16).

Jakobsson and Eriksson also investigated the relationship between seed size and recruitment among 50 plant species liv-ing in the meadows of their study region, using a field experi-ment. At their field sites, Jakobsson and Eriksson planted the seeds of each species in 14 small 10 × 10 cm plots. Each plot was sown with 50 to 100 seeds of the study species. They left half of the study plots undisturbed, while the other plots were disturbed before planting by scratching the soil surface and removing any accumulated litter. In addition to the 14 plots where seeds were sown, Jakobsson and Eriksson established control plots where they did not plant seeds. Again, half of these were disturbed and half left undisturbed. Why did Jakobsson and Eriksson need to establish these control plots? The control plots allowed them to estimate how much germination of each species would occur in the absence of their sowing new seeds. The seeds of many species can lie dormant in soils for long periods of time and additional seeds of their study species might have dispersed into the study plots during the experiment. Therefore, without the control plots, Jakobsson and Eriksson would have no way of knowing if the seedlings they observed had grown from the seeds they had sown or from other seeds.

Of the 50 species of seeds planted, the seeds of 48 species germinated and those of 45 species established recruits. Jako-bsson and Eriksson observed no recruitment of any of the study species on the control plots. Therefore they could be confident that new plants recruited into their experimental plots came from seeds that they had planted. Though plants

Figure 9.17 Seed mass and recruitment rates in grassland plants (data from Jakobsson and Eriksson 2000).

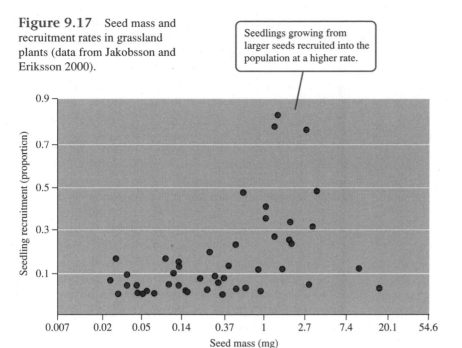

Seedlings growing from larger seeds recruited into the population at a higher rate.

hazards. Seiwa and Kikuzawa were especially focused on the influences of shade on seedling establishment.

The trees studied by Seiwa and Kikuzawa were all broad-leaved deciduous trees that grow in the temperate deciduous forests of Hokkaido either on mountain slopes between 100 and 200 m in altitude or in riparian forests. The fruits of all the study species were collected from trees growing in the arboretum of the Hokkaido Forest Experimental Station. In the laboratory the research team removed any fruit pulp from the seeds, washed them, and then allowed them to air dry for 24 hours. Seiwa and Kikuzawa then estimated average seed mass by weighing one to five groups of 100 to 1,000 randomly chosen seeds. A week after they collected the fruits, Seiwa and Kikuzawa planted the seeds they contained in the arboretum nursery at the Hokkaido Forest Experimental Station. They planted seeds at depths of 1 to 2 cm in a clay loam soil and watered, until the soil was saturated, three times a week.

Seiwa and Kikuzawa's results showed clearly that larger seeds produced taller seedlings (fig. 9.18). They explained this pattern as the result of the larger seeds providing greater energy reserves to boost initial seedling growth. Seiwa and Kikuzawa observed that seedlings from large-seeded species unfolded all of their leaves rapidly in the spring and shed all of their leaves synchronously in the autumn. They concluded

recruited to both undisturbed and disturbed plots, the number of recruits was generally higher in disturbed plots. Further, eight species of plants recruited only on disturbed plots.

What role did differences in seed size play in the rate of recruitment by different species? Jakobsson and Eriksson calculated recruitment success in various ways. One of the most basic ways that they calculated recruitment was by dividing the total number of recruits by the total number of seeds of a species that they planted, giving the proportion of seeds sown that produced recruits. While 45 of 50 species established new recruits in the experimental plots, the rate at which they established varied widely among species from approximately 5% to nearly 90%. Jakobsson and Eriksson found that differences in seed size explained much of the observed differences in recruitment success among species (fig. 9.17). On average, larger seeds, which produce larger seedlings, were associated with a higher rate of recruitment. Therefore it appears that by investing more energy into a seed, the maternal plant increases the probability that the seed will successfully establish itself as a new plant. This advantage associated with large seed size is probably very important in environments such as the grasslands studied by Jakobsson and Eriksson, where competition with established plants is likely to be high.

Jakobsson and Eriksson focused their work on grasslands where the principal growth forms were, using the classification presented in figure 9.15*a,* graminoid or forbs. However, as shown in figure 9.15*a,* woody plants and vines produce substantially larger seeds than herbaceous graminoids and forbs. How might patterns in seed and seedling size vary among woody plants? Kenji Seiwa and Kihachiro Kikuzawa (1991) studied the relationship between seed size and seedling size among tree species native to Hokkaido, the northernmost large island of Japan. The results of their work and their interpretation of the results provide clear insights into how seed size may improve the ability of seedlings to survive environmental

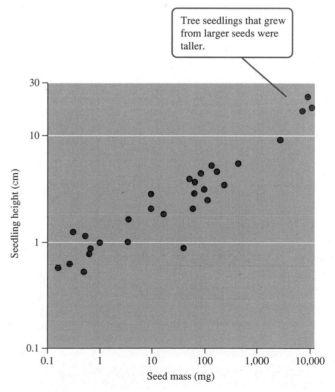

Tree seedlings that grew from larger seeds were taller.

Figure 9.18 Relationship between seed mass and seedling height among trees (Seiwa and Kikuzawa 1991).

that this timing allows the seedlings from large-seeded species to emerge early in the spring before the trees forming the canopy of the forest have expanded their leaves and have shaded the forest floor. Seiwa and Kikuzawa also pointed out that rapid growth would help seedlings penetrate the thick litter layer on the floor of deciduous forests and help them establish themselves as part of the forest understory.

As we can see from these examples in fish, graminoids, and woody plants, there is evidence for an offspring size vs. offspring number trade-off in many species scattered across the planet. But more important than simply quantifying that pattern is the realization that this trade-off has significant implications for other aspects of the ecology and evolution of these species. Offspring size appears to influence both dispersal and competitive ability. Can you imagine how this could influence aspects of behavioural ecology in animals? Does this have any potential impact on mating systems and sexual conflict? As you can see, the reproductive ecology of an organism has the ability to affect nearly all facets of an organism's life, and not simply the number of offspring that it will produce.

In addition to showing variation in the number and sizes of offspring produced, organisms also show a great deal of variation in the age at which they begin reproducing. They also differ greatly in the relative amount of energy they allocate to reproduction versus growth and maintenance. Over the years, life history ecologists have observed patterns in age of reproductive maturity and relative investment in reproduction among species that support some broad generalizations.

Adult Survival & Reproductive Allocation

Is there a relationship between the probability of an organism living from one year to the next and the age at which the organism begins reproducing? What environmental factors are responsible for variation in age at maturity and the amount of energy allocated to reproduction, which has been called **reproductive effort?** (Reproductive effort is the allocation of energy, time, and other resources to the production and care of offspring.) These are two more questions central to life history ecology.

Reproductive effort generally involves trade-offs with other needs of the organism, including allocation to growth and maintenance. Because of these trade-offs, allocation to reproduction may reduce the probability that an organism will survive. However, delaying reproduction also involves risk. An individual that delays reproduction runs the risk of dying before it can reproduce. Consequently, evolutionary ecologists have predicted that variation in mortality rates among adults will be in association with variation in the age of first reproduction, or age of reproductive maturity. Specifically, they have predicted that where adult mortality is higher, natural selection will favour early reproductive maturity; and where adult mortality is low, natural selection has been expected to favour delaying reproductive maturity.

Life History Variation Among Species

The relationship between mortality, growth, and age at first reproduction or reproductive maturity has been examined in a large number of organisms. Early work, which concentrated on fish, shrimp, and sea urchins, suggested linkages between mortality or survival, growth, and reproduction. Richard Shine and Eric Charnov (1992) explored life history variation among snakes and lizards to determine whether generalizations developed through studies of fish and marine invertebrates could be extended to another group of animals living in very different environments.

Shine and Charnov began their presentation with a reminder that, in contrast to most terrestrial arthropods, birds, and mammals (including humans), many animals continue growing after they reach sexual maturity. In addition, most vertebrate species begin reproducing before they reach their maximum body size. Shine and Charnov pointed out that the energy budgets of these other vertebrate species, such as fish and reptiles, are different before and after sexual maturity. Before these organisms reach sexual maturity, energy acquired by an individual is allocated to one of two competing demands: maintenance and growth. However, after reaching sexual maturity, limited energy supplies are allocated to three functions: maintenance, growth, and reproduction. Because they have fewer demands on their limited energy supplies, individuals delaying reproduction until they are older will grow faster and reach a larger size. Because of the increase in reproductive rate associated with larger body size (see fig. 9.10), deferring reproduction would lead to a higher reproductive rate. However again, where mortality rates are high, deferring reproduction increases the probability that an individual will die before reproducing. These relationships suggest that mortality rates will play a pivotal role in determining the age at first reproduction.

Shine and Charnov gathered information from published summaries on annual adult survival and age at which females mature for several species of snakes and lizards. The annual rate of adult survival among snakes in their data set ranged from approximately 35% to 85% of the population, while age at reproductive maturity ranged from 2 to 7 years. Meanwhile, the annual rate of lizard survival ranged from approximately 8% to 67% of the population and their age at first reproduction ranged from a little less than 8 months to 6.5 years. Because most of the species they examined were North American and were members of either one family of snakes or one family of lizards, Shine and Charnov urged that their results not be generalized to snakes and lizards generally until other groups from other regions had been analyzed. Regardless of these cautions, the results of Shine and Charnov's study showed clearly that as survival of adult lizards and snakes increases, their age at maturity also increases (fig. 9.19a).

More recent analyses of the relationship between adult mortality rate and age at maturity among fish species provide additional support for the prediction that high adult survival leads to delayed maturity. Donald Gunderson (1997) explored patterns in adult survival and reproductive effort among several populations of fish. Gunderson suggested that there should be a strong relationship between adult mortality in populations and reproductive effort because some combinations of mortality and reproductive effort have a higher probability of persisting than others. For instance, a population showing a

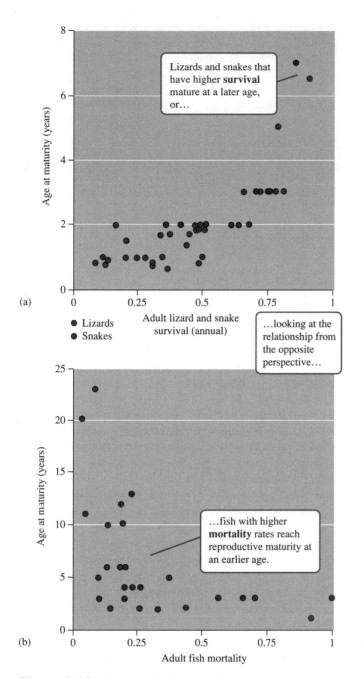

(a)

● Lizards
● Snakes

(b)

Figure 9.19 Relationship between (*a*) adult survival among lizards and snakes and (*b*) adult fish mortality and age of reproductive maturity (data from Shine and Charnov 1992 and Gunderson 1997).

and adjusted for the number of batches of offspring produced by each species per year. For example, because the northern anchovy spawns three times per year, the weight of its ovary was multiplied by 3 for calculating its GSI. Meanwhile, the ovary weight for dogfish sharks, which reproduce only every other year, was divided by 2. However, since most of the species included in the analysis spawn once per year, their ovary weights required no adjustment for GSI calculations.

The fish included in Gunderson's analysis ranged in size from the Puget Sound rockfish, which reaches a maximum size of approximately 15 cm, to northeast Arctic cod that reaches a length of 130 cm. The age at maturation among these fish species ranges from 1 year in northern anchovy populations to 23 years in dogfish shark populations. Like Shine and Charnov, Gunderson gathered information about the life histories of the fish in his analysis from previously published papers and several experts on particular fish species. In his table summarizing life history information for the 28 species included in his analysis, Gunderson lists 72 references. In contrast to Shine and Charnov, Gunderson provides estimates of mortality rates rather than survival rates. In addition his estimates are of "instantaneous" mortality rates instead of annual rates. However, like Shine and Charnov, his results show a clear relationship between adult mortality and age of reproductive maturity (fig. 9.19*b*). These results support the idea that natural selection has acted to adjust age at reproductive maturity to rates of mortality experienced by populations.

Gunderson's analysis also gives information on variation in reproductive effort among species. His calculations of a gonadosomatic index, or GSI, for each of the 28 species included in the analysis spanned more than a 30-fold difference from a value of 0.02 for the rougheye rockfish to 0.65 for the northern anchovy. What do these numbers mean? Remember that the formula for GSI is ovary weight (multiplied by 3 in the case of the northern anchovy because it spawns three times per year) divided by body weight. In other words, reproductive effort is expressed as a proportion of body weight. Converting these proportions to percentages, we can say that the yearly allocation to reproduction by the rougheye rockfish is approximately 2% of its body weight, while the northern anchovy allocates approximately 65% annually! When Gunderson plotted GSI against mortality rates (fig. 9.20), the results supported the prediction from life history theory that species with higher mortality would show higher relative reproductive effort.

Life History Variation Within Species

To this point in our discussion we have emphasized life history differences between species, such as the lizard and snake species compared by Shine and Charnov (fig. 9.19*a*) or the fish species compared by Gunderson (fig. 9.19*b*). Is there evidence that life history differences will evolve within species, where different populations experience different rates of adult mortality? Evidence for the evolution of such intraspecific differences comes from a comparative study of several populations of the pumpkinseed sunfish, *Lepomis gibbosus* (fig. 9.21).

combination of high mortality and high reproductive effort would have a higher chance of persisting than one experiencing high mortality but allocating low reproductive effort. The population with this second combination would likely go extinct in a short period of time.

The life history information Gunderson summarized in his analysis included mortality rate, estimated maximum length, age at reproductive maturity, and reproductive effort. Gunderson estimated reproductive effort as each population's **gonadosomatic index,** or **GSI.** GSI was taken as the ovary weight of each species divided by the species body weight

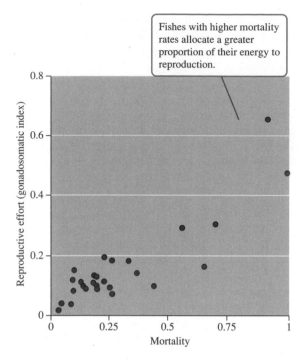

Fishes with higher mortality rates allocate a greater proportion of their energy to reproduction.

Figure 9.20 Relationship between adult fish mortality and reproductive effort as measured by the gonadosomatic index or GSI (data from Gunderson 1997).

Kirk Bertschy and Michael Fox of Trent University (1999) studied the influence of adult survival on pumpkinseed sunfish life histories. One of the major objectives of their study was to test the prediction of life history theory that increased adult survival, relative to juvenile mortality, favours delayed maturity and reduced reproductive effort. What distinguishes this study from those of Shine and Charnov and Gunderson (fig. 9.19)? Again, Bertschy and Fox focused their attention entirely on variation in life histories among populations of *one species*. In other words, their study goal was to explain the evolution of life history variation within a species.

Bertschy and Fox selected five populations of pumpkinseed sunfish living in five lakes from a group of 27 lakes in southern Ontario. Fox had previously studied the pumpkinseed sunfish living in these lakes and so they had a considerable basis for choosing study populations. Bertschy and Fox chose lakes that were similar in area and depth and small enough that they had a reasonable chance of estimating mortality rates and variation in other life history characteristics. Their study lakes varied in area from 7.2 to 39.6 ha and in depth from 2.6 to 11 m. Bertschy and Fox also chose lakes that had no major inflows or outflows. Why did they restrict the study to lakes without major inflows or outflows? One reason is that they wanted to avoid as much movement of individuals in and out of their populations as possible. Such movement could obscure the results of natural selection within the lakes for particular life history characteristics.

Bertschy and Fox estimated life history characteristics from annual samples of approximately 100 pumpkinseed sunfish taken from each of the five study lakes. They caught the fish in their shallow (0.5–2 m depth) littoral habitat using funnel traps

Figure 9.21 Male pumpkinseed sunfish, *Lepomis gibbosus*, build their nests in the shallows of lakes and ponds. They guard their nests against intrusions by other males and attempt to attract females of their species to deposit eggs within them.

and beach seine nets. Bertschy and Fox took their annual population sample in late May or early June just before the beginning or right at the beginning of the spawning season. The individuals caught were sacrificed by placing them in an ice slurry and then freezing them for later analysis. They made several measurements on each individual in their samples, including their age (by counting annual rings in scales), weight (to the nearest 0.1 g), length (in mm), sex, and reproductive status. Because female reproductive effort is largely restricted to egg production while male reproductive effort includes activities such as territory guarding and nest building, Bertschy and Fox studied reproductive traits in females only. A female was considered mature if her ovaries contained eggs with yolk. The ovaries of mature females were dissected out and weighed to the nearest 0.01 g. Bertschy and Fox represented female reproductive effort using the gonadosomatic index, GSI, which they calculated as $100 \times$ (ovary mass) $\div$ (body mass), which yields GSI values expressed as percentages rather than as proportions.

Bertschy and Fox used mark and recapture surveys (see Ecological Tools, chapter 10) to estimate the number of adult pumpkinseed sunfish and the age structure of pumpkinseed populations in each of the study lakes. These surveys, which were conducted each year from 1992 to 1994, gave a basis for estimating rates of adult survival for each age in each lake's population. The lowest rate, or probability, of adult survival was 0.19, while the highest was 0.65. In other words, the proportion of adults surviving from one year to the next ranged from approximately 1 adult out of 5 (0.19) to about 2 adults out of 3 (0.65). This variation among lakes produced striking differences in the pattern of survival (fig. 9.22).

Juvenile survival was estimated by counting the number of pumpkinseed nests and then collecting all the larval fish in a sample of nests. The number of nests in the study lakes varied from 60 to over 1,000 and the number of larval fish produced ranged from approximately 100,000 to over a million. Using their estimate of the number of larvae produced and the number of three-year-old fish in the same lake, Bertschy and Fox estimated juvenile survival. Juvenile survival to adulthood in the study lakes ranged from 0.004, or about 4 out of 1,000 larvae, to 0.016, or about 16 out of 1,000 larvae. Because they were interested in the relative rates of adult and juvenile survival,

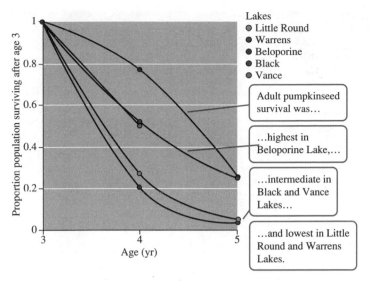

Figure 9.22 Pumpkinseed sunfish survival after age three years in five small lakes (data from Bertschy and Fox 1999).

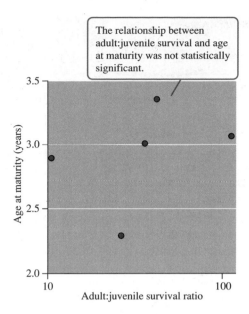

Figure 9.24 Adult:juvenile survival ratios and age at reproductive maturity in populations of pumpkinseed sunfish (data from Bertschy and Fox 1999).

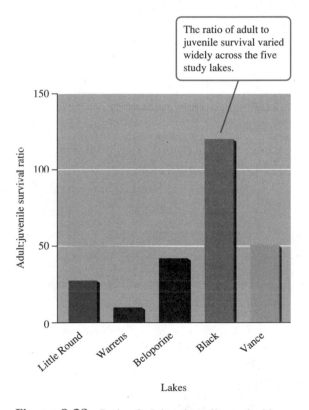

Figure 9.23 Ratio of adult to juvenile survival in pumpkinseed sunfish populations in five small lakes (data from Bertschy and Fox 1999).

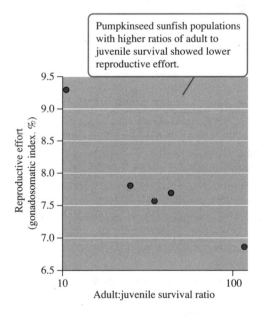

Figure 9.25 Adult:juvenile survival ratio and reproductive effort as measured by the gonadosomatic index or GSI (data from Bertschy and Fox 1999).

Bertschy and Fox represented survival in their study lakes as the ratio of adult to juvenile survival probabilities. Figure 9.23 shows that this ratio ranged widely among study lakes from a low of 10.6 to 116.8, a tenfold difference among lakes.

Bertschy and Fox found significant variation in most life history characteristics across their study lakes. Pumpkinseed sunfish matured at ages ranging from 2.4 to 3.4 years in the different study lakes and they showed reproductive investments (gonadosomatic indexes or GSI) ranging from 6.9% to 9.3%. The relationship between survival rate and age at maturity found by Bertschy and Fox suggests that populations with higher adult survival mature at a greater age (fig. 9.24). The correlation between survival rate and age at maturity was not high enough to be statistically significant; however, the relationship between adult survival and reproductive effort was very clear and highly significant (fig. 9.25). The patterns of life history variation across the pumpkinseed populations studied by Bertschy and Fox support the theory that where adult survival is lower relative to juvenile survival, natural selection will favour allocating greater resources to reproduction.

Ecology In Action

How Life-Histories Influence Extinction Risk

The extinction of species is an issue of global concern. Ecologists are on the forefront of research into understanding the causes and consequences of extinction. The immediate causes of species loss are, in a broad sense, well known and often referred to as the "evil quartet": over-exploitation, habitat loss, competition with introduced species, and trophic dependency leading to cascading chains of extinction (Diamond 1984). All of these topics will be discussed in later chapters of the book. Although we often hear about a global biodiversity crisis, not all species are equally likely to go extinct, even when faced with the same environmental challenges (fig. 9.26). In later chapters we will discuss aspects of how human activities impact population dynamics and viability of a diversity of species. We will also discuss how the Species at Risk Act may be used to help protect some species in Canada. Here, we ask a different question: what aspects of a species' life history increase its susceptibility to extinction? There are a few motives for asking this question. On a practical level, John Reynolds (2003), of Simon Fraser University, has pointed out that the money available for conservation programs is very limited, and having some easily measurable life-history trait, or set of traits, would help managers determine which species should become priorities for recovery. On a more fundamental level, understanding functional linkages between life history and population growth and extinction is a worthy scientific goal, one likely to result in a variety of unintended benefits.

Andy Purvis of Imperial College and his colleagues have been leaders in research to understand how the biology of different species interacts with human-mediated changes to cause increased extinction risks. In a recent paper (Purvis et al. 2000), they summarize and test eight hypotheses gathered from the literature. Here we will focus on one of these. As we have seen throughout this chapter, there are a variety of trade-offs associated with reproduction, and many life-history traits appear to be able to be classified into groupings, representing different strategies (this will be explored more fully later in the chapter). One of the initial hypotheses about extinction risk has been that species that have "slow" life histories will be more at risk than those with "fast" life histories. What do we mean by a slow life history? We mean species that have slow growth rates, reach sexual maturity only late in life, breed infrequently and in small numbers, and similar life-history traits. Purvis and colleagues tested this hypothesis by collecting these life-history traits from previously published studies for Carnivora and Primate mammals. Measures of extinction risk were also collected from the literature, specifically the International Union for the Conservation of Nature and Natural Resources Red List.

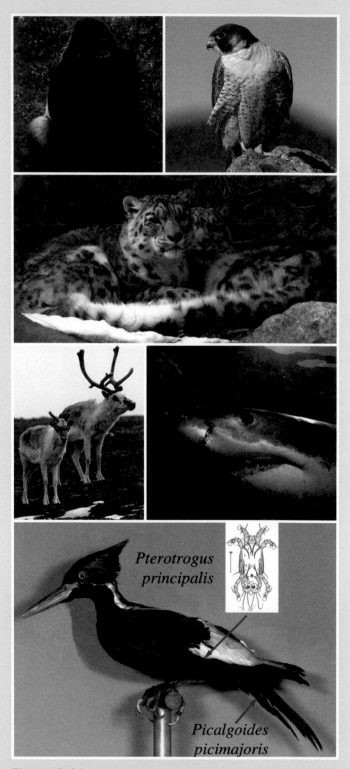

Pterotrogus principalis

Picalgoides picimajoris

Figure 9.26 These species are all at risk of extinction. Species with "slow" life-histories, and species that live in or on endangered species are at increased risk of extinction.

For the carnivores, extinction risk increased with gestation length and age of sexual maturity, supporting the "slow life history" hypothesis. However, these traits were not related to extinction risk in primates. For primates, it was increased size rather than species-specific life-history traits that influenced extinction risk. Purvis and colleagues suggest that primates actually do not exhibit substantial variation in life history independent of size, and thus they question the meaning of that particular result. Purvis and colleagues also present substantial data to show that it is not just size and life history that influence extinction risk, but that other factors such as the geographical range of a species (larger reduces risk), trophic level (higher increases risk), and population density (larger decreases risk) are also important. You may recognize that many of these factors are likely correlated, for example high rates of reproduction likely lead to higher population densities, and due to energetic trade-offs, small body size. Their study highlights that biology matters when it comes to extinction. Although the results of their study may not seem particularly surprising, never before have these ideas been so rigorously tested and explored. Having a degree of certainty in the validity of scientific ideas and conclusions is critical to the ability of ecologists to provide useful information and guidance to policy makers.

The importance of recognizing the inherent interspecific variation in extinction risk can be seen in another paper by Purvis and colleagues (Cardillo et al, 2004). In this study, they build upon the model they developed to predict extinction risk for Carnivora in the previously described study (Purvis et al. 2000). However, this time they also included predicted changes to the population densities of people in Africa as a case study. To do this, they first added the variable of current human population densities to their model, allowing them to include both biological (e.g., life history, geographic range, etc.) and a surrogate for human mediated disturbance (population density) into a single model. When they did this, they found that biological factors are better predictors of extinction risk than is human population density alone. This finding is most pronounced in areas of high population density, where the biology of the species explains over 80% of the variation in extinction risks! In other words, to predict which species are at risk for extinction in areas of high human densities, you need to understand the basic biology of the local species.

In a nice addition to their study, they then changed their measures of population density to demographic projections extending to 2030. By doing this, they were able to predict which species will become at risk, or will increase their level of risk. Such a predictive approach to conservation biology has great potential to help managers respond to conservation needs before they happen, rather than continue in a state of repair. The work by Purvis and his colleagues is a great example of how ecology can be used to address real problems of local and global concern.

Although the public generally sees images of these large carnivores and primates in the media, they represent just a small fraction of the species on the planet, and only a segment of the species at risk of extinction. Many species are dependent upon others for survival, such as butterfly larvae that feed on only a few plant species, and host-specific parasites (chapters 14 and 15). What happens to the butterfly or parasite if its only host species goes extinct? Unless it is immediately able to expand the breadth of its niche to include other hosts, it, too, is doomed. As a result, species that have very specific niche requirements, dependent upon other species, are exposed to increased extinction risk. An international team of researchers, including Heather Proctor of the University of Alberta, decided to determine whether the potential for these "species coextinctions" were of sufficient magnitude to warrant concern (Koh et al. 2004). To address this question, the research team developed a model that calculated the probability of a species going extinct if its host went extinct. To make these numbers meaningful, they compiled information from the literature describing the host-specificity of these "affiliate" species. The model then weighted both the probability of the host going extinct (as some species are more at risk than others), and whether the affiliate had multiple possible hosts. In their database, they had records of nearly 400 host extinctions of plants, fish, birds, and mammals. Their model estimates that around 200 extinctions of affiliate species such as beetles, mites, butterflies, and monogeneans (flukes) were unreported. For the nearly 8,500 host species that are currently endangered, their model estimates that there are another 6,000 affiliate species at risk! In short, their research clearly indicates that aspects of a species' niche, in this case host-specificity, can contribute to a species' risk of extinction.

Although this talk of extinction is often disheartening, particularly when we realize how many species are overlooked by scientists and the media, it is also very important. Extinctions are real, and are happening at an extremely high rate. If we wish to reduce these rates, at least in cases where humans are contributing to the risk, it is essential that we understand how human disturbances and species' biology interact. Work by ecologists studying life-histories and niches can augment governmental protections and recovery programs, providing our society with the greatest hope of reducing the permanent ecological and evolutionary changes associated with extinctions.

Genetic Control of Life History

Variation in life history traits, such as the relationship between adult and juvenile survival, can be due to differences in both the ecological and the environmental conditions faced by individuals and populations. However, this environmentally induced variation can only influence evolution if there is also a genetic, and heritable, component to life-history variation among individuals within and between populations. David Innes, of Memorial University of Newfoundland, has published extensively on one of the most fundamental aspects of life history: sexual versus asexual reproduction. As you will see, his work has clearly shown that aspects of life history can be influenced by both environmental and genetic factors.

Daphnia pulex (fig. 9.27) is a small crustacean commonly referred to as a water flea (Crustacea: Cladocera) that is common in lakes, ponds, and temporary water bodies throughout the world. The reproductive cycle of *D. pulex* is a bit more complicated than what we find in most vertebrate species. There exist two forms of *D. pulex*; the first is similar to most species of *Daphnia* and reproduces by *cyclical* **parthenogenesis**. In this form of reproduction, individuals create *diploid* eggs through *mitosis*, rather than producing *haploid* eggs through *meiosis*, as is the norm for vertebrates. The diploid eggs develop into offspring, resulting in genetic clones of the mother water flea. Since these offspring are clones of their mom, they must be all be females, right? No. *D. pulex* has environmental sex determination (chapter 10), with the eggs developing into females at low population density and males at high population density. As a result, a single female is able to produce genetically identical males and females! Occasionally, these females will undergo meiosis, producing haploid diapausing (resting) eggs that require fertilization by the males to develop. However, a second form of *D. pulex* also exists in which individuals reproduce only through *obligate* parthenogenesis. These clones produce diapausing eggs through mitosis, not meiosis, and thus have no haploid aspect to their life cycle. In a very elegant study, David Innes and his former postdoctoral supervisor, Paul Hebert (now of the University of Guelph but formerly of the University of Windsor), exploited this variation in life history to explore the genetic basis of obligate parthenogenesis in *D. pulex* (Innes and Hebert 1988).

Innes and Hebert grew cultures of several clones collected from natural populations throughout Ontario, Illinois, Michigan, and Iowa. They then took males from an obligately parthenogenetic clone and mated them with females from a cyclically parthenogenetic clone. In total, they conducted 19 such crosses, resulting in 102 hybrid clones. Innes and Hebert collected the diapausing eggs that were produced by 10 of these hybrids. Why the focus on the diapausing eggs? If you recall, the diapausing eggs are produced through mitosis for the clones that use obligate parthenogenesis and meiosis for the clones that use cyclical parthenogenesis. By looking at the variation in allozymes (chapter 4) of the individuals that emerged from the diapausing eggs, Innes and Hebert were able to infer the mode of reproduction. Those eggs derived from mitosis would have uniform allozyme patterns indicating obligate parthenogenesis, while those derived from meiosis would show

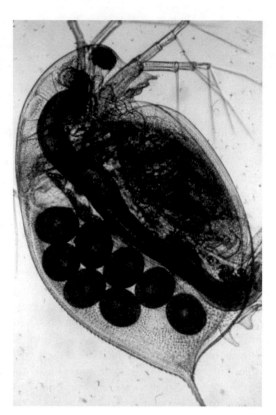

Figure 9.27   Different forms of *Daphnia pulex* can be either sexually reproducing or obligately parthenogenetic. This female is developing a brood of parthenogenetic eggs.

variation, indicating cyclical parthenogenesis. What they found was quite striking: four hybrids reproduced by obligate parthenogenesis like their father, while six hybrids reproduced by cyclical parthenogenesis like their mother! In other words, although all of the mothers reproduced by cyclical parthenogenesis at the start of the experiment, mating with the males derived from obligate parthenogenesis causes a switch in reproductive behaviour in approximately ½ of the hybrids!

Clearly the males contained genes that suppressed meiosis, indicating this extremely fundamental aspect of life history may be under relatively simple genetic control, at least in this species. A related study with the cyclical parthenogens explored variation in the ability to produce males under high levels of crowding (Innes and Dunbrack 1993). Over ⅓ of the clones they tested lacked this ability to produce males. When male-producing lines were mated with themselves, nearly all offspring could also produce males. However, when male-producing lines were mated with non-male producing females, over 50% of the outcrossed progeny were unable to produce males. Once again, these results are strongly suggestive of basic genetic control of this aspect of reproduction in *D. pulex*.

There are numerous examples from a diverse array of other plant, bacterial, and animal species, also showing genetic influences on life history. Because of the heritability of life-history traits, natural selection can result in evolution, altering the basic parameters of how a species lives, grows, and reproduces. Ecology and evolution are linked, and this is rarely made more clear than in the study of life-histories.

As we explored the relationship between offspring size and number and the influence of mortality on the timing of maturation and reproductive effort, we've accumulated a large body of information on life histories. We have also seen that aspects of life history can be under genetic control and thus subject to selection and evolution. Let's step back now and try to organize that information to make it easier to think about life history variation in nature. Several researchers have proposed classification systems for life histories.

Concept 9.2 Review

1. Why did Westoby, Leishman, and Lord (1996) included five floras on three continents in their study?
2. What is a main difference between the study by Bertschy and Fox (1999) and that of Gunderson (1997)?
3. What are the evolutionary implications of life-history traits that are, or are not, influenced by an individual's genotype?

9.3   Life History Classification

The great diversity of life histories may be classified on the basis of a few population characteristics.   While classification systems never capture the full diversity of nature, they make working with the often bewildering variety of nature much easier. It is important to bear in mind when using classification systems, however, that they are an abstraction from nature and that most species fall somewhere in between the extreme types.

r and K Selection

One of the earliest attempts to organize information on the great variety of life histories that occur among species was under the heading of r and K selection (MacArthur and Wilson 1967). The terms r and K selection refer to parameters of population growth models that will be described in chapter 12. The term r selection refers to a measure of population growth rate, and was defined by Robert MacArthur and E. O. Wilson as selection favouring a higher population growth rate. MacArthur and Wilson suggested that r selection would be strongest in species often colonizing new or disturbed habitats. Therefore, high levels of disturbance would lead to ongoing r selection. "r" represents the potential reproductive rate for a population and will be discussed further in chapter 12. MacArthur and Wilson contrasted r selected species with those subject mainly to K selection. The term K selection refers to a measure of the maximum sustainable size of a population. MacArthur and Wilson proposed that K selection favours more efficient utilization of resources such as food and nutrients. They envisioned that K selection would be most prominent in those situations where species populations are near carrying capacity much of the time.

Eric Pianka (1970, 1972) developed the concept of r and K selection further in two important papers. Pianka pointed

Characteristics favoured by *r* versus K selection		
Population attribute	***r* selection**	**K selection**
Potential of population growth rate, *r*	High	Low
Competitive ability	Not strongly favoured	Highly favoured
Development	Rapid	Slow
Reproduction	Early	Late
Body size	Small	Large
Reproduction	Single, semelparity	Repeated, iteroparity
Offspring	Many, small	Few, large

Source: After Pianka 1970.

Figure 9.28

out that r selection and K selection are the endpoints on a continuous distribution and that most organisms are subject to forms of selection somewhere in between these extremes. In addition, he correlated r and K selection with attributes of the environment and of populations. He also listed the population characteristics that each form of selection favours. Following MacArthur and Wilson, Pianka predicted that while r selection should be characteristic of variable or unpredictable environments, fairly constant or predictable environments should create conditions for K selection. Figure 9.28 summarizes Pianka's proposed contrast in population characteristics favoured by r versus K selection.

Pianka's detailed analysis clarified the sharp contrast between the two selective extremes represented by r and K selection by revealing biological details. The most fundamental contrasts are of course between potential growth rates, r_{max}, which should be highest in r selected species, and competitive ability, which should be highest among K selected species. In addition, according to Pianka, development should be rapid under r selection and relatively slow under K selection. Meanwhile, early reproduction and smaller body size will be favoured by r selection, while K selection favours later reproduction and larger body size. Pianka predicted that reproduction under r selection will tend toward a single reproductive event in which many small offspring are produced. This type of reproduction, which is called **semelparity,** occurs in organisms such as annual weeds and salmon. In contrast, K selection should favour repeated reproduction, or **iteroparity,** of fewer larger offspring. Iteroparity, which spaces out reproduction over several reproductive periods during an organism's lifetime, is the type of reproduction seen in most perennial plants and most vertebrate animals. Pianka's contrast puts a name on and fleshes out the comparison we developed in the Ecology In Action example in this chapter, where "small and fast organisms," analogous to r selected species, were less likely to be at an extinction risk than ones that were "large and slow," analogous to K selected species (fig. 9.29).

Figure 9.29   The deer mouse and the African elephant represent extremes among mammals of *r* versus K selection.

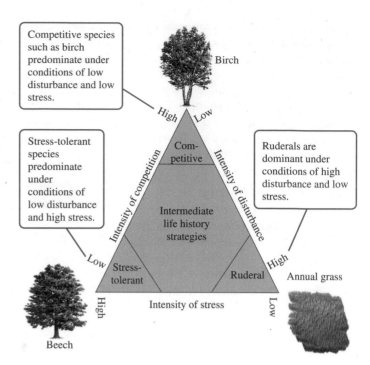

Figure 9.30   Grime's classification of plant life history strategies (after Grime 1979).

The ideas of *r* and K selection helped greatly as ecologists and evolutionary biologists attempted to think more systematically about life-history variation and its evolution. However, ecologists who found that the dichotomy of *r* versus K did not include a great deal of known variation in life histories have proposed alternative classifications.

Plant Life Histories

r and K strategies are a useful shorthand for talking about groups of correlated life-history traits for all taxa. However, some organisms such as plants may be better described using a different shorthand. J. P. Grime (1977, 1979) proposed that variation in environmental conditions has led to the development of distinctive strategies or life histories among plants. The two variables that he selected as most important in exerting selective pressure on plants were the intensity of disturbance and abiotic stress. Grime also argues that competition can exert strong pressures on plants, and that competition should be relatively more important when stress and disturbances are low. Grime contrasted four extreme environmental types, which he characterized by combinations of disturbance intensity and stress intensity. Four environmental extremes envisioned by Grime were: (1) low disturbance–low stress, (2) low disturbance–high stress, (3) high disturbance–low stress, and (4)

high disturbance–high stress. Drawing on his extensive knowledge of plant biology, Grime suggested that plants occupy three of his theoretical environments but that there is no viable strategy among plants for the fourth environmental combination, high disturbance–high stress.

Grime next described plant strategies, or life histories, that match the requirements of the remaining three environments. His strategies were ruderal, stress-tolerant, and competitive (fig. 9.30). **Ruderals** are plants that live in highly disturbed habitats and that may depend on disturbance to persist in the face of potential competition from other plants. Grime summarized several characteristics of ruderals that allow them to persist in habitats experiencing frequent and intense **disturbance,** which he defined as any mechanisms or processes that limit plants by destroying plant biomass. One of the characteristics of ruderals is their capacity to grow rapidly and produce seeds during relatively short periods between successive disturbances. This capacity alone would favour persistence of ruderals in the face of frequent disturbance. In addition, however, ruderals also invest a large proportion of their biomass in reproduction, producing large numbers of seeds that are capable of dispersing to new habitats made available by disturbance. The term ruderal is sometimes used synonymously with the term "weed." Animals that are associated with disturbance, have high reproductive rates, and are good colonists, are also sometimes referred to as ruderals.

Grime (1977) began his discussion of the second type of plant life history, stress-tolerant, with a definition of **stress** as ". . . external constraints which limit the rate of dry matter production of all or part of the vegetation." In other words, stress is induced by environmental conditions that limit the growth of all or part of the vegetation. What environmental conditions might create such constraints? Our discussions in chapters 5, 6, and 7, where we considered temperature, water, and energy and nutrient relations, provide several suggestions. Stress is the result of extreme temperatures, high or low, extreme hydrologic conditions, too little or too much water, or too much or too little light or nutrients. Because different species are adapted to different environmental conditions, the absolute levels of light, water, temperature, and so forth that constitute stress will vary from species to species. In addition, conditions that induce stress will vary from biome to biome. For instance, the amount of precipitation leading to drought stress is different in rain forest and desert, or the minimum temperatures inducing thermal stress are different in tropical forest compared to boreal forest.

The important point that Grime made, however, was that in every biome, some species are more tolerant to the environmental extremes that occur than other species. These are the species that he referred to as "stress-tolerant." Stress-tolerant plants are those that live under conditions of high stress but low disturbance. Grime proposed that, in general, stress-tolerant plants grow slowly, are evergreen, conserve fixed carbon, nutrients, and water, and are adept at exploiting temporary favourable conditions. In addition, stress-tolerant plants are often unpalatable to most herbivores. Because stress-tolerant species endure some of the most difficult conditions a particular environment has to offer, they are there to take advantage of infrequent favourable periods for growth and reproduction.

The third plant strategy proposed by Grime is a competitive life history. In Grime's classification, competitive plants occupy environments where disturbance intensity is low and the intensity of stress is also low. Under conditions of low stress and low disturbance, plants have the potential to grow well. As they do so, however, they eventually compete with each other for resources, such as light, water, nutrients, and space. Grime's model predicts that the plants living under such circumstances will be selected for strong competitive abilities.

In presenting the initial model we have emphasized the extreme strategies that represent each of the corners of "Grime's triangle." However, Grime recognized that life histories in nature will fall along a continuum of these axes, and thus the middle of the triangle represents intermediate plant strategies.

How does Grime's system of classification compare with the r and K selection contrast proposed by MacArthur and Wilson and Pianka? Grime proposed that r selection corresponds to his ruderal strategy of life history, while K selection corresponds to the stress-tolerant end of his classification. Meanwhile, he placed the competitive life history category in a position intermediate between the extremes represented by r selection and K selection. However, while attempting this reconciliation of the two classifications, Grime suggested that a linear arrangement of life histories with r selection and K selection occupying the extremes fails to capture the full variation shown by organisms. He suggested that more dimensions are needed and, of course, Grime's triangular arrangement (fig. 9.30) adds another dimension. The factors varying along the edges of Grime's triangle are intensity of disturbance, stress, and competition. Other ecologists have also recognized the need for more dimensions in representing life history diversity.

Opportunistic, Equilibrium, and Periodic Life Histories

In a review of life history patterns among fish, Kirk Winemiller and Kenneth Rose (1992) proposed a classification of life histories based on some of the aspects of population dynamics. They drew particular attention to survivorship especially among juveniles, fecundity or number of offspring produced, and generation time or age at maturity.

Winemiller and Rose start with the concept of trade-offs. Their trade-offs are among fecundity, survivorship, and age at reproductive maturity. Using variation in fish life histories as a model, Winemiller and Rose proposed that life histories should lie on a semitriangular surface as shown in figure 9.31. They called the three endpoints on their surface "opportunistic," "equilibrium," and "periodic" life histories. The opportunistic strategy, by combining low juvenile survival, low numbers of offspring, and early reproductive maturity, maximizes colonizing ability across environments that vary unpredictably in time or space. It is important to keep in mind, however, that while the absolute reproductive output of opportunistic species may be low, the percentage of their energy budget allocated to reproduction is high. Winemiller and Rose's equilibrium strategy combines high juvenile survival, low numbers of offspring, and late reproductive maturity. Finally, the periodic strategy combines low juvenile survival, high numbers of offspring, and late maturity. Among fish, periodic species tend to be large and produce numerous small offspring. By producing large numbers of offspring over a long life span, periodic species can take advantage of infrequent periods when conditions are favourable for reproduction.

It is difficult to map the exact correspondence of Winemiller and Rose's classification of life history strategies to either the r-K continuum of MacArthur and Wilson and Pianka or the triangular classification of plant life histories developed by Grime. For instance, opportunistic species share characteristics with r selected and ruderal species. However, opportunistic species differ from the typical r selected species because they tend to produce small clutches of offspring. The equilibrium strategy, which combines production of high juvenile survival, low numbers of offspring, and late reproductive maturity, approaches the characteristics of typical K selected species. Winemiller and Rose point out, however, that many fish classified as "equilibrium" are small, while typically K selected species tend toward large body size (see fig. 9.28). Periodic species are not captured by the linear r to K selection gradient. Meanwhile the periodic and equilibrium species in Winemiller and Rose's classification share some characteristics with Grime's stress-tolerant and competitive species but differ in other characteristics.

Thus far in this review of systems for life history classification, we have focused on just three of the many that have been proposed. Even with just these three, however, translation from one classification to another is difficult. What are the sources of these differences in perspective? One of the sources is that different ecologists have worked with different groups of organisms. While MacArthur and Wilson's system

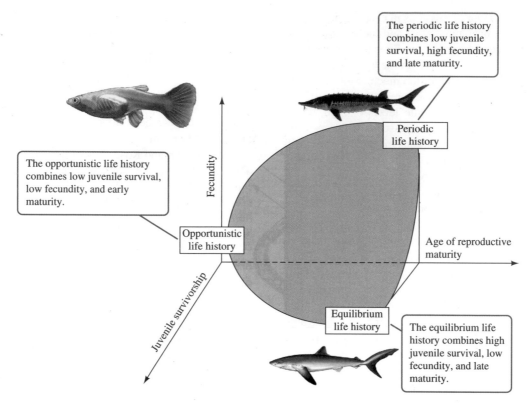

Figure 9.31   Classification of life histories based on juvenile survival, fecundity, and age at reproductive maturity (after Winemiller and Rose 1992).

was built after years of work on birds and insects, respectively, Pianka had worked mainly with lizards. Grime's classification was built on, and intended for, plants. Finally, the perspective of Winemiller and Rose was influenced substantially by their work with fish. Because these ecologists worked with such different groups of organisms, it is not surprising that their classifications of life histories do not overlay precisely.

However, it may be that the analysis by Winemiller and Rose has laid the foundation for a more general theory of life histories. By basing their classification system on some of the most basic aspects of population ecology, Winemiller and Rose (1992) established a common currency for representing and analyzing life history information for any organism. As a model for how such a translation might be done, Winemiller (1992) plotted the distributions of life history parameters of representative animal groups on their life history classification axes (fig. 9.32). By plotting life history variation among vertebrate groups on the same axes using the same variables, figure 9.32 demonstrates differences in the amount of life history variation between the groups. Notice that fish show the greatest variation and mammals the least, while birds and reptiles and amphibians include intermediate levels of variation.

Reproductive Effort, Offspring Size, and Benefit-Cost Ratios

In response to the various attempts to classify life histories, Eric Charnov (2002) developed a new approach to life history classification. His goal was to develop a classification free of the influences of size and time that would facilitate the exploration of life history variation within and among groups of closely related taxa. Why remove the influences of size and time? Our discussion of r and K selection underscored the relationship between size of organisms and timing of life history features (see fig. 9.28). The influences of size and timing are responsible for many of the obvious life history differences among species of closely related taxa, for instance, the differences among large and small mammal species, such as between a deer mouse and an African elephant (see fig. 9.29). By removing size and time effects, we may be able to more clearly detect life history differences among evolutionary lineages.

Charnov's approach was to take a few key life history features and convert them to dimensionless numbers. One of his variables was relative size of offspring. He created this dimensionless variable by dividing the mass of offspring at independence from the parent, I, by the average adult mass, m. The result, I/m, is the size of offspring expressed as a proportion of body mass. While it is clear that an elephant is larger at independence than is a mouse at the same life stage, Charnov's approach allows us to determine whether one is relatively larger than the other. A young, newly independent mouse may represent as large a proportion of its parent's mass as a young elephant. The second variable used by Charnov was a measure of the amount of a lifetime allocated to reproduction. He constructed this variable by dividing the average length (e.g., years) of a species' reproductive life, E, by the average length of time required to reach reproductive age, α. Again because Charnov's index is a ratio of numbers, E/α, with the same units, the units cancel and the ratio is dimensionless. The third

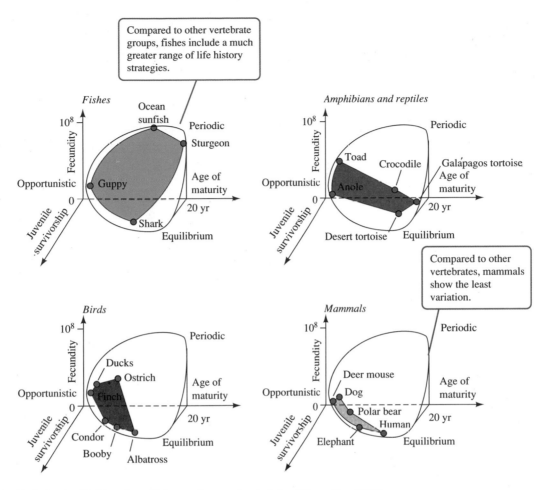

Figure 9.32   Variation in life histories within vertebrate animals (after Winemiller 1992).

measure was proportion of body adult mass allocated to reproduction per unit time, C, divided by the average adult mortality rate E^{-1}. This index C/E^{-1}, which is equivalent to C•E, scales reproductive effort, C, by mortality cost. As we have seen, higher reproductive effort, a benefit, is associated with higher rates of mortality, a cost (see fig. 9.20). Charnov's C•E index is a benefit-cost ratio without dimensions.

For his initial classification of life histories, Charnov chose three groups of well-studied organisms, mammals, fish, and altricial birds. Altricial birds are those birds, ranging from sparrows to eagles, that are born helpless and depend entirely on parental care to mature to independence. One of the striking results of using Charnov's dimensionless analysis is that while there is little variation within mammals, fish, or birds, there are substantial differences between these groups of animals. Figure 9.33 shows that I/m, E/α, and C•E are all higher among birds, intermediate among mammals, and lowest among fish. For instance, while most fish produce very tiny offspring, the average value of I/m for mammals is approximately 0.3 and for altricial birds, which raise their young to adult size, I/m = 1.

Previous classifications of life histories have revealed substantial variation within taxa, such as mammals and fish (see fig. 9.32). In contrast, Charnov's classification, by removing the influences of time and size, allows us to see the great similarities within these groups and reveals the substantial differences among them. Charnov placed values of I/m, E/α, and C•E along the edges of a cube to form what he called a "life history cube." Figure 9.34 shows the results of plotting the average values of I/m, E/α, and C•E for mammals, fish, and altricial birds with a life history cube. The striking separation of these taxa within the cube suggests that mammals, fish, and birds have life histories that are fundamentally different.

This analysis is only the beginning, however, since it raises many unanswered questions. Charnov wonders where bats will appear in his life history cube since they raise their offspring to nearly adult size. He also raises a question about precocial birds, such as pheasants and quail, whose offspring are independent at a very small size. In terms of life history, will bats be more like altricial birds, while precocial birds are more like mammals? Then there are the hundreds of thousands of vascular plants to consider.

The knowledge of species life histories revealed by the studies of life history ecologists has produced a subdiscipline of ecology rich in both theory and biological detail. In the challenges that lie ahead as we work to conserve endangered species, both theory and detailed knowledge of the life histories of individual species will be important. For instance, life history information is playing a key role in understanding the impacts of climate change in natural populations.

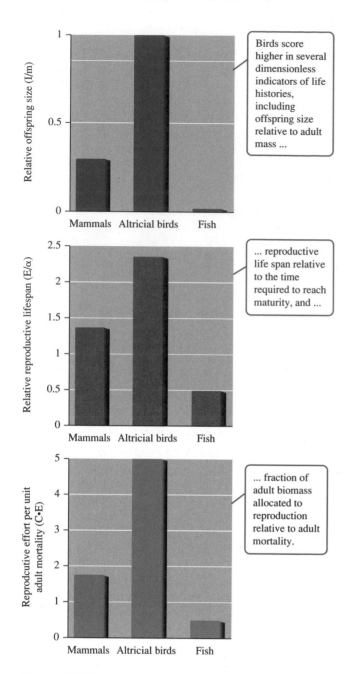

Birds score higher in several dimensionless indicators of life histories, including offspring size relative to adult mass ...

... reproductive life span relative to the time required to reach maturity, and ...

... fraction of adult biomass allocated to reproduction relative to adult mortality.

Figure 9.33   Comparison of life history features mammals, altricial birds, and fish (data from Charnov 2002).

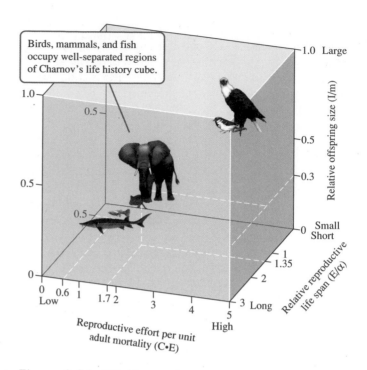

Birds, mammals, and fish occupy well-separated regions of Charnov's life history cube.

Figure 9.34   Life history cube, a classification of fish, mammals, and altricial birds based on three dimensionless indices, indicates little variation within taxa but a great deal of difference among taxa (data from Charnov 2002).

Concept 9.3 Review

1. If a concept, such as *r* and K selection, does not fully represent the richness of life history variation among species, can it still be valuable to science?
2. Where would you place the following plant species, in Grime's and in Winemiller and Rose's classifications of life histories? The plant species lives in an environment where it has access to plenty of water and nutrients but is subject to disturbance by flooding and wind. An average individual produces several million seeds per year and may live several centuries. However, ideal conditions for reproduction by the species occurs only once or twice per decade.

Ecological Tools

Using Life History Information as Indicators of Biological Effects of Climate Change

Throughout the text we have discussed a variety of aspects of climate change, and we will continue to do so in many of the remaining chapters. One of the reasons for this attention should be pretty clear to you by now: interactions with the environment influence nearly every aspect of an organism's life, and thus climate change has the potential to fundamen-

tally alter evolution, populations, and communities. Understanding the ecological consequences of climate change is one of the great challenges faced by ecologists in the twenty-first century. There is an awful lot we just don't know.

Climate change is a very vague term for a very complex topic, one which we will explore in depth in chapter 23. Climate change can include anything from altered temperature, rainfall, snowfall, humidity, and so on, with these factors changing at different rates and intensities in different places across the planet. Here we will focus on one of the more common aspects, temperature. Over the last century, the average global temperature has increased by 0.6°C, with no obvious end in sight (Houghton 2001). This change in temperature is not spread evenly across the planet; instead there can be 3°C–5°C changes in Northwestern Canada, and even slight cooling in other locations. It is difficult to understand what exactly this level of warming means for biological systems. Yes, this rate of change is melting ice caps, will likely lead to massive floods, and could even alter some fundamental aspects of global circulation. All of these things will clearly alter a variety of biological processes, not to mention cause an unprecedented level of destruction to human populations throughout the planet. But how do we actually know when climate change is of a magnitude sufficient to cause ecological change? Is this already occurring, or are we just in a phase where we can predict, but not show, how climate change can alter life on the planet? These questions are being asked by ecologists across the planet, and researchers have found that one of the clearest ways of showing evidence of a biological effect of altered temperatures is by showing changes to one particular aspect of life-histories, **phenology**.

Phenology is the study of the timing of events in an organism's life. Some examples include when leaves flush out, when offspring are born, when hibernation begins and ends, and when migrations occur. These are all examples of critical aspects of an organism's life history, and these are generally closely tuned to the environment. This link between timing and life cycle makes a good deal of sense. You could imagine strong selection against producing a new flush of leaves in the middle of winter, or for initiating a large migration just when food becomes available. This same logic has led ecologists to recognize that phenology is likely one aspect of an organism's life history most sensitive to environmental change. As a result, changes in phenology may serve as an early sign that climate change is having biological consequences. In this section, we will present a variety of examples of research into this branch of ecology, showing how researchers are able to link life-history changes to changes in local environmental temperatures. We start by presenting some general patterns.

Patterns

How do you actually establish that there is a connection between climate change and phenology? How much evidence is necessary to say that this is a global phenomenon, and not just specific to individual locations? When are the effects one observes "important"? These questions were addressed in recent papers by Carmille Parmesan and Gary Yohe (2003) and Terry Root and his colleagues (2003). In both studies, the researchers were looking to determine whether a climate fingerprint exists. In other words, are there data available across the globe that show a biological impact of climate change on natural populations?

Parmesan and Yohe suggest that finding such a fingerprint will be achieved not by focusing solely on detailed studies of individual taxa and single locations, but instead by finding consistent patterns across taxa and throughout the planet. They argue that for most any biological process, the immediate local processes will nearly always be more important than global change over the short-term. For example, even if it is getting warmer on average across the planet, an unusually cold summer can greatly alter plant and animal growth in one location. As a result, they argue that finding a climate fingerprint does not require identifying which particular species are unquestionably responding to climate change, but instead requires finding a recurring pattern across a large spatial scale.

It would be impossible for any pair of researchers to do the field work themselves to try and detect such a fingerprint at such a large spatial scale. Instead, Parmesan and Yohe (2003) conducted a meta-analysis in an attempt to find recurring results. We have discussed such analyses throughout this book, and the importance of meta-analyses in ecology is continuing to grow. The first step of their study was to compile a large database of existing studies of phenological changes. They found data for 677 species, including plants, birds, insects, amphibians, and fishes. The studies measured various phenological events such as bud-break, migration, and so forth over a period that varied from 16 to 132 years. Overall, 27% of the species showed no shift in phenology, 9% showed spring-timed events were delayed, and 62% showed evidence that spring was approaching earlier, a finding consistent with a causal effect of climate change on biology.

Terry Root and his colleagues (2003) also used a meta-analytic approach to try and find a climate fingerprint based on phenological shifts. They had different criteria for which studies would be included in the analysis than did Parmesan and Yohe, resulting in a total of 694 species and species groups in their database. They found that when averaged across all species, spring-timed events are arriving earlier by 5.1 days each decade! This date varies among taxonomic groups (fig. 9.35). Is it surprising that particularly slow-growing groups, such as trees, are showing a slower rate of change than faster growing species, such as insects? When they further divided their data,

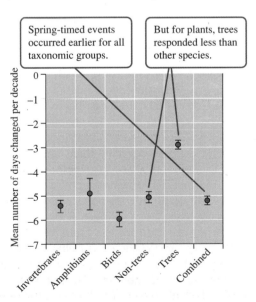

Figure 9.35   Change in the timing of spring-related events (data from Root et al. 2003).

they found that the rate of phenological change is greater near the poles than further from the poles. This, too, supports climate data showing that rates of warming increase as you approach the poles.

These two studies are critical in establishing that yes, climate change has had significant effects on important aspects of life histories for species distributed across the planet. There is little debate among ecologists about whether climate change will alter natural systems, and these studies are just some of the reasons why many view this as a question to which the answer is known. The more difficult questions that remain are in understanding how climate change will impact specific species in specific locations, and the even harder question, what can we do about it? In the remaining parts of this section we will describe a few specific examples of how climate change has influenced phenology, and we will discuss some potential evolutionary and ecological consequences. We begin in Manitoba.

Bird Migration

Since 1939, researchers at the Delta Waterfowl and Wetland Research Station, located in south-central Manitoba, have been recording the dates of the first spring sightings for 231 species of birds. Delta Marsh is among the largest of freshwater marshes in the Canadian prairies, and the research station run by the University of Manitoba is of national importance. Spencer Sealy and a group of students and colleagues at the University of Manitoba decided it was time to explore this long-term database, and find out whether there was an effect of temperature on spring arrivals (Murphy-Klassen et al. 2005).

One of the first issues they needed to contend with was the scope and quality of the data set that had been compiled by countless researchers, students, interns, and others over the previous 63 years. Of particular concern was that although 231 species had been recorded, many of these were only found in a few years, and others were only sighted recently. To ensure that they were looking at long-term trends, they decided to only focus on species found in at least 40 of the 63 years of data collection. They also only used species that were found both in the first and last 10 years of data collection, ensuring a broad span of time for analysis. These choices, along with a few others, reduced the data set down to 96 species from 14 orders—still quite a number to work with! The authors also recognized that due to astronomical reasons, the spring equinox is arriving earlier independent of climate change, and thus they standardized their dates to take this into account. The research team augmented their data set with weather data collected in Winnipeg, 90 km southeast of the study site. Although this distance between bird and weather data is not ideal, it was the nearest location for which weather data were collected for the entire 63 years. Since 1968 such data have been collected at Delta Marsh, and the researchers showed that these two sets of weather data are correlated, justifying their use of the Winnipeg data.

Species varied greatly in their arrival dates, with the Horned Lark arriving (on average) on February 24, and the Common Nighthawk not arriving until May 19. Over the 63 years, mean temperatures for February—May increased. The greatest changes were seen for February, which increased 3.8°C and March, which increased 3.1°C, compared to 0.6°C and 1.4°C for April and May respectively. Twenty-seven of the 96 species showed altered arrivals, with 25 arriving earlier and 2 later. This, too, supports the idea of a climate fingerprint. It is important to note that of the 69 species that did not show a *statistically significant* shift in arrival, 50 of them had a trend towards earlier arrival!

Supporting the idea that these shifts are due to warming is the strong relationship the researchers found between arrival date and the actual temperature of the month which the bird arrived (fig. 9.36). In fact, they found a trend for such a relationship for 84 of their 96 species, strongly supporting the idea that spring arrival is influenced by local climatic conditions.

This study by the research team at the University of Manitoba clearly shows how both current temperatures and general background changes can impact phenology. Across 63 years, there was an increase in temperature, associated with an overall earlier arrival of spring migrants. However, within that time period there were warm and cold years, and the actual date of arrival was highly variable. Overall, birds come to Delta Marsh when it warms up, and if the average temperature continues to increase, we will see birds even earlier in the future. That is, of course dependent upon the assumptions that there are not opposite pressures in the wintering range of these species, that their prey species arrive earlier as well, and that their timing of breeding also accelerates. In other words, although at first glance it may appear that seeing birds a bit earlier is a nice thing (who doesn't like to see birds?), it is important to remember that all species are connected to other species through a network of ecological interactions. All cylinders need to be firing in synch for an organism to meet its niche requirements, and as climate changes, the certainty of this synchronization for some species is less clear. In the last example we will discuss how climate change has influenced one other fundamental aspect of life-histories, reproduction.

Reproduction

The tufted puffin, *Fratercula cirrhata* (fig. 9.37), breeds only on cliffs and islands of the North Pacific. They are found as far south as California, though the only large breeding colony south of Alaska is on Triangle Island off the coast of British Columbia. This breeding colony is the largest in Canada, and several colony-wide reproductive failures have been documented. A team of researchers from Simon Fraser University, University of British Columbia, University of Alberta, and the Canadian Wildlife Service decided to test whether climate change was in part responsible for these reproductive failures of this emblematic species of the North.

The researchers recognized that the factor of potentially greatest importance to the birds wasn't temperature on the island, but instead, sea-surface temperature (SST) in the area. Why? Puffins are near the top of the food chain, feeding upon fish which themselves feed upon phyto- and zooplankton. Increased SST can influence the growth of these small planktonic species, which the researchers reasoned could have cas-

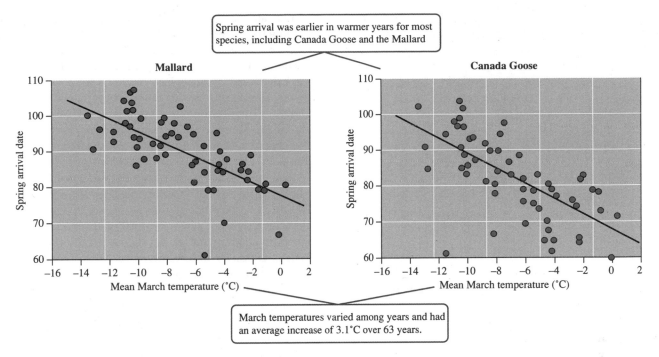

Figure 9.36   Arrival dates of migratory birds is related to temperature at Delta Marsh in Manitoba (data from Murphy-Klassen et al. 2005).

Figure 9.37   A tufted puffin, *Fratercula cirrhata*, on Triangle Island of the Coast of British Columbia.

cading effects on the puffins. To test whether SST was related to breeding success, the authors dug into a 66-year database of SST near the island, and a 28-year database of breeding and fledging success on the island. Since 1940, there has been substantial variation in SST during puffin breeding season (fig. 9.38), with an overall increase of 0.9°C over 66 years. You can notice from figure 9.38 that there was a steady increase in SST from about 1975–1998. From 1999–2002, there was substantial cooling. During the period of warming (1975–1998), there was a significant relationship between SST and the hatch date of chicks (fig. 9.38). However, when the dates from the cooling period were included, there was no overall relationship between SST and hatch date! The research team also found that SST was related to nestling growth rates and overall fledging success. Both of these factors peaked at intermediate levels of breeding-season SST.

Clearly the picture on puffins is not as clear as in the prior examples, but this complexity is likely what we will find for many other species in natural areas. It appears that within a single year, SST impacts the likelihood of fledging success and the growth rates of the young birds. That this relationship peaks at intermediate values is consistent with what we know about physiological ecology, where most processes have an optimum temperature, or range of temperatures. In this case, the researchers believe it is not the birds specifically that are responding to temperature, but instead they are responding to fish which are responding to plankton. More difficult to understand is the relationship between fledging date and SST, and why those "cool" years don't follow the longer pattern. The researchers believe that the birds have some capacity to manipulate when they breed, but that there is a lag in this response. If you look closely at figure 9.38, you will notice that the hatch dates in 2002 fall right onto the longer-term trend. The researchers suggest it may have taken the birds several years to respond to the large temperature drop that occurred in 1999. They point out that although it appears that temperature is playing a role in the breeding success, and failure, of this species, there remain many unanswered questions.

The issue of lags in response is important, and it suggests that some phenological shifts are less likely to change rapidly than others. So far, most of the changes we have discussed regarding phenology and climate change have appeared to be behavioural and physiological changes. Can climate change cause evolutionary changes in populations, which then influence their life history? Or, does climate change happen at a speed much greater than natural selection, meaning that only those species that are phenotypically plastic are able to cope with the changing environment? A team of researchers from

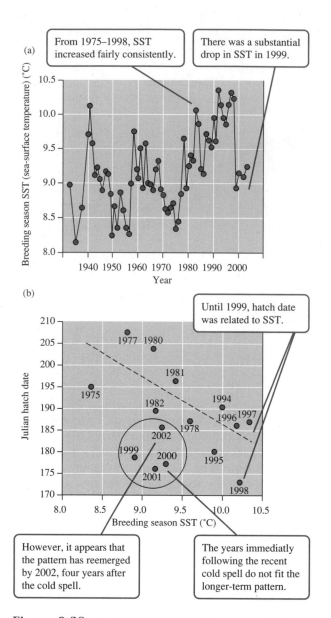

(a) *From 1975–1998, SST increased fairly consistently.*

There was a substantial drop in SST in 1999.

(b) *Until 1999, hatch date was related to SST.*

However, it appears that the pattern has reemerged by 2002, four years after the cold spell.

The years immediately following the recent cold spell do not fit the longer-term pattern.

Figure 9.38 (*a*) Breeding-season SST varied off Triangle Island; (*b*) for much of the record, breeding-season SST was correlated with the hatch date of puffin chicks.

McGill University, University of Alberta, and the Université du Québec à Rimouski decided to test these questions (Réale et al. 2003; Berteaux et al. 2004).

The North American red squirrel (*Tamiasciurus hudsonicus*), is found in much of the forested areas of North America. The research team decided to focus on one phenological measure, the parturition date (timing of birth). Prior work indicated that parturition dates are in part heritable, with an $h^2 = 0.16$ (chapter 4). Additionally, parturition dates generally coincide with food abundance and shifts in spring weather. These factors make it a good candidate for the study of the evolutionary consequences of climate change. The focal population they used was located near Kluane Lake, in the Yukon. The entire population has been studied for years, with all individuals

tagged and reproductive activity monitored from 1989–2001. Because the researchers had tracked the maternity of all squirrels, they were able to estimate how much of the observed phenotype (parturition dates) was heritable, and how much was phenotypic plasticity (see chapter 4 for a review of these terms). During this period, spring temperatures increased by nearly 2°C, and the number of spruce cones available for feeding by the squirrels has increased by 35%. Parturition dates also changed, becoming earlier by two weeks in just ten years (fig. 9.39). Through their understanding of the maternity of the squirrels in their population, they were able to show that nearly 15% of the shift in parturition dates was due to selection on this trait. The rest of the variation was due to phenotypic plasticity and other unidentified factors. This study is important in showing that yes, natural selection can result in phenological shifts of critical life-history parameters over very short periods of time. In other words, although most species have some phenotypic plasticity to climate, prolonged climate change is likely to cause evolutionary shifts in natural populations. In fact, as the researchers have shown, for some species, it already has.

As you can see from the studies we have presented here, there is substantial evidence that climate change is impacting natural populations in biologically significant ways. Shifts in phenology are being used as a climatic fingerprint, providing some of the first biological evidence that change not only might occur, but has in fact already occurred. As ecologists continue to develop the methods needed to detect the importance of climate change, it is certain we will learn much more about how biology and the abiotic environment interact to influence life-histories and niches. Only through continued research will society be able to mitigate some of the negative consequences of these changes, helping protect species that otherwise may be in peril due to human activities.

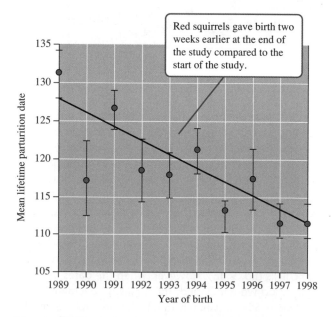

Red squirrels gave birth two weeks earlier at the end of the study compared to the start of the study.

Figure 9.39 Parturition dates became earlier during the course of the study for red squirrel. Source: Data from Reale et al. 2003.

Summary

A niche represents the sets of conditions in which a species could survive. Life history consists of the adaptations of an organism that influence aspects of their biology such as the number of offspring it produces, its survival, and its size and age at reproductive maturity. This chapter presents concept discussions bearing on some of the central concepts of niches and life history.

The fundamental niche reflects the environmental requirements of a species, while the realized niche also includes interactions with other species. The niche concept was developed early in the history of ecology and has had a prominent place ever since. Hutchinson developed the concepts of the *fundamental niche*, the physical conditions under which a species might live in the absence of other species, and the *realized niche*, the more restricted conditions under which a species actually lives as the result of interactions with other species. While a species' niche is theoretically defined by a very large number of biotic and abiotic factors, Hutchinson's *n*-dimensional hypervolume, the most important attributes of the niche of most species, can often be summarized by a few variables. For instance, the niches of Galápagos finches are largely determined by their feeding requirements, while the niche of a salt marsh grass can be defined by tidal levels.

Because all organisms have access to limited energy and other resources there are fundamental trade-offs in how these can be allocated between survival, offspring number, and offspring size. Turner and Trexler found that larger darter species produce larger numbers of eggs. Their results also support the generalization that there is a trade-off between offspring size and number. On average, darters that produce larger eggs produce few eggs. They found a strong positive relationship between gene flow among darter populations and the number of eggs produced by females and a negative relationship between egg size and gene flow. Plant ecologists have also found a negative relationship between sizes of seeds produced by plants and the number of seeds they produce. Westoby, Leishman, and Lord found that plants of different growth form and different seed dispersal mechanisms tend to produce seeds of different sizes. Larger seeds, on average, produce larger seedlings that have a higher probability of successfully recruiting, particularly in the face of environmental challenges such as shade and competition.

Where adult survival is lower, organisms begin reproducing at an earlier age and invest a greater proportion of their energy budget into reproduction. Where adult survival is higher, organisms defer reproduction to a later age and allocate a smaller proportion of their resources to reproduction. Shine and Charnov found that as survival of adult lizards and snakes increases, their age at maturity also increases. Gunderson found analogous patterns among fish. In addition, fish with higher rates of mortality allocate a greater proportion of their biomass to reproduction. In other words, they show higher reproductive effort. These generalizations are supported by comparisons both between and within species. For instance, pumpkinseed sunfish allocate greater energy, or biomass, to reproductive effort where adult pumpkinseed survival is lower. Many life-history traits, such as sexual reproduction in *Daphnia pulex* can be inherited traits subject to evolutionary pressures.

The great diversity of life histories observed in nature can be classified on the basis of a few common characteristics. One of the earliest attempts to organize information on the great variety of life histories that occur among species was under the heading of *r* selection and K selection. *r* selection refers to the per capita rate of increase, *r*, and is thought to favour higher population growth rate. *r* selection is predicted to be strongest in disturbed habitats. K selection refers to the carrying capacity in the logistic growth equation and is envisioned as a form of natural selection favouring more efficient utilization of resources such as food and nutrients. Grime described plant strategies, or life histories, that match the requirements of three environments: (1) low disturbance–low stress, (2) low disturbance–high stress, (3) high disturbance–low stress. His plant strategies matching these environmental conditions were competitive, stress-tolerant, and ruderal. Based on life history patterns among fish, Kirk Winemiller and Kenneth Rose proposed a classification of life histories based on survivorship especially among juveniles, fecundity or number of offspring produced, and generation time or age at maturity. By basing their classification system on some of the most basic aspects of population ecology, Winemiller and Rose established a common currency for representing and analyzing life history information for any organism.

Eric Charnov developed a new approach to life history classification free of the influences of size and time that facilitates the exploration of life history variation within and among groups of closely related taxa. Charnov's classification, based on relative offspring size, I/m, relative reproductive life span, E/α, and reproductive effort per unit adult mortality, C•E, suggests that mammals, fish, and altricial birds have life histories that are substantially different.

Life history information is being used to find evidence that climate change is having effects on natural populations. The search for a climate fingerprint has centred around shifts in phenology, the timing of life events. There is substantial evidence that spring events, such as bud break and mating, are occurring earlier in areas of increased temperature. These changes occur in a diversity of taxa and are the result of phenotypic plasticity, behavioural responses, and natural selection.

Review Questions

1. Researchers have characterized the niches of Galápagos finches by beak size (which correlates with diet) and the niches of salt marsh grasses by position in the intertidal zone. How would you characterize the niches of sympatric canid species such as red fox, coyote, and wolf in North America? What characteristics or environmental features do you think would be useful for representing the niches of arctic plants?

2. The discussion of seed size and number focused mainly on the advantages associated with large seeds. However, research by Westoby, Leishman, and Lord has revealed that the plants from widely separated geographic regions produce a wide variety of seed sizes. If this variation is to be maintained, what are some of the advantages associated with producing small seeds?

3. Under what conditions should natural selection favour production of many small offspring versus the production of a few well provisioned offspring?

4. The studies by Shine and Charnov (1992) and Gunderson (1997) addressed important questions of concern to life history ecologists and their work provided robust answers to those questions. However, the methods they employed differed substantially from those used in most of the studies discussed in this and other chapters. The chief difference is that both relied heavily on data on life histories published previously by other authors. What was it about the nature of the problems addressed by these authors that constrained them to use this approach? In what types of studies would it be most appropriate to perform a synthesis of previously published information?

5. Much of our discussion of life history variation involved variation among species within groups as broadly defined as "fishes," "plants," or "reptiles." However, the work of Bertschy and Fox revealed significant variation in life history within species. In general, what should be the relative amount of variation within a species compared to that among many species? Develop your discussion using relative amounts of genetic variation upon which natural selection might act. You might review the sections discussing the evolutionary significance of genetic variation in chapter 4.

6. Using what you know about the trade-off between seed number and seed size (e.g., fig. 9.14) and patterns of variation among plants, predict the relative number of seeds produced by the various plant growth forms and dispersal strategies listed on figure 9.15.

7. Apply Winemiller's model to plants. If you were to construct a strictly quantitative classification of plant life histories using Winemiller and Rose's approach, what information would you need about the plants included in your analysis? How many plant species would you need to have an idea of how variation in their life histories compares with those of animals (e.g., as in fig. 9.32)? Try to reconcile Grime's plant classification with the scheme offered by Winemiller and Rose. Where are they similar? How are they different?

8. David Innes demonstrated that sexual vs. asexual reproduction in *Daphnia pulex* could be altered depending upon the life-history traits possessed by the parents. Pick another species or organism and a different life-history trait. Design a study that will allow you to determine whether this aspect of life history is heritable. Why does this issue of heritability matter?

9. Climate change consists of variation in many factors other than temperature. How might shifts in precipitation patterns impact phenology for the plants and animals of the prairies? How about for the wetter temperate forest?

10. Will species be able to adjust to climate changes, resulting in no altered risks of extinctions? What factors influence these abilities?

Suggested Readings

Pulliam, H.R. 2000. On the relationship between niche and distribution. *Ecology Letters* 3:349–61.

In this paper Pulliam explands the niche concept, particularly as developed by Hutchinson.

Ardia, D. R. 2005. Tree swallows trade off immune function and reproductive effort differently across their range. *Ecology* 86:2040–46.

Du, W. G., X. Ji, Y. P. Zhang, X. F. Xu, and R. Shine. 2005. Identifying sources of variation in reproductive and life history traits among five populations of a Chinese lizard (*Takydromus septentrionalis*, Lacertidae). *Biological Journal of the Linnean Society* 85:443–53.

Two detailed recent studies of life history variation and trade-offs within species.

Charnov, E. L. 2002. Reproductive effort, offspring size and benefit-cost ratios in the classification of life histories. *Evolutionary Ecology Research* 4:749–58.

Charnov, E. L., T. F. Turner, and K. O. Winemiller. 2001. Reproductive constraints and the evolution of life histories with indeterminate growth. *Proceedings of the National Academy of Sciences of the United States of America* 98:9460–64.

These two works by Eric Charnov and his colleagues provide thought-provoking, cutting-edge insights into the research of one of the leaders in the exploration of life history evolution.

Jakobsson, A. and O. Eriksson. 2000. A comparative study of seed number, seed size, seedling size and recruitment in grassland plants. *Oikos* 88:494–502.

This paper provides an entry into modern experimental research on plant life histories.

Tracy, C. R. 1999. Differences in body size among chuckwalla (*Sauromalus obesus*) populations. *Ecology* 80:259–71.

A complement to the paper by Jakobsson and Eriksson that provides insights into approaches used by animal ecologists.

POPULATION ECOLOGY

In section III we discuss the properties and dynamics of populations. Population ecology is at the interface between physiological ecology (section II), and community and landscape level processes (sections IV and V). We begin by describing their geographic distributions and species ranges (chapter 10). We next discuss dynamic aspects of populations, such as dispersal and rates of population change (chapter 11). We conclude this section with a discussion of several major factors that influence population growth, and the methods ecologists use to describe these changes (chapter 12).

Chapter 10

Distribution and Abundance of Populations and Species

Outline

he distributions and dynamics of populations vary widely among species. While some populations are small and have highly restricted distributions, other populations number in the millions of individuals and may range over vast areas of the planet. Standing on a headland in Nunavut overlooking the Arctic Ocean, a small group of students spots a breeding colony of Arctic terns, *Sterna paradisaea* (fig. 10.1*a*). The population is of mixed sexes, with both males and females defending the nest site from potential threats. These birds are particularly aggressive, as one student learned as he walked just a bit too close in an attempt to get a good picture. When winter comes in the north, this entire population will fly to feeding grounds in the south, reaching the coast of Antarctica. Each bird, even the young fledglings, makes this round trip of over 18,000 km each year. In the process, these birds see more daylight and have the longest regular migration of most any species on the planet.

While several students are watching the birds, others in the group turn around and notice a small herd of muskox, *Ovibos moschatus*, grazing on a variety of plants in a nearby river valley (fig. 10.1*b*). Even a casual observer will recognize that these animals were made to withstand cold temperatures. Most obvious is their fur coat, with numerous thick guard hairs nearly

reaching the ground. These guard hairs are water repellent and help protect the insulative properties of the finer undercoat. On a closer inspection, it appears this herd consists of only males, many of whom are actively competing for dominance within the herd. In winter, these animals do not leave the arctic. Instead, they form herds consisting of both sexes, and move to higher elevations. In these winter grounds, they find less snow, allowing them to more easily find suitable forage for grazing.

Arctic terns and muskox, as different as they may appear, lead parallel lives. As climatic conditions change, and food becomes more scarce or harder to find, the entire population moves to a new area. Although the distance travelled differs among the species, the causes of migration are similar. However, when the students look even more closely they notice that the dominant feature of the landscape, the vegetation, consists of species that don't migrate at all. They are able to find hundreds of species of clubmosses, lichens, ferns, mosses, and flowering plants within just a short distance of their base camp. Even more dramatic, although the colony of terns appeared large with tens of thousands of birds present, that is just a pittance compared to the millions of individual plants that are likely present around the students on the tundra.

With these examples, we begin to consider the ecology of populations. Ecologists usually define a **population** as a group of potentially interbreeding individuals of a single species inhabiting a specific area. A population of plants or animals might occupy a mountaintop, a river basin, a coastal marsh, or an island, all areas defined by natural boundaries. Just as often, the populations studied by biologists occupy artificially defined areas such as a particular country, county, or park. The areas inhabited by populations range in size from the few cubic centimeters occupied by the bacteria in a rotting apple to the millions of square kilometers occupied by a population of migratory terns. A population studied by ecologists may consist of a highly localized group of individuals representing a fraction of the total population of a species, or it may consist of all the individuals of a species across its entire range.

Many attributes of populations are determined by interactions between the physiological ecology of a species and the biotic and abiotic conditions that individuals in population encounter. Because of this, population ecology serves as a bridge between physiological and community ecology, topics discussed in other sections of this book. Ecologists study populations for a number of reasons. First, like all levels of ecological organization, detailed understanding of natural populations can provide insight into the general processes that drive ecological interactions. However, population-level interactions serve as the foundation for many resource-based economies, and thus there are often strong societal pressures to understand population dynamics. Just hearing the words "cod fishery," "pine beetle," or "forest tent caterpillar" sends shudders down the spines of many Canadians. At the core of the economic crises involving these species have been issues related to population ecology. Population ecologists can provide valuable insight into the understanding and possible control of numerous weed, insect, and disease-causing species. Population ecology is also at the centre of many studies of species-at-risk, with

(a)

(b)

Figure 10.1 (*a*) During their annual migration, the entire population of Arctic terns move from the Arctic Ocean in the northern summer to as far south as Antarctica in the southern summer; (*b*) Muskox populations remain in the Arctic all year, though they migrate to higher elevations in the winter to avoid deep snow.

recovery plans often constructed to allow for the recovery of threatened populations. Finally, one of the greatest pressures faced by many plant and animal species around the planet has at its heart a shift in the population of a single species—the exponential growth of human populations.

All populations share several characteristics. The first is its distribution. The distribution of a population includes the size, shape, and location of the area it occupies. A population also has a characteristic pattern of spacing of the individuals within it. It is also characterized by the number of individuals within it and their **density**, which is the number of individuals per unit area. Additional characteristics of populations—their age distributions, sex ratios, birth and death rates, immigration and emigration rates, and rates of growth—are the subject of chapters 11 and 12. In chapter 10 we focus on two population characteristics: **distribution** and **abundance**.

Concepts

10.1   **The physical environment limits the geographic distribution of species.**

10.2   **On small scales, individuals within populations are distributed in patterns that may be random, regular, or clumped; on larger scales, individuals within a population are clumped.**

10.3   **Some populations, called metapopulations, consist of interconnected subpopulations.**

10.4   **Population density declines with increasing organism size.**

10.5   **Commonness and rarity of species are influenced by population size, geographic range, and habitat tolerance.**

10.1   Distribution Limits

The physical environment limits the geographic distribution of species.   A major theme in chapters 4 to 8 is that natural selection has resulted in the evolution of physiological, morphological, and behavioural characteristics that enable individuals to compensate for environmental variation. In chapter 9 we saw how these characteristics were driven in part by a series of trade-offs, resulting in a diversity of life histories and niches. Here we move from our understanding of the conditions that organisms need to persist and thrive, to understanding the locations in which those conditions are found.

Organisms compensate for temporal and spatial variation in the environment by regulating body temperature and water content and by foraging in a way that maintains energy intake at relatively high levels. However, there are limits on how much organisms can compensate for environmental variation.

While there are few environments on earth without life, no single species can tolerate the full range of earth's environments. For each species some environments are too warm, too cold, too saline, or unsuitable in other ways. All species exhibit a range of tolerance to many environmental conditions, beyond which populations are not able to persist. As we saw in chapter 7, organisms take in energy at a limited rate. It appears that at some point, the metabolic costs of compensating for environmental variation may take up too much of an organism's energy budget. Partly because of these energy constraints, the physical environment places limits on the distributions of populations. Let's now turn to some actual species and explore the factors that limit their distributions.

Kangaroo Distributions and Climate

The Macropodidea includes the kangaroos and wallabies, which are some of the best known of the Australian animals. However, this group of large-footed mammals includes many less familiar species, including rat kangaroos and tree kangaroos. While some species of macropods can be found in nearly every part of Australia, no single species ranges across the entire continent.

G. Caughley and his colleagues (1987) found a close relationship between climate and the distributions of the three largest kangaroos in Australia (fig. 10.2). The eastern grey kangaroo, *Macropus giganteus,* is confined to the eastern third of the continent. This portion of Australia includes several biomes (see chapter 2). Temperate forest grows in the southeast and tropical forests in the north. Mountains, with their varied climates, occupy the central part of the eastern grey kangaroo's range. The climatic factor that distinguishes these varied biomes is little seasonal variation in precipitation or dominance by summer precipitation. The western grey kangaroo, *M. fuliginosus,* lives mainly in the southern and western regions of Australia. Most of the western grey kangaroo's range coincides with the distribution of the temperate woodland and shrubland biome in Australia. The climatically distinctive feature of this biome is a predominance of winter rainfall. Meanwhile, the red kangaroo, *M. rufus,* wanders the arid and semiarid interior of Australia. The biomes that cover most of the red kangaroo's range are savanna and desert (chapter 2). Of the three species of large kangaroos, the red kangaroo occupies the hottest and driest areas.

As a group, the distributions of these three large kangaroo species cover most of Australia. However, as you can see in figure 10.2, none of these species lives in the northernmost region of Australia. Caughley and his colleagues explain that these northern areas are probably too hot for the eastern grey kangaroo, too wet for the red kangaroo, and too hot in summer and too dry in winter for the western grey kangaroo. However, they are also careful to point out that these limited distributions may not be determined by climate directly. Instead, they suggest that climate often influences species distributions through factors such as food production, water supply, and habitat. Climate also affects the incidence of parasites, pathogens, and competitors.

Regardless of how the influences of climate are played out, the relationship between climate and the distributions of species can be stable over long periods of time. The distributions of the eastern grey, western grey, and red kangaroos have been stable for at least a century. In the next example, we discuss a species of beetle that appears to have maintained a stable association with climate for 10,000 to 100,000 years.

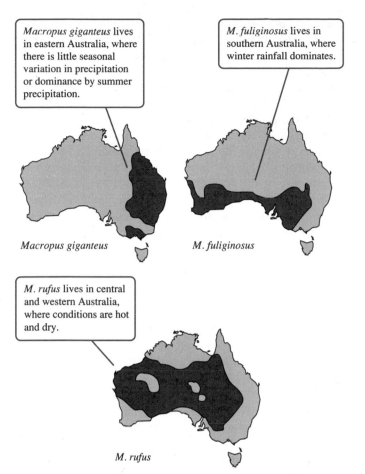

Macropus giganteus lives in eastern Australia, where there is little seasonal variation in precipitation or dominance by summer precipitation.

M. fuliginosus lives in southern Australia, where winter rainfall dominates.

Macropus giganteus

M. fuliginosus

M. rufus lives in central and western Australia, where conditions are hot and dry.

M. rufus

Figure 10.2 Climate and the distributions of three kangaroo species (data from Caughley et al. 1987).

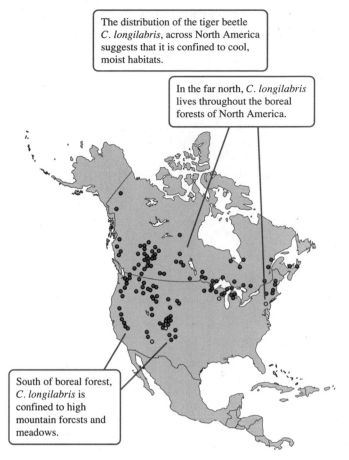

The distribution of the tiger beetle *C. longilabris*, across North America suggests that it is confined to cool, moist habitats.

In the far north, *C. longilabris* lives throughout the boreal forests of North America.

South of boreal forest, *C. longilabris* is confined to high mountain forests and meadows.

Figure 10.3 A tiger beetle, *Cicindela longilabris*, confined to cool environments. Physiological studies conducted on populations indicated by yellow dots (data from Schultz, Quinlan, and Hadley 1992).

A Tiger Beetle of Cold Climates

Tiger beetles have entered our discussions before. In chapter 6, we compared the water loss rates of tiger beetles from desert grasslands and riparian habitats in Arizona. Here we consider the distribution of a tiger beetle that inhabits the cold end of the range of environments occupied by tiger beetles.

The tiger beetle *Cicindela longilabris* lives at higher latitudes and higher elevations than just about any other species of tiger beetle in North America. In the north, *C. longilabris* is distributed from the Yukon Territory in northwestern Canada to the maritime provinces of eastern Canada (fig. 10.3). This northern band of beetle populations coincides with the distribution of northern temperate forest and boreal forest in North America (chapter 2). *C. longilabris* also lives as far south as Arizona and New Mexico. However, these southern populations are confined to high mountains, where *C. longilabris* is associated with montane coniferous forests. As we saw in chapter 2, these high mountains have a climate similar to that of boreal forest.

Ecologists suggest that during the last glacial period *C. longilabris* lived far south of its present range limits. Then with climatic warming and the retreat of the glaciers, the tiger beetles followed their preferred climate northward and up in elevation into the mountains of western North America (fig. 10.3). As a consequence, the beetles in the southern part of this species'

range live in isolated mountaintop populations. This hypothesis is supported by the fossil records of many beetle species.

Intrigued by the distribution and history of *C. longilabris,* Thomas Schultz, Michael Quinlan, and Neil Hadley (1992) set out to study the environmental physiology of widely separated populations of the species. Populations separated for many thousands of years may have been exposed to significantly different environmental regimes. If so, natural selection could have produced significant physiological differences among populations. The researchers compared the physiological characteristics of beetles from populations of *C. longilabris* from Maine, Wisconsin, Colorado, and northern Arizona. Their measurements included water loss rates, metabolic rates, and body temperature preferences.

Schultz and his colleagues found that the metabolic rates of *C. longilabris* are higher and its preferred temperatures lower than those of most other tiger beetle species that have been studied. These differences support the hypothesis that *C. longilabris* is adapted to the cool climates of boreal and montane forests. In addition, the researchers found that none of their measurements differed significantly among populations of *C. longilabris,* Figure 10.4 illustrates the remarkable similarity in preferred body temperature shown by foraging *C. longilabris* from populations separated by as much as

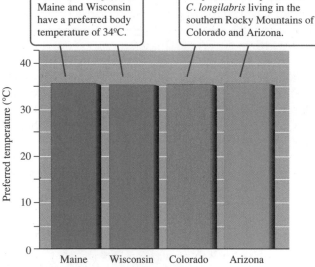

C. longilabris living in the northern regions of Maine and Wisconsin have a preferred body temperature of 34°C.

This is virtually identical to the preferred temperature of C. longilabris living in the southern Rocky Mountains of Colorado and Arizona.

Figure 10.4 Uniform temperature preference across an extensive geographic range (data from Schultz, Quinlan, and Hadley 1992).

3,000 km and, perhaps, by 10,000 years of history. These results support the generalization that the physical environment limits the distributions of species. It also suggests that those limits may be stable for long periods of time.

Now, let's consider how the physical environment may limit the distribution of plants. Our example is drawn from the arid and semiarid regions of the American Southwest.

Distributions of Plants along a Moisture-Temperature Gradient

Variation in leaf pubescence among plants in the genus *Encelia* appears to correspond directly to the distributions of these species along a moisture-temperature gradient from the California coast eastward (Ehleringer and Clark 1988). *Encelia californica*, the species with the least pubescent leaves, occupies a narrow coastal zone that extends from southern California to northern Baja California (fig. 10.5). Inland, *E. californica* is replaced by *E. actoni*, which has leaves that are slightly more pubescent. Still farther to the east, *E. actoni* is in turn replaced by *E. frutescens* and *E. farinosa*.

These geographic limits to these species' distributions correspond to variations in temperature and precipitation. The coastal environments where *E. californica* lives are all relatively cool. However, average annual precipitation differs a great deal across the distribution of this species. Annual precipitation ranges from about 100 mm in the southern part of its distribution to well over 400 mm in the northern part. By comparison, *E. actoni* occupies environments that are only slightly warmer but considerably drier. The rainfall in areas occupied by *E. frutescens* and *E. farinosa* is similar to the amount that falls in the areas occupied by *E. actoni* and *E. californica*. However, the environments of *E. frutescens* and *E. farinosa* are much hotter.

Variation in leaf pubescence does not correspond entirely to the macroclimates inhabited by *Encelia* species. The leaves of *E. frutescens* are nearly as free of pubescence as the coastal species *E. californica*. However, *E. frutescens* grows side by side with *E. farinosa* in some of the hottest deserts in the world. Because they are sparsely pubescent, the leaves of *E. frutescens* absorb a great deal more radiant energy than the leaves of *E. farinosa* (fig. 10.6). Under similar conditions, however, leaf temperatures of the two species are nearly identical. How does *E. frutescens* avoid overheating? The leaves do not overheat because they transpire at a high rate and are evaporatively cooled as a consequence.

Evaporative cooling solves one ecological puzzle but appears to create another. Remember that these two shrubs live in some of the hottest and driest deserts in the world. Where does

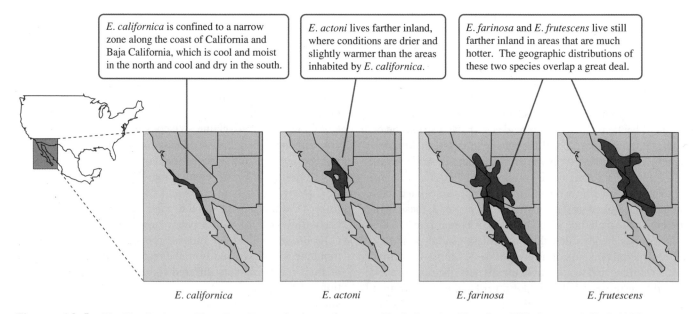

E. californica is confined to a narrow zone along the coast of California and Baja California, which is cool and moist in the north and cool and dry in the south.

E. actoni lives farther inland, where conditions are drier and slightly warmer than the areas inhabited by E. californica.

E. farinosa and E. frutescens live still farther inland in areas that are much hotter. The geographic distributions of these two species overlap a great deal.

E. californica   E. actoni   E. farinosa   E. frutescens

Figure 10.5 The distributions of four *Encelia* species in southwestern North America (data from Ehleringer and Clark 1988).

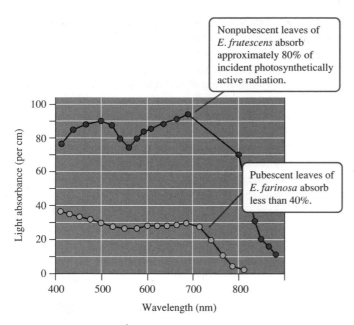

> Nonpubescent leaves of *E. frutescens* absorb approximately 80% of incident photosynthetically active radiation.

> Pubescent leaves of *E. farinosa* absorb less than 40%.

Figure 10.6   Light absorption by leaves of *Encelia frutescens* and *E. farinosa* (data from Ehleringer and Clark 1988).

E. frutescens get enough water to evaporatively cool its leaves? Though the distributions of *E. frutescens* and *E. farinosa* overlap a great deal on a geographic scale, these two species occupy distinctive microenvironments. As shown in figure 10.7, *E. farinosa* grows mainly on upland slopes, while *E. frutescens* is largely confined to ephemeral stream channels, or desert washes. Along washes, runoff combined with deep soils increases the availability of soil moisture. This example reminds us of a principle that we first considered in chapter 5: organisms living in the same macroclimate may, because of slight differences in local distribution, experience substantially different microclimates. This is certainly true of the two barnacle species we consider in the following example.

Distributions of Barnacles along an Intertidal Exposure Gradient

The marine intertidal zone presents a steep gradient of physical conditions from the shore seaward. As we saw in chapter 3, the organisms high in the intertidal zone are exposed by virtually every tide while the organisms that live at lower levels in the intertidal zone are exposed by the lowest tides only. Exposure to air differs at different levels within the intertidal zone. Organisms that live in the intertidal zone have evolved different degrees of resistance to drying, a major factor contributing to zonation among intertidal organisms (chapter 3).

Barnacles, one of the most common intertidal organisms, show distinctive patterns of zonation within the intertidal zone. For example, Joseph Connell (1961a, 1961b) described how along the coast of Scotland, adult *Chthamalus stellatus* are restricted to the upper levels of the intertidal zone, while adult *Balanus balanoides* are limited to the middle and lower levels (fig. 10.8). What role does resistance to drying play in the intertidal zonation of these two species? Unusually calm and warm weather combined with very low tides gave Connell some insights into this question. In the spring of 1955, warm weather coincided with calm seas and very low tides. As a consequence, no water reached the upper intertidal zone occupied by both species of barnacles. During this period, *Balanus* in the upper intertidal zone suffered much higher mortality than *Chthamalus* (fig. 10.9). Meanwhile, *Balanus* in the lower intertidal zone showed normal rates of mortality. Of the two species, *Balanus* appears to be more vulnerable to desiccation. Higher rates of desiccation may exclude this species of barnacle from the upper intertidal zone.

Vulnerability to dessication, however, does not completely explain the pattern of intertidal zonation shown by *Balanus* and *Chthamalus*. What excludes *Chthamalus* from the lower intertidal zone? Though the larvae of this barnacle settle in the lower intertidal zone, the adults rarely survive there. Connell

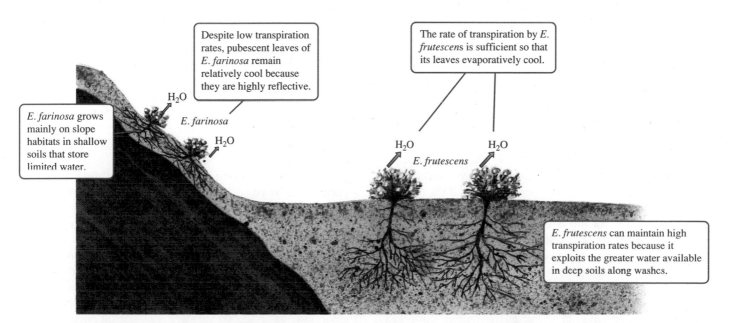

> Despite low transpiration rates, pubescent leaves of *E. farinosa* remain relatively cool because they are highly reflective.

> The rate of transpiration by *E. frutescens* is sufficient so that its leaves evaporatively cool.

> *E. farinosa* grows mainly on slope habitats in shallow soils that store limited water.

> *E. frutescens* can maintain high transpiration rates because it exploits the greater water available in deep soils along washes.

H_2O *E. farinosa* H_2O H_2O *E. frutescens* H_2O

Figure 10.7   Temperature regulation and distributions of *Encelia farinosa* and *E. frutescens* across microenvironments.

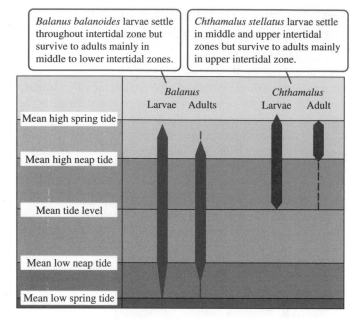

Balanus balanoides larvae settle throughout intertidal zone but survive to adults mainly in middle to lower intertidal zones.

Chthamalus stellatus larvae settle in middle and upper intertidal zones but survive to adults mainly in upper intertidal zone.

Figure 10.8 Distributions of two barnacle species within the intertidal zone (data from Connell 1961a, 1961b).

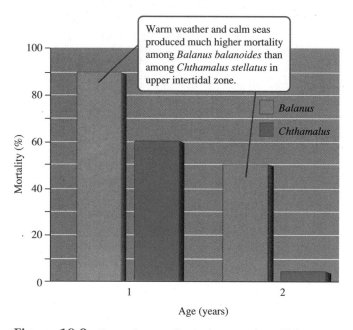

Warm weather and calm seas produced much higher mortality among Balanus balanoides than among Chthamalus stellatus in upper intertidal zone.

Figure 10.9 Barnacle mortality in the upper intertidal zone (data from Connell 1961a, 1961b).

explored this question by transplanting adult *Chthamalus* to the lower intertidal zone and found that transplanted adults survive in the lower intertidal zone very well. If the physical environment does not exclude *Chthamalus* from the lower intertidal zone, what does? It turns out that this species is excluded from the lower intertidal zone by competitive interactions with *Balanus*. We discuss the mechanisms by which this competitive exclusion is accomplished in chapter 13, which covers interspecific competition.

These barnacles remind us that the environment consists of more than just physical and chemical factors. An organism's environment also includes biological factors. In many

situations, biological factors may be as important or even more important than physical factors in determining the distribution and abundance of species. Often the influences of biological factors remain hidden, however, because of the difficulty of demonstrating them. In ecology, we must usually probe deeper to see beyond outward appearances, as Connell did when he transplanted *Chthamalus* from the upper to the lower intertidal zone. The influence of biological factors, such as competition, predation, and disease, on the distribution and abundance of organisms is a theme that enters our discussions frequently in the remainder of this book, especially in chapters 13, 14, and 15.

Now that we have considered factors limiting the distributions of individuals, let's consider the patterns of distribution of individuals within their habitat. Let's begin by considering three basic patterns of distribution.

Concept 10.1 Review

1. How might climate change influence the distribution of a species?
2. What role does life history play in determining how a species responds to changes in the biotic or abiotic environment?

10.2   Distribution Patterns

On small scales, individuals within populations are distributed in patterns that may be random, regular, or clumped; on larger scales, individuals within a population are clumped. We have just considered how the environment limits the distributions of species. When you map the distribution of a species such as the red kangaroo in Australia (see fig. 10.2), or the zoned distribution of *Chthamalus* and *Balanus* in the intertidal zone (see fig. 10.8), the boundaries on your map indicate the range of the species. In other words, your map shows where at least some individuals of the species live and where they are absent. Knowing a species' range, as defined by presence and absence, is useful, but it says nothing about how the individuals that make up the population are distributed in the areas where they are present. Are individuals randomly distributed across the range? Are they regularly distributed? As we shall see, the distribution pattern observed by an ecologist is strongly influenced by the scale at which a population is studied.

Ecologists refer frequently to large-scale and small-scale phenomena. What is "large" or "small" depends on the size of organism or other ecological phenomenon under study. For this discussion, **small scale** refers to distances of no more than a few hundred meters, over which there is little environmental change significant to the organism under study. **Large scale** refers to areas over which there is substantial environmental change. In this sense, large scale may refer to patterns over an entire continent or patterns along a mountain slope, where environmental gradients are steep. Let's begin our discussion with patterns of distribution observed at small scales.

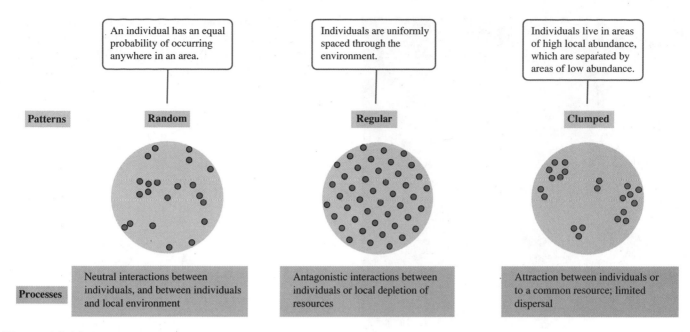

Figure 10.10   Random, regular, and clumped distributions.

Distributions of Individuals on Small Scales

Three basic patterns of distribution are observed on small scales: random, regular, or clumped. A **random distribution** is one in which individuals within a population have an equal chance of living anywhere within an area. A **regular distribution** is one in which individuals are uniformly spaced. In a **clumped distribution,** individuals have a much higher probability of being found in some areas than in others (fig. 10.10).

These three basic patterns of distribution are produced by the kinds of interactions that take place between individuals within a population, by the structure of the physical environment, and by a combination of interactions and environmental structure. Individuals within a population may *attract* each other, *repel* each other, or *ignore* each other. Mutual attraction creates clumped, or aggregated, patterns of distribution. Clumped distributions can also occur if individuals produce offspring that fail to disperse far from the parents. Regular patterns of distribution are produced when individuals avoid each other or claim exclusive use of a patch of landscape. Neutral responses contribute to random distributions.

The patterns created by social interactions may be reinforced or reduced by the structure of the environment. An environment with patchy distributions of nutrients, nesting sites, water, and so forth fosters clumped distribution patterns. An environment with a fairly uniform distribution of resources and frequent, random patterns of disturbance (or mixing) tends to reinforce random or regular distributions. Let's now consider factors that influence the distributions of some species in nature.

Distributions of Tree Species on Vancouver Island

Both competition and habitat characteristics (e.g., soil fertility) can influence the distribution of individuals within a population.

Further complicating the situation is that these processes may interact, such that competition may be more, or less, important at some levels of fertility than other levels. As a result, discerning the mechanisms that cause spatial patterns in natural populations can be a challenge. A team of researchers from Canada and Germany decided to tackle this issue, and to try to understand what factors influenced the small scale distribution of trees in a Douglas-fir forest (fig. 10.11) on Vancouver Island, British Columbia (Getzin et al. 2006).

They chose as a study site a set of forest stands on southeastern Vancouver Island. These stands differed in ages, ranging from old-growth (254 years old) to relatively immature (39 years old). The research team mapped the locations of all the dead and living trees in several plots within each stand (fig. 10.12). They also recorded the species identity of each tree, focusing primarily on Douglas-fir (*Pseudotsuga menziesii*), Western Hemlock (*Tsuga heterophylla*), and Western Red Cedar (*Thuja plicata*). If competition is important in structuring these populations, they predict that trees in clumps are likely to suffer mortality. As a result, the distribution of trees should become more regular over time (moving from the young stand to the old stand). Strong influences of local site characteristics would likely be seen as clumped distributions, with trees of a given species found only in areas that have the necessary site-conditions for its survival and growth.

They found that at the smallest spatial scales, trees tended to be clumped together, suggesting influence of the local habitat. However, they also found there was a positive correlation between spatial aggregation and competition. For all three species, the highest levels of aggregation were found in the stands for which competition was strongest! They were able to measure competition as the relationship between the distance of a tree to its nearest neighbour and its growth rate, showing that the closer other trees were, the slower the tree grew. When competition was greatest varied among species,

Figure 10.11 The small-scale distribution of different tree species in a Douglas-fir forest is determined by both biotic and abiotic interactions.

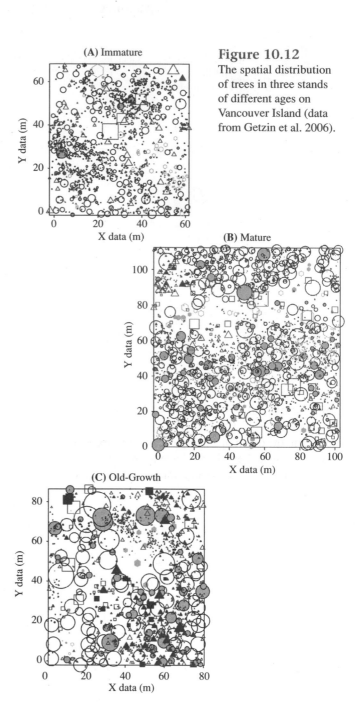

Figure 10.12 The spatial distribution of trees in three stands of different ages on Vancouver Island (data from Getzin et al. 2006).

but in general strong competition did not necessarily result in an even distribution of plants.

Why did these surprising results occur? One possible explanation is that although competition was strong and significantly reduced plant growth rates, it was not strong enough to kill them. In other words, competition should impact spatial patterns if it kills the plants involved (or, if looking at animal populations, it would need to cause the animals to either die or leave the area). An additional possibility is that clumped trees may somehow facilitate the growth of the other trees (chapter 15), thereby mitigating the negative consequences of competition. Finally, within the large data set that Getzin and colleagues generated was another clue to this answer. For one species, Western Hemlock, spatial distributions of the trees were more regular post-mortality than pre-mortality, a result consistent with competition. This suggests that the factors that influence spatial distributions of individuals within a population are going to vary among species. Although we use generalizations frequently, more meaningful answers only come from detailed studies and the hard work of many individuals.

Below Ground Distributions of Desert Shrubs

As we have seen in the forests of British Columbia, competition between plants may influence the distribution of individuals within a population. However, in many systems competition among plants will be predominantly below ground (chapter 13) for resources such as water and nitrogen. How do researchers study these sorts of below ground interactions? For a classic example, we turn to the work of Jacques Brisson and James Reynolds (1994) describing the below ground side of creosote bush distributions. These researchers carefully excavated and mapped the distributions of 32 creosote bushes in the Chihuahuan Desert. They proposed that if creosote bushes compete, their roots should grow in a way that reduces overlap with the roots of nearby individuals.

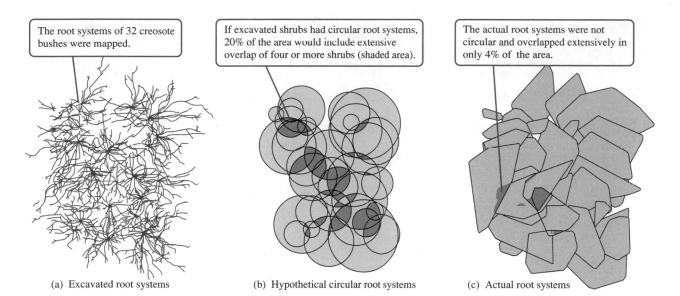

The root systems of 32 creosote bushes were mapped.

(a) Excavated root systems

If excavated shrubs had circular root systems, 20% of the area would include extensive overlap of four or more shrubs (shaded area).

(b) Hypothetical circular root systems

The actual root systems were not circular and overlapped extensively in only 4% of the area.

(c) Actual root systems

Figure 10.13 Creosote bush root distributions: hypothetical versus actual root overlap (data from Brisson and Reynolds 1994).

The 32 excavated creosote bushes occupied a 4 by 5 m area on the Jornada Long Term Ecological Research site near Las Cruces, New Mexico. The creosote bush was the only shrub within the study plot. Their roots penetrated to only 30 to 50 cm, the depth of a hardpan calcium carbonate deposition layer. Because they did not have to excavate to great depths, Brisson and Reynolds were able to map more root systems than previous researchers. Still, their excavation and mapping of roots required two months of intense labour.

The complex pattern of root distributions uncovered confirmed the researchers' proposal: Creosote bush roots grow in a pattern that reduces overlap between the roots of adjacent plants (fig. 10.13a). We can make the root distributions of individual plants clearer by plotting their perimeters only. Figure 10.13b shows the hypothetical distributions of creosote bushes with circular root systems, while figure 10.13c shows their actual root distributions. Notice that the root systems of creosote bushes overlap much less than they would if they had circular distributions. Brisson and Reynolds conclude that competitive interactions with neighbouring shrubs influence the distribution of creosote bush roots. Their work suggests that creosote bushes compete for belowground resources.

As we have seen, numerous factors can influence both the above and below ground distributions of plants. In the following section we find distributions are predominantly clumped.

Distributions of Individuals on Large Scales

We have considered how individuals within a population are distributed on a small scale. Now let's step back and ask how individuals within a population are distributed on a larger scale over which there is significant environmental variation. For instance, is population density fairly regularly distributed across the entire area occupied by a species, or are there a few centres of high density surrounded by areas in which the species is present but only in low densities?

Bird Populations Across North America

Terry Root (1988) mapped patterns of bird abundance across North America using the "Christmas Bird Counts." These bird counts provide one of the few data sets extensive enough to study distribution patterns across an entire continent. Christmas Bird Counts, which began in 1900, involve annual counts of birds during the Christmas season. The first Christmas Bird Count was attended by 27 observers, who counted birds in 26 localities—2 in Canada and the remainder in 13 states of the United States. In the 1985–86 season, 38,346 people participated in the Christmas Bird Count. The observers counted birds in 1,504 localities throughout the United States and most of Canada. In 2006, a record 57,156 observers recorded 2,060 localities! Included in these numbers were 12,201 observers in Canada alone. In fact, the two locations with the greatest number of participants in all of North America were Edmonton, Alberta and North Bay, Ontario. This annual count continues to produce a unique record of the distribution and population densities of wintering birds across most of a continent.

Root's analysis centres around a series of maps that show patterns of distribution and population density for 346 species of birds that winter in the United States and Canada. Although species as different as swans and sparrows are included, the maps show a consistent pattern. At the continental scale, bird populations show clumped distributions. Clumped patterns occur in species with widespread distributions, such as the American crow, *Corvus brachyrhynchos,* as well as in species with restricted distributions, such as the fish crow, *C. ossifragus.* Though the winter distribution of the American crow includes most of the continent, the bulk of individuals in this population are concentrated in a few areas. These areas of high density, or "hot spots," appear as red dots in figure 10.15a. For the American crow population, hot spots are concentrated along river valleys, especially the Cumberland, Mississippi, Arkansas, Snake, and Rio Grande.

Ecology In Action

Using Ecology to Protect Threatened Species

In the media we often hear reports of species on the verge of extinction, and of government efforts underway to protect remaining populations and individuals. The laws protecting these species vary widely among countries, and in Canada, we have the Species at Risk Act (SARA). By November, 2006, there were 389 species formally listed and given legal protection in Canada under SARA (Government of Canada, 2006; fig. 10.14). But what exactly does this mean? Who actually makes this determination, what happens after such a designation is made, and what role does ecology play in this process?

As stated in the summary of SARA itself, "The purposes of this enactment are to prevent Canadian indigenous species, subspecies and distinct populations of wildlife from becoming extirpated or extinct, to provide for the recovery of endangered or threatened species, to encourage the management of other species to prevent them from becoming at risk" (Canada. Species At Risk Act Public Registry 2007). To achieve these goals there are two very important steps (1) the identification of species that are at risk, and (2) the development and implementation of a recovery and/or protection plan. Both of these steps require substantial research effort into understanding issues such as species distributions and changes to population size.

Figure 10.14   Species currently endangered in Canada include (*a*) the Burrowing Owl, *Athene cunicularia*; (*b*) Taylor's Checkerspot, *Euphydryas editha taylori*; (*c*) Aurora trout, *Salvelinus fontinalis timagamiensis*; and (*d*) the Western spiderwort, *Tradescantia occidentalis*.

Decisions about at-risk designations are not taken lightly, and involve substantial deliberation among an independent body of experts, the Committee on the Status of Endangered Wildlife in Canada, or COSEWIC. In 2006, COSEWIC consisted of 30 members. These include governmental members from the wildlife agency of each of the 13 territories or provinces, and members from four federal agencies (Canadian Wildlife Service, Parks Canada, Department of Fisheries and Oceans, and the Federal Biodiversity Partnership). Non-governmental representatives included three science members, nine members from the Species Specialist Subcommittees, and one co-chair from the Aboriginal Traditional Knowledge Subcommittee. COSEWIC makes decisions about whether the best science and traditional knowledge support a case for listing a particular species as endangered. It is then up to the Minister of the Environment to act upon that recommendation. However, listing many species can present significant economic and political challenges, and thus not all species recommended for listing by COSEWIC are listed by the Minister of the Environment. In other words, science and politics both influence the legal status of species in Canada.

The first step in giving a species an at-risk designation is for COSEWIC to become aware of a potential threatened species. This is not a trivial undertaking considering that there are over 70,000 known wild species in Canada. These efforts are assisted by biologists at the provincial, territorial, and federal governmental levels who regularly assess a number of species, forwarding species of concern to COSEWIC. Additional inputs on species for consideration can come from non-governmental organizations and private citizens. Assessments are based mainly on changes in abundance and distribution of the species in Canada using quantitative benchmarks based upon those elaborated by the International Union for the Conservation of Nature (IUCN). Factors that get considered include species range (chapter 10), population size (chapter 10), rates of population decline (chapters 11, 12), habitat fragmentation (chapter 21), and the existence of current or expected threats to the species (e.g., introduced species, disease, habitat destruction, etc.). As we discuss in this chapter, rarity of species can take many different forms, and both the spatial extent of a species' range and local population densities can contribute to different forms of rarity. However, rarity alone is not enough to warrant listing, as some species are "naturally" rare. The committee is looking for evidence of a likely sustained decrease in population size, rather than a species which has stable, but low, population densities.

Although only species thought to be at risk are brought to COSEWIC, upon further study of the data, the committee often finds that not all of these species are actually at risk. For example, by April 2006, COSEWIC evaluated 727 species

(COSEWIC 2006). Of these, 157 (22%) were found to be not-at-risk, meaning the best science to date suggests that these species will continue to persist without special protection. An additional 41 species (5%) were deemed "data-deficient," which means there are not enough data available to make a sound scientific decision for or against protection. The remaining 529 species (73%) were recommended for listing by COSEWIC. However, you may recall from the beginning of this section that by November 2006, only 389 species were actually listed under SARA. What happened to the other 140 species COSEWIC recommend for listing? Some are likely in the pipeline, and are simply experiencing expected delays within the government. Others, however, are intentionally not listed by the Minister of the Environment.

The Minister of the Environment has the ability to make a non-science-based discretionary decision that reflects concerns about potential economic or political implications of a listing. In contrast to the Endangered Species Act in the United States, Canada's SARA does not provide the opportunity for private citizens to appeal such discretionary decisions. Although SARA does provide some protections, it is a substantially weaker act than is in place in the United States. A team of researchers including Arnie Mooers from Simon Fraser University, Laura Prugh from the University of British Columbia, Marco Festa-Bianchet from the Université de Sherbrooke, and Jeff Hutchings from Dalhousie University, have recently published a study investigating bias in which species were given legal protection under SARA (Mooers et al. 2007). The team explored all decisions regarding listing of species as at risk of extinction made by the Minister of Environment between 2004–2006. During this period, COSEWIC recommended listing 186 species, of which 30 were not listed by the Minister. Analyses indicated that only 17% of the COSEWIC recommended fish and mammals species harvested by humans were listed, while 93% of the non-harvested species were given legal protection. These results were particularly evident for marine fish, where nearly all of the recommended species were denied listing. The researchers note that the one marine fish that was listed, the green sturgeon, has a "disagreeable taste" and there is no commercial fishery. A second bias appeared in a reluctance to list northern species. None of the 10 species that occurred in Nunavut recommend for listing by COSEWIC were listed, and in general only 28% of northern species were listed, compared to 90% of non-northern species. Clearly science only plays a partial role in the protection of species in Canada, with politics getting the final say.

Despite clear evidence of politics influencing the decision to protect species, some species do end up with legal protection. Being at-risk can take several forms, from the most extreme forms of being already extinct or extirpated (no longer found in Canada, but found in other countries), to less extreme forms of risk such as endangered (facing imminent extirpation or extinction), threatened (likely to become extinct or extirpated unless actions are taken), and of special concern (may become threatened without actions being taken). Once a species has been listed, a recovery plan is developed that is designed to meet the unique needs of that species. Actions can include harvest moratoriums, captive breeding programs, control of competing or predating species, translocation of individuals to enhance existing or establish new populations, and education programs that promote changes in land use. These efforts are made through the cooperation of government agencies, a variety of non-governmental organizations, scores of local volunteers, and with the help of land-owners and industrial stakeholders. Although not every species will be able to be successfully recovered, several populations of several protected species have improved. For example, the Swift Fox (*Vulpes velox*) is a small fox found in southern Alberta and Saskatchewan. It was listed as extirpated in 1978. Between 1983 and 1997, foxes were reintroduced, resulting in a population of 279 foxes in the wild in Canada in 1999, and the species was thus downgraded to endangered. The populations appear to be continuing to grow, and though this species is still endangered, there has been improvement over the last several decades. There are other successes, such as the downlisting of the red-shouldered hawk from special concern to not-at-risk as populations increase, and populations of peregrine falcon continue to grow. For all listed species, continued monitoring to assess the effectiveness of recovery efforts is critical, with the eventual hope to be able to de-list recovered species.

Although being listed as at-risk provides legal protection to many species, it is important to recognize that we do not have good data on all species in Canada. For example, it is widely acknowledged that there is currently a bias in data collection towards vertebrates. In fact, over 60% of the species brought forward to COSEWIC have been vertebrates, with only 2% being insects, even though vertebrates make up only a small fraction of Canada's biodiversity. These biases mean that many inconspicuous species likely at risk are unprotected. Yet these species can be extremely important to ecosystem function and have equal ethical rights for consideration under both IUCN and COSEWIC guidelines. It is the job of future generations of ecologists to learn more about the biodiversity of Canada and other locations in the world, with these efforts critical to our ability to preserve a diverse world for future generations.

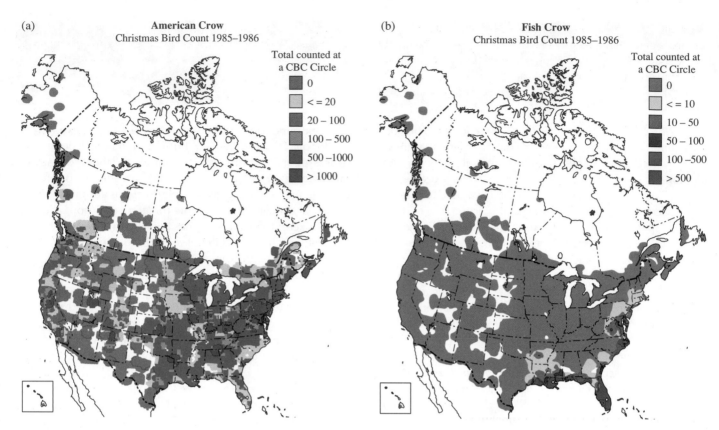

Figure 10.15   (*a*) Winter distribution of the American crow, *Corvus brachyrynchos*. (*b*) Winter distribution of the fish crow, *C. ossifragus* (data from National Audubon Society).

Away from these hot spots the winter abundance of American crows diminishes rapidly.

The fish crow population, though much more restricted than that of the American crow, is also concentrated in a few areas (fig. 10.15*b*). Fish crows are restricted to areas of open water near the coast of the Gulf of Mexico and along the southern half of the Atlantic coast of the United States. Within this restricted range, however, most fish crows are concentrated in a few hot spots—one on the Mississippi Delta, another on Lake Seminole west of Tallahassee, Florida, and a third in the everglades in southern Florida. Like the more widely distributed American crow, the abundance of fish crows diminishes rapidly away from these centres of high density.

Might bird populations have clumped distributions only on the wintering grounds? James H. Brown, David Mehlman, and George Stevens (1995) analyzed large-scale patterns of abundance among birds across North America during the breeding season, the opposite season from that studied by Root. In their study these researchers used data from the Breeding Bird Survey, which consists of standardized counts by amateur ornithologists conducted each June at approximately 2,000 sites across the United States and Canada under the supervision of the Fish and Wildlife Services of the United States and the National Wildlife Research Centre run by the Canadian Wildlife Service. For their analyses, they chose species of birds whose geographic ranges fall mainly or completely within the eastern and central regions of the United States, which are well covered by study sites of the Breeding Bird Survey.

Like Root, Brown and his colleagues found that a relatively small proportion of study sites yielded most of the records of each bird species. That is, most individuals were concentrated in a fairly small number of hot spots. For instance, the densities of red-eyed vireos are low in most places (fig. 10.16). Clumped

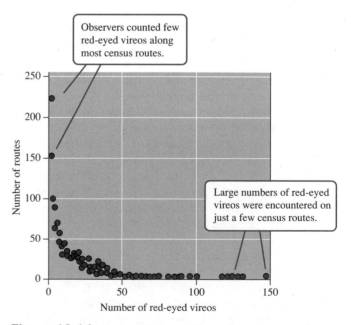

Figure 10.16   Red-eyed vireos, *Vireo olivaceus*, counted along census routes of the Breeding Bird Survey (data from Brown, Mehlman, and Stevens 1995).

distributions were documented repeatedly. When the numbers of birds across their ranges were totalled, generally about 25% of the locations sampled supported over half of each population. By combining the results of Root and Brown and his colleagues we can say confidently that at larger scales, bird populations in North America show clumped patterns of distribution. In other words, most individuals within a bird species live in a few hot spots, areas of unusually high population density.

Brown and his colleagues propose that these distributions are clumped because the environment varies and individuals aggregate in areas where the environment is favourable. What might be the patterns of distribution for populations distributed along a known environmental gradient? Studies of plant populations provide interesting insights.

Plant Abundance Along Moisture Gradients

Several decades ago, Robert Whittaker gathered information on the distributions of woody plants along moisture gradients in several mountain ranges across North America. This work has since proven to be a foundation of ecology. As we saw in chapter 2 environmental conditions on mountainsides change substantially with elevation. These steep environmental gradients provide a compressed analog of the continental-scale gradients to which the birds studied by Root and Brown and his colleagues were presumably responding.

Let's look at the distributions of some tree species along moisture gradients in two of the mountain ranges studied by Whittaker. Robert Whittaker and William Niering (1965) studied the distribution of plants along moisture and elevation gradients in the Santa Catalina Mountains of southern Arizona. These mountains rise out of the Sonoran Desert near Tucson, Arizona, like a green island in a tan desert sea. Vegetation typical of the Sonoran Desert, including the saguaro cactus and creosote bush, grow in the surrounding desert and on the lower slopes of the mountains. However, the summit of the mountains is topped by a mixed conifer forest. Forests also extend down the flanks of the Santa Catalinas in moist, shady canyons.

There is a moisture gradient from the moist canyon bottoms up the dry southwest-facing slopes. Whittaker and Niering found that along this gradient the Mexican pinyon pine, *Pinus cembroides,* is at its peak abundance on the uppermost and driest part of the southwest-facing slope (fig. 10.17). Along the same slope, Arizona madrone, *Arbutus arizonica,* reaches its peak abundance at middle elevations. Finally, Douglas-firs, *Pseudotsuga menziesii,* are restricted to the moist canyon bottom. Mexican pinyon pines, Arizona madrone, and Douglas-fir are all clumped along this moisture gradient, but each reaches peak abundance at different positions on the slope. These positions appear to reflect the different environmental requirements of each species.

Whittaker (1956) recorded analogous tree distributions along moisture gradients in the Great Smoky Mountains of eastern North America. Again, the gradient was from a moist valley bottom to a drier southwest-facing slope. Along this moisture gradient, hemlock, *Tsuga canadensis,* was concentrated in the moist valley bottom and its density decreased rapidly upslope (fig. 10.18). Meanwhile red maple, *Acer rubrum,* grew at highest densities in the middle section of the slope, while table

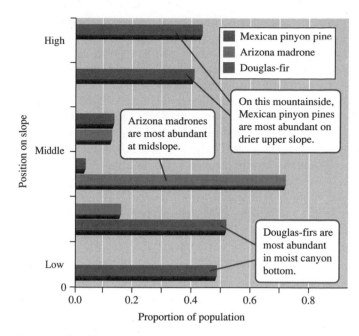

Figure 10.17 Abundances of three tree species on a moisture gradient in the Santa Catalina Mountains, Arizona (data from Whittaker and Niering 1965).

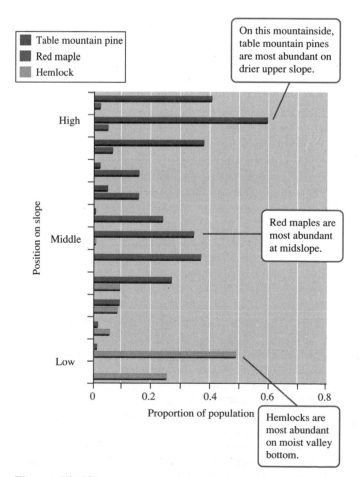

Figure 10.18 Abundance of three tree species on a moisture gradient in the Great Smoky Mountains, Tennessee (data from Whittaker 1956).

mountain pine, *Pinus pungens,* was concentrated on the driest upper sections. As in the Santa Catalina Mountains of Arizona, these tree distributions in the Great Smoky Mountains reflect the moisture requirements of each tree species.

The distribution of trees along moisture gradients seems to resemble the clumped distributional patterns of birds across the North American continent but on a smaller scale. All species of trees discussed here showed a highly clumped distribution along moisture gradients, and their densities decreased substantially toward the edges of their distributions. In other words, like birds, tree populations are concentrated in hot spots. As we shall see in the next concept discussion, some populations are subdivided into separate subpopulations that exchange individuals over time.

Concept 10.2 Review

1. How could you test the hypothesis that low overlap in the root systems of creosote bush populations is the result of ongoing competition, and not due to variation in underlying soil nutrient distributions?
2. Why do population densities generally decline as you move from the centre to the edge of a species' range?

10.3   Metapopulations

Some populations, called metapopulations, consist of interconnected subpopulations.   Populations of many species occur not as a single, continuously distributed population but in spatially isolated patches, with significant exchange of individuals among patches. A group of subpopulations living on such patches connected by exchange of individuals among patches make up a **metapopulation**. Why are some populations divided into subpopulations and other populations able to persist as single integrated population?

Metapopulations develop due to interactions between the biology of the species of interest and the landscape upon which it lives. For example, some species have very specific habitat requirements, such as a butterfly that can only oviposit on certain meadow plants. If meadows exist as large and continuous areas, then you would also expect the butterfly population to be large and continuous. However, if the meadows are only found as small patches of land surrounded by forest, agricultural fields, or other habitat unsuitable for this butterfly, then you would expect this species to form small populations in these meadows. If the biology of the organism allows for dispersal of individuals from one meadow to another, this then forms a metapopulation. If dispersal does not occur, this species would form several small and unconnected populations on the landscape. More information about the characteristics of metapopulations can be found in figure 10.19.

The population of Glanville fritillary butterflies, *Melitaea cinxia,* which lives in dry meadows scattered through the landscape of southern Finland (see chapter 4) is a metapopulation. In our earlier discussion of this butterfly metapopulation we reviewed how the exchange of individuals among sub-

Metapopulations are complex networks of movement and residency that have important consequences for species abundances, extinctions, and gene flow. Here are a few essential points about metapopulations:

1. Metapopulations are a population of subpopulations.
2. The subpopulations are connected by movement of individuals from one subpopulation to another.
3. Any subpopulation can go extinct and be re-colonized repeatedly over time.
4. The risk of subpopulation extinction is generally greatest for small subpopulations, which usually occur in small patches on the landscape.
5. Density-dependent and density-independent population dynamics (chapters 11, 12) occur within each subpopulation.

Figure 10.19

populations has been well documented (Saccheri et al. 1998). However, the metapopulation of *Melitaea* in southern Finland is only one of many that are well known. Here is another example of a butterfly metapopulation.

A Metapopulation of an Alpine Butterfly

Once population biologists began to include the concept of metapopulations in their thinking, they found them everywhere. Butterflies have been well represented in studies of metapopulations. One of these butterflies is the Rocky Mountain Parnassian butterfly, *Parnassius smintheus* (figure 10.20). The range of *P. smintheus* extends from northern New Mexico along the Rocky Mountains to southwest Alaska. Along this range *P. smintheus* caterpillars feed mainly on the leaves and flowers of stonecrop, *Sedum* sp., in areas of open forest and meadows. Because of their tie to a narrow range of host plants, *P. smintheus* populations are often distributed among the habitat patches occupied by their host plant, appearing to form metapopulations.

One such metapopulation was studied by Jens Roland, Nusha Keyghobadi and Sherri Fownes of the University of Alberta in Edmonton, Canada (Roland, Keyghobadi, and Fownes 2000). Roland, Keyghobadi, and Fownes focused their attention on a series of 20 alpine meadows on ridges in the Kananaskis region of the Canadian Rocky Mountains. The study meadows ranged in area from about 0.8 ha to 20 ha. While some meadows were adjacent to each other, others were separated by up to 200 m of coniferous forest. The host plant of *P. smintheus* in the study meadows was the lanceleaf stonecrop, *Sedum lanceolatum.*

A combination of fire suppression and global warming appears to be decreasing the size of alpine meadows and increasing their isolation from each other by intervening forest. In 1952, the study meadows averaged approximately 36 ha in area. By 1993, the average area of these meadows had declined to approximately 8 ha, a decrease in area of approximately 77%. These changes motivated the research team of Roland, Keyghobadi, and Fownes to study the influences of meadow size and isolation on movements of *P. smintheus* during the summers of 1995 and 1996.

Figure 10.20 Jens Roland and colleagues marked (notice the QME on the wing) and recaptured many Rocky Mountain Parnassian butterflies to understand metapopulation dynamics for this species. Because this species is tied to meadows and open forest where its larval host plants grow, *P. smintheus* lives in scattered subpopulations connected by dispersal.

The research team used mark and recapture techniques (see Ecological Tools) to estimate population size in each meadow and to follow their movements. Butterflies were hand netted and marked on the hind wing with a three-letter identification code, using a fine-tipped permanent marker (fig. 10.20). The team recorded the sex of *P. smintheus* captured and its location within 20 m. Upon recapture, dispersal distance of an individual was estimated as the straight line distance from its last point of capture.

Roland, Keyghobadi, and Fownes marked 1,574 *P. smintheus* in 1995 and 1,200 in 1996. Of these marked individuals, they recaptured 726 in 1995 and 445 in 1996. Over the course of the study, the size of *P. smintheus* populations in the 20 study meadows ranged from 0 to 230. The average movement distance by males and females in 1995 was approximately 131 m. In 1996, the average movement distances of males and females was 162 m and 118 m respectively. The maximum dispersal distance for a butterfly in 1995 was 1,729 m and in 1996 the maximum dispersal distance was 1,636 m. Most of the movements determined by recaptures were the result of dispersal within meadows. In 1995 5.8% of documented dispersal movements were from one meadow to another and in 1996 dispersal between meadows accounted for 15.2% of total recaptures.

One of the questions posed by Roland, Keyghobadi, and Fownes was how meadow size and population size might affect dispersal by *P. smintheus*. As shown in figure 10.21, average butterfly population size increased with meadow area. It turned out that butterflies are more likely to leave small populations than large populations. Butterflies leaving small populations generally immigrate to larger populations. The results of this study by Roland, Keyghobadi, and Fownes indicate that as alpine meadows in the Rocky Mountains decline in area, populations of *P. smintheus* will become progressively more compressed into fewer and fewer small meadows, perhaps disappearing entirely in parts of their range.

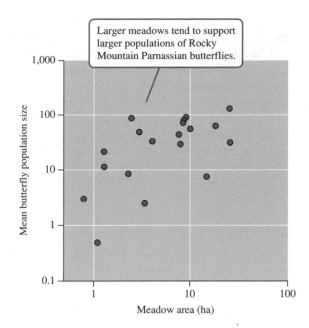

Figure 10.21 The relationship between meadow area and the size of Rocky Mountain Parnassian butterfly, *Parnassius smintheus*, populations. With forest encroachment into alpine meadows in the Rocky Mountains, populations of *P. smintheus* will likely decline.

In the last two discussions, we have reviewed patterns of distribution within populations. We have seen that those patterns vary from one population to another and may depend upon the scale at which ecologists make their observations. Now we turn from patterns of spatial variation within populations to compare the average densities of different populations. Is there any way to predict the average population density of populations? While it is not possible to make precise predictions, the following examples show that population densities are very much influenced by organism size.

Concept 10.3 Review

1. How can you determine whether the population of a species you are studying is a single population, or a connected subpopulation of a larger metapopulation?
2. If a subpopulation of a metapopulation collapses to n = 0, does the entire metapopulation crash? Why or why not?

10.4 Organism Size and Population Density

Population density declines with increasing organism size. If you estimate the densities of organisms in their natural environments, you will find great ranges. Bacterial populations in soils or water can exceed 10^9 per cubic centimeter. Phytoplankton densities often exceed 10^6 per cubic meter. Populations of large mammals and birds can average considerably less than one individual per square kilometer. What factors produce this variation in population density? The densities of a wide variety of organisms are highly correlated with body size. In general, population densities decrease with increasing size.

While it makes common sense that small organisms generally live at higher population densities than larger ones, quantifying the relationship between body size and population density provides valuable information. Measuring the relationship between body size and population density for a wide variety of species reveals different relationships for different groups of organisms. Differences in the relationship between size and population density can be seen among major groups of animals.

Animal Size and Population Density

John Damuth (1981) produced one of the first clear demonstrations of the relationship between body size and population density. He focused his analysis on herbivorous mammals, ranging from small rodents with a mass of about 10 g, to rhinoceros, with a mass well over 10^6 g. Meanwhile, average population density ranged from about 0.1 individual (10^{-2}) per 1 km^2 to about 10,000 (10^4) per 1 km^2. As figure 10.22 shows, the population density of 307 species of herbivorous mammals decreases with increased body size.

Building on Damuth's analysis, Robert Peters and Karen Wassenberg (1983) explored the relationship between body size and average population density for a wider variety of animals, including terrestrial invertebrates, aquatic invertebrates, mammals, birds, and poikilothermic vertebrates. Animal mass ranged from 10^{-11} to about $10^{2.3}$ kg, while population density ranged from less than 1 per square kilometer to nearly 10^{12} per square kilometer. Peters and Wassenberg, like Damuth, found that population density decreased with increased body size.

If you look closely at the data in figure 10.23, however, it is clear that there are differences among the animal groups. First, aquatic invertebrates of a given body size tend to have higher population densities than terrestrial invertebrates of similar size. Second, mammals tend to have higher population densities than birds of similar size. Peters and Wassenberg suggest that it may be appropriate to analyze aquatic invertebrates and birds separately from the other groups of animals.

The general relationship between animal size and population density has held up under careful scrutiny and reanalysis. Plant ecologists have found a qualitatively similar relationship in plant populations, as we see next.

Plant Size and Population Density

James White (1985) summarized the relationship between size and density for a large number of plant species spanning a wide range of plant growth forms (fig. 10.24).

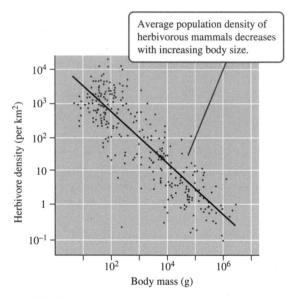

Figure 10.22   Body size and population density of herbivorous mammals (data from Damuth 1981).

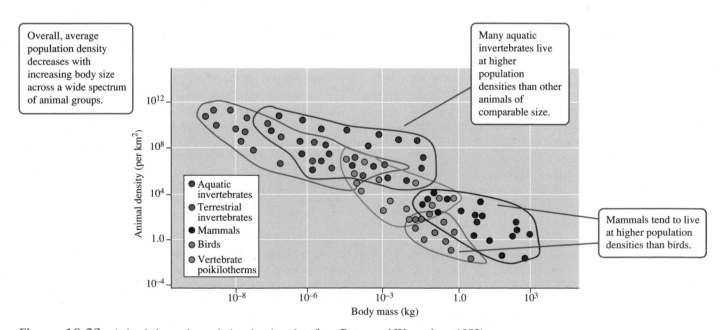

Figure 10.23   Animal size and population density (data from Peters and Wassenberg 1983).

The pattern in figure 10.24 illustrates that as in animals, plant population density decreases with increasing plant size. However, the biological details underlying the size–density relationship shown by plants are quite different from those underlying the size–density patterns shown by animals. The different points in figures 10.22 and 10.23 represent different species of animals. A single species of tree, however, can span a very large range of sizes and densities during its life cycle. Even the largest trees, such as the giant sequoia, *Sequoia gigantea,* start life as small seedlings. These tiny seedlings can live at very high densities. As the trees grow, density declines progressively until the mature trees live at low densities. We discuss this process, which is called *self-thinning,* in chapter 13. Thus, the size–density relationship changes dynamically within plant populations and also differs significantly between populations of plants that reach different sizes at maturity. Despite differences in the underlying processes, the data summarized in figure 10.24 indicate a predictable relationship between plant size and population density.

The value of such an empirical relationship, whether for plants or animals, is that it provides a standard against which we can compare measured densities and gives an idea of expected population densities in nature. For example, suppose you go out into the field and measure the population density of some species of animal. How would you know if the densities you encounter are unusually high, low, or about average for an animal of the particular size and taxon? Without an empirical relationship such as that shown in figures 10.23 and 10.24 or a list of species densities, it would be impossible to make such an assessment. One question that we might attempt to answer with a population study is whether a species is rare. As we shall see next, rarity is a more complex consideration than it might seem at face value.

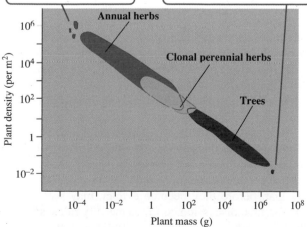

As in animals, plant population density decreases with increasing plant size across a wide range of plant growth forms.

Duckweed, *Lemna,* one of the smallest flowering plants, lives at very high population densities.

The coastal redwood, *Sequoia sempervirens,* one of the largest trees, lives at one of the lowest population densities.

Annual herbs

Clonal perennial herbs

Trees

Figure 10.24 Plant size and population density (data from White 1985).

Concept 10.4 Review

1. What are some advantages of Damuth's strict focus on herbivorous mammals in his analysis of the relationship between body size and population density?
2. How might energy and nutrient relations explain the lower population densities of birds compared to comparable sized mammals?

10.5 Commonness and Rarity

Commonness and rarity of species are influenced by population size, geographic range, and habitat tolerance. Viewed on a long-term, geological timescale, populations come and go and extinction seems to be the inevitable punctuation mark at the end of a species' history. However, some populations seem to be more vulnerable to extinction than others. What makes some populations likely to disappear, while others persist? At the heart of the matter are patterns of distribution and abundance. Species that are rare even in the absence of human activity seem to be more vulnerable to extinction. In order to understand extinction, we need to first understand the seven forms of rarity.

Seven Forms of Rarity and One of Abundance

Deborah Rabinowitz (1981) devised a classification of *commonness* and *rarity,* based on combinations of three factors: (1) the geographic range of a species (*extensive* versus *restricted*), (2) habitat tolerance (*broad* versus *narrow*), and (3) local population size (*large* versus *small*). Habitat tolerance is related to the range of conditions in which a species can live. For instance, some plant species can tolerate a broad range of soil texture, pH, and organic matter content, while other plant species are confined to a single soil type. As we shall see, tigers have broad habitat tolerance; however, within the tiger's historical range in Asia lives the snow leopard, which is confined to a narrow range of conditions in the high mountains of the Tibetan Plateau. Small geographic range, narrow habitat tolerance, and low population density are attributes of rarity.

As shown in figure 10.25, there are eight possible combinations of these factors, seven of which include at least one attribute of rarity. The most abundant species and those least threatened by extinction have extensive geographic ranges, broad habitat tolerances, and large local populations at least somewhere within their range. Some of these species, such as starlings, Norway rats, and house sparrows, are associated with humans and are considered pests. However, many species of small mammals, birds, and invertebrates not associated with humans, such as the deer mouse, *Peromyscus maniculatus,* or the marine zooplankton, *Calanus finmarchicus,* also fall into this most common category.

Ecologists exploring the relationship between size of geographic range and population size have found that they are not independent. Instead, there is a strong positive correlation between the two variables for most groups of organisms. In

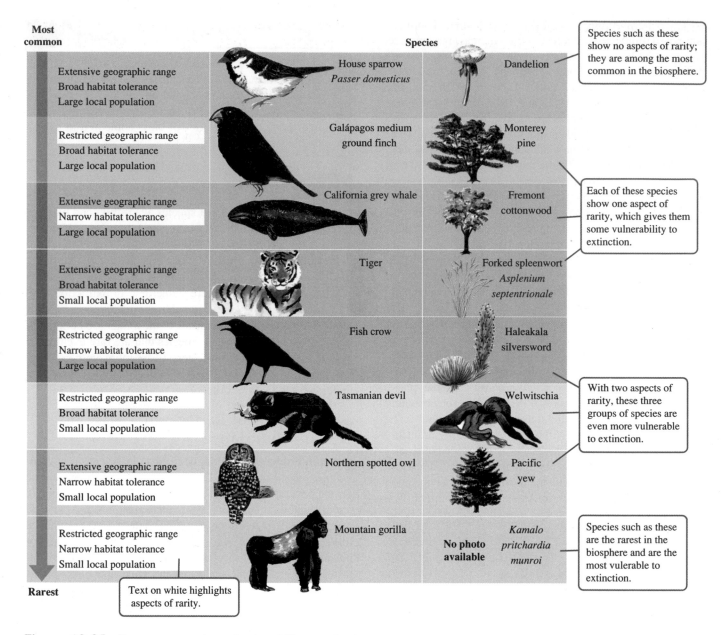

Figure 10.25   Commonness, rarity, and vulnerability to extinction.

other words, species abundant in the places where they occur are generally widely distributed within a region, continent, or ocean, while species living at low population densities generally have small, restricted distributions. The positive relationship between range and population density was first brought to the attention of ecologists by Ilka Hanski (Hanski 1982) and James H. Brown (Brown 1984). Kevin Gaston (Gaston 1996, Gaston et al. 2000) points out that in the two decades since the early work by Hanski and Brown, ecologists have found a positive relationship between range and population density for many groups, including plants, grasshoppers, scale insects, hoverflies, bumblebees, moths, beetles, butterflies, birds, frogs, and mammals. Several mechanisms have been proposed to explain the positive relationship between local abundance and range size. Many of the explanations focus on

breadth of environmental tolerances and differences in metapopulation dynamics. However, as Gaston and his colleagues point out (Gaston et al. 2000) there is still no concensus on the most likely explanations.

Most species are uncommon; seven combinations of range, tolerance, and population size each create a kind of rarity. As a consequence, Rabinowitz referred to "seven forms of rarity." Let's look at species that represent the two extremes of Rabinowitz's seven forms of rarity. The first two discussions concern species that are rare according to only one attribute. These are species that, before they become extinct, may seem fairly secure. The final discussion concerns the very rarest species, which show all three attributes of rarity. Though these rarest species are the most vulnerable to extinction, rarity in any form appears to increase vulnerability to extinction.

Rarity I: Extensive Geographic Range, Broad Habitat Tolerance, Small Local Population

It is easy to understand how people were drawn to the original practice of falconry. The sight and sound of a peregrine falcon, *Falco peregrinus,* in full dive at over 200 km per hour must have been one of the great experiences of a lifetime. To have held such a bird on your arm and launched it at its avian prey must have seemed liked controlling the wind. The peregrine, which has a geographic range that circles the Northern Hemisphere and broad habitat tolerance, is uncommon throughout its range. Apparently, this one attribute of rarity was enough to make the peregrine vulnerable to extinction. The falcon's feeding on prey containing high concentrations of DDT, which produced thin eggshells and nesting failure, was enough to drive the peregrine to the brink of extinction. Peregrine falcons were saved from extinction by control of the use of DDT, strict regulation of the capture of the birds, captive breeding, and reintroduction of the birds to areas where local populations had become extinct.

The range of the tiger, *Panthera tigris* (fig. 10.26), once extended from Turkey to eastern Siberia, Java, and Bali and included environments ranging from boreal forest to tropical rain forest. The tigers in this far-flung population varied enough from place to place in size and coloration that many local populations were described as separate subspecies, including the Siberian, Bengal, and Javanese tigers. Like peregrine falcons, tigers had an extensive geographic range and broad habitat tolerance but low population density. Over the centuries, relentless pursuit by hunters reduced the tiger's range from nearly half of the largest continent on earth to a series of tiny fragmented populations. Many local populations have become extinct and others, such as the magnificent Siberian tiger, teeter on the verge of extinction in the wild. These populations may survive only through captive breeding programs in zoos. The next example shows that narrow habitat tolerance can also lead to extinction.

Rarity II: Extensive Geographic Range, Large Local Population, Narrow Habitat Tolerance

When Europeans arrived in North America, they encountered one of the most numerous birds on earth, the passenger pigeon. The range of the passenger pigeon extended from the eastern shores of the present-day United States to the Midwest, and its population size numbered in the billions. However, the bird had one attribute of rarity: it had a narrow requirement for its nesting sites. The passenger pigeon nested in huge aggregations in virgin forests. As virgin forests were cut, its range diminished and market hunters easily located and exploited its remaining nesting sites, finishing off the remainder of the population. By 1914, when the last passenger pigeon died in captivity, one of the formerly most numerous bird species on earth was extinct. Extensive range and high population density alone do not guarantee immunity from extinction.

The rivers in the same region inhabited by the passenger pigeon harboured an abundant, widely distributed but narrowly tolerant fish, the harelip sucker, *Lagochila lacera.* This fish was found in streams across most of the east-central United States and was abundant enough that early ichthyologists cited it as one of the commonest and most valuable food fishes in the region. However, the harelip sucker, like the passenger pigeon, had narrow habitat requirements. It was restricted to large pools with rocky bottoms in clear, medium-sized streams about 15 to 30 m wide. This habitat was eliminated by the silting of rivers that followed deforestation and by the erosion of poorly managed agricultural lands. The last individuals of this species collected by ichthyologists came from the Maumee River in northwestern Ohio in 1893.

Extreme Rarity: Restricted Geographic Range, Narrow Habitat Tolerance, and Small Local Population

Species that combine small geographic ranges with narrow habitat tolerances and low population densities are the rarest of the rare. This group includes species such as the mountain gorilla, the giant panda, and the California condor. Species showing this extreme form of rarity are clearly the most vulnerable to extinction. Many island species have these attributes,

Figure 10.26   The tiger, *Panthera tigris*, was historically found throughout much of Asia, but at low population densities throughout its range.

so it is not surprising that island species are especially vulnerable. Of the 171 bird species and subspecies known to have become extinct since 1600, 155 species have been restricted to islands. Of the 70 species and subspecies of birds known to have lived on the Hawaiian Islands, 24 are now extinct and 30 are considered in danger of extinction.

Organisms on continents that are restricted to small areas, have narrow habitat tolerance, and small population size are also vulnerable to extinction. Examples of populations in such circumstances are common. More than 20 species of plants and animals are confined to about 200 km² of mixed wetlands and upland desert in California called Ash Meadows. The Ash Meadows stick-leaf, *Mentzelia leucophylla,* inhabits an area of about 2.5 km² and has a total population size of fewer than 100 individuals. Another plant, the Ash Meadows milk vetch, *Astragalus phoenix,* has a total population of fewer than 600 individuals. Human alteration of Ash Meadows appears to have caused the extinction of at least one native species, the Ash Meadows killifish, *Empetrichthys merriami.*

Amazingly, there are species with ranges even more restricted than those of Ash Meadows, California. In 1980, the total population of the Virginia round-leaf birch, *Betula uber,* was limited to 20 individuals in Smyth County, Virginia.

Until recently the total habitat of the Socorro isopod, *Thermosphaeroma thermophilum,* of Socorro, New Mexico, was limited to a spring pool and outflow with a surface area of a few square meters. Meanwhile, a palm species, *Pritchardia munroi,* which is found only on the island of Maui in the Hawaiian Islands, has a total population in nature of exactly one individual!

Examples such as these fill books listing endangered species. In nearly all cases, the key to a species' survival is increased distribution and abundance. One of the most fundamental needs for managing species, endangered or not, is making accurate estimates of population size. Some of the conceptual and practical issues that population ecologists must consider when censusing a population are the subject of the Ecological Tools section.

Concept 10.5 Review

1. How can the type of rarity displayed by a particular species influence its risk of going extinct? In other words, do low population sizes and restricted ranges present equal risks for extinction?
2. How does the life history influence whether it will be common, or rare? Which types of life histories are more prone to restricted ranges? Small population sizes?

Ecological Tools

Estimating Abundance— From Whales to Sponges

The abundance of organisms and how abundance changes in time and space are among the most fundamental concerns of ecology. These factors are so basic that some authors define ecology as the study of distribution and abundance of organisms. Because abundance is so important, ecologists should understand how to estimate it for a wide variety of organisms. Keep in mind, however, that ecologists do not measure abundance as an end in itself but as a tool to understand the ecology of populations. Knowing how abundant an organism is can tell us whether its population is growing, declining, or stable. However, to estimate the abundance of species the ecologist must contend with a variety of practical challenges and conceptual subtleties. Some of these are discussed here.

Estimating Whale Population Size

In 1989, the journal *Oceanus* published a table that listed the estimated sizes of whale populations. The table included the following note: "All estimates . . . are highly speculative." Why is it difficult to provide firm estimates of whale population size? Briefly, whales live at low population densities and may be distributed across vast expanses of ocean. They also spend much time submerged and move around a great deal. As large

as they are, you cannot count all the whales in the ocean. Instead, marine ecologists rely on population estimation. Each method of estimation has its own limitations and uncertainties.

One method used to estimate population sizes of elusive animals involves marking or tagging some known number of individuals in the population, releasing the marked individuals so they will mix with the remainder of the population, and then sampling the population at some later time. The ratio of marked to unmarked individuals in the sample gives an estimate of population size. The simplest formula expressing this relationship is the Lincoln-Peterson index:

$$M/N = m/n$$

where:

M = the number of individuals marked and released
N = the actual size of the study population
m = the number of marked individuals in a sample of the population
n = the total number of individuals in the sample

The major assumption of the Lincoln-Peterson index is that the ratio of marked to unmarked individuals in the population as a whole equals the ratio of marked to unmarked individuals in a sample of the population. If this is approximately so, then the population size is estimated as:

$$N = Mn/m$$

Figure 10.27   A humpback whale, *Megaptera novaeangliae*.

However, on average, the Lincoln-Peterson index overestimates population size. To reduce this tendency to overestimate, N. Bailey (1951,1952) proposed a corrected formula:

$$N = \frac{M(n+1)}{m+1}$$

Some of the assumptions of mark and recapture studies are:

• All individuals in the population have an equal probability of being captured.
• The population is not increased by births or immigration between marking and recapture.
• Marked and unmarked individuals die and emigrate at the same rates.
• No marks are lost.

Although real populations rarely meet all these assumptions, mark and recapture estimates of population size are often the best estimates available.

    Whale populations have been studied using mark and recapture techniques for some time. In the early days of whale population studies, population biologists marked whales by shooting a numbered metal dart into their blubber. Refined mark and recapture methods do not require artificially marking or capturing whales. In the "marking" phase of newer procedures, a whale is photographed and its distinguishing marks are identified. These photographs, along with information such as where the photograph was taken and whether the whale was accompanied by an offspring, are catalogued for future reference. In the "recapture" phase the whale is photographed at a later date and identified from previous photos. This method is called *photoidentification*.

    For more than two decades, Steven Katona (1989) has used photoidentification to study the humpback whales, *Megaptera novaeangliae*, of the North Atlantic (fig. 10.27). Humpback whales are particularly rich in individual marks, especially on the tail or flukes. This is convenient for photographic studies because humpback whales generally raise their flukes above the water before they dive. This behaviour, called "fluking," exposes the flukes to the photographer and reveals potentially unique markings (fig. 10.28).

(a)

(b)

Figure 10.28   Unique markings identify individual humpback whales. A humpback whale called "Siphon," #700, photographed in Frenchman Bay, Maine: (*a*) in 1995 and (*b*) in 1993.

Using photographs of these marks, Katona and his colleagues have produced the North Atlantic Humpback Catalog, which includes photographs of more than 4,000 individual whales. The photographs included in the catalog, along with information on where each photograph was taken, whether the whale was accompanied by an offspring, and other available observations, are curated for future reference. This photographic record is an invaluable source of information for determining the migration routes, feeding grounds, breeding grounds, and size of the North Atlantic humpback whale population (fig. 10.29).

    From 1979 to 1986, Scott Baker, Janice Straley, and Anjanette Perry (1992) photographed and identified 257 humpback whales along the coast of southeastern Alaska. In one part of their study the researchers used photoidentification to estimate the number of humpback whales in Frederick Sound, Alaska. In their first sampling period, from July 31 to August 3, 1986, the team photographed and identified 72 humpback whales. In a second sampling period, from August 29 to September 1, 1986, they photographed and identified 78 humpback whales. Of the 78 whales photographed in the second

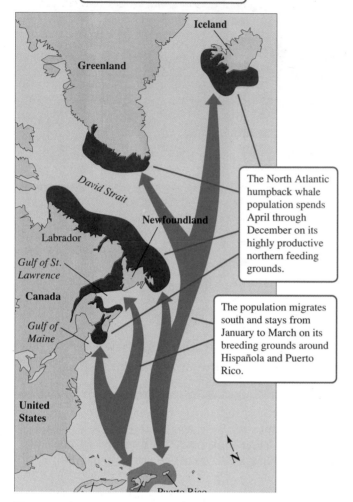

Mark and recapture estimates based on photographs place the current population of humpback whales in the North Atlantic at about 5,000.

The North Atlantic humpback whale population spends April through December on its highly productive northern feeding grounds.

The population migrates south and stays from January to March on its breeding grounds around Hispañola and Puerto Rico.

Figure 10.29 Photoidentification and the North Atlantic humpback whale population.

Puget Sound and around Vancouver Island, revealing information about births, deaths, and the size of the population. An advance in this research approach is the use of computerized image analysis to help identify and match photos of whales. While not providing all the information necessary for conserving and managing whale populations, photographic studies are clearly making an important contribution.

Though it may be more challenging physically, the process of counting whales is much like counting many other kinds of animals such as humans, lynxes, trout, or lady beetles. However, ecologists must use different methods to estimate the abundance of organisms that have a more variable growth form or differ greatly in size. As we shall see in the next example, this is particularly true when the relative abundances of very different organisms are compared.

The Relative Abundance of Corals, Algae, and Sponges

The reefs along the north coast of Jamaica were once dominated by corals. Thickets of staghorn coral rose from the seafloor like marine bramble bushes, and elkhorn coral grew in abundance in the surging waves. Then dramatic change came in 1980 with Hurricane Allen, which generated waves large enough to flatten the staghorn coral thickets and dislodge elkhorn corals. Most of the branching corals in shallow water were reduced to rubble. However, Hurricane Allen and its devastation was not the only problem. The reefs seemed to be changing even at depths below 25 m, where there was little hurricane damage. Assessing the extent and nature of changes on the reef would require detailed population studies.

Fortunately, Terence Hughes (1996) had started long-term studies of coral populations near Discovery Bay, Jamaica, in 1977, three years before Hurricane Allen. One of his goals was to document and understand apparent shifts in dominance from corals to algae. He was also concerned with documenting possible changes in sponge populations. But how can the relative abundance of organisms so different in size and growth form be estimated? A coral colony may cover several square meters or just a few square centimeters. Sponges also differ greatly in size. Algae of several species may grow together in a tangled mat covering several square meters or as a few isolated individuals. Ecologists studying terrestrial plants encounter similar size differences among plants of different ages and species. In the face of this variation, ecologists resort to measures of abundance that take into account differences in size. For instance, ecologists studying shrubs, herbaceous vegetation, or marine organisms such as corals, algae, and sponges often measure coverage, the area of landscape or reef covered by a species.

Hughes estimated percent cover by corals, algae, and sponges on his study reef nearly every year from 1977 to 1993. He made his estimates from photographs of 12 study plots 1 m^2 in size taken from a standard distance using slide film. He then mapped the positions and sizes of all coral and sponge colonies within the quadrats. He used a computer

sampling period, 56 were photographed for the first time, while 22 had also been photographed during the first sampling period. These 22 whales were the "recaptures." We can use these data and the corrected Lincoln-Peterson index to estimate the total number of whales in Frederick Sound from August 29 to September 1, 1986:

$$N = M (n + 1)/m + 1 = 72 (78 + 1)/22 + 1 = 247$$

In other words, Baker and his colleagues estimated that there were 247 humpback whales in Frederick Sound during the time of their study. Population estimates such as this are very important for monitoring the state of populations. In addition, photographic studies provide information on movements, calving intervals, and survival because photoidentified whales can go on yielding information throughout their lives.

In another study, population ecologists photographed and identified the entire population of 325 killer whales in

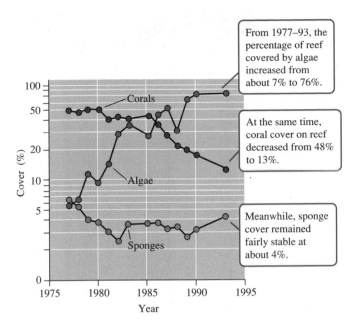

From 1977–93, the percentage of reef covered by algae increased from about 7% to 76%.

At the same time, coral cover on reef decreased from 48% to 13%.

Meanwhile, sponge cover remained fairly stable at about 4%.

Figure 10.30 Estimating abundance as percent cover: corals, sponges, and algae (data from Hughes 1996).

program to measure the areas on his maps that were covered by corals and sponges and then converted these measurements of absolute area to percent cover. Hughes estimated percent cover of algae by projecting the slide images of his study plots on a screen and superimposing a uniform grid of points on the image. The grid contained 100 points per square meter. The percentage of these points contacting algae in the image gave him an estimate of percent algal cover.

Hughes' 16-year study shows clear changes in the abundances of corals and algae (fig. 10.30). During the study, algal cover increased tenfold from 7% to 76%. At the same time, coral cover decreased from about 48% to 13%, while sponge populations remained fairly constant. Verifying the status of populations such as these is one of the most basic aspects of ecological research. Such measurements are the first step toward identifying the factors that determine the distribution and abundance

of organisms. With his photographs Hughes was able to show that this shift from a coral-dominated reef to one dominated by algae was due to increased mortality of coral colonies and reduced recruitment of new corals to the population. These are aspects of population dynamics that we cover in chapter 11.

Estimating Animal Abundances in Winter

Animals are tracked on land throughout the year. Though we may be most familiar with using traps and mist-nets to catch animals in the summer months (chapter 11), the winter can be an effective time of year to measure population sizes of many animals. Any ecologist with even a basic understanding of natural history will understand that measures of populations based only on summer numbers are likely less informative than those that include winter data, at least for species that are active and resident year round. How, though, does an ecologist measure populations in winter?

In much of Canada the ground is snow covered and much of the vegetation has died back during winter (chapter 5). As a result, large animals have relatively few places to hide, and can be easily identified and counted from the air. Ecologists regularly use surveys in helicopters and fixed-wing aircraft to estimate population sizes of large mammals such as elk over large expanses of land. Small animals, such as insects, can still be caught directly during winter. Subnivean traps can be placed below the snow to trap small animals that are active in the warm space between the ground and the surface of the snow (chapter 5).

Population sizes can also be estimated using a number of indirect measures based upon evidence of animal activity, rather than direct capture or observation. By counting tracks in snow of animals such as wolves, accurate estimates of local activity and population size can be constructed. These measures can be made even more accurate by including pellet/dung counts, potentially even using molecular means to identify individuals within the population (chapter 4). Other animals, such as hare, leave tell-tale signs of their presence through unique damage left on the stems of the browse they leave behind.

Summary

Ecologists define a population as a group of individuals of a single species inhabiting an area delimited by natural or human-imposed boundaries. Population studies hold the key to solving practical problems such as saving endangered species, controlling pest populations, or managing fish and game populations. All populations share a number of characteristics. Chapter 10 focused on two population characteristics: distribution and abundance.

While there are few environments on earth without life, no single species can tolerate the full range of earth's environments. Because all species find some environments too warm, too cold, too saline, and so forth, **the physical environment limits the geographic distribution of species.** For instance, there is a close relationship between climate and the distributions of the three largest kangaroos in Australia. The tiger beetle *Cicindela longilabris* is limited to cool boreal and mountain environments. Large- and small-scale variation in temperature and moisture limits the distributions of certain plants. However, differences in the physical environment only partially explain the distributions of some species, a reminder that biological factors constitute an important part of an organism's environment.

On small scales, individuals within populations are distributed in patterns that may be random, regular, or clumped. Patterns of distribution can be produced by the social interactions within populations, by the structure of the physical environment, or by a combination of the two. Social organisms tend to be clumped; territorial organisms tend to be regularly spaced. An environment in which resources are patchy also fosters clumped distributions. The distribution of trees in a Douglas-fir forest changes as the forest ages and varies among species. **On larger scales, individuals within a population are clumped.** In North America, populations of both wintering and breeding birds are concentrated in a few hot spots of high population density. Clumped distributions are also shown by plant populations living along steep environmental gradients on mountainsides.

Some populations, called metapopulations, consist of interconnected subpopulations. Populations of many species occur not as a single continuously distributed population but in spatially isolated patches, with significant exchange of individuals among patches. A group of subpopulations living on such patches connected by exchange of individuals among patches make up a metapopulation, such as is found for the Rocky Mountain Parnassian butterfly, *Parnassius smintheus,* in Alberta, Canada.

Population density declines with increasing organism size. In general, animal population density declines with increasing body size. This negative relationship holds for animals as varied as terrestrial invertebrates, aquatic invertebrates, birds, poikilothermic vertebrates, and herbivorous mammals. Plant population density also decreases with increasing plant size. However, the biological details underlying the size–density relationship shown by plants are quite different from those underlying the size–density patterns shown by animals. A single species of tree can span a very large range of sizes and densities during its life cycle. The largest trees start life as small seedlings that can live at very high population densities. As trees grow, their population density declines progressively until the mature trees live at low densities.

Commonness and rarity of species are influenced by population size, geographic range, and habitat tolerance. Rarity of species can be expressed as a combination of extensive versus restricted geographic range, broad versus narrow habitat tolerance, and large versus small population size. The most abundant species and those least threatened by extinction combine large geographic ranges, wide habitat tolerance, and high local population density. All other combinations of geographic range, habitat tolerance, and population size include one or more attributes of rarity. Rare species are vulnerable to extinction. Populations that combine restricted geographic range with narrow habitat tolerance and small population size are the rarest of the rare and are usually the organisms most vulnerable to extinction.

The abundance of organisms and how abundance changes in time and space are among the most fundamental concerns of ecology. To estimate the abundance of species the ecologist must contend with a variety of practical challenges and conceptual subtleties. Mark and recapture methods are useful in the study of populations of active, elusive, or secretive animals. Mark and recapture techniques, which use natural distinguishing marks, are making an important contribution to the study of populations of whales. Ecologists studying organisms, such as corals, algae, and sponges or many types of terrestrial plants, that differ a great deal in size and form, often estimate abundance as coverage, the area covered by a species. Population size can be estimated in the winter for many species using a variety of methods that take advantage of the snow. Patterns of distribution and abundance are ultimately determined by underlying population dynamics.

Review Questions

1. What confines *Encelia farinosa* to upland slopes in the Mojave Desert? Why is it uncommon along desert washes, where it would have access to much more water? What may allow *E. frutescens* to persist along desert washes while *E. farinosa* cannot?

2. Spruce trees, members of the genus *Picea,* occur throughout the boreal forest and on mountains farther south. For example, spruce grow in the Rocky Mountains south from the heart of boreal forest all the way to the deserts of the southern United States and Mexico. How do you think they would be distributed in the mountains that rise from the southern deserts? In particular, how do altitude and aspect (see chapter 5) affect their distributions in the southern part of their range? Would spruce populations be broken up into small local populations in the southern or the northern part of the range? Why?

3. What kinds of interactions within an animal population lead to clumped distributions? What kinds of interactions foster a regular distribution? What kinds of interactions would you expect to find within an animal population distributed in a random pattern?

4. How might the structure of the environment, for example, the distributions of different soil types and soil moisture, affect the patterns of distribution in plant populations? How should interactions among plants affect their distributions?

5. Suppose one plant reproduces almost entirely from seeds, and that its seeds are dispersed by wind, and a second plant reproduces asexually, mainly by budding from runners. How should these two different reproductive modes affect local patterns of distribution seen in populations of the two species?

6. Suppose that in the near future, the fish crow population in North America declines because of habitat destruction. Now that you have reviewed the large-scale distribution and abundance of the fish crow, devise a conservation plan for the species that includes establishing protected refuges for the species. Where would you locate the refuges? How many refuges would you recommend?

7. Use the empirical relationship between size and population density observed in the studies by Damuth (1981) (see fig. 10.22) and Peters and Wassenberg (1983) (see fig. 10.23) to answer the following: For a given body size, which generally has the higher population density, birds or mammals? On average, which lives at lower population densities, terrestrial or aquatic invertebrates? Does an herbivorous mammal twice the size of another have on average one-half the population density of the smaller species? Less than half? More than half?

8. Outline Rabinowitz's classification (1981) of rarity, which she based on size of geographic range, breadth of habitat tolerance, and population size. In her scheme, which combination of attributes makes a species least vulnerable to extinction? Which combination makes a species the most vulnerable?

9. Can the analyses by Damuth (1981) and by Peters and Wassenberg (1983) be combined with that of Rabinowitz (1981) to make predictions about the relationship of animal size to its relative rarity? What two attributes of rarity, as defined by Rabinowitz, are not included in the analyses by Damuth and by Peters and Wassenberg?

10. Suppose you have photoidentified 30 humpback whales around the island of Oahu in one cruise around the island. Two weeks later you return to the same area and photograph all the whales you encounter. On the second trip you photograph a total of 50 whales, of which 10 were photographed previously. Use the Lincoln-Peterson index with the Bailey correction to estimate the number of humpback whales around Oahu during your study.

Suggested Readings

Brisson, J. and J. F. Reynolds. 1994. The effects of neighbors on root distribution in a creosote bush (*Larrea tridentata*) population. *Ecology* 75:1693–1702.

The paper by Brisson and Reynolds demonstrates extended studies of creosote bush distributions belowground.

Brown, J. H., D. W. Mehlman, and G. C. Stevens. 1995. Spatial variation in abundance. *Ecology* 76:2028–43.

Root, T. 1988. *Atlas of Wintering North American Birds.* Chicago: University of Chicago Press.

These two references provide excellent entries into the area of large-scale distribution patterns in bird populations. These are pioneering efforts.

Gaston, K. J., T. M. Blackburn, J. J. D. Greenwood, R. D. Gregory, R. M. Quinn, and J. H. Lawton. 2000. Abundance-occupancy relationships. *Journal of Applied Ecology* 37:39–59.

A thorough review of the relationship between population size and geographic range.

King, S. R. B. and J. Gurnell. 2005. Habitat use and spatial dynamics of takhi introduced to Hustai National Park, Mongolia. *Biological Conservation* 124:277–90.

Fascinating population study following the successful reintroduction of captive-bred takhi or Przewalski's horse into Mongolia in the 1990s. This is one of the few examples of the reestablishment of a species following its extinction in the wild.

Konvicka, M., M. Maradova, J. Benes, Z. Fric, and P. Kepka. 2003. Uphill shifts in distribution of butterflies in the Czech Republic: effects of changing climate detected on a regional scale. *Global Ecology and Biogeography* 12:403–10.

Wilson, R. J., D. Gutiérrez, J. Gutiérrez, D. Martinez, R. Agudo, and V. J. Monserrat. 2005. Changes to the elevational limits and extent of species ranges associated with climate change. *Ecology Letters* 8:1138–46.

Two studies showing how butterfly species distributions shifted in response to warming temperatures during the twentieth century.

Rabinowitz, D., S. Cairns, and T. Dillon. 1986. Seven forms of rarity and their frequency in the flora of the British Isles. In M. E. Soule, ed. *Conservation Biology: The Science of Scarcity and Diversity.* Sunderland, Mass.: Sinauer Associates.

This paper provides an introduction and application of the concept of rarity developed by Deborah Rabinowitz.

Chapter 11

Population Dynamics

Outline

$\mathcal{U}$ncovering patterns of survival within natural populations of animals or plants often requires extended field studies. As Adolph Murie watched, the gray wolf ran downhill toward a herd of 20 Dall sheep, *Ovis dalli.* As the wolf approached, the herd of white sheep split into two bands. One band circled the wolf and ran up the slope, while the other ran downhill. In response, the wolf stopped. The two bands of sheep also stopped, only 30 to 40 m away from the wolf. Suddenly the wolf sprinted after the lower band, but they easily outran him on the steep terrain. Again, the sheep and the wolf stopped and rested. After an hour, the wolf broke the stalemate and again charged the lower band. The sheep avoided him, circling the wolf and rejoining the other half of their herd. A few minutes later the wolf abandoned the hunt, trotting away as the herd of Dall sheep watched from the ridge above (fig. 11.1).

Despite this particular wolf's failure, wolves kill enough Dall sheep to cause some people to suggest that wolf populations should be reduced to protect the sheep. Murie (1944) had been hired by the U.S. National Park Service to study the interactions between wolves and Dall sheep in Mount Danali National Park, Alaska. The main purpose of his study was to determine whether wolves kill enough sheep to justify the call for reducing the wolf population.

Murie pursued several lines of research. As in this example, he directly observed wolves and sheep. He also tracked wolves through winter snow to find their kills. The tracks left a record of wolf interactions with their prey. Where wolves had killed Dall sheep, they often left the skulls, which provided a record as rich as the telltale tracks. Murie could age the skulls by the size of the horns. The horns also indicated the sex of the individual. The teeth provided an indication of the sheep's general condition; worn teeth were a sign of poor nutrition and weakness. A careful search of Mount Danali National Park yielded a sample of 608 sheep skulls, which Murie used to explore the causes and age of death. The skulls showed Murie that death within the Dall sheep population fell mainly on the very young and the very old. Most sheep in the population could, as his direct observations had shown, avoid attack by wolves.

Fifty years later in the rocky desert terrain of eastern Egypt, Ahmad Hegazy (1990) used similar care to study an endangered plant species. The plant, *Cleome droserifolia,* is heavily exploited by desert dwellers and herbalists as a medicinal plant. Hegazy's study was prompted by concern that harvesting was leading to the extinction of this valuable plant species. Like Murie, Hegazy collected information that would give him insights into patterns of life and death within his study population. He collected information on the number of seeds produced by the population, on seed dispersal, and on the number of seeds in the soil. Hegazy also studied the establishment of seedlings and juvenile plants, as well as the survival of adults.

Though Hegazy did not have to pursue his study organisms through deep winter snows, the *Cleome* population presented him with challenges no less daunting than those faced by Murie. First, *Cleome* has a large number and diversity of life stages, including flowers, fruits, seeds, seedlings, juvenile plants, and adult plants. In addition, where Murie's study population numbered in the hundreds, Hegazy's seed population num-

Figure 11.1 Dall sheep, *Ovis dalli*, a mountain sheep of far northern North America, was the subject of one of the classic studies of suvivorship.

bered in the millions. While Murie had to contend with estimating survival and reproduction of an organism with a life span of about a dozen years, Hegazy had to estimate patterns of survival and reproduction of an organism that lives nearly 80 years. Hegazy's careful analysis of the *Cleome* population provided a means for managing the species that promotes its survival and allows its use in traditional medicine.

Adolph Murie's studies of wolves and Dall sheep and Hegazy's more recent study of a desert plant introduce us to another area of population biology, population dynamics. In chapter 10, we explored population distribution and abundance. However, to do so, we had to freeze populations at a particular instant in time. In fact, patterns of distribution and abundance result from a dynamic balance between rates of birth, death, immigration, and emigration. These dynamic processes are the subject of chapter 11.

Population dynamics involve what we might call the "behaviour" of populations. However, population behaviour differs from the behaviour of individual organisms. Population dynamics occur at a different level of biological organization, at the level of groups of individuals. Another major difference is that except for highly localized populations of microorganisms, population processes are played out at larger spatial, and longer temporal, scales. This difference in scale largely hides all but the most obvious population phenomena from the unaided human observer. To see and probe the dynamics of populations we use mathematical tools to provide us with a window to otherwise largely invisible phenomena.

It is difficult to keep track of everything going on in populations. Distributions may expand and contract. Numbers may increase for some time and then fall precipitously. A new population of a previously unrecorded species may suddenly appear in an area, persist for a season or a decade, and then disappear. Estimating characteristics such as survival and birthrates requires a great deal of information. Numbers of individuals alone, which may range from dozens to millions, can overwhelm the population ecologist. In addition, individuals of different ages and sexes may make different contributions to population dynamics and so must be followed separately. To organize our exploration of population dynamics, we first consider patterns of survival in populations and then age and sex distributions. Populations sometimes increase or decrease in size, and we next acquire the quantitative tools for perceiving such changes. Finally, we examine the effects of individuals' moving into and out of populations.

Concepts

11.1 **A survivorship curve summarizes the pattern of survival in a population.**

11.2 **The age distribution of a population reflects its history of survival, reproduction, and potential for future growth.**

11.3 **Population sex ratios can change depending upon the relative fitness of different sexes within a population.**

11.4 **A life table combined with a fecundity schedule can be used to estimate net reproductive rate (R_0), geometric rate of increase (λ), generation time (T), and per capita rate of increase (r).**

11.5 **Dispersal can increase or decrease local population densities.**

11.1   Patterns of Survival

A survivorship curve summarizes the pattern of survival in a population.   Patterns of survival vary a great deal from one species to another and, depending on environmental circumstances, can vary substantially even within a single species. Some species produce young by the millions, which, in turn, die at a high rate. Other species produce few young, invest heavily in their care, and have high rates of juvenile survival. Still other species show intermediate patterns of reproductive rate, parental care, and juvenile survival. In response to practical challenges of discerning patterns of survival, ecologists have invented bookkeeping devices called **life tables** that list the births, the survivorship, and the deaths, or *mortality,* in populations.

Estimating Patterns of Survival

There are three main ways of estimating patterns of survival within a population. The first and most reliable way is to identify a large number of individuals that are born at about the same time and keep records on them from birth to death. A group born at the same time is called a **cohort**, and a life table made from data collected in this way is called a **cohort life table.** The cohort studied might be a group of plant seedlings that matured at the same time or all the lambs born into a population of mountain sheep in a particular year.

While understanding and interpreting a cohort life table may be relatively easy, obtaining the data upon which a cohort life table is based is not. Imagine yourself lying face down in a meadow painstakingly counting thousands of tiny seedlings

of an annual plant. You must mark their locations and then come back every week for six months until the last member of the population dies. Or, if you are studying a moderately long-lived species, such as a barnacle or a perennial herb like a buttercup, imagine checking the cohort repeatedly over a period of several years. If your study organism is a mobile animal such as a whale or falcon, the problems multiply. If your species is very long-lived, such as a giant sequoia, such an approach is impossible within a single human lifetime. In such circumstances population biologists usually resort to other techniques.

A second way to estimate patterns of survival in wild populations is to go into the field for a narrow window of time and record the age at death of a large number of individuals. This method differs from the cohort approach because the individuals in your sample are born at different times. This method produces a **static life table.** The table is called *static* because the method involves a snapshot of survival within a population during a short interval of time. Estimating the age of dealth can be done by tagging individuals when they are born and then recovering the tags after death. An alternative procedure is to somehow estimate the age of dead individuals. For instance, mountain sheep can be aged by counting the growth rings on their horns. There are also growth rings on the carapaces of turtles, in the trunks of trees, and in the "stems" of soft or hard corals.

A third way of determining patterns of survival is from the **age distribution.** An age distribution consists of the proportion of individuals of different ages within a population. You can use an age distribution to estimate survival by calculating the difference in proportion of individuals in succeeding age classes. This method, which also produces a static life table, assumes that the difference in numbers of individuals in one age class and the next is the result of mortality. What are some other major assumptions underlying the use of age distributions to estimate patterns of survival? This method requires that a population is neither growing nor declining and that it is not receiving new members from the outside or losing members because they migrate away. Since most of these assumptions are often violated in natural populations, a life table constructed from this type of data tends to be less accurate than a cohort life table. Static life tables are often useful, however, since they may be the only information available.

High Survival Among the Young

As we saw in the introduction, Adolph Murie studied patterns of survival among Dall sheep in what is now Mount Danali National Park, Alaska. Murie estimated survival patterns by collecting the skulls of 608 sheep that had died from various causes. He determined the age at which each sheep in his sample died by counting the growth rings on their horns and by studying tooth wear.

Figure 11.2 summarizes the survival patterns for Dall sheep based on Murie's sample of skulls. The upper portion of the figure shows the static life table that Murie constructed. The first column lists the ages of the sheep, the second column lists the number surviving in each age class, and the third column lists the numbers dying in each age class. Notice

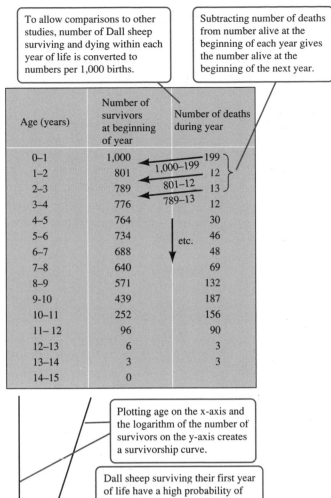

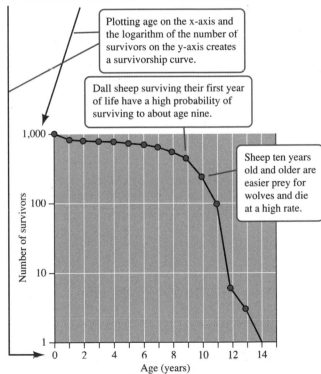

Figure 11.2 Dall sheep: from life table to survivorship curve (data from Murie 1944).

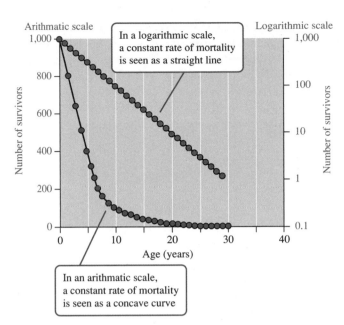

Figure 11.3 In this hypothetical population, 20% of individuals at the start of a given age class die prior to their next birthday. Using a logarithmic scale, the resulting survivorship curve is a straight line, while in the arithmetic scale the line is curved. As a result, the use of a logarithmic scale makes it easier to understand mortality patterns in populations.

The major assumption of this study is that the proportion of skulls in each age class represented the typical proportion of individuals dying at that age. For example, the proportion of sheep in the sample that died before the age of 1 year (199/1000) represents the proportion that generally dies during the first year of life. While this assumption is not likely to be strictly true, the pattern of survival that emerges probably gives a reasonable picture of survival in the population, particularly when the sample is as large as Murie's.

Plotting number of survivors per 1,000 births against age produces the **survivorship curve** shown in the lower portion of figure 11.2. A survivorship curve shows patterns of life and death within a population. You will notice that the y-axis of the survivorship curve is presented in a logarithmic scale. Why is this and what happens if we use the arithmetic, rather than logarithmic scale? First, it is important to understand why we draw survivorship curves in the first place, which quite simply is to have a quick way of knowing whether mortality rates for a given population change with age. If we used the arithmetic scale changes in slope would occur even without changes in survivorship rates (fig. 11.3), while in the logarithmic scale a flat line represents constant mortality rates with age.

Notice that in this population of Dall sheep, there are two periods when mortality rates are higher: during the first year and during the period between 9 and 13 years. Juvenile mortality and mortality of the aged are higher in this population, while mortality in the middle years is lower. The overall pattern of survival and mortality among Dall sheep is much like that for a variety of other large vertebrates, including red deer, *Cervus elaphus*, Columbian black-tailed deer, *Odocoileus hemionus columbianus*, East African buffalo, *Syncerus caffer*,

that although Murie studied only 608 skulls, the numbers in the table are expressed as numbers per 1,000 individuals. This adjustment is made to ease comparisons with other populations. The upper portion of figure 11.2 also shows how to translate numbers of deaths into numbers of survivors.

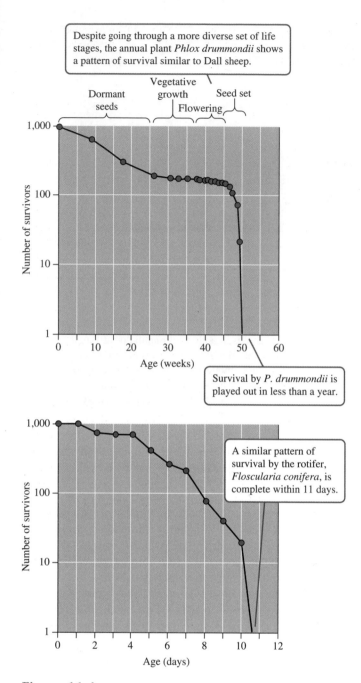

Despite going through a more diverse set of life stages, the annual plant *Phlox drummondii* shows a pattern of survival similar to Dall sheep.

Dormant seeds

Vegetative growth

Flowering

Seed set

Survival by *P. drummondii* is played out in less than a year.

A similar pattern of survival by the rotifer, *Floscularia conifera*, is complete within 11 days.

Figure 11.4   High rates of survival among the young and middle-aged in plant and rotifer populations (data from Deevey 1947, *bottom*, Leverich and Levin 1979, *top*).

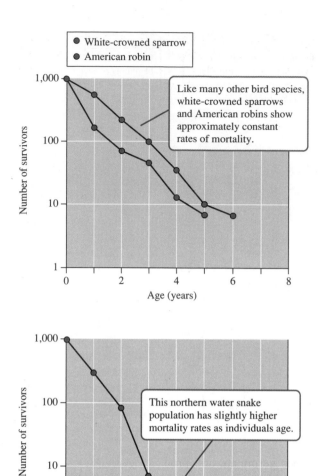

● White-crowned sparrow
● American robin

Like many other bird species, white-crowned sparrows and American robins show approximately constant rates of mortality.

This northern water snake population has slightly higher mortality rates as individuals age.

Figure 11.5   Constant rates of survival in sparrows and robins (data from Deevey 1947, Baker, Mewaldt, and Stewart 1981) Water snakes have higher juvenile survival rates than older individuals (Brown and Weatherhead 1999).

tern of survival is played out in less than 1 year and in the rotifer population in less than 11 days. These survivorship curves are based on cohort life tables.

Survival patterns can be quite different in other species. In the next example, mortality is not delayed until old age but occurs at approximately equal rates throughout life.

Constant Rates of Survival

The survivorship curves of many species are nearly straight lines. In these populations, individuals die at approximately the same rate throughout life. This pattern of survival has been commonly observed in birds, such as the American robin, *Turdus migratorius,* and the white-crowned sparrow, *Zonotrichia leucophrys nuttalli* (fig. 11.5). Life expectancy remains relatively constant over the whole period a cohort is in existence. While birds are the most well known for showing a linear pattern of survival, many other taxa do as well. For instance, figure 11.5 also shows the same pattern of survival for a population of the

and humans. The key characteristics of survival among these populations are relatively high rates of survival among the young and middle-aged and high rates of mortality among the older members.

This pattern of survival has also been observed in populations of annual plants and small invertebrate animals. Notice in figure 11.4 that patterns of survival in a population of a plant, *Phlox drummondii,* and a rotifer, *Floscularia conifera,* are remarkably similar to that of Dall mountain sheep. Following an initial period of higher juvenile mortality, mortality is relatively low for a period, and then mortality is high among older individuals. In the *Phlox* population, however, this pat-

northern water snake *Nerodia Sipedon*. Though the water snake has a high rate of mortality during the first year of life, thereafter, survival follows a straight line.

As we shall see next, some organisms die at a much higher rate as juveniles than we have seen in any of the populations we have considered to this point.

High Mortality Among the Young

Some organisms produce large numbers of young with very high rates of mortality. The eggs produced by marine fish such as the mackerel, *Scomber scombrus,* may number in the millions. Out of 1 million eggs laid by a mackerel, more than 999,990 die during the first 70 days of life either as eggs, larvae, or juveniles. Survival rates are similar in populations of the prawn *Leander squilla* off the coast of Sweden. For each 1 million eggs laid by *Leander,* only about 2,000 individuals survive the first year of life. This period of high mortality among young prawns is followed by a fairly constant mortality over the remainder of the life span.

Similar patterns of survival are shown by other marine invertebrates and fish and by plants that produce immense numbers of seeds. One of these plants is *Cleome droserifolia,* the desert shrub studied by Ahmad Hegazy (1990) that we discussed briefly in the introduction. Hegazy estimated that a local population of approximately 2,000 plants produce almost 20 million seeds each year. Of these, approximately 12,500 seeds germinate and produce seedlings. Only 800 seedlings survive to become juvenile plants. Figure 11.6 traces this pattern of survival by *Cleome* expressed as survivors per million seeds. Hegazy estimated that for each 1 million seeds produced about 39 survive to the age of one year, a survival rate of only 0.0039%. Survival in this desert plant population contrasts sharply with that seen in Dall sheep. The striking difference in patterns of survival between populations such

as *Cleome,* birds such as the American robin, and large mammals such as Dall sheep led early population biologists to propose a classification of survivorship curves.

Three Types of Survivorship Curves

Based on studies of survival by a wide variety of organisms, population ecologists have proposed that most survivorship curves fall into three major categories (fig. 11.7). A relatively high rate of survival among young and middle-aged individuals followed by a high rate of mortality among the aged is known as a **type I survivorship curve.** This is the pattern of survival we saw in populations of Dall sheep, *P. drummondii,* and rotifers (see figs. 11.2 and 11.4). Constant rates of survival throughout life produce the straight-line pattern of survival known as a **type II survivorship curve.** American robins, white-crowned sparrows, and northern water snakes show this pattern of survival (see fig. 11.5). A **type III survivorship curve** is one in which a period of extremely high rates of mortality among the young is followed by a relatively high rate of survival. The desert plant *Cleome* provides an excellent example of a type III survivorship curve (see fig. 11.6).

How well does this classification of survivorship represent natural populations? Most populations do not conform perfectly to any one of the three basic types of survivorship but show virtually every sort of intermediate form of survivorship between the curves. Even single species can show considerable variation in survivorship from one environment to another. For example, while human survivorship generally follows a type I survivorship curve, in difficult environments, human survivorship approaches a type II curve. This variation in patterns of human survival prompted G. Evelyn Hutchinson (1978) to muse: "One can only conclude that sometimes man is constrained to die randomly like a bird, but in other circumstances he may aspire to as ripe an old age as that of a wild sheep or an African

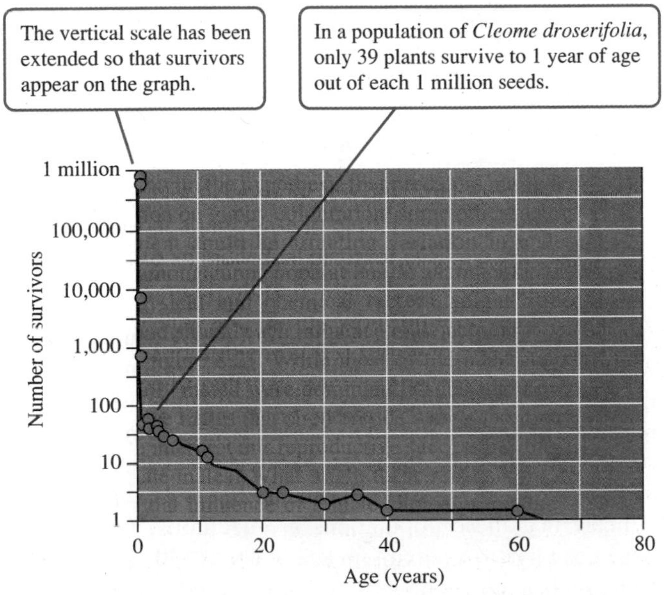

The vertical scale has been extended so that survivors appear on the graph.

In a population of *Cleome droserifolia*, only 39 plants survive to 1 year of age out of each 1 million seeds.

Figure 11.6 A high rate of mortality among the young of a perennial plant population (data from Hegazy 1990).

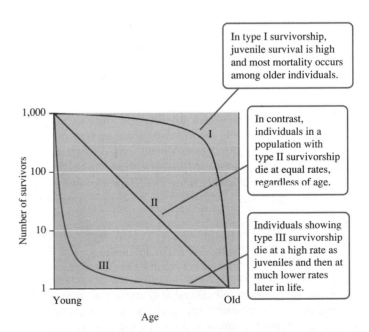

In type I survivorship, juvenile survival is high and most mortality occurs among older individuals.

In contrast, individuals in a population with type II survivorship die at equal rates, regardless of age.

Individuals showing type III survivorship die at a high rate as juveniles and then at much lower rates later in life.

Figure 11.7 Three types of survivorship curves.

buffalo." If survivorship can be so variable within species, what good are these idealized, theoretical survivorship curves? Their most important value, like most theoretical constructs, is that they set boundaries that mark what is possible within populations. Regardless of how closely actual survivorship curves approximate the theoretical curves, they serve excellent summaries of survival patterns within populations.

We now turn to the age distributions of populations, a topic closely related to survivorship. As we have seen, the age distribution of a population can be used to construct a static life table from which a survivorship curve can be drawn. However, as we shall see next, a population's age distribution offers other insights into population dynamics.

Concept 11.1 Review

1. How would substantial emigration and immigration affect estimates of survivorship within a population, where estimates are based on age distributions?
2. Female cottonwood trees (*Populus*; chapter 6) produce millions of seeds each year. Does this information give you a sound basis for predicting their survivorship pattern?

11.2 Age Distribution

The age distribution of a population reflects its history of survival, reproduction, and potential for future growth. Population ecologists can tell a great deal about a population just by studying its age distribution. Age distributions indicate periods of successful reproduction, periods of high and low survival, and whether the older individuals in a population are replacing themselves or if the population is declining. By studying the history of a population, population ecologists can make predictions about its future.

Stable and Declining Tree Populations

In 1923, R. B. Miller published data on the age distribution of a population of white oak, *Quercus alba,* in a mature oak-hickory forest in Illinois. In his study, Miller first determined the relationship between the age of a white oak and the diameter of its trunk. To do this, he measured the diameters of 56 trees of various sizes and then took a core of wood from their trunks. By counting the annual growth rings from each of the cores he could determine the ages of the trees in his sample. With the relationship between oak age and diameter in hand, Miller used diameter to estimate the ages of hundreds of trees.

Most white oaks in Miller's study forest were concentrated in the youngest age class of 1 to 50 years, with progressively fewer individuals in the older age classes (fig. 11.8). The oldest white oaks in the forest were over 300 years old. In other words, the age distribution of white oak in this forest was biased toward the young trees. What might we infer from this age distribution? The age distribution indicates that reproduction is sufficient to replace the oldest individuals in the population as they die. That is, this population of white oaks appeared to be stable, neither growing nor declining, at the time it was studied.

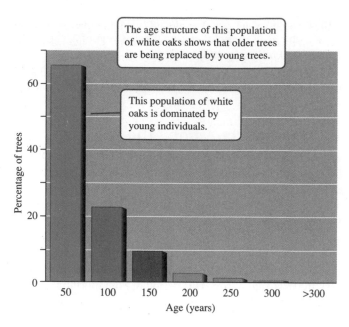

Figure 11.8   The age distribution of a white oak, *Quercus alba*, population in Illinois (data from Miller 1923).

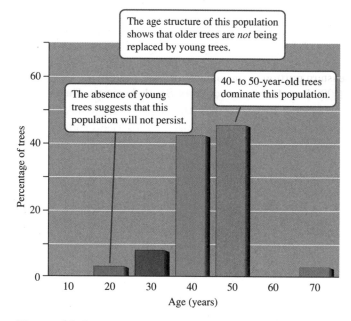

Figure 11.9   The age distribution of a population of Rio Grande cottonwoods, *Populus deltoides* subsp. *wislizenii*, near Belen, New Mexico (data from Howe and Knopf 1991).

The age distribution of this white oak population contrasts sharply with the age distributions of populations of Rio Grande cottonwoods, *Populus deltoides* spp. *wislizenii*. The most extensive cottonwood forests remaining in the southwestern United States grows along the Middle Rio Grande in central New Mexico. However, studies of age distributions indicate that these populations are declining. Older trees, which can live to a maximum age of about 130 years, are not being replaced by younger trees (fig. 11.9). In contrast to the white oak population in Illinois, the Rio Grande cottonwood population is dominated by older individuals. At the study site represented by figure 11.9, there has been no reproduction for over a decade. At other sites along the Rio Grande there has been little reproduction for over three decades.

Why have Rio Grande cottonwoods failed to reproduce? As we discussed in chapter 6, regeneration by Rio Grande cottonwoods depends upon seasonal floods, which play two key roles. First, floods create areas of bare soil without a surface layer of organic matter and without competing vegetation. Floods also keep these nursery areas of bare soil moist until cottonwood seedlings can grow their roots deep enough to tap into the shallow water table. The annual rhythm of seed bed preparation and seeding has been interrupted by the construction of dams on the Rio Grande for flood control and irrigation.

The age distributions of tree populations change over the course of many decades or centuries. Meanwhile, other populations can change significantly on much shorter timescales. One of these dynamic populations has been thoroughly studied on the Galápagos Islands.

A Dynamic Population in a Variable Climate

Rosemary Grant and Peter Grant (1989) have spent decades studying Galápagos finch populations. One of their most thorough studies has concerned the large cactus finch, *Geospiza conirostris*, on the island of Genovesa, which lies in the northeastern portion of the Galápagos archipelago, approximately 1,000 km off the west coast of South America. The Galápagos Islands have a highly variable climate, which is reflected in the highly dynamic populations of the organisms living on the islands, including populations of the large cactus finch.

The age distributions of the large cactus finch during 1983 and 1987 show that the population can be very dynamic (fig. 11.10). The 1983 age distribution shows a fairly regular distribution of individuals among age classes. However, there were no 6-year-old individuals in the population. This gap is due to a drought in 1977, during which no finches reproduced. Now, compare the 1983 and 1987 age distributions. The distributions contrast markedly, though they are for the same population separated by only 4 years!

The 1977 gap is still present in the 1987 age distribution and another has been added for two- and three-year-old finches. This second gap is the result of two years of reproductive failure during a drought that persisted from 1984 to 1985. Another difference is that the 1987 age distribution is dominated by four-year-old birds that were fledged during 1983. The 1983 class dominates because wet weather that year resulted in very high production of food that the finches depend upon for reproduction. The 1987 age distribution also shows evidence of high mortality among older finches. Might this decline be due to high adult mortality during the 1984–85 drought? Whatever the cause of these declines, the reproductive output of this population of large cactus finches is dominated by birds hatched in one exceptionally favourable year, 1983. This long-term study of the large cactus finch population of Genovesa Island demonstrates the responsiveness of population age structure to environmental variation.

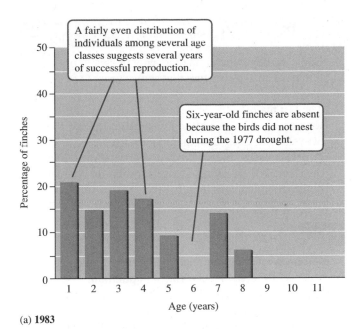

(a) **1983**

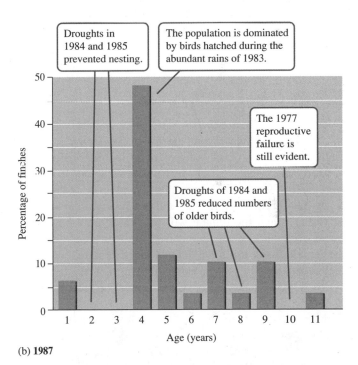

(b) **1987**

Figure 11.10 The age distribution of a population of large cactus finches, *Geospiza conirostris*, on the island of Genovesa in the Galápagos Islands during 1983 (*a*) and 1987 (*b*) (data from Grant and Grant 1989).

In this section, we have seen that an age distribution tells population ecologists a great deal about the dynamics of a population, including whether a population is growing, declining, or approximately stable. We can look even more closely at populations, and find differences among populations in the relative frequency of different sexes within the populations. In the next section we will find these differences are often the result of natural selection.

Concept 11.2 Review

1. Can a healthy population that is not in danger of extinction have an age structure that shows years of reproductive failure?
2. The last major natural reproduction by Rio Grande cottonwoods, which produced the large number of 40- and 50-year-old trees documented by Howe and Knopf (1991) occurred before the last major dam was built on the river. Is there any evidence for reproductive failure before that dam was built?

11.3   Sex Ratios

Population sex ratios can change depending upon the relative fitness of different sexes within a population.   As we have seen in prior chapters, sexual reproduction is widespread among plant and animal species, and there can be strong evolutionary advantages to sexual recombination. However, if we look closely at sex types in populations of many species, we find a puzzling pattern: although species and populations differ in many attributes such as population growth rates and size, males and females are generally found in approximately equal numbers. As a result, many populations of many species have approximately 1:1 **sex ratios** (fig. 11.11). Sex ratios can be defined as the relative frequency of each sex type (e.g., male, female) in a population. What factors influence the sex ratio of a population?

Fisher (1930) was among the first to suggest that sex ratios could be the result of natural selection. Imagine a population that had 100 individuals, 1 of which was female, and 99 of which were male. If we assume that mating is random (with the caveat being that it requires one male and one female to produce an offspring), then the female will most assuredly be able to mate, while the males will experience strong competition for the female. As a result, the parents of the female will have a high fitness (as they will have grandchildren), while the parents of nearly all the males will have zero fitness (no grandchildren).

If the ability to produce males or females has a genetic basis, then the relative frequency of female-producing individuals will increase. As the relative frequency of females approaches a 1:1 sex ratio, the fitness benefit for producing females instead of males decreases. If the population contains more females than males, then the selection will favour the production of sons, and not daughters. This process is a form of **frequency-dependent selection**, where the relative fitness of producing males or females is not inherent in the gender of the offspring itself, but instead is dependent upon the relative frequency of both alternative phenotypes. Through this process of frequency-dependent selection, populations should reach equilibrium at approximately a 1:1 sex ratio.

Although this theoretical model may be useful in explaining the many populations that do have 1:1 sex ratios, it fails to explain the many populations that have biased sex ratios. This issue has not escaped the attention of many evolutionary biologists over the last several decades, and here we will discuss just a few of the mechanisms that can cause unequal sex ratios. First, sex ratios can change as individuals age due to differential mortality of the sexes. For example, in human populations across the world there is a slight bias towards males at birth (World Factbook 2007), with 1.07 males to every female. However, for people older than 65, there is a strong female bias, with 0.78 males to every female. Across all age classes, the sex ratio is 1.01:1, very close to the theoretical prediction. Second, for many species, the body sizes of the different sexes are different, even at birth. As a result, so too is the cost to the parent of producing a son or a daughter. In general, natural selection will favour producing more individuals of the least costly sex, such that if males cost twice as much to produce as females, the population sex ratio should be female biased. Finally, Fisher's model assumed that all individuals had an equal probability of mating, but as we saw in chapter 8, there are many mating systems found in plant and animal species where this assumption is not met. For example, in harem-forming systems, dominant males generally receive more than an equal share of mating opportunities, while subordinate

(a)   (b)

Figure 11.11   (*a*) Male and (*b*) female individuals of the Banded Uromastyx, *Uromastyx flavofasciata*, are different colours. Most natural populations of animals have equal numbers of males and females.

males receive few, if any, opportunities. If it is only the biggest and healthiest males that become dominant in a population, then there should be selection against producing small sons, but not against producing smaller females (nearly all females will mate regardless of size in most harem mating systems). This can then result in increased costs in producing males relative to females (as described above), or instead it could result in only the healthiest females producing sons. In both scenarios, sex ratios should be female biased.

Although we do not generally consider the gender of one's offspring as a factor under evolutionary control, there is substantial research identifying a variety of specific genes and processes that increase or decrease the likelihood of producing males or females. The most obvious examples of how easily parents can influence gender are in cases of environmental sex determination. In a variety of species, there do not exist specific sex chromosomes (e.g., XY), but instead the gender of an offspring is determined by the environmental conditions in which the embryo develops, which may be under parental control. For example, the sex of many reptile species is determined by the temperature of incubation of the egg during the middle trimester of development. This is controlled in many species by changes in nest construction and egg burial depth.

In this section we have seen that sex ratios can vary among populations and through time. Natural selection can be a powerful force, and in a constant environment should lead toward a stable sex ratio for a given population. In the next section, we move beyond differences in sexes within a population, and focus on changes in population size over time. Although sexually reproducing species have more than one sex, you will see in the next section that population biologists generally focus only on the females of the population. Why? It is much easier to count the number of eggs laid, offspring birthed, or seeds set by a female than it is to determine paternity on all individuals in a population.

Concept 11.3 Review

1. Is frequency-dependent selection likely to influence the sex ratio of individual populations, or the average ratio among all populations of a species? Why?
2. How can a sex ratio of 2:1 males:females be stable? Is such a skewed sex ratio an indication of extinction risk for a population?

11.4 Rates of Population Change

A life table combined with a fecundity schedule can be used to estimate net reproductive rate (R_0), geometric rate of increase (λ), generation time (T), and per capita rate of increase (r). In addition to survival rates, population ecologists are concerned about another major influence on local population density—birthrates. In mammals and other live-bearing organisms, from sharks to humans, the term **birthrate** means the number of young born per female in a period of time. Population biologists also use the term *birth*

more generally to refer to any other processes that produce new individuals in the population. In populations of birds, fish, and reptiles, births are usually counted as the number of eggs laid. In plants, the number of births may be the number of seeds produced or the number of shoots produced during asexual reproduction. In bacteria, the birth, or reproductive, rate is taken as the rate of cell division.

Tracking birthrates in a population is similar to tracking survival rates. In a sexually reproducing population, the population biologist needs to know the average number of births per female for each age class and the number of females in each age class. In practice, the ecologist counts the number of eggs produced by birds or reptiles, the number of fawns produced by deer, or the number of seeds or sprouts produced by plants. The numbers of offspring produced by parents of different ages are then tabulated. The tabulation of birthrates for females of different ages in a population is called a **fecundity schedule.** If we combine the information in a fecundity schedule with that in a life table we can estimate several important characteristics of populations. To a population ecologist, one of the most important things to know is whether a population is growing or declining.

Estimating Rates for an Annual Plant

Figure 11.12 combines survivorship with seed production by the annual plant *P. drummondii*. The first column, x, lists age intervals in days. The second column, n_x, lists the number of individuals in the population surviving to each age interval. The third column, l_x, lists survivorship, the proportion of the population surviving to each age x. The fourth column, m_x, lists the average number of seeds produced by each individual in each age interval. Finally, the fifth column, $l_x m_x$, is the product of columns 3 and 4.

We've already used the data in column 3, l_x, to construct the survivorship curve for this species (see fig. 11.4). Now, let's combine those survivorship data with the seed production for *P. drummondii*, m_x, to calculate the **net reproductive rate, R_0.** The calculations of reproductive rates in this section assume that birthrates and death rates for each age class in a population are constant and that the population under study has a **stable age distribution.** In a population with a stable age distribution, the proportion of individuals in each of the age classes is constant. In general, the net reproductive rate is the average number of offspring produced by an individual in a population during its lifetime or per generation. In the case of the annual plant *P. drummondii,* the net reproductive rate is the average number of seeds left by an individual. You can calculate the net reproductive rate from figure 11.12 by adding the values in the final column. The result is:

$$R_0 = \sum l_x m_x = 2.4177$$

To calculate the total number of seeds produced by this population during the year of study, multiply 2.4177 by 996, which was the initial number of plants in this population. The result, 2,408, is the number of seeds that this population of *P. drummondii* will begin with the next year.

Figure 11.12

Combining survivorship with seed production by *P. drummondii* to estimate net reproductive rate, R_0

Age (days)	Number surviving to day x	Proportion surviving to day x	Average number of seeds per individual during time interval	Multiplication of l_x and m_x
x	n_x	l_x	m_x	$l_x m_x$
0–299	996	1.0000	0.0000	0.0000
299–306	158	0.1586	0.3394	0.0532
306–13	154	0.1546	0.7963	0.1231
313–20	151	0.1516	2.3995	0.3638
320–27	147	0.1476	3.1904	0.4589
327–34	136	0.1365	2.5411	0.3470
334–41	105	0.1054	3.1589	0.3330
341–48	74	0.0743	8.6625	0.6436
348–55	22	0.0221	4.3072	0.0951
355–62	0	0.0000	0.0000	0.0000

Data from Leverich and Levin 1979.

Each individual leaves an average of 2.4177 offspring.

$$R_0 = \sum l_x m_x = 2.4177$$

The value of R_0, which is greater than 1.0, indicates that this population of *P. drummondii* is growing.

Summing the final column yields R_0, the net reproductive rate per individual.

Since *P. drummondii* has pulsed reproduction, we can estimate the rate at which its population is growing with a quantity known as the **geometric rate of increase, λ.** The geometric rate of increase is the ratio of the population size at two points in time:

$$\lambda = \frac{N_{t+1}}{N_t}$$

In this equation, N_{t+1} is the size of the population at some future time and N_t is the size of the population at some earlier time (fig. 11.13). The time interval t may be years, days, or hours; which time interval you use to calculate the geometric rate of increase for a population depends on the organism and the rate at which its population grows.

Let's calculate λ for the population of *P. drummondii.* What time interval should we use for our calculation? Since *P. drummondii* is an annual plant, the most meaningful time interval would be one year. The initial number, N_t, of *P. drummondii* in the population was 996. The number of individuals (seeds) in the population at the end of a year of study was 2,408. This is the number in the next generation, which is N_{t+1}. Therefore, the geometric rate of increase for the population over the period of this study was:

$$\lambda = \frac{2,408}{996} = 2.4177$$

This is the same value we got for R_0. But, before you jump to conclusions, you should know that R_0, which is the number of

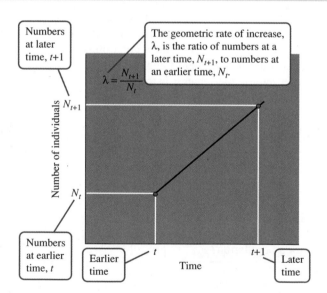

Figure 11.13 The geometric rate of increase.

offspring per female per generation, does not always equal λ. In this case, λ equaled R_0 because *P. drummondii* is an annual plant with pulsed reproduction. If a species has overlapping generations and continuous reproduction, R_0 will usually not equal λ.

How long do you think this plant can continue to reproduce at the rate of λ, or $R_0 = 2.4177$? Not long, but we'll get back to this point in chapter 12. Before we do that, let's do some calculations for organisms with overlapping generations.

Estimating Rates When Generations Overlap

The population of the northern water snake, *Nerodia sipedon*, whose mortality we examined in figure 11.5, contrasts with the *P. drummondii* population in various ways. Let's examine some of the details of this snake and study to better understand life tables. The data presented in figure 11.14 were collected in a marsh near Queen's University Biological Station in Ontario. Snakes were captured, marked, and recaptured regularly over a period of nine years. Approximately 70% of adult females will breed in any particular year. In contrast to annual plants, individual snakes do not die following breeding and thus there is overlap in survival among generations (parents and children coexist). Further complicating matters is that individuals can mate multiple times in their life. Females are not generally sexually mature until age four, and even then larger females tend to produce larger litters than smaller females. Across all ages and sizes of females that do breed, the average litter size is 19.7 offspring. Multiplying the proportion of females that breed (0.7) by the average litter size (19.7), gives us an estimate of the average number of offspring produced by an adult (reproductively mature) female each year = 13.79. On average, half of these offspring will be male, and half will be female. However, population biologists generally keep track of only females and thus we are concerned here with only the production of daughters. Since the sex ratio in this population is 1:1, we multiply 13.79 by 0.50 to calculate the number of daughters per adult female per year in the population = 6.9. However, if you look at figure 11.14, you will not find the value 6.9 listed under the m_x column. Why? Because 6.9 is an average value across all adult females, while in this snake population older females tended to be larger than younger females, and also produced more offspring per litter.

Figure 11.14 includes the life table information used to construct figure 11.5 plus the fecundity information estimated during the study. The sum of $l_x m_x$ provides an estimate of R_0, the net reproductive rate of females in this population. In this case, $R_0 = 0.787$. We can interpret this number as the average number of daughters produced by each female in this population over the course of her lifetime. If this number is correct, the mothers in this population are not producing enough daughters to replace themselves. What value of R_0 would suggest a stable snake population? In a stable population, R_0 would be 1.0, which means that each female would replace just herself during her lifetime. In a growing population, such as the population of Phlox, R_0 would be greater than 1.0.

Population ecologists are also interested in several other characteristics of populations. One of those is the generation time, T, which is the average time from egg to egg, seed to seed, and so forth. We can use the information in figure 11.14 to calculate the average generation time for the northern water snakes of Barb's Marsh as:

$$T = \frac{\sum x l_x m_x}{R_0}$$

In this equation x is age in years. To calculate T, sum the last column and divide the result by R_0. The result shows that the average generation time is 5.04 years.

How could you tell if 5.0 years is an unusually long, or short, generation time? Figure 11.15 plots the generation time for a broad range of organisms against body size. As we saw for population density in chapter 10, there is a significant positive correlation between body size and generation time. The largest organisms have the longest generation times and the smallest have the shortest. While this relationship might not be particularly surprising, its consistency across such a wide range of organisms is impressive. In addition, the relationship isn't restricted to a narrow taxon such as herbivorous mammals. John Bonner (1965) found the trend shown in figure 11.15, which is rooted in the bacteria and extends all the way to the largest organisms in the biosphere, the giant sequoia, *Sequoia gigantea*. Humans and water snakes lie somewhere in the middle range of the distribution.

Knowing R_0 and T allows us to estimate r, the **per capita rate of increase** for a population:

$$r = \frac{\ln R_0}{T}$$

(ln is the base of the natural logarithms). We can interpret r as birthrate minus death rate: $r = b - d$. Using this method, the estimated per capita rate of increase for the northern water snake population is:

$$r = \frac{\ln 0.787}{5.04} = -0.048$$

x (years)	l_x	m_x	$l_x m_x$	$x l_x m_x$
0	1.0000	0	0	0
1	0.4000	0	0	0
2	0.1640	0	0	0
3	0.1000	0	0	0
4	0.0640	5.5400	0.3547	1.4188
5	0.0307	6.7600	0.2078	1.0388
6	0.0148	7.8100	0.1152	0.6913
7	0.0071	8.8900	0.0629	0.4406
8	0.0034	9.1000	0.0309	0.2474
9	0.0016	9.2400	0.0151	0.1357

Source: Table based on Brown and Weatherhead 1999, CJ277:1358-1366 (Survival of northern water snakes).

$$R_0 = \sum l_x m_x = 0.787$$

> The value of R_0 is less than 1.0 which indicates the population is declining.

$$T = \frac{\sum x l_x m_x}{R_0} = \frac{3.97}{0.787} = 5.04$$

> Dividing $\sum x l_x m_x$ by R_0 gives an estimate of generation time.

> The generation time for this population is 5.04 years.

Figure 11.14 Calculating net reproductive rate, R_0, and generation time, T, for a population of the northern water snake, *Nerodia sipedon*.

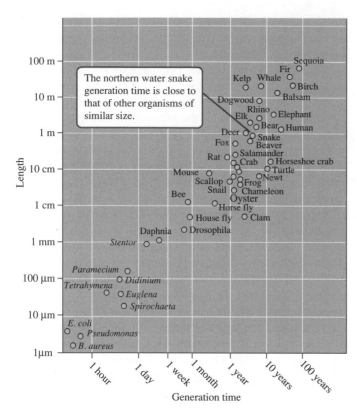

Figure 11.15   Size and generation time (data from Bonner 1965).

The northern water snake generation time is close to that of other organisms of similar size.

The negative value of *r* in this case indicates that birthrates are lower than death rates and the population is declining. A value of *r* greater than 0 would indicate a growing population, and a value equal to 0 would indicate a stable population. While there are ways to make more accurate estimates of *r*, this method is accurate enough for our discussion. We will return to *r* in chapter 12 as we discuss population growth.

In this section we have seen how a life table combined with a fecundity schedule can be used to estimate net reproductive rate, R_0, geometric rate of increase, λ, generation time, *T,* and per capita rate of increase, *r*. Population dynamics are clearly influenced by patterns of survival and reproduction. However, births and deaths are not the only processes that make populations dynamic. As we shall see in the next concept discussion, population dynamics are also influenced by the movements of organisms.

Concept 11.4 Review

1. Suppose that you are managing a population of an endangered species that has been reduced in numbers throughout its historic range and that your goal is to increase the size of the population. What values of R_0 would meet your management goals?
2. Both R_0 and *r* indicate that the water snake population at Barb's Marsh is in decline. Is there any way that this population could persist, without human intervention, for many generations even with such negative indicators?

11.5   Dispersal

Dispersal can increase or decrease local population densities.   As we saw in chapter 10 where we considered metapopulations, dispersal is an important aspect of population dynamics. The seeds of plants disperse with wind or water or may be transported by a variety of mammals, insects, or birds. Adult barnacles may spend their lives attached to rocks, but their larvae travel the high seas on far-ranging ocean currents. A host of other sessile marine invertebrates, algae, and many highly sedentary reef fishes also disperse widely as larvae. Some young spiders spin a small net that catches winds and carries them for distances up to hundreds of kilometers. Young mammals and birds often disperse from the area where they were born and may join other local populations. As a consequence of movements such as these (fig. 11.16), the population ecologist trying to understand local population density must consider dispersal *into* (**immigration**) and *out of* (**emigration**) the local population.

Despite its importance, dispersal is one of the least-studied aspects of population dynamics. Its study is clearly a difficult undertaking. But dispersal is worth studying; the health and survival of many local populations may depend upon this underappreciated aspect of population dynamics. One of the richest sources of information on dispersal and some of the clearest examples come from studies of expanding populations.

Dispersal of Expanding Populations

Expanding populations are in the process of increasing their geographic range. Why should this type of population provide us with some of the best records of species dispersal? The appearance of a new species in an area is quickly noted and recorded, especially if the species impacts the local economy or human health or safety. For instance, the expansion of Africanized bees through South and North America is well documented (fig. 11.17). The legendary aggressiveness of these bees ensures that their dispersal into an area does not escape notice for long.

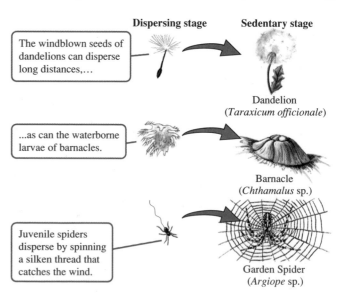

The windblown seeds of dandelions can disperse long distances,...

...as can the waterborne larvae of barnacles.

Juvenile spiders disperse by spinning a silken thread that catches the wind.

Dandelion
(*Taraxicum officionale*)

Barnacle
(*Chthamalus* sp.)

Garden Spider
(*Argiope* sp.)

Figure 11.16   Dispersing and sedentary stages of organisms.

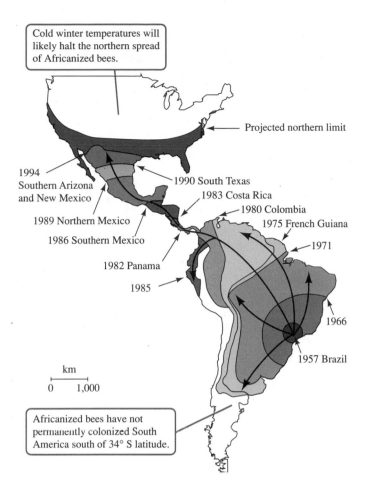

Figure 11.17   The expansion of Africanized bees from South America through Central and North America, 1956 to 1994 (data from Winston 1992)

Africanized Honeybees

Honeybees, *Apis melifera,* evolved in Africa and Europe, where their native range extends from tropical to cold, temperate environments. Across this extensive environmental range, this species has differentiated into a number of locally adapted subspecies. In an attempt to improve the adaptability of managed honeybees to their tropical climate, Brazilian scientists imported queens of the African subspecies *Apis melifera scutellata* in 1956. These queens mated with the European honeybees used by Brazilian beekeepers, producing what we now call Africanized bees.

Africanized honeybees differ in several ways from European honeybees. Temperate and tropical environments have apparently selected for markedly different behaviour and population dynamics. Natural selection by a high diversity and abundance of nest predators has probably produced the greater aggressiveness shown by Africanized bees. The warmer climate and greater stability of nectar sources eliminates the advantages of storing large quantities of honey and maintaining large colonies for survival through the winter. Most important to this discussion of dispersal, Africanized honeybees produce swarms that disperse to form new colonies at a much higher rate than do European honeybees.

High rates of colony formation and dispersal have caused a rapid expansion of Africanized honeybees through South and North America. Their rate of dispersal has ranged from 300 to 500 km per year. Within 30 years, Africanized honeybees occupied most of South America, all of Central America, and most of Mexico. The estimated number of wild colonies of these bees in South America alone is 50 to 100 million. Africanized bees reached southern Texas in 1990 and southern Arizona and New Mexico in 1994. The honeybees stopped spreading southward through South America by about 1983, stopping at about 34° S latitude. However, they continue to spread northward through North America and will continue to do so until stopped by cold climates. Population ecologists predict that Africanized honeybees will reach the northern limit of their distribution within North America sometime early in the twenty-first century.

How does this rate of expansion by African honeybees compare to rates of expansion by other populations? Figure 11.18, which summarizes rates of dispersal for a variety of mammals and birds, shows that rates of dispersal differ by three orders of magnitude. While some species such as Africanized bees spread at rates of tens or hundreds of kilometers per year, others disperse only a few hundred meters per year. This is about the same rate at which North American trees expanded their distributions following the retreat of the glaciers.

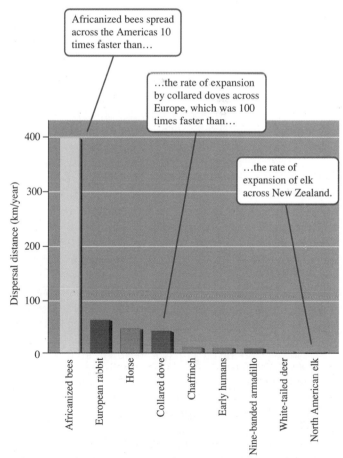

Figure 11.18   Rates of expansion by animal populations (data from Caughley 1977, Hengeveld 1988, Winston 1992).

Unintended Consequences of Ecological Research

When we look at life tables and other measures of populations, it is easy to forget that each data point often represents an actual organism that an ecologist located, measured, marked, and released back into the wild (chapter 10). The numbers of organisms that are marked in a given year can be amazingly high. For example, the United States and Canada have a joint effort coordinated by the Bird Banding Laboratory (BBL) to catch, band, and release birds. Recaptures and recoveries are used for a variety of population measures. Over 1,000,000 birds are banded annually in North America, and since the BBL program began in 1908, over 60,000,000 birds have been banded. Of these, a total of about 3,000,000 birds have been recovered or recaptured. Studies of other species also involve the capture and release of large numbers of individuals. Because the biology of species differ so greatly, so too do the methods of capture and release. Many birds are caught in fine "mist-nets" installed in flight paths. Birds are removed from the nets by hand, measured, and a small metal band is placed on one leg. Many large mammals are caught by being followed with a helicopter and then shot with a tranquilizer. Marking can involve tattooing, insertion of tags around ears or other body parts, and in some cases, the removal of a tooth for age determination. Lizards and frogs have historically been captured in snares and pitfall traps and marking often involves "toe-clipping," in which the ecologist snips off various combinations of toes to give each animal a unique pattern. With increased technological advances over the last several decades, many organisms are outfitted with VHF (very high frequency) or GPS (global positioning systems) telemetry devices which can be inserted internally or attached externally. So what? Do these ecologists need to concern themselves with the effects of these methods on their organisms?

Yes, and many ecologists have been concerned for quite some time. In Canada, all research on vertebrates, and on some invertebrates, requires formal approval by Animal Care Committees. These procedures are not trivial, and they require the researcher to fully describe the research protocols that will be used, the justification for the need for these protocols, and the steps that will be taken to minimize stress, the number of animals handled, and the risk of physical harm to the animals and researchers. Failure to show due diligence during the study can result in significant penalties, including the loss of funding, inability to publish, and a variety of more severe disciplinary actions. Aside from these "sticks" associated with animal welfare and scientific research, and the associated ethical considerations they are designed to protect, ecologists are increasingly concerned about their activities based upon scientific grounds.

Concerns are generally raised on two issues (1) immediate harm to individuals during the capture and marking process, and (2) longer-term harm through altered physiology and/or morphology. For example, capture and handling can cause significant stress to animals. When this is coupled with inadequate training, chance events, and other factors, trapping and handling can lead to mortality in a variety of species. Although exact numbers of capture-related deaths are difficult to find in the literature, mortality rates in excess of 2% for large mammals due to capture and handling have been suggested to be of concern (Arnemo et al. 2006). Due to the magnitude of some mark-recapture efforts, large numbers of animals may be adversely affected. For example, one study in Australia suggested a 1% rate of mortality associated with mist-nests and bird banding (Recher et al. 1985). If we assume this value to be constant, then banding activity in North America alone may cause the death of over 10,000 birds annually, and 600,000 birds since 1908. Though these numbers are dwarfed in comparison to mortality associated with habitat loss, power lines, and other human-mediated causes, it is important to recognize that trapping and handling of animals does cause mortality. When these activities are on a large scale like the BBL, the numbers of deaths due to research activity will also be large. Aside from immediate mortality, some organisms will continue to show negative consequences of capture and handling for days, weeks, or years after the capture event. For example, toe-clipping can reduce the clinging ability of an arboreal lizard (Bloch and Irschick 2005), outfitting marine birds with transmitters reduces their foraging efficiency (Wilson et al. 1986), capturing butterflies alters their subsequent behaviour (Singer and Wedlake 1981), and even repeated measures of plants can alter rates of herbivory (Cahill et al. 2001). Few studies have determined the impacts of marking on population dynamics, with one main exception.

Gauthier-Clerc and colleagues (2004) investigated the impact of flipper bands on population dynamics of king pen-

Range Changes in Response to Climate Change

In response to climate change following retreat of the glaciers northward in North America beginning about 16,000 years ago, organisms of all sorts began to move northward from their ice age refuges. Temperate forest trees have left one of the best preserved records of this northward dispersal. In chapter 1 we saw how Margaret Davis was able to show the migration of tree species through well preserved pollen records in lake sediment. For example, the northward advance of maple and hemlock is shown in figure 11.20.

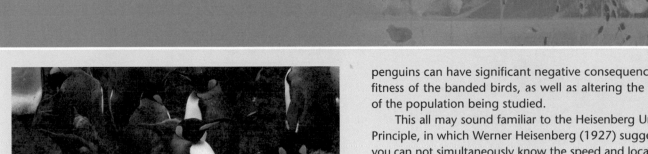

Figure 11.19   Flipper tags have been extensively used in the study of penguin population dynamics.

guins (fig. 11.19). Due to the shape of penguin ankles, leg bands that are commonly used for songbirds can not be used, and instead bands are placed on penguin flippers. To test the hypothesis that flipper bands could alter population dynamics, they followed 100 adult King Penguins (*Aptenodytes patagonicus*) in a colony of 25,000 breeding pairs for five years. To 50 of these birds they attached standard flipper tags. To the other 50 birds they inserted a transponder tag below each bird's skin. They also buried antennae under paths between the water and the colony, which recorded each time individual birds crossed the paths. Over five years, the 50 banded birds produced 28 chicks, while the unbanded birds produced 54 chicks, a very large difference in fecundity between groups. Additionally, each year the banded birds arrived to the breeding colony several days later than unbanded birds, which may have negative consequences for mate selection. In a related study in which researchers inserted transponders into 300 chicks (their prior results led them to conclude it would be unethical to place flipper bands on any more penguins), they found survival rates nearly twice as high as those in published studies that used banded chicks (Gauthier-Clerc et al. 2004). Taken together, these data strongly suggest banding these

penguins can have significant negative consequences for the fitness of the banded birds, as well as altering the dynamics of the population being studied.

This all may sound familiar to the Heisenberg Uncertainty Principle, in which Werner Heisenberg (1927) suggested that you can not simultaneously know the speed and location of an electron, as the act of measuring one alters the value of the other. Ecologists are recognizing that they are not invisible monitors of the natural world, and the very act of conducting ecological research can cause changes in the behaviour of natural systems. Does this mean we should stop doing ecological research or that all field work is inherently flawed and unethical? Of course not, and there are recent efforts to help develop positive solutions. First, ecologists have become more aware of these issues, and studies documenting unintended consequences are being published in high profile journals and receiving extensive media coverage. This encourages other scientists to test the effects of the methods they use, and helps us develop less invasive methods. For example, many GPS-recording devices, transponders, and other attachments have greatly decreased in size, which should reduce the stress associated with wearing the device. Genetic approaches can allow researchers to follow individual organisms not by recording the number on an ear tag, but by using DNA samples from hair snags or fecal collections, reducing the need for live-captures. At the same time, technological advances are reducing the cost of many recording devices that can be attached to animals, resulting in a proliferation of studies that place measuring devices on wild animals themselves. Wilson and McMahon (2006) have called for the development of a framework to establish acceptable practices for ecologists. Such a step is a clear sign that ecologists are working to reduce unnecessary harm to study organisms.

All research activity results in unintended and potentially confounding effects. However, it is important to remember that many of the questions that ecologists are addressing have the potential to positively impact the health and sustainability of numerous wild populations. It is unfortunate that the process of study causes mortality of some individuals; however, without these studies even larger numbers of individuals are likely at risk. Ecologists work hard to minimize these negative effects, both because it is ethically sound and because it provides better data.

Figure 11.20 illustrates a number of ecologically significant messages. Though the distributions of maple and hemlock overlap today, they did not during the height of the last ice age. In addition, maple colonized the northern part of its present range from the lower Mississippi Valley region, while hemlock colonized its present range from a refuge along the

Atlantic coast. The two trees dispersed at very different rates. Of the two species, maple dispersed faster, arriving at the northern limits of its present-day range about 6,000 years ago. In contrast, hemlock didn't reach the northwestern limit of its present distribution until 2,000 years ago.

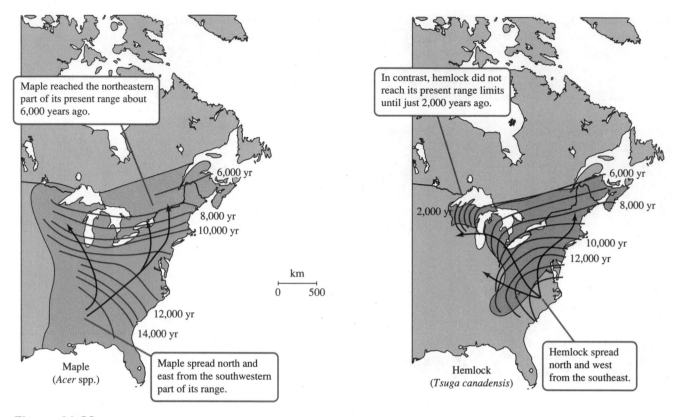

Figure 11.20   The northward expansion of two tree species in North America following glacial retreat (data from Davis 1981).

The pollen preserved in lake sediments indicates that forest trees in eastern North America spread northward following the retreat of the glaciers at the rate of 100 to 400 m (0.1–0.4 km) per year. This rate of dispersal is similar to that of some large mammals such as the North American elk. However, it is 1/1,000 the dispersal rate of Africanized bees across South, Central, and North America.

It is easy to take some comfort from the work of Davis, in that trees are able to move large distances over relatively short periods of time in response to climate change. As we will discuss in depth later (chapter 23) the planet is facing another period of rapid climatic change, which should cause many populations to find themselves in inhospitable conditions. In theory, dispersal will allow species ranges to move along with the climate. However, since the last ice age, there has been substantial human alteration of the landscape (chapters 21–23). It remains unclear to what extent these alterations will prevent, or slow down, the migration of plant and animal species in response to the current climate change that many parts of the planet are experiencing. Additionally, in some regions, the rate of climate change is quite high (chapter 23). Dispersal is only an effective mechanism to colonize habitable areas if the rate of climate change is low enough to allow dispersal before conditions become inhospitable. For many species, particularly those with very short dispersal distances, it is unclear whether natural processes will allow for species migration. In short, dispersal will play a critical role in determining the impact of climate change on the distribution and abundances of species.

The previous examples concern dispersal by populations in the process of expanding their ranges. Significant dispersal also takes place within established populations whose ranges are not changing. Movements within established ranges can be an important aspect of local population dynamics. We will consider two examples.

Dispersal in Response to Changing Food Supply

Predators show several kinds of responses to variation in prey density. In addition to the functional response we discussed in chapter 7, C. S. Holling (1959) also observed **numerical responses** to increased prey availability. Numerical responses are changes in the density of predator populations in response to increased prey density. Holling studied populations of mice and shrews preying on insect cocoons and attributed the numerical responses he observed to increased reproductive rates. He commented that "because the reproductive rate of small mammals is so high, there was an almost immediate increase in density with increase in food." However, some other predators, with much lower reproductive rates, also show strong numerical responses. These numerical responses to prey density are almost entirely due to dispersal.

In some years, northern landscapes are alive with small rodents called voles, *Microtus* spp. Go to the same place during other years and it may be difficult to find any voles. In northern latitudes, vole populations usually reach high densities every 3 to 4 years. Between these peak times, population densities crash. Population cycles in different areas are not synchronized, however. In other words, while vole population density is very low in one area, it is high elsewhere.

Erkki Korpimäki and Kai Norrdahl (1991) conducted a 10-year study of voles and their predators. The study began in 1977 during a peak in vole densities of about 1,800 per square kilometer and continued through two more peaks in 1982 (960/km^2) and 1985–86 (1,980 and 1,710/km^2). The researchers estimated that between these population peaks vole densities per square kilometer fell to as low as 70 in 1980 and 40 in 1984. During this period, the densities of the European kestrel, *Falco tinnunculus,* short-eared owls, *Asio flammeus,* and long-eared owls, *Asio otus,* closely tracked vole densities (fig. 11.21). How do kestrel and owl populations track these variations in vole densities?

What mechanisms produce the numerical responses by kestrels and owls to changing vole densities? Look at figure 11.21 for a clue. The peaks in raptor densities in 1977, 1982, and 1986 match the peaks in vole densities almost perfectly. If reproduction was the source of numerical response by kestrels and owls, there would have been more of a delay, or time lag, in kestrel and owl numerical response. From this close match in numbers, Korpimäki and Norrdahl proposed that kestrels and owls must move from place to place in response to local increases in vole populations.

Is there any supporting evidence for high rates of movement by kestrels and owls? Korpimäki (1988) marked and recaptured 217 kestrels, a large proportion of their study population. Because European kestrel populations have an annual survival rate of 48% to 66%, he predicted a high rate of recapture of the marked birds. However, only 3% of the female and 13% of the male kestrels were recaptured. These very low rates of recapture indicated that kestrels were moving out of the study area. From their data, Korpimäki and Norrdahl concluded that the hawks and owls in western Finland are nomadic, moving from place to place in response to changing vole densities.

These studies documented the contribution of dispersal to local populations of kestrels and owls. Earlier in this section,

we saw how studies of expanding populations have shed light on the contribution of dispersal to local population density and dynamics. Many other local populations are strongly influenced by dispersal. One of the environments in which dispersal has a major influence on local populations is in streams and rivers.

Dispersal in Rivers and Streams

One of the most distinctive features of the stream and river environment is *current,* the downstream flow of water. What effect does current have on the lives of stream organisms? As you may recall from chapter 3, the effects of current are substantial and influence everything from the amount of oxygen in the water to the size, shape, and behaviour of stream organisms. In this section, we stop and consider how stream populations are affected by current.

Let's begin with a question. Why doesn't the flowing water of streams eventually wash all stream organisms, including fish, insects, snails, bacteria, algae, and fungi, out to sea? All stream dwellers have a variety of characteristics that help them maintain their position in streams. Some fish such as trout are streamlined and can easily swim against swift currents, while other fish like sculpins and loaches are well designed for avoiding the full strength of currents by living on the bottom and seeking shelter among or under stones. Microorganisms resist being washed away by adhering to the surfaces of stones, wood, and other substrates. Many stream insects are flattened and so stay out of the main force of the current, while others are streamlined and fast-swimming.

Despite these means of staying in place, stream organisms do get washed downstream in large numbers, particularly during flash floods, or **spates.** To observe this downstream movement of organisms, put a fine or medium mesh net in a stream or river and you will soon capture large numbers of stream insects and algae along with fragments of leaves and wood. If you place some of the organic matter washed into your net under a microscope, you will find it laden with all sorts of microorganisms. Stream ecologists refer to this downstream movement of stream organisms as **drift.** Some drift is due to displacement of organisms during flash floods. However, some is due to the active movement of organisms downstream.

Whatever its cause, stream organisms drift downstream in large numbers. Why doesn't drift eventually eliminate organisms from the upstream sections of streams? Karl Müller (1954, 1974) hypothesized that drift would eventually wash entire populations out of streams unless organisms actively moved upstream to compensate for drift. He proposed that stream populations are maintained through a dynamic interplay between downstream and upstream dispersal that he called the **colonization cycle.** The colonization cycle is a dynamic view of stream populations in which upstream and downstream dispersal, as well as reproduction, have major influences on stream populations (fig. 11.22).

Many studies support Müller's hypothesized colonization cycle, especially among aquatic insects. As larvae, aquatic insects disperse upstream as well as downstream by swimming, crawling, and drifting. Because of continuous dispersal, which

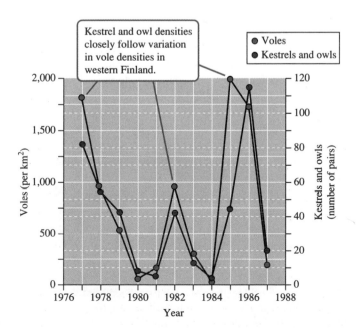

Figure 11.21   Dispersal and numerical response by predators (data from Korpimäki and Norrdahl 1991).

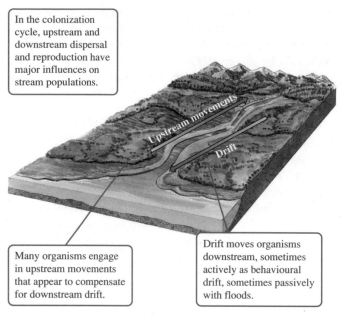

In the colonization cycle, upstream and downstream dispersal and reproduction have major influences on stream populations.

Many organisms engage in upstream movements that appear to compensate for downstream drift.

Drift moves organisms downstream, sometimes actively as behavioural drift, sometimes passively with floods.

Figure 11.22   The colonization cycle of stream invertebrates.

reshuffles stream populations, new substrates put into streams are quickly colonized by a wide variety of stream invertebrates, algae, and bacteria. Most of these dynamics are difficult to observe because they occur too quickly, within the substratum, or at night, or they involve microorganisms impossible to observe directly without the aid of a microscope. However, a snail that lives in a tropical stream in Costa Rica provides a well-documented example of the colonization cycle.

The Rio Claro flows approximately 30 km through tropical forest on the Osa Peninsula of Costa Rica before flowing into the Pacific Ocean. One of the most easily observed inhabitants of the Rio Claro is the snail *Neritina latissima,* which occupies the lower 5 km of the river. The eggs of *Neritina* hatch to produce free-living planktonic larvae that drift down to the Pacific Ocean. After the larvae metamorphose into small snails they reenter the Rio Claro and begin moving upstream in huge migratory aggregations of up to 500,000 individuals (fig. 11.23). These aggregations move slowly and may take up to one year to reach the upstream limit of the population.

The population of *Neritina* in the Rio Claro consists of a mixture of migrating and stationary subpopulations, with exchange between them. Individual snails migrate upstream for some distance and then leave the migrating wave and enter a local subpopulation. At the same time individuals from the local subpopulation enter the migratory wave and move upstream. Thus, individuals move upstream in steps and immigration continuously adds to local subpopulations, while emigration removes individuals. Because an organism that is visible to the naked eye does all this in a clear stream, and does it at a snail's pace, we are provided with a unique opportunity to observe that dispersal can strongly influence local population density. Dispersal dynamics, though difficult to study, deserve greater attention.

(a)

(b)

Figure 11.23   The colonization cycle in action. (*a*) A wave of migrating snails, *Neritina latissima*, in the Rio Claro, Costa Rica; (*b*) a close-up of the migrating snails.

How can information on population dynamics be used to address environmental problems? For instance, how would you go about evaluating the possible effects of a potential pollutant on natural populations? Making such a judgment is usually not as simple as it might sound. If a toxin kills everything in its path, at virtually all detectable concentrations, the situation is clear enough but often the effects of pollutants are not so obvious. One of the most promising approaches to assessing the impact of pollutants is to study their effects on population dynamics.

Concept 11.5 Review

1. Why might a species like Africanized honeybees be less threatened by climate change than maple trees?
2. Some ecologists who have hung clear plastic sheets (coated with adhesive capable of trapping flying insects) from river bridges have found that the side of the sheets facing downstream trap more adult aquatic insects than the upstream-facing side. Explain.

Ecological Tools

Using Population Dynamics to Assess the Impact of Pollutants

Many scientists are studying the effects of sublethal concentrations of pollutants (concentrations too low to kill within a short period of time) on the population biology of a diverse set of organisms. Recently, there has been increased attention given to the potential of pollution to impact organisms located in arctic habitats. At first glance it is difficult to understand why researchers in the Arctic would be concerned about pollutants, as the Arctic is far removed from areas of high industrial development. However, as we saw in chapters 2 and 3, there are global patterns of air and water movement, and these bring large quantities of pollutants to these seemingly isolated areas. Of particular concern is the movement of persistent organic pollutants (POPs), such as polychlorinated biphenyls (PCBs), and heavy metals such as mercury (Hg). POPs are able to volatize in warmer southern latitudes and move north through global air circulation. As these POPs reach colder air, they condense and become redeposited in the Arctic, resulting in high pollutant concentrations in arctic communities (Barrie et al. 1997). Similar effects are found in alpine communities (Blais et al. 1998), where the POPs carried in warm air from lower elevations condense in the cool air at higher elevations. POPs are particularly troublesome because they are hydrophobic, and thus they tend to accumulate rapidly in biological (i.e., fatty) tissues. These compounds can be ingested or absorbed at higher rates than they can be excreted or detoxified. As a result, toxin concentrations gradually increase within an individual through the process of **bioaccumulation**. If the contaminated individuals are consumed (e.g., when a seal eats a fish), the predator gains both the nutritive value and toxin load of its prey. Because bioaccumulation has resulted in the prey item having elevated toxin levels compared to its environment, the levels in the predator will become even greater, through a process called **biomagnification**. This process continues up the food chain (chapter 18) where the top predators have very high concentrations of pollutants due to the consumption of prey items with lower levels of pollutant concentrations. Arctic food webs generally include species with particularly high fat reserves (e.g., seal, walrus, etc.), making them particularly prone to accumulation of POPs. These pollutants enter the systems of all individuals that consume polluted prey species. For example, PCB concentrations in human breast milk of individuals from Inuit communities can be much higher than those found in southern areas where PCBs are actually used and produced (Dewailly et al. 1989). There is some thought that this is related to processes of bioaccumulation and biomagnification. A detailed discussion of the potential effects of pollution in the north on human populations is beyond the scope of this text, and we will instead focus on the potential, and documented, impacts on non-human populations.

One of the central themes running through the ecological study of pollution is the attempt to connect the effects of pollutants on animal physiology with their effects on population dynamics. In terms of the organization of this book, this research topic bridges the gap between section II, the ecology of individuals, and section III, population ecology. An energy balance equation provides the key to bridging physiological and population ecology:

Energy assimilated = Respiration + Excretion + Production

In this equation, the amount of energy assimilated by an animal equals the sum of that expended in respiration, the amount of energy excreted (perspiration, urination, defecation, etc.), and the amount of energy available for production. This production energy is that amount of energy that an organism can use for growth and reproduction.

How does this equation connect the physiological effects of pollutants with their effects on populations? The connection derives from the principle of allocation. The principle of allocation assumes that energy supplies available to organisms are limited and predicts that any increase in the allocation of energy to any one of life's functions decreases the amount of energy available to other functions. In terms of our energy balance equation, if an organism is exposed to a toxin that induces physiological stress, energy expended in respiration generally increases. This increased respiration includes energy expended to excrete the toxin, to convert the toxin into a non-toxic chemical form, and to repair cellular damage caused by the toxin. The important point is that the processes that increase the energy spent for respiration decrease the energy available for growth and reproduction. This trade-off between reproduction and respiration provides the bridge between physiological and population ecology.

Now that we understand the reasons why pollutants might alter population dynamics, what information is actually needed to determine whether such effects are actually occurring? There are three critical pieces of information needed: (1) identification of a pollutant in a population of interest, (2) evidence that observed concentrations have a negative physiological effect on individual performance, and (3) evidence that the level of pollutants in all individuals in the population will alter population parameters, such as the per capita rate of increase.

POPs and heavy metals have been found in a disappointingly large number of wild species (Gamberg et al. 2005; Evans et al. 2005; Braune et al. 2005); however, documenting causal effects on populations can be difficult and requires extensive research. It is in trying to meet criteria numbers 2 and 3 where desired scientific information comes into conflict with scientific ethics and the difficult logistics associated with field work in remote locations. As we discussed in chapter 1, experiments are very useful tools for determining the direct effects of a factor of interest. For example, if one wanted to understand the impacts of PCBs on polar bears, the cleanest approach

Figure 11.24   Polar bears feed upon a number of marine mammals. They are currently at the centre of international efforts to understand the impact of bioaccumulation and biomagnification on marine mammal populations in the Arctic.

would be a controlled experiment in which different individuals are exposed to different amounts of PCBs and the resulting changes measured. This is exactly the approach routinely used in toxicology labs, though centred on a few model species such as lab mice and rats. It is not a viable option for many wild species for a variety of reasons including naturally low population densities, where removing individuals for study could put the population at risk, many species' inability to thrive in captivity, and the extreme expenses associated with large-scale and long-term experiments in the north. Instead, in the study of pollution in wild species a correlative approach is generally used, in which correlations are found between factors (such as PCB levels in individuals and their fertility) and causality is inferred. So what have ecologists learned about pollutants in northern and alpine populations over the last few decades? To address this issue we will focus on one well-studied and dramatic example, the polar bear, *Ursus maritimus* (fig. 11.24).

Polar bears are the largest extant land predator, and are at the top of the food chain in the Arctic, with males often weighing more than 450 kg, and females generally less than 400 kg. Polar bears can be found throughout the Arctic, with their range limited to areas where sea-ice persists for much of the year. Ringed seals are their primary food source, and polar bears tend to preferentially consume the fatty tissues over the protein. This preference for consuming fat makes sense from an evolutionary perspective, given that nearly 50% of the calories of a seal are in the fat tissues, but it poses a potential risk due to the accumulation of lipophilic POPs. As a result, the bears are preferentially consuming the parts of the seal that contain the highest levels of pollutants. Additionally, these levels of pollutants are magnified in the seals as they themselves are con-

suming fish and other prey items that contain pollutants. By understanding the basic aspects of the ecology of this species and the system, it is reasonable to believe that this species is particularly at risk for detrimental effects of pollution on its population dynamics. So what have ecologists learned?

Over the last several decades, teams of researchers from Canada, Russia, Norway, Sweden, and the United States have been investigating POP impacts on polar bears. A variety of POPs, including PCBs and pesticides, have been found in tissue samples of polar bears from many populations (Verreault et al. 2005). There were complex spatial patterns in terms of which populations had high levels of specific compounds, though in general PCB concentrations were higher in the eastern populations from Svalbard, Norway and Eastern Greenland than from the western populations of Alaska. Even within a single population there is substantial variation in PCB concentrations among individuals. Olsen et al. (2003) conducted a study to explore potential causes of this variation in which they tagged 54 female polar bears from around Svalbard with transmitters to monitor bear movement. At the end of the study, they found that the size of the home range of individual bears was the strongest predictor of total PCB levels found within the bear, with bears with larger home ranges having higher PCB levels. Why might this be the case? Going back to our theory of allocation, if an animal is moving a lot, it either needs to burn existing fat reserves for energy, or it needs to eat more food, both of which can influence the amount of PCBs found in the blood. By eating more food, the animal may simply be consuming more pollutants contained in their prey, and the authors believe that was likely occurring in their study. However, what happens when an animal burns fat for energy? Lipophilic compounds previously stored in the fat, such as PCBs, become liberated, and can now affect the physiology of the animals. These results show that not only can regional differences in pollutant levels cause large-scale gradients in PCB concentrations, but the behaviour of individual animals can influence their own pollutant levels. If PCBs reduce an individual's fitness, do you think natural selection would favour larger or smaller home range sizes?

Now that we have established that POPs are found in wild polar bear populations, what evidence is there that they have any physiological effect on the bears? Polar bear females, like all mammals, feed their cubs milk postpartum. Where does the energy for that milk come from? In large part, it comes from the stored fat reserves. In this process, PCBs and other POPs are liberated, and high concentrations of these pollutants are found in the milk itself (Polischuk 2002). Not all cubs will survive, and there is some evidence that the POP concentrations in the milk of mothers whose cubs were lost are higher than the POP concentrations of mothers who kept their cubs (Polischuk 2002). This provides us with a hint that there may be a reproductive cost to POP concentrations on cub survival. However, without a decisive experiment, it is difficult to refute alternative explanations, and more research is needed. Other studies by Lie et al. (2004, 2005) also suggest that PCBs and other POPs can negatively impact the immune system of adult bears. In these studies, the authors captured bears in Canada and Norway and measured their POP levels and collected blood samples for in vitro immunological assays (e.g., lymphocyte proliferation). They also gave the bears immunizations for a variety of compounds such as influenza virus, and upon recapture they measured antibody levels. They found that for many variables the level of immune response was negatively correlated with the level of PCBs in the bear. In other words, it appears that high PCB concentrations can increase the risk of infection of polar bears. If infection is a natural cause of mortality for these bears, then this again suggests that POPs pollution can negatively impact population dynamics.

The final piece of this puzzle requires us to see if there is a link between POPs and population dynamics, and here the data are fairly sparse. The best study to date comes from Andy Derocher, now at the University of Alberta, and his colleagues (Derocher et al. 2003) in which they measured POP contents in polar bear blood samples that were collected and stored from the Svalbard population in 1967, and then related those values to observed patterns in population age distributions. In 1973, hunting of polar bears was banned in Svalbard, and in the absence of pollutants, populations were expected to show growth during the last 30 years. During this same time period, Derocher et al. (2003) found an increase in PCBs, potentially posing an increased stress to this population. The authors found that in the Svalbard population, there were fewer older females (>16 year) compared to other polar bear populations where hunting is also restricted. Additionally, this age distribution more closely resembles a Canadian population, which is managed for maximal harvest yet experiences relatively little pollution. These data suggest that although the Svalbard population has grown following the hunting ban, its rate of growth is well below that expected, and mortality and decreased reproduction associated with pollution is a likely contributing factor.

What you can see in this series of studies is not the end product of decades of research, which have resulted in a firm and certain conclusion, but instead, a view of what science-in-progress looks like. There are hints that PCBs will reduce population growth, but the data are not completely firm. There are great scientists hard at work trying to fill in the missing pieces, but the inherent difficulty in working with large and dangerous animals in very remote locations under often brutal conditions makes this a very expensive, and slow process. However, these are important questions being addressed, with significant implications for this species. It is only through continued work by future ecologists that we can hope to further unravel this, and related questions.

The implications of the work of these researchers goes well beyond the effects of particular pollutants on particular animal species. Their results suggest that organisms that are seemingly isolated from industrial development and large-scale human activity are connected through global patterns of water and air circulation. Their results also suggest that variation in population dynamics among populations can be an indicator of different levels of pollution. Their work also raises concern in the context of global warming, which is placing additional stresses on many species of the north. How these populations will respond to multiple stressors remains the future work of ecologists. It is also significant that this research at the population level is rooted in phenomena at the level of the individual organism. This successful bridging between physiological and population ecology suggests that similar connections exist between the population level and higher organizational levels that we examine in the later sections of the book.

Summary

A survivorship curve summarizes the pattern of survival in a population. Patterns of survival can be determined either by following a cohort of individuals of similar age to produce a cohort life table or by determining the age at death of a large number of individuals or the age distribution of a population to produce a static life table. Life tables can be used to draw survivorship curves, which generally fall into one of three categories: (1) type I survivorship, in which there is low mortality among the young but high mortality among older individuals; (2) type II survivorship, in which there is a fairly constant probability of mortality throughout life; and (3) type III survivorship, in which there is high mortality among the young and low mortality among older individuals.

The age distribution of a population reflects its history of survival, reproduction, and potential for future growth. Age distributions indicate periods of successful reproduction, high and low survival, and whether the older individuals in a population are replacing themselves or if the population is declining. Population age structure may be highly complicated in variable environments, such as that of the Galápagos Islands. Populations in highly variable environments may reproduce episodically.

Population sex ratios can change depending upon the relative fitness of different sexes within a population. Many populations contain approximately equal numbers of males and females. This balanced sex ratio can be the result of frequency-dependent selection, in which there should be selection favouring the rarer sex. In species in which there are complicated mating systems, sex-dependent survivorship differences, or differential costs associated with producing offspring of each gender, sex-ratios can diverge from 1:1.

A life table combined with a fecundity schedule can be used to estimate net reproductive rate (R_0), geometric rate of increase (λ), generation time (T), and per capita

rate of increase (*r*). Because these population parameters form the core of population dynamics, it is important to understand their derivation as well as their biological meaning. Net reproductive rate, R_0, the average number of offspring left by an individual in a population, is calculated by multiplying age-specific survivorship rates, l_x, times age-specific birthrates, m_x, and summing the results:

$$\sum l_x m_x$$

The geometric rate of increase, λ, is calculated as the ratio of population sizes at two successive points in time. Generation time is calculated as:

$$T = \frac{\sum x l_x m_x}{R_0}$$

The per capita rate of increase, *r*, is related to generation time and net reproductive rate as:

$$r = \frac{\ln R_0}{T}$$

The per capita rate of increase may be positive, zero, or negative depending on whether a population is growing, stable, or declining.

Dispersal can increase or decrease local population densities. The contribution of dispersal to local population density and dynamics is demonstrated by studies of expanding populations of species such as Africanized bees in the Americas. Climate changes can induce massive changes in the ranges of species. As availability of prey changes, predators may disperse, which increases and decreases their local population densities. Stream organisms actively migrating upstream or drifting downstream increase densities of stationary and migrating populations by immigrating and decrease them by emigrating.

Ecologists are studying the impacts of pollutants on the population dynamics of many species in arctic communities. Working with wild species imposes constraints on the methods available to physiological and population ecologists, and correlative rather than experimental approaches are often used. Pollutants can alter population-level processes by changing the physiology of individual organisms. The results of this research suggest that variation in population growth rates for some species can be an indicator for pollutant levels, though much more research is needed before making broad conclusions.

Review Questions

1. Compare cohort and static life tables. What are the main assumptions of each? In what situations or for what organisms would it be practical to use either?

2. Of the three survivorship curves, type III has been the least documented by empirical data. Why is that? What makes this pattern of survivorship difficult to study?

3. Population ecologists have assumed that populations of species with very high reproductive rates, those with offspring sometimes numbering in the millions per female, must have a type III survivorship curve even though very few survivorship data exist for such species. Why is this a reasonable assumption? In general, what is the expected relationship between reproductive rate and patterns of survival?

4. Draw hypothetical age structures for growing, declining, and stable populations. Explain how the age structure of a population with highly episodic reproduction might be misinterpreted as indicating population decline. How might population ecologists avoid such misinterpretations?

5. From a life table and a fecundity schedule, you can estimate the geometric rate of increase, λ, the average reproductive rate, R_0, the generation time, T, and the per capita rate of increase, *r*. That is a lot of information about a population. What minimum information do you need to construct a life table and fecundity schedule?

6. C. S. Holling (1959) observed predator numerical responses to changes in prey density. He attributed the numerical responses to changes in the reproductive rates of the predators.

Discuss a hypothetical example of reproductive-rate numerical response by a population of predators in terms of changes in fecundity schedules and life tables. Include the terms R_0, T, and *r* in your discussion.

7. Outline Müller's (1954, 1974) colonization cycle. If you were studying the colonization cycle of the freshwater snail *N. latissima*, how would you follow colonization waves upstream? How would you verify that these colonization waves gain individuals from local populations and also contribute individuals to those same local populations?

8. Persistent organic pollutants have the potential to greatly impact the population dynamics of many species of the arctic and alpine environments. Why are species so far removed from industry at risk from an industrial pollutant? Draw a hypothetical graph relating the levels of PCBs you would expect in a polar bear population as a function of latitude, and explain why.

9. Which aspects of our understanding of the impacts of POPs on polar bear populations came from manipulative experiments, and which came from correlative studies? What are the strengths and weaknesses of each approach?

10. Suppose you measure the sex ratio of a population, and find 1.2 males per female. Is this an indication of a skewed sex ratio? What additional information would you seek to help determine whether this result is due to chance events or due to stabilizing selection?

Suggested Readings

Carey, J. R. 2001. Insect biodemography. *Annual Review of Entomology* 46:79–110.

A comprehensive review of life tables and survivorship in insect populations, including a complete cohort life table for 1.2 million Mediterranean fruit flies.

Fisher, R. A. 1930. *The genetical theory of Natural Selection.* Claredon Press, Oxford.

One of the most important texts on biology. Ever. Among other things, Fisher presents his argument for 1:1 sex ratios.

Grant, R. B. and P. R. Grant. 1989. *Evolutionary Dynamics of a Natural Population.* Chicago: University of Chicago Press.

Exceptional long-term study of the large cactus finch on Genovesa Island—destined to be a classic study in ecology.

Hellgren, E. C., R. T. Kazmaier, D. C. Ruthven, and D. R. Synatzske. 2000. Variation in tortoise life history: demography of *Gopherus berlandieri. Ecology* 81:1297–1310.

Excellent study providing a life table and estimates of demographic parameters along with comparisons to other tortoise populations.

Hengeveld, R. 1989. *Dynamics of Biological Invasions.* New York: Chapman and Hall.

Excellent and readable introduction to biological invasions. Includes a quantitative approach to studying population expansion.

Hyrenbach, K. D. and R. C. Dotson. 2003. Assessing the susceptibility of female black footed albatross (*Phoebastria nigripes*) to longline fisheries during the post-breeding dispersal: an integrated approach. *Biological Conservation* 112:391–404.

A modern approach to following dispersal of a far-ranging pelagic seabird, using satellite tracking.

Stirling, I. 1999. *Polar Bears.* Ann Arbor: University of Michigan Press.

A classic book integrating the science and beauty of polar bears, written by one of the world's experts.

Chapter *12*

Population Growth

Outline

iven suitable environmental conditions, populations will grow rapidly. Each spring, in temperate seas and lakes around the globe, planktonic populations of diatoms explode as these single-celled protists survive, mature, and reproduce. Populations of zooplankton respond to the "spring blooms" of diatoms, on which they feed, by increasing their own numbers (fig. 12.1). Later in the annual cycle, the numbers of individuals in the diatom and zooplankton populations decrease, responding to decreases in sunlight and nutrients and increases in competition and predation. Populations are dynamic—increasing, decreasing, and responding to changes in the biotic and abiotic environments.

In chapter 12 we examine the factors that determine rates and patterns of population growth. We also review the environmental forces that limit population size. We look at population growth in the presence of abundant resources, growth where resources are limiting, how the environment can act to change birth and death rates, and, finally, how rates of population growth are affected by the size of organisms. In this chapter we discuss two approaches to understanding populations. One approach uses mathematics to model population growth. The second approach focuses on studies of laboratory

(a)

(b)

Figure 12.1   Lake plankton populations undergo explosive population growth each spring in mid- and high-latitude lakes as a result of favourable environmental conditions. Shown here are (*a*) diatoms and (*b*) a copepod.

and natural populations. Our knowledge of population growth has progressed through an interplay between modelling and observations of actual populations. Let's turn now to studies of population growth in the presence of abundant resources.

Concepts

12.1   In the presence of abundant resources, populations can grow at geometric or exponential rates.

12.2   If resources become limited, population growth rate slows and eventually stops; this is known as logistic population growth.

12.3   The environment limits population growth by changing birth and death rates.

12.1   Geometric and Exponential Population Growth

In the presence of abundant resources, populations can grow at geometric or exponential rates.   Suppose a population had access to abundant resources, such as food, space, nutrients, and so forth. How fast could it grow? Imagine a plant, animal, or bacterial population reproducing at its maximum reproductive rate. What would the resulting pattern of population growth be? Regardless of the species you choose, the pattern will be the same. A population growing at its maximum rate grows slowly at first and then faster and faster. In other words, population growth accelerates.

When growing at their maximum rates, some populations are said to grow *geometrically* and others *exponentially*. We examine what causes these two ways of modelling population growth in this section.

Geometric Growth

Because it is an annual plant, populations of *Phlox drummondii* grow in discrete annual pulses. Populations of insects that produce a single generation a year also grow in pulses. Growth by any population with pulsed reproduction can be modelled as **geometric population growth,** in which successive generations differ in size by a constant ratio.

We can use the population of *Phlox* studied by Leverich and Levin (1979) to build a model of geometric population growth. In chapter 11, we calculated a geometric rate of increase, $1 = N_{t+1}/N_t$, for this population of 2.4177. At the end of that discussion, we asked rhetorically how long the *Phlox* population could continue growing at this rate. Let's address that question here.

As we saw in chapter 11, we can compute the growth of a population of organisms whose generations do not overlap by simply multiplying λ times the size of the population at the beginning of each generation. The initial size of the population studied by Leverich and Levin was 996 and the number of offspring produced by this population during their year of study was:

$$N_1 = N_0 \times \lambda, \text{ or } 996 \times 2.4177 = 2,408$$

Now let's repeat this calculation for a few generations. The population size at the beginning of the next generation, N_2, would be $N_1 \times \lambda$. However, because

$$N_1 = N_0 \times \lambda, N_2 = N_0 \times \lambda \times \lambda, \text{ or } N_0 \times \lambda^2,$$

which is

$$996 \times 2.4177 \times 2.4177 = 5,822.$$

At the third generation, N_3,

$$N_0 \times \lambda^3 = 14,076$$

and in general, the size of a population growing geometrically at any time, t, can be modelled as:

$$N_t = N_0\lambda^t$$

In this model, N_t is the number of individuals at any time t, N_0 is the initial number of individuals, λ is the geometric rate of increase, and t is the number of time intervals or generations. The interpretation of this model and the definitions of each of its terms are summarized in figure 12.2. We can use this model to project the future size of our hypothetical *Phlox* population. Notice in figure 12.3 that in only 8 years the population has grown from 996 to 1.16×10^6, to over 1 million individuals. By

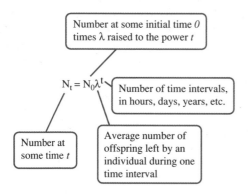

Figure 12.2 Anatomy of the equation for geometric population growth.

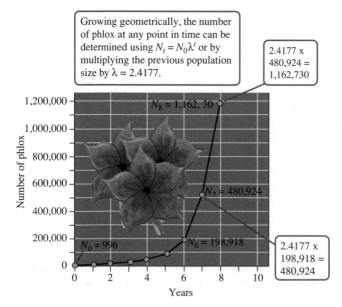

Figure 12.3 Geometric growth by a hypothetical population of *Phlox drummondii*.

16 years, the population would be over a billion, by 24 years the population would top 1 trillion individuals, and by year 40 it would increase to over 10^{18}, or 1 billion billion individuals.

We can get a feeling for how large this hypothetical *Phlox* population would be by calculating how much space the growing population would occupy. Since the *Phlox* population studied by Leverich and Levin was from Texas, let's confine our hypothetical population to North America and scale population growth against the area of the North American continent, which is about 24 million km^2. Assuming a uniform density across the continent, by 32 years our population would reach a density of nearly 80 million individuals per square kilometer or about 80 individuals per square meter across the entire continent, from southern Mexico to northern Canada and Alaska. Eight years later, the density would be nearly 90,000 individuals per square meter!

There are many reasons why this exercise is unrealistic. The population would soon be so dense that plants would die because they lacked sufficient nutrients, light, and water; and the population would soon spread beyond the physical climates to which *P. drummondii* is adapted. However, out of this unrealistic exercise comes an important fact about the natural world. Natural populations have a tremendous capacity for increase, and geometric population growth cannot be maintained in any population for very many generations. You may also recognize how this type of realization influenced the development of the theory of natural selection (chapter 4). It is apparent that populations can not grow without bounds for extended periods of time, and thus the relative performance of individuals within a population will have strong influences on their overall fitness.

Now let's consider population growth by organisms such as bacteria, forest trees, and humans, which have overlapping generations. Because growth by these populations can be continuous, the geometric model is usually not appropriate.

Exponential Growth

Continuous population growth in an unlimited environment can be modelled as **exponential population growth:**

$$\frac{dN}{dt} = r_{max}N$$

The exponential growth equation (fig. 12.4) expresses the rate of population growth, dN/dt, which is the change in numbers of individuals with change in time, as the per capita rate of increase, r_{max}, times population size, N. The exponential model is appropriate for populations with nonpulsed reproduction because it represents population growth as a continuous process. Notice that the per capita rate of increase, r_{max}, has a subscript $_{max}$. The subscript here indicates that this is the *maximum* per capita rate of increase, achieved by a species under ideal environmental conditions, where birthrates, death rates, and age structure are constant. The per capita rate of increase attained under such circumstances, r_{max}, is called the **intrinsic rate of increase.** When we calculated the rate of increase from a life table in chapter 11, we determined r, the *realized* or *actual* per capita rate of increase. As we saw, realized r may be positive,

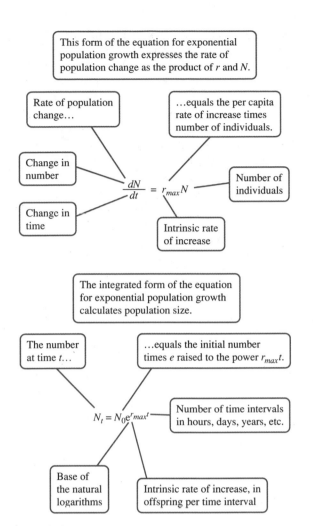

Figure 12.4   Anatomy of equations for exponential population growth. The first equation is the derivative of the second.

Exponential Growth in Nature

Some of the assumptions of the exponential growth model, such as a constant rate of per capita increase, may seem a bit unrealistic, so it is reasonable to ask whether populations in nature ever grow at an exponential rate. The answer is a qualified yes. Natural populations may grow at exponential rates for relatively short periods of time in the presence of abundant resources.

Exponential Growth by Tree Populations

As we saw in chapters 1 and 11, as the last ice age was ending, tree populations in the Northern Hemisphere followed the retreating glaciers northward. Ecologists have documented these movements by studying the sediments of lakes, where the pollen of wind-pollinated tree species is especially abundant. The appearance of pollen of a tree species in a lake sediment is a record of its establishment near the lake. The date of each establishment can be determined using carbon-14 concentration to determine the age of organic matter along a sediment profile.

Pollen records have also been used to estimate the growth of several postglacial tree populations in Britain. K. Bennett (1983) estimated population sizes and growth by counting the number of pollen grains of each tree species deposited within lake sediments. By counting the number of pollen grains per square centimeter deposited each year, Bennett was able to reconstruct changes in tree population densities in the surrounding landscape. This approach is a bit different from going out in a forest and estimating population density directly by counting trees. What is the main assumption of this method? Bennett's assumption was that the rate of pollen deposition is proportional to the size of tree populations around a lake. This assumption, which seems reasonable, leads to an interesting picture of growth by postglacial tree populations in the British Isles. Populations of the tree species studied grew at exponential rates for 400 to 500 years following their initial appearance in the pollen record. Figure 12.5 shows the exponential increase in abundance of Scots pine, *Pinus sylvestris,* which first appeared in the pollen record of the study lake about 9,500 years ago.

Conditions for Exponential Growth

Natural populations of organisms as different as diatoms, birds, and trees can grow at exponential rates. However, as different as these organisms are, the circumstances in which their populations grow at exponential rates have a great deal in common. All begin their exponential growth in favourable environments at low population densities. The trees studied by Bennett began at low densities because they were invading new territory previously unoccupied by the species. Spring blooms of planktonic diatoms are also the result of exponential population growth in response to seasonal increases in nutrients and light.

The whooping crane provides another example of exponential growth following protection and careful management (fig. 12.6). Hunting and habitat destruction reduced the population of whooping cranes to 15 individuals by 1941–42. At that time it was known that this remnant population of whooping

zero, or negative, depending on environmental conditions. Because natural populations are usually subject to factors such as disease, competition, and so forth, the actual per capita rate of increase, realized *r,* is generally less than r_{max}. In the exponential model, r_{max} is a constant, while *N* is a variable. Therefore, as population size, *N,* increases the rate of population increase, *dN/dt,* gets larger and larger. The rate of increase gets larger because the constant *r* is multiplied by a larger and larger population size, *N.* Consequently, during exponential growth, the rate of population growth increases over time.

For a population growing at an exponential rate, the population size at any time *t* can be calculated as:

$$N_t = N_0 e^{r_{max}t}$$

In this form of the exponential growth model, N_t is the number of individuals at time *t,* N_0 is the initial number of individuals, *e* is the base of the natural logarithms, r_{max} is the intrinsic rate of increase, and *t* is the number of time intervals. Notice that this form of the exponential model of population growth is virtually the same as our equation for geometric growth but with $e^{r_{max}}$ taking the place of λ. The two forms of the exponential growth equation are presented and explained in figure 12.4.

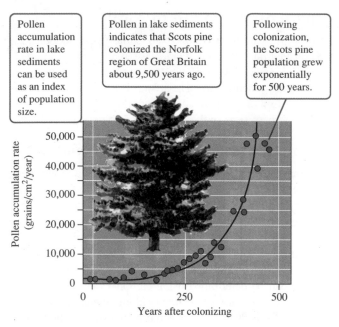

Pollen accumulation rate in lake sediments can be used as an index of population size.

Pollen in lake sediments indicates that Scots pine colonized the Norfolk region of Great Britain about 9,500 years ago.

Following colonization, the Scots pine population grew exponentially for 500 years.

Figure 12.5 Exponential growth of a colonizing population of Scots pine, *Pinus sylvestris* (data from Bennett 1983).

Figure 12.6 Whooping cranes in the breeding grounds found within Wood Buffalo National Park, Alberta.

cranes wintered on the Texas Gulf Coast but its northern breeding grounds were unknown. It was later discovered that they breed in Wood Buffalo National Park in Canada. Under full protection and careful management in both Canada and the United States, the migratory whooping crane population has grown exponentially from 22 in 1942 to over 220 individuals in 2005 (fig. 12.7).

These examples suggest that exponential population growth may be very important to populations during the process of establishment in new environments, during exploitation of transient, favourable conditions, and during the process of recovery from some form of exploitation. However, as we saw with *P. drummondii,* geometric or exponential growth cannot continue indefinitely. In nature, population growth eventually slows and population sizes level off.

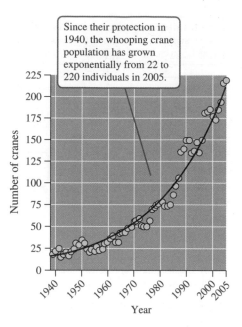

Since their protection in 1940, the whooping crane population has grown exponentially from 22 to 220 individuals in 2005.

Figure 12.7 Hunting and habitat destruction reduced the whooping crane, which is endemic to North America, to a single natural population. Protection and intensive management of this population has led to its dramatic recovery (data from USGS 2005, USFWS Whooping Crane Coordinator).

Slowing of Exponential Growth

The collared dove, *Streptopelia decaocto,* expanded beyond its historical range into western Europe during the latter half of the twentieth century. As the bird spread into new territory, its populations grew at exponential rates for a decade or more. For instance, from 1955 to 1972, the expanding population in the British Isles followed a typical exponential curve (fig. 12.8). However, if you examine figure 12.8 closely, you will see evidence that the rate of growth by the collared dove population began to slow by 1970.

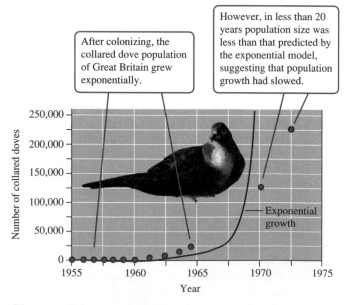

After colonizing, the collared dove population of Great Britain grew exponentially.

However, in less than 20 years population size was less than that predicted by the exponential model, suggesting that population growth had slowed.

Figure 12.8 Exponential growth of the collared dove population of Great Britain (data from Hengeveld 1988).

The pattern for the collared dove indicates that its population grew at a higher rate, from 1955 to 1964, and then, between 1965 and 1970, its rate of population growth began to slow. This slowdown suggests that between 1965 and 1970, this invading population was approaching some environmental limits. Environmental limitation is incorporated into another model of population growth called **logistic population growth.**

Concept 12.1 Review

1. What was the major assumption underlying Bennett's (1983) use of pollen deposited in lake sediments to estimate the postglacial population size of Scots pine?
2. Why do many populations of exotic species, such as zebra mussels in the Great Lakes or Eurasian collared doves in Europe, often grow at exponential rates for some time following their introductions into a new environment?
3. African annual killifish live in temporary pools, where their populations survive the dry season as eggs that lie dormant in the mud, developing and hatching only when the pools fill each wet season. In contrast, the guppy, a common aquarium fish, lives in populations consisting of mixed-age classes in which reproduction occurs year-round. Which model of population growth, exponential or geometric, would be most appropriate for each of these fish species?

12.2 Logistic Population Growth

If resources become limited, population growth rate slows and eventually stops; this is known as logistic population growth. Exponential growth cannot continue indefinitely. Eventually, populations run up against environmental limits to further increase. The effect of the environment on population growth is reflected in the shapes of population growth curves. As population size increases, growth rate eventually slows and then ceases as population size levels off. This pattern of growth produces a **sigmoidal,** or S-shaped, **population growth curve** (fig. 12.9). The population size at which growth stops is generally called the **carrying capacity,** or **K,** which is the number of individuals of a particular species that the environment can support. At carrying capacity, birthrates equal death rates and population growth is zero.

Sigmoidal growth curves have been observed in a wide variety of populations. In the course of his laboratory experiments, G. F. Gause (1934) obtained sigmoidal growth curves for populations of several species of yeast (fig. 12.10) and protozoa (fig. 12.11). Similar patterns of population growth have been recorded for other populations, including barnacles (fig. 12.12) and African buffalo (fig. 12.13).

What causes these populations to slow their rates of growth and eventually stop growing at carrying capacity? The idea behind the concept of carrying capacity is that a given environment can only support so many individuals of a particular species. For the barnacles studied by J. H. Connell (1961*a*, 1961*b*), carrying capacity is largely determined by

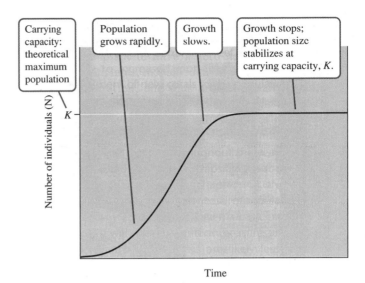

Figure 12.9 Sigmoidal, or logistic, population growth results from environmental limitation on population size.

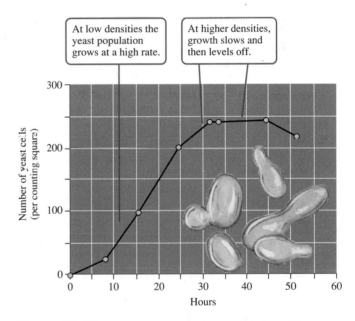

Figure 12.10 Sigmoidal growth by a population of the yeast *Saccharomyces cerevisiae* (data from Gause 1934).

the amount of space available on rocks for attachment by new barnacles. For African buffalo, Tony Sinclair of the University of British Columbia has found carrying capacity appears largely determined by the amount of grass available as food (Sinclair 1977). Yeast feed on sugars and produce alcohol. As the density of a population of yeast increases, their environment contains less and less sugar and more and more alcohol, which is toxic to them. So, yeast populations are eventually limited by their own waste products. For most species, carrying capacity is likely determined by a complex interplay among factors such as food, parasitism, disease, and space. While we can discuss these factors in a general way, the mathematical models of population biology help us to discuss population processes in a more precise way.

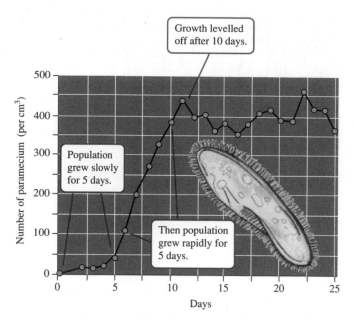

Figure 12.11   Sigmoidal growth by a population of *Paramecium caudatum* (data from Gause 1934).

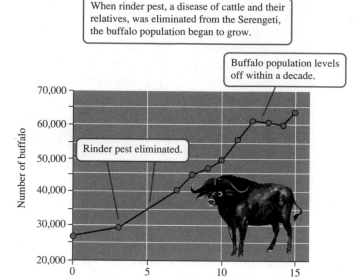

Figure 12.13   Sigmoidal population growth by African buffalo, *Syncerus caffer*, on the Serengeti Plain (data from Sinclair 1977).

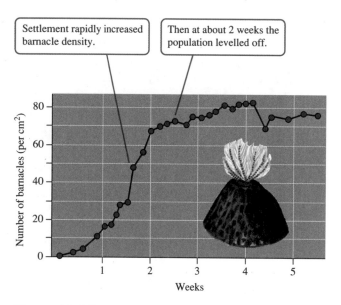

Figure 12.12   Settlement by the barnacle *Balanus balanoides* in the intertidal zone (data from Connell 1961*a*, 1961*b*).

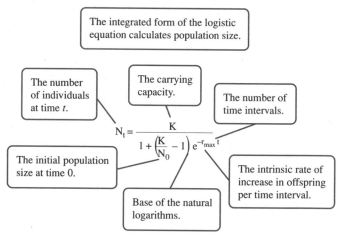

Figure 12.14   Anatomy of the logistic equation for population growth.

The logistic model was proposed to account for the patterns of growth shown by populations as they begin to deplete environmental resources. Population ecologists built the logistic growth model by modifying the exponential growth model. The exponential model of population growth, $dN/dt = r_{max}N$, can be modified to produce a model in which population growth is sigmoidal. The simplest way to do this is to add an element that slows growth as population size approaches carrying capacity, K:

$$\frac{dN}{dt} = r_{max}N\left(\frac{K-N}{K}\right)$$

The inventor of this equation for sigmoidal population growth, P. F. Verhulst, called it the **logistic equation** (Verhulst and Quetelet 1838). Rearranging the logistic equation shows more clearly the influence of population size, N, on rate of population growth:

$$\frac{dN}{dt} = r_{max}N\left(\frac{K-N}{K}\right) = r_{max}N\left(\frac{K}{K} - \frac{N}{K}\right) = r_{max}N\left(1 - \frac{N}{K}\right)$$

In the logistic equation, the rate of population growth, dN/dt, slows as population size increases because the difference, $(1 - N/K)$, becomes a smaller and smaller value as N approaches K. When N equals K, the right side of the equation becomes zero. Therefore, as population size increases, the logistic growth rate becomes a smaller and smaller fraction of the exponential growth rate and when $N = K$, population growth ceases (fig. 12.14).

The ratio N/K has been called the "environmental resistance" to population growth. As the size of a population, N, gets closer and closer to carrying capacity, environmental factors increasingly impede further population growth.

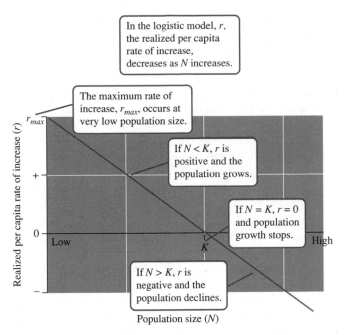

Figure 12.15 The relationship between population size, *N*, and realized per capita rate of increase, *r*, in the logistic model of population growth.

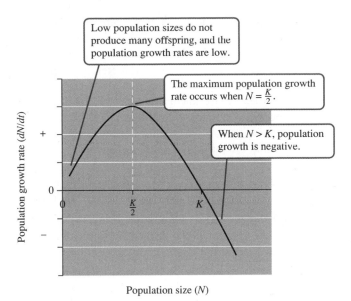

Figure 12.16 Relationship of population growth rate, *dN/dt*, as a function of population size, *N*, in the logistic model of population growth.

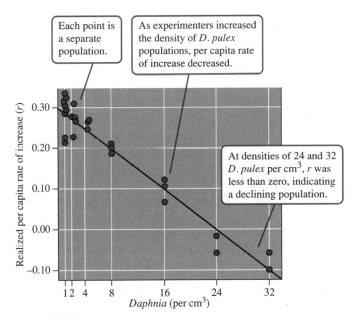

Figure 12.17 Relationship of density to per capita rate of increase in populations of *Daphnia pulex* (data from Frank, Boll, and Kelly 1957).

In the logistic growth model, the *realized* per capita rate of increase, which is $r = r_{max}(1 - N/K) = r_{max} - r_{max}(N/K)$, depends upon population size. Therefore, when population size, *N,* is very small, the per capita rate of increase is approximately r_{max}. As *N* increases, however, realized *r* decreases until *N* equals *K*. At that point, realized *r* is zero. The relationship between realized *r* and population size in the logistic model, which follows a straight line, is shown in figure 12.15.

If according to the logistic equation, per capita growth rates are highest at low population sizes, when will population growth itself be greatest? Or put another way, at what population size will the largest number of individuals be added during a given time interval? We know the answer can not be at population sizes above *K*, as that results in either zero or negative population growth (fig. 12.15). What about at the other extreme, when population sizes are very low? Under these conditions, *r*, the realized per capita growth rate (the value that we measured in the life tables of chapter 11), is at its highest point, equal to r_{max} (fig. 12.15). However, because the population size is low, although the population is growing rapidly on a per capita basis, it is not increasing rapidly in absolute numbers. Instead, the growth rate of a population, *dN/dt*, is influenced both by population size, N, and the realized per capita growth rate. If a population is demonstrating logistic growth, *dN/dt* is greatest when $N = K/2$ (fig. 12.16).

When working with mathematical models, it is always useful for the ecologist to keep the biology behind the model firmly in mind. A mathematical model is only a formal description of an idea. It's not magic, it's not law, it's just an idea. These equations can be very helpful in trying to understand and predict changes in population sizes. In the case of models of population growth, we should remember that *r* is the difference between birth and death rates in a population. Let's think about figure

12.15 from this perspective. At very low population size, the per capita birthrate, *b,* greatly exceeds the per capita death rate, *d*. As population size increases, the logistic model assumes that per capita birthrates will decrease and per capita death rates will increase. Then, when population size reaches carrying capacity, or *K*, *b = d* and since *b − d = 0*, population growth stops.

The response of per capita rate of increase by *Daphnia pulex,* a water flea, to population density closely matches the assumptions of the logistic growth model. When *D. pulex* are grown at densities ranging from 1 to 32 individuals per cubic centimeter, *r* decreases with increasing population size (fig. 12.17). As assumed by the logistic growth model, per capita rate of increase was highest at the lowest population densities. Per capita rate of increase was positive in *D. pulex* populations with densities of 16 individuals per cubic centimeter or lower. However, at densities of 24 and 32 individuals per cubic centimeter, per capita rate of increase was negative.

Ultimately the environment limits the growth of populations by modifying birth and death rates. In the following concept discussion section, we examine in detail a few examples of environmental effects on population growth.

Concept 12.2 Review

1. Interpret the pattern of population growth shown by figure 12.12 in terms of the information given in figure 12.15, and discuss the relationship between population size and *r*.
2. How could you test the hypothesis that carrying capacity for the *Paramecium* population shown in figure 12.11 was set by the availability of their main food—yeast cells?
3. Why might a manager of an exploited population, such as a commercially important fish, want to keep fish population size near one-half *K* and not much lower?

12.3 Limits to Population Growth

The environment limits population growth by changing birth and death rates.   Most of us could recite an impressive list of factors affecting the size of populations. Such lists generally include food, competitors, shelter, rainfall, disease, floods, and predators—a mixture of abiotic and biotic factors. Ecologists have long been concerned with the effects of factors such as these on populations. Out of this concern came a long period of debate between the champions of the importance of abiotic factors and those who argued for the importance of biotic factors. Because the effects of factors, such as competitors, disease, and predation, are often influenced by population density, biotic factors are often referred to as **density-dependent factors.** Meanwhile, abiotic factors, such as floods and extreme temperature, can exert their influences independently of population density and so are often called **density-independent factors.** However, many ecologists were (and are) quick to point out that abiotic factors can also influence populations in a density-dependent fashion. For instance, think of the effect on mortality of an unusually cold period. At high population densities a larger proportion of the population may inhabit less sheltered sites, and so mortality rate in the population is greater at high population density than at low population density. Similarly, biotic factors such as disease can affect populations in a density-independent way—for example, a particularly virulent pathogen, such as Dutch elm disease, which causes total mortality in infected populations regardless of their local density. The major point of this section is that biotic and abiotic factors act on populations by modifying birth and death rates. The significance of biotic and abiotic factors on populations has been well demonstrated by studies of Galápagos finches and their major food sources.

Environment and Birth and Death Among Galápagos Finches

Since Charles Darwin's visit in the 1830s, the Galápagos Islands have continued to provide scientists with a rich source of information concerning ecological and evolutionary processes. More than two decades ago Peter Grant and Rosemary Grant and their students and colleagues began a long-term study of the evolution and ecology of Galápagos finches. This long-term project has yielded information extending well beyond the finch populations and the Galápagos Islands. Knowledge of the influences of the environment on birth and death rates in natural populations could not have been gained from a short-term study.

Highly variable rainfall and responsive plant populations provided the environmental setting for these finch studies (fig. 12.18). In 1976, Peter. T. Boag and Peter Grant began a study of the populations of Darwin's finches inhabiting Daphne Major, an island of only 0.4 km^2 situated in the middle of the Galápagos Archipelago (Boag and Grant 1984*a*). At the time of this research, Peter Boag was a graduate student working with Peter Grant at McGill University. Boag is now a Professor at Queen's University. This study has since become a classic, cited in over 100 other papers. At its heart is an elegant study of the numbers of birds found on islands. The numerically

(a)

(b)

Figure 12.18   The abundant rains of 1983 (*a*) greatly increased plant growth on the Galápagos Islands compared to (*b*) periods of lower rainfall.

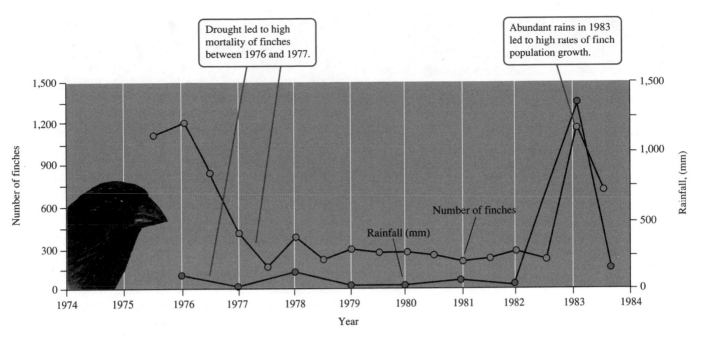

Figure 12.19   Rainfall and the medium ground finch, *Geospiza fortis,* population of Daphne Major Island (data from Gibbs and Grant 1987).

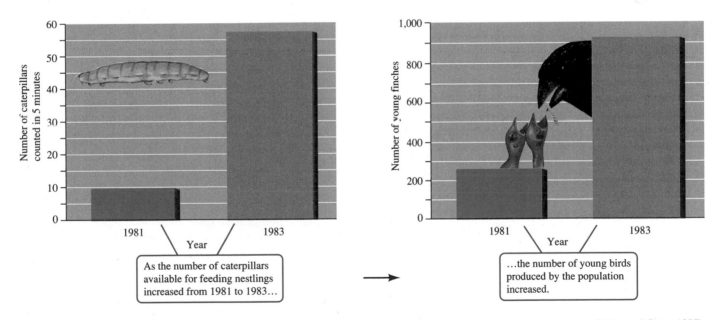

Figure 12.20   Availability of caterpillars and fledgling of young medium ground finches on Daphne Major (data from Gibbs and Grant 1987).

dominant finch on Daphne Major at the beginning of the study was the medium ground finch, *Geospiza fortis,* with about 1,200 individuals. In 1977, a drought struck the Galápagos Islands and by the end of the year the population of *G. fortis* had fallen to about 180 individuals. This decrease represents a decline in population size of about 85% in just one year.

Though a few birds may have emigrated to other nearby islands, most of this population decline was due to starvation. During the drought, the plants that normally produce an annual crop of seeds, upon which the finches depend for food, failed to do so. From 1977 to 1982, the population of *G. fortis*

on Daphne Major averaged about 300 individuals. Then in 1983, about 10 times the average amount of rainfall fell and the population grew to about 1,100 individuals (fig. 12.19). This population growth was due to an increased birthrate as a consequence of an abundance of seeds that the adult finches eat and an abundance of caterpillars that the finches feed to their young (fig. 12.20). As you can see, *G. fortis* populations declined in 1977 because death rates due to starvation far exceeded birthrates. However, the situation was reversed in 1983, when, in the presence of abundant food, birthrates greatly exceeded death rates.

Fisheries

Commercial fishing has a long history in Canada, serving as the economic and social foundation of many communities on the Atlantic, Pacific, and Northern coasts. In 2006, the economic value of the marine fisheries was in excess of two billion dollars ($Cdn) annually, with over 80% of that coming from the Atlantic fisheries. However, Atlantic fish harvests have declined from around 1.2 million tonnes annually in the late 1980s to about 850,000 tonnes annually in the early 2000s. Hidden within these numbers are harvests of a diversity of species, some of which have shown particularly dramatic declines in population sizes over a relatively short time period. For example, the cod harvest in Newfoundland and Labrador declined from approximately 250,000 tonnes (valued at approximately $133 million) in 1990 to 20,000 tonnes (valued at approximately $27 million) in 2002. Clearly these changes carry significant challenges for the local and national economies. Underlying collapses of fisheries are big changes in the population dynamics of species of commercial interest. We begin here with a general discussion of fisheries management, and the potential influence that ecologists can have in the collection and interpretation of data. We will then provide a more detailed analysis of the Atlantic Cod fishery collapse off the coast of Newfoundland and Labrador.

What is a fishery? A fishery includes the fish, fishers, marketplace, local communities, and other related industries. Fisheries are themselves embedded into natural ecosystems that influence the population dynamics of the fish, and they are influenced by local and national governments. A principle goal of sustainable fishery management is to provide the maximum long-term economic return while also maintaining a stable fish population. Successful fisheries will combine sound ecological and scientific knowledge with accurate local knowledge, helping construct appropriate governmental policies that provide incentives to protect the resource while also allowing for the economic viability of communities and industry. This is not an easy task, and over the last 50 years, 366 of the world's 1519 fisheries have experienced a collapse (Mullon et al. 2005), and many more fisheries are likely to collapse in the upcoming decades. Daniel Pauly and Johanne Dalsgaard from the University of British Columbia, along with colleagues from the Philippines, have documented that over the last several years there has been a global move to "fish down the food chain" (Pauly et al. 1998). In a survey of catches from fisheries across the globe, they found that there has been a shift away from large piscivorous fish towards small planktivorous fish and invertebrates. This pattern is likely due to rapid population declines of the "desired" species, causing a shift in the fishing effort towards fish that historically did not support commercial fisheries. Global

changes in fishing efforts suggest a general failure in managing these "renewable" resources. Why? Critical to the management of a sustainable fishery is a sound understanding of the ecology of the species of interest, and knowledge of the factors that influence population growth. It also is dependent upon governments and individuals choosing to maintain long-term sustainability, even at the cost of short-term profits. This is complicated by the fact that many marine species migrate through the territorial waters of many countries, and thus international cooperation is often necessary. Global politics is bit beyond the scope of this book, and instead we limit ourselves to a simpler question: What does ecological theory tell us about sustainable harvest levels?

If we believe that a population is following the logistic growth curve, then we already know a few pieces of information that may help us manage the fishery. Although there are countless numbers of fishery models currently in use (Caddy 1999), we will talk about the most basic idea of the **maximum sustainable yield, MSY**. MSY represents the maximum harvest (catch) of a population that can occur without decreasing population growth rates (fig 12.21). In an ideal population, such as one that follows the very simple and easy to understand logistic model of population growth, MSY is achieved when harvests maintain population densities at $N = K/2$. Why this value? When $N = K/2$, population growth rates are highest (fig. 12.16)! If harvests are greater than that, then dN/dt is reduced because there are relatively few individuals in the population left to reproduce. If harvest rates are reduced N below $K/2$, density-dependent factors will reduce per capita reproduction (fig. 12.15), and thus population growth rates are suppressed. It is important to recognize that MSY is generally higher than the **optimum sustainable yield, OSY** (fig. 12.21). OSY incorporates economics of harvesting as well as population growth rates, with the OSY being at the point which maximizes the difference between total revenue and total costs. The exact shape of the cost and revenue curves will depend on the value of the fish, as well as the type of equipment and intensity of harvest.

This all sounds so simple, yet why do fisheries so frequently collapse? We need to remember that fisheries are set within a social context, and the actions of individuals and governments are not necessarily those that will result in a sustainable harvest. In many cases, local economic pressures to maximize economic returns over the short-term, even at the risk of fishery collapse, can place significant political pressures to set harvest targets that are not necessarily biologically justified. At the same time, the logistic growth model has a variety of assumptions built into it, which if not true, means the resulting predictions are also not true. For example, to calculate dN/dt, you need actual numbers for r, K, and N, and these are not necessarily easy to get for large popula-

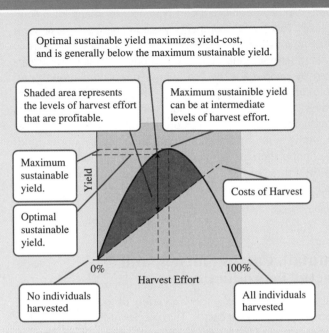

Figure 12.21 By integrating harvest intensity, costs, yields, and population growth, fishery managers can develop predictions of maximum and optimal sustainable yields.

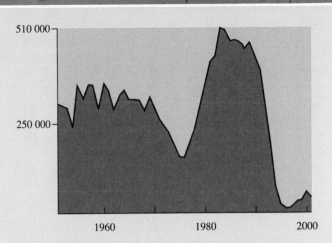

Figure 12.22 A 50-year time series of harvest of Atlantic cod in Canada.

tions of deep ocean fish. Inaccurate assessments of these measures, or of age of maturity, generation time, and sample size can result in equally inaccurate predictions of MSY and OSY. Additionally, mathematical models of population growth are simply that, models. Sometimes, despite the best efforts of population biologists the models that are constructed are simply wrong for a given species of interest. When this is the case, even accurate measures of population parameters will result in inaccurate predictions of population dynamics. Taking into consideration that faulty data, misguided governmental decisions, selfish behaviour, and incomplete ecological knowledge can all lead to fishery collapses, It may be less surprising that many of the world's fisheries are not particularly healthy. We end this section with one specific example, the recent collapse of Cod (*Gadus morhua*) fisheries off the coast of several Maritime Provinces in eastern Canada.

During the late 1980s and early 1990s there was a dramatic collapse in cod fisheries off the coasts of Nova Scotia and Newfoundland and Labrador (fig. 12.22), leading to a fishing moratorium declared in the early 1990s. Particularly striking about this collapse was that the decades prior showed relatively little variation in harvests. This fishery is rapidly becoming a model for study among ecologists, with the exact reasons behind the collapse still an issue of intense social debate. The central question for ecologists to answer is whether this collapse was the result of natural events (e.g., shifting habitats,

altered climate, increase in natural predation rates, etc.) or if it was due to overexploitation through commercial fishing.

The population density of cod has historically been measured by recording the catch rate by industry. This methodological choice is based upon the assumption that there is a linear relationship between fish population density and catch rate (proxy measure). Figure 12.22 clearly shows that catch rates were constant just prior to the fishery collapse. Does this mean that the population densities were themselves constant? Jeffrey Hutchings (1996) suggests otherwise, and instead argues that the data suggest that population densities off the coast of Newfoundland and Labrador were decreasing since the middle 1980s, and thus the apparent sudden collapse had longer-term biological explanations. Hutchings found that the cod population appears to have become more clumped as fishing mortality increased and population size decreased throughout the 1980s. By focusing fishing efforts primarily in areas of high fish density, commercial catch rates did not decrease substantially, even though the underlying fish population was experiencing a substantial decline. The idea of the population becoming more clumped assumes there is a fitness benefit to cod for being part of a group, such as increased foraging success, predator avoidance, or increased mating success. Another risk of relying on catch rates as a measure of population size is that technical advances in fishing can cause increases in catch rates even when the underlying population is declining.

It is difficult to overestimate the political and social sensitivities to the idea that fishing caused the collapse of the cod fishery, and it is important to point out there exist several other hypotheses. Here we briefly discuss one of the more commonly discussed hypotheses, the idea that the fishery collapse was due to increased predation by seals, rather than fishing.

Fu and colleagues at the Department of Fisheries and Oceans conducted a set of mathematical analyses designed to determine the relative impacts of several factors on the collapse of a cod population off the coast of Nova Scotia (2001). Of particular interest was the role of seals, which are natural predators of the Atlantic cod. The researchers simulated the effects of seal on cod populations by developing a population growth model for the fish. More specifically, this model accounted for different sources of mortality and rates of increase in different age classes. In their analyses, they manipulated the values given to the different parameters to determine the overall sensitivity of cod populations to each value. They found no evidence that predation by seals was strong enough to cause the initial population collapse. However, they have found that the intensity of seal predation has increased since 1993, and seals may in part be responsible for a failure of this fish population to recover.

Understanding the population dynamics of natural populations can have significant consequences for many local communities. There can be competing pressures between maximizing instantaneous rates of harvest and providing good stewardship of a long-term sustainable fishery. Responding to all of the actions taken by people are the fish, whose population growth and evolutionary trajectories will be a direct function of changes in birth and death rates. Ecologists are essential to any hopes of reducing the pressures put on natural fisheries throughout the world, as without accurate data and scientific understanding of population growth, there will be no hope for maintaining healthy fish stocks as human populations continue to grow, placing even higher demands on wild fish stocks.

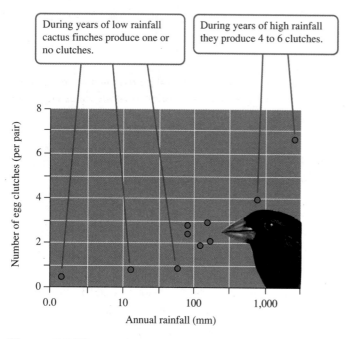

During years of low rainfall cactus finches produce one or no clutches.

During years of high rainfall they produce 4 to 6 clutches.

Figure 12.23   Relationship between annual rainfall and the number of egg clutches produced by large cactus finches, *Geospiza conirostris*, on Genovesa Island (data from Grant and Grant 1989).

Over this same period, Rosemary Grant and Peter Grant (1989) were studying a population of the large cactus finch, *Geospiza conirostris*, on Genovesa, a small, highly isolated island in the extreme northeastern portion of the Galápagos Archipelago. The study continued from 1978 to 1988, long enough for the researchers to observe the effects of two droughts and two wet periods on reproductive biology. In this population of cactus finches, there was a positive correlation between the number of clutches of eggs laid by birds and the total annual rainfall (fig. 12.23). This study also showed how wet and drought cycles and cactus finches affect populations of prickly pear cactus.

Rainfall, Cactus Finches, and Cactus Reproduction

The Galápagos finches harvest a variety of foods from several species of prickly pear cactus. Two species of finches, *Geospiza scandens* and *G. conirostris*, are well-known specialists on cacti. The Grants documented several ways in which these finches make use of cacti, including (1) opening flower buds in the dry season to eat pollen, (2) consuming nectar and pollen from mature flowers, (3) eating a seed coating called the aril, (4) eating seeds, and (5) eating insects from rotting cactus pads and from underneath bark. In return, the finches disperse some cactus seeds and pollinate cactus flowers.

Finches also damage many cactus flowers, however. When they open flower buds or partially opened flowers, they snip the style and destroy the stigmas. As a consequence, the ovules of these flowers cannot be fertilized and they do not produce seeds. The Grants found that up to 78% of a population of flowers can be damaged in this way. These activities, which take place during the wet season, may reduce the seeds available to finches during the dry season.

Opuntia helleri, one of the main sources of food for cactus finches on Genovesa Island, was negatively impacted by the El Niño of 1983. This El Niño damaged the cacti in three ways: (1) Many *O. helleri* simply absorbed so much water that their roots could no longer support them and they were blown over by wind; (2) *O. helleri* on sea cliffs were bathed in salt spray during the many storms that hit the island during 1983, which may have produced osmotic stress (see chapter 6); and (3) increased rainfall stimulated growth by a fast-growing vine that smothered many *O. helleri* (fig. 12.24). Though outright mortality of the cactus was not common, flower and fruit production was severely reduced for several years.

Reduced reproductive output by *O. helleri* was at least partly due to the activities of the cactus finches on Genovesa. The stigma snipping behaviour of cactus finches was especially damaging during the drought years of 1984 and 1985. During

Figure 12.24 High rainfall during the El Niño of 1983 caused increased mortality of the cactus *Opuntia helleri* on Genovesa Island.

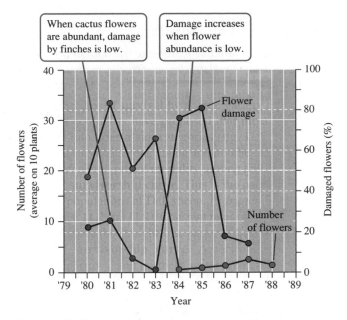

When cactus flowers are abundant, damage by finches is low.

Damage increases when flower abundance is low.

Flower damage

Number of flowers

Figure 12.25 Cactus flower abundance on Genovesa Island and extent of flower damage by large cactus finches (data from Grant and Grant 1989).

normal years, stigma damage is mainly confined to the early part of the wet season from January to March. During the extremely wet 1983 season, there was very little damage to the stigmas of cactus flowers. However, during the drought years of 1984 and 1985, up to 95% of stigmas were snipped (fig. 12.25). This extensive damage to flowers helped delay recovery of flower and fruit production until 1986, when another El Niño brought heavy rains to the Galápagos Islands.

Populations of Galápagos finches and their food plants are an instructive model of how the environment can affect birth and death rates. Sometimes, as when the cactus fell because they were engorged with water during the El Niño of 1983, the effect of the physical environment is clear and direct. Sometimes, as when *G. fortis* starved in response to reduced seed supplies during the drought of 1977, the effect of the physical environment on a population is clearly mediated through a biological resource (in this case, seeds). In other cases, such as reduced fruit production by *O. helleri* on Genovesa, populations respond to a complex mixture of abiotic (drought) and biotic (damage by finches) factors that are themselves interrelated. The message to remember from these detailed studies is that both biotic and abiotic factors have important influences on birth and death rates in populations and that their effects are often tightly interconnected. In the examples just presented,

environmental variation essentially changed the carrying capacity (*K*) of the environment for Galápagos finch populations. In section II, we have focused on how various aspects of the physical environment affect the performance of organisms, including their reproductive performance. In chapters 13, 14, and 15 of section IV we will consider at length how biological interactions affect populations. Let's now explore patterns of population groups in one common species, humans.

Concept 12.3 Review

1. Why can we be sure that all animal and plant populations are under some form of environmental control?
2. What appears to set the carrying capacity for medium ground finches on Daphne Major Island?
3. Why might medium ground finch population responses to short-term, episodic increases in rainfall differ from their responses to increases in rainfall lasting for years or decades?

Ecological Tools

The Human Population

Most of the environmental concerns expressed by human society trace their origins to the effects of the human population itself on the environment. Therefore, it is very important that students of ecology be familiar with the history, current state, and projected growth of human populations. This knowledge serves as a critical tool in understanding the root cause of many ecological issues students may be called upon to fix in the future. Let's use some of the conceptual tools we discussed in chapters 10 and 11 and in this chapter to review patterns of human distribution and abundance, population dynamics, and growth.

Distribution and Abundance

One of the most distinctive features of the human population is its distribution. Our species is virtually everywhere. We occupy all the continents—even the Antarctic includes a population of scientists and support staff—and most oceanic islands. What other species, except those dependent upon humans, is so ubiquitous? Except for the Antarctic population, the current distribution of humans did not require modern technological advances. People with stone-age technology nearly reached the present limits of our distribution over 10,000 years ago. Colonization of only the most isolated oceanic islands had to await the development of sophisticated navigational techniques by the Polynesians and Europeans.

Like other populations, human populations are highly clumped at large scales (see chapter 10). In 2006, 60.7% of the global population, or about 3.9 billion people, were concentrated in Asia (fig. 12.26). In turn, most Asians live in two countries, China and India, the most populous countries on the planet. The remainder of the human population is spread across Africa (13.9%), Europe (11.2%), North America (7.9%), and South America (5.8%). The remainder (0.5%) live in Oceania (Australia and scattered oceanic islands).

Within continents, human populations attain their highest densities in eastern, southeastern, and southern Asia. Other areas of high population density include western and central Europe,

northern and western Africa, and eastern and western North America. The patterns shown in figure 12.27 suggest that the highest human population densities are in coastal areas and along major river valleys.

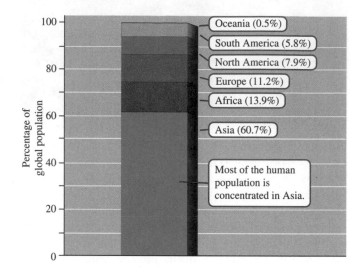

Figure 12.26   Distribution of the human population by continent in 2006 (data from the U.S. Bureau of the Census, International Data Base 2006).

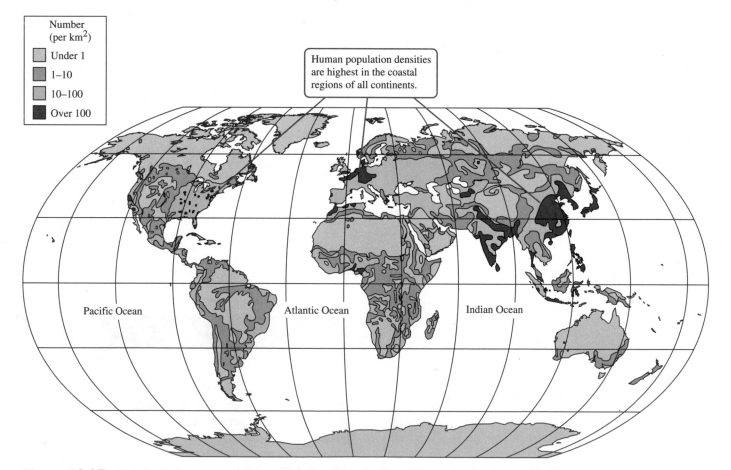

Figure 12.27   Variation in human population density (data from the United Nations Population Information Network).

There is even more variation in human population density if viewed on a smaller scale. Within Asia, Singapore has a population density of over 6,800 persons per square kilometer, while Mongolia has a population density of only 1.8 persons per square kilometer. This is slightly less than the density on the continent of Australia, which is 2.6 persons per square kilometer. Within Europe, The Netherlands harbours about 400 persons per square kilometer, while Spain and Greece have population densities of about 80 per square kilometer. In North America, Canada has an average population density of about 3.5 people per square kilometer. However, this population is concentrated in the southern part of the country, with nearly ¾ of the population living within 200 km of the southern border with the United States. Within Canada, population densities are lowest in Nunavut (0.02 people per square kilometer) and highest in Prince Edward Island (24.5 people per square kilometer). In contrast, the United States has an average population density of about 30 per square kilometer. This ranges from nearly 450 people per square kilometer in New Jersey to less than 1 person per square kilometer in Alaska. Again, on a large scale, human populations are highly clumped and as a consequence, population density is highly variable. Population dynamics also vary a great deal.

Population Dynamics

Population dynamics vary widely from region to region and from country to country. Let's examine the age distributions, birthrates, and death rates of three countries that have stable, declining, and rapidly growing populations. As we saw in chapter 11, population ecologists can surmise a great deal about a population by examining its age distribution. Sweden has an age distribution that is approximately the same width near its base as it is higher up (fig. 12.28). This indicates that the individuals in this population are producing just enough offspring to approximately replace losses due to death. Compare this distribution with that of Hungary. The age distribution of Hungary's population is much narrower at its base, which indicates a declining population. In contrast, the very broad base of Rwanda's age distribution indicates a rapidly growing population.

The impressions we get by examining the age distributions of these three countries are confirmed if we calculate their birth and death rates. In 2006, the annual per capita birthrate, b, of Sweden's population was 0.010. This exactly matched the death rate, d, in Sweden's population, which was 0.010. If we subtract Sweden's death rate from its birthrate (0.010 − 0.010), the result is a zero per capita rate of increase, r, of 0.000. In contrast, Hungary's birthrate (0.010) was lower than its death rate (0.013), which results in a per capita rate of increase, r, of −0.003. This negative value for r confirms our impression that Hungary's population is declining. At the other end of the population dynamics spectrum, Rwanda's population has a birthrate that is over two times its death rate. As a consequence, this country's annual per capita rate of increase is 0.024, which is strongly positive growth. Let's move from these estimates of the present rates of change to examine the longer-term population trends in these countries.

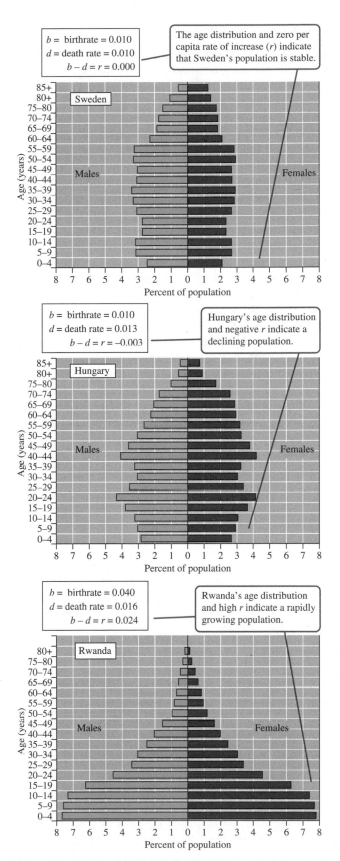

Figure 12.28 Age distributions for human populations in countries with stable, declining, and rapidly growing populations (data from the U.S. Bureau of the Census, International Data Base 2006).

Population Growth

Figure 12.29 presents the historical and projected populations of Sweden, Hungary, and Rwanda. In 1950, the population of Rwanda was much smaller than either Hungary's or Sweden's population. Rwanda's population is projected to continue growing and to exceed that of Hungary and Sweden in the year 2020. Meanwhile, Sweden's population is expected to stabilize and then decline gradually, while the population of Hungary declines at a faster rate.

How is the global human population changing? While the populations of many developed countries are either stable or declining, those of most developing countries are growing, and the trend for the entire global population is continued growth. While the rate of growth has begun to slow, the global population is expected to exceed 9 billion by the middle of the twenty-first century (fig. 12.30*a*).

There are signs that global population growth is slowing. While the global population continues to grow, it is not now growing exponentially. The *rate* of global population growth has declined substantially over the past 40 years, as shown in figure 12.30*b*. The size of the global population is not rising as steeply as it once was and is projected to level off sometime after the middle of the twenty-first century. Figure 12.30*b* also displays the proximate cause of this leveling off in population size, a decline in annual growth of the global population. The rate of annual growth by the global population rose steadily from 1950 to 1957 and then took a sharp dip during a major famine in China that lasted from 1958 to 1961, resulting

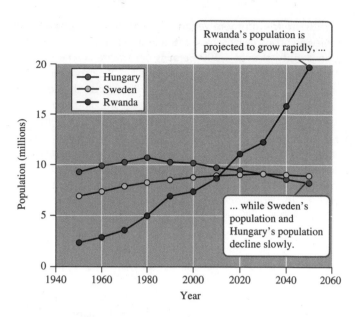

Figure 12.29 Historical and projected human populations of countries with growing, declining, and stable populations (data from the U.S. Bureau of the Census, International Data Base 2005).

in the deaths of an estimated 16 to 33 million Chinese. Annual growth rate, which peaked from 1962 to 1963 at 2.19%, has been decreasing in the four decades since, reaching 1.14% in 2006. The global growth rate is projected to decline to less than 0.5% by 2050. However, this is a projection based on

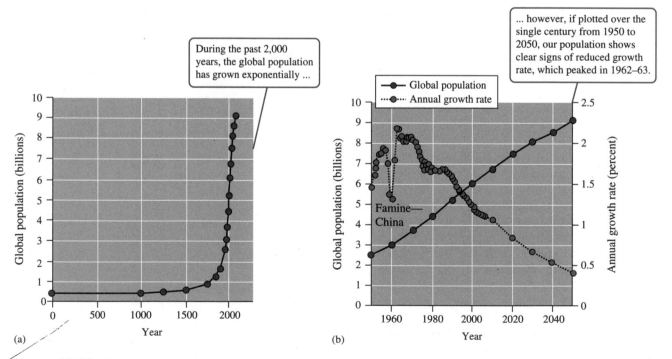

Figure 12.30 Temporal perspectives on global population growth: (*a*) Exponential growth during the past 2000 years is evident but (*b*) the past 40 years have been a period of slowing growth by the global human population; growth is projected to continue to slow over the next half century (data from the United Nations Population Information Network and the U.S. Bureau of the Census, International Data Base 2006).

current conditions and recent dynamics of the global and regional populations. Since rates of growth in human populations are currently very dynamic, projections of future global population sizes are being adjusted frequently. During the past five years, most of these adjustments have produced lowered estimates of future global population size. However, the cost that the present human population exacts upon the global environment is already substantial (see chapter 23). One of the greatest environmental challenges of the twenty-first century will be to establish a sustainable global population.

Summary

In the presence of abundant resources, populations can grow at geometric or exponential rates. Population growth by organisms with pulsed reproduction can be described by the geometric model of population growth. Population growth that occurs as a continuous process, as in human or bacterial populations, can be described by the exponential model of population growth. Examples of exponential growth from natural populations suggest that this type of growth may be very important to populations during establishment in new environments, during recovery from some form of exploitation, or during exploitation of transient, favourable conditions.

If resources become limited, population growth rate slows and eventually stops; this is known as logistic population growth. As population size increases, population growth eventually slows and then ceases, producing a sigmoidal, or S-shaped, population growth curve. Population growth stops when populations reach a maximum size called the carrying capacity, the number of individuals of a particular population that the environment can support. Sigmoidal population growth can be modelled by the logistic growth equation, a modification of the exponential growth equation that includes a term for environmental resistance. In the logistic model, per capita growth rates decrease linearly with increasing population density. In contrast, the growth rate of the population itself, dN/dt, shows a unimodal relationship with density, with maximal population growth when $N = K/2$. Population growth is a function both of per capita growth rates and population size. Research on laboratory populations indicates that zero population growth at carrying capacity can be due to a variety of combinations of reduced birthrates and increased death rates.

The environment limits population growth by changing birth and death rates. The factors affecting population size and growth include biotic factors such as food, disease, competitors, and predators and abiotic factors such as rainfall, floods, and temperature. Because the effects of biotic factors, such as disease and predation, are often influenced by population density, biotic factors are often referred to as density-dependent factors. Meanwhile, abiotic factors such as floods and extreme temperature can exert their influences independently of population density and so are often called density-independent factors. As we have already seen, both abiotic and biotic forces have important influences on populations. The significant effects of biotic and abiotic factors on populations have been well-demonstrated by studies of Galápagos finches and their major food sources.

The present state of the human population can be examined using the conceptual tools of population biology discussed in chapters 10 and 11 and in chapter 12. Though humans live on every continent, their population density differs by several orders of magnitude in different regions. In 2006, 60.7% of the global population, or about 3.9 billion people, were concentrated in Asia. The remainder of the human population was spread across Africa (13.9%), Europe (11.2%), North America (7.9%), South America (5.8%), and Oceania (0.5%). Population densities in different regions vary from less than 1 person per square kilometer to nearly 7,000 persons per square kilometer. While the populations of some countries are stable, and some are declining, the global population is expected to continue growing past the year 2050. One of the greatest environmental challenges of the twenty-first century will be to establish a sustainable global human population.

Review Questions

1. For what types of organisms is the geometric model of population growth appropriate? For what types of organisms is the exponential model of population growth appropriate? In what circumstances would a population grow exponentially? In what circumstances would a population not grow exponentially?

2. In chapters 10, 11, and 12 we have presented a number of mathematical models that describe natural populations? Why are models used extensively in population biology? How can models enhance, or hinder, understanding of the underlying concepts of population biology?

3. How do you build the logistic model for population growth from the exponential model? What part of the logistic growth equation produces the sigmoidal growth curve?

4. In question 3, you thought about how the logistic growth equation produces a sigmoidal growth curve. Now, let's think about nature. What is it about the natural environment that produces sigmoidal growth? Pick a real organism living in an environment with which you are familiar and list the things that might limit the growth of its population.

5. What is the relationship between per capita rate of increase, r, and the intrinsic rate of increase, r_{max}? In chapter 11, we estimated r from the life tables and fecundity schedules of two species. How would you estimate r_{max}?

6. Both abiotic and biotic factors influence birth and death rates in populations. Make a list of abiotic and biotic factors that are potentially important regulators of natural populations.

7. Population biologists may refer to abiotic factors, such as temperature and moisture, as density-independent because such factors can affect population processes independently of local population density. At the same time, biotic factors, such as disease and competition, are called density-dependent factors because their effects may be related to local population density. Explain how abiotic factors can influence populations in a way that is independent of local population density. Explain why the influence of a biotic factor is often affected by local population density. Now, explain how the impact of an abiotic factor may also be affected by the local population density, that is, may behave at least partly as a density-dependent factor.

8. Where on earth is human population density highest? Where is it lowest? Where on earth do no people live? Where are human populations growing the fastest? Where are they approximately stable?

9. What factors will determine the earth's carrying capacity for Homo sapiens? Explain why the earth's long-term (thousands of years) carrying capacity for the human population may be much lower than the projected population size for the year 2050. Now argue the other side. Explain how the numbers projected for 2050 might be sustained over the long term.

10. What role can ecologists play in developing a sustainable fishery? Does the source of harvest mortality (e.g., seals vs. people) have differential impacts on population growth and/or evolution?

Suggested Readings

Bennett, K.D. 1983. Post-glacial population expansion of forest trees in Norfolk, UK. *Nature* 303:164–67.

This short paper offers a reconstruction of population growth by trees following the end of the last glacial period.

Dobson, F.S. and M.K. Oli. 2001. The demographic basis of population regulation in Columbian ground squirrels. *The American Naturalist* 158:236–47.

Clear demonstration of the influence of food availability on populations of Columbian ground squirrels. This study explores the details of population regulation in the study populations.

Grant, P.R. and B.R. Grant. 2002. Unpredictable evolution in a 30-year study of Darwin's finches. *Science* 296:707–11.

Grant, B.R. and P.R. Grant. 2003. What Darwin's finches can teach us about the evolutionary origin and regulation of biodiversity. *BioScience* 53:965–75.

Excellent reviews of discoveries resulting from Rosemary and Peter Grant's long-term ecological and evolutionary studies of the Galápagos, or Darwin's, finches.

Hixon, M.A., S.W. Pacala, and S.A. Sandin. 2002. Population regulation: historical context and contemporary challenges of open vs. closed systems. *Ecology* 83:1490–1508.

Careful overview of the concept of population regulation which brings the historical ideas into a contemporary focus.

Snell, T.W., B.J. Dingmann, and M. Serra. 2001. Density-dependent regulation of natural and laboratory rotifer populations. *Hydrobiologia* 446/447:39–44.

Yoshinaga, T., A. Hagiwara, and K. Tsukamoto. 2001. Why do rotifer populations present a typical sigmoid growth curve? *Hydrobiologia* 446/447:99–105.

A pair of papers that thoroughly document density-dependent regulation of r and the resulting pattern of sigmoidal or logistic population growth in natural and laboratory populations of rotifers.

Wauters, L.A., E. Matthysen, F. Adriaensen, and G. Tosi. 2004. Within-sex density dependence and population dynamics of red squirrels *Sciurus vulgaris*. *Journal of Animal Ecology* 73:11–25.

Very detailed study of the influences of density-dependent and density-independent factors on the population dynamics of European red squirrels.

Section IV

INTERACTIONS

Interactions among species can take a variety of forms, and have varying effects on an organism's fitness, population dynamics, and community structure. In this section we will explore several of the more dominant types of interactions: competition, predation, herbivory, mutualism, and parasitism. These topics build from our understanding of populations (section III) and interactions with the abiotic environment (section II), and are critical to our ability to understand how communities are structured, the topic of section V.

Chapter *13*

Competition

Outline

Careful observation and experimentation can reveal competition between species in nature. Along a coral reef off the north coast of Jamaica, threespot damselfish guard small territories of less than 1 m² (fig. 13.1). These territories are regularly dispersed across the reef and contain most of the resources upon which the damselfish depend: nooks and crannies for shelter against predators, a carefully tended patch of fast-growing algae for food, and in the territories of males, an area of coral rubble kept clean for spawning. The damselfish constantly patrol and survey the borders of their territories, vigorously attacking any intruder that presents a threat to their eggs and developing larvae, or to their food supply. If you look carefully, however, you may find that not all members of the population have a territory. Damselfish without territories live in marginal areas around the territorial members, wandering from one part of the reef to another.

If you create a vacancy on the reef by removing one of the damselfish holding a territory, other damselfish appear within minutes to claim the vacant territory. Some of the new arrivals are threespot damselfish like the original resident, and some are cocoa damselfish, which generally live a bit higher on the reef face. These new arrivals fight fiercely for the vacated territory. The damselfish chase each other, nip each other's flanks, and slap each other with their tails. The melee ends within minutes, and life among the damselfish settles back into a kind of tense tranquility. The new resident, which may have driven off a half dozen rivals, is usually another threespot damselfish.

This example demonstrates several things. First, individual damselfish maintain possession of their territories through ongoing competition with other damselfish, and this competition takes the form of *interference competition,* which involves direct aggressive interactions between individuals. Second, though it may not appear so to the casual observer, there is a limited supply of suitable space for damselfish territories, a condition that ecologists call **resource limitation.** Third, the threespot damselfish are subject to **intraspecific competition**, competition with members of their own species, as well as **interspecific competition**, competition between individuals of different species. The effects of competition on the fitness of the competitors are not necessarily the same for all individuals. Instead, competitive effects can be asymmetric, with some

individuals harmed (the losers), while others (the winners) are not. In this chapter we will explore some of the factors that lead to competition, some of the strategies employed to enhance competitive abilities, and we will discuss some evolutionary consequences of prolonged conflict over limited resources.

Competition is not always as dramatic as fighting damselfish nor is it always resolved so quickly. In a mature white pine forest in New Hampshire, tree roots grow throughout the soil taking up nutrients and water as they provide support. In 1931, J. Toumey and R. Kienholz designed an experiment to determine whether the activities of these tree roots suppress the activities of other plants. The researchers cut a trench, 0.92 m deep, around a plot 2.74 m by 2.74 m in the middle of the forest. In so doing, they cut 825 roots, which removed potential competition by these roots for soil resources. They also established control plots on either side of the trenched plot and then watched as the results of their experiment unfolded. The experiment continued for eight years, with retrenching every two years and over 100 roots cut each time. By retrenching, the researchers maintained their experimental treatment, suppression of potential root competition.

In the end, this eight-year experiment yielded results as dramatic as those with the damselfish. Vegetative cover on the section of forest floor that had been released from root competition was 10 times that present on the control plots. Apparently the roots of white pines exert interspecific competition for limited supplies of nutrients and water that is strong enough to suppress the growth of forest floor vegetation (fig. 13.2). In addition, the growth of young white pines was much greater

Figure 13.2 Competition in a forest can be as intense as competition on a coral reef. However, much of the competition in a forest takes place underground, where the roots of plants compete for water and nutrients.

Figure 13.1 Territorial reef fish such as threespot damselfish and the two blennies shown in this photo compete intensely for space.

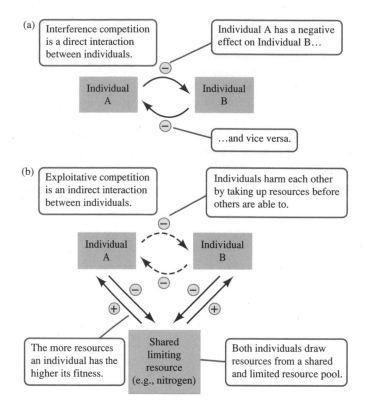

Figure 13.3 Competition can be (*a*) direct, or (*b*) indirect interaction among individuals of the same or different species.

within the trenched plots than in the control plots, demonstrating considerable intraspecific competition was occurring.

In both the forest floor and damselfish examples, individuals are competing for limited resources. A critical difference is that the damselfish compete by actively attacking other individuals, in the hopes of preventing access to the desired resource contained on the reef. In the forest example the plants are not competing by preventing access to the soil nutrients and water, instead, competition occurs when some individuals acquire these resources before other individuals are able to capture the resources. The damselfish were demonstrating *interference competition*, while the plants are demonstrating **exploitative competition** (fig. 13.3). Both plants and animals are able to demonstrate exploitative and interference competition, depending upon the details of the specific competitive interaction.

Ecologists have long thought that competition is pervasive in nature, and in many circumstances competitive interactions can affect fitness and evolution of species. However, competition is not always important in all natural communities for all species. Instead, abiotic stress (section II), predation, or parasites may most strongly limit individual fitness, population dynamics, and community structure. In this chapter we will discuss the many approaches ecologists have taken to understanding the potential role of competition in influencing fitness, population dynamics, and species distributions. As you will see, the research ranges from mathematical equations to field experiments and most everything in between. The answers obtained from the research are farther reaching than simply saying that competition is, and always will be, a powerful force in natural communities. Instead, there is wide agreement that competition can be powerful, and understanding when, where, and why competition exists is an important set of goals for the ecologists of today and tomorrow.

Concepts

13.1 **Mathematical and laboratory models provide a theoretical foundation for studying competitive interactions in nature.**

13.2 **Field and mesocosm studies show that resource limitation and competition are widespread.**

13.3 **Competition can have significant ecological and evolutionary influences on species.**

13.1 Mathematical and Laboratory Models

Mathematical and laboratory models provide a theoretical foundation for studying competitive interactions in nature. Ecologists have used both mathematical and laboratory models to explore the ecology of competition. Models are generally much simpler than the natural circumstances the ecologist wishes to understand. However, while sacrificing accuracy, this simplicity offers a degree of control that ecologists would not have in most natural settings.

D. B. Mertz (1972) began a review of four decades of research on *Tribolium* beetle populations with an astute summary of the characteristics of models in general and of the "*Tribolium* model" in particular: (1) It is an abstraction and simplification, not a facsimile, of nature; (2) except for the beetles themselves, it is a man-made construct, partly empirical and partly deductive; and (3) it is used to provide insights into natural phenomena. The predictions of these simplified models can be tested in natural systems and either supported or falsified. If falsified, a theory can be modified to accommodate the new information. Ideally, scientific understanding proceeds as a consequence of this dialog between theory and observation, between theoretician and empiricist.

Modelling Interspecific Competition

As we saw in chapter 12, the model of logistic population growth includes a term for intraspecific competition, $\frac{K-N}{K}$. This model can be expanded to include the influence of interspecific competition on population growth. The first to do so was Vito Volterra (1926), who was interested in developing a theoretical basis for explaining changes in the composition of a marine fish community in response to reduced fishing during World War I. Alfred Lotka (1932b) independently repeated Volterra's analysis and extended it using graphics to represent changes in the population densities of competing species during competition.

Let's retrace the steps of Lotka's and Volterra's modelling exercise, beginning with the logistic model for population growth discussed in chapter 12:

$$\frac{dN}{dt} = r_{max}N\left(\frac{K-N}{K}\right)$$

We can express the population growth of two species of potential competitors with the logistic equation:

Change in population growth of species 1 =

$$\frac{dN_1}{dt} = r_{max1}N_1\left(\frac{K_1-N_1}{K_1}\right) \text{ and}$$

Change in population growth of species 2 =

$$\frac{dN_2}{dt} = r_{max2}N_2\left(\frac{K_2-N_2}{K_2}\right)$$

Where N_1 and N_2 are the population sizes of species 1 and 2, K_1 and K_2 are their carrying capacities, and r_{max1} and r_{max2} are the intrinsic rates of increase for species 1 and 2. In these models, population growth slows as N increases and the relative level of intraspecific competition is expressed as the ratio of numbers to carrying capacity, either N_1/K_1 or N_2/K_2. The assumption here is that resource supplies will diminish as population size increases due to intraspecific competition for resources. Resource levels can also be reduced by interspecific competition.

Lotka and Volterra included the effect of interspecific competition on the population growth of each species as:

$$\frac{dN_1}{dt} = r_{max1}N_1\left(\frac{K_1-N_1-\alpha_{12}N_2}{K_1}\right)$$

and

$$\frac{dN_2}{dt} = r_{max2}N_2\left(\frac{K_2-N_2-\alpha_{21}N_1}{K_2}\right)$$

In these models, the rate of population growth of a species is reduced both by conspecifics (individuals of the same species) and by individuals of the competing species, that is, interspecific competition. The effect of interspecific competition is incorporated into the Lotka–Volterra model by introducing the terms $-\alpha_{12}N_2$ and $-\alpha_{21}N_1$. The terms α_{12} and α_{21} are called **competition coefficients** and express the interspecific competitive effects of the two species. Specifically, α_{12} is the effect of an individual of species 2 on the rate of population growth of species 1, while α_{21} is the effect of an individual of species 1 on the rate of population growth of species 2. By multiplying α_{12} and α_{12} by N_1 and N_2 respectively, interspecific competitive effects are expressed in terms of intraspecific equivalents. If, for example, $\alpha_{12} > 1$, then the competitive effect of an individual of species 2 on the population growth of species 1 is greater than that of an individual of species 1. If, on the other hand, $\alpha_{12} < 1$, then the competitive effect of an individual of species 2 on the population growth of species 1 is less than that of an individual of species 1.

In general, the Lotka–Volterra model predicts coexistence of two species when, for both species, interspecific competition is weaker than intraspecific competition. Otherwise, one species is predicted to eventually exclude the other. How can you determine that these species are predicted to coexist under some conditions, while not under other conditions? The answer to this question involves a bit of mathematical rearrangement, and shows how simple theoretical models can provide great ecological insight. To determine the conditions for coexistence of two competing species, we begin by determining the conditions under which the population growth of both species is zero. This can be determined through simple rearrangement of the Lotka–Voterra equations.

Populations of species 1 and 2 stop growing when:

$$\frac{dN_1}{dt} = r_{max1}N_1\left(\frac{K_1-N_1-\alpha_{12}N_2}{K_1}\right) = 0$$

and

$$\frac{dN_2}{dt} = r_{max2}N_2\left(\frac{K_2-N_2-\alpha_{21}N_1}{K_2}\right) = 0$$

That is, when:

$$(K_1-N_1-\alpha_{12}N_2) = 0 \text{ and } (K_2-N_2-\alpha_{21}N_1) = 0$$

Or, further rearranging these equations, we predict that population growth for the two species will stop when:

$$N_1 = K_1-\alpha_{12}N_2 \text{ and } N_2 = K_2-\alpha_{21}N_1$$

Here is some good news: the resulting equations are simply equations that describe two straight lines ($y = $ (slope)(x) + y-intercept)! In the first equation, the population size of species 1 (N_1) is our y value, the effects of species 2 on species 1 (α_{12}) is the slope, and the population size of species 2 (N_2) is the x-value, and the carrying capacity of species 1 is the y-intercept (when $x = 0$). The second equation has a similar form. Since you learned all about straight lines back in first grade, you certainly can understand this next step. We will start by giving these lines a special name, **isoclines of zero population growth**. At every point along these lines, population growth is stopped:

$$\frac{dN_1}{dt} = 0 \text{ and } \frac{dN_2}{dt} = 0$$

Above an isocline of zero growth, the population of a species is decreasing ($\frac{dN}{dt} < 0$); below it the population is increasing (fig. 13.4) ($\frac{dN}{dt} > 0$).

The isoclines of zero growth show how the environment can be filled up or, in other words, the relative population sizes of species 1 and species 2 that will deplete the critical resources. At one extreme, for example, for species 1, the environment is completely filled by species 1 and species 2 is absent. This occurs where $N_1 = K_1$. At the other extreme, again for species 1, the environment can be saturated entirely by species 2, while species 1 is absent. This occurs where $N_2 = K_1/\alpha_{12}$. In between these extremes, the environment is saturated with a mixture of species 1 and 2. The graph of the isocline for zero growth for species 2 can be interpreted in a similar way.

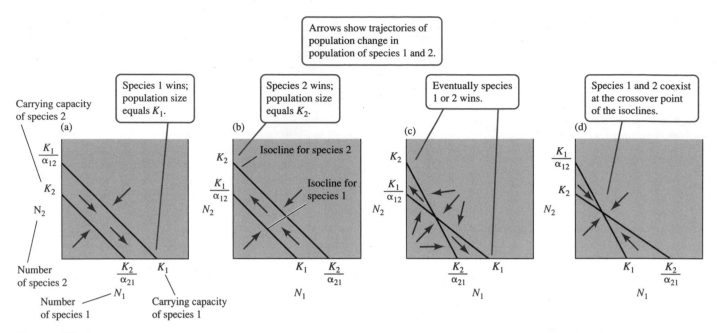

Figure 13.4   The orientation of isoclines for zero population growth and the outcome of competition according to the Lotka–Volterra competition model.

Putting the isoclines of zero growth for the two species on the same axis allows us to predict if one species will exclude the other or whether the two species will coexist. The precise prediction depends upon the relative orientation of the two isoclines. As shown in figure 13.4, there are four possibilities.

The Lotka–Volterra model predicts that one species will exclude the other when the isoclines do not cross. If the isocline for species 1 lies above that of species 2, species 1 will eventually exclude species 2. This exclusion occurs because all growth trajectories lead to the point where $N_1 = K_1$ and $N_2 = 0$ (fig. 13.4a). Figure 13.4b portrays the opposite situation in which the isocline for species 2 lies completely above that of species 1 and species 2 excludes species 1. In this case, all trajectories of population growth lead to the point where $N_2 = K_2$ and $N_1 = 0$.

Coexistence is possible only in the situations in which the isoclines cross. However, only one of these situations leads to stable coexistence. Figure 13.4c shows the situation in which coexistence is possible at the point where the isoclines of zero population growth cross but coexistence is unstable. In this situation, $K_1 > K_2/\alpha_{21}$ and $K_2 > K_1/\alpha_{12}$ and most population growth trajectories lead either to the points where $N_1 = K_1$ and $N_2 = 0$, or to where $N_2 = K_2$ and $N_1 = 0$. The populations of species 1 and 2 may arrive at the point where the lines cross, but any environmental variation that moves the populations off this point eventually leads to exclusion of one species by the other. Figure 13.4d represents the only situation that predicts stable coexistence of the two species. In this situation, $K_2/\alpha_{21} > K_1$ and $K_1/\alpha_{21} > K_2$ and all growth trajectories lead to the point where the isoclines of zero growth cross.

What is the biological meaning of saying that all growth trajectories lead to the point where the isoclines of zero growth cross? What this means is that the relative abundances of species 1 and 2 will eventually arrive at the point where the isoclines cross, a point where the abundances of both species are greater than zero. In this situation, each species is limited more by members of their own species than they are by members of the other species. In other words, the Lotka–Volterra model predicts that species coexist when intraspecific competition is stronger than interspecific competition. This is a central finding of competition theory and it is supported by the results of laboratory experiments on interspecific competition.

Laboratory Models of Competition

Experiments with *Paramecia*

G. F. Gause (1934) used laboratory experiments to test the major predictions of the Lotka-Volterra competition model. During the course of his work Gause experimented with many organisms, but the most well known of his experimental subjects were paramecia. Paramecia are freshwater, ciliated protozoans that offer several advantages for laboratory work. First, since they are small, they can be kept in large numbers in a small space and some of their natural habitats are fairly well simulated by laboratory aquaria. In addition, paramecia feed on microorganisms, which can be easily cultured in the laboratory and provided in whatever concentration desired by the experimenter.

In one of his most famous experiments, Gause studied competition between *Paramecium caudatum* and *P. aurelia*. The question he posed was: Would one of these two species drive the other to extinction if grown together in microcosms where they were forced to compete with each other for a limited food supply?

Gause demonstrated resource limitation by growing pure populations of *P. caudatum* and *P. aurelia* in the presence of two different concentrations of their food, the bacterium *Bacillus pyocyaneus*. If food supplies limit the growth of laboratory populations of these paramecia, what kind of

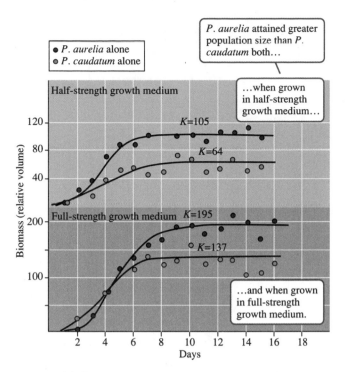

Figure 13.5 Population growth and population sizes attained by *Paramecium aurelia* and *P. caudatum* grown separately (data from Gause 1934).

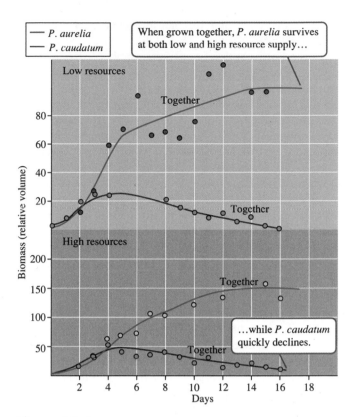

Figure 13.6 Population growth and population sizes attained by *Paramecium aurelia* and *P. caudatum* grown together.

population growth would you expect them to show? As you probably expect, Gause observed sigmoidal growth with a clear carrying capacity at both full- and half-strength concentrations of the food supply (fig. 13.5). When grown in the presence of a full-strength concentration of food, the carrying capacity of *P. aurelia* was 195. When food availability was halved, the carrying capacity of this species was reduced to 105. *P. caudatum* showed a similar response to food concentration. In the presence of a full-strength concentration of food, *P. caudatum* had a carrying capacity of 137. At a half-strength concentration, the carrying capacity was 64. The nearly one-to-one correspondence between food level and the carrying capacities of these two species provides evidence that when grown alone, the carrying capacity was determined by intraspecific competition for food. These results set the stage for Gause's experiment to determine whether interspecific competition for food, the limiting resource in this system, would lead to the exclusion of one of the competing species.

When grown together, *P. aurelia* survived, while the population of *P. caudatum* quickly declined (fig. 13.6). The difference in results obtained at the two food concentrations support the conclusion that competitive exclusion results from competition for food. At a full-strength food concentration, the decline in the *P. caudatum* population was approaching exclusion by 16 days but exclusion was not complete. In contrast, at a half-strength food concentration, *P. caudatum* had been entirely eliminated by day 16. What does this contrast in the time to exclusion suggest about the influence of food supply on competition? It suggests that reduced resource supplies increase the intensity of competition.

Competitive Exclusion Principle and Mechanisms of Coexistence

The results of Gause, and others led to the development of the **competitive exclusion principle**, which in its simplest form states that "complete competitors cannot coexist" (Hardin 1960). What does this actually mean? Quite simply, it states that if two species that are nearly identical in their basic ecology (feeding, nesting, etc.) come into competition, one of them will persist while the second will go locally extinct. This idea has become a central tenet in ecological theory. However, like all theories, the world is full of exceptions. For example, if you go for a walk in a field, you may find 20 different species of plants all growing within a meter of where you are standing. These plants may appear similar, all needing light, nitrogen, and water, and yet they appear to coexist. As we will see in later chapters, one obvious explanation is that competition is not occurring in all communities, and thus competitive exclusion should not occur! For example, in many communities the "struggle for existence" of individuals within a population may be primarily with extreme environmental conditions, rather than interspecific competitors. Populations may also be limited through predation and disease (chapters 14 and 15), rather than competition. Even with these exceptions, we can still find a large number of situations where species coexist, *and* competition is occurring among the species. How is this possible if the competitive exclusion principle is true? For the last several decades, ecologists have explored the question: what mechanisms allow for the coexistence of competing species? There have been many potential mechanisms proposed and demonstrated in the literature; here we will discuss only a few.

In the Lotka–Volterra equations, stable coexistence can occur when competition between species (interspecific) is low relative to competition within a species (intraspecific). What does this mean in the context of the competitive exclusion principle? In short, species are unlikely to cause the extinction of similar species if they don't compete very strongly with them! This leads to the first of our potential mechanisms of coexistence: *spatial heterogeneity*. As we saw in Gause's work, the speed with which *P. caudatum* went extinct was a function of the amount of food provided. If we think more broadly and consider two species that have overlapping distributions across a landscape we could imagine that in some areas resources will be limiting, and in other areas resources may be abundant. A requirement of exploitative competition is that resources must be limiting, and thus in areas of high resource abundance competition will be low or non-existent, and the species can coexist. In areas of lower resources, competition may be more intense and one species will go locally extinct. The heterogeneity in resources and competition can allow for coexistence on the landscape, even if not within every single patch on the landscape.

Varied resource levels are not the only factor that can cause disparity in the strength of competition. Instead, we could imagine that disease, predation, herbivory, extreme climatic conditions, and countless of other factors all will influence population growth, densities, behaviour, and ultimately the strength (or lack thereof) of competition. If there is heterogeneity on the landscape in any of these factors, we can then expect the potential for species coexistence, even if they compete strongly elsewhere on the landscape.

Species coexistence can also occur even if competition is everywhere, if there is *variation in competitive ability within a species*. In other words, the Lotka–Volterra model assumes that the competition coefficients are fixed values for each species. However, evidence suggests this is not always the case, and instead competitive abilities are often influenced by local climatic conditions, and even the genotype of individuals. Why might climate alter a species' competitive ability? As we discussed in section II, there are tradeoffs in the ability to perform different physiological and ecological functions, including competitive ability. A classic laboratory study demonstrating the role that variation in the local microclimate can have on competitive outcomes was published by Thomas Park in 1954. *Tribolium* beetles infest stored grains and grain products. Since all of the life stages of *Tribolium* live in finely milled flour, small containers of flour provide all the environmental requirements necessary to sustain a population, and thus *Tribolium* are ideal subjects of laboratory research. Thomas Park (1954) worked extensively on interspecific competition between two species, *T. confusum* and *T. castaneum*, under varied levels of temperature and humidity. Under hot (34°C) and wet (70% RH) conditions, and without competition, both species were able to persist over the course of the experiment (fig. 13.7*a*). However, when grown together under these conditions, *T. castaneum* usually excluded *T. confusum* (fig. 13.7*b*). In contrast, cool-dry conditions generally favoured *T. confusum*,

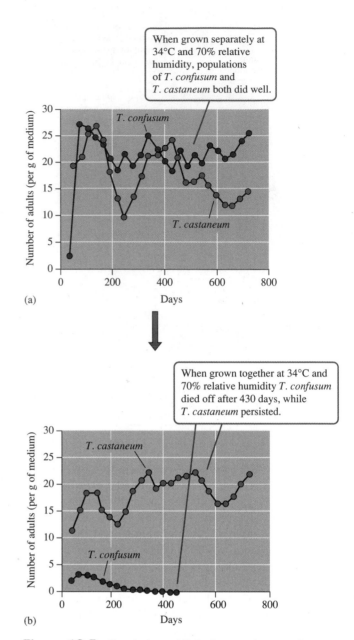

Figure 13.7   Populations of *Tribolium confusum* and *T. castaneum* grown separately (*a*) and together (*b*) at 34°C and 70% relative humidity (data from Park 1954).

with *T. castaneum* going extinct under these conditions even without competition (fig. 13.8). These results demonstrate that competitive outcomes can be influenced by altered climatic conditions. If such variation exists in natural setting (think about the temperature and humidity differences you experience sitting under a tree versus sitting in an open field), then coexistence should occur across the landscape.

A third mechanism of coexistence is the idea of *competitive equivalence*. We have so far been assuming that under some conditions, one species is able to displace another, causing competitive exclusion. In some situations we may find that species are completely equal in their competitive abilities, such that the outcome of competition is not predictable. Although individually one species may win or lose a competitive contest, on average across a landscape, these species

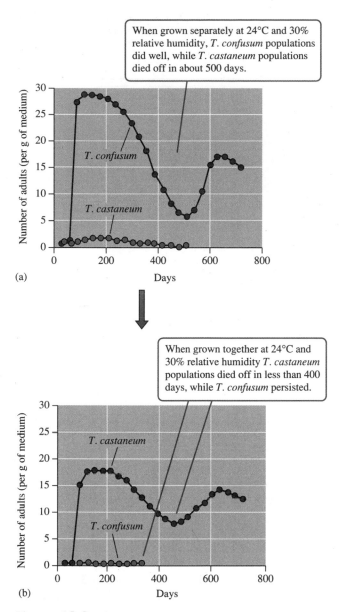

(a)

When grown separately at 24°C and 30% relative humidity, *T. confusum* populations did well, while *T. castaneum* populations died off in about 500 days.

When grown together at 24°C and 30% relative humidity *T. castaneum* populations died off in less than 400 days, while *T. confusum* persisted.

(b)

Figure 13.8 Populations of *Tribolium confusum* and *T. castaneum* grown separately (*a*) and together (*b*) at 24°C and 30% relative humidity (data from Park 1954).

should win and lose an approximately equal number of times. As a result, coexistence should occur.

The final mechanism of coexistence we will discuss here is that of *nonequilibrium conditions.* Competitive exclusion is not instantaneous, and instead is a process that may take many generations to occur. Both Gause and Park found for fast growing species, exclusion took weeks, or even years to occur. What this means is that prior to exclusion, coexistence occurred, it just wasn't stable. In many communities, the environment may be variable and unlikely to ever reach equilibrium. At the same time, we must keep in mind that competition can alter the fitness of the individuals that are competing, and this may cause an evolutionary response. Most models of competition, such as Lotka–Volterra, are based upon the assumption that competitive ability is a fixed trait of a species. Park has shown how this isn't true when you have variation in climate.

Later in the chapter we will discuss examples showing how competition can cause evolutionary changes, which may themselves promote coexistence. However, before we explore the evolutionary impacts of competition on natural populations, we will discuss some of the evidence which demonstrates the prevalence of competition in natural systems.

Concept 13.1 Review

1. *Paramecium aurelia* and *P. caudatum* coexisted for a long period before competitive exclusion when fed full-strength food compared to when they were fed half that amount. What does this contrast in time suggest about the role of food supply on competition between these two species?
2. Competitive exclusion can, but does not necessarily, occur when species interact. How can competitive equivalence among species prevent exclusion?
3. Using the isoclines in figure 13.4*a* and 13.14*b*, is there any way that predation on one of the two competing species could alter the outcome of competition?

13.2 Resource Competition

Field and mesocosm studies show that resource limitations and competition are widespread. In chapter 12, we saw that slowing population growth at high densities produces a sigmoidal, or S-shaped, pattern in which population size levels off at carrying capacity. Our assumption in that discussion was that intraspecific competition for limited resources plays a key role in slowing population growth at higher densities. The effect of intraspecific competition is included in the model of logistic population growth. If competition is an important and common phenomenon in nature, then we should be able to observe it among individuals of the same species, individuals with identical or very similar resource requirements. Gause found such evidence in a laboratory population of paramecium. Here, we discuss evidence from field studies.

Self-Thinning in Plant Populations

The development of a stand of plants from the seedling stage to mature individuals suggests competition for limited resources. Each spring as the seeds of annual plants germinate, their population density often numbers in the thousands per square meter. However, as the season progresses and individual plants grow, population density declines. This same pattern occurs in the development of a stand of trees. As the stand of trees develops, more and more biomass is composed of fewer and fewer individuals. In populations of long- or short-lived plants, this process is called **self-thinning.**

Self-thinning results from intraspecific competition for limited resources. As a local population of plants develops, individual plants take up increasing quantities of nutrients, water, and space for which some individuals compete more successfully. The losers in this competition for resources die, and population density decreases, or "thins," as a consequence. Over time the population is composed of fewer and fewer large individuals.

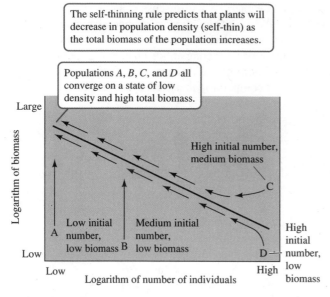

Figure 13.9   Self-thinning in plant populations (data from Westoby 1984).

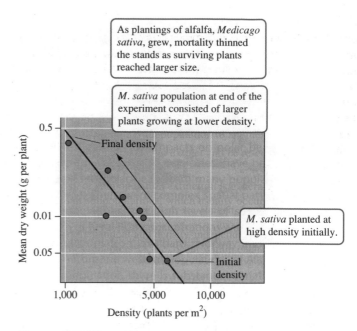

Figure 13.10   Self-thinning in populations of alfalfa, *Medicago sativa* (data from White and Harper 1970).

One way to represent the self-thinning process is to plot total plant biomass against population density. If we plot the logarithm of plant biomass against the logarithm of plant density, the slope of the resulting line averages around $-1/2$. In other words, there is an approximately one-unit increase in total plant biomass with each two-unit decrease in population density; plant population density declines more rapidly than biomass increases (fig. 13.9).

Another way to represent the self-thinning process is to plot the average weight of individual plants in a stand against density (fig. 13.10). The slope of the line in such plots averages around $-3/2$. Because self-thinning by many species of plants comes close to a $-3/2$ relationship, this relationship has come to be called the **$-3/2$ self-thinning rule.** The $-3/2$ self-thinning rule was first proposed by K. Yoda and colleagues (1963) and amplified by White and Harper (1970), who provided many additional examples (e.g., fig. 13.10). Subsequently, the self-thinning rule became widely accepted among ecologists.

Recent analyses have shown that self-thinning in some plant populations deviates significantly from the $-3/2$ (or $-1/2$ for biomass-numbers) slope. However, regardless of the precise trajectory followed by different plant populations, self-thinning of plant populations has been demonstrated repeatedly. The important points, from the perspective of our present discussion, is that self-thinning occurs and appears to be the consequence of intraspecific competition for limited resources. Additionally the self-thinning law appears to be found in most plant species tested, suggesting this is a very generalizable phenomenon. Resource limitation has also been demonstrated in experiments on intraspecific competition within animal populations.

Intraspecific Competition Among Planthoppers

Ecologists have often failed to demonstrate that insects, particularly herbivorous insects, compete. However, one group of insects in which competition has been repeatedly demonstrated are the Homoptera, including the leafhoppers, planthoppers, and aphids. Robert Denno and George Roderick (1992), who studied interactions among planthoppers (Homoptera, Delphacidae), attribute the prevalence of competition among the Homoptera to their habit of aggregating, to rapid population growth, and to the mobile nature of their food supply, plant fluids.

Denno and Roderick demonstrated intraspecific competition within populations of the planthopper *Prokelesisia marginata*, which lives on the salt marsh grass *Spartina alterniflora* along the Atlantic and Gulf coasts of the United States. The population density of *P. marginata* was controlled by enclosing the insects with *Spartina* seedlings at densities of 3, 11, and 40 leafhoppers per cage, densities that are within the range at which they live in nature. At the highest density, *P. marginata* showed reduced survivorship, decreased body length, and increased developmental time (fig. 13.11). These signs of intraspecific competition were probably the result of reduced food quality at high leafhopper densities. Plants heavily populated by planthoppers show reduced concentrations of protein, chlorophyll, and moisture. Therefore, competition between these leafhoppers was probably the result of limited resource supplies. However, as demonstrated in the following example, interference competition may occur in the absence of obvious resource limitation.

Interference Competition Among Song Sparrows

Peter Arcese (1987) used a field study on Mandarte Island, British Columbia, to understand how male song sparrows, *Melospiza melodia*, defend their territories. These sparrows are primarily monogamous. Starting at age one, males set up territories in which they sing and present visual displays to attract females as potential mates. However, appropriate space

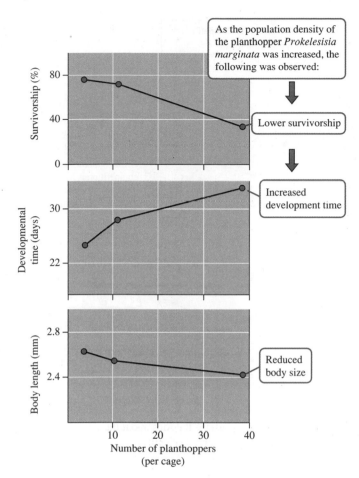

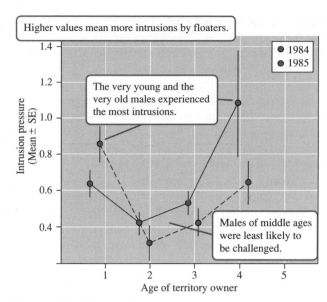

Figure 13.11 Population density and planthopper performance (data from Denno and Roderick 1992).

Figure 13.12 Intrusion pressure by floaters varies as a function of the age of the territorial male (data from Arcese 1987).

for territories is limited, and many males are left without established territories (around 20% of males on this island). These males, called *floaters*, live within the territories of other males, rarely singing or perching on visually obvious branches. In other words, they generally hide, waiting for the territorial male to die and thus allow them to take over the territory, or they will challenge the territorial male in the hope of winning the contest and claiming the territory. When a territorial male sees a floater intruding in his territory, there is a rapid and obvious response of a song followed by a chase, a very clear example of *interference competition*.

For 10 years prior to Arcese's study, the sparrows on this island had been extensively studied, with every bird individually marked. Arcese and his field crew then spent 294 hours over the course of two years observing the behaviour of many floaters and territorial males. Of particular interest to Arcese were intrusions by the floaters into the territories of other males, and whether some territorial males were more likely to be intruded upon than others. This question is similar to our discussion of how the strength of exploitative competition can vary with some factors, such as resource availability. Here, however, Arcese is trying to determine what factors influence intraspecific interference competition. Prior research and theories suggested that territory size, male age, and male health may all influence the likelihood of an intrusion by a floater.

Intrusion pressure was not related to territory size, nor was it related to the presence of fertile females in the territory. Instead, there was a strong relationship between the age of the territory owner and intrusion pressure (fig. 13.12). These sparrows typically live up to four years, and both the youngest and the oldest males were most likely to be challenged by floaters. These intrusions appeared to come at a real cost to the resident males, as the youngest and oldest males held on to their territories for a shorter duration than two- and three-year-old males. In many cases the physical chase that ensued resulted in broken limbs or other injuries, often followed by the presumed death of the previously territorial male. In looking in more detail at the data, Arcese was also able to determine that those males that lost their territory often had a broken limb or other physical handicap, and were more likely to show weight loss (a sign of poor health) than males that retained their territories. The one-year-olds did not generally show physical handicaps, and instead Arcese reasoned that they were less experienced and less able to defend a territory than slightly older males.

Overall, Arcese's field study shows that interference competition can occur in a natural setting, with potentially strong consequences for the competing individuals. He also shows that, like exploitative competition, a variety of factors can influence the strength of competition experienced by different individuals in the population. In this case, it appears that the floating males were choosing to challenge the weakest and most inexperienced males, while generally avoiding the stronger males. These results show that for some organisms, behavioural choices also can influence competitive interactions. Next we will provide a more general discussion of evidence for competition in natural systems.

An Overview of Competition in Natural Systems

In the years since Darwin focused our attention on the potential importance of competition to the ecology and evolution of natural species, there have been literally thousands of ecological studies conducted. The study of competition has gone through several phases. There was an early theoretical phase, followed by work with laboratory models, which was in turn followed by intensive observation and experimentation in the field. At the same time, there has been persistent questioning about the basic assumption that competition is an important force in nature. Here we will first discuss some of the results from large reviews of the literature, and then will follow with an example of a manipulative field experiment.

In the early 1980s, there was a very basic question unanswered in ecology: is competition common in natural populations? Two of the first analyses designed to provide a broad test of this question were by Thomas Schoener (1983) and Joseph Connell (1983), both of whom reviewed the evidence provided by field experiments. Schoener, who reviewed over 150 experiments on interspecific competition, reported that competition was found in 90% of the studies and among 76% of the species. Connell, who reviewed 527 experiments on 215 species, found evidence of interspecific competition in about 40% of the experiments and about 50% of the species. Why is there such a difference in these results? One reason is that the researchers analyzed different groups of studies and used different criteria for including studies in their analyses. This idea is supported by Jessica Gurevitch and her colleagues (1992) who analyzed field experiments published during the 1980s. She found that although competition had a very strong and negative impact on biomass in general, there was substantial variation among taxa and trophic level. Despite the differences found in these studies, the best evidence to date shows that competition is an important force in the lives of many species in natural systems. However, the data also indicates that competition is not omnipresent, and instead is just one of many factors that can influence an individual's fitness, population dynamics, and species distributions.

Many of the questions about whether competition plays an important role in natural populations were raised by animal ecologists. As you will see in later chapters (section V), animals are generally rare on the landscape relative to plants, and direct encounters between individuals are not quite as apparent. Looking at the plants, however, the role of competition appears a bit different. Plants are generally growing in very close proximity to their neighbours, and their leaves and roots likely interact for their entire lives! The impact of these interactions can be obvious, as any gardener knows if they don't pull weeds from their strawberry beds. So for plant ecologists, the big question about competition was not in whether it occurred, but instead it was in trying to understand whether competition should be strongest when resources are rare or when resources are common.

This debate originated with Phil Grime who developed one of the theories of plant life history strategies we discussed in chapter 9. Grime (1973) argued that competition among plants will be unimportant in unproductive areas, areas of low resource availability and little plant growth. Edward Newman (1973), and later David Tilman (1987) disagreed with this position, and instead argued that competition will be important at both high and low resource availability. What will

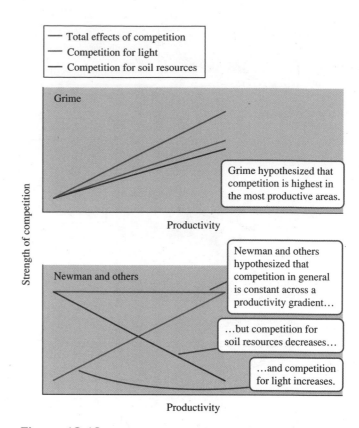

Figure 13.13 Contrasting theories about the relationship between plant competition and productivity.

differ, they hypothesized, is that in unproductive environments competition will be primarily belowground, while in productive environments competition will be predominantly aboveground (fig. 13.13). Of course, is it really too surprising that people that study competition for a living are often themselves embroiled in competitive encounters?

Throughout the 1980s and early 1990s there were numerous experiments designed to resolve this debate, generally with conflicting results. One concern had been that each of these experiments was conducted over a relatively small spatial scale, and thus differences observed could have been due to site-specific differences. Richard Reader, of the University of Guelph, initiated an ambitious study to try to finally resolve what had been a long-standing and very combative debate amongst ecologist. Reader assembled a team of 20 researchers located throughout the world (Canada, United States, the Netherlands, Sweden, and Australia). The team conducted identical experiments at each of 12 study sites, allowing a broad test of the research question (Reader et al. 1994). To minimize variation among sites, they used similar types of communities (grasslands and abandoned fields) in all locations, and they chose sites that had naturally occurring variation in productivity (an indirect measure of resource availability). Within each site they laid out a number of plots from which they either removed the neighbouring vegetation by spraying an herbicide, or left the neighbouring vegetation intact. They then transplanted one individual of the species *Poa pratensis* (Kentucky bluegrass) into every plot, measuring its growth over the

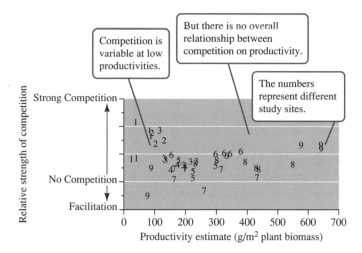

Figure 13.14 Reader and colleagues found no evidence that the strength of competition varied as a function of habitat productivity.

course of the season. This sort of design is called a *focal plant study*, in which measures are taken from a specific individual within each plot (the transplanted bluegrass seedlings). The strength of competition was measured in several ways, but is most widely reported as some function of the growth of the focal plants when neighbours were present relative to their growth when neighbours were removed. Using this relative measure of competition, Reader and his colleagues found no evidence that competition varied in intensity along this intercontinental productivity gradient (fig. 13.14). They also found that within their study there was substantial variation in the relationship between competition and productivity among study sites, and the results changed slightly if they used a different method of measuring competition. These findings support Reader's initial motivations for this unprecedented study in plant ecology—to investigate whether site- and experiment-specific variation might obscure any overall patterns which are, or are not, occurring. This study continues to serve as an outstanding example of how large-scale collaborative work can be used to address issues of particular conflict in the ecological literature.

We have now provided several examples of competition occurring in models, in the laboratory, and in the field. In this next section we explore the potential impacts of competition on populations and species distributions.

Concept 13.2 Review

1. The self-thinning rule appears to apply to most species of plants; however, whether the slope is closer to $-\frac{3}{2}$ or $-\frac{1}{2}$ depends upon species. What factors about a species' biology are likely to influence the slope of the relationship between plant density and average plant weight?

2. Richard Reader and his colleagues (1994) found no overwhelming evidence that, across a broad geographic gradient competition among plants varied as a function of productivity. How is it possible that even when resources vary, competition may stay constant?

13.3 Competition and Niches

Competition can have significant ecological and evolutionary influences on species. Competition can have short-term ecological effects on species' distributions by restricting them to realized niches (chapter 9). These species may retain their capacity to inhabit the fuller range of environments we call the fundamental niche. However, if competitive interactions are strong and pervasive enough, they may produce an evolutionary response in the population that can change the dimensions of the fundamental niche. In this section, we explore the evidence for both ecological and evolutionary influences on the niches of natural populations.

Niches and Competition Among Plants

A. Tansley (1917) conducted one of the first experiments to test whether competition was responsible for the separation of two species of plants on different soil types. In the introduction to his paper, Tansley pointed out that while the separation of closely related plants had long been attributed to mutual competitive exclusion, it was necessary to perform manipulative experiments to demonstrate that this interpretation is correct. That is exactly what Tansley did to account for the mutually exclusive distributions of *Galium saxatile* and *G. sylvestre* (now *G. pumilum*), two species of small perennial plants commonly called bedstraw (fig. 13.15). In the British Isles, *G. saxatile* is largely confined to acidic soils and *G. sylvestre* to basic limestone soils.

Tansley conducted his experiment at the Cambridge Botanical Garden from 1911 to 1917, where seeds of the two species of plants were sown in planting boxes (i.e., a **mesocosm**) of acidic and basic soils. The seeds were sowed in single-species plantings and in mixtures of the two species. Both species germinated on both soil types, in both single- and mixed-species plantings (fig. 13.16). Like the paramecia studied by Gause, both *Galium* species established healthy populations on both soil types when grown by themselves and these single-species plantings persisted to the end of the six-

Figure 13.15 These two species of bedstraw grow predominately on different soil types: *Galium saxatile* (shown here) grows mainly on acidic soils, while *G. sylvestre* (*G. pumilum*) grows mainly on basic limestone soils.

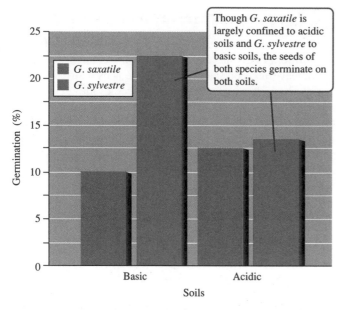

Figure 13.16 Percentage seed germination by *Galium saxatile* and *G. sylvestre* in basic calcareous soils and acidic peat soil (data from Tansley 1917).

year study. However, as the two species grew in mixed plantings, Tansley observed clear competitive dominance by each species on its normal soil type.

On limestone soils, *G. sylvestre,* the species naturally found on limestone soils, overgrew and eliminated *G. saxatile,* the acidic soil species, by the end of the first growing season. On acidic soils, the relationship was reversed and *G. saxatile* was competitively dominant but competitive exclusion was not completed. Growth by both species was so slow on the acidic soils that it took until the end of the six-year experiment for *G. saxatile* to completely cover the planting boxes containing acidic soils, a density attained by *G. sylvestre* on limestone soils in just one year. However, among the abundant *G. saxatile* Tansley found a few "quite healthy" plants of *G. sylvestre.* What do you think would have happened to the *G. sylvestre* on acidic soils if the experiment had been continued for a few more years? Of course it's impossible to say with certainty, but it is likely that *G. saxatile* would eventually exclude *G. sylvestre.* The delayed exclusion was probably due to the extremely slow growth of both species on acidic soils.

Tansley was one of the first ecologists to use experiments to demonstrate the influence of interspecific competition on the niches of species. The fundamental niche of both species of *Galium* included a wider variety of soil types than they inhabit in nature. The results of this experiment suggest that interspecific competition restricts the realized niche of each species to a narrower range of soil types.

Niche Overlap and Competition Between Barnacles

The barnacles *Balanus balanoides* and *Chthamalus stellatus* are restricted to predictable bands in the intertidal zone. We saw in chapter 10 that adult *Chthamalus* along the coast of

Scotland are restricted to the upper intertidal zone, while adult *Balanus* are concentrated in the middle and lower intertidal zones. Joseph Connell's observations (1961a, 1961b) indicate that *Balanus* is limited to the middle and lower intertidal zones because it cannot withstand the longer exposure to air in the upper intertidal zone. However, physical factors only partially explain the distribution of *Chthamalus.* Connell noted that larval *Chthamalus* readily settle in the intertidal zone below where the species persists as adults but that these colonists die out within a relatively short period. In the course of field experiments, Connell discovered that interspecific competition with *Balanus* plays a key role in determining the lower limit of *Chthamalus* within the intertidal zone.

Because barnacles are sessile, small, and grow in high densities, they are ideal for field studies of survivorship. Their exposure at low tide is an additional convenience for the researcher. Connell established several study sites from the upper to the lower intertidal zones where he kept track of barnacle populations by periodically mapping the locations of every individual barnacle on glass plates. He established his study areas and made his initial maps in March and April of 1954, before the main settlement by *Balanus* in late April. He divided each of the study areas in half and kept one of the halves free of *Balanus* by scraping them off with a knife. Connell determined which half of each study site to keep *Balanus*-free by flipping a coin.

By periodically remapping the study sites, Connell was able to monitor interactions between the two species and the fates of individual barnacles. The results showed that in the middle intertidal zone *Chthamalus* survived at higher rates in the absence of *Balanus* (fig. 13.17). *Balanus* settled in densities up to 49 individuals per square centimeter in the middle intertidal zone and grew quickly, crowding out the second species in the process. In the upper intertidal zone, removing *Balanus* had no effect on survivorship by the second species because the population density of *Balanus* was too low to compete seriously. Connell's results provide direct evidence that *Chthamalus* is excluded from the middle intertidal zone by interspecific competition with *Balanus.*

How does interspecific competition affect the niche of *Chthamalus?* In the absence of *Balanus,* it can live over a broad zone from the upper to the middle intertidal zones. Using the terminology of Hutchinson (1957), we can call this broad range of physical conditions the fundamental niche of *Chthamalus.* However, competition largely restricts *Chthamalus* to the upper intertidal zone, a more restricted range of physical conditions constituting the species' realized niche (fig. 13.18).

Does variation in interspecific competition completely explain the patterns seen by Connell? At the lowest levels in the lower intertidal zone, *Chthamalus* suffered high mortality even in the absence of *Balanus.* What other factors might contribute to high rates of mortality by *Chthamalus* in the lower intertidal zone? Experiments have shown that this species can withstand periods of submergence of nearly two years, so it seems that it is not excluded by physical factors. It turns out that the presence of predators in the lower intertidal zone introduces complications that we will discuss in chapter 14 when we examine the influences of predators on prey populations.

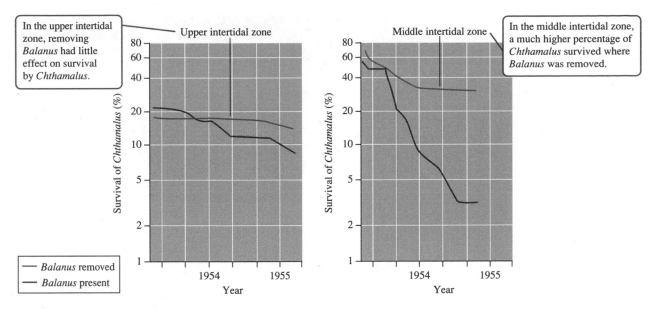

In the upper intertidal zone, removing *Balanus* had little effect on survival by *Chthamalus*.

In the middle intertidal zone, a much higher percentage of *Chthamalus* survived where *Balanus* was removed.

— *Balanus* removed
— *Balanus* present

Figure 13.17 A competition experiment with barnacles: removal of *Balanus* and survival by *Chthamalus* in the upper and middle intertidal zones (data from Connell 1961a, 1961b).

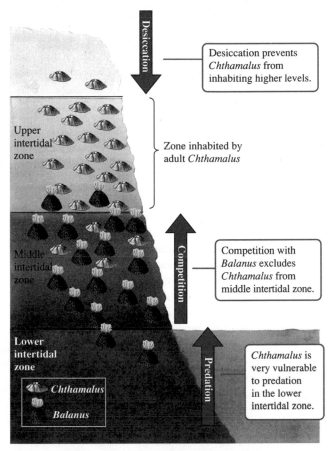

Desiccation prevents *Chthamalus* from inhabiting higher levels.

Zone inhabited by adult *Chthamalus*

Competition with *Balanus* excludes *Chthamalus* from middle intertidal zone.

Chthamalus is very vulnerable to predation in the lower intertidal zone.

Figure 13.18 Environmental factors restricting the distribution of *Chthamalus* to the upper intertidal zone.

Competition and the Niches of Small Rodents

One of the most ambitious and complete of the many field experiments ecologists have conducted on competition among rodents focused on desert rodents in the Chihuahuan Desert near Portal, Arizona. This experiment, conducted by James H. Brown and his students and colleagues (Munger and Brown 1981, Brown and Munger 1985), is exceptional in many ways. First, it was conducted at a large scale; the 20 ha study site includes 24 study plots each 50 m by 50 m (fig. 13.19). Second, the experimental trials have been well replicated, both in space and in time. Third, the project has been long term; it began in 1977 and is ongoing. These three characteristics combine to demonstrate subtle ecological relationships and phenomena that would not otherwise be apparent.

The rodent species living on the Chihuahuan Desert study site can be divided into groups based upon size and feeding habits. Most members of the species are **granivores,** rodents that feed chiefly on seeds. The large granivores consist of three species of kangaroo rats (fig. 13.20*a*) in the genus *Dipodomys*—*D. spectabilis,* 120 g; *D. ordi,* 52 g; and *D. merriami,* 45 g. In addition, the study site is home to four species of small granivores (fig. 13.20*b*)—*Perognathus penicillatus,* 17 g; *P. flavus,* 7 g; *Peromyscus maniculatus,* 24 g; *Reithrodontomys megalotis,* 11 g—and two species of small insectivorous rodents—*Onychomys leucogaster,* 39 g; and *O. torridus,* 29 g. Many of these species have very broad distributions, found throughout parts of Canada, the United States, and Mexico

In one experiment, Brown and his colleagues set out to determine whether large granivorous rodents (*Dipodomys* spp.) limit the abundance of small rodents on their Chihuahuan Desert study site. They also wanted to know whether the rodents might be competing for food. The researchers addressed their questions with a field experiment in which they enclosed 50 m by 50 m study plots with mouse-proof fences. The fences were constructed with a wire mesh with 0.64 cm openings, which were too small for any of the rodent species to crawl through. They also buried the fencing 0.2 m deep so the mice couldn't dig under it, and they topped the fences with aluminum flashing so the mice couldn't climb over it. This may sound like a lot of

Figure 13.19 Aerial photo showing the placement of 24 study plots, each 50 m by 50 m, in the Chihuahuan Desert near Portal, Arizona (courtesy of J. H. Brown).

work, but to answer their questions, the researchers had to control the presence of rodents on the study plots.

The researchers next cut holes 6.5 cm in diameter in the sides of all the fences to allow all rodent species to move freely in and out of the study plots. With this arrangement in place, the rodents in the study plots were trapped live and marked once a month for 3 months. Following this initial monitoring period, the holes on four of eight study plots were reduced to 1.9 cm, small enough to exclude *Dipodomys* but large enough to allow free movement of small rodents. Brown and his colleagues refer to these fences with small holes as semipermeable membranes, since they allow the movement of small rodents but exclude *Dipodomys,* the large granivores in this system.

If *Dipodomys* competes with small rodents, how would you expect populations of small rodents to respond to its removal? The density of small rodent populations should increase, right? If food is the limiting resource, would you expect granivorous and insectivorous rodents to respond differently to *Dipodomys* removal? The researchers predicted that if competition among rodents is mainly for food, then small granivorous rodent populations would increase in response to *Dipodomys* removal, while insectivorous rodents would show little or no response.

The results of the experiment were consistent with the predictions. During the first three years of the experiment, small granivores were approximately 3.5 times more abun-

(a)

(b)

Figure 13.20 Two species of granivorous rodents living in the Chihuahuan Desert: (*a*) the kangaroo rat, *Dipodomys* spp., a large granivore; (*b*) a pocket mouse, *Perognathus* sp., a small granivore.

dant on the *Dipodomys* removal plots compared to the control plots, while populations of small insectivorous rodents did not increase significantly (fig. 13.21).

The results presented in figure 13.21 support the hypothesis that *Dipodomys* spp. competitively suppress populations of small granivores. But would they do so again in response to another experimental manipulation? We cannot be certain unless we repeat the experiment. That's just what Edward Heske, James H. Brown, and Shahroukh Mistry (1994) did. In 1988, they selected eight other fenced study plots that they had been monitoring since 1977, installed their semipermeable barriers on four of the plots, and removed *Dipodomys* from them. The result was an almost immediate increase in small granivore populations on the removal plots (fig. 13.22). By reproducing the major results of the first experiment, this second experiment greatly strengthens the case for competition between large and small granivores at this Chihuahuan Desert site.

Character Displacement

Because competition can reduce an individual's fitness, it can exert selective pressure within a population. If this pressure is strong enough, it can cause evolutionary changes, including (1) selection favouring improved competitive abilities, increasing the rewards of competition to the "winners," or (2) selection

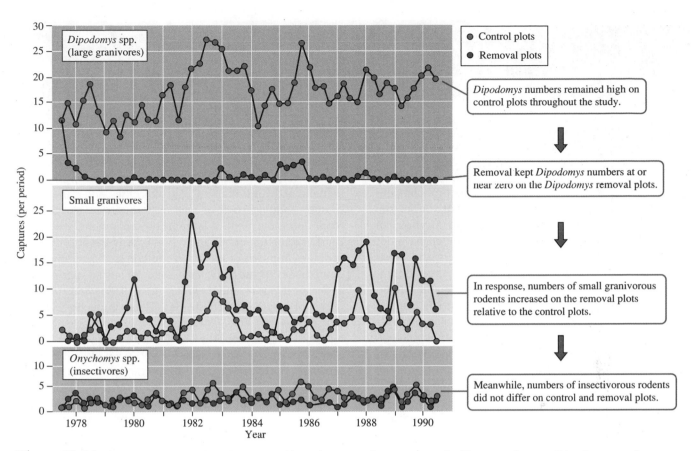

Figure 13.21 Responses by small granivorous and insectivorous rodents to removal of large granivorous *Dipodomys* species (data from Heske, Brown, and Mistry 1994).

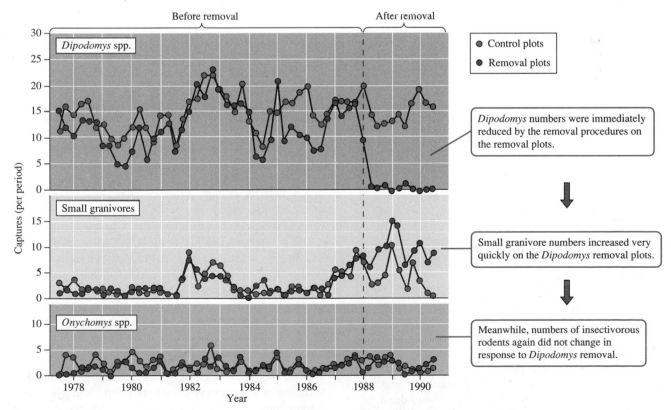

Figure 13.22 Responses of small granivorous and insectivorous rodents to a second removal experiment, which was preceded by several years of study before initiating *Dipodomys* removal (data from Heske, Brown, and Mistry 1994).

The Role of Competition in Forest Management

Competition is not an abstract scientific concept with little relevance to broader society; instead, the effects of competition on the growth of economically important species can result in economic losses in the millions, and maybe even billions, of dollars. The economics of competition have not escaped the attention of farmers, ranchers, fishers, and foresters. Modifying the strengths of intra- and interspecific competition is often an integral aspect of resource management. Canada is home to numerous researchers studying the impacts of competition on crop production and developing management strategies to reduce the economic cost of this ecological process. For example, Paul Cavers of the University of Western Ontario links population ecology and the study of interspecific competition by focusing his research on understanding how weed species use temporal dispersal (a seed bank) to escape competition from crop plants. His work also explores how crop litter may suppress future weed growth. There are numerous other examples of ecological research being applied to agricultural systems; however, here we will focus on another important "crop" grown in Canada: trees. Approximately 50% of the Canadian landbase is covered by forests and woodlands (402 million hectares). On a global scale, Canada is home to nearly 30% of the world's boreal forest and about 10% of all global forests. Within Canada, approximately 0.9 million hectares of forest are harvested annually (0.4%), and in 2006, Canadian exports of forest products were valued at $38.2 billion ($Cdn) (Canada, Natural Resources Canada 2007). In short, Canada is home to a large reserve of forests, and the harvest of this area makes a significant contribution to the national and local economies. The impacts of forestry on local communities are also important, providing jobs to over 350,000 people. At the same time, logging activities dramatically alter the landscape, both through logging itself as well as through construction of roads and movement of large heavy equipment, which can cause fragmentation (chapter 21). Forests are also home to countless numbers of species in addition to the commercially desired trees. These can include other harvested species, such as deer and moose, and the much more diverse and abundant group of non-harvested species. These understory plants, mosses, insects, birds, mammals, fungi, and other species represent a large proportion of Canada's biodiversity. Forests provide much more than wood, and there is often conflict in some areas between continued expansion of the forest industry and the preservation of existing forests. The realities of Canadian society are such that forest activities are likely to continue for the foreseeable future, and thus forest biologists and ecologists are actively working on ways to both minimize the environmental damage associated with logging, as well as increasing potential economic returns. This research has led to changes in tree planting programs, minimization of soil disturbance, reduced road development, and changes in the methods used for harvesting timber. These efforts are greatly influenced by our understanding of succession in the boreal forest, a topic we discuss in chapter 18. Here we focus on efforts to increase yields in regrowth forests (forests that have been previously logged). In theory, the overall footprint of logging activity can be kept smaller if we are able to increase the yields from the areas we currently harvest. Competition

favouring reduced niche overlap and reduced competition (and thus the cost of competition). We discuss some traits associated with good competitors in the next section. Here we will focus on the issue of evolution towards niche divergence (reduced niche overlap) in the face of competition, an evolutionary process called **character displacement**.

The basic idea of character displacement was presented by Brown and Wilson in 1956, where they suggested that two species that live apart (allopatric) may be nearly identical in form and function, though when these species live together (sympatric) competition will cause the evolution of some meaningful differences between them. Although the idea that evolution can cause a reduction in competition seems to be a modest proposal, it resulted in a very prolonged and often inflammatory debate amongst ecologists. At the core of the debate were broad concerns that competition was being used as a mechanism to explain observed patterns without sufficient data. These issues were presented most succinctly in a paper by Joseph Connell (1980) in which he criticized the invoking of the "Ghost of Competition Past." He pointed out that just because one observes morphological differences between sympatric species does not prove that competition caused those differences. Connell's paper, and others, contributed to concerns about whether there was truly any strong evidence for character displacement in natural systems. To help resolve this issue, Dolph Schluter and John McPhail (1992) compiled a list of criteria that would be necessary to vigorously show character displacement has occurred:

1. Chance should be ruled out as an explanation for the differences in phenotypes among allopatric and sympatric populations.

2. Phenotypic differences must have a genetic basis.

plays an important role in determining yields by causing a reduction in the harvestable biomass in Canada's forests.

To understand the impact of competition in stand development and forestry, it is first important to understand what an area that has been recently logged looks like (fig. 13.23). The removal of the tall overstory trees causes a dramatic increase in light reaching the soil floor, and the dead roots and leaf litter often result in a flush of nutrients. In other words, conditions are ideal for the establishment of large numbers of *r*-selected, ruderal species. At the same time, forestry practices often involve a replanting effort, generally with economically desirable tree species. As you can imagine, it would be very easy for these trees to be rapidly overtaken by the ruderal species, causing high tree mortality and slower wood production. In other words, competition by "weeds" can kill and stunt trees desired by the forest industry, causing a loss of

Figure 13.23 Open space is found in a Lodgepole pine stand after thinning.

wood production and economic benefit. We use the term "weed" for a specific reason. **Weeds** are species that a person does not want in a certain location at a certain point in time. If our goal is to maximize harvestable biomass of trees, then species that reduce this are undesired weeds. However, if our goal is instead to maximize biodiversity, then those same species would be desired as they contribute to species diversity, and thus would not be called weeds. In other words, a weed is a human designation of a species based upon what people want, it is not an inherent characteristic of a species.

These unwanted plants, which include both weeds and even overly high densities of some commercial trees (e.g., Aspen), can be managed through a variety of practices including herbicide application, grazing, burning, and other methods of weed removal. All of these practices cost money, and it is thus not surprising that there exist several long-term studies testing whether vegetation management practices (i.e., reducing interspecific competition) result in increased tree growth and economic benefit. Responses can be large. Full removal of neighbouring vegetation increased growth of Lodgepole pine 150% over 15 years in British Columbia; Balsam fir in New Brunswick increased 250% after 28 years; and White spruce in Ontario increased by up to 90% over 30 years (Wagner et al. 2006).

Whether these increases in yield offset the cost of the vegetation management itself depends upon market conditions (e.g., price of timber, labour costs, etc.), and is beyond the scope of ecology. What is clear is that applying knowledge of ecological processes such as competition can have significant impacts on the harvest and management of Canada's natural resources.

3. Phenotypic differences in sympatry should be the outcome of evolutionary shifts, and not just the inability of similar-sized species to coexist (e.g., because of competitive exclusion).

4. Phenotypic differences should be related to differences in resource use.

5. Sites of sympatry and allopatry should not differ in food or major environmental features.

6. There should be evidence that similar phenotypes actually compete for food.

You can see how difficult demonstrating character displacement can be, and you can see the rigours of doing good, strong science. We will end this section with one of the best examples of character displacement, the threespine stickle-

backs. You may remember this species from chapter 4 in our discussion of sympatric speciation. Character displacement and speciation are related topics, and so it should come at no surprise that the same researcher, Dolph Schluter of the University of British Columbia, is investigating both phenomena.

There are numerous species of closely related sticklebacks (*Gasterosteus aculeatus* complex) that live in small lakes. Some sympatric species appear to exhibit character displacement such that one species feeds on benthic organisms in the littoral zone with the second species feeding on planktonic species in the littoral zone. These species are morphologically dissimilar, with the benthic species having few, short gill rakers and a wide gape, and the limnetic species having many, long gill rakers and a narrow gape (fig. 13.24). Prior work indicates that these phenotypes improve efficiency at capturing specialized food items. What is particularly inter-

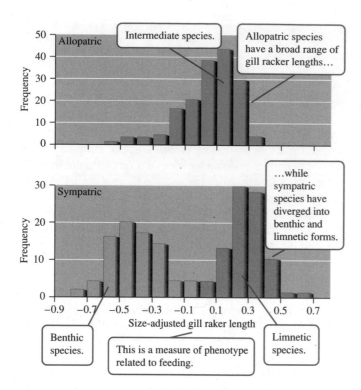

Figure 13.24 With character displacement, phenotypes differ among allopatric and sympatric populations (data from Schluter and McPhail 1992).

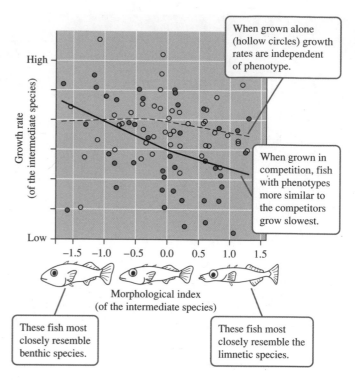

Figure 13.25 Growth rates among the intermediate species of Stickleback varied as a function of phenotype and the presence of a competitor species (data from Schluter 1994).

esting is that when these species live allopatrically, they demonstrate intermediate phenotypes (fig. 13.24) and feed in both the littoral and benthic zones. Knowing these pieces of natural history, it becomes easy to understand why Schluter would believe this to be a potential case of character displacement. But is it? To answer this, we will work through the list of criteria that Schluter himself published.

Detailed work on these populations has shown that the phenotypic variations found between sympatric and allopatric populations are greater than expected by chance (Schluter and McPhail 1992), that these phenotypes have a heritable component, and that the phenotype influences feeding. To address the remaining three issues (#3, #5, #6), Schluter (1994) designed an elegant experiment in which he controlled environmental conditions (eliminating the concern of #5), tested whether there was competition for food (#6), and tested whether there was directional selection due to sympatry (#3). Schluter reasoned that a prediction of character displacement would be that if you put an intermediate species in the same pond as a limnetic species, there should be directional selection on the intermediate species towards a benthic form. In other words, those individuals of the intermediate form that were most similar to its competitor (the limnetic species) would have lower fitness than those individuals that were most dissimilar to the competitor. To see if this actually occurred, Schluter constructed two experimental ponds on the campus of the University of British Columbia. He divided each pond in half, placing individuals of the intermediate species into both halves of both ponds. On one half of each pond, he also added individuals of a limnetic species. After three months, he harvested

all the remaining fish and was able to measure growth rates. Overall growth rates were negatively correlated with fish density, suggesting competition was occurring. Additionally, as predicted by theory, individuals of the intermediate species that most resembled the competitor species had the lowest growth rates (fig. 13.25). Since these fish all grew under identical environmental conditions, this directional selection can not be due to any factor other than competition, providing very clear and convincing evidence that competition can cause evolutionary shifts in populations over short ecological timescales.

In the final section of this chapter, we will look below the level of the population and investigate some of the mechanisms organisms use in competition. It is one thing to talk about competition as a process that has occurred, but what traits actually confer competitive advantage, and how would an ecologist know?

Concept 13.3 Review

1. What do you think would have happened to the *Galium sylvestre* on acidic soil if Tansley had continued his experiment for a few more years?
2. What does the increase in small granivore populations but the lack of response by populations of insectivorous rodents suggest about the nature of competition between rodents in Brown's Arizona study area?
3. Why does phenotypic differences among populations need to be partly heritable to believe character displacement may have occurred?

Ecological Tools

Identifying the Mechanisms by Which Plants Compete

Discussions of competition often centre on the consequences of competition, such as reduced fitness, altered population dynamics and distributions, or changes in community structure. However, there is another side of competition that is explored by ecologists, and this is the study of the mechanisms by which individuals actually compete. This research is most actively pursued by plant ecologists, and we will explore two case studies in which the researchers were trying to identify the factor(s) that influence competitive ability in plants. You will see that experiments are a critical experimental tool when one wants to understand the mechanisms or interactions among individuals. You will also see that there is a great diversity in the types of experiments that can be used to address similar research questions.

Size Does Matter

One of the pioneers in the study of mechanisms of competition among plants has been Paul Keddy, formerly of the University of Ottawa. For the past several decades he and a large number of students and post-docs have published a series of papers designed to understand which plant traits are most closely associated with competitive ability in plants. When Keddy began his work, the standard experimental approach was to choose one, or just a few species and study them very intensely. The hope was that by understanding the specific ecology of one species you would gain an understanding of many species. However, by using this approach the literature rapidly filled with a series of "special cases" without a clear understanding of general processes across large numbers of taxa. Keddy understood that to make truly broad generalizations about the relationship between plant traits and competitive abilities, he would need to develop a unique methodological approach.

Keddy, along with graduate student Connie Gaudet (Gaudet and Keddy 1988), developed a comparative method in which they could study large numbers of species simultaneously. In their study they chose 44 species of plants that were found in the wetlands near the campus of the University of Ottawa. One of the first problems they faced was in deciding how to conduct an experiment from which they could determine a standard measure of competitive performance. If they used two species, this would be easy, as they would simply need to put these plants together in a pot, or grow them individually. With three species, it is still manageable, pair-wise contests result in only 3 competition treatment (species A vs. B, A vs. C, B vs. C). However, the number of pair-wise contests is equal to $N(N–1)/2$, where N is the number of species used. With 44 species, this would result in 946 different competition treatments. Clearly this is not feasible, no matter how many undergraduate assistants they hired! Gaudet and Keddy instead used what is now called a *phytometer*. They chose one

species, *Lythrum salicaria*, which would compete against all 44 species. By measuring the growth of the phytometer against the different competitors, they could then establish which species were strong competitors and which were weak. In other words, if *Lythrum* was small in a pot, it was against a strong competitor. It if was large, it was against a weak competitor. By using this approach Gaudet and Keddy were able to reduce the size of the experiment from 946 treatments down to 44. This was a major advance in competition studies, and is widely used today.

Now that they had measures of competitive ability, they needed a way to determine which plant traits were most likely the cause of enhanced competitive ability. To assess this, they measured a variety of traits of each of their study species, such as above and below ground biomass, height, leaf shape, canopy diameter, etc. Using a multiple regression analysis (appendix A), they were able to explain most of the variation in competitive abilities of the species (74%) using their measures of plant traits. In other words, if they knew what a plant looked like (quantitatively), they were fairly accurate in predicting its competitive ability. Looking at the traits individually, it was plant biomass that was most strongly associated with competitive ability (fig. 13.26), with the largest plants being the best competitors.

There have been numerous studies conducted since Gaudet and Keddy. Plant size remains one of the major correlates of competitive ability in plants. However, as we see in the next example, size is not the only weapon available to plants.

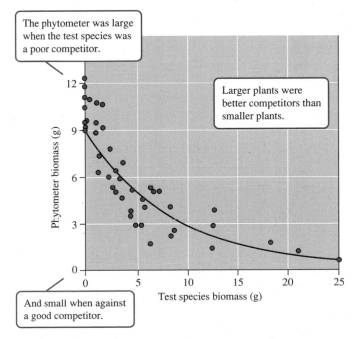

Figure 13.26   Results of Gaudet and Keddy's experiment investigating the relationship between plant traits and competitive ability.

Perceiving One's Environment Allows for Adaptation

As we saw in section II, plants exhibit a diverse set of mechanisms which allow them to adapt to changes in their abiotic environment. They do not simply "sit and take it," but instead are able to change their morphologies and physiologies to be better suited to the specific microenvironment they find themselves rooted in. From an evolutionary perspective, this makes sense, as selection will favour those genotypes (plants or animals) with the highest fitness within a population. Using the same logic, there is no reason to believe that plants should just suffer the consequences of competition, with no evolutionary response. Instead, if competition is strong it should favour a response by the competing plants. Such a response is obvious to see when animals compete, as you can see one bird attacking another, but what can plants do? The major difference in responses between plants and mobile animals is that plants respond by altered morphology, while many animals respond with movement. However, both approaches can be adaptive and can have a genetic basis. Johanna Schmitt and her students have published a series of papers describing one response in plants: shade avoidance.

Many plants exhibit an interesting trait: in response to low light levels, they grow taller than they would under high light conditions. More specifically, many plants are not just responding to low light levels, but instead they are responding primarily to light that has low levels of red wavelengths (relative to far-red wavelengths). Why? First we can ask what makes leaves green? Leaves are green because chlorophyll reflects green light, absorbing red and blue. That means that light that travels through a leaf will have a lower R:FR ratio than light that has not passed through another plant. This physical fact results in a signal that many plants are able to perceive: if low R:FR light hits their leaves, that means a neighbouring plant is above them. This is potentially really bad news for the plant, and a very common response is for the lower plant to grow tall quickly, trying to overtop its neighbour. This process is mediated through the phytochrome system, which is extremely sensitive to changes in R:FR ratios and influences a variety of aspects of plant growth and development. Theory predicts that plants that exhibit this shade avoidance response have the potential to access direct sunlight at the top of the canopy, while plants that are unable to exhibit this response are likely doomed to subordinate status where they will receive very little light. Although this response is well documented, and the logic behind its adaptive advantage makes sense, Schmitt realized that tests to determine whether it actually was an adaptive behavioural response were lacking.

Schmitt and colleagues (1995) reasoned that support for the adaptive hypothesis would require demonstrating that elongated plants have higher fitness in dense stands than unelongated plants in a dense stand. However, Schmitt immediately reached an impasse: if all plants in a population elongate in response to being part of a dense stand, there is no way of measuring the fitness of short and tall individuals! Schmitt and her colleagues devised a novel solution, and were amongst the first researchers to incorporate transgenic plants in ecological research. Schmitt and her colleagues developed two transgenic strains of tobacco, *Nicotiana tabacum*, in which they inserted a gene from oats, which greatly reduces the shade avoidance response. By doing this they produced plants that even in deep shade were unable to elongate, and thus she could now begin her experiment. The experimental design was very straightforward, growing plants at low and high density in both monocultures and mixtures. As expected, the transgenic plants exhibited a reduced shade avoidance response at high density. After the plants had experienced significant competition for light, the transgenic plants were smaller than the wild type plants when grown at high density. As we know from Keddy's work, reduced size could further reduce a plant's competitive ability. Small size is also commonly associated with reduced survival and fecundity, and thus this reduction in size likely is a demonstration of a real fitness cost of not possessing the shade avoidance response.

These results support the adaptive hypothesis. Even more importantly, the creative experimental design by Schmitt and her colleagues shows that by blending molecular biology with traditional approaches in ecology researchers are able to find answers to questions that previously were impossible to address.

Summary

Competition is generally divided into *intraspecific competition*, competition between individuals of the same species, and *interspecific competition*, competition between individuals of different species. Competition can take the form of interference competition, which consists of direct aggressive interactions between individuals, or exploitative competition in which individuals interact indirectly through use of a shared and limiting resource.

Mathematical and laboratory models provide a theoretical foundation for studying competition in nature. Lotka and Volterra independently expanded the logistic model of population growth to represent interspecific competition. In the Lotka–Volterra competition model, the growth rate of species depends both upon numbers of conspecifics and numbers of the competing species. In this model, the effect of one species upon another is summarized by competition coefficients. In general, the Lotka–Volterra competition model predicts coexistence of species when interspecific competition is less intense than intraspecific competition. Competitive exclusion of one species by another is a common outcome of laboratory experiment. However, changes to experimental conditions can impact the outcome of competition, enhancing the possibility of coexistence. Observations in nature suggest the competitive exclusion principle is not inviolate. Competition theory suggests that competing species can coexist if there is spatial heterogeneity in resources or in the strength of competition, if there is variation in competitive abilities within a species or equivalence in competitive ability among species, or if the natural system is not at equilibrium.

Field and mesocosm studies show resource limitation and competition are widespread. Experiments under field and semi-natural conditions (mesocosms) show that competition occurs outside of the laboratory. Growing plant populations can experience self-thinning in which the average plant size varies with plant density. Resource competition among leafhoppers also varies with population density, and results in reduced survivorship and growth of the competing individuals. A field study with song sparrows shows that even in the absence of a clear limiting resource interference competition

can occur, with individual birds choosing to enter or avoid competitive encounters due to the relative experience and health of their potential competitor. Several large reviews show that competition is widespread in natural systems, but is not omnipresent. Plant ecologists have investigated the roles of resource availability and habitat productivity on the strength of competition, and have developed contrasting models. An intercontinental field experiment was conducted to try to provide a critical test, lending support to the idea that competition is strong across a broad resource gradient.

Competition can have significant ecological and evolutionary influences on species. Field experiments involving a diversity of organisms have demonstrated that competition can restrict the niches of species to a narrower set of conditions than they would otherwise occupy in the absence of competition. Natural selection can lead to divergence in the niches of competing species, a phenomenon called character displacement. Stringent requirements for a definitive demonstration of character displacement have limited the documented number of cases. However, studies like those of the threespine stickleback indicate that character displacement does occur under natural condition. After many decades of work on competition, we can conclude that competition is a common and strong force operating in nature, but not always, and not everywhere.

Due to the potential importance of competition to ecologists, foresters, farmers, fishers, ranchers, and other members of society, it is not surprising the study of competition continues to be a major focus of attention by ecologists. At the core of resolving genuine scientific and societal issues in science is a strong scientific method and creative experimental designs. Ecologists have incorporated theory, laboratory studies, observations, and experiments to develop a body of knowledge about competition. Continued improvements are gained through novel approaches such as using phytometers in comparative studies and the incorporation of transgenic plants to address ecological questions. Continued expansion of research methodologies will allow for improved understanding of this topic, which is central to much of ecology and society.

Review Questions

1. How can the results of greenhouse experiments on competition help us understand the importance of competition among natural populations? How can a researcher enhance the correspondence of results between greenhouse experiments and the field situation?

2. Explain how self-thinning in field populations of plants can be used to support the hypothesis that intraspecific competition is a common occurrence among natural plant populations.

3. Explain why species that overlap a great deal in their fundamental niches have a high probability of competing. Now explain why species that overlap a great deal in their realized niches and live in the same area probably do not compete significantly.

4. Draw the four possible ways in which Lotka's (1932a) isoclines of zero growth (see fig. 13.4) can be oriented with respect to each other. Label the axes and the points where the isoclines intersect the horizontal and vertical axes. Explain how each situation represented by the graphs leads to either competitive exclusion of one species or the other or to stable or unstable coexistence.

5. How was the amount of food that Gause (1934) provided in his experiment on competition among paramecia related to carrying capacity? In Gause's experiments on competition, *P. aurelia* excluded *P. caudatum* faster when he provided half the amount of food than when he doubled the amount of food. Explain.

6. Discuss how mathematical theory, laboratory models, and field experiments have contributed to our understanding of the ecology of competition. List the advantages and disadvantages of each approach.

7. One of the conclusions that seems justified in light of several decades of studies of interspecific competition is that competition is a common and strong force operating in nature, but not always and not everywhere. List the environmental circumstances in which you think intraspecific and interspecific competition would be most likely to occur in nature. In what circumstances do you think competition is least likely to occur? How would you go about testing your ideas?

8. The study of competition has been filled with contentious debates among researchers, such as was seen in the study of character displacement. Schluter and McPhail (1992) compiled a list of criteria that would be necessary to convincingly show character displacement had occurred. Develop a similar list of criteria to convincingly show that competition is a strong influence on the current distribution of any particular species.

9. The study of competition can increase economic benefits associated with forestry. This, in turn, has the potential to increase forest activity by making previously marginal forests economically viable for harvest. What role do ecologists have in deciding how their results are used by industry and science, and should ecologists advocate specific policy positions?

10. Discuss potential reasons why we observe competitors coexisting in natural systems when the competitive exclusion principle predicts this should not occur.

Suggested Readings

Aarssen, L. W. and T. Koegh. 2002. Conundrums of competitive ability in plants: what to measure? *Oikos* 96:531–42.

A careful analysis of plant competition studies that calls for greater caution when estimating competitive ability. The authors emphasize the need for measuring the allocation of plants to survival and fecundity as indicators of competitive ability.

Byers, J. E. 2000. Competition between two estuarine snails: implications for invasions of exotic species. *Ecology* 81:1225–39.

A modern experimental study that reveals the rich details of interspecific competition between a native and an invasive snail species.

Byers, J. E. 2002. Impact of non-indigenous species on natives enhanced by anthropogenic alteration of selection regimes. *Oikos* 97:449–58.

The author reviews how human-caused environmental change can reverse the outcome of competition among species.

Chuine, E. and E. G. Beaubien. 2001. Phenology is a major determinant of tree species range. *Ecology Letters* 4:500–10.

An application of the concepts of realized and fundamental niches at a large geographic scale, with applications to studies of plant responses to global warming and the spread of invasive plant species.

Grant, P. R. 1994. Ecological character displacement. *Science* 266:746–47.

Schluter, D. 1994. Experimental evidence that competition promotes divergence in adaptive radiation. *Science* 266:798–801.

These papers provide some of the best documented examples and concise reviews of the topic of character displacement.

Heske, E. J., J. H. Brown, and S. Mistry. 1994. Long-term experimental study of a Chihuahuan Desert rodent community: 13 years of competition. *Ecology* 75:438–45.

This paper reports on the first 13 years of one of the most ambitious experiments on interspecific competition among terrestrial animals. Destined to become a classic.

Keddy, P. A. 2001. *Competition*, 2nd Edition. Kluwer Academic Publishers: Dordrecht.

This is a comprehensive book describing current understanding in the mechanisms and consequences of competition among animals and plants.

Chapter 14

Predation and Herbivory

Outline

*I*n nature, the consumer eventually becomes the consumed. A moose browses intently on the twigs and buds of a willow barely protruding above the deep snow of midwinter (fig. 14.1). With each mouthful it chews and swallows, the moose reduces the mass of the willows and adds to the growing energy store in its own large and complex stomach, energy stores that the moose will need to make it through one more northern winter. Then, a familiar scent catches the moose's attention and startled, it runs off.

Suddenly, the clearing where the moose had been feeding is a blur of bounding forms dashing headlong in the direction the moose has gone—a pack of wolves in pursuit of its own meal. A portion of the pack has already run ahead of the moose and is cutting off its retreat. This time, unlike so many times before, the old moose will not escape. After a fierce struggle, the moose is down and the wolves settle in to feed.

Some of the strongest links between populations are those between herbivore and plant, and between predator and prey. The conceptual thread that links these interactions between species is that the interaction enhances the fitness of one individual—the predator or herbivore, etc.—while reducing the fitness of the exploited individual—the prey or host. Because of this common thread we can group these interactions under the heading of *exploitation.*

Predation and herbivory are not the only forms of exploitative relationships we will encounter. Recall from chapter 8 that some social interactions among individuals were manipulative, such as the cowbirds that lay eggs in the nests of other species. Parasitic interactions in general are considered exploitative, and they, along with a closely related form of interaction, mutualism, will be discussed in chapter 15. Competition, the subject of chapter 13, can occur due to common exploitation of a limiting resource, however this differs from the idea of exploitation that we discuss in chapters 14 and 15. In competition, individuals exploit a resource, while in predation, herbivory, parasitism, and mutualism, individuals exploit another individual. As you will see, this is much more than a subtle difference in wording.

Figure 14.1 This moose exploits the twigs and buds of woody plants for the food it needs to survive the cold northern winter. Eventually, wolves may prey upon the moose to meet their needs for food.

Let's consider some of the most common types of exploitation. *Herbivores* consume live plant material but do not usually kill plants. Typical herbivores include caterpillars, aphids, ants, and ungulates. **Predators** kill and consume other organisms. Typical predators are animals that feed on other animals—wolves that eat moose, snakes that eat mice, etc.

As clear as all these definitions may seem, they are fraught with semantic problems. Once again, we are faced with capturing the full richness of nature with a few restrictive definitions. For instance, not all predators are animals, a few are plants, some are fungi, and many are protozoans. When an herbivore kills the plant upon which it feeds, should we call it a predator? If an ant eats a seed killing a baby plant, is it an herbivore or a predator? If an herbivore does not kill its food plants, would it be better to call it a parasite? The point of these questions is not to argue for more terminology but to argue for fewer, less restrictive terms. As is often the case, we are faced with a continuum of interesting and sometimes bewildering interactions involving millions of organisms. Let's recognize the diversity and continuous variation facing the ecologist, put the restrictive definitions aside for the moment, and recognize what is common to all these interactions: **exploitation,** that is, one organism makes its living at the expense of another.

Concepts

14.1 Predation and herbivory are common ecological interactions, influencing the distribution, abundance, and structure of prey and host populations.

14.2 Predator–prey and herbivore–host relationships are dynamic.

14.3 To persist in the face of exploitation, hosts and prey need refuges.

14.4 The impacts of exploitation of host and prey have resulted in a variety of defenses that increase their ability to avoid attack.

14.1 Widespread Interactions

Predation and herbivory are common ecological interactions that influence the distribution, abundance, and structure of prey and host populations.   By conservative estimates, there are at least 10 million species on the planet. This number is sure to grow as researchers explore the biodiversity of soils, oceans, and small microbial and invertebrate life. But there is another way of looking at the diversity on the planet, one based on interactions rather than taxonomic affiliation. There are somewhere on the order of 350,000 species of photosynthetic plants, and some unknown number of autotrophic bacteria. Combined, these make up just a tiny fraction of the life on the planet, which means that most species obtain essential resources through some sort of exploitative relationship with other species. It is perhaps then no surprise that ecologists have focused on many aspects of these exploitative relationships, using terms like plant–animal interactions, tri-trophic interactions, predator–prey, herbivore–host, disease–host, and others to describe the branch of ecology in which they work.

The effect of predation on prey is pretty obvious: death. The effect of herbivory on the host plant is less clear. Herbivory rarely immediately kills a plant, and following the departure of the herbivore, many plants appear to recover very well. As we will see in this chapter, under some conditions herbivory may actually stimulate plant growth. However, to find out what typically happens, Christine Hawkes and Jon Sullivan (2001) decided to comb through the extensive literature on herbivory, and conduct a meta-analysis. The found a total of 81 cases in which growth or reproduction were measured on plants grown with and without herbivory under experimental conditions. When averaged across all species, they found that herbivory does typically harm plants, reducing plant growth and reproduction. However, the exact effects of herbivory varied among species, with monocots generally increasing their growth rates following herbivory when nutrients were abundant. So, although herbivory is generally detrimental for a typical plant, there will be times in which herbivory may actually stimulate growth, at least for some species. We will discuss this issue of overcompensation shortly.

Although there is widespread recognition that nearly all species are involved in some sort of exploitative relationship, and these interactions can have negative consequences for the individuals being consumed, what is often less clear is whether these relationships have important consequences for population growth, community structure, landscape processes, and evolutionary trajectories. The answer to this will depend upon exactly how many individuals within the population are being consumed. As we will show in chapter 19, most of the plant biomass that is produced is never consumed while still alive. In other words, most plant matter is NOT exploited until death, as opposed to exploitation being the cause of death! We will find similar results when we look at causes of mortality for a variety of animal species, where most individuals do not die due to being food to another animal, but instead death arises from competition, abiotic stressors, and even simple age-related failings of physiology. However, in some systems herbivory and predation occur at extremely high rates, and can have dramatic effects on populations and communities. It is important to remember that even though we are discussing individual types of interactions, these take place in a broader context during which competition, physical constraints, and social interactions are occurring simultaneously.

As we will see here, sometimes exploitative interactions are a dominant influence on populations and individuals, and thus to understand the functioning of ecological systems, it is critical we understand the nature of predator–prey and herbivore–host relationships.

Snow Goose Grazing and a Sub-Arctic Salt Marsh

Bob Jefferies, of the University of Toronto, has for several decades conducted research in the sub-arctic wetlands at La Pérouse Bay, Manitoba (chapter 3). La Pérouse Bay is at the northern limit of the boreal forest, just east of Churchill, Man-

(a)

(b)

Figure 14.2 (*a*) Geese are the dominant herbivores in many northern wetlands, such as this marsh at La Pérouse Bay, Manitoba, (*b*) Exclosures can be used to experimentally manipulate grazing intensity.

itoba. These wetlands are the summer home to large numbers of herbivores, whose feeding behaviour has the ability to change the landscape. When we think of herbivores, it is often images of bison, caterpillars, and deer that come to mind. However, in La Pérouse Bay and other wetlands of the North, geese are the dominant herbivores, having the potential to completely devegitate areas (fig. 14.2). Within La Pérouse Bay, there is a large expanse of marsh dominated by two plant species, *Puccinellia phryganodes* and *Carex subspathacea*. These two plant species alone can make up nearly 95% of all plant biomass in the marsh, and thus changes in their growth would indicate changes in the overall biomass production of this community. In 1979–1980 there were approximately 4,000 nesting pairs of snow geese, along with many more non-breeding geese. The birds graze heavily, often leaving only 1–2 cm of vegetation unclipped (Cargill and Jefferies 1984). One of the first questions that Jefferies and his colleagues asked was quite simple: what is the effect of this grazing on the growth of these two plant species?

To determine the effects of geese grazing on plant growth, Jefferies created areas of the marsh that were protected from

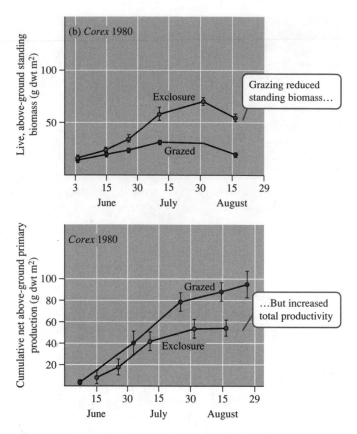

Figure 14.3 Grazing decreased standing biomass, but increased productivity of a sub-arctic wetland (data from Cargill and Jefferies 1984).

the herbivores. By building a series of 5 × 5 m *exclosures* out of wood and chicken wire, they were able to keep geese out of their study plots. Some of these exclosures were temporary, and some were permanent, allowing them to determine both the short, and longer-term effects of grazing on plant growth. They then measured plant biomass inside and outside the exclosures over the course of the growing season for two years. There was no surprise when they found grazing reduced above-ground biomass (fig. 14.3). In other words, at any point in time, there was more **standing biomass** in the ungrazed plots than the grazed plots. Standing biomass is a measure of how much plant biomass is found at a specific point in time, per unit area. What was surprising, however, was when they added up all the production from the plots over the course of the summer, taking into account the amount of biomass the geese ate, the grazed plots actually had higher **primary productivity** than the ungrazed ones (fig. 14.3)! As you may recognize, primary productivity is a measure of plant growth per unit area, per unit time. Herbivory can cause increased productivity, even if standing biomass is reduced. This is an example of **overcompensation**, where growth following herbivory is greater than growth without herbivory. This concept should be vaguely familiar to you, as it is similar to the idea that populations that follow the logistic growth curve will have maximal population growth rates at intermediate population densities (chapter 12).

Overcompensation seems very counterintuitive. How can plant growth increase when plants are being consumed? Jefferies

and his students have explored this issue, finding this pattern is much more complex than it first appears. David Hik (now at University of Alberta) and Jefferies conducted an experiment designed to understand why overcompensation occurs (Hik and Jefferies 1990). Researchers had quickly zeroed in on three ideas that could influence plant recovery. (1) Not all grazing is of the same intensity. Minor grazing could be beneficial if herbivores consumed dead/dying parts of the plant, increasing light availability to the rest of the plant. At high levels of herbivory, however, herbivores may consume the whole plant, with negative impact. (2) Grazers don't only eat, they also defecate. As a result, the geese may be converting nitrogen into a form that plants can take up, stimulating growth. (3) Plants may be more vulnerable to grazing at different times of the year, and early-season grazing may give plants the most opportunity to recover. Hik and Jefferies conducted a series of experiments where they manipulated the duration of grazing, removed feces from the experimental plots (yes, that couldn't have been fun!), and altered the timing of herbivory. To do this, they used *enclosures*, rather than exclosures. The difference here is that they added geese inside of the enclosures, permitting them to graze for known durations during different times of year, thereby controlling the level of herbivory experienced by the plants. To manipulate nutrient remobilization, they removed feces by hand from several plots. They found that overall productivity increased in response to light grazing and when feces were present. This response was greatest early in the summer, and absent later. When the plants were grazed heavily, growth was reduced. When feces were removed, growth was reduced. When herbivory happened late in the season, plants couldn't recover. In short, overcompensation only occurred if a very narrow set of conditions were met.

One may think of this as a nice story about the balance of nature, and how these geese are able to coexist with their food resources, increasing the production of the food they depend upon, with all members living happily ever after. Nature doesn't work like that. Peter Kotanen and Jefferies have shown that over 12 years there has been a significant shift in this plant–animal interaction (Kotanen and Jefferies 1997). At the heart of this change has been rapid population growth of geese; the numbers of breeding pairs of lesser snow geese at La Pérouse Bay have increased from less than 2,000 in 1968 to over 20,000 in 1990. This population growth has a variety of causes, though it is primarily driven by decreased mortality on the geese's wintering grounds in the United States, due to increased food availability in agricultural fields and reduced hunting activity. As you might imagine, this population growth has resulted in an increase in the intensity of grazing in the breeding grounds. Knowing what we do through the work of Hik and Jefferies, it should come as no surprise that during this period there has been nearly a 65% decrease in the abundances of *Puccinellia* and *Carex*. In their place have emerged carpets of moss, plants the geese do not eat, and large expanses of completely devegetated soil (fig. 14.4).

These studies by Jefferies and his colleagues show that herbivory isn't inherently bad for plant growth. Instead, its effects will depend upon a variety of issues such as nutrient

Figure 14.4 Rapid population growth of geese has resulted in extensive areas of La Pérouse Bay becoming devegetated.

relations, plant phenology, and the intensity of the grazing event. Next we show, in a different system, how the same issues can impact the food resources available for the herbivore.

An Herbivorous Stream Insect and Its Algal Food

One of the main reasons ecologists are interested in exploitative interactions between species is that these interactions have the potential to influence prey and host populations. Gary Lamberti and Vincent Resh (1983) studied the influence of an herbivorous stream insect on the algal and bacterial populations upon which it feeds. The herbivorous insect was the larval stage of the caddisfly (order Trichoptera) *Helicopsyche*

borealis. This insect inhabits streams across most of North America and is most notable for the type of portable shelter it builds as a larva. The larvae cement sand grains together to form a helical portable home that looks just like a small snail shell. In fact, the species was originally described as a freshwater snail. Larval *Helicopsyche* graze on the algae and bacteria growing on the exposed surfaces of submerged stones. This feeding habit requires that *Helicopsyche* spend considerable time out in the open, where it would be far more vulnerable to predators were it not for its case.

Lamberti and Resh found that larval *Helicopsyche* grow and develop through the summer and fall, attaining densities of over 4,000 individuals per square meter in Big Sulphur Creek, California. At this density, they make up about 25% of the total biomass of benthic animals. A consumer that reaches such high population densities clearly has the potential to reduce the density of its food supply. Lamberti and Resh got an indication of the potential of *Helicopsyche* to influence its food supply in a preliminary experiment. In this first experiment they placed unglazed ceramic tiles (15.2 cm × 7.6 cm) on the bottom of the creek and followed colonization of these artificial substrates by algae and *Helicopsyche* over a period of seven weeks.

Algae rapidly colonized the tiles, reaching peak density two weeks after the tiles were placed in Big Sulphur Creek. The *Helicopsyche* population reached its highest density one week later. Algal biomass decreased from week two to week five of the study and then rose again during the last two weeks, as *Helicopsyche* numbers declined. These results (fig. 14.5) suggest that the caddisfly larvae depleted their food supply. However, Lamberti and Resh could not be certain. Why is that? First, there are many other benthic invertebrates living

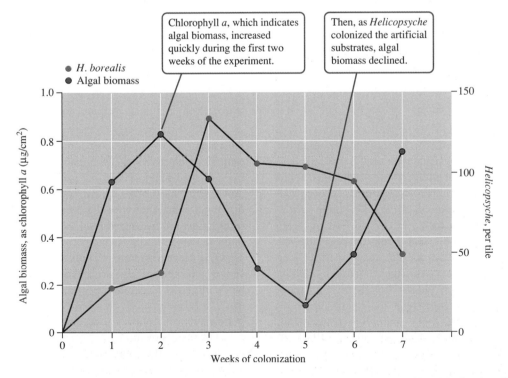

Figure 14.5 Biomass of algae and numbers of the grazing caddisfly *Helicopsyche borealis* (data from Lamberti and Resh 1983).

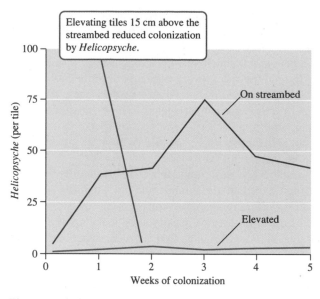

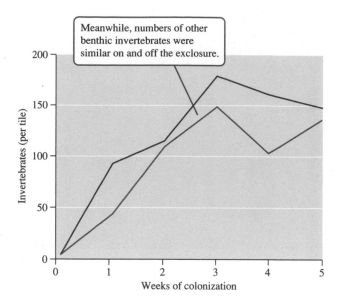

Figure 14.6   The influence of elevating tiles on colonization by *Helicopsyche borealis* and other benthic invertebrates (data from Lamberti and Resh 1983).

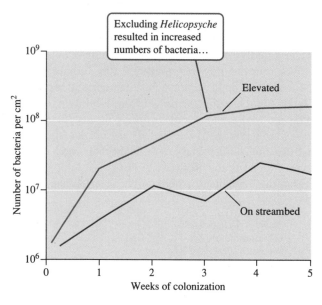

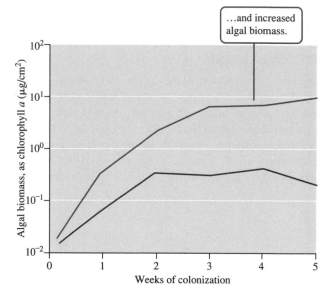

Figure 14.7   Influence of excluding *Helicopsyche borealis* on abundance of bacteria and algae (data from Lamberti and Resh 1983).

in Big Sulphur Creek, some of which might be depleting the algal populations. Second, physical factors could have changed during the seven weeks of the study, and these changes could have produced the fluctuations in both algal and *Helicopsyche* populations. This initial experiment provided valuable indications but was not a definitive test.

In a follow-up study, the researchers used an exclusion experiment to test for the effect of *Helicopsyche* on its food supply. They placed unglazed ceramic tiles in two 3-by-6 grids of 18 tiles each. One grid was placed directly on the stream bottom, while the other was placed on a metal plate supported by an upside-down J-shaped metal bar. This arrangement, which raised the tiles 15 cm above the bottom but still 35 cm below the stream surface, allowed colonization of tiles by algae and most invertebrates while preventing colonization by *Helicopsyche*. *Helicopsyche* could not colonize the tiles because

their heavy snail-shaped case confines them to the stream bottom. To reach the tiles, *Helicopsyche* would have to crawl up the J-shaped support bar, out of the water, and then back down, while most other invertebrates could colonize by either drifting downstream with the current or by swimming to the raised tiles. Lamberti and Resh coated the above-water parts of the bar with an adhesive to prevent adult *Helicopsyche* from crawling down to the tiles to deposit their eggs. As figure 14.6 shows, the experimental arrangement excluded *Helicopsyche* while allowing large numbers of other invertebrates to colonize the raised tiles. Such selective manipulations of natural populations are not easy to attain.

The results of this experiment clearly show that *Helicopsyche* reduces the abundance of its food supply. Figure 14.7 shows that the tiles without *Helicopsyche* supported higher abundances of both algae and bacteria. The large effect of

(a)

(b)

Figure 14.8 Effects of excluding *Helicopsyche borealis* on benthic algal biomass: (*a*) two sets of tiles at the beginning of experiment; exclusion tiles in foreground; (*b*) same tiles five weeks into the experiment.

Helicopsyche on its food supply is apparent from paired photos of the experimental and control tiles at the beginning and the end of the experiment (fig. 14.8). In this next example we find predators can also significantly alter prey densities.

Moose, Wolves, and Populations

Moose, *Alces alces*, are distributed throughout much of Canada and the northern United States. Across this range, there exists substantial variation in moose density, and researchers have long searched for potential explanations. A long-standing debate had existed in the literature as to whether low abundances of prey (i.e., moose) could be caused by predation by wolves, or whether they were the result of low food availability or abiotic stress. Françoise Messier, of the University of Saskatchewan, set off to test a variety of potential explanations (Messier 1994).

In the first step towards disentangling these different factors, Messier developed several graphical models describing how moose growth could vary as a function of moose density under different predation and food regimes (fig. 14.9). Messier reasoned that if predation is absent, moose should reach an equilibrium density equal to their population carrying capacity.

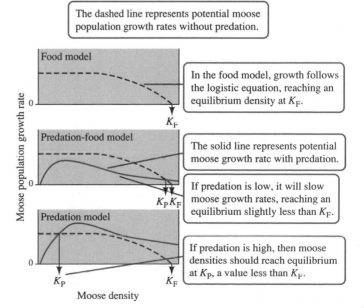

Figure 14.9 Three possible relationships between moose density, moose population growth rates, food, and predation (data from Messier 1994).

Invasive Species and Exploitative Relationships

One of the most ecologically damaging activities that humans regularly engage in is the intentional and accidental release of organisms into novel habitats. These activities occur through the introduction of new horticultural plants, in ballast water released near shore, as contaminants to imported agricultural products, and as simple stowaways in our cars and backpacks as we leave our houses for cottages or decide to see how long it really takes to travel from St. John's to Nanaimo. Most of these **introduced** (i.e., exotic or non-native) **species** will quickly flounder before establishing a sustainable population. Perhaps the new home is too hot, too cold, or too crowded. Others will establish and maintain small populations, being simply another minor component of a complex ecological system. In fact, nearly one-third of all vascular plant species in Canada are non-native. A small subset of introduced species will not only establish populations, but under some conditions will rapidly expand, reducing the abundance and diversity of the pre-existing native species. These **invasive species** are an issue of global concern (Mack et al. 2000). Ecologists throughout the world are actively pursuing research designed to understand both the causes of species invasion, and potential ways to control their spread.

What allows introduced species to establish in novel habitats? What allows invasive species to spread? In a classic view of ecological systems, ecologists have often thought of all species as being essential components to the system, where bending one part will cause bends elsewhere. In this model, the community was also viewed as closed (chapter 16), where all the available niches were full and thus competitive exclusion (chapter 13) would keep out new species. We realize now, however, that this model was woefully incorrect. Introduced species are able to establish in nearly every ecological community across the planet. How is this possible? Why don't the regular processes of exploitation and resource limitation keep these species in check? We will discuss here the "enemy release hypothesis," one of several putative explanations for the spread of species into new communities. One of the interesting findings that many researchers have uncovered is that many species that spread in novel habitats are relatively minor members of the community in their native environments. The enemy release hypothesis suggests that at home, population growth is reduced due to exploitation, such as we saw for moose and wolves. In new habitats, these species do not bring with them their native predators and herbivores, nor are they eaten extensively by the predators and herbivores in their new home, and thus their populations grow, restricted only by resources. Making things even worse is that with enemy release, organisms may grow a bit bigger and have increased vigour, making them better able to compete with the native organisms. In other words, by not bringing along their pests, these new species do not suffer the costs of exploitation, and may actually accrue the benefit of increased competitive ability. But does this really occur?

Anurag Agrawal and Peter Kotanen, of the University of Toronto, are skeptical of this idea. They conducted a large field experiment at the Koffler Scientific Reserve at Jokers Hill, about an hour away from campus (Agrawal and Kontanen 2003). They planted seeds of 30 species into a ploughed field, measuring rates of herbivory on each at the end of the growing season. Making this study particularly well-designed is that these species were divided into different pairs of congeneric species, such that within each pair, one species was native to Joker's hill and its congener was introduced. By using this taxonomic pairing, they controlled for a variety of confounding effects that could be associated with differences among species. In contrast to the enemy release hypothesis, they found that leaf damage by herbivores was about 40% higher on exotic species compared to their native relatives! Importantly, they also found that overall levels of herbivory were low (around 6% leaf damage). They suggest that not only is the pattern opposite to that which was predicted, the low magnitude of leaf damage suggests that herbivory itself is not a significant stressor on most of the species they tested. In other words, if herbivory doesn't hurt plants too much, being released from herbivory is not likely to be of much benefit.

A similar result was found by Michael Stastny and Elizabeth Elle of Simon Fraser University, in collaboration with a colleague in Switzerland (Stastny et al. 2005). They conducted an experiment in Switzerland where the plant, *Senecio jacobaea*, is native to much of Europe. *Senecio* has been introduced and has become invasive to rangelands throughout North America, Australia, and New Zealand. They were interested in whether the genotypes that invaded new habitats were less susceptible to damage by the specialist herbivore, *Longitarsus jacobaeae*, a flea beetle (fig. 14.10), than the genotypes commonly found in the native habitat. To do this, they collected seed from eight populations of *Senecio* from their introduced and native ranges. The plants were then planted into a meadow in Switzerland, where *Senecio* and *Longitarsus* naturally occur. They

---

If predation is severe, this will prevent food from ever being limiting, and instead moose densities should fall well below their carrying capacity. If predation is light, there remains the potential for intraspecific competition for food resources, though the predation will remove enough individuals to result in equilibrium slightly below carrying capacity.

(a)

Figure 14.10
(a) *Senecio jacobaea;*
(b) *Longitarsus jacobaeae.*

(b)

measured herbivory and growth of the plants throughout the growing season. They found that the introduced genotypes grew larger, had greater reproductive output, *and* were eaten more than the native genotypes! These results also are not consistent with the enemy release hypothesis, and instead suggest that invasive genotypes are likely to be larger and better competitors than native ones. The researchers suggest that the increased vigour of the introduced species allows them to tolerate the increased levels of herbivory, which, as in the Agrawal and Kotanen study, are thought not to be of a magnitude great enough to reduce fitness. This is another example of the importance of both understanding the diversity of ecological interactions that individuals encounter, and not assuming that increased levels of herbivory will necessarily reduce plant fitness.

These findings have very significant implications for the management of invasive species in natural and managed systems. Invasive species can be managed in a variety of ways, including ignoring them, mechanical removal (i.e., weeding), herbicides, and **biocontrol**. Biocontrol is the deliberate introduction of some agent (herbivore, pathogen, etc.) that will exploit an invasive species, reducing its population size. You can see that the ideas presented in this chapter lend some support to this approach: under some conditions, exploitation can

reduce population growth. However, you likely also recognize that information in this chapter raises significant questions about how effective these programs will be, and whether there will be any **nontarget effects**. Nontarget effects are changes to species other than the intended invasive target. It may come as no surprise that there is substantial divide amongst ecologists as to whether biocontrol is an ecologically responsible, or dangerous, idea (Louda et al. 2003). On one side, proponents of biocontrol programs point out that once an agent is identified, it is inexpensive to use, self-replicates, and reduces the need to use potentially toxic compounds. There is also substantial evidence that biocontrol can be effective in reducing populations of many species. In a recent review of the effects of herbivores on plant population growth, John Maron and Elizabeth Crone (formerly of the University of Calgary) report that biocontrol agents have a 7 times stronger negative effect on plant population growth than do native herbivores (Maron and Crone 2006). Clearly, biocontrol agents can be effective in reduced plant growth. However, there are serious ecological risks associated with using biocontrol agents (Louda et al. 2003), including: (1) there is substantial evidence that relatives of the target species are also likely to be attacked, including endangered native species; (2) biocontrol agents can have undesired cascading effects on the trophic dynamics of ecological communities; and (3) in many cases, exploitation is not of a magnitude sufficient to cause declines in abundance of the invasive species. In other words, if, as in the examples above, enemy release is not the driver of a species' spread, it is unlikely that the introduction of an enemy will slow it down. Finally, there is often a difference of goals, with many biocontrol agents designed to tackle agricultural pests, where success is measured as reduction in weed densities and increased crop yield, while many ecologists are concerned about what happens when these organisms spread outside the fields and into native communities.

Understanding the causes of species invasion, as well as mechanisms of control, is a critical issue for the current and next generation of ecologists. By identifying which aspects of a species' life history limits, or encourages, population growth, one may be able to design more appropriate control measures. However, it is clear that the world isn't as simple as saying that enemies control growth. The outcome of one interaction is dependent upon other interactions, and only by understanding these connections can we hope to learn how to control species invasion.

These animals roam over very large ranges, and experimental manipulations like those used by Jefferies for snow geese just are not feasible. Instead, Messier used a modelling approach, drawing data from the literature on moose and wolf populations throughout North America. By analyzing these data with a variety of population growth models, and calculating functional and numerical responses, Messier concludes that on average, wolves reduce moose density from 2.0 to 1.3 moose/km². This value can be further reduced in the presence of other predators of moose, such as bear and humans.

As we are seeing in many examples, the impacts of exploitation on populations are not fixed, but instead are dependent upon a variety of other factors, such as the presence of alternative predators and/or resource availability. The models presented by Messier provide a useful first step in our attempts to understand what the potential role of predation and food will be on limiting prey population growth. Messier himself recognized this, and actually presented a fourth conceptual model that allows for alternative equilibrium densities of the moose. This, it turns out, most closely approximates what occurs in nature. In the next section, we continue our discussion of exploitation, now extending our studies to variation through time.

Concept 14.1 Review

1. How can geese cause an increase in productivity but a decrease in standing biomass in La Pérouse Bay?
2. In many natural communities there are numerous herbivorus species that feed simultaneously. How did Lamberti and Resh determine the specific effects of *Helicopsyche* on algal biomass?
3. What influence can predators have on plant–herbivore interactions?

14.2   Dynamics

Predator–prey and herbivore–host relationships are dynamic.   In the last section we saw how some predators and herbivores affect the populations they exploit. The picture that emerges from these studies is that the biology of exploitation is complex. As complex as this emerging picture of exploitation may be, it belies an even deeper underlying complexity. In this section, we add another level of complexity as we take up the topic of *temporal dynamics*. Populations of a wide variety of predators and prey are not static but cycle in abundance over periods of days to decades.

Cycles of Abundance in Snowshoe Hares and Their Predators

Population cycles are well documented for a wide variety of animals living at high latitudes, including lemmings, voles, muskrats, red fox, arctic fox, ruffed grouse, and porcupines. We have already seen in chapter 11 how periodic outbreaks of voles lead to local increases in the abundance of avian predators due to numerical responses by owls and hawks (Korpimäki and Norrdahl 1991).

One of the best-studied cases of animal population cycles is that of the snowshoe hare, *Lepus americanus,* and the lynx, *Lynx canadensis,* one of the snowshoe hare's chief predators. The population cycles of these two species are especially well documented because the Hudson Bay Company kept trapping records during most of the eighteenth, nineteenth, and twentieth centuries. Drawing on this unique historical record ecologists were able to estimate the relative abundances of Canada lynx and snowshoe hare over a period of about 200 years. That record, shown in figure 14.11, demonstrates a remarkable match in the cycles of the two populations.

By the 1950s several hypotheses had been proposed to explain these and other cycles among northern populations. Charles Elton (1924) proposed that cycles of abundance in snowshoe hare and lynx populations are driven by variation in amount of solar radiation as a consequence of sunspot cycles. He proposed that variation in intensity of solar radiation may directly affect snowshoe hares and their food supply and that lynx populations, in turn, respond to the changing abundance of the snowshoe hare, their main prey.

The sunspot hypothesis was rejected by D. MacLulich (1937) and P. Moran (1949), who showed that sunspot cycles do not match snowshoe hare population cycles. The second group of hypotheses, which Lloyd Keith (1963) referred to as

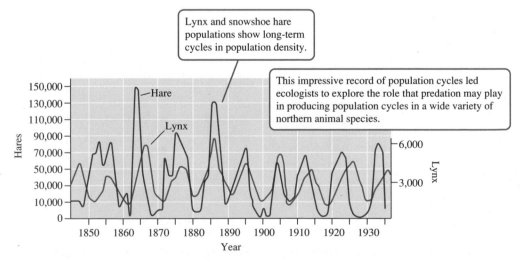

Figure 14.11   Historical fluctuations in lynx and snowshoe hare populations based on the number of pelts purchased by the Hudson Bay Company (data from MacLulich 1937).

"overpopulation theories," suggested that periods of high population growth are followed by (1) decimation by disease and parasitism, (2) physiological stress at high densities leading to increased mortality as a consequence of nervous disorders, and (3) starvation due to reduced quantity and quality of food at high population densities. An alternative to the overpopulation hypothesis was that cycles like that of the snowshoe hare are driven by predators. According to this hypothesis, predators increase in number in response to increasing prey availability and then eventually reduce prey populations.

Keith observed that none of these hypotheses completely accounts for population cycles in snowshoe hare and other northern populations. He went on to say that "the 10-year cycle is not likely to become better understood by further theorizing. Clearly the present need is for comprehensive long-term investigations by a diversified team of specialists." Heeding his own advice, Keith organized such studies. After three decades of research by his team and several other groups in North America and Europe, we now have a reasonable picture of the roles played by predators and food supply in producing population cycles in the far north.

The Role of Food Supply

Snowshoe hares live in the boreal forests of North America. As we saw, the boreal forest is dominated by a variety of conifers such as spruce, *Picea* spp., jackpines, *Pinus banksiana,* and tamarack, *Larix laricina,* and deciduous trees such as balsam poplar, *Populus balsamifera,* aspen, *Populus tremuloides,* and paper birch, *Betula papyrifera.* Within the boreal forest, snowshoe hares associate with dense growths of understory shrubs, which provide both cover and winter food, the most critical portion of the snowshoe hare's food supply.

Snowshoe hares have the potential to reduce the quantity and quality of their food supply. The hares live up to the legendary reproductive capacity of rabbits and hares. Estimated geometric rate of increase, λ (see chapter 11), during the growth phase of a hare population cycle can average as high as 2.0. In other words, snowshoe hare populations can double in size each generation. Keith and his colleagues (1984) have observed snowshoe hare population densities of up to 1,100 to 2,300 per square kilometer. However, local densities are highly dynamic. Keith cites 100-fold fluctuations in snowshoe hare densities in some areas and states that 10- to 30-fold fluctuations are common. Similar densities are sometimes observed in populations of the mountain hare, *Lepus timidus,* which shows pronounced population cycles across the Eurasian taiga (Keith 1983) and which destroys considerable vegetation at high densities.

Snowshoe hares spend the long northern winter (six to eight months) browsing on the buds and small stems of shrubs such as rose, *Rosa* spp., and willow, *Salix* spp. Where deep snow provides access, snowshoe hares browse on the saplings of trees such as spruce and aspen. The most nutritious portions of these shrubs and trees are the small stems (< 4–5 mm diameter). Over the winter, each hare requires about 300 g of these stems each day. In some areas, however, snowshoe hares have been observed to remove over 1,500 g of food biomass per day, possibly wasting a great deal of potential food in the process. Feeding at these rates, one population of snowshoe hares reduced food biomass from 530 kg per hectare in late November to 160 kg per hectare by late March. Many ecologists have demonstrated food shortage during winters of peak snowshoe hare density.

Snowshoe hares also influence the quality of their food supply. Feeding by snowshoe hares induces chemical defenses in their food plants, defenses like those we discussed in chapter 7. Shoots produced after substantial browsing contain elevated concentrations of terpene and phenolic resins, defensive chemicals that repel hungry hares. Elevated concentrations of plant defensive chemicals can persist for up to two years after browsing by hares. The effect of these induced chemical defenses reduces *usable* food supplies during the population decline. Some ecologists suggest that plant defensive responses may be the "timer" that produces 10-year population cycles in snowshoe hares.

The Role of Predators

The long historical record of lynx population cycles may have distracted ecologists from the fact that lynxes are only one of several predators that feed on snowshoe hares. Other major predators of snowshoe hares include goshawks, *Accipiter gentilis,* great horned owls, *Bubo virginianus,* mink, *Mustela vison,* long-tailed weasels, *Mustela frenata,* red foxes, *Vulpes vulpes,* and coyotes, *Canis latrans.* Populations of these predators are known to cycle synchronously with snowshoe hare populations. Though the lynx is considered to be a specialist on snowshoe hares, the diet of a generalist predator such as the coyote may also be dominated by snowshoe hares. This is particularly true when snowshoe hare populations are at peak density. Arlen Todd and Lloyd Keith (1983) report that snowshoe hares made up 67% of the coyote diets in central Alberta, Canada. Ecologists have estimated that predation can account for 60% to 90% of snowshoe hare mortality during peak densities.

Research by a team of researchers from British Columbia, Alaska, the Yukon, Alberta, and Argentina (O'Donoghue et al. 1997, 1998) provide clear evidence of predator *functional response* and *numerical response* to increased hare densities. O'Donoghue and his colleagues focused their research on two of the most important predators of adult snowshoe hares: lynx and coyotes. Their study shows that coyote and lynx numbers increase six to seven fold, a numerical response, following increases in snowshoe hare populations. The two predators also showed functional responses to increased hare densities. However, coyote and lynx functional responses differed in their timing and form. The lynx killed more hares when hare numbers were declining, while coyotes showed higher predation rates when the hare population was increasing. O'Donoghue and colleagues discovered that lynx show a clear type 2 functional response to increasing hare densities, reaching a maximum number of 1.2 hares per day at medium hare densities. In contrast, coyotes preyed on up to 2.3 hares per day at the highest hare densities and their functional response showed no signs of levelling off. At high hare densities, coyote and lynx predation rates exceeded their daily energetic needs. Coyotes killed more hares early in the winter, caching many and retrieving them later in the season. In some instances individual coyotes returned to eat hares over four months after they were cached. The combination of numerical and functional responses by lynx and coyotes indicate great potential for these predators to reduce snowshoe hare populations.

In summary, several decades of research provided evidence that both predation and food can make substantial contributions to snowshoe hare population cycles (Haukioja et al. 1983, Keith 1983, Keith et al. 1984). The food availability and predation hypotheses are not mutually exclusive alternatives but rather are complementary. As hare populations increase, they reduce the quantity and quality of their food supply. Reduced food availability, which leads to starvation and weight loss, would itself likely produce population decline. This potential decline is ensured and accelerated by high rates of mortality due to predation. As hare population density is reduced, predator populations decline in turn, plant populations recover, and the stage is set for another increase in the hare population. This scenario was tested through a series of long-term experiments.

Experimental Test of Food and Predation Impacts

Charles J. Krebs of the University of British Columbia and several colleagues from UBC, University of Alberta, and the University of Toronto (Krebs et al. 1995) conducted a large-scale, long-term experiment designed to sort out the tangle of conflicting evidence regarding the impacts of food and predation on snowshoe hare population cycles. Over a period of eight years, Krebs and colleagues conducted one of the most ambitious field experiments to date. This project is on the scale of the large manipulate experiments conducted by David Schindler at the experimental lakes area (chapter 1), and will certainly be remembered by ecologists as a project of grand objectives and strong science. As a sign of the scope of the project, the main findings of the study are best absorbed as a book (Krebs, Boutin, and Boonstra 2001), rather than individual papers!

Their experimental plots consisted of nine 1-km^2 blocks of undisturbed boreal forest near Kluane, Yukon, each separated from other experimental blocks by a minimum of 1 km. Three blocks served as controls for comparison to the six other blocks where experimental treatments were applied. To test the impact of food, hares were given unlimited supplemental food on two experimental blocks during the entire period of the study. To test for the possible influences of plant tissue quality on hare numbers, the researchers applied a nitrogen-potassium-phosphorus fertilizer from the air to two of the experimental blocks. Finally, they built electric fences around two of the 1-km^2 blocks, which excluded mammalian predators but not hawks and owls. One of these predator reduction blocks received supplemental food. Krebs and his colleagues report that, due to maintenance requirements, they could not replicate the predator reduction and predator reduction + food experimental manipulations. The fences on both predator reduction areas (8 km of fence) had to be checked every day through the winter, when temperatures would sometimes dip as low as −45°C. Krebs' research team maintained these experimental conditions through one cycle in snowshoe hare numbers.

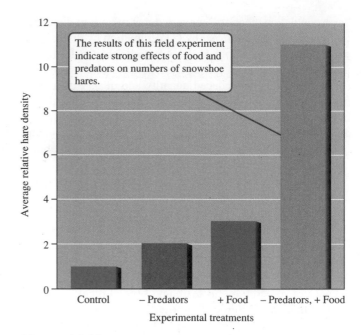

Figure 14.12   The densities of snowshoe hares averaged from the peak in hare density through the period of declining density observed during the study. Hare densities are expressed relative to the densities on the control plots where no experimental manipulation was applied (data from Krebs et al. 1995, 2001).

During the eight years of the experiment, the researchers observed an increase in hare numbers to a peak, followed by a decline on all the study plots. The application of fertilizer increased plant growth within the fertilizer treatment blocks but did not increase numbers of snowshoe hares. Meanwhile compared to control plots, hare numbers increased substantially on food addition, predator reduction, and predator reduction + food study plots. Averaged over the peak and decline phases during the study, reducing predators doubled hare density, adding food tripled hare density, and excluding predators and adding food increased hare density to 11 times that of the controls (fig. 14.12). What factors contributed to these increased densities within treatment blocks? Krebs and his colleagues found that higher densities on experimental plots were the result of both higher survival and higher reproduction.

After approximately 70 years of research, we can conclude that the population cycle in snowshoe hares is the result of an interaction between three trophic levels: the hares, their food supply, and their predators. Krebs and colleagues (2001) point out, however, that to understand the controls on hare numbers, researchers have had to work with all three trophic levels simultaneously. In addition, the critical experiment had to be done on a large scale and in the field. Still, a great deal of insight into this large-scale predator–prey system has come from laboratory and mathematical studies.

Population Cycles in Mathematical and Laboratory Models

Now let's shift our focus from population cycles in the vast world of the boreal forest to population cycles in mathematical models and controlled laboratory conditions. Mathematical and laboratory models offer population ecologists the opportunity to manipulate variables that they cannot control in the field. Our question here is whether predator-prey cycles can be produced in mathematical and laboratory models without the complications introduced by factors such as the effects of the prey on its food supply and uncontrolled weather cycles. In other words, can the interactions among exploited populations themselves generate population cycles of the type observed in snowshoe hares? The answer to this question is a qualified yes.

Mathematical Models

The first ecologists to model predator-prey interactions mathematically were Alfred Lotka (1925) and Vito Volterra (1926). These names should be familiar, as they were also involved in the early development of a model for competition (chapter 13) Both researchers built their models based on observations of interactions among natural populations. Lotka was impressed by the reciprocal oscillations of populations of moth and butterfly larvae and the parasitoids that attack them. Volterra was inspired by the response of marine fish populations to cessation of fishing during World War I. Volterra observed that the response of fish populations was uneven. Predaceous fish, particularly sharks, increased in abundance, while the populations upon which they fed decreased. This reciprocal change in numbers suggested that predators have the potential to reduce the abundance of their prey. In this single observation, Volterra somehow saw the potential for predator-prey population cycles. With these observations in mind, Lotka and Volterra then set out to build mathematical models that would produce the cycles that they thought occurred in nature.

The Lotka–Volterra predator–prey equations demonstrated that very simple models will produce cycling of predator and prey populations. It is important to note that their model also applies to host–pathogen interactions, though we limit discussion here to predator–prey. The basic Lotka–Volterra model assumes that the host population grows at an exponential rate and that host population size is limited by its predators:

$$\frac{dN_h}{dt} = r_h N_h - p N_h N_p$$

N_h represents the host (prey) population size, and $r_h N_h$ represents exponential growth by the host (prey) population. In the Lotka–Volterra model, exponential growth by the host (prey) population is opposed by deaths due to predation, which is represented by $-p N_h N_p$, where p is the rate predation, N_h is again the number of hosts, and N_p is the number of predators.

The Lotka–Volterra model assumes that the rate of growth by the predator population is determined by the rate at which it converts the hosts it consumes into offspring (new predators) minus the mortality rate:

$$\frac{dN_p}{dt} = c p N_h N_p - d_p N_p$$

Here again N_h and N_p are the numbers of hosts and predators respectively. The rate at which the predators convert hosts into offspring is $c p N_h N_p$, which is the rate at which the exploiters destroy hosts, $p N_h N_p$, times a conversion factor, c, the rate at

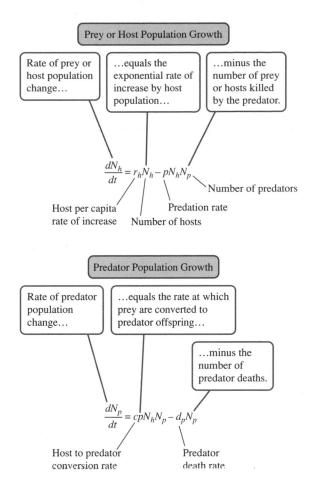

Figure 14.13 Anatomy of the Lotka Volterra equations for predator-prey population growth.

which hosts are converted to predator offspring. In the Lotka–Volterra equation, the growth rate of the predator population is opposed by predator deaths, $d_p N_p$. Notice that in these equations the only variables are N_h and N_p. All the other terms in the Lotka–Volterra model, p, c, d_p, and r_h, are constants. The Lotka–Volterra predator–prey model is summarized in figure 14.13.

Now let's reflect on the behaviour of this model. Because the host population grows at an exponential rate, its population growth accelerates with increasing population size. However, this tendency to grow faster and faster with increasing N_h is opposed by exploitation. As N_h increases, the rate of exploitation, $p N_h N_p$, also increases. Consequently, in the Lotka–Volterra model, reproduction by the host is translated immediately into destruction of hosts by the predator. In addition, increased predation, $p N_h N_p$, is translated directly and immediately into more predators by $c p N_h N_p$. Increased numbers of predators increase the rate of exploitation since increasing N_p increases $p N_h N_p$. Growth of the predator population eventually reduces the host population, which in turn leads to declines in the predator population. So, like the host, exploiter success carries the seeds of its own destruction.

These reciprocal effects of host and exploiter produce oscillations in the two populations, which we can represent in two

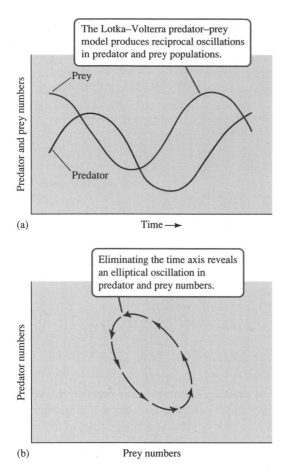

The Lotka–Volterra predator–prey model produces reciprocal oscillations in predator and prey populations.

(a)

Eliminating the time axis reveals an elliptical oscillation in predator and prey numbers.

(b)

Figure 14.14   A graphical view of the Lotka–Volterra predator–prey model (data from Gause 1934).

ways. In figure 14.14*a*, population oscillations are presented as we looked at them in snowshoe hare and lynx populations (see fig. 14.11), while figure 14.14*b* gives an alternative representation. The time axis has been eliminated and the two remaining axes represent the numbers of predators and hosts. When we plot population data in this way we see that the Lotka–Volterra model produces oscillations in exploiter and host populations that follow an elliptical path whose size depends upon the initial sizes of host and exploiter populations. Whatever the ellipse size, however, the host and exploiter populations just go round and round on the same path forever.

The prediction of eternal oscillations on a very narrowly defined path is obviously unrealistic. Another unrealistic assumption is that neither the host nor the exploiter populations are subject to carrying capacities. Another is that changes in either population are instantaneously translated into responses in the other population. Despite these unrealistic assumptions, Lotka and Volterra made valuable contributions to our understanding of predator–prey systems. They showed that simple models with a minimum of assumptions produce reciprocal cycles in populations of predator and prey analogous to those that biologists had observed in natural populations. They demonstrated that exploitative interactions themselves can, in theory, produce population cycles without any influences from an outside force such as climatic variation.

Laboratory Models

One of the most successful attempts to produce Lotka–Volterra-type population cycles in the laboratory was that of Syunro Utida (1957) of Kyoto University, Japan. Utida studied interactions between the adzuki bean weevil, *Callosobruchus chinensis,* and a hymenopteran parasitoid wasp, *Heterospilus prosopidis,* which attacks the bean weevil. Adult weevils lay their eggs on adzuki beans, *Paseolus angularis,* and upon hatching the larvae feed on the beans until they metamorphose into pupae. When they emerge from the pupal stage, the adult weevils mate and seek out new beans on which to lay their eggs. The entire life cycle, from egg to egg, takes approximately 20 days. While the weevil works at completing its life cycle, the parasitoid wasp searches for weevil larvae and pupae, where they lay their eggs. The larvae of the wasps feed on the larvae and pupae of the weevils and in the process, kill them. Though the details of their behaviour differ, the wasps are predators of the weevils, no less than are lynx predators of snowshoe hares.

Utida's experimental populations lived in petri dishes 1.8 cm tall by 8.5 cm in diameter where temperature was maintained at a constant 30°C and relative humidity at 75%. Within the petri dishes Utida placed 10 g of adzuki beans with a water content of 15% and added a mixture of adult adzuki bean weevils and parasitoid wasps: either 64 weevils and 8 wasps (population A), 8 weevils and 8 wasps (population C), or 512 weevils and 128 wasps (population E). Every 10 days 10 g of fresh beans were added, and the leavings of the old beans were placed in another dish. Any beetles moved with the spent food were recorded over a period of 20 days.

Utida followed population C for 47 beetle generations, approximately 940 days, after which a mistake in handling killed the population. He followed population E for 82 generations, approximately 1,640 days, after which the weevils died out. Population A was followed the longest, 112 generations, over six years, after which the population was accidentally destroyed. It was only by following the beetle and wasp populations for so many generations that Utida was able to see the pattern we look at now.

All three of the experimental populations showed the same cyclic behaviour (fig. 14.15). For several generations Utida observed reciprocal fluctuations in his beetle and parasitoid populations that look very similar to those we saw for lynx and hare populations (see fig. 14.11). After an initial phase of high-magnitude oscillations the population cycles were decreased in amplitude, remained in a situation of low-amplitude fluctuations for some time, and then increased in amplitude once again. In population A, high-amplitude cycles continued for the first 20 generations, dampened out until about generation 30, and then resumed high-amplitude cycling until about generation 54, when the oscillations dampened out once again.

Utida's results are analogous to the patterns of reciprocal fluctuation seen in the Lotka–Volterra model along with some behaviour not predicted by the mathematical model. However, despite these differences, like the Lotka–Volterra model, Utida's laboratory model shows that parasitoid–host populations can show reciprocal oscillations without significant temporal variation in the physical environment.

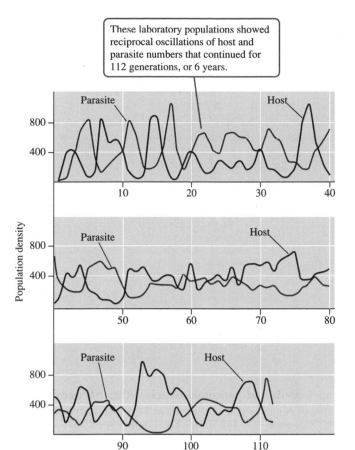

These laboratory populations showed reciprocal oscillations of host and parasite numbers that continued for 112 generations, or 6 years.

Figure 14.15   Laboratory populations of a host, the adzuki bean weevil, and a parasitoid wasp (data from Utida 1957).

G. Gause (1935) produced similar results when he studied a laboratory population of *Paramecium aurelia* preying upon yeast. He followed the populations through three cycles, which took only 20 days. Though Gause's experiments were much shorter than Utida's, they also produced oscillations like those predicted by the Lotka–Volterra model.

Utida's and Gause's successes make work with laboratory models look far easier than it is. Most attempts to produce Lotka–Volterra-type oscillations in laboratory populations have failed. Most laboratory experiments have led to extinction of the predator or prey population in a fairly short period of time. To sustain oscillations even for a short period researchers have generally had to provide the prey with refuges of some sort, which indicates another generalization about natural predator–prey systems. It appears that to persist in the face of exploitation by predators and herbivores, hosts and prey need refuges.

Concept 14.2 Review

1. When the coupled cycling of lynx and snowshoe hare populations (see fig. 14.11) was first described, many concluded that lynx control snowshoe hare populations. Why are lynx not the primary factor controlling snowshoe hare populations even though their population cycles are highly correlated?

2. Why is it not surprising that snowshoe hare populations are controlled by a combination of factors, food and predators and not by a single environmental factor?

3. Both mathematical and laboratory models offer valuable insights into the dynamics of predator–prey systems. What are some advantages and limitations of each approach?

14.3   Refuges

To persist in the face of exploitation, hosts and prey need refuges.   This section is about *refuges*, situations in which members of an exploited population have some protection from predators. When we think of refuges, we generally think of an inaccessible place. There are, however, many other kinds of refuges. Many have nothing to do with places and most do not provide complete security—just enough.

Refuges and Host Persistence in Laboratory and Mathematical Models

Gause's success at producing cycles in populations of *Paramecium aurelia* and its prey, *Saccharomyces exiguus,* gives no hint of the difficulties he experienced in his earlier attempts. Gause's first attempts to produce Lotka–Volterra population cycles involved *Paramecium caudatum* and one of its predators, another aquatic protozoan called *Didinium nasutum.* If Gause grew these organisms in a simple laboratory microcosm, *Didinium* quickly consumed all the *Paramecium* (fig. 14.16). The absence of a refuge for the prey led eventually to extinction of the predator and prey populations. Gause responded by putting some sediment on the bottom of his microcosm to provide a refuge for *Paramecium.* In this case once *Didinium* had eaten all of the *Paramecium* not hiding in bottom sediments, it starved and became extinct. Following the disappearance of *Didinium* and the removal of predation pressure, the population of *Paramecium* quickly increased. Here, a simple refuge for the prey population led to extinction of the predator.

Gause was only able to maintain oscillations in predator-prey populations if he periodically restocked the populations from his laboratory cultures. In this experiment, the microcosm contained no refuges for *Paramecium,* but every three days Gause would take one of each organism from his pure laboratory cultures and add them to the experimental microcosm. Using these periodic immigrations he was able to produce Lotka–Volterra-type predator–prey oscillations (see fig. 14.16). To do so, however, the experimental system had to include a refuge for the prey and a reservoir for the predator (the laboratory cultures) and Gause had to create periodic immigrations from those populations to the experimental microcosm.

Are these experimental requirements entirely artificial or do they correspond with anything we already know about natural populations? Actually, Gause's experimental results match many of our observations in natural populations. In chapter 10, we saw that on larger scales populations show clumped distributions. Most species are much more common in some parts of their range than in others. Then in chapter 11, we saw how dispersal is an important contributor to population dynamics

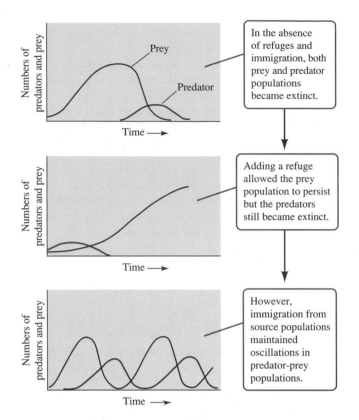

Figure 14.16 Refuges and the persistence of predator–prey oscillation in laboratory populations of prey (*Paramecium aurelia*) and predators (*Didinium nasutum*) (data from Gause 1934).

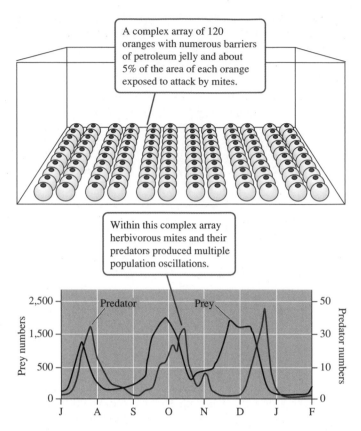

Figure 14.17 Environmental complexity and oscillations in laboratory populations of an herbivorous mite and a predatory mite (data from Huffaker 1958).

and that some local populations are maintained entirely by dispersal from other areas. Some biologists have combined observations such as these to hypothesize the existence of population sources and population sinks—local populations maintained by immigration from source populations. In Gause's experiment, the laboratory cultures were population hot spots, or sources, while the microcosms where predator and prey interacted were population sinks. The requirements of Gause's experiment are consistent with the results of later experiments.

C. Huffaker (1958) set out to test whether Gause's results could be reproduced in a situation in which the predator and prey are responsible for their own immigration and emigration among patches of suitable habitat. Huffaker chose the six-spotted mite, *Eotetranychus sexmaculatus,* a mite that feeds on oranges, as the prey and the predatory mite *Typhlodromus occidentalis,* which attacks *E. sexmaculatus,* as the predator. Huffaker's experimental setups, or "universes" as he called them, consisted of various arrangements of oranges, or combinations of oranges and rubber balls, separated by partial barriers to mite dispersal consisting of discontinuous strips of petroleum jelly.

An important point of natural history is that the predatory mite had to crawl in order to disperse from one orange to another, while the herbivorous mite can disperse either by crawling or by "ballooning," a means of aerial dispersal. A mite balloons by spinning a strand of silk that can catch wind currents. Huffaker gave the herbivorous mite the chance to balloon by providing small wooden posts that could serve as launching pads and by having a fan circulate air across his experimental setup.

While Huffaker's simpler experimental universes did not produce predator–prey oscillations, his most elaborate setup of 120 oranges did. These oscillations spanned several months (fig. 14.17). Huffaker observed three oscillations that spanned about six months. They were maintained by the dispersal of predator and prey among oranges in a deadly game of hide-and-seek, in which the prey managed to keep ahead of the predator for three full oscillations. These results are similar to those obtained by Gause, but we need to remember that Huffaker did not directly manipulate dispersal. In Huffaker's experiment both predator and prey moved from patch to patch under their own power.

The importance of refuges was recognized by Lotka (1932a) and incorporated into his mathematical theory of predator–prey relations. The starting point for his discussion were the Lotka–Volterra predator–prey equations that we discussed previously:

$$\frac{dN_h}{dt} = r_h N_h - p N_h N_p \text{ and } \frac{dN_p}{dt} = cp N_h N_p - d_p N_p$$

The part of this equation that provided the starting point for Lotka's discussion was p, the capture or consumption rate of the predator. Lotka pointed out that while it may be reasonable to assume that p is a constant for a particular environment, its value should change from one environment to another if the environments differ structurally, particularly if there is a difference in the availability of refuges in the two environments. Specifically, p should be lower where the prey or hosts have access to more refuges. This refinement of the Lotka–Volterra predator–prey model anticipated recent theoretical analysis of the role that refuges and spatial diversity in general play in the persistence of predator–prey and parasite–host systems. While Lotka's analysis concentrated on physical refuges that could shelter terrestrial prey, he recognized the wide variety of forms that refuges could take. He pointed out, for instance, that flight is a refuge for birds from terrestrial predators.

Exploited Organisms and Their Wide Variety of "Refuges"

Space

Most of our discussion has focused on what we might call "spatial" refuges, places where members of the exploited population have some protection from predators and parasitoids. Many forms of spatial refuge are familiar: burrows, trees, air, water (if faced with terrestrial predators), and land (if faced with aquatic predators). However, some spatial refuges differ in subtle ways from other areas.

St. John's Wort, *Hypericum perforatum,* persists in refuges in the face of attacks by the beetle *Chrysolina quadrigemina,* one of the chief enemies of *Hypericum* in the Pacific Northwest region of the United States. *Hypericum* was introduced into areas along the Klamath River around 1900, and its population quickly grew to cover about 800,000 ha by 1944. Following the release of the beetles, the area covered by St. John's Wort was reduced to less than 1% of its maximum coverage. This remnant population of the plant was concentrated in shady habitats, where, though it grows more poorly than in sunny areas, it is protected from the beetles, which avoid shade.

Protection in Numbers

Living in a large group provides a type of refuge. Aside from the potential of social groups to intimidate would-be predators, numbers alone can reduce the probability of an individual prey or host being eaten. We can make this prediction based solely on the work of C. S. Holling (1959) on the responses of predators to prey density. Holling is a fellow of the Royal Society of Canada, and has worked at the University of British Columbia and the Department of the Environment for the Canadian Government. His research on predator–prey relationships has been central to the theoretical understanding of this ecological process. In chapter 8 we looked at the functional responses of several predators and herbivores. Briefly, predator functional response results in increasing rate of food intake as prey density increases. Eventually, however, the predator's feeding rate levels off at some maximum rate. In chapter 11, we looked at numerical response, a second component of predator response to prey density that results in increased predator density as prey density increases. As with functional response, the numerical response eventually levels off at the point where further increases in prey density no longer produce increased predator density.

Now let's put functional response and numerical response together to predict the predator's **combined response** to

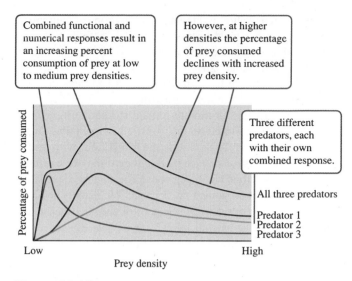

Figure 14.18   Prey density and the percentage of prey consumed due to combined functional and numerical responses (data from Holling 1959).

increased prey density. We can combine the two responses by multiplying the number of prey eaten per predator times the number of predators per unit area:

$$\frac{\text{Prey consumed}}{\text{Predator}} \times \frac{\text{Predators}}{\text{Area}} = \frac{\text{Prey consumed}}{\text{Area}}$$

By dividing the prey consumed per unit area by the population density of the prey (prey consumed/area), we can determine the percentage of the prey population consumed by the predator. If we plot percentage of the prey consumed against prey density over a broad range of prey densities, the prediction is that the percentage of the prey population consumed will be lower at high prey densities (fig. 14.18).

Why should the percentage of the prey consumed by the predator decline at high prey densities? The answer to this question, which may not be obvious at first, lies in the predator functional and numerical responses. We see this effect because both numerical and functional responses level off at intermediate prey densities; that is, beyond a certain threshold, further increases in prey density do not lead to either higher predator densities or increased feeding rates. Meanwhile, the density of the prey population continues to increase and the proportion of the prey eaten by predators declines. This work by Holling suggests that prey can reduce their individual probability of being eaten by occurring at very high densities. It appears that this defensive tactic, which is called **predator satiation,** is employed by a wide variety of organisms from insects and plants to marine invertebrates and African antelope.

Predator Satiation by an Australian Tree

A great number of plants flower and produce seeds synchronously over large areas, including bamboo, pine, beech, and oak. This phenomenon of synchronous widespread seed and fruit production is called **masting.** Daniel Janzen (1978) proposed that a major selective force favouring the production of mast crops is seed predation. You may recall Janzen from chapter 1, when we highlighted his work in tropical rainforests. He suggested that mast crops may lead to satiation of seed predators, allowing some seeds to escape predation, germinate, and successfully establish.

Many Australian trees in the genus *Eucalyptus* disperse their seeds in large numbers following forest fires. Seeds are produced each year but mostly remain stored in closed seed capsules that are retained on the tree. Following a fire, a massive, synchronized release floods the forest floor with seeds.

Synchronous seed release by *Eucalyptus* may be a defense against seed predators, but which ones? The chief seed predators in Australian forests appear to be ants. We usually think of Australia as the continent of kangaroos and koalas, but the region could be just as well known for its ants. Australia harbours a tremendous diversity of ants. For instance, while North American deserts support about 160 species of ants, the deserts of Australia contain an estimated 2,000 species and the continent as a whole may harbour nearly 4,000 species. The ants in Australian forests have been reported to prevent forest regeneration by removing up to 80% of the seeds broadcast by foresters.

D. O'Dowd and A. Gill (1984) used field experiments to determine whether synchronous seed dispersal by *Eucalyptus* might be a means to reduce seed losses to ants. They set up study plots in two forests of Australian alpine ash, *Eucalyptus delgatensis,* a gigantic tree found in the Australian Alps and Tasmania, where it commonly grows to 50 to 60 m in height. One of the study sites was to serve as a reference site and the second as an experimental site. *E. delgatensis* constituted nearly 90% of the tree biomass at both study sites. The researchers monitored a number of physical and biological variables at the control and experimental sites and then set a controlled high-intensity fire at the experimental site. The area burned was approximately 98 ha; 93% of the trees were killed.

The results of O'Dowd and Gill's field experiments support their hypothesis that synchronous seed dispersal by *Eucalyptus* reduces losses of seeds to ants. As expected, the fire stimulated the release of massive numbers of seeds. During the three weeks following the fire, seed fall was approximately 405 fertile seeds per square meter, compared with a peak seed fall of 10 seeds per square meter per week at the control site, which was not burned. The fire also seemed to stimulate ant activity. Prior to the fire, researchers trapped an average of 176 ants belonging to 14 species each week. After the fire, the number of ants trapped each week rose to an average of 680 individuals belonging to 23 species. Despite this strong numerical response, the rate at which ants removed seeds dropped following the fire. The rate of seed removal from seed trays at the experimental site dropped from an average of about 65% per week during the five weeks prior to the fire to an average of about 14% per week during the five weeks following the fire. This result is consistent with the predator satiation hypothesis proposed by O'Dowd and Gill and is consistent with Holling's prediction of reduced predator combined response at high prey densities.

So, what does O'Dowd and Gill's experiment tell us? We know that *E. delgatensis* stores seeds in closed seed capsules, that these seeds are released synchronously following intense

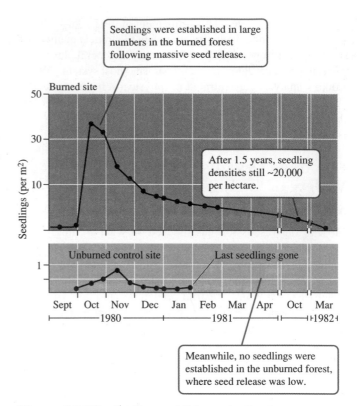

Figure 14.19   Seedling establishment by Eucalyptus delgatensis at burned and unburned sites (data from O'Dowd and Gill 1984).

fires, and that a substantial proportion of these seeds escape predation even in the face of strong numerical response by seed-eating ants. Is this information sufficient to conclude that the apparent predator satiation strategy of *E. delgatensis* provides an effective "refuge" from predation? It seems that we should also know whether greater seed survival is translated into greater seedling establishment, an evolutionary bottom line. O'Dowd and Gill also showed that seedling establishment was greater on the burned experimental plot than on the control plot (fig. 14.19). About 1.5 years after the experimental fire, seedling survival at the experimental site was approximately two individuals per square meter, or 20,000 individuals per hectare. This seems a respectable level of reproductive success for trees that could eventually reach 50 to 60 m in height. Predator satiation also provides protection to many kinds of insects, but nowhere is this more apparent than among the cicadas.

Predator Satiation by Periodical Cicadas

Periodical cicadas, *Magicicada* spp., emerge as adults once every 13 years in the southern part of their range in North America and once every 17 years in the northern part of their range. Though these insects emerge only once every 13 or 17 years in any particular area, virtually every year sees a brood emerging somewhere in eastern North America. An emergence of periodical cicadas produces a sudden flush of singing insects whose density can approach 4×10^6 individuals per hectare, which translates into a biomass of 1,900 to 3,700 kg of cicadas per hectare, the highest biomass of a natural population of terrestrial animals ever recorded.

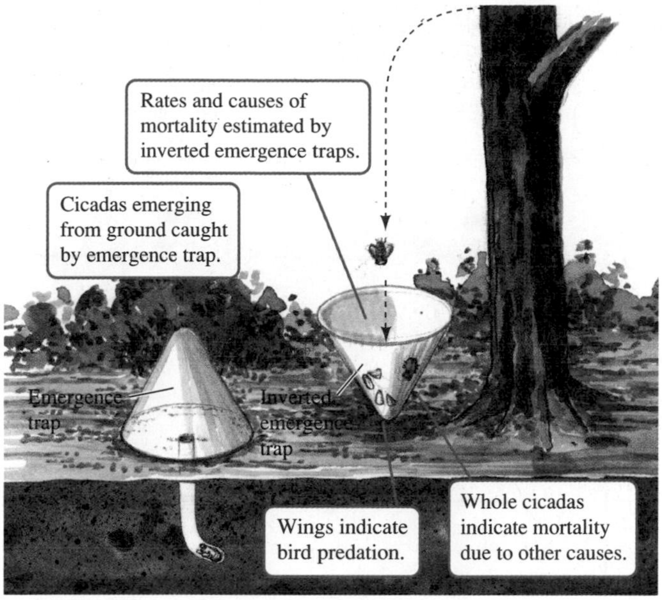

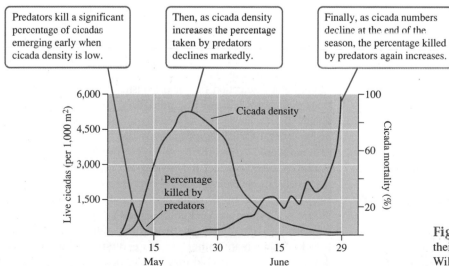

Figure 14.20 Estimating cicada population size and predation rates by birds.

Periodical cicadas are insects of the order Homoptera, which includes the leafhoppers and aphids. Like their relatives, cicadas make their living by sucking the fluids of plants and spend either 13 or 17 years of their life as nymphs underground, where they feed on the xylem fluids in roots. When mature, nymphs dig their way to the soil surface, where they shed their nymphal skin and emerge as winged adults. Among periodical cicadas this emergence is so synchronized that millions of adults emerge over a period of only a few days. Following emergence males fly to the treetops, where they sing the mating songs to which females are attracted. After they mate, females lay their eggs in living twigs of shrubs and trees. When the nymphs hatch in about six weeks, they immediately drop to the ground and burrow down to a root, where they begin to feed, moving around very little for the next 13 or 17 years. A mass emergence of periodical cicadas, one of the most memorable biological phenomena nature has to offer, appears aimed at predator satiation.

Kathy Williams and her colleagues (1993) tested the effectiveness of predator satiation in a population of 13-year periodical cicadas in northwest Arkansas. They monitored emergence of cicadas using conical emergence traps constructed of plastic mesh and inverted their traps to measure predation rates (fig. 14.20). Nymphs emerging from the ground below the traps could be counted to estimate the numbers of emerging nymphs. Then, as adult cicadas died from a variety of factors, including physical factors, senescence, and pathogens, they fell from the trees to the ground, where some were caught in the inverted traps. Because the major predators were birds, predation rates could be estimated because birds discard the wings of cicadas as they feed upon them. The wings falling into the inverted traps gave an estimate of predation rates.

Patterns of mortality and predation rates relative to population size support the predator satiation hypothesis. Williams and her colleagues estimated that 1,063,000 cicadas emerged from their 16 ha study site and that 50% of these emerged during four consecutive nights. Cicada abundance peaked in late May and then declined rapidly during the first two weeks of June. Part of this decline was due to mortality from severe thunderstorms during the first week of June. Figure 14.21 shows that losses due to birds were low throughout the period of peak cicada abundance and then climbed to 100% as cicada populations declined during June. These results indicate that the predator satiation tactic was sufficiently effective to reduce cicada losses to birds to only 15% of the total population.

Size as a Refuge

We first encountered size-selective predation in chapter 7 among bluegills, *Lepomis macrochirus,* and pumas, *Felis concolor.* However, many other organisms select their prey by size. In fact, average prey size shows a significant correlation with predator size across taxa ranging from lizards to small mammals. The reason for size selective predation among such a diverse array of organisms is that prey capture and consumption are mechanical problems, and as we saw in chapter 7, size can influence the time required to handle prey and therefore the rate of energy intake. The bottom line is that for a given

Figure 14.21 Cicada population density and their percent mortality due to predation (data from Williams, Smith, and Stephan 1993).

Figure 14.22 Large size can provide a refuge from predators. While young African elephants may be vulnerable to predation by African lions, mature elephants are not.

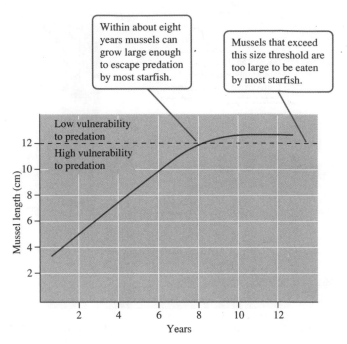

Figure 14.24 Growth by mussels in an intertidal area from which the sea star, *Pisaster ochraceus*, was excluded (data from Paine 1976).

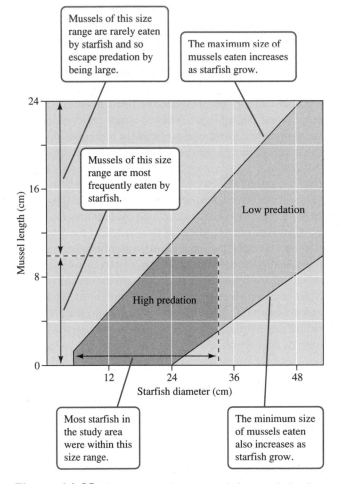

Figure 14.23 Large mussels are eaten infrequently by the sea star *Pisaster ochraceus* (data from Paine 1976).

predator some prey are simply too large to be profitable and so are not attacked.

Now let's look at size from the perspective of the prey. If large individuals are ignored by predators, then large size may offer a form of refuge. An obvious example is on the African savanna. While a variety of predators may attack the calves of elephants or rhinoceros, the same predators avoid the adults,

which have been observed to kill adult lions (fig. 14.22). On a smaller scale, Robert Paine (1976) found that the sea star *Pisaster ochraceus* does not consume the largest individuals in populations of one of its chief prey species, the mussel *Mytilus californianus*. Figure 14.23 shows that the maximum size of mussels eaten by sea stars is a function of sea star size. Notice that most of the successful predation observed by Paine involved small- to medium-sized sea stars attacking mussels less than 11 cm long. Most sea stars cannot eat the largest mussels, and the largest sea stars that can were limited to a few areas of coastline in the study area. What this means is that if a mussel can manage to escape predation long enough to reach 10 to 12 cm in length, it will be immune from attack by most sea stars. When Paine removed the sea stars from an area of the intertidal zone, resident mussels survived at higher rates and therefore grew to a larger average size (fig. 14.24). When Paine allowed sea stars to recolonize the area, many of the mussels were large enough that they effectively escaped predation by sea stars. This result has implications that reach far beyond higher survival within a single prey population.

If predators pass up prey above a particular size threshold, might natural selection favour organisms that project a "large" body size to some would-be predators? It appears that some aquatic insects have been selected to do just that. Barbara Peckarsky (1980, 1982) observed that mayflies in the family Ephemerellidae would "stand their ground" in the face of a foraging predatory stonefly. In fact, they would not only stand their ground, they would curve their abdomens over their backs and point the tips of their abdominal cerci into the face and antennae of a stonefly, a behaviour Peckarsky called a "scorpion" posture (fig. 14.25). Usually a stonefly greeted in this way does not attack. While many other stream ecologists had seen this behaviour in ephemerellid mayflies, Peckarsky was the first to

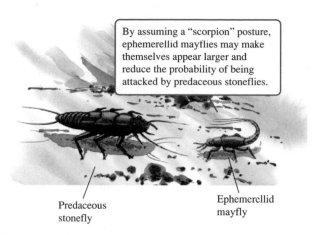

By assuming a "scorpion" posture, ephemerellid mayflies may make themselves appear larger and reduce the probability of being attacked by predaceous stoneflies.

Predaceous stonefly

Ephemerellid mayfly

Figure 14.25 Posturing by an ephemerellid mayfly confronted by a predaceous stonefly.

suggest that the scorpion posture was a defensive tactic in which the mayfly projected a larger image to a tactile, size-selective predator.

Why should a large stonefly avoid large ephemerellid mayflies? Large ephemerellids have been observed attacking stoneflies trying to prey on them, and so like lions that avoid rhinoceros, stoneflies that avoid ephemerellids may be protecting themselves from injury. Most ephemerellids, however, present no danger to large predaceous stoneflies, so self-protection only partially answers our question. For the bulk of encounters between stoneflies and ephemerellid mayflies, large apparent size would probably indicate low profitability, low E/T in terms of optimal foraging theory (see chapter 7), and send the predator looking for a prey that would yield a higher energy return. It may be that the display by ephemerellids is not a bluff, however, since they require an exceptionally long handling time for a prey of their size. The scorpion posture of ephemerellids may be a case of "truth in advertising." As you will see in the next section, organisms possess a variety of mechanisms of defense against predators and herbivores.

Concept 14.3 Review

1. O'Dowd and Gill demonstrated that the release of large numbers of seeds by *Eucalyptus delgatensis* allows a substantial number of seeds to escape predation by ants. Is this information sufficient to conclude that the apparent predator satiation of *Eucalyptus delgatensis* provides an effective "refuge" from ant predation?
2. Why should a large predaceous stonefly avoid ephemerellid mayflies that assume a scorpion posture to project a large appearance?
3. Why should there be strong selection on periodical cicadas for highly synchronous emergence?

14.4   Mechanisms of Defense

The impacts of exploitation of host and prey have resulted in a variety of defenses that increase their ability to avoid attack. We have seen how herbivory and predation can have

significant consequences for the population dynamics of the host and prey species. These in turn can result in feedbacks that alter the predator and herbivore populations themselves. Refuges serve as an important mechanism by which predators and herbivores are unable to fully exploit their prey and host populations. However, there is another equally important mechanism that reduces the efficiency of predation and herbivory: evolution by natural selection.

Prey and host are not passive creatures that simply exist to be eaten by others. Instead, these organisms are subject to natural selection, just like every other living thing on this planet. If being eaten reduces the reproductive output and/or survival of an organism, there will obviously be selection for traits that result in the individual either being less likely to be eaten (resistance) or, that reduce the harm associated with being eaten (tolerance). For example, imagine there is a caterpillar that can eat only one species of plant. When it finds the plant, it will consume a large portion of the leaves, reducing the plant's photosynthetic capacity and potential to produce seeds. Some aspects of this plant–animal interaction are likely related to genotype, and with genetic variation in the plant population, there can be variation in this association. Some plants may produce a toxin that reduces feeding, others may grow smaller and be harder to find, others may produce leaves of low nutritive value, decreasing the cost of replacement. These are examples of possible adaptations that increase the resistance to exploitation or increase the ability of the organism to tolerate exploitation. As you might recognize, these changes would then have impacts on the herbivore, potentially resulting in a co-evolutionary response (See Ecological Tools).

In this section we will discuss common mechanisms of defense in plants and animals. We will also discuss some evolutionary consequences of long-term predator–prey and herbivore–host relationships, further demonstrating that ecological interactions have the potential to profoundly alter species, populations, and communities.

Animal Display

Most prey species are masters of defense, one of the most basic means of which is camouflage. Quite simply, predators can not eat prey they can not find. The efficiency of this defense can be astounding, as shown by Bernd Heinrich (1984) in a study of predatory bald-faced hornets. The hornets hunt other insects by flying rapidly among the plants in their environment and pouncing on objects that may be prey. Because their prey are well camouflaged, the hornets often pounce on inanimate objects. Heinrich was able to observe 260 pounces by hornets. About 70% of these were directed at inanimate objects, such as bird droppings and brown spots on leaves. Another 20% were directed at insects, such as bumblebees and other wasps, insects too well defended to be prey. Only 7% of the pounces were on potential insect prey! The hornets managed to capture two of these, a moth and a fly. Heinrich's observations indicate bald-faced hornets have a prey capture rate of less than 1%!

Not all prey species are hidden to predators, and instead many prey are coloured to be extremely visually apparent. This can be seen in the striking colours displayed by many butterflies,

(a)

(b)

Figure 14.26   Poisonous Müllerian (*a*) and nonpoisonous Batesian (*b*) mimics.

snakes, and nudibranchs. How can prey persist with such colouration? Many of these animals are toxic. Prey that carry a threat to predators often advertise that fact, usually by being brightly coloured or conspicuous in some other way. The conspicuous colours, or **aposematic colouration**, of many distasteful or toxic animals warn predators that "feeding on me may be hazardous to your health." However, such a signal is not perfect. For example, one of the authors of this text (J.C.) enjoyed catching butterflies as a young boy. I recall well the bright sunny day that I decided the Monarch just looked so beautiful that I promptly licked its wings for a taste. Needless to say, the Monarch was advertising truthfully: its colouration is associated with a variety of foul tasting compounds. Lest you think that I am the sole potential predator of species with aposematic colouration, many predatory species need to learn to associate colouration with toxicity. Only for a subset of species is this "knowledge" an innate trait of the species. The curious predator is not the only potential threat to species with warning colouration.

In **Batesian mimicry**, a perfectly harmless (nontoxic) species will exhibit colouration similar to that of a noxious species that lives in the same area. For example, king snakes mimic the poisonous coral snakes, Viceroy butterflies mimic the noxious Monarch butterfly, and syphid flies mimic stinging bees. Batesian mimics elude predation not through the actual ability to defend themselves from attack, but instead by using the learned (and innate) abilities of predators to associate harm with particular colours and patterns. What do you imagine might happen if in a given community the frequency of mimics exceeds the frequency of actually toxic models?

Müllerian mimicry is also common, and can enhance the learning by potential predators associated with aposematic colouration. Müllerian mimics are *all* toxic/noxious, and share similar colouration. For example, you may have noticed that many stinging flies, wasps, and bees, three distantly related groups of taxa, have superficially similar appearances that include yellow and black stripes. These are Müllerian mimics. One likely advantage of similar colouration is that potential predators are likely to encounter toxic/noxious organisms with similar colouration more frequently than if only one species has such colouration. As a result, it is thought that Müllerian mimicry systems enhance the rate at which predators learn to associate a particular colour/pattern with risk, thereby reducing predation risk for these species. However, you may have noticed that some flies share the same colouration, yet do not sting. These are Batesian mimics of Müllerian mimics!

Plant Defenses

Although aposematic colouration is widespread among animals, it is generally absent among plants (with possible exceptions of some fruits and seeds). Why don't plants colour their leaves to warn herbivores? The most obvious explanation is that plants use chlorophyll to absorb most of the light used in photosynthesis, and this pigment reflects green light, absorbing reds and blues. To reduce chlorophyll content would reduce photosynthetic capacity, likely causing a greater loss of fitness than would be experienced by some degree of herbivory. However, just because plants don't use colouration as a warning doesn't mean that they are just sitting there waiting to be eaten. In fact, many plants are simply bad food for many animals.

We have already discussed how plants have high C:N ratios (chapter 7), decreasing their nutritive value. Many plants also employ a variety of morphological defenses, such as thorns, which deter herbivores (fig. 14.27). Why do thorns reduce herbivory? These small defenses are non-lethal, and are simply an irritant rather than a real risk to the large herbivores which they generally deter. As we discussed previously (chapter 7), animals generally engage in some sort of optimal foraging. To eat a thorny plant, the animal will need to move its head and body more precisely, which slows down the rate of feeding. It may be more energetically advantageous for the animal to keep walking and find a less prickly bush than to stop walking and feed slowly. In other words, thorns work as defenses because plants are able to use animal behaviour to their own advantage. Did you really think plants just sat back and took whatever came to them?

Figure 14.27 Herbivores must overcome the wide variety of physical and chemical defenses evolved by plants.

Although morphological defenses are widespread among plants, plants also contain a variety of chemical defenses that can be roughly divided as (1) toxins, and (2) digestion-reducing substances. Toxins are chemicals that kill, impair, or repel most would-be herbivores. The compounds are widely used by humans as medicines, and include such compounds as cocaine, morphine, digitalis, and others. Digestion-reducing substances are generally phenolic compounds such as tannins, that bind to plant proteins, inhibiting their breakdown by digestive enzymes and further reducing the value of plants as food for the hungry herbivore. Humans are familiar with tannins as the bitter taste one gets when eating an unripe banana, or as the dark colouration in the morning cup of Earl Grey tea.

Chemists have isolated thousands of toxins from plant tissues, and the list continues to grow. The great variety of plant toxins defies easy description and generalization. However, one interesting pattern is that more tropical plants contain toxic alkaloids than their temperate counterparts. Despite these higher levels of chemical defense, herbivores appear to remove approximately 11%–48% of leaf biomass in tropical forests, while only about 7% in temperate forests. These higher levels of herbivore attack on tropical plants suggest that natural selection for chemical defense is more intense in tropical plant populations. However, clearly no defense is perfect.

Plant chemical defenses often work against some herbivores, but not all. The tobacco plant uses nicotine, a toxic alkaloid, to repel herbivorous insects, most of which die immediately upon ingestion (really, this stuff isn't good for you!).

However, several insects specialize in eating tobacco plants and manage to avoid the toxic effects of nicotine (no, humans do not fall into this group of specialist insects). Some of these insects simply excrete nicotine, while others convert it to non-toxic molecules. Similarly, toxins and repellents produced by plants in the cucumber family repel most herbivorous insects but attract the spotted cucumber beetle. This beetle is a specialist that feeds mainly on members of the cucumber family. Some specialized herbivores go even further by using plant toxins as a source of nutrition. Even more amazing is that some species, such as the Monarch butterfly and the dogbane leaf beetle, are able to sequester plant toxins, using these as chemical deterrents against predation!

As we have seen with competition and foraging, plants are able to alter their physiology and morphology in response to changes in their environment, such as the deposition of a nutrient patch or the presence of a competitor. Plants show similar plasticity in response to herbivores. Many morphological and chemical defenses are **constitutive defenses**, produced continuously, independent of what happens to a plant. Many, however, are also **induced defenses**, where concentrations of defensive chemicals increase rapidly in response to the first indication of herbivore damage. Such induced defenses make sense in the context of the theory of allocation, where allocating energy and limited resources to defenses when insects are not around seems maladaptive. It seems likely that the benefit of producing constitutive or induced defenses will depend upon the likelihood of a plant being attacked.

The world may appear green to us, but to herbivores only some shades of green are edible. Plant defenses and the adaptations of herbivores that overcome those defenses are complex. In the next section, we will explore how scientists are beginning to understand the evolutionary consequences of this widespread ecological interaction.

Concept 14.4 Review

1. Plants can possess traits that make them resistant to herbivores, or tolerant of herbivory. Are the same plant traits likely to confer both of these abilities? Why?
2. What advantage do animals gain from aposematic colouration? What advantages may arise from induced, rather than constitutive defenses?
3. What is the difference between Batesian and Müllerian mimics?

Ecological Tools

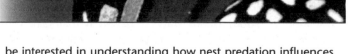

Evolution and Exploitation

Research in ecology can take place at a variety of spatial and temporal scales. At the shortest and smallest scales might be an ecologist interested in understanding which predator consumes the eggs of nesting birds in a single field. Another ecologist may

be interested in understanding how nest predation influences population dynamics. At an even broader scale may be a study showing how nest predation and egg production vary across a landscape. At a deeper time scale may be the evolutionary ecologist studying how predation alters selective pressures on nesting birds, resulting in evolutionary shifts in nesting strategy.

At an even broader scale may be the scientist trying to understand how evolutionary shifts in nesting strategies could cause an evolutionary shift in foraging practices of a predator. Seemingly simple ecological questions can be addressed in a variety of ways using a diversity of research tools.

In this section we focus on aspects of the evolutionary ecology of exploitation. We will show how by studying interactions over longer time scales new insights about interactions emerge. It is difficult to understand the ecology of exploitation without also understanding its evolutionary causes and consequences, and thus sometimes significant advances come not through the development of a new research technology, but instead through the adoption of different conceptual approaches to a single research question. Specifically, we will discuss two issues related to exploitation (1) does exploitation place selective pressures on organisms, and (2) how do prolonged periods of exploitation alter evolutionary trajectories? In these studies, you will see how molecular methods can enhance an ecologist's ability to answer research questions.

Selection

Does predation cause selective pressure and evolutionary responses in prey populations? The answer to this question is dependent upon a variety of factors. For example, is predation common or rare within a population? If rare, then few individuals will likely experience predation risk and thus it would be difficult for predation to cause an evolutionary response. If it is common, then there is the possibility for natural selection to favour genotypes that are either better protected or better able to avoid predation, and evolution could occur. If predation is extremely strong, it may be possible for evolution to not only occur, but to occur rapidly. Showing evolutionary change requires being able to measure the genotypic composition of a population over several generations. For slow-growing species, generation times can be on the order of decades, and thus it isn't practical for a single researcher to actually document evolutionary shifts in ecological time scales. However, for fast-growing species, ecologists may be able to observe many generations within a single year, and thus studies documenting evolutionary shifts in response to predation are possible.

Justin Meyer, now of the University of Ottawa, and colleagues at Cornell University tested the evolutionary effects of predation using rotifer-algal microcosms as their experimental system (fig. 14.28). **Microcosms** are small models of natural systems that allow experimental manipulation. Meyer and his colleagues use a particular type of microcosm, called a *chemostat*, that allows for continuous population growth of small-bodied organisms, such as the algae and rotifers used here (Meyer et al. 2006). Chemostats are generally maintained at constant temperatures and nutrient levels, and consist of glass beakers or vials that allow for flow-through of waste and nutrients. These microcosms are obviously poor approximations of the complexity of the natural world, however, their strength as research tools lies in their ability to let researchers focus on very specific questions. In this case, Meyer was able to address

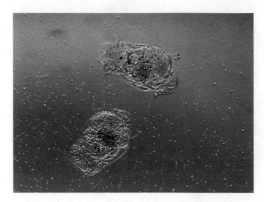

Figure 14.28   The rotifer, *Brachionus calyciflorus*, is a large predator that consumes the smaller algae, *Chlorella vulgaris*.

the impact of predation on algal evolution, independent of changes in nutrients and population growth rates.

Meyer chose a single predatory rotifer, *Brachionus calyciflorus*, and a single algal species, *Chlorella vulgaris* as focal species. The rotifer is considered a predator, as it consumes the entire single-celled algae. Because Meyer was interested in understanding evolution, it was critical that he be able to show shifts in gene frequencies of the algal population over time. To do this, he used nine distinct strains of the algae, each of which he was able to distinguish using microsatellite markers (chapter 4). The experimental design was rather straightforward: Meyer placed two of the algal strains in the chemostat, added the rotifer, and then sampled the populations daily. The results were dramatic. After 30 days of predation, the algal populations consisted almost exclusively of only one of the two clones, even though both were present at the start (Fig. 14.29). This is a shift in gene frequency within a population, and this is evolution. But why did this happen? Why did one clone consistently outperform the other in the presence of this predator?

There appears to be a trade-off in the competitive ability of these algal clones when grown without predation, and their ability to defend against predation. Those clones that grew fastest when alone, grew slowest when a rotifer was present. Such a trade-off makes sense in the view of the theory of allocation (chapter 7), where allocation to one ecological ability (e.g., competitive ability), likely results in less energy available for allocation to other traits (e.g., defense). The trade-off may also exist if morphological defenses to predation harden cell walls or have some other physical effect of possible growth rates. What was the nature of the defense? Both clones were consumed with equal frequency by the rotifers, indicating the "defended" clone did not deter predation. Instead, the defended clone had a much higher probability of still being alive after passage through the rotifer gut than did the "competitive" clone. In other words, the competitive clone was digested when consumed, while the defended clone was not. This is a fairly effective defense against predation! It may come as no surprise that the clone that dominated the populations after 30 days of predation was the "defended" clone, while the "competitive" clone neared extinction when grown with the predator.

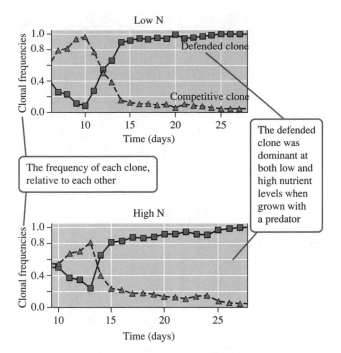

Figure 14.29 Changes in relative frequency of two clones of algae in the presence of a predatory rotifer.

Meyer's study is an example of how strong levels of predation can cause rapid evolution. In this case, one genotype nearly went extinct after only 30 days of predation. This example also highlights the role that trade-offs can play in maintaining genetic diversity and thus altering ecological interactions. One might expect areas lacking rotifers to be dominated by competitive algal lines, while areas with rotifers to be dominated by well-defended clones. However, this evolutionary response by the prey should impact the predators too. Clearly, a rotifer that is unable to digest its prey will be at a selective disadvantage relative to a rotifer that is able to overcome this prey defense. In this next section, we explore these potential evolutionary feedbacks.

Evolutionary Dynamics

Coevolution

As we can see from Meyer's example, predators can cause evolution in prey. If this can cause a reciprocal evolutionary response in the predator populations, this would be an example of coevolution. The study of coevolution in exploitative relationships has been an active area of research for evolutionary ecologists. At the base of this research lie two alternative models for coevolution: Red Queen and Stable Cycling.

Red Queen

In 1973, Leigh van Valen suggested that over geological time, the probability of a taxonomic family going extinct does not change. This finding was a bit surprising, as we know that there is substantial evolution occurring within families over this timescale, and yet there appears to be no "improvement"

in the extinction levels with time. This finding highlights the fact that evolution is not directional, nor does it reach an end state. Instead, natural selection is a continuous process. Van Valen viewed species interactions as analogous to an "evolutionary arms race" in which all members are actively changing (through evolution), with each adaptation leading to a counter-adaptation. The idea of an evolutionary arms race was named the "Red Queen Hypothesis" by van Valen, after the line from Lewis Carroll's book, *Through the Looking Glass* in which the Red Queen says "It takes all the running you can do, to keep in the same place." This has been applied extensively to predator–prey and herbivore–host dynamics, suggesting that the reason there hasn't been a "winner" to these exploitative interactions is because both participants are involved in a complex coevolutionary dance.

One prediction of the Red Queen hypothesis is that prey/plant defenses and predator/herbivore countermeasures should become increasingly sophisticated and complex over evolutionary times. The idea is of an arms race, and it is likely not by chance that this terminology was coined during the cold war between the United States and the Soviet Union. Although there are examples supporting the idea of an arms race for some exploitative interactions, there are other examples where no such escalation occurs. Does this mean coevolution is not occurring? Not necessarily. John Thompson (1994) has presented an alternative model for coevolution, one based on *stable cycling*, rather than escalation, of the phenotypes of the interacting species.

Stable Cycling

At the heart of stable cycling is frequency dependent selection (chapter 4), and the idea that different populations will have different dominant genotypes, resulting in a *geographic mosaic* of the genotypes and phenotypes of the interacting species across the species' distributions. In general the argument for stable cycling is that some defenses and countermeasures will be controlled by single genes. For instance, a given allele may cause a particular shape and toxicity of a certain plant chemical defense, while a different allele may cause a different shape and toxicity. The ability of an insect to detoxify a particular compound may be dependent upon having the allele that produces the correct detoxification enzyme for the particular plant defense that it experiences. For example, let's suppose the plant toxin produced by the allele T_1 at the T locus could be detoxified by the insect enzyme produced by the allele E_1 at the E locus.

Now suppose that all plants in a population had the same allele, T_1, and that there were different genotypes of herbivores that had enzymes that ranged from E_1–E_5. What should happen to gene frequencies in the population of the herbivore? Natural selection should favour those herbivores that have E_1, as they will be able to eat the plant. But let's not stop here. If this happens, this means that the herbivore population will soon become full of individuals that are E_1, which means that nearly every herbivore would be able to eat this plant. What should now happen to the plant population? Well, any new mutant that produces any other form of the defense, perhaps

T_2, will be at a selective advantage and increase in frequency. This in turn reduces the fitness of herbivores that have E_1, and increases that of those with E_2. As you can see, this can go on forever. What is most important is that this is coevolution without escalation. This process can occur independently in each population of the plant and herbivore, such that across the landscape there is a mosaic of dominant phenotypes in each population.

These ideas are supported by a variety of field and lab studies, showing that there will not be a "single" answer to how coevolution works in natural systems. Instead, these insights from evolution help ecologists understand that exploitative interactions are dynamic. We end this section by looking at a slightly deeper time-scale, asking what could happen if exploitative interactions continue to exist for many generations.

Speciation

Although only a fraction of insect species are described in science, a current estimate suggests that there are around 5–10 million insects, with perhaps 35%–40% of these being plant-eating, or **phytophagous**, species (Ødegaard 2000). The number of phytophagous insect species alone is greater than the total number of birds, fish, and mammal species combined (9,000 species of birds, 20,000 species of fish, and 4,500 species of mammals). This level of diversity has led many researchers to wonder whether there was something about the herbivore–host interaction that could cause such high levels of diversity. Of particular interest was the realization that although many insects were **generalists**, feeding upon a diverse set of host plants, other species were **specialists**, feeding upon a more restricted diet—perhaps limited to even a single plant species. Could this specialization lead to speciation?

When people began to explore this issue, it soon became apparent that a single species of insect could form **host races**, genetically distinct subpopulations that are differentiated as a function of the host species. For example, *Rhagoletis pomonella*, the apple maggot, forms two main host races. One of these feeds upon the common apple, while a second feeds upon a related species, the hawthorn. Such differentiation may be the first step in the evolution of isolating mechanisms that could lead to sympatric speciation (chapter 4). What is unclear, however, is how common such differentiation is among herbivores. Unfortunately, broad surveys of large numbers of species have not yet been conducted, and there is not yet enough information to make a conclusive statement. However, Steve Heard at the University of New Brunswick and colleagues in Iowa used a different approach, leading them to conclude that host differentiation may, in fact, cause the levels of diversity we see.

Heard and colleagues decided to address this question in a novel way (Stireman, Nason, and Heard 2005). Rather than focus in-depth on a single insect species, they instead chose two common host plants (*Solidago altissima* and *S. gigantea*), and looked at many of the herbivore species that feed upon these plants. These two plant species are ideal for such a study, as they are found growing together over most of southern

(a)

(b)

(c)

Figure 14.30   (*a*) Adult moths oviposit within stems of *Solidago*, forming (*b*) galls. (*c*) Within the galls are the developing larvae of the moths.

Canada and the United States, and thus there is substantial opportunity for host-race formation. They found nine common herbivores, which include leaf-feeding beetles and gall-forming midges, flies, and moths (fig. 14.30). To test for divergence, they collected insects from both plant species throughout much of Canada and the United States. They flash froze the insects in the field, allowing them to later sequence segments of mitochondrial DNA. Divergence was then estimated by looking at the differences in sequences for a given species as a function of its two hosts. In other words, was a particular insect species genetically homogeneous or genetically distinct across the two plant species?

They found that four of their nine insect species showed evidence of genetic divergence among host plants. This high number supports the idea that variation among host species can lead to genetic specialization, which could be the first step towards speciation. In a follow-up study, the authors show that such differentiation is not limited to the plant and herbivore, but can also extend to the parasitoids of the herbivores (Stireman et al. 2006). They again sampled a broad geographic range, this time focusing exclusively on the common gall-forming insects of these plant species. Many of these insects will themselves serve as host to a variety of parasitoid species. Again using genetic analysis, Heard and his colleagues were able to show that the parasitoid populations themselves were genetically differentiated as a function of the plant species their host insect was feeding upon, even though the parasitoid had no direct interactions with the plant itself! They suggest that host-race formation can cascade to these top predators, potentially contributing to increased diversity for them as well.

The studies by Heard and colleagues leave many questions unanswered, such as what about the other 100 species of insects that feed on these plants? What are the mechanisms?

When did this occur? Heard and colleagues readily acknowledge their study is not the end to the story, but instead just the beginning. Continued research by them, and by the next generation of ecologists, will lead to more answers, and of course, even more questions. By combining ecology, evolution, field work, and genetic analysis, details of exploitation are being unveiled that could never before be seen.

Summary

Predator–prey and host–herbivore interactions are two common forms of exploitation that occur among species. These interactions increase the fitness of one member at the expense of the other, and can have significant consequences on population dynamics and evolutionary trajectories.

Predation and herbivory are common ecological interactions, influencing the distribution, abundance, and structure of prey and host populations. Exploitative interactions are a fact of life for the majority of species on the planet. These generally have negative consequences for the consumed and positive benefits for the consumer. However, light grazing by geese can cause overcompensation in a subarctic salt marsh, while heavy grazing by the same geese can cause reductions in plant growth. Predation by wolves contributes to reduced moose population growth rates, though this interacts with variation in food supply. Herbivorous stream insects have been shown to control the density of their algal and bacterial food.

Predator–prey and herbivore–host relationships are dynamic. Populations of a wide variety of predators and prey show highly dynamic fluctuations in abundance ranging from days to decades. A particularly well-studied example of predator–prey cycles is that of snowshoe hares and their predators, which have been shown to result from the combined effects of the snowshoe hares on the food and of the predators on the snowshoe hare population. Mathematical models of predator–prey interaction by Lotka and Volterra suggest that exploitative interactions themselves can produce population cycles without any influences from outside forces such as weather. Predator–prey cycles have also been observed in a few laboratory populations under restricted circumstances.

To persist in the face of exploitation, hosts and prey need refuges. The refuges that promote the persistence of hosts and prey include secure places to which the exploiter has limited access. However, living in large groups can be considered as a kind of refuge since it reduces the probability that an individual host or prey will be attacked. It appears that predator satiation is a defensive tactic used by a wide variety of organisms from rain forest trees to temperate insects. Growing to large size can also represent a kind of refuge when the prey species is faced by size-selective predators. Size is used as a refuge by prey species ranging from stream insects and intertidal invertebrates to the rhinoceros.

The impacts of exploitation of host and prey have resulted in a variety of defenses that increase their ability to avoid attack. Two main strategies for prey defense are resistance and tolerance. Resistance can include camouflage, toxicity, and spines. Tolerance can include the ability to regrow tissues following consumption and protection from digestion. Many animal species are Batesian mimics, in which they display the warning colouration that is associated with a toxic model species. Other animal species are Müllerian mimics, in which there has been convergence towards a common warning colouration for unrelated toxic species, such as the black and yellow stripes of stinging insects. Plants often contain numerous morphological and chemical defenses that can deter feeding or cause illness in the herbivore if consumed. Some of these defenses will be constitutive, while others will be induced following an attack.

Exploitative interactions can cause evolution in the prey species. For example, predatory rotifers caused an algal population to consist primarily of well-defended genotypes, even though these genotypes grew more slowly when the predators were absent. These evolutionary changes can also influence the predator species, resulting in coevolution. The Red Queen hypothesis and Stable Cycling are two models of coevolution regularly used to describe exploitative relationships. Populations of herbivores can become genetically subdivided if they feed upon multiple host species. This could be the first step towards sympatric speciation, and may contribute to the large number of phytophagous insect species that exist on the planet.

Review Questions

1. Predation is one of the processes by which one organism exploits another. Others are herbivory, parasitism, and disease. What distinguishes each of these processes, including predation, from the others? We can justify discussing these varied processes under the heading of exploitation because each involves one organism making its living at the expense of another. By what "currency" would you measure that expense (e.g., energy, fitness)?

2. Researchers have suggested that predators could actually increase the population density of a prey species heavily infected by a pathogenic parasite (Hudson, Dobson, and Newborn 1992). Explain how predation could lead to population increases in the prey population.

3. Explain the roles of food and predators in producing cycles of abundance in populations of snowshoe hare. Populations of many of the predators that feed on snowshoe hares also cycle substantially. Explain population cycles among these predator populations.

4. What contributions have laboratory and mathematical models made to our understanding of predator–prey population cycles? What are the shortcomings of these modelling approaches? What are their advantages?

5. We included spatial refuges, predator satiation, and size in our discussions of the role played by refuges in the persistence of exploited species. How could time act as a refuge? Explain how natural selection could lead to the evolution of temporal "refuges."

Joseph Culp and Gary Scrimgeour (1993) studied the timing of feeding by mayfly larvae in streams with and without fish. These mayflies feed by grazing on the exposed surfaces of stones, where they are vulnerable to predation by fish, which in the streams studied are size-selective feeders and feed predominantly during the day. In the study streams without fish, both small and large mayflies have a slight tendency to feed during the day but feed at all hours of the day and night. In the streams with abundant fish populations, small mayflies fed around the clock, while large mayflies fed mainly at night. Explain these patterns in terms of time as a refuge and size-selective predation.

6. The growth of all populations must be controlled by some factor. What factors are potentially limiting to population growth? How can ecologists figure out which factors are operating on a particular population at any given point in time?

7. Batesian mimics confer an advantage from the toxicity of the model species, yet do not incur any of the energetic costs associated with the actual production of the toxic chemical. Why do the Batesian model species allow this to happen?

8. Having induced, rather than constitutive, plant defenses seems like a very cost-effective mechanism to protect oneself against attack. However, many plant species contain constitutive defenses. Why?

9. Snow geese can cause changes in the growth of their food plants, either positive or negative depending upon the intensity of grazing. When grazing is most severe, a variety of low-growing moss species become dominant. Why aren't these moss species dominant when grazing is light? How can grazing alter competitive interactions among these plant species?

10. Ecological interactions, such as exploitation, can have significant evolutionary consequences, such as host-race formation. To understand this, it is critical that researchers be able to blend techniques from different disciplines, such as evolutionary biology and ecology. Are ecology and evolution truly distinct disciplines, or do they look at similar questions, but in different time scales?

Suggested Readings

Lamberti, G. A. and V. H. Resh. 1983. Stream periphyton and insect herbivores: an experimental study of grazing by a caddisfly population. *Ecology* 64:1124–35.

A classic field experiment that reveals the controlling influence of a benthic invertebrate grazer on a stream community. A model for the design of field experiments.

Prugh, L. R., C. E. Ritland, S. M. Arthur, and C. J. Krebs. 2005. Monitoring coyote population dynamics by genotyping faeces. *Molecular Ecology* 14:1585–96.

This study shows how the tools of molecular biology are offering exciting new possibilities for better understanding of the population dynamics of elusive species.

Williams, K. S., K. G. Smith, and F. M. Stephen. 1993. Emergence of 13-yr periodical cicadas (Cicadidae: *Magicicada*): phenology, mortality, and predator satiation. *Ecology* 74:1143–52.

Beautifully designed field study of a complex problem. Demonstrates predator satiation by periodical cicadas.

Krebs, C. J., S. Boutin, and R. Boostra. 2001. *Ecosystem dynamics of the boreal forest: The Kluane project.* Oxford University Press.

A comprehensive book describing the complexity of plant–herbivore–predator dynamics in the boreal forest near Kluane, Yukon.

Thompson, J. N. 1994. *The Coevolutionary Process.* Chicago, University of Chicago Press.

An overview of the causes and consequence of coevolution.

Karban R. and I. T. Baldwin. 1997. *Induced responses to herbivory.* University of Chicago Press

A well written overview of induced defenses in plants in response to herbivory.

Bazely D. R. and R. L. Jefferies. 1986. Changes in the composition and standing crop of salt-marsh communities in response to the removal of a grazer. *Journal of Ecology* 74:693–706.

Kotanen, P. M. and R. L. Jefferies. 1997. Long-term destruction of sub-arctic wetland vegetation by lesser snow geese. *Ecoscience* 4:179–82

These papers describe some of the impacts snow geese have on sub-arctic wetland communities.

Chapter *15*

Mutualism, Parasitism, and Disease

Outline

*I*n chapters 13 and 14 we discussed a variety of interactions that were primarily negative for at least one participant, such as the plant that captures sunlight before its neighbours, or the moose eaten by a wolf. In chapter 15, we continue our discussion of exploitation, but now suggest that in some situations exploitation can be beneficial for both participants. We again emphasize that the human desire to classify interactions as either negative or positive does not represent the true variation found in nature. Instead, there is great complexity in the effects of exploitative interactions on all participants, and the mutualist–parasite continuum is the main theme of this chapter.

At one end of this continuum are parasites, organisms that live in or on the tissues of their host, drawing resources from their host. Similarly, pathogens live inside their host, often inducing disease. The negative consequences to the host and positive benefits to the parasite/pathogen are obvious, and they can be viewed as simple exploitative relationships just like predation and herbivory. However, other organisms, such as the epiphytes of chapter 2, are able to live on their host, causing no apparent harm. Some fungi live in plant tissues, consuming plant resources with no apparent effect on plant growth. Many scavenger fish follow sharks and other predators, consuming food that otherwise would be left behind, again without apparent harm to the predators. All of these interactions are neutral for at least one participant. And then at the other extreme, there are interactions in which both participants appear to benefit, such as the butterfly that feeds upon nectar and the flower that receives pollination services. In this chapter we show the rich variety of ecological interactions, and how the relative costs and benefits of a particular interaction will be dependent on the specifics of the interaction, and will be subject to natural selection.

Positive interactions among species are common. We are all familiar with the plant–pollinator interaction (fig. 15.1), but there are many more. For example birds and fish that remove the parasites of other animals (chapter 8) gain food for themselves, and reduce the parasite load for the host. Below ground there exists a world of partnerships as well. The roots of most plants are intimately connected with fungi in an association called a **mycorrhizae**. The fungal hyphae extend far from the roots of the plant, increasing the capacity of the plant to forage for nutrients. Also located in the mycorrhizae are specialized structures that allow the fungi to draw large amounts of sugars from the plant.

These are just a few examples of **mutualisms**, interactions between individuals of different species that benefit both partners. Not all mutualisms are alike, and the differences have important consequences for the ecology of the different species involved in the interactions. Some species can live without their mutualistic partners and so the relationship is called **facultative mutualism**. Other species are so dependent upon the mutualistic relationship that they cannot live in its absence. Such a relationship is an **obligate mutualism**.

Historically, the study of mutualisms has fallen well behind that of the exploitative interactions; though in recent years ecologists have realized that this bias in research greatly skewed

Figure 15.1 Hummingbirds feeding on nectar transfer pollen from flower to flower.

our understanding of the natural world. Mutualisms are widespread and involve large numbers of individuals and species, likely with great impacts on population dynamics and community organization. Without mutualisms the biosphere would be entirely different. For example, without mutualisms we can erase the Great Barrier Reef, the largest biological structure on earth. The deep sea would have not luminescent fishes or invertebrates, and the deep sea life around ocean floor hydrothermal vents would not exist (chapter 7). On land, there would be no orchids, sunflowers, apples, or other animal-pollinated plants and produce. No bumblebees, hummingbirds, or monarch butterflies would be left. Many wind pollinated plants, such as conifers and grasses would exist; however, over 90% of these form mycorrhizae, and what they would look like without these belowground mutualists is unclear. Even if the grasses remained, the large herbivores such as bison, elephants, and camels, and even the smaller rabbits and caterpillars, would not. They have a variety of mutualistic relationships with microbes in their guts that allow them to eat plants.

The effect mutualisms have on extant life is even greater than we might expect. Lynn Margulis and René Fester (1991) have amassed convincing evidence that all eukaryotes, both heterotrophic and autotrophic, originated as mutualistic associations between different organisms. Eukaryotes are apparently the product of a mutualistic relationship so ancient that the mutualistic partners have become cellular organelles (e.g. mitochondria and chloroplasts) whose mutualistic origins long went unrecognized. Consequently, without mutualisms, all eukaryotes—from *Homo sapiens* to protozoans—would be gone.

In this chapter, we will review what is known about parasitism and mutualism, and show why many ecologists are moving away from the idea that exploitation and mutualism are fundamentally different types of interactions. Instead, there is an increasing understanding that exploitation and mutualisms are simply different extremes on a continuum of possible interactions. We will begin with a discussion of the diversity of interactions that are found in nature.

Concepts

15.1 There is great diversity in the types of parasitic and mutualistic interactions that exist, defying easy generalization.

15.2 Basic ecological principles can be applied to our understanding of disease, and the population dynamics of pathogens can be predicted using a compartmental model.

15.3 Many forms of interactions can switch from parasitic to mutualistic, depending upon the specific conditions of the local environment.

15.4 Theory predicts that mutualism will evolve where the benefits of mutualism exceed the costs.

15.1 Complex Interactions

There is great diversity in the types of parasitic and mutualistic interactions that exist, defying easy generalization.
Most species on the planet are host to at least one species of specialist parasite, and several species of generalist parasites. As a result, most species on the planet are parasites (and small!). However, not all interactions between species are inherently exploitative, or even competitive. Instead, there also exist a variety of mutualistic relationships among species. It is impossible to present the full diversity of these interactions in a single section of a chapter, and instead we present just a few examples that demonstrate what great variability exists in nature.

Control: Behaviour Modification by Parasites

A number of parasites alter the behaviour of their hosts in ways that benefit transmission and reproduction of the parasite. Acanthocephalans, or spiny-headed worms, change the behaviour of amphipods, small aquatic crustaceans, in ways that make it more likely that infected amphipods will be eaten by a suitable vertebrate host. Janice Moore (1983, 1984a, and 1984b) studied a parasite–host interaction involving an acanthocephalan, *Plagiorhynchus cylindraceus*, a terrestrial isopod or pill bug, *Armadillidium vulgare,* and the European starling, *Sturnus vulgaris.* In this interaction, the pill bug serves as an intermediate host for *Plagiorhynchus,* which completes its life cycle in the starling (fig. 15.2).

At the outset of her research, Moore predicted that *Plagiorhynchus* would alter the behaviour of *Armadillidium.* She based this prediction on several observations. One was the relative frequency of infection of *Armadillidium* and starlings by *Plagiorhynchus.* Field studies had demonstrated that even where *Plagiorhynchus* infects only 1% of the *Armadillidium* population, over 40% of the starlings in the area were infected. Some factor was enhancing rates of transmission to the starlings, and Moore predicted that it was altered host behaviour. Moore thought that the size of *Plagiorhynchus* might also be a factor. At maturity, the cystacanth stage of *Plagiorhynchus* grows to about 3 mm, a substantial fraction of the internal environment of an 8 mm pill bug!

Moore brought *Armadillidium* into the laboratory and established two populations: an uninfected control group and an infected experimental group. After three months, the *Plagiorhynchus* in the infected populations matured to the

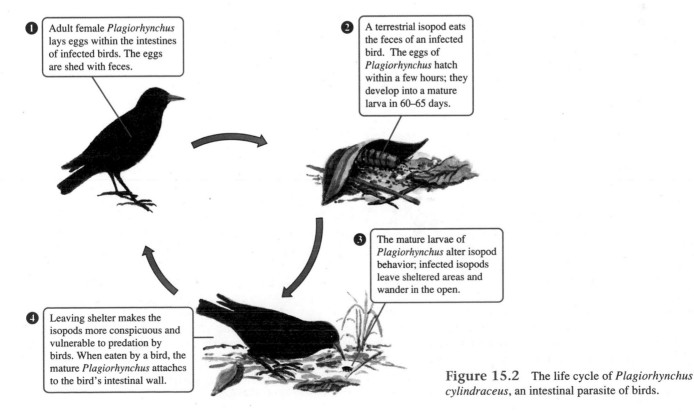

❶ Adult female *Plagiorhynchus* lays eggs within the intestines of infected birds. The eggs are shed with feces.

❷ A terrestrial isopod eats the feces of an infected bird. The eggs of *Plagiorhynchus* hatch within a few hours; they develop into a mature larva in 60–65 days.

❸ The mature larvae of *Plagiorhynchus* alter isopod behavior; infected isopods leave sheltered areas and wander in the open.

❹ Leaving shelter makes the isopods more conspicuous and vulnerable to predation by birds. When eaten by a bird, the mature *Plagiorhynchus* attaches to the bird's intestinal wall.

Figure 15.2 The life cycle of *Plagiorhynchus cylindraceus*, an intestinal parasite of birds.

cystacanth stage. At this point Moore mixed the infected and uninfected populations.

Moore found that *Plagiorhynchus* alters the behaviour of *Armadillidium* in several ways. Infected *Armadillidium* spend less time in sheltered areas and more time in low-humidity environments and on light-coloured substrates. These changes in behaviour would increase the time an *Armadillidium* spends in the open, where it could be easily seen by a bird. In other words, infected *Armadillidium* behave in a way that is likely to increase the probability that they will be discovered by foraging birds.

A critical step in this research was to determine whether the changed behaviour of infected *Armadillidium* translates into their being eaten more frequently by wild birds. Moore collected the arthropods that starlings feed to their nestlings and from these collections estimated the rate at which they delivered *Armadillidium*—about one every 10 hours. Using this delivery rate and the proportion of the *Armadillidium* population infected by *Plagiorhynchus* (about 0.4%), she was able to predict the expected rate of infection among starling nestlings if the adults capture *Armadillidium* at random from the natural population. The proportion of infected nestlings was 32%, about twice the rate of infection predicted if starlings fed randomly on the *Armadillidium* population. These results support Moore's hypothesis that the altered behaviour of infected *Armadillidium* increases their probability of being eaten by starlings.

Moore emphasized that *Plagiorhynchus* does not just alter *Armadillidium*'s behaviour, but alters its behaviour in a particular way—in a way that increases the rate at which the final host of the parasite, starlings, is infected. As you might expect, parasites can have impacts on host population dynamics.

Infestation: Ghost Moose and Winter Ticks

Moose, *Alces alces*, are found throughout most of Canada (fig. 15.3*d*), and are the subject of many myths, legends, and stories. One of the more common stories is about the "ghost moose," white moose seen walking across the landscape (fig. 15.3*b*). Bill Samuel, of the University of Alberta, has studied these "ghost" moose, and has been able to clearly show the cause: winter ticks (Samuel 2004).

Dermacentor albipictus is a tick that can feed on a variety of hosts, including moose, elk, and white-tailed deer (fig. 15.3*c*). Winter ticks are unique compared to all other ticks in Canada in that the larval, nymph, and adult stages feed upon the blood of a single host. These ticks are found throughout most of the southern range of moose in North America (fig. 15.3*d*). Although these ticks are large relative to other ticks, reaching 1.5 cm in length as a blood-engorged adult, their size is dwarfed in comparison to an adult moose standing nearly 2 m in height. How is it possible that this little parasite can cause a dramatic shift in the appearance, and health, of this large animal? The answer lies primarily in numbers.

Over the years, Samuel and his students have examined the hides of hundreds of moose collected in the winter. Amazingly, on 214 hides collected from western Canada, there was an average of 33,000 winter ticks per moose, with 3% of the moose having in excess of 100,000 ticks. As a point of reference, 50,000 ticks correspond to approximately 3.0 ticks per cm^2 on a calf moose (Samuel 2004). Samuel compared tick densities on co-occurring hosts in Elk Island National Park, Alberta, and found tick densities to be more than 25 times

Figure 15.3 (*a*) With few ticks, moose retain a brown coat; (*b*) at high numbers of ticks, moose self-groom, destroying the winter coat of hair, giving the whitish image of a "ghost" moose; (*c*) winter ticks can occur at extremely high densities on the skin of a moose; (*d*) the ranges of winter ticks and moose overlap over much of Canada and the northern United States.

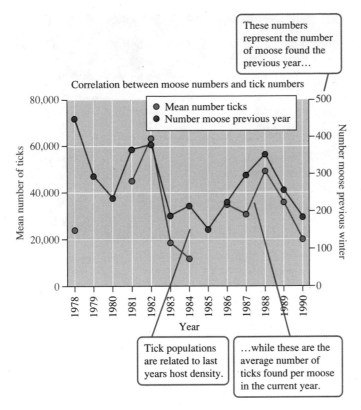

These numbers represent the number of moose found the previous year…

Correlation between moose numbers and tick numbers

- Mean number ticks
- Number moose previous year

Tick populations are related to last years host density.

…while these are the average number of ticks found per moose in the current year.

Figure 15.4   Relationship between average number of ticks on a moose and moose population sizes in Elk Island National Park, Alberta (data from Samuel 2004).

greater on moose than elk, deer, or bison. In other words, these ticks infest this particular host, even though other hosts are available in the area.

The consequence of this infestation can be severe. Using estimates on the amount of blood that individual female ticks can consume, along with his knowledge of tick densities, Samuel (2004) made some rough calculations about blood loss. He estimated that naturally occurring tick densities consume approximately 17% of the blood volume of a bull moose, 11% of the blood volume of cows (though this is during the last trimester of pregnancy), and 58% of the blood volume of calves. Also, moose groom in response to high tick numbers. Grooming can include biting and licking, scratching with hind hooves, and rubbing against trees. In a study of captive moose, in which he was able to control tick infestation, Samuel found that tick-infested moose groom up to two hours each day when the ticks are most actively feeding in March and April, while the tick-free moose groom less than five minutes per day! The direct outcome of this high level of grooming is hair loss, with increased grooming of wild moose associated with increased hair loss (Mooring and Samuel 1999). The "ghost" moose have broken off the dark outer portion of their hair on over 80% of the body surface, exposing the white-coloured lower portion, giving rise to an overall whitish appearance.

Knowing what you do about the theory of allocation and physiological ecology (section II), it should be readily apparent that increased expenditure of energy to replace blood,

increased time spent grooming, and decreased insulative properties of the coat likely increase stress and reduce the health of infested individuals. For nearly a century, ticks have been seen as reducing the strength of moose, and a likely source of mortality. Samuel (2004) lists a variety of accounts throughout Canada linking moose die-offs to tick numbers. Within Elk Island National Park, moose and tick numbers seem to track in synch (fig. 15.4), similar to what we saw with predator–prey dynamics in chapter 14. In figure 15.4, the average number of ticks found on moose appears to be tightly linked to the number of moose present the previous year. This is similar to the number of predators responding to the number of potential prey available.

Whether these winter ticks are the actual cause of the moose population swings, or if they are simply responding to changes in host densities, is a question not yet answered. Samuel and his students have done an excellent job in describing the general ecology of the host–parasite interaction, with many questions left for the next generation of students. We now turn to a different example, and show that parasites can not only alter behaviour, but also influence the outcome of competitive interactions.

Interactions: Predation, Parasitism, and Competition

During their work on competition among flour beetles, Thomas Park and his colleagues (Park 1948, Park et al. 1965) uncovered one of the very first examples of competitors eating each other. As we saw in chapter 13, the outcome of competition between *Tribolium castaneum* and *T. confusum* depended upon temperature and moisture. It turns out that the presence or absence of a protozoan parasite of *Tribolium*, *Adelina tribolii*, also influences the competitive balance between flour beetle species. The effects of this parasite are also entangled with predation among the flour beetles and cannibalism, which we might think of as a form of intraspecific exploitation.

Of the two species, *T. castaneum* is the most cannibalistic but it preys on the eggs of *T. confusum* at an even higher rate than it cannibalizes its own eggs. In the light of its predatory behaviour, it's not surprising that *T. castaneum* eliminated *T. confusum* in 84% of 76 competition experiments spanning a period of about 10 years. This predatory strategy works best, however, in the absence of *Adelina*.

Several biologists before Park had noted that *Adelina* caused "sickness" and death among *Tribolium* populations. It was Park, however, who demonstrated that *Adelina* reduces the density of *Tribolium* populations and can alter the outcome of competition between *T. confusum* and *T. castaneum*. *Adelina* strongly reduces the population density of *T. castaneum* populations but has little effect on *T. confusum* populations. In the absence of the parasite, *T. castaneum* won 12 of 18 competitive contests against *T. confusum*. When the parasite was included, however, *T. confusum* won 11 of 15 contests (fig. 15.5). In other words, parasitism can completely reverse the outcome of competitive interactions between species. We now move to an example where having one species live within and on the host confers benefits to the host.

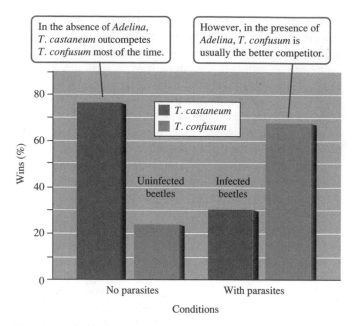

In the absence of *Adelina*, *T. castaneum* outcompetes *T. confusum* most of the time.

However, in the presence of *Adelina*, *T. confusum* is usually the better competitor.

Figure 15.5   The influence of the protozoan parasite *Adelina tribolii* on competition between the flour beetles *Tribolium castaneum* and *T. confusum* (data from Park 1948).

Figure 15.6   Split thorn of a bullshorn acacia, revealing a nest of its ant mutualists.

Protection: Ants and Bullshorn Acacia

Writing about the natural history of mutualism, Daniel Janzen (1985) included "plant–ant protection mutualisms" as one of his general categories of mutualism. Janzen (1966, 1967a, 1967b) himself is responsible for studying one of the best known of these mutualisms, the obligate mutualism between ants and swollen thorn acacias in Central America. The ants mutualistic with swollen thorn acacias are members of the genus *Pseudomyrmex* in the subfamily Pseudomyrmecinae. This subfamily of ants is dominated by species that have evolved close relationships with trees, and show several characteristics that Janzen suggested are associated with arboreal living. They are generally fast and agile runners, have good vision, and forage independently. The *Pseudomyrmex* spp. associated with swollen thorn acacias, or "acacia-ants," are also aggressive toward vegetation and animals contacting their home tree, maintain large colony sizes, and exhibit 24-hour activity outside of the nest. This combination of characteristics means that any herbivore attempting to forage on an acacia occupied by acacia-ants is met by a large number of fast, agile, and highly aggressive defenders.

Worldwide, the genus *Acacia* includes over 700 species. Distributed throughout the tropical and subtropical regions around the world, acacias are particularly common in drier tropical and subtropical environments. The swollen thorn acacias, which form obligate mutualisms with *Pseudomyrmex* spp., are restricted to the New World, where they are distributed from southern Mexico, through Central America, and into Venezuela and Columbia in northern South America. Across this region, swollen thorn acacias occur mainly in the lowlands up to 1,500 m elevation in areas with a dry season of one to six months. Swollen thorn acacias show several character-

istics related to their obligate association with ants, including enlarged thorns with a soft, easily excavated pith; year-round leaf production; enlarged foliar nectaries; and leaflet tips modified into concentrated food sources called Beltian bodies. The thorns provide living space for ants, while the foliar nectaries provide a source of sugar and liquid. Beltian bodies are a source of oils and protein. Resident ants vigorously guard these resources against encroachment by nearly all comers, including other plants.

Janzen's detailed natural history of the interaction between bullshorn acacia and ants suggests interactions of mutual benefit to both partners (fig. 15.6). Newly mated *Pseudomyrmex* queens move through the vegetation searching for unoccupied seedlings or shoots of bullshorn acacia. When a queen finds an unoccupied acacia, she excavates an entrance in one of the green thorns or uses one carved previously by another ant. The queen then lays her first eggs in the thorn and begins to forage on her newly acquired home plant. She gets nectar for herself and her developing larvae from the foliar nectaries and gets additional solid food from the Beltian bodies. Over time, the number of workers in the new colony increases, and the queen shifts to a mainly reproductive function.

Ants protect acacias from attack by herbivores and competition from other plants. Workers have several duties, including foraging for themselves, the larvae, and the queen. One of their most important activities is protecting the home plant. Workers will attack, bite, and sting nearly all insects they encounter on their home plant, or any large herbivores such as deer and cattle that attempt to feed on the plant. They will also attack and kill any vegetation encroaching on the home tree. Workers sting and bite the branches of other plants that come in contact with their home tree or that grow near its base. These activities keep other plants from growing near the base of the home tree and prevent other trees, shrubs, and vines from shading it. Consequently the home plant's access to light and soil nutrients is increased.

Once a colony has at least 50 to 150 workers, which takes about nine months, they patrol the home plant day and night.

Eventually, colonies grow so large that they occupy all the thorns on the home tree and may spread to neighbouring acacias. The queen, however, generally remains on the shoot that she colonized originally. When the colony reaches a size of about 1,200 workers, it begins producing a more or less steady stream of winged reproductive males and females, which fly off to mate. The queens among them may eventually establish new colonies on other bullshorn acacias or one of the other Central American swollen thorn acacias.

Experimental Evidence for Mutualism

While much of the natural history of this mutualism was known at the time Janzen conducted his studies, no one had experimentally tested the strength of its widely supposed benefits. Janzen took his work beyond natural history to experimentally test for the importance of ants to bullshorn acacias. It was clear that the ant needs swollen thorn acacias, but do the acacias need the ants? Janzen's experiments concentrated on the influence of ants on acacia performance. He also tested the effectiveness of the ants at keeping acacias free of herbivorous insects. Janzen removed ants from acacias by clipping occupied thorns or by cutting out entire shoots with their ants. He then measured the growth rate, leaf production, mortality, and insect population density on acacias with and without ants.

Janzen's experiments demonstrated that ants significantly improve plant performance. Differences in plant performance were likely the result of increased competition with other plants and increased attack by insects faced by acacias without their tending ants. Suckers growing from stumps of acacias occupied by ants lengthened at seven times the rate of suckers without ants (fig. 15.7). Suckers with ants were also more than 13 times heavier than suckers without ants and had more than twice the number of leaves and almost three times the number of thorns. Suckers with ants also survived at twice the rate of suckers without ants (fig. 15.8).

What produces the improved performance of acacias with ants? One factor appears to be reduced populations of herbivorous insects. Janzen found that acacias without ants had more herbivorous insects on them than did acacias with ants (fig. 15.9). Janzen's experiments provide strong evidence that bullshorn acacias need ants as much as the ants need the acacia. It appears that this is a truly mutualistic situation and that it is obligate for both partners.

Construction: Zooxanthellae and Corals

Because of the importance of mutualism in the lives of reef-building corals, it appears that the ecological integrity of coral reefs depends upon mutualism. Coral reefs show exceptional productivity and diversity. Recent estimates put the number of species occurring on coral reefs at approximately 0.5 million, and coral reef productivity is among the highest of any natural ecosystem. As we saw in chapter 3, the paradox is that this overwhelming diversity and exceptional productivity occurs in an ecosystem surrounded by nutrient-poor tropical seas. The key to explaining this paradox lies with mutualism; in this case, between reef-building corals and unicellular algae called zooxanthellae, members of the phylum Dinoflagellata. Most of these organisms are free-living unicellular marine and freshwater photoautotrophs. Together, these organisms create the foundation ecosystem.

Zooxanthellae live within coral tissues at densities averaging approximately 1 million cells per square centimeter of coral surface. Like plants, zooxanthellae receive nutrients from their animal partner. In return, the coral receives organic compounds synthesized by zooxanthellae during photosynthesis.

One of the most fundamental discoveries concerning the relationship between corals and zooxanthellae is that the release of organic compounds by zooxanthellae is controlled by the coral partner. Corals induce zooxanthellae to release

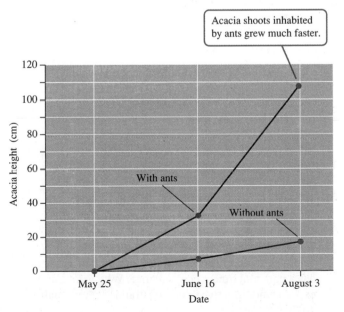

Figure 15.7 Growth by bullshorn acacia with and without resident ants (data from Janzen 1966).

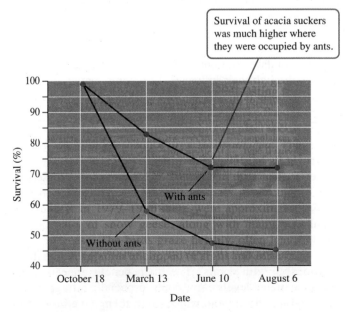

Figure 15.8 Survival of bullshorn acacia shoots with and without resident ants (data from Janzen 1966).

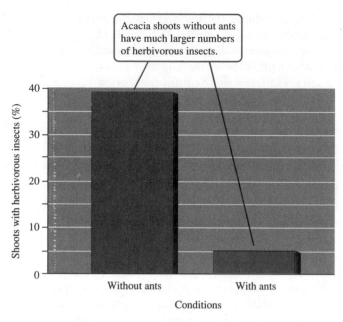

Figure 15.9   Ants and the abundance of herbivorous insects on bullshorn acacia (data from Janzen 1966).

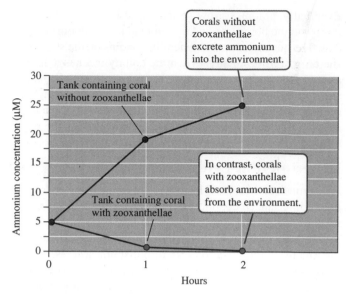

Figure 15.10   Zooxanthellae, corals, and ammonium flux (data from Muscatine and D'Elia 1978).

organic compounds with "signal" compounds, which alter the permeability of the zooxanthellae cell membrane. Zooxanthellae grown in isolation from corals release very little organic material into their environment. However, when exposed to extracts of coral tissue, zooxanthellae immediately increase the rate at which they release organic compounds. This response appears to be a specific, chemically mediated communication between corals and zooxanthellae. Zooxanthellae do not respond to extracts of other animal tissues, and coral extracts do not induce leaking of organic molecules by any other algae that have been studied.

Corals not only control the secretion of organic compounds by zooxanthellae, they also control the rate of zooxanthellae population growth and population density. In corals, zooxanthellae populations grow at rates 1/10 to 1/100 the rates observed when they are cultured separately from corals. Corals exert control over zooxanthellae population density through their influence on organic matter secretion. Normally, unicellular algae show **balanced growth,** growth in which all cell constituents, such as nitrogen, carbon, and DNA, increase at the same rate. However, zooxanthellae living in coral tissues show unbalanced growth, producing fixed carbon at a much higher rate than other cell constituents. Moreover, the coral stimulates the zooxanthellae to secrete 90% to 99% of this carbon, which the coral uses for its own respiration. Carbon secreted and diverted for use by the coral could otherwise be used to produce new zooxanthellae, which would increase population growth.

What benefits do the zooxanthellae get out of their relationship with corals? The main benefit appears to be access to higher levels of nutrients, especially nitrogen. Corals feed on zooplankton, which gives them a means of capturing nutrients, especially nitrogen and phosphorus. When corals metabolize the protein in their zooplankton prey, they

excrete ammonium as a waste product. L. Muscatine and C. D'Elia (1978) showed that coral species such as *Tubastrea aurea* that do not harbour zooxanthellae continuously excrete ammonium into their environment, while corals such as *Pocillopora damicornis* do not excrete measurable amounts of ammonia (fig. 15.10). What happens to the ammonium produced by *Pocillopora* during metabolism of the protein in their zooplankton prey? Muscatine and D'Elia suggested that this ammonium is immediately taken up by zooxanthellae as the coral excretes it. In addition to internal recycling of the ammonium produced by their coral partner, zooxanthellae also actively absorb ammonium from seawater. By absorbing nutrients from the surrounding medium and leaking very little back into the environment, corals and their zooxanthellae gradually accumulate substantial quantities of nitrogen. So, as in tropical rain forest, large quantities of nutrients on coral reefs accumulate and are retained in living biomass.

Concept 15.1 Review

1. Many parasites cause their hosts to alter their behaviour. What impact can this have on the parasite's ability to complete its life cycle?
2. Winter ticks are small relative to the size of their hosts. Even with this size disparity, there is reason to believe they can increase moose mortality. Why?
3. There is a big difference between describing an interaction and experimentally showing that the interaction has a potential fitness consequence. Why were Janzen's experiments effective in demonstrating that mutualisms do exist under natural conditions?

15.2   Ecology of Disease

Basic ecological principles can be applied to our understanding of disease, and the population dynamics of pathogens can be predicted using a compartmental model. What is disease? Does ecology apply to disease? Of course. The pathogens that cause disease are living organisms, just like the caribou, pine trees, and whales that are more often associated with "ecology." Although there are certainly debates about what types of pathogens are alive (e.g., bacteria, fungi, etc.) and which are not (e.g., prions, viruses, etc.), this debate is irrelevant to applying ecological principles to our understanding of disease. Instead, it is important to recognize that natural selection is not dependent upon life to operate! Instead, there simply need to be traits that are heritable (the pathogen must be able to reproduce or replicate), and there need to be different levels of fitness (rates of reproduction or replication) among genotypes. This applies just as well to viruses as to wolves. The population size of the pathogen will be determined by processes within the host (e.g., immune response, competition with other pathogens), and processes outside the host (e.g., transmission rates).

Taking an ecological approach to understand disease also provides insights that may be helpful in reducing the spread of disease through population of concern, be they human or wildlife. In an influential paper entitled "The Dawn of Darwinian Medicine," the evolutionary biologists George Williams and Randolph Nesse (1991) argued that human health could be better improved by understanding the evolutionary and ecological basis of disease. How so? Quite simply, the goal of disease management programs is to reduce the spread of the disease among the host population. Some of our population management decisions (such as many medical treatments) may reduce pathogen growth rates, others may not. To get a better understanding of why, we need to understand what factors actually influence the population growth of diseases.

Compartmental Models

In chapters 10, 11, and 12, we spent a good deal of time discussing models used to describe population growth, such as the exponential and logistic growth models. In chapter 13 we extended that model to include competition, and in chapter 14 we presented a model to account for predation and herbivory. These models, unfortunately, are not usually very effective in describing the population dynamics of disease, and thus we present a new model here. What is unique about disease is that there are two scales at which pathogen populations can grow: pathogen levels within the body of a single host (e.g., viral load) and the number of new hosts a pathogen is able to colonize. As you will see, it is often the rate of spread to new hosts that most severely limits the spread of disease, and this too is a main target of vaccination and quarantine programs. A new approach to understanding disease growth was developed in a foundational paper by Roy Anderson and Robert May (1979).

The growth rate of a pathogen is dependent upon its ability to move from one host to another. Some pathogens are particularly good at this, and have very high transmission rates, ß, while others are less efficient at this, and have lower transmission rates. Pathogens with a high ß, will move quickly through a host population, and not surprisingly, will tend to have a high population growth rate.

A second factor that is important is the virulence, α, of the pathogen. Highly virulent pathogens cause the presentation of many symptoms in the host, and can lead to high rates of mortality. Pathogens with low virulence may result in hosts that are asymptomatic, with very low rates of mortality. It is worth considering this issue a bit more, from the perspective of the pathogen. All else being equal, what is likely to confer the greatest fitness to a pathogen, high or low virulence? If a pathogen quickly kills its host, it has less time to find a new host, and thus its growth rate is likely lower than a pathogen whose host persists longer. In other words, high rates of virulence are often counter to the best interests, evolutionarily, of a disease. In fact, many diseases become less virulent over time, likely due to natural selection within the pathogen's population.

A third major influence on pathogen population growth rates is the number of susceptible hosts available. These are individuals who are not immune, either through naturally acquired immunity (e.g., recovered from the disease), or through a vaccination program. The number will of course also be influenced by the host population birth and death rates (independent of disease), which are in turn influenced by all the other ecological processes discussed so far in this book!

These three factors can then be connected using a graphical compartmental model (fig. 15.11). This model is an elegant way of showing how these basic aspects of pathogen population growth are connected. These ecological models allow researchers to address questions of great public concern. A major public

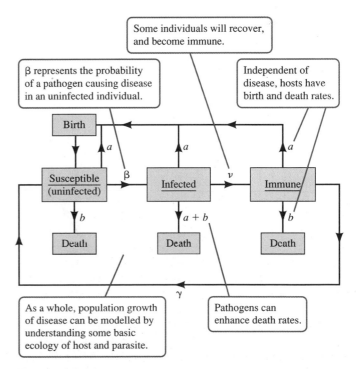

Figure 15.11   A compartmental model of the population growth of a disease-causing organisms (data from Anderson and May 1979).

health goal is to reduce the rate of spread of disease in human populations. Here we present two strategies, quarantine and vaccination, and show how ecologists are able to provide insight into effective control measures for human disease.

Quarantine During a SARS Outbreak

Severe acute respiratory syndrome, SARS, was first reported in November 2002 in China. SARS has a high mortality rate, killing about 15% of those infected, and up to 50% of elderly individuals who contract the disease. SARS left China, reaching 32 countries, killing over 750 people, and infecting over 7,000 more (Gumel et al. 2004). In 2003, there was a SARS outbreak in the greater Toronto area, killing 44 people. Vaccines have yet to be successfully developed for SARS. Isolation and quarantine of individuals suspected of having SARS have been used as means of reducing the spread of the disease. Isolation means separating sick individuals from people that are healthy. Quarantine also involves separating people who have been exposed to the illness, even if they are not presenting any symptoms of the disease. As you may recognize, isolation and quarantine disrupt the lives of many people, and thus should only be implemented if they are likely to improve public health. Troy Day, of Queen's University, along with colleagues from the University of Manitoba, the University of New Brunswick, the University of British Columbia, the University of Victoria, York University, several Canadian health groups, and other researchers in the United States, used compartmental models to determine the effectiveness of isolation and quarantine during the SARS outbreak (Gumel et al. 2004).

The research team developed a compartmental model, consisting of six potential sub-populations (fig. 15.12): susceptible, asymptomatic, quarantined, symptomatic, isolated, and recovered. They parameterized their model using data from the SARS outbreaks in Toronto, Hong Kong, Singapore, and Beijing. Using a variety of mathematical equations, they were then able to explore which of the parameters of the model most strongly influences the spread of the disease in these populations. They found that isolation, if rigorously applied, can be effective in reducing the rate of spread of SARS. However, if isolation is not complete, then mortality rates will increase unless quarantine is also implemented. Of critical concern is the timing of implementation of isolation and quarantine. For example, their model suggests that delaying an isolation and quarantine program around Toronto by only five more days would have led to an additional 16 deaths. The overall importance of speed-of-response can be seen in figure 15.13, which shows the predicted mortality results as a function of the average number of days before individuals are isolated or quarantined in the greater Toronto area.

The results from this team's research clearly demonstrate that fast responses by the health care system can be critical in reducing mortality of SARS. Next we show that vaccination programs may also be effective in reducing the spread of disease in human populations.

Using Vaccination to Provide Herd Immunity

Why do humans spend billions of dollars annually on immunization programs? There are two main answers. At the individual level, people are concerned about individuals they know contracting a variety of diseases, many of which have very significant negative consequences for individual health. However, many of the diseases that we currently vaccinate for are actually rare in Canada, though that was certainly not always the case. What is the point in vaccinating for a rare disease, one that even an unvaccinated individual is unlikely to contract?

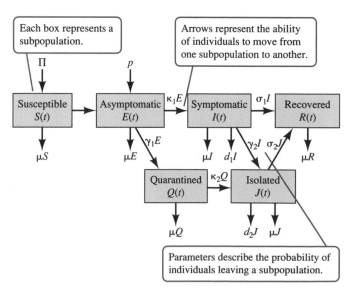

Figure 15.12 A compartmental model was constructed to determine the effectiveness of isolation and quarantine during the SARS outbreak of 2003.

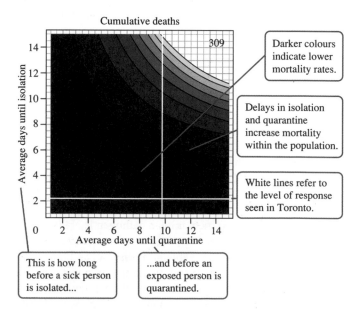

Figure 15.13 Delays in isolation and quarantine would have increased mortality due to SARS during the 2003 outbreak in Toronto.

Some Epidemiological Properties of Vaccine-Preventable Childhood Viral and Bacterial Infections

Infection/infectious agent	Average age at infection in yr	Inter-epidemic period (yr)	R_0	Critical vaccination coverage to block transmission (%)
Measles	4–5	2	15–17	92–95
Pertussis	4–5	3–4	15–17	92–95
Mumps	6–7	3	10–12	90–92
Rubella	9–10	3–5	7–8	85–87
Diphtheria	11–14	4–6	5–6	80–85
Polio virus	12–15	3–5	5–6	80–85

This is the potential growth rate of the pathogen based upon its transmission rate.

Figure 15.14 Several common human diseases, their population growth rates, and vaccination levels needed to provide herd immunity (data from Anderson and May 1990).

By understanding the ecology of diseases, the answer should come as no surprise. Vaccination programs serve a significant benefit to public health through modifying the growth rates of diseases. At the extreme, a very effective vaccination program can lead to negative pathogen population growth rates, such that the pathogen goes extinct in that host population (e.g., Canada). At that tantalizing point, **herd immunity** has been achieved, and a great public health objective has been met. Why does this work? Let us go back to our model (fig 15.11). Vaccination moves previously susceptible hosts to an "immune" sub-population, with direct negative consequences for the rate of pathogen growth.

Unfortunately, herd immunity is unlikely to be achieved for every population of every disease. What types of diseases do you think are more likely to be effectively controlled? The answer can be found in figure 15.14, which provides population growth rates (R_0) and the estimated percent of a population that would need to be vaccinated to confer herd immunity. Pathogens with naturally low levels of transmission have low population growth rates, and are the most susceptible to vaccination programs. It may then be no surprise that polio, with a relatively low R_0, has been eradicated throughout many countries by using aggressive vaccination programs. It is important to recognize that this happened not because every person in a population was vaccinated, but instead because the rates of vaccination were high enough to cause negative population growth of the disease. In contrast, measles has a very high R_0, and is unlikely to ever be eliminated through vaccination.

In the next section we move back to the more traditional organisms studied by ecologists, and begin to explore the mutualist–exploiter continuum.

Concept 15.2 Review

1. Why is life not a necessary condition for application of ecological models of population growth to diseases?
2. Describe the similarities and differences between quarantine and vaccination as means to reduce the spread of a disease in a human population.
3. Why is herd immunity hard to achieve for diseases with high transmission rates?

15.3 Mutualist–Exploiter Continuum

Many interactions can switch from parasitic to mutualistic, depending upon the specific conditions of the local environment. So far in this chapter we have seen what appears to be a very static portrayal of parasitic and mutualistic interactions. Similarly, we have presented examples that generally involve few individuals, such as the ant–acacia mutualism, where there are highly specialized adaptations that link species. Although this view is helpful in contrasting different types of ecological interactions, they give a skewed perspective of the complexity that actually exists in nature. To understand that mutualism and parasitism are actually different points on a continuum of possible ecological interactions, we must first recognize that most mutualistic interactions are facultative, not obligatory. Additionally, the more common mutualisms generally involve sets of species, rather than single species pairs, such as the ant–acacia example. Two examples we will discuss here, pollination and mycorrhizae, are typical of the complexity of mutualisms. Only in rare exceptions can a single flower be pollinated by a single animal; instead, most animal-pollinated flowers can be serviced by a diversity of insects (fig. 15.15). Similarly, insects are not usually dependent upon a single plant host for nectar or other food, but instead often have a broad selection to choose from. The fact that multi-species interactions are involved, rather than the simpler idea of one-to-one interactions, has required ecologists to take a fresh look at mutualistic and exploitative interactions. We begin, once again, with natural selection.

Recall from chapter 8 that altruism and cooperation required stringent conditions to be evolutionarily stable. There is strong selection against an individual decreasing its fitness, as cheaters in the population would gain benefits from others, while expending no cost. This same logic applies to facultative mutualisms. Individuals are selected most strongly based upon traits that increase their own fitness, not the fitness of others. If an individual in the population "donates" a portion of its fitness to an unrelated individual (here of a different species), and receives less that that amount in return, that behaviour will be selected against. Mutualisms are not "friendly" interactions that occur among species, but instead are exploitative interactions that happen to be reciprocal.

This shift in thinking about mutualisms is not simply a semantic issue. As you will see in the following examples, viewing mutualisms as cases of reciprocal exploitation helps provide

Figure 15.15 Mutualisms, such as those that occur among plants and pollinators, generally involve large numbers of species. Here are three pollinators of *Camas quamash*, a plant found throughout southwestern Canada.

us with greater insight into how individuals actually interact. In these examples we highlight that interactions can switch from parasitic to neutral to mutualistic depending upon which species are participating, the local environmental conditions, and even the energetic status of the individuals involved.

Pollination: Optimal Foraging vs. Pollen Movement

Let us imagine pollination for a minute. Most of us will picture a sunny summer day, a field of flowers, and bees moving from one to the next, fertilizing the plants and in turn, receiving nectar from the flowers. We can, however, look at it another way. Plants that undergo sexual reproduction have a problem: they can't move. As a result, they are unable to actively pursue potential mates, and instead require a **pollen vector** to move pollen from the anther to a stigma. In many cases, this pollen vector is abiotic, such as the wind moving the pollen of grasses and many boreal and temperate tree species. Other plant species use a biotic pollen vector, such as bees, flies, ants, birds, butterflies, or even small mammals. It is this group of "animal-pollinated" plants that we will discuss here. From the plant's perspective, traits that (1) increase visitation rates by pollinators, (2) enhance rates of pollen deposition, and (3) ensure that pollen moves from one individual to another individual of the same species at a minimum energetic cost, should all be favoured by natural selection. Let us now look at it from the perspective of a pollinator, perhaps a bee. The bee is not interested in pollination; instead it is searching for food while trying to spend the minimum amount of energy foraging (chapter 5). Traits that help the bee locate food efficiently and reduce handling time will be favoured. This presents a problem. For the bee, it is best to fly from one flower to another on a single plant, as this will reduce travel time. Additionally, the bee should spend very little time on each flower, just taking the nectar and leaving. Unfortunately, for the plant, it is best if the bee visits very few flowers on a single plant (or else there is a good chance of inbreeding), and spends some time at each flower (ensuring pollen deposition). We clearly see that the mutualism of pollination is the outcome of conflicting exploitative interactions: the plants need sex, the bees need food. I don't think this is what parents have in mind when they teach their children about the "birds and the bees."

These conflicts of interest have been studied by many ecologists, and show how evolutionary self-interest of members of mutualistic associations drives these exploitative interactions. Let us first consider an example of a non-obligate pollination mutualism, and the issue of how long flowers "should" stay open. Plant species vary greatly in how long their flowers stay open, with some lasting a few hours, others several weeks. Why? Tia-Lynn Ashman, a former post-doc of Daniel Schoen at McGill University, has addressed this issue in a series of papers (Ashman and Schoen 1994, 1997). She began by developing a model based upon the potential costs and benefits of keeping flowers open for different lengths of time. What does a plant gain from having its flowers open? Only when open is there a chance that a pollinator will bring or remove pollen, and thus the male and female function of the plant is dependent upon the flower being open. But this lasts only to a point. Although not all pollen is removed during a single visit by a pollinator, nor are all ovules generally fertilized, the fitness gained from subsequent visits by a pollinator is likely less than that gained on the first visit. In other words, there are diminishing returns from staying open longer (fig 15.16). At the same time, there are a variety of costs associated with keeping flowers open, such as increased evaporation of nectar, increased respiration costs, and even increased risk of acquiring a sexually transmitted disease. The shapes of the cost and benefit curves will vary among species, but the point is the same. Maintaining open flowers is a balance between potential rewards and costs. In experimental work, they showed that seed set decreases when flowers are fertilized long after opening as opposed to soon after opening (Ashman and Schoen 1997), supporting their model. From the pollinator perspective, having the plant close flowers is not in the insect's best interest but is a perfectly understandable "selfish" behaviour of the plant, one that is likely favoured by natural selection. Any thoughts as to what selective pressures this would place on the pollinators?

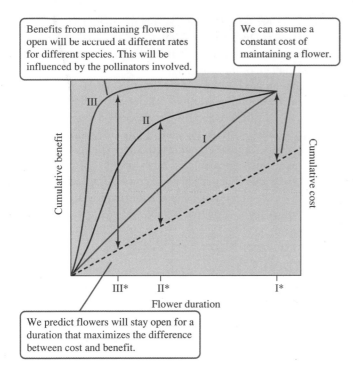

Figure 15.16 Cost-benefit analyses can be helpful in trying to understand mutualisms, such as the optimal time for a plant to keep its flowers open.

Benefits from maintaining flowers open will be accrued at different rates for different species. This will be influenced by the pollinators involved.

We can assume a constant cost of maintaining a flower.

We predict flowers will stay open for a duration that maximizes the difference between cost and benefit.

Cumulative benefit

Cumulative cost

Flower duration

The costs and benefits of mutualisms to each partner are variable, even within an obligate mutualism. John Addicott, of the University of Calgary, has spent decades unravelling details of the obligate mutualism occurring between the Yucca plant and its pollinator, the Yucca moth. Yuccas are a group of species (*Yucca* spp.) common throughout the dry areas of the western United States, also existing as small populations in southern Alberta, and are common to gardens throughout Canada. Yuccas are pollinated by specialist moths (*Tegeticula* spp.). This is a highly specialized system where neither the plant nor moth can complete their life cycle without the other (fig. 15.17).

We begin in spring, where the moths emerge from cocoons in the soil, and quickly mate. The gravid females fly to a nearby Yucca plant, which is now in bloom. The moth enters the flower, and picks many packets of pollen. Using specialized appendages, she forms the pollen into a ball and carries it with her out of the flower. She flies to a new flower, and lays her eggs in its ovary. She then moves to the stigma of the flower and inserts the pollen ball, ensuring fertilization of the ovules of the plant. The moth larvae emerge from their eggs, consuming many of the developing seeds within the Yucca fruit. Fall eventually arrives, and the fruits split open, releasing whatever seeds were not consumed. The fruit falls to the ground, and soon the moth larvae will crawl out, go belowground, and form a cocoon, repeating this cycle in the spring. Some Yucca–Yucca moth pairs are species specific, some Yuccas can be pollinated by a few species of this moth, and some of these moths can pollinate a few species of Yucca. However, Yucca can not be pollinated by anything other than Yucca moths, and these moths can not complete their life cycle without Yucca plants.

(a)

(b)

Figure 15.17 (a) *Yucca baccata* in full flower; (b) a Yucca moth, *Tegeticula planella*, ovipositing on a Yucca flower.

You may recognize in this description that there are a variety of places where cheating could happen. Why does the plant use a pollinator that eats its babies? Why does the moth take the time to pollinate the plant? Why don't the larvae eat all the seeds? Why doesn't the plant just drop the fruit that are being eaten? Over the years, Addicott and his students have been able to learn much about this system.

One of his initial discoveries was that though most Yucca and Yucca-moth associations are similar in terms of their general mode of operation; there is substantial variation in the potential costs and rewards of this mutualism among Yucca species. One measure of the benefit of this mutualism to the plant is the ratio of viable seeds to available ovules (the female structures that become seeds with fertilization). A ratio of 1.0 would indicate that all ovules developed into seeds (maximal benefit), a ratio of 0.5 would indicate that half the ovules developed into seeds, and a ratio of 0.0 would indicate that there were no mature seeds (no benefit). Across populations, Addicott (1986) found the benefits to the plant ranged from 0.36 to 0.60, a substantial degree of variability. This variability was caused by variation among populations and species in the probability of certain parts of the fruit being occupied by larvae, and by variation in the level of feeding of larvae. He found that many fruit were unoccupied by larvae (they likely died during development), resulting in high seed set, while other fruits had many larvae (and low seed set). This variation highlights that even this elaborate obligate mutualism is dynamic, and the costs and benefits vary in natural systems.

Feeding by pollinators is not the only risk to the Yucca plant. The morphology of the moth greatly influences its ability to place pollen on the stigma, and the morphology of the plant's reproductive structures influences the ability of the moth to successfully lay her eggs. Variation in these traits can lead to cheating, receiving benefit from the mutualistic partner, while not providing a service in return. In fact, upon closer examination of several species, Addicott (1996) found that cheating was common in the Yucca–Yucca-moth system. After capturing a number of female Yucca moths, he was able to show that a number of the females of this "mutualist" species were lacking the specialized appendages necessary to move pollen! These females continued to lay their eggs in the ovules of the Yucca ovary, but did not display any of the behaviour associated with pollen ball formation and deposition. As it turns out, these cheaters are not rare, and can represent 30% of all larvae in the fruits of at least five Yucca species. Needless to say, such cheaters represent an increased cost for these Yucca species, one for which no apparent reward is obtained. This is a further example of how the field of ecology has moved away from viewing mutualism as associated species that "do things" for each other, to seeing mutualisms as cases of reciprocal exploitation. There are a number of questions left unanswered. How common can cheaters be in a population before Yucca populations decline? Do cheater females lay eggs in flowers they know have been pollinated by other moths? If not, how do her offspring get fed?

Cheaters are not unique to the obligate mutualism of Yucca and the Yucca moths. The next time you are in a field full of flowers, sit down and look closely. You will likely see many animals, ants, flies, wasps, bees, beetles, and bugs, moving in and out of the flowers. Some of these will be carrying or leaving pollen, but many of these won't. Instead, they are called **nectar robbers**, who exploit an energy-rich resource (nectar) while providing no pollination services. This exploitation is not limited to insects, and plants too deceive their pollination "partners." A variety of orchid species produce flowers similar in shape, size, and odour to reproductively receptive female wasps, inducing pseudocopulation by male wasps. These males land on the flowers and "mate," taking away and depositing

pollen in the process. Clearly the plant benefits from these services provided by the wasp. I will leave it to your own imagination as to whether the plant is providing a service or instead taking advantage of the wasp.

Pollination services are of enormous economic importance in Canada, contributing millions of dollars annually to the economy as a critical aspect to the successful production of many agricultural crops. At the core of this critical agricultural process is a very familiar ecological theme, exploitation. What we learn in ecology does not just apply to our National Parks and wilderness areas but instead these processes affect our lives every day. We see in this next example that exploitation is common in another interaction that involves plants, mycorrhizae.

Mycorrhizae: Nutrient Gain vs. Carbon Gain

The study of mutualisms has largely been centred on interactions between plants and other organisms. This is in part because plants are the dominant life form on land. It would be no exaggeration to say that the integrity of the terrestrial portion of the biosphere depends upon plant-centred mutualisms. However, there is another reason so much research has been done on plant mutualisms: plants make very good experimental subjects! Researchers can often learn much more, more quickly, by being able to experimentally alter environmental conditions and thus the potential costs and benefits of associations, and plants are ideally suited for this. We thus continue our discussion on mutualisms, once again involving plants, but now move from the colourful flowers and diverse pollinators to a less well-understood web of interactions in the soil.

The fossil record shows that mycorrhizae arose early in the evolution of land plants, perhaps as long as 400 million years ago. Over evolutionary time, a relationship between plants and fungi evolved in which mycorrhizal fungi provide plants with greater access to inorganic nutrients while feeding off the root exudates of plants. The two most common types of mycorrhizae are (1) **arbuscular mycorrhizal fungi (AMF),** in which the mycorrhizal fungus produces **arbuscules,** sites of exchange between plant and fungus; **hyphae,** fungal filaments; and **vesicles,** fungal energy storage organs within root cortex cells, and (2) **ectomycorrhizae (ECM),** in which the fungus forms a mantle around roots and a netlike structure around root cells (fig. 15.18). Mycorrhizae are especially important in increasing plant access to phosphorus and other immobile nutrients (nutrients that do not move freely through soil) such as copper and zinc, as well as to nitrogen and water.

Mycorrhizae and the Water Balance of Plants

Mycorrhizal fungi appear to improve the ability of many plants to extract soil water. Edie Allen and Michael Allen (1986) studied how mycorrhizae affect the water relations of the grass *Agropyron smithii* by comparing the leaf water potentials of plants with and without mycorrhizae. Figure 15.19 shows that *Agropyron* with mycorrhizae maintained higher leaf water potentials than those without mycorrhizae. This means that

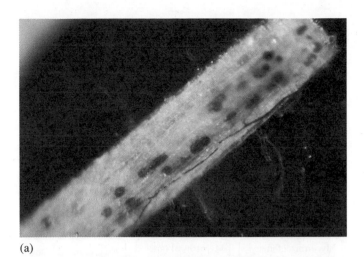

(a)

(b)

Figure 15.18 Mutualistic associations between fungi and plant roots: (*a*) arbuscular mycorrhizal fungus stained so that fungal structures appear blue; and (*b*) ectomycorrhizae, which give a white fuzzy appearance to these roots.

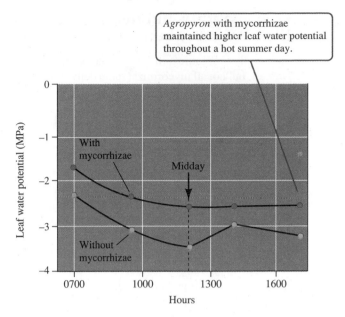

Figure 15.19 Influence of mycorrhizae on leaf water potential of the grass *Agropyron smithii* (data from Allen and Allen 1986).

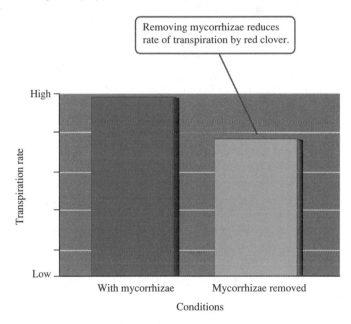

Figure 15.20 Effect of removing mycorrhizal hyphae on rate of transpiration by red clover (data from Hardie 1985).

when growing under similar conditions of soil moisture, the presence of mycorrhizae helped the grass maintain a higher water potential. Does this comparison show that mycorrhizae are directly responsible for the higher leaf water potential observed in the mycorrhizal grass? No, they do not. These higher water potentials may be an indirect effect of greater root growth resulting from the greater access to phosphorus provided by mycorrhizae.

Plants with greater access to phosphorus may develop roots that are more efficient at extracting and conducting water; mycorrhizal fungi may not be directly involved in the extraction of water from soils. Kay Hardie (1985) tested this hypothesis directly with an ingenious experimental manipulation of plant growth form and mycorrhizae. First, she grew mycorrhizal and nonmycorrhizal red clover, *Trifolium pratense,* in conditions in which their growth was not limited by nutrient availability. These conditions produced plants with similar leaf areas and root:shoot ratios. Under these carefully controlled conditions, mycorrhizal red clover showed higher rates of transpiration than nonmycorrhizal plants.

Hardie took her study one step further by removing the hyphae of mycorrhizal fungi from half of the red clover with

mycorrhizae. She controlled for possible side effects of this manipulation by using a tracer dye to check for root damage and by handling and transplanting all study plants, including those in her control group. Removing hyphae significantly reduced rates of transpiration (fig. 15.20), indicating a direct role of mycorrhizal fungi in the water relations of plants. Hardy suggests that mycorrhizal fungi improve water relations of plants by giving more extensive contact with moisture in the rooting zone and provide extra surface area for absorption of water.

So far, it seems that plants always benefit from mycorrhizae. That may not always be the case. Environmental conditions may change the flow of benefits between plants and mycorrhizal fungi.

Nutrient Availability and the Mutualistic Balance Sheet

Mycorrhizae supply inorganic nutrients to plants in exchange for carbohydrates, but not all mycorrhizal fungi deliver nutrients to their host plants at equal rates. The relationship between fungus and plant ranges from mutualism to parasitism, depending on the environmental circumstance and mycorrhizal species or even strains within species.

Nancy Johnson (1993) performed experiments designed to determine whether fertilization can select for less mutualistic mycorrhizal fungi. Before discussing her experiments, we have to ask what would constitute a "less mutualistic" association. In general, a less mutualistic relationship would be one in which there was a greater imbalance in the benefits to the mutualistic partners. In the case of mycorrhizae, a less mutualistic mycorrhizal fungus would be one in which the fungal partner received an equal or greater quantity of photosynthetic product in trade for a lower quantity of nutrients.

Johnson pointed out that there are several reasons to predict that fertilization would favour less mutualistic mycorrhizal fungi. The first is that plants vary the amount of soluble carbohydrates in root exudates as a function of nutrient availability. Plants release more soluble carbohydrates in root exudates when they grow in nutrient-poor soils and decrease the amount of carbohydrates in root exudates as soil fertility increases. Consequently, fertilization of soils should favour strains, or species, of mycorrhizal fungi capable of living in a low-carbohydrate environment. Johnson suggested that the mycorrhizal fungi capable of colonizing plants releasing low quantities of carbohydrates will probably be those that are aggressive in their acquisition of carbohydrates from their host plants, perhaps at the expense of host plant performance. She addressed this possibility using a mixture of field observations and greenhouse experiments.

In the first phase of her project, Johnson examined the influence of inorganic fertilizers on the kinds of mycorrhizal fungi found in soils. She collected soils from 12 experimental plots in a field on the Cedar Creek Natural History Area in central Minnesota that had been abandoned from agriculture for 22 years. Six of the study plots had been fertilized with inorganic fertilizers for eight years prior to Johnson's experiment, while the other six had received no fertilizer over the same period.

Johnson sampled the populations of mycorrhizal fungi from fertilized and unfertilized soils and showed that the composition of mycorrhizal fungi differed substantially. Of the 12 mycorrhizal species occurring in the samples, unfertilized soil supported higher densities of three mycorrhizal fungi, *Gigaspora gigantea, G. margarita,* and *Scutellispora calospora,* while fertilized soil supported higher densities of one species, *Glomus intraradix.* Spores of *G. intraradix* accounted for over 46% of the spores recovered from fertilized soils but only 27% of the spores from unfertilized soils.

Johnson used greenhouse experiments to assess how these differences in the composition of mycorrhizal fungi might affect plant performance. She chose big bluestem grass, *Andropogon gerardii,* as a study plant for these experiments because

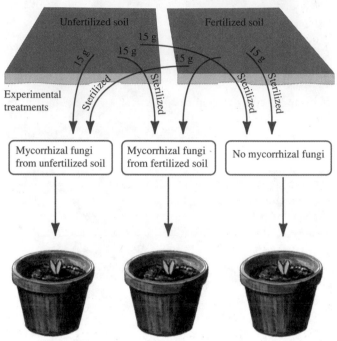

Question: Does fertilizing soil select for less mutualistic mycorrhizal fungi?

Experimental Design

Two sources of mycorrhizal fungi

Compare: Growth, root:shoot ratios, and number of inflorescences produced by three treatments.

Figure 15.21   Testing the effects of long-term fertilizing on interactions between mycorrhizal fungi and plants on agricultural lands.

it is native to the Cedar Creek Natural History Area and is well adapted to the nutrient-poor soils of the area. Seedlings of *Andropogon* were planted in pots containing sand. Johnson also added a composite sample of other soil microbes living in the soils of the fertilized and unfertilized study plots.

To each pot Johnson added a mycorrhizal "inoculum" of 30 g of soil of one of three types: (1) a fertilized inoculum consisting of 15 g of soil from fertilized study plots mixed with 15 g of sterilized unfertilized soil, (2) an unfertilized inoculum consisting of 15 g of soil from unfertilized study plots mixed with 15 g of sterilized fertilized soil, or (3) a nonmycorrhizal inoculum consisting of 30 g of a sterilized composite from the soils of fertilized and unfertilized study plots. The first two inocula acted as a source of mycorrhizal fungi for colonization of *Andropogon*. The design of Johnson's experiment is summarized in figure 15.21.

Why did Johnson create her inocula by mixing sterilized and unsterilized soils from the fertilized and unfertilized study areas? She did so to control for the possibility that some nonbiological factor such as trace nutrients in one of the two soil types might have a measurable effect on plant performance. The completely sterilized inoculum acted as a control to assess the performance of plants in the absence of mycorrhizae. Why did Johnson's control consist of sterilized composite soil from all the study areas? Again, she had to guard against the possibility that the soils themselves without mycorrhizal fungi might affect plant performance.

Pots were next assigned to one of four nutrient treatments in which Johnson (1) added no supplemental nutrients (None), (2) added phosphorus only (+P), (3) added nitrogen only (+N), or (4) added both nitrogen and phosphorus (+N+P). The sand from the Cedar Creek Natural History Area contained a fairly low concentration of nitrogen but considerably higher concentrations of phosphorus. Nutrient additions were adjusted so that the supplemented treatments offered nitrogen and phosphorus concentrations comparable to those of the topsoil in the fertilized study plots.

Johnson harvested five replicates of each of the treatments at two points in time: at 4 weeks, when *Andropogon* was actively growing, and at 12.5 weeks, when the grass was fully grown. At each harvest she measured several aspects of plant performance: plant height, shoot mass, and root mass; and at 12.5 weeks she also recorded the number of inflorescences per plant.

At 12.5 weeks shoot mass was significantly influenced by nutrient supplements and by whether or not plants were mycorrhizal but not by the source of the mycorrhizal inoculum (fig. 15.22). Shoot mass was greatest in the double nutrient supplement treatment (+N+P), somewhat lower in the nitrogen supplement (+N), and very low in the other two treatments (None and +P). Figure 15.22*a* also indicates a definite influence of mycorrhizae on performance. Shoot mass was significantly greater for mycorrhizal plants across all nutrient treatments.

Nutrient supplements and mycorrhizae also significantly influenced root:shoot ratios (fig. 15.22*b*). As we saw in chapter 7, plants invest differentially in roots and shoots depending on nutrient and light availability. It also appears that variation in investment is aimed at increasing supplies of resources in short supply. For instance, in nutrient-poor environments many plants invest disproportionately in roots and consequently have high root:shoot ratios, which decline with increasing nutrient availability. The results of Johnson's experiments are consistent with this generalization. Root:shoot ratios were highest in the treatments without nitrogen supplements (None and +P) and lowest in the treatments with nitrogen supplements (+N and +N+P). In other words, higher plant investment in roots in the low-nitrogen treatments suggests greater nutrient limitation than in the high-nitrogen treatments.

In summary, Johnson's study produced two pieces of evidence that bear on the question posed at the outset of her study: Can fertilization of soil select for less mutualistic mycorrhizal fungi? First, in the early stages of her experiment, *Andropogon* inoculated with fertilized soil had lower shoot mass than those inoculated with unfertilized soil. Second, *Andropogon* inoculated with unfertilized soils produced more inflorescences than did *Andropogon* inoculated with fertilized soils. In other words, *Andropogon* inoculated with mycorrhizal fungi from unfertilized soils showed faster shoot growth as young plants. These results suggest that plants receive more benefit from association with the mycorrhizal fungi from unfertilized soils. Johnson's simultaneous studies of the

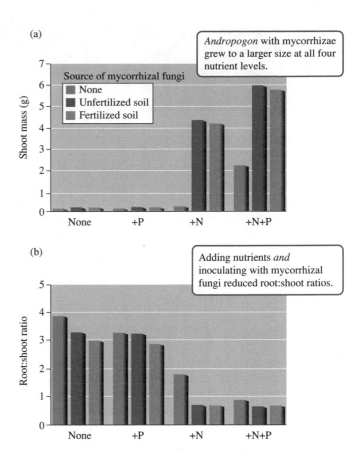

Figure 15.22 Effect of nutrient additions and mycorrhizae on the grass *Andropogon gerardii* (data from Johnson 1993).

mycorrhizal fungi indicate the mechanisms producing these patterns. It appears that altering the nutrient environment does alter the mutualistic balance sheet, an influence of potential importance to agricultural practice.

John Klironomos, from the University of Guelph, has also delved deeply into complex world of plant–fungal interactions. He has found that the form of interaction between plants and fungi is even more variable and complex than people had imagined. Klironomos asked a very important question: Are AMF generally mutualists, or parasites? In a very straightforward experiment he subjected individual plants of 64 plant species to one of two treatments: Plants were planted in a greenhouse pot with either propagules of one species of AMF (*Glomus etunicatum*), or sterile soil (Klironomos 2003). He used 10 replicates of each plant species × AMF combination, resulting in 1,280 pots. After 16 weeks, he measured plant biomass, comparing growth with, and without, AMF. The results were dramatic (fig. 15.25). The growth of most species did not differ between the AMF and sterile soil treatments! In other words, this relationship was generally neutral—not mutualistic nor parasitic. However, for some species the interaction was strongly parasitic, and others strongly beneficial. Across this broad range of species, Klironomos found a broad range of plant responses. Ecological interactions, like mycorrhizae, fall along a continuum of effect for the partners. Understanding why requires we look a bit at the evolution of mutualisms.

Impacts of Mycorrhizae on Forest Sustainability

As we have discussed, mycorrhizae have the potential to impact a plant's life positively or negatively, and the position along the mutualism–exploitation continuum depends upon the exact costs and benefits at any particular time. This issue has enormous implications for agriculture and forestry, and here we will discuss two examples in which mycorrhizal interactions may have significant consequences for forest regeneration and community composition.

Suzanne Simard, of the University of British Columbia, has studied the ecology of ectomycorrhizae and their potential impact on forest dynamics extensively. Forest dynamics are an important issue for the forest industry, and having a detailed understanding of the factors that influence regeneration can be of broad economic importance. One of the interesting aspects of mycorrhizae is that many of the fungi involved are generalists, able to colonize the roots of different species of plants. This aspect of fungal biology is not restricted to pots in a greenhouse, but also can occur in the field, where you can regularly find one individual fungus associated with the roots of many individuals of plant species—simultaneously. Simard developed an elegant design to test whether these shared connections could result in sugar moving toward or away from some plants (Simard 1997). In other words, could some plants partially parasitize others through these shared mycorrhizal connections? In her study she used three focal species, *Betula payrifera*, *Pseudotsuga menziesii*, and *Thuja plicata* (fig. 15.23), all of which are important to the forestry industry of British Columbia. Simard planted young plants of these three species together in forest soil, and after some time, fed the leaves of the plants with ^{13}C or ^{14}C. Why did she use these tracers? Very simply, to follow the carbon. For example, if she fed *Betula* with ^{13}C, but found ^{13}C in the other plants, that would tell her the carbon moved. But does that mean it moved through hyphae? No. It is certainly possible that the carbon went from the leaves, to the roots, and then entered the soil as dead roots, or root exudate. Part of the elegance of her design is that she included *Thuja* in her study. This species does not share fungal species with *Betula* and *Pseudotsuga*, and so the amount of labelled carbon in *Thuja* would indicate

Figure 15.23   A number of tree species can be interconnected by mychorrhizal fungi in the forests of British Columbia.

how much passed through the plants to the soils, with any excess found in the other species coming through mycorrhizal connections.

Why did she use two tracers in this study? She wasn't interested in simply whether carbon moved from one plant to another (as prior studies have shown it could); instead she wanted to find whether there was *net* movement from one plant to another. Net movement, if it occurs, would indicate parasitism by the recipient on the host, and would be quite a surprise to many forest biologists! So, in a single trial she would feed *Betula* with one tracer and *Pseudotsuga* with the other. In her analyses, she was particularly interested in knowing the net movement of sugars into, or out of, *Pseudotsuga*. Net movement could be measured as the difference in tracer concentrations between *Pseudotsuga* and *Betula*. For instance, if *Betula* was labelled with ^{13}C and Pseudotsuga with ^{14}C, net movement would be the difference between the ^{14}C found in *Betula* and the ^{13}C found in *Pseduotsuga*.

What did Simard find? There was very little tracer in *Thuja*, indicating the plant-to-soil pathway was not likely important. However, there was substantial net movement of sugars to *Pseudotsuga*, indicating it was exploiting *Betula*! Even more interesting, the amount of parasitism expressed increased when she shaded *Pseudotsuga* (fig. 15.24), reaching up to 6% of its entire carbon budget! Why would *Betula* feed this unrelated host? We can once again return to our understanding of mutualisms as reciprocal exploitation. Not everything that happens in such an interaction is "good" for each member, instead the net effect is positive. So, in this example it is possible that the potential benefit *Betula* receives from this mutualism with the fungus is greater than the costs of feeding other plants. But there is also an alternative explanation. Perhaps *Pseduotsuga* simply can't do anything about it, and that at this point in the evolution of this interaction, the parasite is winning! We can't lose site of the fact that parasites, be they fungal or plant, are also subject to natural selection, and will certainly evolve traits that allow them to circumvent the defense systems of the host organisms.

John Klironomos, of the University of Guelph, also has evidence that ectomycorrhizae may also serve as parasites to some living animals (Klironomos and Hart 2001). Klironomos found that one species of fungus, *Laccaria bicolor*, was able to infect the small soil-dwelling arthropod, *Folsomia candida* (a springtail). This infection appears to kill large numbers of the springtails. By using ^{15}N tracers, he was able to show that the nitrogen in the springtails was moved into new tissue in seedlings of *Pinus strobus*. In other words, this ectomycorrhizal fungus is a predator to the springtail, and a mutualist

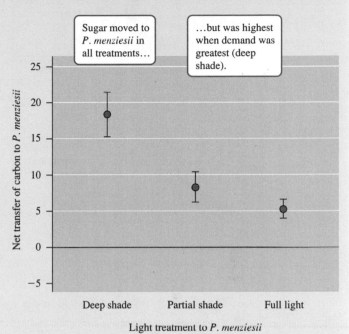

Figure 15.24 Sugar can move from one individual to another through mycorrhizal connections (data from Simard 1997).

to the tree! Similar results were not found for a second species of fungus, suggesting that even within mycorrhizal fungi there is substantial variation in the mechanisms by which resources are captured.

So what does this mean for forests sustainability? The answer to that question is unknown. Many ecologists continue to work in this area, with a growing realization that it is much more complicated than simply saying mycorrhizae are "good" for the forests. Although there may be some feeding going on through mycorrhizae, it remains unclear whether that is greater than the negative effects of competition for light and nutrients. In other words, resource sharing is yet another type of interaction among species, one that happens in addition to the other forms of interaction we have already discussed. Because of the enormous potential impact on forest regeneration, it is fair to say we will hear more of this story in the years to come.

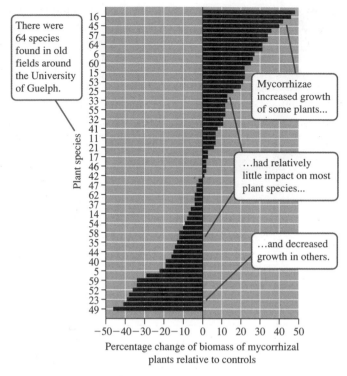

There were 64 species found in old fields around the University of Guelph.

Mycorrhizae increased growth of some plants...

...had relatively little impact on most plant species...

...and decreased growth in others.

Figure 15.25 Change in growth of 64 plant species as a function of the presence or absence of a mycorrhizal fungal species (data from Klironomos 2003).

Concept 15.3 Review

1. What similarities do nectar robbers and "cheating" Yucca moths share? What risk may then encounter if they represent a large proportion of the insects that visit the host flowers?
2. Explain why plants and pollinators have competing interests about how long flowers should be kept open.
3. Why should selection favour mycorrhizal fungi that are "less mutualistic" when soil nutrients are high?

15.4 Evolution of Mutualism

Theory predicts that mutualism will evolve where the benefits of mutualism exceed the costs. We have reviewed several complex mutualisms both on land and in marine environments. There are many others, every one a fascinating example of the intricacies of nature. Ecologists not only study the present biology of those mutualisms but also seek to understand the conditions leading to their evolution and persistence. We have also seen evidence that interactions are not fixed in time, but can vary according to changes in local conditions. Theoretical analyses point to the relative costs and benefits of a possible relationship as a key factor in the evolution of mutualism.

Modelling of mutualism has generally taken one of two approaches. The earliest attempts involved modifications of the Lotka–Volterra equations to represent the population dynamics of mutualism. The alternative approach has been to model mutualistic interactions using cost-benefit analysis to explore the conditions under which mutualisms can evolve and persist. In chapters 13 and 14, where we discussed models of competition and predation, we focused on the population dynamic approach to modelling species interactions. Here, we concentrate on cost-benefit analyses of mutualism.

Kathleen Keeler (1981, 1985) developed models to represent the relative costs and benefits of several types of mutualistic interactions. Among them are two of the mutualistic interactions we discussed in chapter 15: ant-plant protection mutualisms and mycorrhizae. Keeler's approach requires that we consider a population polymorphic for mutualism containing three kinds of individuals: (1) *successful mutualists,* which give and receive measurable benefits to another organism; (2) *unsuccessful mutualists,* which give benefits to another organism but, for some reason, do not receive any benefit in return; and (3) *nonmutualists,* neither giving nor receiving benefit from a mutualistic partner. The bottom line in Keeler's approach is that for a population to be mutualistic, the fitness of successful mutualists must be greater than the fitness of either unsuccessful mutualists or nonmutualists. In addition, the combined fitness of successful and unsuccessful mutualists must exceed that of the fitness of nonmutualists. If these conditions are not met, Keeler proposed that natural selection will eventually eliminate the mutualistic interaction from the population.

In general, we can expect mutualism to evolve and persist in a population when and where mutualistic individuals have higher fitness than nonmutualistic individuals.

Keeler represented the fitness of nonmutualists as:

$$w_{nm} = \text{fitness of nonmutualists}$$

(Fitness has been traditionally represented by the symbol *w* and though it might be clearer to use another symbol, such as *f,* the traditional symbol is used here.) Keeler represents the fitness of mutualists as:

$$w_m = pw_{ms} + qw_{mu} \tag{1}$$

where:

p = the proportion of the population consisting of successful mutualists

w_{ms} = the fitness of successful mutualists

q = the proportion of the population consisting of unsuccessful mutualists

w_{mu} = the fitness of unsuccessful mutualists.

We can represent Keeler's conditions for the evolution and persistence of mutualism as:

$$w_m > w_{nm} \tag{2}$$

or

$$pw_{ms} + qw_{mu} > w_{nm} \tag{3}$$

Keeler predicts that mutualism will persist when the combined fitness of successful and unsuccessful mutualists exceeds the fitness of nonmutualists. Why do we have to combine the fitness of successful and unsuccessful mutualists? Remember that both confer benefit to their partner, but only the successful mutualists receive benefit in return.

The analysis is more convenient if we think of these relationships in terms of **selection coefficients (s),** the relative selective costs associated with being either a successful mutualist, an unsuccessful mutualist, or a nonmutualist:

$$s = 1 - w \text{ and } w = (1 - s).$$

Using selective coefficients, Keeler expressed the selective cost of being a successful mutualist, an unsuccessful mutualist, or a nonmutualist as:

$$s_{ms} = (H)(1 - A)(1 - D) + I_A + I_D \tag{4}$$

$$s_{mu} = (H)(1 - D) + I_A + I_D \tag{5}$$

$$s_{nm} = H(1 - D) + I_D \tag{6}$$

where:

H = the proportion of the plant tissue damaged in the absence of any defenses

D = the amount of protection given to the plant tissues by defenses other than ants (e.g., chemical defenses); so, 1 − D is the amount of tissue damage that would occur in spite of these alternative defenses

A = the amount of herbivory prevented by ants (so, again, 1 − A is the amount of herbivory that occurs in spite of ants)

I_A = the investment by the plant in benefits extended to the ants

I_D = investment in defenses other than ants

Using these selective coefficients we can express Keeler's conditions for evolution and persistence of the ant–plant mutualism as:

$$p(1 - s_{ms}) - q(1 - s_{mu}) > 1 - s_{nm}$$

into which Keeler substituted the relationships given in equations (4), (5), and (6). By simplifying the resulting equation, she produced the following expression of benefits relative to costs:

$$p[H (1 - D) A] > I_A$$

Facultative Ant–Plant Protection Mutualisms

Keeler applied her cost-benefit model to facultative mutualisms involving plants with extrafloral nectaries and ants that feed at the nectaries and provide protection to the plant in return. Her model is not appropriate for obligate mutualisms like that between swollen thorn acacias and their mutualistic ants but instead applies to situations in which both the plant and ant can live without its partner. In addition, Keeler wrote her model from the perspective of the plant side of the mutualism. Let's step through the general model and connect each of the terms with the ecology of facultative plant–ant protection mutualisms.

In this model, w_{ms} is the fitness of a plant that produces extrafloral nectaries and that successfully attracts ants effective at guarding it, while w_{mu} is the fitness of a plant that produces extrafloral nectaries but that has not attracted enough ants to mount a successful defense. For example, these plants may be too far from an ant nest. In addition, Keeler includes the fitness of nonmutualistic plants, w_{nm}, which would be the fitness of individuals of a plant that does not produce extrafloral nectaries. Are there such individuals in natural populations? We don't know, but that is not the point. The reason Keeler includes nonmutualists in her model is to provide an assessment of the potential costs and benefits of such a strategy against which she can weigh the mutualistic strategy. This is analogous to the approach used in game theory in chapter 8.

Keeler's model represents potential benefits to the host plant as:

$$p [H (1 - D) A]$$

where:

p = the proportion of the plant population attracting sufficient ants to mount a defense

Keeler's model represents the plant's costs of mutualism as:

$$I_A = n[m + d (a + c + h)]$$

where:

n = the number of extrafloral nectaries per plant

m = the energy content of nectary structures

d = the period of time during which the nectaries are active

a = costs of producing amino acids in nectar

c = costs of producing the carbohydrates in nectar

h = costs of providing water for nectar

Again, Keeler's hypothesis is that for mutualism to persist, benefits must exceed costs. In terms of her model:

$$p[H(1 - D)A] > I_A$$

This model proposes that for a facultative ant–plant mutualism to evolve and persist, the proportion of the plant's energy budget that ants save from destruction by herbivores must exceed the proportion of the plant's energy budget that is invested in extrafloral nectaries and nectar.

The details of Keeler's model offer insights into what conditions may produce higher benefits than costs. First, and most obviously, I_A, the proportion of the plant's energy budget that is invested in extrafloral nectaries and nectar should be low. This means that plants living on a tight energy budget, for example, plants living in a shady forest understory, should be less likely to invest in attracting ants than those living in full sun. Higher benefits result from (1) a high probability of attracting ants, that is, high p; (2) a high potential for herbivory, H; (3) low effectiveness of alternative defenses, low D, and (4) highly effective ant defense, high A.

The task for ecologists is to determine how well these requirements of the model match values of these variables in nature. By finding the conditions under which mutualisms are, or are not most likely to occur, ecologists can begin to unravel the complexity of interactions that occur in the natural world.

Concept 15.4 Review

1. Suppose you discover a mutant form of plant that does not produce extrafloral nectaries. What does Keller's theory predict concerning the relative fitness of these mutant plants and the typical ones that produce extrafloral nectaries?
2. According to Keller's theory, under what general conditions would the mutant, lacking extrafloral nectaries, increase in frequency in a population and displace the typical plants that produce extrafloral nectaries?

Ecological Tools

Mutualism and Humans

Mutualism has been important in the lives and livelihood of humans for a long time. Historically, much of agriculture has depended upon mutualistic associations between species and much of agricultural management has been aimed at enhancing mutualisms, such as nitrogen fixation, mycorrhizae, and pollination to improve crop production. Agriculture itself has been viewed as a mutualistic relationship between humans and crop and livestock species. However, there may be some qualitative differences between agriculture as it has been generally practiced and mutualisms among other species. How much of agriculture is pure exploitation and how much is truly mutualistic remains an open question. Here we discuss how understanding the ecology of mutualisms can help us understand some human behaviours.

There is, however, at least one human mutualism that fits comfortably in chapter 15, a mutualism involving communication between humans and a wild species with clear benefit to both. This mutualism joins the traditional honey gatherers of Africa with the greater honeyguide, *Indicator indicator* (fig. 15.26). Honey gathering has long been an important aspect of African cultures, important enough that there are scenes of honey gathering in rock art painted over 20,000 years ago (Isack and Reyer 1989). No one knows how long humans have gathered honey in Africa, but it is difficult to imagine the earliest hominids resisting such sweet temptation. Whenever honey gathering began, humans have apparently had a capable and energetic partner in their searches.

The Honeyguide

Honeyguides belong to the family Indicatoridae in the order Piciformes, an order that also includes the woodpeckers. The family Indicatoridae includes a total of 17 species, 15 of which are native to Africa. Honeyguides have the unusual habit of feeding on waxes of various sorts—most feed on beeswax and insects. Of the 17 species of honeyguides, only the greater honeyguide, *I. indicator,* is known to guide humans and a few other mammals to bees' nests.

The greater honeyguide is found throughout much of sub-Saharan Africa. It avoids only dense forests and very open grass-

Figure 15.26
The greater honeyguide,
Indicator indicator.

lands and desert, and its distribution corresponds broadly with the distributions of tropical savanna and tropical dry forest. Like all of the honeyguides, the greater honeyguide is a brood parasite that, like cuckoos, lays its eggs in the nests of other birds. This way of life is reflected in the early morphology of nestling honeyguides, which retain "bill hooks" on their upper and lower bills for the first 14 days of life that they use to lacerate and kill their nest mates. However, nests sometimes contain two honeyguide nestlings, so apparently there is some mechanism by which nestlings of the same species can coexist. After the deaths of their nest mates, honeyguide nestlings receive all the food brought by their foster parents, which continue to feed young honeyguides until they are completely independent, approximately 7 to 10 days after leaving the nest.

Greater honeyguides are capable of completely independent life without mutualistic interactions with humans, so we would classify their mutualism as facultative. Living independently, honeyguides feed on beeswax, and on the adults, larvae, pupae, and eggs of bees. They also feed on a wide variety of other insects. Greater honeyguides show highly opportunistic feeding behaviour and sometimes join flocks of other bird species foraging on the insects stirred up by large mammals. The most distinguishing feature of the greater honeyguide, however, is its habit of guiding humans and ratels, or honey badgers, to bees' nests.

Guiding Behaviour

The first written report of the guiding behaviour of *I. indicator* was authored in 1569 by João Dos Santos, a missionary in the part of East Africa that is now Mozambique. Dos Santos first noticed honeyguides because they would enter the mission church to feed upon the bits of beeswax on candlesticks. He went on to describe their guiding behaviour by saying that when the birds find a beehive, they search for people and attempt to lead them to the hive. He noted that the local people eagerly followed the birds because of their fondness for honey, and he observed that the honeyguide profits by gaining access to the wax and dead bees left after humans raid the hive. Dos Santos's report of this behaviour was confirmed by other European visitors to almost all parts of Africa for the next four centuries. However, it wasn't until the middle of the twentieth century that the mutualism of honeyguides with humans was examined scientifically. The foundation work of these studies was that of H. Friedmann (1955), who reviewed and organized the observations of others, including those of Dos Santos, and who conducted his own extensive research on the honeyguides of Africa.

Friedmann's report of some of the African legends surrounding the greater honeyguide suggests that a wide variety of African cultures prescribed rewarding the bird for its guiding behavior and that native Africans recognized the need for reciprocity in their interactions with honeyguides. One proverb reported by Friedmann was, "If you do not leave anything for the guide [*I. Indicator*], it will not lead you at all in the future." Another proverb stated more ominously, "If you do not leave anything for the guide, it will lead you to a dangerous animal the next time." Friedmann also observed that many African cultures forbid killing a honeyguide and once "inflicted severe penalties" for doing so. These observations suggest long association between humans and honeyguides and that the association has been consciously mutualistic on the human side of the balance sheet.

The mutualistic association between humans and honeyguides may have developed from an earlier association between the bird and the ratel, or honey badger, *Mellivora capensis*. The honey badger is a powerful animal, well equipped with strong claws and powerful muscles to rip open bees' nests, that readily follows honeyguides to bees' nests. The honey badger, though secretive, has been observed often following honeyguides while vocalizing. African honey gatherers also vocalize to attract honeyguides, and Friedmann reported that some of their vocalizations imitate the calls of honey badgers.

The most detailed and quantitative study of this mutualism to date is that of H. Isack of the National Museum of Kenya and H.-U. Reyer of the University of Zurich (Isack and Reyer 1989), who studied the details of the interaction of the greater honeyguide with the Boran people of northern Kenya. The Boran regularly follow honeyguides and have developed a penetrating whistle that they use to attract them. The whistle can be heard over 1 km away, and Isack and Reyer found that it doubles the rate at which Boran honey gatherers encounter honeyguides. If they are successful in attracting a honeyguide, the average amount of time it takes to find a bees' nest is 3.2 hours. Without the aid of a honeyguide the average search

time per bees' nest is about 8.9 hours. This is an underestimate of the true time, however, since Isack and Reyer did not include days in which no bees' nests were found in their analysis. The benefit of the association to the bird seems apparent from Isack and Reyer's analysis, since they report that 96% of the nests to which the Boran were guided would have been inaccessible to the birds without human help.

The greater honeyguide attracts the attention of a human by flying close and calling as it does so. Following this initial attention-getting behaviour the bird will fly off in a particular direction and disappears for up to one minute. After reappearing, the bird again perches in a conspicuous spot and calls to the following humans. As the honey gatherers follow, they whistle, bang on wood, and talk loudly to "keep the bird interested." When the honey gatherers approach the perch from which the honeyguide is calling, the bird again flies off, calling and displaying its white tail feathers as it does so, only to reappear at another conspicuous perch a short time later. This sequence of leading, following, and leading is repeated until the bird and the following honey gatherers arrive at the bees' nest.

Isack, who is a Boran, interviewed Boran honey gatherers to determine what information they obtained from honeyguides. The main purpose of the study was to test assertions by the honey gatherers that the bird informs them of (1) the direction to the bees' nest, (2) the distance to the nest, and (3) when they arrive at the location of the nest. The data gathered by Isack and Reyer support all three assertions.

Honey gatherers reported that the bird indicated direction to the bees' nest on the basis of the direction of its guiding flights. One method used by Isack and Reyer to test how well flight direction indicated direction was to induce honeyguides to guide them from the same starting point to the same known bees' nest on five different occasions. Figure 15.27*a* shows the highly restricted area covered by these five different guiding trips. Another approach was to induce the bird to guide them to a bees' nest from seven different starting points (fig. 15.27*b*). The result was a consistent tendency by the bird to lead directly to the site of the bees' nest.

The Boran honey gatherers said that three variables decrease as distance to the nest decreases: (1) the time the bird stays out of sight during its first disappearance following the initial encounter, (2) the distance between stops made by the bird on the way to the bees' nest, and (3) the height of the perch on the way to the nest. Data gathered by Isack and Reyer support all three statements (fig. 15.28).

The honey gatherers also report that they can determine when they arrive in the vicinity of a bees' nest by changes in the honeyguide's behaviour and vocalizations (fig. 15.29). Isack and Reyer observed several of these changes. While on the path to a bees' nest a honeyguide emits a distinctive guiding call and will answer human calls by increasing the frequency of the guiding call. On arriving at a nest, the honeyguide perches close to the nest and gives off a special "indication" call. After a few indication calls, it remains silent and does not answer to human sounds. If approached by a honey gatherer, a honeyguide flies in a circle around the nest location before perching again nearby.

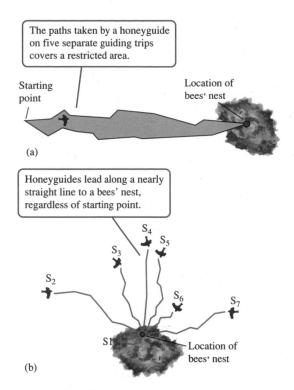

The paths taken by a honeyguide on five separate guiding trips covers a restricted area.

Starting point

Location of bees' nest

(a)

Honeyguides lead along a nearly straight line to a bees' nest, regardless of starting point.

S₄

S₃   S₅

S₂

S₆

S₇

S1

Location of bees' nest

(b)

Figure 15.27   Paths taken by honeyguides leading people to bees' nests (data from Isack and Reyer 1989).

Isack and Reyer observe that their data do not allow them to test other statements by the Boran honey gatherers, including that when bees' nests are very far away (over 2 km) the honeyguide will "deceive" the gatherers about the real distance to the nest by stopping at shorter intervals. Isack and Reyer add, however, that they have no reason to doubt these other statements, since all others have been supported by the data they were able to collect. What these data reveal is a rich mutualistic interaction between wild birds and humans. It remains unclear how widely mutualisms alter human behaviour. Using ecological tools and methods of study may provide further insights into the social biology of people.

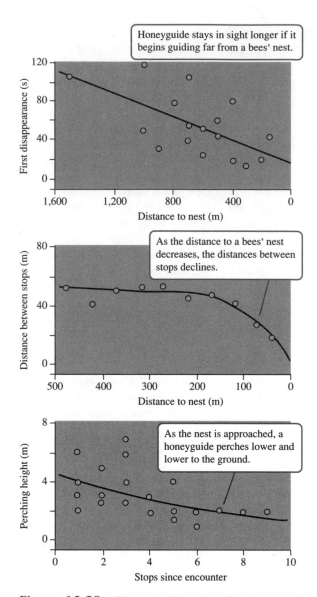

Honeyguide stays in sight longer if it begins guiding far from a bees' nest.

As the distance to a bees' nest decreases, the distances between stops declines.

As the nest is approached, a honeyguide perches lower and lower to the ground.

Figure 15.28   Changes in behaviour of the honeyguide as it nears a bees' nest (data from Isack and Reyer 1989).

After arriving at a bees' nest, the honeyguide gives a few distinctive indication calls and then perches silently near the nest.

On the way to a bees' nest a honeyguide uses a particular call and responds to a human voice by increasing call frequency.

Figure 15.29
Vocal communication between honeyguides and humans.

Summary

Many interactions between individuals are difficult to classify, and range along a continuum of exploitation and mutualism. Mutualisms, interactions between individuals that benefit both partners, are common in nature, and form the foundation of most of life as we know it within the biosphere. Mutualisms can be divided into those that are facultative, where species can live without their mutualistic partners, and obligate, where species are unable to complete their life cycle without their partner.

There exists great diversity in the types of parasitic and mutualistic interactions that exist, defying easy generalization. Despite the ubiquity of mutualistic interactions, most species on the planet are parasites. The specific interactions between parasites and hosts, and between mutualistic partners are extremely diverse. Many pathogens alter behaviour of their hosts in ways that increase the transmission rate of the pathogen. Such changes can have negative consequences for the host, such as increased predation rates and altered competitive abilities. Some parasites, such as winter ticks, can infest their hosts, causing shifts in appearance, behaviour, and likely population dynamics. Other interactions appear to benefit both partners, such as the obligate mutualism that occurs between ants and Acacia trees. Acacia trees provide food and housing for ants, which provide protection from herbivores and potential competitors for the tree. The mutualism between Zooxanthellae and corals results in the construction of the foundation of an entire ecosystem, coral reefs. The Zooxanthellae live within their animal partners (the coral), receiving nutrients from the coral while returning organic compounds for the coral to synthesize.

Basic ecological principles can be applied to our understanding of disease, and the population dynamics of pathogens can be predicted using a compartmental model. Disease can be viewed as an exploitative interaction between a host and a pathogen. Population growth of the disease can be modelled by the use of a compartmental model. One key parameter is the transmission rate of the disease, which is a measure of how efficiently an infected host can infect a susceptible member of the population. Virulence is a measure of how symptomatic an infection is, along with any increased mortality. Population growth of a disease is highest when transmission rates are high and virulence low, and natural selection often favours decreased virulence over time. Humans can use these models to control the growth of disease within human populations. For example, having basic ecological measures of SARS can lead to evaluation of the effectiveness of isolation and quarantine programs. Basic ecological data on common human diseases allows public health professionals to design vaccination programs to provide herd immunity to the target population.

Many interactions can switch from parasitic to mutualistic, depending upon the specific conditions of the local environment. Although many mutualisms appear as though individuals are doing things "for each other," mutualisms are better viewed as reciprocal exploitation. Most mutualisms are facultative, and the net effect can be parasitic, neutral, or mutualistic, depending on the specific environmental conditions and species involved. For example, plants modify flower longevity to maximize their own fitness, even though this comes at the cost of reduced foraging opportunities for their "partners," the pollinators. Even in the obligate mutualism of Yucca–Yucca moths, the costs and benefits of the interaction can vary greatly among populations. Many of populations contain high densities of cheater phenotypes of the moths, which do not posses the physical ability to pollinate their host plants. Pollination services are of great importance to the economy of Canada, and to the sustainability of natural systems. This interaction is based upon an exploitative interaction that is generally reciprocal. Mycorrhizae are another form of mutualism involving plants, also with enormous economic importance. Mycorrhizae, which are mostly either vesicular-arbuscular mycorrhizae or ectomycorrhizae, are important in increasing plant access to water, nitrogen, phosphorus, and other nutrients. In return for these nutrients, mycorrhizae receive energy-rich photosynthate. Experiments have shown that the balance sheet between plants and fungi can be altered by nutrient availability, and that the net effects of mycorrhizae on plant growth vary greatly among plant species. These results further emphasize the idea that interactions fall along a continuum of net effects.

Theory predicts that mutualism will evolve where the benefits of mutualism exceed the costs. Keeler built a cost-benefit model for the evolution and persistence of facultative plant–ant protection mutualisms in which the benefits of the mutualism to the plant are represented in terms of the proportion of the plant's energy budget that ants protect from damage by herbivores. The model assesses the costs of the mutualism to the plant in terms of the proportion of the plant's energy budget invested in extrafloral nectaries and the water, carbohydrates, and amino acids contained in the nectar. The model predicts that the mutualism will be favoured where there are high densities of ants and potential herbivores and where the effectiveness of alternative defenses are low.

Humans have developed a variety of mutualistic relationships with other species, but one of the most spectacular is that between the greater honeyguide and the traditional honey gatherers of Africa. In this apparently ancient mutualism, humans and honeyguides engage in elaborate communication and cooperation with clear benefit to both partners. The mutualism offers the human side a higher rate of discovery of bees' nests, while the honeyguide gains access to nests that it could not raid without human help. Careful observations have documented that the honeyguide informs the honey gatherers of the direction and distance to bees' nests as well as of their arrival at the nest.

Review Questions

1. Why do scientists view mutualisms as one point along an exploitation–mutualism continuum? Why can some interaction switch from parasitic to mutualistic?
2. Why don't individuals "do things for each other," even if at a cost to their own fitness? Simard's studies with mycorrhizae suggest that in some cases this may occur. How can you reconcile your understanding of ecology and natural selection with her finding that one tree feeds unrelated individuals of another species?
3. Outline the experiments of Johnson (1993), which she designed to test the possibility that artificial fertilizers may select for less mutualistic mycorrhizal fungi. What evidence does Johnson present in support of her hypothesis?
4. Explain how mycorrhizal fungi may have evolved from ancestors that were originally parasites of plant roots. Is there any evidence that present-day mycorrhizal fungi may act like parasites to plants or animals? Be specific.
5. Janzen (1985) encouraged ecologists to take a more experimental approach to the study of mutualistic relationships. Outline the details of Janzen's own experiments on the mutualistic relationship between swollen thorn acacias and ants.
6. Explain how human diseases can be viewed as an ecological interaction. What benefits may come from using ecological models to describe population growth of a pathogen? Is medicine connected to ecology?
7. How are the coral-centred mutualisms similar to the plant-centred mutualisms we discussed in chapter 15? How are they different? The exchanges between mutualistic partners in both systems revolve around energy, nutrients, and protection. Is this an accident of the cases discussed or are these key factors in the lives of organisms?
8. Outline the benefits and costs identified by Keeler's (1981, 1985) cost-benefit model for facultative ant–plant mutualism. From what perspective does Keeler's model view this mutualism? From the perspective of plant or ant? What would be some of the costs and benefits to consider if the model was built from the perspective of the other partner?
9. How could you change the Lotka–Volterra model of competition we discussed in chapter 13 into a model of mutualism? Would the resulting model be a cost-benefit model or a population dynamic model?
10. Outline how the honeyguide–human mutualism could have evolved from an earlier mutualism between honeyguides and honey badgers. In many parts of Africa today, people have begun to abandon traditional honey gathering in favour of keeping domestic bees and have also begun to substitute refined sugars bought at the market for the honey of wild bees. Explain how, under these circumstances, natural selection might eliminate guiding behaviour in populations of the greater honeyguide. (In areas where honey gathering is no longer practiced, the greater honeyguide no longer guides people to bees' nests.)

Suggested Readings

Allen, M. F. 1991. *The Ecology of Mycorrhizae*. Cambridge, England: Cambridge University Press.

A thorough, concise, and readable overview of the ecology of mycorrhizae.

Bever, J. D., P. A. Schultz, A. Pringle, and J. B. Morton. 2001. Arbuscular mycorrhizal fungi: more diverse than meets the eye and the ecological tale of why. *BioScience* 51:923–31.

Interesting account of diversity among arbuscular mycorrhizal fungi.

Bronstein, J. L. 1994. Our current understanding of mutualism. *The Quarterly Review of Biology* 69:31–51.

Bronstein reviews studies of mutualism set within the perspective of approaches used to study competition and predation. She identifies several key research questions to guide future studies of mutualism.

Hoeksema, J. D. and E. M. Bruna. 2000. Pursuing the big questions about interspecific mutualism: a review of theoretical approaches. *Oecologia* 125:321–30.

An overview of the fundamental questions regarding the evolution of interspecific mutualisms.

Huntzinger, M., R. Karban, T. P. Young, and T. M. Palmer. 2004. Relaxation of induced indirect defenses of acacias following exclusion of mammalian herbivores. *Ecology* 85:609–14.

The researchers found that following exclusion of herbivores swollen thorn acacias reduce their allocation to defensive ant mutualists.

Lindstrom, E.R., H. Andrén, P. Angelstam, G. Cederlund, B. Hörnfeldt, L. Jäderberg, P.A. Lemnell, B. Martinsson, K. Sköld, and J. E. Swenson. 1994. Disease reveals the predator: sarcoptic mange, red fox predation, and prey populations. *Ecology* 75:1042–49.

Large-scale, long-term study of interactions between a pathogenic parasite, a predator, and its prey.

Moore, J. 1984. Parasites that change the behaviour of their host. *Scientific American* 250:108–15

An excellent reveiw of the influences of parasites on prey behaviour.

Samuel, W.M. 2004. White as a ghost. *Federation of Alberta Naturalists.*

A very readable overview of the relationship between winter ticks and moose.

Williams, G.C. and R.M. Neese. 1991. The dawn of Darwinian Medicine. *The Quarterly Review of Medicine.* 66:1–22.

The paper that started the field of Darwinian medicine.

COMMUNITIES AND ECOSYSTEMS

In this section we move beyond specific interactions between individuals and their environment and discuss communities and ecosystems. In chapter 16 we discuss different approaches to describing communities. In chapter 17 we show how species interactions can have strong influences on various aspects of community structure and functioning. In chapter 18 we discuss how these interactions can vary in time and in response to disturbances, altering succession and stability of communities. We end this section with chapters 19 and 20, in which we discuss primary and secondary production, and how these are related to nutrient cycling.

Chapter 16

Species Abundance and Diversity

Outline

ifferent areas within the same region may differ substantially in the number of species they support. Vast areas of flat or gently sloping land in the hot deserts of North America are dominated by a single species of shrub, the creosote bush, *Larrea tridentata*. While grasses and forbs grow in the spaces between these shrubs, creosote bushes make up most of the plant biomass. In these areas, you can travel many kilometers and see only subtle changes in a landscape dominated by a single species of plant (fig. 16.1).

The uniformity of the creosote flats contrasts sharply with the biological diversity of other places in these hot deserts (fig. 16.2). For instance, a rich variety of plant life-forms cover Organ Pipe National Monument in southern Arizona. Here grow ocotillo, consisting of several slender branches 2 to 3 m tall springing from a common base, palo verde trees with green bark and tiny leaves, and mesquite, which reach the size of medium-sized trees. In addition, there are cactus such as the low-growing prickly pears and the shrublike teddy bear chollas. The most striking are the column-shaped squat barrel cactus, the organ pipe cactus, with its densely packed slender columns, and the saguaro, a massive cactus that towers over all the other plant species. Among these larger plants also grow a wide variety of small shrubs, grasses, and forbs.

The creosote flats, dominated by one species of shrub, convey an impression of great uniformity. The vegetation of Organ Pipe National Monument, consisting of a large number of species of many different growth forms, gives the impression of high diversity. The ecologist is prompted to ask what factors control this difference in diversity?

In chapters 13 to 15 we focused on competition, predation, and mutualism, primarily between pairs of species. As you can see, we are now considering patterns and processes that involve a larger number of species in a community. A **community** is an association of interacting species inhabiting some defined area. Communities generally consist of many species that potentially interact in all of the ways discussed in chapters 13 to 15. At the same time, species within a community must continue to cope with the abiotic environment, and thus the issues discussed in chapters 5–9 are also relevant.

Community ecologists seek to understand how various abiotic and biotic aspects of the environment influence the structure of communities. **Community structure** includes attributes such as the number of species, the relative abundance of species, and the kinds of species comprising a community. As you may recognize, these measures rely on population dynamics, the focus of chapters 10–12.

Because it is difficult to study large numbers of species, many community ecologists work with restricted groups of organisms, focusing, for example, on plants, mammals, or insects (see Ecological Tools for an understanding of how communities are sampled). Some community ecologists restrict their focus even more by studying guilds of species. A **guild** is a group of organisms that all make their living in a similar way. Examples of guilds include the seed-eating animals in the boreal forest, the fruit-eating birds in a tropical rain forest, or the filter-feeding invertebrates in a stream. Some guilds consist of closely related species, while others are taxonomically heteroge-

Figure 16.1   Desert landscape dominated by the creosote bush, *Larrea tridentata*.

Figure 16.2   Species-rich Sonoran Desert landscape.

neous. For instance, the fruit-eating birds on many South Pacific islands consist mainly of pigeons, while the seed-eating guild in the boreal forest includes mammals, birds, and ants.

The main users of the guild concept have been animal ecologists. Similar terms used by plant ecologists are life-form, growth form, or functional group. The life-form of a plant is a combination of its structure and its growth dynamics. Plant life-forms have been classified in various ways and we have used an informal classification since chapter 1, where we discussed life-forms such as trees, vines, annual plants, sclerophylous vegetation, grasses, and forbs. Functional groups generally refer to some aspect of how plants live, such as C_3 vs. C_4 plants.

Like the members of an animal guild, plants of similar life-form and functional groups exploit the environment in similar ways. As a consequence, plant community ecologists have often concentrated their attention on plants of similar life-form by studying the ecology of tree, herb, C_3, C_4, or shrub communities. By using these approaches, ecologists focus their energies on a manageable and coherent portion of the community, manageable in terms of number of species and coherent in terms of ecological requirements. Of course, it is fair to ask if ignoring other groups of species limits our understanding of communities.

In 1959, G. Evelyn Hutchinson wrote a landmark paper with the captivating title, "Homage to Santa Rosalia or Why Are There So Many Kinds of Animals?" This paper stimulated generations of ecologists to explore biological diversity. One of the most fundamental questions that we still address today is what controls the number and relative abundance of species in communities. There have been a number of foundational papers published since 1959, and they will serve as the focus for this chapter.

Concepts

16.1 Most species are moderately abundant; few are very abundant or extremely rare.

16.2 A combination of the number of species and their relative abundance defines species diversity.

16.3 Species diversity is higher in complex environments.

16.4 Intermediate levels of disturbance promote higher diversity.

16.1 Species Abundance

Most species are moderately abundant; few are very abundant or extremely rare.   The relative abundance of species is one of the most fundamental aspects of community structure. This property is so fundamental that George Sugihara (1980) referred to it as "minimal community structure." We began our discussion of the abundance of species in chapter 10, where we explored the relationship between body size and abundance and considered the various forms of rarity. In this section, we expand our perspective by addressing the following question: What will you find if you go out into a community and quantify the abundance of species within a group of taxonomically or ecologically related organisms such as beetles, birds, shrubs, or diatoms?

It turns out that there are regularities in the relative abundance of species in communities that hold whether you examine plants in a forest, moths in that forest, or algae inhabiting a nearby stream. If you thoroughly sample groups of organisms such as these, you will come across a few abundant species and a few that are very rare. Most species will be moderately abundant. This pattern was first quantified by Frank Preston (1948, 1962a, 1962b), who carefully studied the relative abundance of species in collections and communities. Preston worked throughout the Canadian Prairies, and his "distribution of commonness and rarity" among species is one of the best documented patterns in natural communities.

The Lognormal Distribution

How do we think about the abundance of organisms? Preston suggested that we think of abundance in relative terms and say, for example, that one species is twice as abundant as another. This common way of expressing relative abundance led Preston to graph the abundance of species in collections as frequency distributions, where the classes of species abundance were intervals of 1–2, 2–4, 4–8, 8–16, etc., individuals. Preston made each interval twice the preceding one and plotted them on a $\log_2$ scale (e.g., $\log_2$ of $1 = 0$, $\log_2$ of $2 = 1$, $\log_2$ of $4 = 2$, etc.). Preston's graphs plot $\log_2$ of species abundance against the number of species in each abundance interval. When the relative abundance of species were plotted in this way, he consistently obtained results like those shown in figure 16.3.

Figure 16.3a shows the relative abundance of desert plants. Robert Whittaker (1965) plotted these abundances using coverage rather than numbers of individuals, which accords well with our discussions in chapter 10 of how to represent the relative abundance of plants. Notice that few species were represented by more than 8% cover or less than 0.15% cover. Most species had intermediate coverage. Whittaker's plot shows the most distinctive feature of Preston's distributions, that is, they are approximately "bell-shaped," or "normal." Since abundance is plotted on a log scale, Preston's curves are called "lognormal" distributions.

Figure 16.3b shows the relative abundance of 86 species of birds breeding near Westerville, Ohio, over a 10-year period (Preston 1962a). Notice that few species were represented by over 64 individuals or by a single individual. Like Whittaker's plants, most species showed intermediate levels of abundance, producing another lognormal distribution.

In most lognormal distributions, only a portion of a bell-shaped curve is apparent. For instance, neither figure 16.4a nor b presents a complete normal curve. However, figure 16.4b, a sample of moths from Lethbridge, Alberta, comes closer to a complete curve than does figure 16.4a, a sample of moths from Saskatoon, Saskatchewan. Preston suggested that much of the difference between the two curves results from a difference in sample size. While the sample of moths from Saskatoon contained approximately 87,000 individuals belonging to 277 species, the sample from Lethbridge contained an incredible 303,251 individuals belonging to 291 species. If the sample from Saskatoon had contained 300,000 individuals, it would have contained more species, producing a more complete lognormal curve. Ecologists have found that the more you sample a community, the more species you will find. The common species show up in even small samples, but a great deal of sampling effort is needed to capture the rare species.

So, how do we explain the lognormal distribution of commonness and rarity? Robert May (1975) proposed that the lognormal distribution is the product of many random environmental variables acting upon the populations of many species. In other words, the lognormal distribution is a statistical expectation.

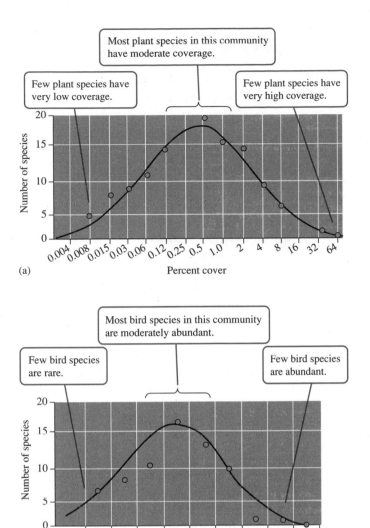

Figure 16.3   Lognormal distributions of (*a*) desert plants, and (*b*) forest birds (data from Whittaker 1965, Preston 1962a).

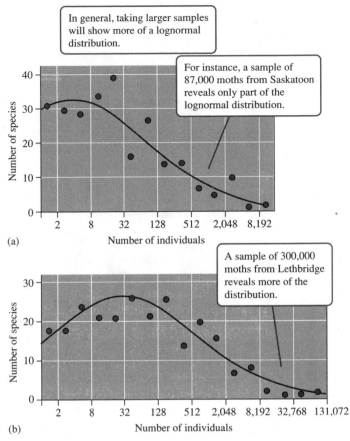

Figure 16.4   Sample size and the lognormal distribution (data from Preston 1948).

Is the lognormal distribution just a mathematical artifact or does it reflect important biological processes? George Sugihara (1980) suggested that the lognormal distribution is a consequence of the species within a community subdividing niche space. However, regardless of its origins, the lognormal distribution is important because it allows us to predict the distribution of abundance among species.

Concept 16.1 Review

1. Why do smaller samples result in only part of the bell-shaped curve that is characteristic of the lognormal distribution?

2. Why did the massive sampling efforts associated with the moth collections shown in figure 16.4 reveal only a portion of the lognormal distribution, while the studies of birds and plants produced the nearly complete lognormal distributions shown in figure 16.3?

16.2   Species Diversity

A combination of the number of species and their relative abundance defines species diversity.   What is diversity? This seemingly simple question can prove extraordinarily complex to answer. To begin to simplify this, we will focus on biological diversity, rather than social and abiotic aspects of diversity. This, however, still leaves us with many options. Diversity could represent variation in genotypes among individuals, differences in the physical structure of communities (e.g., low-growing peatland vs. tall forest), variation in the types of organisms found (mites, springtails, plants, etc.), or perhaps variation in the actual species that are found in a community. It is this later form of diversity, **species diversity**, which is generally studied by community ecologists. However, it is important to recognize that species diversity represents just one type of diversity that can be found in a single community.

Ecologists define species diversity on the basis of two factors: (1) the number of species in the community, which ecologists usually call **species richness,** and (2) the relative abundance of species, or **species evenness.** The influence of species richness on community diversity is clear. A community with 20 species is obviously less diverse than one with 80 species. The effects of species evenness on diversity are more subtle but easily illustrated.

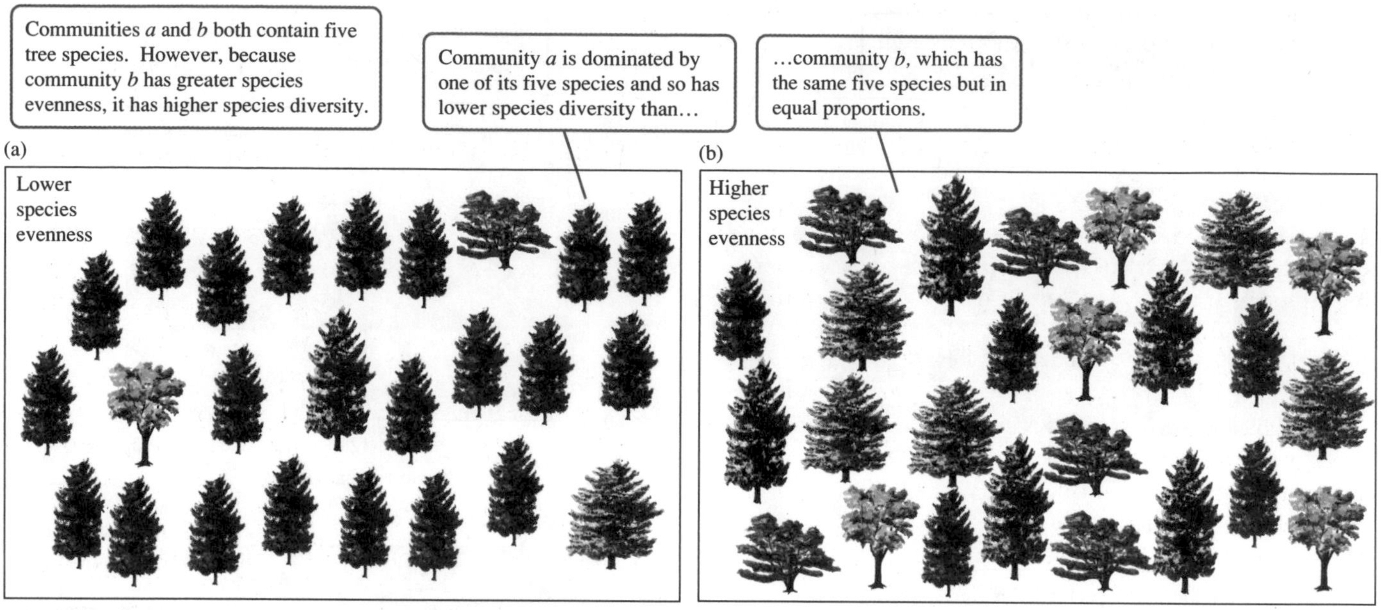

Communities *a* and *b* both contain five tree species. However, because community *b* has greater species evenness, it has higher species diversity.

Community *a* is dominated by one of its five species and so has lower species diversity than...

...community *b*, which has the same five species but in equal proportions.

(a)

Lower species evenness

(b)

Higher species evenness

Figure 16.5   Species evenness and species diversity.

Figure 16.5 contrasts two hypothetical forest communities. Both forests contain five tree species, so they have equal levels of species richness. However, community *b* is more diverse than community *a* because its species evenness is higher. In community *b*, all five species are equally abundant, each comprising 20% of the tree community. In contrast, 84% of the individuals in community *a* belong to one species, while each of the remaining species constitutes only 4% of the community. On a walk through the two forests, you would almost certainly form an impression of higher species diversity in community *b*, despite equal levels of species richness in the two forests.

This issue is of critical importance to understanding and describing communities. Diversity is generated though an increase in the number of species *and* through an increase in the evenness among those species. As you will see in the remainder of the text, different factors can affect species numbers and evenness, and these two measures of diversity may themselves differentially affect other community and ecosystem processes. Because of this importance of this issue, it should come as no surprise that these measures of diversity have been incorporated into a single index of diversity.

An Integrative Index of Species Diversity

Getting ecologists to agree on the "best" index for species diverse is slightly more difficult than herding cats. A quick search through the literature will yield a diversity of indices seemingly as great as the diversity of the species they are intended to describe. These indices go by the names of Simpson's index (named after Edward, not Homer), Margalef's index, and Brillouin's index of diversity to name just a few. These indices all share a core trait: their values depend upon levels of species richness and evenness. Here we apply one of the more widely used indices, the Shannon–Wiener index, to our hypothetical forest communities.

The Shannon–Wiener index is:

$$H' = -\sum_{i=1}^{s} p_i \log_e p_i$$

where:

H' = the value of the Shannon–Wiener diversity index

p_i = the proportion of the *i*th species

$\log_e$ = the natural logarithm of p_i

s = the number of species in the community

To calculate H', determine the proportions of each species in the study community, p_i, and the $\log_e$ of each p_i. Next, multiply each p_i times $\log_e p_i$ and sum the results for all species from species 1 to species *s*, where *s* = the number of species in the community, that is:

$$\sum_{i=1}^{s}$$

Since this sum will be a negative number, the Shannon–Wiener index calls for taking its opposite, that is:

$$-\sum_{i=1}^{s}$$

The minimum value of H' is 0, which is the value of H' for a community with a single species, and increases as species richness and species evenness increase.

Figure 16.6 shows how to calculate H' for our two hypothetical forest communities. The different values of H' for the two communities reflect the difference in species evenness that we see when we compare the two forests depicted in figure 16.5. H' for community *b*, the community with higher species evenness, is 1.610, while H' for community *a* is 0.662.

The Shannon–Wiener index is a great way to get a snapshot of the diversity of the community, capturing aspects of both the number and evenness of species. However, sometimes an ecologist may be interested in these two components of diversity individually. Not surprisingly, ecologists have a few standard ways of measuring them. *Species richness*, s, is simply the number of species found in a given location (quadrat, community, landscape, etc.). It is the most basic of measures, truly just a count of species, but it serves as the backbone of many studies of biodiversity.

There are many metrics used to measure evenness, though one of the more commonly used is Pielou's J, named after the influential mathematical ecologist Evelyn Pielou, formerly of Queen's University, Dalhousie University, and University of Lethbridge. Pielou was influential in developing appropriate mathematical tools to answer questions in community ecology. Her influence in the field is in part evidenced by the Statistical Ecology section of the Ecological Society of America naming an annual award given to graduate students in her honour. Pielou's measure of evenness, J, is key to many studies of biodiversity. The simplicity of the measure itself is evidence of the elegance of Pielou's research, as J is developed and supported by a large body of mathematical research in information science (Pielou 1966), yet has been presented in a very usable form. Simply:

$$J = \frac{H'}{H_{max}}$$

where:

H' = the value of the Shannon–Wiener diversity index
H_{max} = the total possible H for the number of species in the sample.

H_{max} is calculated by assuming all individuals in a sample are evenly distributed among the species contained in the sample. For example, if there were 5 species ($s = 5$), then you would assume each has a p_i of 0.20, and calculate H accordingly. As Pielou shows, H_{max} will equal log s, and thus you can rewrite the equation for evenness as:

$$J = \frac{H'}{\log s}$$

By doing this, both evenness and species richness can be directly measured, providing ecologists with more tools for understanding communities. As you will see next, we can also use a graphical approach to contrast communities.

Rank-Abundance Curves

We can portray the relative abundance and diversity of species within a community by plotting the relative abundance of species against their rank in abundance. The resulting **rank-abundance curve** provides us with important information about a community, information accessible at a glance. Figure 16.7 plots the abundance rank of each tree species in communities a and b (see fig. 16.5) against its proportional abundance. The rank-abundance curve for community b shows that all five species are equally abundant, while the rank-abundance curve for community a shows its dominance by the most abundant tree species.

Now let's examine the more realistic differences shown by the rank-abundance curves for two actual communities. Figure 16.8 shows rank-abundance curves for the understory

Calculating species diversity (H′) for two hypothetical communities of forest trees

Community a

Species	Number	Proportion (p_i)	$\log_e p_i$	$p_i \log_e p_i$
1	21	0.84	−0.174	−0.146
2	1	0.04	−3.219	−0.129
3	1	0.04	−3.219	−0.129
4	1	0.04	−3.219	−0.129
5	1	0.04	−3.219	−0.129
Total	25	1.00		−0.662

$$H' = -\sum_{i=1}^{s} p_i \log_e p_i = 0.662$$

Community b

Species	Number	Proportion (p_i)	$\log_e p_i$	$p_i \log_e p_i$
1	5	0.20	−1.609	−0.322
2	5	0.20	−1.609	−0.322
3	5	0.20	−1.609	−0.322
4	5	0.20	−1.609	−0.322
5	5	0.20	−1.609	−0.322
Total	25	1.00		−1.610

$$H' = -\sum_{i=1}^{s} p_i \log_e p_i = 1.610$$

Figure 16.6

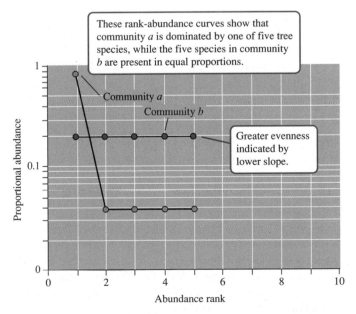

These rank-abundance curves show that community a is dominated by one of five tree species, while the five species in community b are present in equal proportions.

Community a
Community b

Greater evenness indicated by lower slope.

Figure 16.7 Rank-abundance curves for two hypothetical forests.

vegetation found in burned and unburned forests just north of Thunder Bay, Ontario (Lamb et al. 2003). The researchers from Lakehead University measured the diversity and abundance of the vegetation in areas that were burned about four

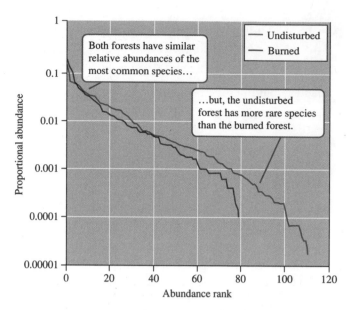

Figure 16.8   Rank-abundance curves for burned and undisturbed forests near Thunder Bay, Ontario (unpublished data courtesy of E. Lamb).

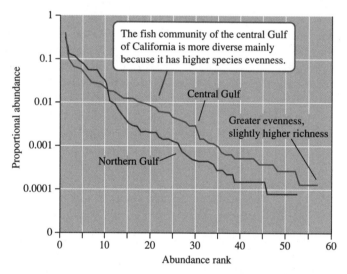

Figure 16.9   Rank-abundance curves for two reef fish communities in the Gulf of California (data from Molles 1978, Thomson and Lehner 1976, and courtesy of D. A. Thomson and C. E. Lehner 1976).

years prior to data collection, and undisturbed forest. The undisturbed forests contained 110 species, while the burned forest only held 79. Additionally, you will notice that although the proportional representation of the common species was similar in both forest types, the less common species were rarer in the burned forests than the undisturbed forests. You can see this because for most ranks, the undisturbed forest line is above the burned forest line, indicating that the xth most common species in the forest has a higher proportional representation in the undisturbed forest.

Two reef fish communities from the Gulf of California provide a more subtle contrast in rank-abundance patterns. The reef fish communities yielded approximately similar numbers of

species (52 versus 57) but differed substantially in species evenness. The community of the central Gulf of California showed a more even distribution of individuals among species. This greater evenness is depicted in figure 16.9, which shows that after about the tenth most abundant species, the rank-abundance curve for the central Gulf of California lies above the curve for the northern Gulf. Rank-abundance curves will provide a useful representation of community structure in later discussions.

Concept 16.2 Review

1. Burning of forests can cause a reduction in the diversity of plants (see fig. 16.8). Why?
2. Suppose you sample an area and find the five species of forest trees listed in figure 16.6 in the following proportions: 0.35, 0.25, 0.15, 0.15, and 0.10. What is the Shannon-Wiener diversity of this community, "*c*," compared to communities *a* and *b* in figure 16.6?

16.3   Environmental Complexity

Species diversity is higher in complex environments.   How does environmental structure affect species diversity? This is one of the most fundamental questions we can ask about communities. In general, species diversity increases with environmental complexity or heterogeneity. However, an aspect of environmental structure important to one group of organisms may not have a positive influence on another group. Consequently, you must know something about the ecological requirements of species to predict how environmental structure affects their diversity. In other words, you must know something about their niches.

Forest Complexity and Bird Species Diversity

In chapter 13, we saw that competition can significantly influence the niches of species. If competition acts to produce divergence in the niches of species, what would you expect to find if you characterized the niches of closely related, coexisting species? The competitive exclusion principle (see chapter 13) leads us to predict that coexisting species will have significantly different niches. As we saw in chapter 1, that is precisely what Robert MacArthur (1958) found when he examined the ecology of five species of warblers that live together in the forests of northeastern North America.

What does MacArthur's study of warbler niches have to do with the influence of environmental complexity on species diversity? MacArthur's results suggest that since these species forage in different vegetative strata, their distributions may be influenced by variation in the vertical structure of vegetation. He explored this possibility on Mount Desert Island, Maine, where he measured the relationship between volume of vegetation above 6 m and the abundance of warblers (fig. 16.10). The number of warbler species at the study sites increased with forest stature. The study sites with greater

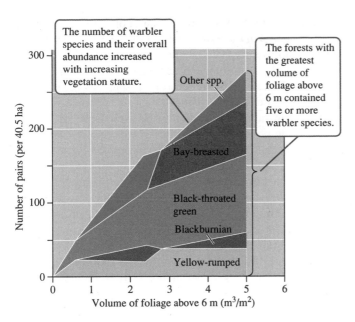

Figure 16.10   Stature of vegetation and number of warbler species (data from MacArthur 1958).

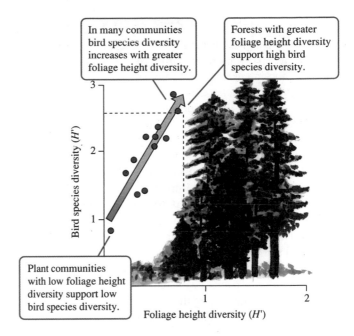

Figure 16.11   Foliage height diversity and bird species diversity (data from MacArthur and MacArthur 1961).

volume of vegetation above 6 m supported more warbler species. In other words, MacArthur found that warbler diversity increased as the stature of the vegetation increased. These results formed the foundation of later studies of how foliage height diversity influences bird species diversity.

MacArthur was one of the first ecologists to quantify the relationship between species diversity and environmental heterogeneity. He quantified the diversity of species and the complexity of the environment using the Shannon–Wiener index, H'. He measured environmental complexity as foliage height diversity, which increased with the number of vegetative layers and with an even distribution of vegetative biomass among three vertical layers, 0 to 0.6 m, 0.6 to 7.6 m, and > 7.6 m. MacArthur's foliage height diversity, like species diversity, increases with richness (the number of vegetative layers) and evenness (how evenly vegetative biomass is distributed among layers).

Robert MacArthur and John MacArthur (1961) measured foliage height diversity and bird species diversity in 13 plant communities in northeastern North America, Florida, and Panama. The vegetative communities included in their study ranged from grassland to mature deciduous forest, with foliage height diversity that ranged from 0.043 to 1.093. Plant communities with greater foliage height diversity supported more diverse bird communities (fig. 16.11). MacArthur and his colleagues went on to study the relationship between foliage height diversity and bird species diversity in a wide variety of temperate, tropical, and island settings, from North America to Australia. They again found a positive correlation between foliage height diversity and bird species diversity. The combined weight of the evidence from North and Central America and Australia suggests that the relationship is not one of chance but reflects something about the way that birds in these environments subdivide space.

How is environmental complexity related to the diversity of other organisms besides birds? Ecological studies have

shown positive relationships between environmental complexity and species diversity for many groups of organisms, including mammals, lizards, plankton, marine gastropods, and reef fish. Notice, however, that this list of organisms is dominated by animals. How does environmental complexity affect diversity of plants?

Niches, Heterogeneity, and the Diversity of Algae and Plants

The existence of approximately 300,000 species of terrestrial plants presents a multitude of opportunities for specialization by animals. Consequently, high plant diversity can explain much of animal diversity. However, how do we explain the diversity of primary producers? G. Evelyn Hutchinson (1961) described what he called "the paradox of the plankton." He suggested that communities of phytoplankton present a paradox because they live in relatively simple environments (the open waters of lakes and oceans) and compete for the same nutrients (nitrogen, phosphorus, silica, etc.), yet many species can coexist without competitive exclusion. This situation seemed paradoxical because it appears to violate the competitive exclusion principle. The diversity of terrestrial plants presents a similar paradox. This paradox is sufficiently vexing that Joseph Connell (1978) proposed that environmental heterogeneity is not sufficient to account for terrestrial plant diversity, especially in tropical rain forests.

After some decades of theoretical and empirical work, however, it appears that environmental complexity can account for a significant portion of the diversity among both planktonic algae and terrestrial plants. As with animals, to study the influence of environment on diversity of plants and algae we need to understand the nature of their niches.

The Niches of Algae and Terrestrial Plants

The niches of algae appear to be defined by their nutrient requirements. The importance of nutrient requirements to the niches of phytoplankton was demonstrated by David Tilman (1977). Tilman conducted experiments on competition between freshwater diatoms. His experiments were similar to those conducted by G. F. Gause (1934) (see chapter 13) on competition between paramecium. However, in addition to demonstrating competitive exclusion, Tilman's experiments also showed the conditions that allowed coexistence of diatom species. Exclusion or coexistence depended upon the ratio of two essential nutrients, silicate, SiO_2^{-2}, and phosphate, PO_4^{-3}.

When Tilman grew the diatoms *Asterionella formosa* and *Cyclotella meneghiniana* by themselves, they established and maintained stable populations. However, when he grew them together, *Asterionella* sometimes excluded *Cyclotella,* and sometimes the two species coexisted. The outcome of Tilman's experiments depended upon the ratio of silicate to phosphate (fig. 16.12). At high ratios *Asterionella* eventually excluded *Cyclotella*. However, at lower ratios the two species coexisted. At the lowest ratio, *Cyclotella* was numerically dominant over *Asterionella*.

How are Tilman's results different from those obtained by Thomas Park (1954) when he studied competition between *Tribolium* beetles (see chapter 13)? In Park's experiments, the outcome of competition experiments also depended upon physical conditions (temperature and moisture) but in all cases, Park eventually observed competitive exclusion of one *Tribolium* species or the other. In contrast, Tilman found experimental conditions allowing coexistence. Do Tilman's results violate the competitive exclusion principle? They do not because the diatoms he studied had different nutrient requirements. In other words, *Cyclotella* and *Asterionella* have different trophic niches.

How can we explain Tilman's results? It turns out that *Asterionella* takes up phosphorus at a much higher rate than does *Cyclotella*. Tilman reasons that at high ratios of silicate to phosphate *Asterionella* is able to deplete the environment of phosphorus and consequently eliminate *Cyclotella*. However, when ratios are low, silicate limits the growth rate of *Asterionella* and it cannot deplete phosphate. Consequently, when ratios are low, *Asterionella* cannot exclude *Cyclotella*. At these low ratios, silicate limits the growth rate of *Asterionella,* while phosphate limits the growth rate of *Cyclotella*. Consequently, in the presence of low ratios of silicate to phosphate, the two diatoms coexist.

What do the results of Tilman's experiments have to do with the relationship of environmental complexity to species diversity? The implication is that if the ratio of silicate to phosphate varies across a lake, then *Asterionella* will dominate some areas, while elsewhere *Cyclotella* will dominate.

Now, how might we characterize the niches of terrestrial plants? A. Tansley's experiments (1917) on competition between *Galium* species, which we discussed in chapter 13, provide insights into the niches of terrestrial plants. You may recall that Tansley studied two species: *G. saxatile,* which grows mainly on acidic soils, and *G. sylvestre,* which grows mainly on basic soils. When these two plants competed against each other in an experimental garden, each did best on the soil type that it occupies in nature. Like the diatoms *Asterionella* and *Cyclotella,* the niches of *G. saxatile* and *G. sylvestre* are significantly influenced by the chemical characteristics of the environment, in this case of the soil.

So what does this say about environmental complexity from the viewpoint of algae and plants? Because of the feeding niches of the warblers he studied, MacArthur could quantify environmental complexity from his birds' perspectives as foliage height diversity. Forests with higher foliage height diversity provided more distinctive environments for foraging birds. We can define the niches of algae and plants on the basis of their nutrient requirements and responses to constraining physical or chemical conditions, such as moisture and pH. Therefore, from the perspective of plants and algae, variation in the availability of limiting nutrients, such as silicate and phosphate, and variation in physical and chemical conditions, such as temperature, moisture, and pH, contribute to environmental complexity.

Complexity in Plant Environments

How much do plant nutrients vary across the environments inhabited by plants and algae? Let's look first at environmental heterogeneity in an aquatic environment. Martin Lebo and his colleagues (1993) studied spatial variation in nutrient and particulate concentrations in Pyramid Lake, Nevada, which has a surface area of approximately $450 \, km^2$ and a maximum depth of 102 m.

Pyramid Lake, like other lakes, is not a uniform chemical solution. All of the nutrients studied by the researchers showed substantial variation across the lake. Figure 16.13 shows that nitrate (NO_3) ranged from $> 20 \, \mu g$ per litre (L^{-1}) near the inflow of the Truckee River to $< 5 \, \mu g L^{-1}$ along the western and northeastern shores. Silicate (SiO_2) reached maximum concentrations of $> 300 \, \mu g L^{-1}$ at the inflow of the Truckee River and then decreased progressively northward,

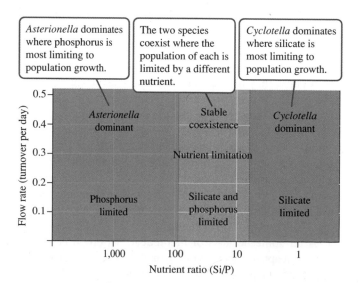

Figure 16.12   The ratio of silicate (SiO_2^{-2}) to phosphate (PO_4^{-3}) and competition between the diatoms *Asterionella formosa* and *Cyclotella meneghiniana* (data from Tilman 1977).

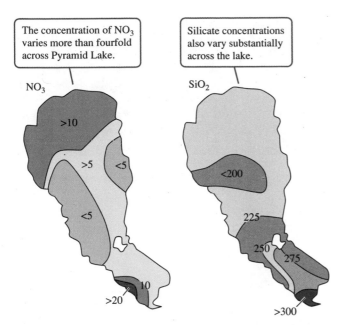

The concentration of NO₃ varies more than fourfold across Pyramid Lake.

Silicate concentrations also vary substantially across the lake.

Figure 16.13 Concentrations (mg/L) of nitrate (NO₃) and silicate (SiO₂) in the surface waters of Pyramid Lake, Nevada (data from Lebo et al. 1993).

reaching a minimum of $< 200\ \mu gL^{-1}$ in the north-central portion of the lake. Other nutrients also showed substantial variation across Pyramid Lake, but their pattern of variation differed from that shown by nitrate and silicate. In other words, different parts of the lake offer distinctive growing conditions for phytoplankton. This environmental complexity should allow for phytoplankton diversity.

Now, let's look at variation in nutrient concentrations in a terrestrial environment. Our example concerns an abandoned agricultural field, a situation where we might expect low environmental heterogeneity. We can expect reduced heterogeneity in an abandoned field because agricultural practices such as plowing, land levelling, and fertilizer applications would reduce spatial variation across fields.

G. Robertson and a team of researchers (1988) quantified variation in nitrogen and moisture across an abandoned agricultural field. Their study site was located in southeast Michigan, on the E. S. George Reserve, a 490 ha natural area maintained by the University of Michigan. Farmers cleared the field of its original oak-hickory forest and plowed the land sometime before 1870. Crop raising continued on the field until the early 1900s, when most of the land was converted to pasture. Then in 1928, the cattle were removed and the nature reserve was established. Though grazing by cattle has ceased, a dense population of white-tail deer, *Odocoileus virginianus,* continue to graze the site.

Robertson and his colleagues focused their measurements on a 0.5 ha (69 m × 69 m) subplot within the old field in which they measured several soil variables, including nitrate concentration and soil moisture, at 301 sampling points. This large number of sampling points over a small area provided sufficient data to construct a detailed map of soil properties. Figure 16.14 shows considerable patchiness in both nitrate and moisture. Both variables show at least tenfold differences across the study plot. In addition, nitrate concentration and moisture don't appear to correlate well with each other; hot spots for nitrates were not necessarily hot spots for moisture. The researchers concluded that soil conditions show sufficient spatial variability to affect the structure of plant communities.

We can see from these studies that algal and plant resources change substantially across aquatic and terrestrial environments. Now let's examine how spatial heterogeneity in these resources may affect the distribution and diversity of plants.

Influences of Environmental Heterogeneity on the Diversity of Forest Sedges

Graham Bell, Martin Lechowicz, and Marcia Waterway of McGill University have teamed up to identify the factors that influence the distribution of sedges in the deciduous forests of Quebec (Bell et al. 2000; fig. 16.15). The research team chose

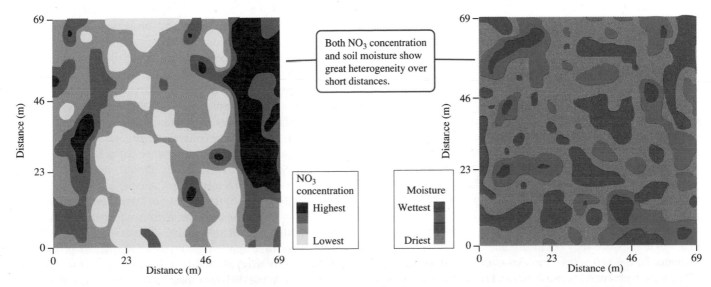

Both NO₃ concentration and soil moisture show great heterogeneity over short distances.

NO₃ concentration: Highest / Lowest

Moisture: Wettest / Driest

Figure 16.14 Variation in nitrate (NO₃) and soil moisture in a 4,761 m² area in an old agricultural field (data from Robertson et al. 1988).

Figure 16.15 McGill University's Gault Nature Reserve on Mont-Sainte-Hilaire, Quebec.

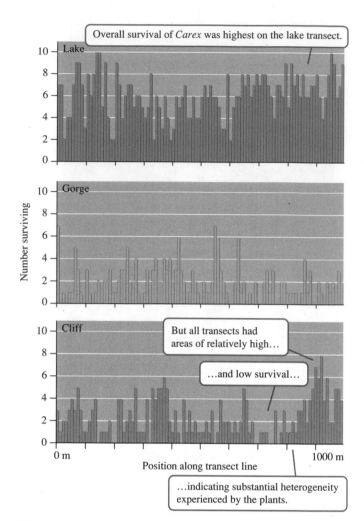

Figure 16.16 Plant survival varied along three 1000 m transects in a deciduous forest in Quebec (data from Bell et al. 2000).

to focus on sedges, more specifically the genus *Carex*, as there are more *Carex* species in forest and wetland habitats of these northern areas than any other genus of seed plant. Additionally, there are over 500 species of *Carex* in North America, and over 50 are found within the 1,000 ha study site used by the research team. In other words, this is an ideal group of organisms to explore the linkages between heterogeneity and diversity.

One of the difficulties that ecologists face when trying to identify whether heterogeneity influences diversity is in figuring out what to measure. We have already discussed a variety of measures for diversity, such as species number and evenness, but what about heterogeneity? We have seen that many animal ecologists measure heterogeneity and complexity as a function of the plant community (figs. 16.10, 16.11), and many plant ecologists measure complexity as heterogeneity in nutrient distributions (figs. 16.12, 16.13). In all these cases it has been a person choosing a specific factor to measure, and then trying to relate variation in that factor to diversity. However, from our discussions of niches (chapter 9), it is clear that niches are multidimensional, and the performance of individuals is influenced by multiple co-occurring factors. So, what if researchers choose the wrong factor for their study? How can they be certain they are choosing the most important niche axes? Bell, Lechowicz, and Waterway (2000) used a very ingenious method to get around this problem. They decided to let the plants "speak" for themselves.

The research team went out into the forest and collected several healthy individuals of 11 *Carex* species. These plants grow by forming numerous *ramets*, genetically identical modules of the plant. The team separated each individual into its ramets, planted those individually, and ended up with a large number of clones for each of their 11 species. They then went back to the field and laid out three 1,000 m transects, planting one individual of each species every 10 m. By ensuring they only used a single genetic individual of a given plant species on a single transect, they could say that any variation in performance of the plants they found was due to environmental, not genetic, influences. Very clever, and once again wonderful evidence as to why plants make such excellent study organisms

for ecological research. Trying to clone birds would be a bit more difficult, not to mention likely run the researcher into some problems with the university ethics review board!

After a year, the research team went back to their sites and recorded which plants were alive, and which had died. As you can see in figure 16.16, there was substantial variation in the number of survivors at each position along the three transects. In addition to the number of survivors, the researchers recorded the identity of the survivors. Why? Just because five species may have survived at each of two locations does not necessarily mean it was the same five species. Shifts in the **species composition** of a community, even without shifts in species richness, would indicate a shift in community structure.

What does this variation in survival (and composition) indicate? Since the use of clones allowed the research team to rule out genetic factors, they can conclude that there was biologically meaningful variation in the environment for these 11 species. The next question is whether this variation was actually related to species diversity. To test this, the researchers first applied a variety of statistical procedures allowing them to quantify the variation in performance among the species in the different locations. They were then able to use a variety of regression analyses to relate environmental

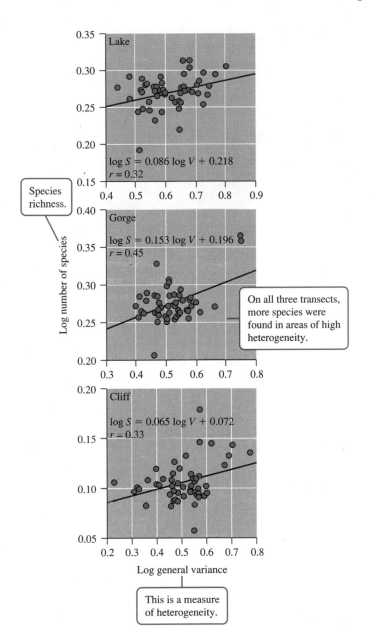

Species richness.

Log number of species

$\log S = 0.086 \log V + 0.218$
$r = 0.32$

Lake

$\log S = 0.153 \log V + 0.196$
$r = 0.45$

Gorge

On all three transects, more species were found in areas of high heterogeneity.

$\log S = 0.065 \log V + 0.072$
$r = 0.33$

Cliff

Log general variance

This is a measure of heterogeneity.

Figure 16.17 The diversity of forest sedges increased with increased environmental heterogeneity (data from Bell et al. 2000).

heterogeneity found among nearby sites to the number of species in those sites. In general, they found that environmental variation between sites increased with the distance between sites. More interestingly, as environmental variation increased among sites, there was also increased variation in how each of the 11 species performed. In other words, as environmental heterogeneity increased, so too did the variability in species responses. This supports the idea that species have different niches, and that different factors will more strongly influence different species. This also supports the experimental approach the research team took: not measuring a single environmental factor, but instead looking for variation in responses in the plants themselves. Finally, the researchers found that overall species diversity in their plots increased with environmental heterogeneity (fig. 16.17), providing an answer to the initial question of this study.

The work here by Bell, Lechowicz, and Waterway provides an example of how focusing on a single group of species, *Carex*, can reveal patterns of community structure. In the next section, we explore the role of another factor in altering community composition: disturbance.

Concept 16.3 Review

1. Does Tilman's finding that *Asterionella* and *Cyclotella* exclude each other under certain conditions but coexist under other conditions violate the competitive exclusion principle?
2. Suppose you discover that the fish species inhabiting small isolated patches of coral reef use different vertical zones on the reef face—some species live down near the sand, some live a bit higher on the reef, and some higher still. Based on this pattern of zonation, can you predict how reef structure should affect the diversity of fish living on such reefs?
3. Why did Bell et al (2000) use plants as indicators of heterogeneity rather than rely on measures of abiotic variables such as light and nitrogen?

16.4 Disturbance and Diversity

The Nature of Equilibrium

Intermediate levels of disturbance promote higher diversity. For several chapters we have assumed that environmental conditions remain more or less stable. Ecologists refer to this state as one of **equilibrium.** In an equilibrial system, stability is maintained by opposing forces. The Lotka–Volterra competition models (see chapter 13), all predator-prey models (see chapter 14), and models of disease (chapter 15) assumed a constant physical environment. Even in chapter 16 when we discussed the influences of environmental complexity on species diversity, there was an underlying assumption of a stable environmental equilibrium. However, most natural environments are subject to various forms of disturbance.

The Nature and Sources of Disturbance

What is disturbance? The answer to this question is not as simple as it may seem. What constitutes disturbance varies from one organism to another and from one environment to another. A disturbance for one organism may have little or no impact on another, and the nature of disturbance may be quite different in different environments. It is difficult to define disturbance because it involves a departure from average conditions. Because the organisms of a particular environment have been selected to cope with average conditions, disturbance must be defined in terms of average conditions. Average conditions for a particular environment may involve substantial variation. Normal daily variation in the salinity of an estuary would cause massive disruption on a coral reef. Similarly, the normal seasonal variation in temperature experienced in a temperate deciduous forest would devastate populations in a tropical rain forest. Conversely, stabilizing either an estuary or the seasonal variation in a deciduous forest, which would be departures from average conditions, would disturb the biota of those systems. Based on these ideas, do you view the elimination of the large, natural, herbivores, bison, from the Prairies as causing or eliminating a disturbance?

Wayne Sousa (1984), who examined the role of disturbance in structuring natural communities, defined disturbance as "a discrete, punctuated killing, displacement, or damaging of one or more individuals (or colonies) that directly or indirectly creates an opportunity for new individuals (or colonies) to become established." P. S. White and S. Pickett (1985) defined disturbance as "any relatively discrete event in time that disrupts ecosystem, community or population structure and changes resources, substrate availability, or the physical environment." They also caution, however, that we must be mindful of spatial and temporal scale. For instance, disturbance to bryophyte (mosses and liverworts) communities growing on boulders along the margin of a stream can occur at spatial scales of fractions of meters and annual temporal scales that are irrelevant to the surrounding forest community.

There are innumerable potential sources of disturbance to communities. White and Pickett listed 26 major sources of disturbance roughly divided into abiotic forces such as fires, hurricanes, ice storms, and flash floods; biotic factors such as disease and predation; and human-caused disturbance. Regardless of the source, we can classify disturbances by a smaller set of characteristics. We will focus our discussion of disturbance on two characteristics: frequency and intensity.

The Intermediate Disturbance Hypothesis

Joseph Connell (1975, 1978) proposed that disturbance is a prevalent feature of nature that significantly influences the diversity of communities. He questioned the assumption of equilibrial conditions made by most competition-based models of diversity. As you may recall from chapter 13, high levels of diversity are contrary to the predictions of the competitive exclusion principle. This led many researchers to find ways in which organisms could persist even in the face of competition. Connell took a different approach, proposing that high diversity is a consequence of continually changing conditions, not of competitive accommodation at equilibrium, and predicted that intermediate levels of disturbance promote higher levels of diversity (fig. 16.18).

Connell suggested that both high and low levels of disturbance would lead to reduced diversity. He reasoned that if disturbance is frequent and intense, the community will consist of those few species able to colonize and complete their life cycles between the frequent disturbances. He also predicted that diversity will decline if disturbances are infrequent and of low intensity. In the absence of significant disturbance, the community is eventually limited to the species that are the most effective competitors, effective either because they are the most efficient at using limited resources or the most effective at interference competition. You may notice that this argument is based upon the assumption that species vary in life histories. As we saw in chapter 9, such variation does exist, and both the K and CSR

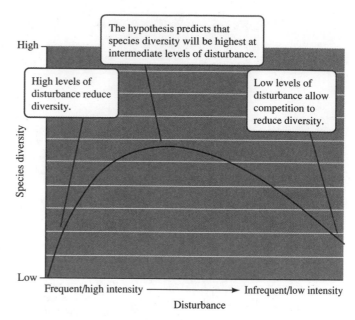

Figure 16.18   The intermediate disturbance hypothesis (data from Connell 1978).

models could apply here. What types of species groups do you expect to find at different locations on figure 16.18?

Even if we can understand the extremes of this diversity gradient favouring specific life histories, how can intermediate levels of disturbance promote higher diversity? Connell suggested that at intermediate levels of disturbance there is sufficient time between disturbances for a wide variety of species to colonize but not enough time to allow competitive exclusion.

Disturbance and Diversity in the Intertidal Zone

Wayne Sousa (1979a) studied the effects of disturbance on the diversity of marine algae and invertebrates growing on boulders in the intertidal zone. Disturbance to this community comes mainly from ocean waves generated by winter storms. These waves, which can exceed 2.5 m in height, are large enough to overturn intertidal boulders, killing the algae and barnacles growing on their upper surfaces. Meanwhile, the newly exposed underside of the boulder is available for colonization by algae and marine invertebrates.

Because boulders of different sizes turn over at different frequencies and in response to waves of different heights, Sousa predicted that the level of disturbance experienced by the community living on boulder surfaces depends upon boulder size. Smaller boulders are turned over more frequently and therefore experience a high frequency of disturbance, middle-sized boulders experience an intermediate level of disturbance, and large boulders experience the lowest frequency of disturbance.

Sousa quantified the relationship between boulder size and probability of being moved by waves by measuring the force required to dislodge boulders of different sizes. He measured the exposed surface area of a series of boulders and then measured the force required to dislodge each. To make a measurement he wrapped a chain around a boulder, attached a

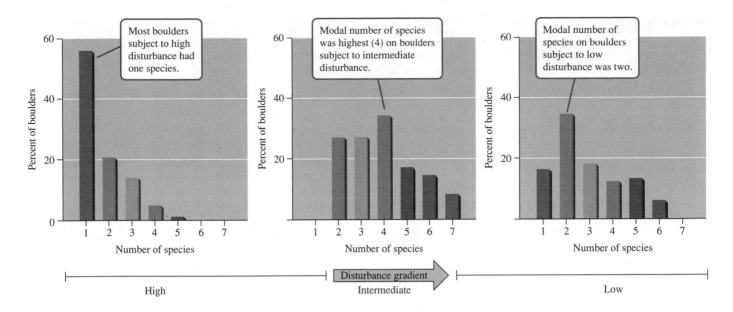

Figure 16.19 Levels of disturbance and diversity of marine algae and invertebrates on intertidal boulders (data from Sousa 1979a).

spring scale to the chain, and pulled in the direction of incoming waves until the boulder moved. He recorded the number of kilograms registered on the scale when the boulder moved and then converted his measurements to force expressed in newtons (newtons [N] = kg × 9.80665). As you might expect, there was a positive relationship between size and the force required to move boulders. What was Sousa assuming as he made these measurements? He assumed that the force required to move a boulder with his apparatus was proportional to the force required for waves to move it.

Sousa verified this assumption by documenting the relationship between his force measurements and movement by waves. He established six permanent study sites and measured the force required to move the boulders in each. He next mapped the locations of boulders by photographing the study plots and then checked for boulder movements by taking additional photographs monthly for two years. Sousa divided the boulders in the study sites into three classes based on the force required for movement: (1) ≤ 49 N, (2) 50 to 294 N, and (3) > 294 N. These classes translated into frequent movement (42% per month = frequent disturbance), intermediate movement (9% per month = intermediate disturbance), and infrequent movement (1% per month = infrequent disturbance).

The number of species living on boulders varied with frequency of disturbance (fig. 16.19). Most of the frequently disturbed boulders supported a single species, few supported five species, and none supported six or seven species. Most of the boulders experiencing a low frequency of disturbance supported one to three species, few supported six species, and none supported seven. The boulders supporting the greatest diversity of species were those subject to intermediate levels of disturbance. Most of these supported three to five species, many supported six species, and some supported seven species.

Disturbance and Diversity in Temperate Grasslands

Can several species coexist where there is a single limiting resource? The Lotka–Volterra competition equations (see chapter 13) predict that under such circumstances, one species will eventually exclude all others. However, as Sousa's work shows, even where species compete for a single resource, such as space in the intertidal zone, several species may coexist if disturbance prevents competitive exclusion. David Tilman (1994) reached a similar conclusion in regard to plant diversity within North American prairies.

What sorts of disturbance have been important in grasslands? Historically, the magnitude of disturbance on the North American prairie ranged from trampling by bison herds and fire to the death of an individual plant. One of the most important and ubiquitous sources of disturbance to grasslands is burrowing by mammals.

April Whicker and James Detling (1988) proposed that prairie dogs (*Cynomys* spp.), which occupied about 40 million ha of North American grasslands as late as 1919, were an important source of disturbance on the North American prairies. Prairie dogs are herbivorous rodents that weigh approximately 1 kg as adults and live in colonies containing 10 to 55 individuals per hectare. Prairie dogs build extensive burrow systems that are 1 to 3 m deep and about 15 m long, with tunnel diameters of 10 to 13 cm and two entrances. To build a burrow with these dimensions a prairie dog must excavate 200 to 225 kg of soil, which it deposits in mounds 1 to 2 m in diameter around burrow entrances.

Burrowing and grazing by prairie dogs have substantial effects on the structure of plant communities at several spatial scales. Figure 16.20 shows the areas of Wind Cave National Park occupied by prairie dogs. Because of the activities of these rodents, each of these areas supports vegetative communities

Human Impacts on Community Structure

We will often hear a variety of concerned citizens, non-governmental organizations, and environmental activists discuss the negative impacts of human development on the environment. This is of course an extremely broad issue, and can range from direct impacts of pollution decreasing the health of people and other species, the loss of systems due to harvesting, or more subtle impacts such as gradual declines in species abundances due to factors such as climate change. What is the role of the ecologist in these public debates? The issues of scientists as advocates is a contentious one, with some groups believing scientists should provide "just the facts," while others believe scientists should also provide suggestions for public policy. This is not the place to attempt to resolve this debate. Instead, we can show that at least one critical role ecologists can serve is providing information on how humans have historically interacted with their environment. Human impacts on the environment have been occurring for millennia. It is through the work of ecologists that we are able to take a much broader perspective on interactions between people and the environment.

Near the border between Panama and Columbia there is a region so laced with rivers and swamps and so thick with tropical rain forest that the Pan American Highway cannot pass. This region, called the Darien, has become a symbol of raw tropical nature, impenetrable and pristine. Though the Darien has resisted the passage of the Pan American Highway, it is not as pristine as it has seemed. Indiginous populations occupied and farmed the Darien continuously for about 4,000 years. They abandoned the region only after the Spanish conquest about three centuries ago. This challenge to the generally held view of the "pristine" Darien comes from work by Mark Bush and Paul Colinvaux (1994). As a consequence of their studies, we now know that these rain forests are not "virgin" but have grown up since the abandonment of agriculture, covering most traces of previous human occupation.

How did Bush and Colinvaux penetrate the secrets of the Darien? They used paleoecological methods similar to those of John Smol in chapter 3. Bush and Colinvaux looked for lakes and swamps whose sediments might preserve a record of the Darien's past. However, rather than focusing on changes in aquatic species like Smol, Bush and Colinvaux recorded pollen and spores in the cores as an indication of the plants in the area. They found such a record in a swamp and a small lake, Lake Wodehouse, approximately 15 km apart, near a small mining settlement called Cana near Panama's border with Columbia.

The researchers collected 10 m cores of sediment from Lake Wodehouse and Cana Swamp. At the bottom of the cores from Lake Wodehouse were an abundance of spores from ferns (e.g., *Triletes*) and pollen from other forest plants and little pollen from plants associated with disturbed landscapes (fig. 16.22). This portion of the pollen record indicates a swamp community dominated by ferns surrounded by mature tropical forest. Then, about 3,900 years ago, the sediment record changed abruptly with the appearance of charcoal and corn pollen, which are present throughout the subsequent record until nearly 310 years ago. Similar patterns occurred in Cana Swamp except that corn pollen constituted a greater proportion of the total pollen (about 2%), indicating that corn was being grown right on the swamp during the dry season. The sediments containing corn pollen and charcoal also contained pollen from wild plants that live in disturbed areas (e.g., Melastomataceae, *Cecropia*, *Trema,* and *Pilea*). Then, about 310 years ago, about 1.6 to 1.7 m deep in the Lake Wodehouse sediment core, charcoal and corn pollen disappear, while the pollen of forest species increases in abundance.

Other studies reveal even longer histories of human occupation and disturbance. Mark Bush, Dolores Piperno, and Paul Colinvaux (1989) provide evidence of 6,000 years of corn cultivation in the Amazon River basin. They recovered this record from the sediments of Lake Ayauch, Ecuador, a small lake within the eastern Amazon River basin at an elevation of 500 m.

As impressive as this 6,000-year history of agriculture may be, substantial human disturbance of the forests of Panama began about 11,000 years ago. Evidence comes from the sediments of Lake La Yeguada in central Panama. Lake La Yeguada yielded a 17.5 m sediment core containing a 14,300-year record of the surrounding landscape. This sediment core contains no record of human disturbance for about 3,300 years. Then, about 11,000 years ago, the charcoal content of sediment rises abruptly.

distinct from the surrounding landscape. Within a colony, prairie dog activities create patchiness on a smaller scale, with areas of forbs and shrubs, grass and forbs, and grass within the surrounding matrix of prairie grassland. Whicker and Detling estimate that plant species diversity is greatest in areas experiencing intermediate levels of disturbance by prairie dogs (fig. 16.21).

How does disturbance by prairie dogs foster higher diversity? The mechanisms underlying this effect are essentially the same as those operating in the intertidal boulder field studied by Sousa. By burrowing and piling earth and by grazing and clipping vegetation, prairie dogs remove vegetation from areas around their burrows. These bare patches are then open for colonization by plants. However, some plant species are more likely to colonize these open patches. Those species investing most heavily in dispersal are usually the first to arrive. However, these early colonists can be displaced by better competitors

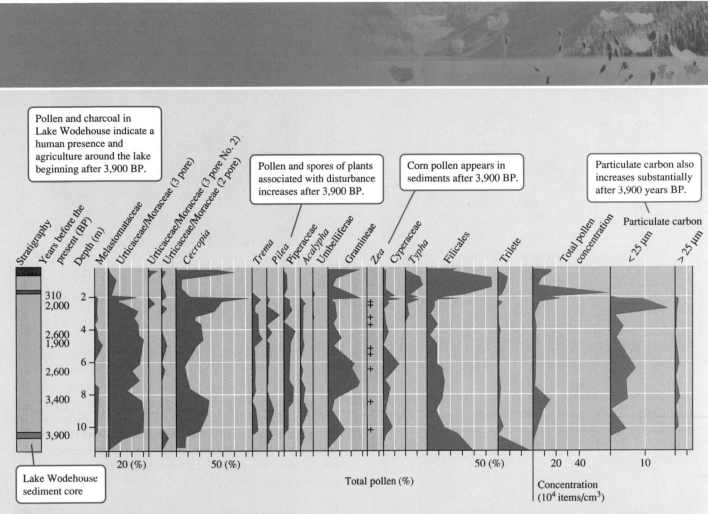

Figure 16.22 Pollen and particulate carbon in the sediments of Lake Wodehouse, Panama, dating from the present to 3,900 years before the present (BP) (data from Bush and Colinvaux 1994).

The increase in charcoal in the sediment record of La Yeguada also coincided with the presence of Paleo-Indian artifacts across Panama. We can conclude that humans have played a substantial role in shaping the communities and ecosystems of Panamanian rain forests for at least 11,000 years. At the very least we can say that the exceptionally high diversity of the New World tropics has coexisted with moderate levels of human disturbance for at least 11,000 years. However, the present rate of clear-cutting of Amazonian rain forest has no historical precedent.

Ecologists throughout the world are continuing their research on current and historical pressures on the structure of the tropical forests, as well as other systems such as the boreal forest, arctic tundra, and alpine meadows. Researchers are consistently finding that humans influenced these systems for millennia, yet they now face an unprecedented challenge from human activities. It is the role of the ecologist to understand what is happening, what will happen if conditions persist, and what will happen if human activities continue to increase, or even if they decrease. This work will require the efforts of a new generation of ecologists.

that arrive later. The persistence of both good colonizers and good competitors in a plant community depends upon intermediate levels of disturbance. Too much disturbance and the community is dominated by the good colonizers; too little disturbance and the better competitors dominate.

Because they have been considered an agricultural pest, various control programs have reduced prairie dog populations by about 98% during the last century. The extermination also

eliminated their dynamic influences on plant communities. However, other burrowing mammals remain in large numbers. One of the most important of these are the pocket gophers of the family Geomyidae. Though pocket gophers are much smaller than prairie dogs, weighing from 60 to 900 g, their effects on grassland and arid land communities are considerable. The mounds that gophers create during their burrowing may cover as much as 25% to 30% of the ground surface, which

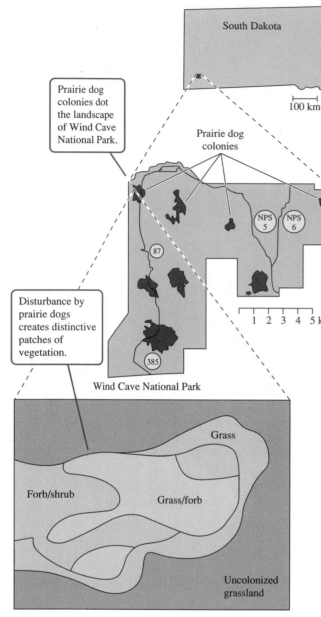

Prairie dog colonies dot the landscape of Wind Cave National Park.

Prairie dog colonies

Disturbance by prairie dogs creates distinctive patches of vegetation.

Wind Cave National Park

Figure 16.20 Disturbance by prairie dogs and patchiness of vegetation (data from Coppock et al. 1983, Whicker and Detling 1988).

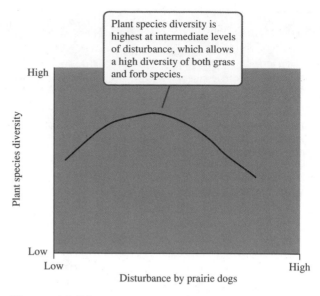

Plant species diversity is highest at intermediate levels of disturbance, which allows a high diversity of both grass and forb species.

Figure 16.21 Disturbance by prairie dogs and plant species diversity (data from Whicker and Detling 1988).

increases heterogeneity in light availability and soil nitrogen, which in turn fosters increased plant species richness.

Throughout this chapter we have explored a variety of ways to describe communities. We have also discussed several factors that may structure communities. All of this information is dependent upon researchers actually being able to go out in the field and collect accurate data on natural populations. In the next section we describe a variety of the ways ecologists sample communities.

Concept 16.4 Review

1. Could suppressing fires in forests that once burned with regular frequency due to lightening strikes be considered a disturbance?
2. According to the intermediate disturbance hypothesis, could human disturbance sustain higher levels of species diversity than in the absence of human disturbance?

Ecological Tools

Sampling Communities

At the very heart of community ecology is the need to accurately and reliably measure the composition of a community. This may seem to be a trivially easy task, as we all know that ecology professors simply go out into the field, lay down a few transects or plots, write down a few numbers, and then return home ready to devise a difficult exam for the undergraduates in their introductory courses. Except for that last part, this is

a woefully inaccurate overview of how community ecology is actually done, and takes no account of the numerous pitfalls that lie along the way.

The question of how many species are found in a community is one of the most fundamental questions an ecologist can ask. With increasing threats to biodiversity, species richness is also one of the most important community attributes we might measure. Estimates of species richness are critical for determining areas suitable for conservation, for diagnosing the impacts of environmental change on a community, or for identifying critical habitat for rare and threatened species. However, determining species richness of an actual community is not a simple undertaking. Sound estimates require a carefully designed, standardized sampling program; and great accuracy by those collecting the data. This section will focus on several fundamental aspects of study design.

One of the positions that Evelyn Pielou advocated was that advancement in ecology would come through integration of models, lab studies, and data-rich studies from the field. Mathematical ecology would then serve a critical role in "processing large bodies of observational data in such a way that interesting regularities, hitherto buried from sight, become apparent" (Pielou 1977). This approach by Pielou is important in that it emphasizes a link between question development (modelling, lab studies) and testing in real world conditions (field studies; statistics). Over the decades, ecologists have grappled with developing the appropriate research methods that will provide society not only with large volumes of data, but more importantly, with large volumes of high quality and accurate data. In chapter 1 we presented a general overview of the scientific method. Here we explore some of the issues that ecologists face when they work at that point between research idea and statistical analysis (fig. 16.23).

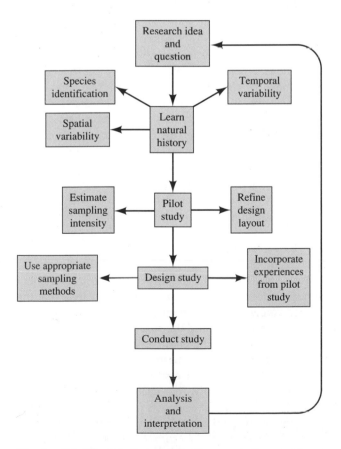

Figure 16.23 Much time and effort occurs between the development of a research idea and the statistical analysis of the data.

Where, When, and How Much?

One of the critical first steps in a study is knowing exactly where and when you should sample. For some projects, this may be trivially easy. For example, if you are "contracted" to measure the number of native plant species growing in your parents' native flower garden, and there is only one weekend left before you return to campus for the fall term, then this study has clearly defined boundaries, in both space and time. However, suppose your contract was to measure the number of plant species found in gardens throughout your home town. If you happen to live in a very small town, with only a handful of gardens, it is possible that you would be able to measure every single garden and get an actual count of species richness. However, suppose you lived in Victoria, British Columbia. It simply isn't possible to measure every garden over the entire summer, let alone your last weekend home. Instead, you will need to sub-sample. Additionally, because the growing season in Victoria is quite long, there is likely going to be variation in which species you see at different points of the year, and thus sampling only in the fall is likely inadequate to measure the actual diversity of the system.

Timing

We will first discuss a few issues related to deciding when and how often you should sample. In general, you want to sample with a frequency that allows you to accurately identify all species that are likely present. What that frequency is will depend upon the organisms. For example, you likely only want to sample for flying insects during the months and times of day that they are active. If you are working with plants, there is little value in sampling during the winter months throughout much of the Northern hemisphere. However, some regions are too hot to support plant growth during the summer, and thus are best surveyed during the winter! Some groups of organisms are likely to have little change in species composition over their period of activity (e.g., small mammals over summer), while others may change substantially. As a result, you will need to sample high-turnover taxa more frequently than low-turnover taxa. For example, Elise Bolduc and her colleagues at McGill University sampled the diversity of ground-dwelling spiders in vineyards in southern Quebec (Bolduc et al. 2005). Their data shows that the abundances of five of the more common species vary greatly over the summer months, and thus if they used a single "snapshot" of the community, they likely would have missed several of these species (fig. 16.24). It is clearly important to sample when your species are active! At the same time, you do not want to oversample your community, as this would be wasted effort, costing you money, loss of time, and even increasing risk to your study populations for little scientific value (chapter 9). Whether the right frequency means you should sample once a week, once a month, or once a year will depend on the organisms you work with and this is why having a strong basis in natural history is critical to doing good ecological research (fig. 16.23).

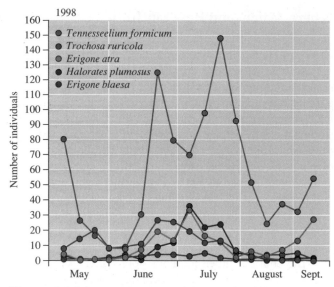

Figure 16.24   The abundances of five co-occurring species of spiders can vary greatly over the summer (data from Bolduc et al. 2005).

Location

Deciding where to sample poses difficulties similar to deciding when to sample. If all species were distributed evenly across a community, the life of a field ecologist would often be quite simple, as we could simply throw down a quadrat and what we'd find would be representative of every other location in the community. The real world, however, is much more heterogeneous. As we have discussed throughout the text, different species have different niche requirements, and even more restricted realized niches, and thus only a narrow set of locations within a community are likely suitable for growth for any particular species. As a result, even if we placed two quadrats down on the forest floor, separated only by 1–2 m, and measured the diversity of plant species in each, there is a very good chance we would not find identical results. If we assume that it isn't possible to sample every square inch of the forest floor, we need to instead use sub-samples. Where do we lay them? How many do we use?

Let's suppose we have the time, energy, and budget to sample the vegetation of only 100 m² of a 10 ha forest community, or 0.1% of the actual community (fig. 16.25). How do we decide what size of plots we should use, and where do we lay them? (It is worth noting that many ecological questions can also be measured using "plotless" sampling techniques, though that is beyond the scope of this text). The most basic consideration given to determining the size of study plots is the size of the organisms you are going to study. Plots need to be larger than many individuals of all the species you are measuring. In other words, you can use a 50 × 50 cm plot if you are measuring mosses, but not if you are measuring trees. Second, your plot size needs to be small enough that you can accurately measure all the individuals within the plot. For organisms such as mosses that are very small, large plots result in substantial error. You learn the appropriate size of plot for

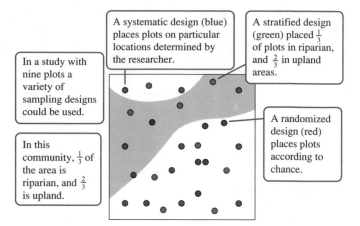

Figure 16.25   Systematic, random, and stratified sampling in a community.

your system through experience. Again, a solid grounding in natural history is critical to good ecological research.

We will now suppose that you are focusing your work on the diversity of understory seedlings, and you have decided that plots of 1 × 1 m are most appropriate. How do you distribute those plots throughout the community? You have three main choices: random, systematic, and stratified random. Random is simply that. You use a random number generator to develop coordinates for each of your 100 samples. This will give a completely unbiased sample (which is good), sometimes (which is bad). Why only sometimes? We know that species distributions are not random, or at least not completely random. Some species are going to be found only in some locations. When you randomly assign plots to locations, the plots may—by chance—aggregate in certain areas of the community. Remember from chapter 9 that random is not the same as even. Random distributions of plots work best in communities that do not have any obvious major "sub-communities" within them. For instance, random plot assignments might work well in a homogeneous forest, but not one that has a stream going through it, as you would expect differences in species composition as a function of distance to the stream. The potential negative effects of random plot placement are greatest when you are using relatively few plots.

So does this mean that we should generally place our plots in certain places, using instead some sort of systematic plot design? No. Systematic designs can come in a variety of flavours. One design would be to place plots in areas that the researcher "knows" are important areas of diversity. This will obviously bias the results and the study, as the areas sampled are not representative of the entire area. In the wrong hands, such a biased design could be used to either artificially inflate or deflate measures of biodiversity of a single community, even if the data collected within each plot is accurate. It is because of this reason that scientists pay particular attention to the details of study designs in their own work, as well as that of others. There is another form of systematic plot layout that is often used, and that is to spread plots out evenly over the community. For example, in this study you could devise a grid with 100 evenly spaced intersections, sampling in each location. This design introduces a new bias, one that is based upon the natural distribution of the organisms in the system. If the organisms are distributed according to any particularly spatial pattern, then superimposing any new spatial pattern (e.g. a grid) imposes a new bias! For example, imagine that competition for light results in a recurring pattern of tall tree — small tree — tall tree — small tree. Sampling on a grid that overlays a regular spatial pattern will cause a biased sample, overestimating the number of either large or small trees. As a result, systematic designs are generally avoided, unless substantial prior research is available showing such underlying patterns do not exist.

The final design, and one that is often used, particularly when only a few plots are available, is the stratified random design. This approach takes the best parts of both the randomized and systematic design, without falling prey to their statistical traps. Quite simply, suppose you are working in a forest that has riparian and upland habitats, and you think that these "subcommunities" will contain different species. You can stratify your study into two parts, upland and riparian, and then you assign plots to those strata in proportion to their abundance on the landscape. For example, if 30% of the area was riparian, you would assign 30 of your 100 plots to riparian, and the remaining 70 to upland. Within a given strata, you would randomly locate those 30 (or 70) plots. This design is very commonly used, and works best when a community is only subdivided into a few strata, allowing for many plots within each.

The Need for Pilot Studies

In this section we have only touched upon a few of the common issues field ecologists encounter when they attempt to sample communities. There exist many more problems that we have not yet even touched upon. For example, how do we know when we have sampled enough? In other words, when is sampling the same plot for longer worse than sampling a new plot for a shorter duration? Even more basic is the issue of species identification. How do we know we are right in the names we are assigning to our samples? Without a high level of accuracy in that most basic of skills, much of the time and money spent on a project is wasted.

How does one acquire those skills? Practice and patience. There is no substitute for actual field experience if you want to become a field researcher. The idea of natural history being important in ecology is not because all ecologists are granola eating (I hate granola) relics of the sixties (I was only alive for 23 days of the 1960s). Rather, natural history is important because a sound understanding of the system that you will explore is critical to the development of a sound experimental design. Do you want to do a field experiment? Then stop spending all your free time sitting in the library discussing Sartre and Heidegger, and get to the field!

Summary

A *community* is an association of interacting species inhabiting some defined area. Examples of communities include the plant community on a mountainside, the insect community associated with a particular species of tree, or the fish community on a coral reef. Community ecologists often restrict their studies to groups of species that all make their living in a similar way. Animal ecologists call such groups *guilds*, while plant ecologists use the terms *life-form* and functional groups. The field of community ecology concerns how the environment influences *community structure*, including the relative abundance and diversity of species, the subjects of this chapter.

Most species are moderately abundant; few are very abundant or extremely rare. Frank Preston (1948) graphed the abundance of species in collections as distributions of species abundance, with each abundance interval twice the preceding one. Preston's graphs were approximately "bell-shaped" curves and are called "lognormal" distributions. Lognormal distributions, which describe the relative abundance of organisms ranging from algae and terrestrial plants to birds, may result from many random environmental variables acting upon the populations of a large number of species or may be a consequence of how species subdivide resources. Regardless of the underlying mechanisms, the lognormal distribution is one of the best-described patterns in community ecology.

A combination of the number of species and their relative abundance defines species diversity. Two major factors define the diversity of a community: (1) the number of species in the community, which ecologists usually call *species richness*, and (2) the relative abundance of species, or *species evenness*. One of the most commonly applied indices of species diversity is the Shannon–Wiener index:

$$H' = -\sum_{i=1}^{s} p_i \log_e p_i$$

Species eveness is generally measured with Pielou's J. The relative abundance and diversity of species can also be portrayed using *rank-abundance curves*. Accurate estimates of species richness require carefully designed sampling programs.

Species diversity is higher in complex environments. Robert MacArthur (1958) discovered that five coexisting warbler species feed in different layers of forest vegetation and that the number of warbler species in North American forests increases with increasing forest stature. Various investigators have found that the diversity of forest birds increases with increased foliage-height diversity. Heterogeneity in physical and chemical conditions across aquatic and terrestrial environments can account for a significant portion of the diversity among planktonic algae and terrestrial plants. Heterogeneity in forests is positively associated with the diversity of *Carex* communities.

Intermediate levels of disturbance promote higher diversity. Joseph Connell (1975, 1978) proposed that high diversity is a consequence of continually changing conditions, not of competitive accommodation at equilibrium. He predicted that intermediate levels of disturbance would foster higher levels of diversity. At intermediate levels of disturbance, a wide array of species can colonize open habitats, but there is not enough time for the most effective competitors to exclude the other species. Wayne Sousa (1979a), who studied the effects of disturbance on the diversity of sessile marine algae and invertebrates growing on intertidal boulders, found support for the intermediate disturbance hypothesis. Diversity in prairie vegetation also appears to be higher in areas receiving intermediate levels of disturbance. The effect of disturbance on diversity appears to depend upon a trade-off between dispersal and competitive abilities.

Studies in community ecology are complicated by variation in the distributions of species in both space and time. Appropriate study designs require detailed knowledge of the natural history of the study system and the organisms that live within it. It is critical to consider aspects of the timing and frequency of measurements, as well as the shape, number, and distribution of study plots. Designs not founded in an understanding of the study system are likely to result in biased findings. In order to learn how to conduct field research, it is critical to do field research.

Review Questions

1. What is the difference between a community and a population? What are some distinguishing properties of communities? What is a guild? Give examples. What is a plant life-form? Give examples.
2. Draw a "typical" lognormal distribution. Include properly labelled horizontal (x) and vertical (y) axes. You can use the lognormal distributions included in chapter 16 as models.
3. Suppose you are a biologist working for an international conservation organization concerned with studying and conserving biological diversity. On one of your assignments you are sent out to explore the local biotas of several regions. As part of your survey work you are to take large quantitative samples of the copepods of the North Atlantic, the butterflies of central New Guinea, and the ground-dwelling beetles of southwest Africa. Using the lognormal distribution, predict the patterns of relative abundance of species you expect to see within each of these groups of organisms.
4. What are species richness and species evenness? How does each of these components of species diversity contribute to the value of the Shannon–Wiener diversity index (H')? How do species evenness and richness influence the form of rank-abundance curves?
5. Why is it important that the ecologist be familiar with the niches of study organisms before exploring relationships between environmental complexity and species diversity?
6. Communities in different areas may be organized in different ways. For instance, C. Ralph (1985) found that in Patagonia in Argentina, as foliage height diversity increases, bird species diversity decreases. This result is exactly the opposite of the pattern observed by MacArthur (1958) and others reviewed in chapter 16. Design a study aimed at determining the environmental factors determining variation in bird species diversity across Ralph's Patagonian study sites.
7. According to the intermediate disturbance hypothesis, both low and high levels of disturbance can reduce species diversity. Explain possible mechanisms producing this relationship. Include trade-offs between competitive and dispersal abilities in your discussion.
8. The dams that have been built on many rivers often stabilize river flow by increasing flows below the dam during droughts and decreasing the amount of flooding during periods of high rainfall. Explain how these stabilized flows can be considered as a "disturbance." Using the intermediate disturbance hypothesis, predict how stabilized flows would affect the diversity of river organisms below reservoirs.
9. Humans have been living in the tropical rain forests of the New World for at least 11,000 years. During this period, disturbance by humans has been a part of these tropical rain forests. Use the intermediate disturbance hypothesis to explain how recent disturbances threaten the biological diversity of these forests, while earlier disturbances apparently did not.
10. You have been contracted to determine the diversity of the species of your favourite group of organisms in your favourite part of the world. Money is tight, and you can only sample 1% of the area of your study community. Design a sampling protocol that is most likely to give an unbiased estimate of the number of species in the community. How would you know if you are right?

Suggested Readings

Bush, M. B. and P. A. Colinvaux. 1994. Tropical forest disturbance: paleoecological records from Darien, Panama. *Ecology* 75:1761–68.

Bush, M. B., D. R. Piperno, and P. A. Colinvaux. 1989. A 6,000 year history of Amazonian maize cultivation. *Nature* 340:303–5.

Bush, M. B., D. R. Piperno, P. A. Colinvaux, P. E. De Oliveira, L. A. Krissek, M. C. Miller, and W. E. Rowe. 1992. A 14,300-yr paleoecological profile of lowland tropical lake in Panama. *Ecological Monographs* 62:251–75.

Colinvaux, P. A. 1989. The past and future Amazon. *Scientific American* 260:102–8.

This series of papers reviews the long history of human disturbance in tropical communities of Central and South America.

WallisDeVries, M. F., P. Poschlod, and J. H. Willems. 2002. Challenges for the conservation of calcareous grasslands in northwestern Europe: integrating the requirements of flora and fauna. *Biological Conservation* 104:265–73.

Willems, J. H. 2002. Problems, approaches, and results in restoration of Dutch calcareous grassland during the last 30 years. *Restoration Ecology* 9:147–54.

Two studies that describe another long-term, human-impacted community: the chalk grasslands of northwestern Europe.

Cao, Y., D. D. Williams, and D. P. Larsen. 2002. Comparison of ecological communities: the problem of sample representativeness. *Ecological Monographs* 72:41–56.

In this study, Cao, Williams, and Larsen point out that equalizing sampling efforts across communities may not result in representative estimates of species richness.

Fleishman, E., J. R. Thomson, R. Mac Nally, D. D. Murphy, and J. P. Fay. 2005. Using indicator species to predict species richness of multiple taxonomic groups. *Conservation Biology* 19:1125–37.

The authors successfully predict overall bird and/or butterfly diversity using a few species of birds, butterflies, or a combination of birds and butterflies as diversity indicators.

Gotelli, N. J. and R. K. Colwell. 2001. Quantifying biodiversity: procedures and pitfalls in the measurement and comparison of species richness. *Ecology Letters* 4:379–91.

This study examines some of the subtle issues involved in making quantitative comparisons of species richness.

Joern, A. 2005. Disturbance by fire frequency and bison grazing modulate grasshopper assemblages in tall-grass prairie. *Ecology* 86:861–73.

This study shows how fire and grazing influence grasshopper species richness and diversity through their effects on vegetation heterogeneity and plant species diversity.

Mac Nally, R. and C. A. R. Timewell. 2005. Resource availability controls bird-assemblage composition through interspecific aggression. *Auk* 122:1097–1111.

In this study, the researchers find that a combination of resource availability (nectar), size of habitat, and aggression among honeyeater birds controls the composition of local bird assemblages.

Martikainen, P. and J. Kouki. 2003. Sampling the rarest: threatened beetles in boreal forest biodiversity inventories. *Biodiversity and Conservation* 12:1815–31.

A detailed analysis of the sampling efforts required to sample rare beetle species in boreal forests. This study shows that the amount of earth's biodiversity and the challenges of characterizing that diversity are substantial even far from the tropics.

Tilman, D. 1994. Competition and biodiversity in spatially structured habitats. *Ecology* 75:2–16.

A pioneering study on diversity among organisms that contrasts sharply with the birds studied by MacArthur and his colleagues.

Chapter 17

Species Interactions and Community Structure

Outline

*S*o far in this book we have presented a number of isolated facts: mutualisms, herbivory, parasitism, and competition are but a few of the ways species can interact; population growth can be exponential or regulated, and may cycle; species richness and evenness are two measures of biodiversity. Community ecology requires integration of this information. In this chapter we begin to explore how complex interactions among diverse groups of species result in changes in community structure.

Feeding relationships provide some of the most visually obvious examples of interaction in communities. We can see around the Antarctic waters krill, shrimp-like crustaceans named *Euphausia superba*, feeding upon large numbers of diatoms. The krill are themselves prey to many other species, including crabeater seals, penguins, seabirds, and many fish and squid. You may be most familiar with the large baleen whales that once gathered in huge numbers to feed upon krill in these waters (fig. 17.1). Of course, the krill-eating fish and squid are eaten by other predators, including emperor penguins, other fish, and Weddel and Ross seals. These seals are themselves fed upon by Leopard seals, and all of these are fed upon by orcas. How do we go beyond this verbal description to one which more accurately summarizes these feeding relationships? This question is at the heart of one of the earliest approaches to studying communities, descriptions of who eats whom. Since the beginning of the twentieth century, ecologists have meticulously described the feeding relationships of hundreds of communities, each producing a tangle of relationships called a **food web**. These summaries of feeding interactions within a community can reveal many basic aspects of community structure, serving as a portrait of a community (fig. 17.2).

But as you know, there is so much more than predation that happens in communities. These species that feed and are fed upon also engage in a multitude of interactions within and across species, each of which can itself alter the structure of communities. Although feeding relations are one aspect of communities, ecologists are now well aware that these processes are not independent, and instead interact with many other factors. It is these combinations of interactions that result in the diversity of communities that we now see. In this chapter we will explore how species interactions combine to influence community structure.

Concepts

17.1 **A food web summarizes the feeding relationships in a community**

17.2 **Strong competitors can alter community structure**

17.3 **The activities of a few keystone species may control the structure of communities**

17.4 **Mutualists can act as keystone species**

17.1 Food Webs

A food web summarizes the feeding relations in a community. The earliest work on food webs concentrated on simplified communities. In 1927, Charles Elton pointed out that the number of well-described food webs, which he called "food cycles," could be counted on the fingers of one hand. One of the first of those food webs described the feeding relations on Bear Island off the coast of Northern Norway in the high Arctic (fig. 17.3). Summerhayes and Elton (1923) studied the feeding relations there because they believed that the high Arctic, with few species, would be the best place to begin the study of food webs.

Summerhayes and Elton used a food web to present the feeding relations on Bear Island in a single picture. The primary producers in the Bear Island food web are terrestrial plants and aquatic algae. These primary producers are fed upon by several kinds of terrestrial and aquatic invertebrates, which are in turn consumed by birds. The birds on Bear Island are attacked by arctic foxes. Arctic foxes also feed on marine mammals that have washed up onto the beaches, and on the dung of polar bears. The polar bears of Bear Island subsist on a diet of seals and beached marine mammals. Seabirds harvest food from the sea around Bear Island but enter the Bear Island food web because they are attacked by foxes, feed on beached marine animals and on the freshwater invertebrates of Bear Island, and contribute dung that fertilizes the primary producers of the island.

The work of Summerhayes and Elton revealed that even in these "impoverished faunas," feeding relations are complex and difficult to study. For instance, they failed to document several probable feeding relations in their Bear Island food web, which they indicated with dotted lines. However, the level of food web complexity increased dramatically as ecologists studied more diverse communities.

In more recent years, there has been growing recognition that even though food webs are cartoons of just one type of relationship among species (predation and herbivory), they are woefully incomplete even in accomplishing that task. What is missing from these diagrams? Or perhaps it is easier to ask, who eats the predators? The answer is parasites, decomposers, and detritivores. We have talked about these organisms throughout the book, and they are a diverse group of organisms. As

Figure 17.1 A marine food web in action: feeding baleen whales and birds.

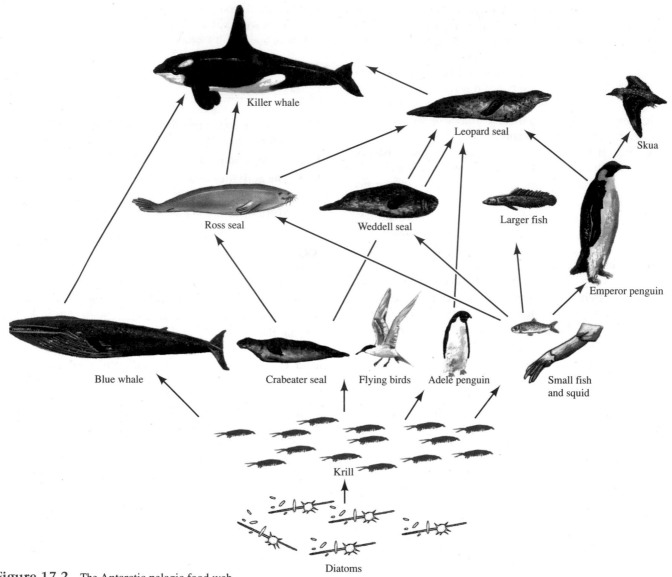

Figure 17.2   The Antarctic pelagic food web.

we will discuss in more depth in chapters 19 and 20, most biomass in a community is consumed only after death, and not as a predation or herbivory event. Missing from the classic cartoons of most food webs is a large proportion of the biological diversity on the planet, and the links that connect the bulk of biomass to its consumers! This is another example of the gross oversight that has resulted in a historical bias against understanding those things that are small, and those things that occur in the soil and sediments of the world (chapters 2 and 3). The sad reality of the state of ecology is that the ecology of parasites, pathogens, microbes, and other small consumers is woefully understudied. These disciplines in ecology will remain open areas of research for enterprising students for decades to come. Because our understanding of the details of these aspects of food webs is so incomplete, we must ignore them for now, coming back to decomposition in chapters 19 and 20. But first we show that even when we do ignore this aspect of feeding relationships, there exists great complexity in food webs.

We turn now to the work of Ralph Bird, who in 1930 published a paper entitled "Biotic Communities of the Aspen Parkland of Central Canada". Bird traveled throughout the Parkland region (Fig. 17.4) and provided the first detailed survey of the feeding relationships among species in each of the major community types of the parkland: prairie, Aspen forest, and willow stands (Fig. 17.5). We have presented the original hand-drawn versions of these food webs, as presented in Bird's papers, to give a sense of the level of care and detail that was necessary to publish such monumental work. This is even without consideration of the difficulty in travelling across Canada prior to the construction of the major road systems, and all in the name of ecological research.

There are several things that are important to point out in these figures. First, the number of connections in each community does not appear to be particularly troublesome, and certainly a level of complexity a scientist should be able to handle. However, if you look closely at the figures, you will notice that these webs do not usually list all of the species

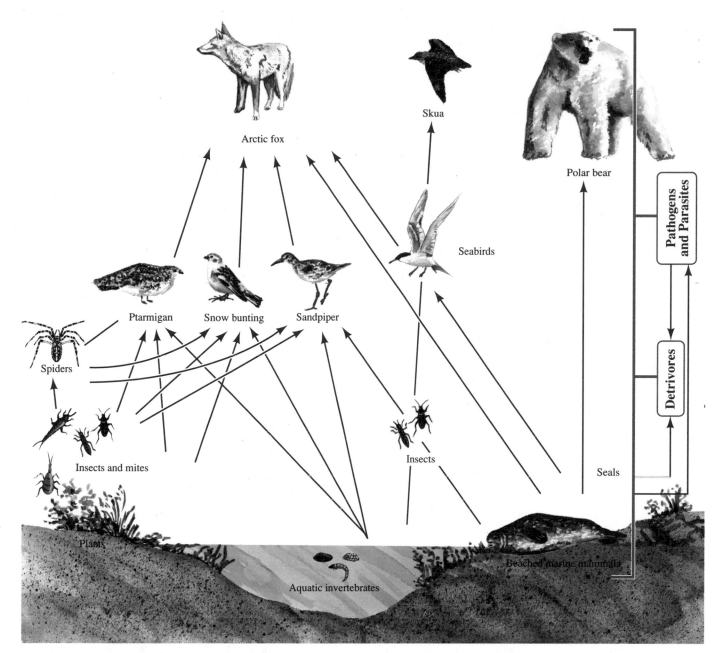

Figure 17.3   Simple food web of an Arctic island.

involved, but instead list guilds and functional groups. In particular, the smaller organisms, such as snails, insects, spiders, etc. are lumped together, while the vertebrates are separated by species. Why? Obviously this is in large part because of historical patterns of taxonomic bias towards larger organisms. However, there may be a biological basis as well. It is possible that some connections between species may be more important in influencing community structure than others. In other words, some species may be substitutable in terms of the overall community structure, while other species may be critical by themselves. However, it is important to note that the lumping of species we see here was not based upon experiments that can test for such strong or weak effects.

In addition to providing food webs for each of the three communities, Bird also drew the connections he observed

among species in different communities (fig. 17.5). This is a critical point to make, as it shows that as early as 1930, ecologists were recognizing that community boundaries are "fuzzy," and that there can be direct interactions of species among "communities." This issue has recently received substantially more attention among ecologists, and it is now recognized that feeding relations across communities (e.g., streams and forests) can play a substantial role in energy and nutrient cycles (chapters 19 and 20).

Before we return to the idea that some interactions are likely more functionally important in influencing community structure than others, let's first return to the idea of competition. Like we see for feeding relations, there can be predictable linkages of competition across species, which may itself influence community structure.

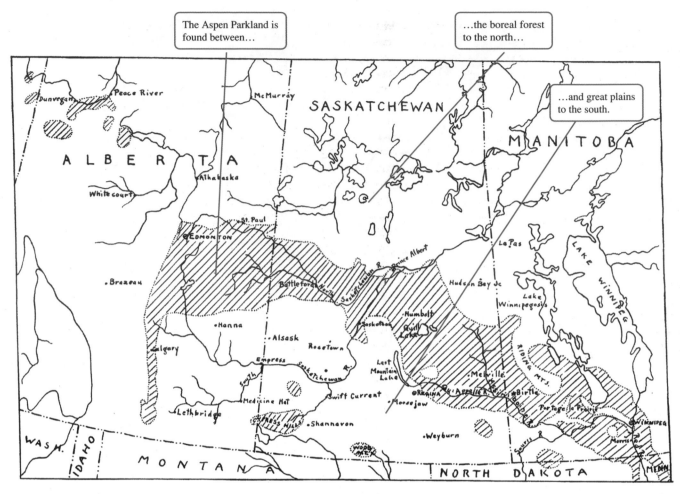

Figure 17.4   Map of the Aspen Parkland as presented in Bird, 1930.

Concept 17.1 Review

1. What are the main advantages of including only strong linkages in a food web?
2. What was the primary way by which Bird simplified the food web representing the interactions of species in the Aspen Parkland?
3. Why are parasites and detritivores generally left out of food webs?

17.2 Competitive Asymmetries

Strong competitors can alter community structure. In chapter 13 we discussed competition, and described many of the potential effects it could have on populations. We also talked about the most extreme potential impact of competition in a community: competitive exclusion. However, potentially competing species can coexist through a variety of mechanisms (chapter 13), which leaves us a bit unclear about whether competition can actually influence community structure. In this section we provide several examples in which competition is seen to have very strong effects on critical aspects of community structure.

Competition and Diversity

What should happen to species diversity of a community if the strength of competition increases? The answer to this question is going to be dependent upon whether species are similar in their competitive abilities, or instead if communities contain **competitive hierarchies**. A competitive hierarchy is a very simple idea: some species are consistently better competitors than other species. For example, if there were four species in a community (A, B, C, and D), and if a competitive hierarchy existed, then you could rank their competitive abilities as A>B>C>D. You may notice that this hierarchy is also transitive (think back to introductory algebra!), meaning that if A>B and B>C, then A>C. This is the most extreme possible version of a hierarchy, and one could imagine others such as A>B=C>D. Regardless of the details of the rankings, the implications of hierarchies and transitivity for community structure are broad. If there is no competition in the community then a hierarchy is irrelevant and competitive exclusion will not occur. Similarly, if intransitivity occurs (such that a complete hierarchy is not formed), species coexistence can also occur, even if competition is strong (Laird and Schamp, 2006). However, if competition is strong, and transitivity occurs, then in the above example A, B, and C will start to

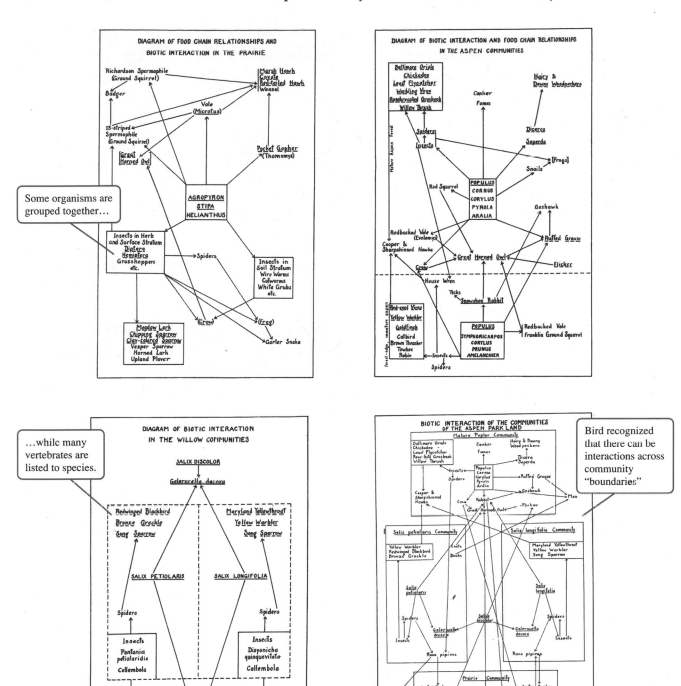

Figure 17.5 Biotic interactions within and among three Aspen Parkland community types, drawn by Bird (1930).

squeeze species D out, potentially causing it to be lost from the community. If competition continues to increase, the community may lose species C, and perhaps even B, resulting in a community consisting only of species A. In other words, if the species of a community differ consistently in their competitive abilities, then increased competition should cause a drop in species diversity. Does it?

Competitive Hierarchies

We begin, once again, with plants. We do this for several reasons. The first is practical: plant ecologists have a long history studying competition, and thus much of the best data on competition in communities is from studies of plant ecology. The second reason is more conceptual: as we discussed in chapter 16, the diversity of animals in a community often

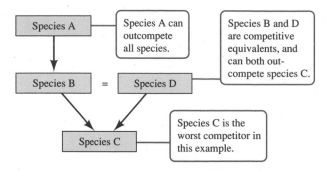

Figure 17.6 Competitive relationships among species can be displayed in a manner similar to that of food webs.

varies as a function of the heterogeneity of the plants. As a result, changes to plant community structure due to competition can cause changes in animal community structure, even if the animals themselves are not competing with each other! This critical issue is often overlooked when examining the impact of competition on community structure.

Bill Shipley is a professor at the Université de Sherbrooke, and has spent many years combining mathematical and community ecology. He has been quite interested in the importance of competitive hierarchies in plant communities. In fact, he contributed to the initial concept of competitive transitivity (Keddy and Shipley 1989) which he then refined (Shipley 1993). In his 1993 paper, Shipley developed an analytical method allowing one to test whether competitive relationships among plants are, or are not, transitive. Shipley was able to find 10 published studies of matrices that recorded the competitive relationships (analogous to feeding relationships in food webs; fig. 17.6) of different species of plants. In 9 of 10 cases, relationships were transitive, supporting the idea that competition has the potential to alter plant community structure.

As we will see next, the idea of competitive hierarchies can be combined with the theory of allocation (chapter 7), leading to a theory that could be helpful in explaining the distribution of species along environmental gradients.

Centrifugal Organization of Species

Paul Keddy, formerly of the University of Ottawa, has been a strong promoter of the idea of "centrifigul organization of plant communities." Paul has spent decades studying the wetlands of North America. In the freshwater wetlands in Ontario he kept observing a repeating pattern: much of the area would be dominated by a single genus of grass, *Typha*, while many other species could be found nearby in small patches of much higher diversity (fig. 17.7). What caused these patterns in this system? Answering this question has served as the foundation of research for many students and postdocs from the Keddy lab, many of whom continue their research in plant community ecology in universities and government agencies throughout Canada. The combined work of Keddy and former lab members including Scott Wilson, Lauchlan Fraser, Evan Weiher, Connie Gaudet, Bill Shipley, and Irene Wisheu resulted in an innovative approach to understanding community organization, one that extends far beyond the wetlands of Ontario.

(a)

(b)

Figure 17.7 Areas of differing productivity and diversity in a wetland. (*a*) *Typha* dominates core habitats, while (*b*) a diversity of species live in peripheral habitats.

The theory of centrifugal organization of species is most thoroughly explained in a 1992 paper by Irene Wisheu and Paul Keddy entitled *Plant competition and centrifugal organization of plant communities: theory and test*. The theory is based upon the idea of core and peripheral habitats existing within a landscape. The core habitat is the "prime" real estate in the community, with no abiotic stresses, lots of resources, and few pests or pathogens. In short, the core habitat meets the requirements of the fundamental niche for nearly all species of the community (fig. 17.8). However, because species differ in competitive abilities, and there exists a competitive hierarchy in this system, not all species will be able to occupy the core habitat. Instead, the core habitat will be dominated by the best competitor, which in

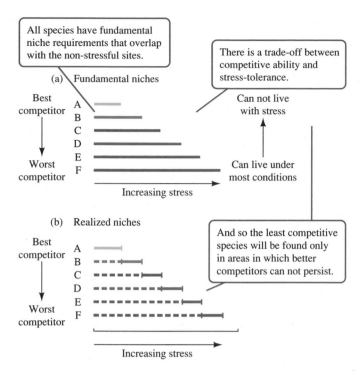

All species have fundamental niche requirements that overlap with the non-stressful sites.

(a) Fundamental niches

There is a trade-off between competitive ability and stress-tolerance.

Can not live with stress

Can live under most conditions

(b) Realized niches

And so the least competitive species will be found only in areas in which better competitors can not persist.

Figure 17.8 Competitive hierarchies form the basis of the theory of centrifigul organization of plant communities (data from Wisheu and Keddy 1992).

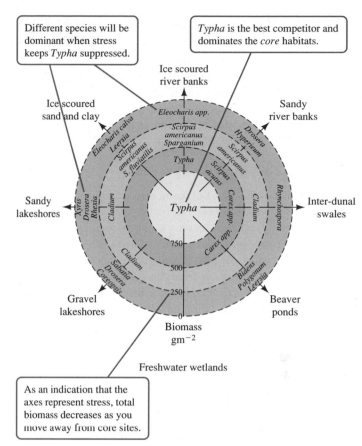

Different species will be dominant when stress keeps *Typha* suppressed.

Typha is the best competitor and dominates the *core* habitats.

As an indication that the axes represent stress, total biomass decreases as you move away from core sites.

Figure 17.9 Centrifigul organization of a freshwater wetland (data from Wisheu and Keddy 1992, originally from Moore et al. 1989).

these wetlands is *Typha*. But why do you find so many other species in this system? As we discussed in chapter 16, the world is a heterogeneous place. Some places will freeze up and be subjected to frequent ice scouring. Other areas will be sandy and low in nutrient content. Others will be near beaver dams and subjected to repeated flooding. In the theory of centrifugal organization of species diversity, Keddy makes the assumption that plants require specific adaptations to perform well under these less-than-ideal conditions. He further assumes that not all plants are able to perform at their optimum under all environmental conditions, and instead there will exist trade-offs between competitive ability and the ability to cope with the different types of environmental stresses. As we saw in our discussion of life histories (chapter 9), this assumption is quite reasonable, and likely valid for many plant communities.

As a result of these trade-offs, Keddy argues that you will find the competitively inferior species occupying areas that are dominated by these stresses, as under those conditions they either are able to outcompete *Typha*, or competition itself no longer occurs. Each community will have its own set of stress gradients along which stress-competition trade-offs will occur, and Keddy would expect a predictable arrangement of species along each of those gradients. These gradients can be arranged graphically (fig. 17.9), with the core habitat in the centre, and each stress gradient radiating out. If you have a detailed understanding of the species of the system, you can then include likely species found along each of these gradients. Once this is developed, you could then go out to a community, identify what stressors are, or are not, occurring in a

given location, and then see whether you find the species you expect to occur. In other words, this relatively simple model of community organization, based in the ideas of competition and theory of allocation, is a powerful tool to explain observed patterns of species occurrence.

Of course, this model is just one of many possible models to explain species distributions, and it has built into it several assumptions. For example, species hierarchies and trade-offs between competitive ability and stress tolerance are key aspects of the model. There will certainly be examples of communities where these assumptions are not met, and thus this model would not apply. However, there are other communities, such as the wetlands that Keddy has spent his professional life studying, which seem to be very well described by this model (Wisheu and Keddy 1992), and thus it is an important tool to help ecologists understand how species interactions can alter community structure.

But the story does not end here. Although feeding relations and competitive interactions can both influence community structure, we need to recognize that these processes do not occur in isolation of each other. Instead, organisms will potentially need to deal with prey, predators, and competitors simultaneously. As we will see in the next section, interactions between feeding relations and competition can be critical to structuring some communities.

Concept 17.2 Review

1. Why are the effects of competition on community structure dependent upon whether competitive hierarchies are transitive or non-transitive?
2. Explain how the theory of allocation is an important aspect of Keddy's theory of centrifugal organization of plants.

17.3   Keystone Species

The activities of a few keystone species may control the structure of communities.   Robert Paine (1966, 1969) proposed that the feeding activities of a few species have inordinate influences on community structure. He called these **keystone species**. Paine's keystone species hypothesis emerged from a chain of reasoning. First, he proposed that predators might keep prey populations below their carrying capacity. Next, he reasoned the potential for competitive exclusion would be low in populations kept below carrying capacity. Finally, he concluded that if keystone species reduce the likelihood of competitive exclusion, their activities would increase the number of species that could coexist in communities. In other words, Paine predicted that some predators may increase species diversity. As we will see in this section, the idea of keystone species is an important one, and a great deal of ecological research has resulted in a clearer understanding of what being a keystone species entails.

Food Web Structure and Species Diversity

Paine began his studies by examining the relationship between overall species diversity within food webs and the proportion of the community represented by predators. He cited studies that demonstrated that as the number of species in marine zooplankton communities increases, the proportion that are predators also increases. For instance, the zooplankton community in the Atlantic Ocean over continental shelves includes 81 species, 16% of which are predators. In contrast, the zooplankton community of the Sargasso Sea contains 268 species, 39% of which are predators. Paine set out to determine if similar patterns occur in marine intertidal communities.

Paine described a food web from the intertidal zone at Mukkaw Bay, Washington, which lies in the north temperate zone at 49° N. This food web is typical of the rocky shore community along the west coast of North America (fig. 17.10) and similar to what is found around the B.C. coast. The base of this food web consists of algae and phytoplankton. However, Paine was particularly interested in nine dominant intertidal invertebrates: two species of chitons, two species of limpets, a mussel, three species of acorn barnacles, and one species of gooseneck barnacle. Paine pointed out that *Pisaster*, a starfish, commonly consumes two other prey species in other areas, a snail and another bivalve, bringing the total food web diversity to 13 species. Ninety percent of the energy consumed by the middle level predator, *Thais,* consists of barnacles. Meanwhile the top predator, *Pisaster,* obtains 90% of its energy from a mixture of chitons (41%), mussels (37%), and barnacles (12%).

Paine also described a subtropical food web (31° N) from the northern Gulf of California, a much richer web that included 45 species. However, like the food web at Mukkaw Bay, Washington, the subtropical web was topped by a single predator, the starfish *Heliaster kubinijii* (fig. 17.10). However, six predators occupy middle levels in the subtropical web, compared to one middle level predator at Mukkaw Bay. Because four of the five species in the snail family Columbellidae are also predaceous, the total number of predators in the subtropical web is 11. These predators feed on the 34 species that form the base of the food web. Despite the presence of many more species in this subtropical web, the top predator, *Heliaster,* obtains most of its energy from sources similar to those used by *Pisaster* at Mukkaw Bay. *Heliaster* obtains 74% of its energy directly from a mixture of bivalves, herbivorous gastropods, and barnacles.

Paine found that as the number of species in his intertidal food webs increased, the proportion of the web represented by predators also increased. As Paine went from Mukkaw Bay to the northern Gulf of California, overall web diversity increased from 13 species to 45 species, a 3.5-fold increase. However, at the same time, the number of predators in the two webs increased from 2 to 11, a 5.5-fold increase. According to Paine's predation hypothesis, this higher proportion of predators produces higher predation pressure on prey populations, which in turn promotes the higher diversity in the Gulf of California intertidal zone.

Does this pattern confirm Paine's predation hypothesis? No, it does not. First, Paine studied a small number of webs—not enough to make broad generalizations. Second, while the patterns described by Paine are consistent with his hypothesis, they may be consistent with a number of other hypotheses. To evaluate the keystone species hypotheses, Paine needed a direct experimental test.

Experimental Removal of Starfish

For his first experiment, Paine removed the top predator from the intertidal food web at Mukkaw Bay and monitored the response of the community. He chose two study sites in the middle intertidal zone that extended 8 m along the shore and 2 m vertically. One site was designated as a control and the other as an experimental site. He removed *Pisaster* from the experimental site and relocated them in another portion of the intertidal zone. Each week Paine checked the experimental site for the presence of *Pisaster* and removed any that might have colonized since his last visit.

Paine followed the response of the intertidal community for two years. Over this interval, the diversity of intertidal invertebrates in the control plot remained constant at 15, while the diversity within the experimental plot declined from 15 to 8, a loss of 7 species. This reduction in species diversity supported Paine's keystone species hypothesis. However, if this reduction was due to competitive exclusion, what was the resource over which species competed?

The most common limiting resource in the rocky intertidal zone is space. Within three months of removing *Pisaster* from the experimental plot, the barnacle *Balanus glandula* occu-

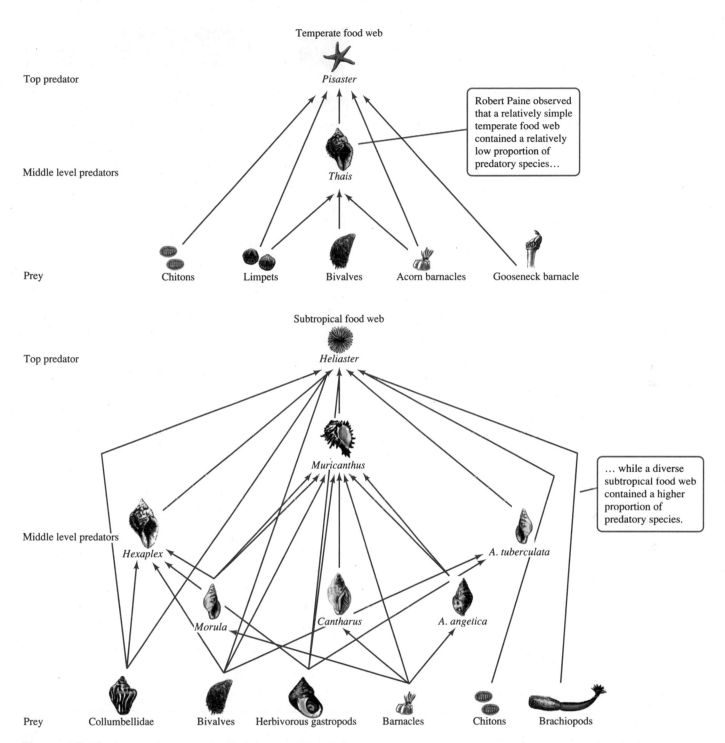

Figure 17.10   Roots of the keystone species hypothesis: does a higher proportion of predators in diverse communities indicate that predators contribute to higher species diversity? Algae and phytoplankton are not included in these diagrams.

pied 60% to 80% of the available space. One year after Paine removed *Pisaster*, *B. glandula* was crowded out by mussels, *Mytilus californianus,* and gooseneck barnacles, *Pollicipes polymerus.* Benthic algal populations also declined because of a lack of space for attachment indicating that algae and animals compete for the same resources. The herbivorous chitons and limpets also left, due to a lack of space and a shortage of food. Sponges were also crowded out and a nudibranch that feeds on sponges also left. After five years, the *Pisaster* removal plot

was dominated by two species: the mussel, *M. californianus,* and the gooseneck barnacle, *P. polymerus.*

This experiment showed that *Pisaster* is a keystone species. When Paine removed it from his study plot, the community structure changed dramatically. Paine's studies provide substantial support for the keystone species hypothesis. Many other studies quickly followed the lead taken by Paine's pioneering work. Next we will provide three examples where a mammal, a fish, and a bird all can serve as keystone species.

Fish as Keystone Species in River Food Webs

Mary Power (1990) tested the possibility that fish can significantly alter the structure of food webs in rivers. She conducted her research on the Eel River in northern California, where most precipitation falls during October to April, sometimes producing torrential winter flooding. During the summer, however, the flow of the Eel River averages less than 1 m³ per second.

In early summer, the boulders and bedrock of the Eel River are covered by a turf of the filamentous alga *Cladophora* (fig. 17.11). However, the biomass of the algae declines by midsummer and what remains has a ropy, prostrate growth form and a "webbed" appearance. These mats of *Cladophora* support dense populations of larval midges in the fly family Chironomidae. One chironomid, *Pseudochironomus richardsoni,* is particularly abundant. *Pseudochironomus* feeds on *Cladophora* and other algae and weaves the algae into retreats, altering their appearance in the process.

Chironomids are eaten by predatory insects and the young (known as *fry*) of two species of fish: a minnow called the California roach, *Hesperoleucas symmetricus,* and three-spined sticklebacks, *Gasterosteus aculeatus.* These small fish are eaten by young steelhead trout, *Oncorhynchus mykiss.* Steelhead and large roach eat predatory invertebrates, and large roach also feed directly upon benthic algae. These interactions form the Eel River food web pictured in figure 17.12.

Power asked whether or not the two top predators in the Eel River food web, roach and steelhead, significantly influence web structure. She tested the effects of these fish on food web structure by using 3 mm mesh to cage off 12 areas 6 m² in the riverbed. The mesh size of these cages prevented the passage of large fish but allowed free movement of aquatic insects and stickleback and roach fry. Power excluded fish from six of her cages and placed 20 juvenile steelhead and 40 large roach in each of the other six cages. These fish densities were within the range observed around boulders in the open river.

Significant differences between the exclosures and enclosures soon emerged. Algal densities were initially similar; however, enclosing fish over an area of streambed significantly reduced algal biomass (fig. 17.13). In addition, the *Cladophora* within cages with fish had the same ropy, webbed appearance as *Cladophora* in the open river.

How do predatory fish decrease algal densities? The key to answering this question lies with the Eel River food web (see fig. 17.12). Predatory fish feed heavily on predatory insects, young roach, and sticklebacks. Lower densities of these smaller predators within the enclosures decreased predation on chironomids. Higher chironomid density increased the feeding pressure of these herbivores on algal populations. This explanation is supported by Power's estimate that enclosures contained lower densities of predatory insects and fish fry and higher densities of chironomids (fig. 17.14). By enclosing and excluding fish from sections of the Eel River, Power, like Paine and Lubchenko, who worked in the intertidal zone, demonstrated that fish act as keystone species in the Eel River food web.

(a)

(b)

Figure 17.11   Seasonal changes in biomass and growth form of benthic algae in the Eel River, California: (*a*) in early summer, June 1989; (*b*) in late summer, August 1989.

All of the examples that we have discussed so far have been aquatic. Do terrestrial communities also contain keystone species? An increasing body of evidence indicates that they do.

We have already discussed several keystone species throughout this text, such as the geese in arctic wetland habitats and their role in herbivory (chapter 14). As you may recall,

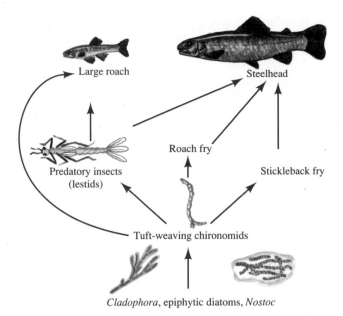

Figure 17.12 Food web associated with algal turf during the summer in the Eel River, California.

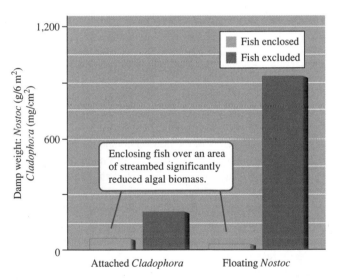

Figure 17.13 The influence of juvenile steelhead and California roach on benthic algal biomass in the Eel River (data from Power 1990).

under moderate rates of grazing, plant growth actually increased, while in response to high levels of grazing there was a drop in production as only herbivory-resistant species were able to survive. This is a clear example of how one form of species interaction (grazing) can strongly influence community organization. Here we provide another example of how a keystone species can influence patterns of diversity and community organization. You all should be familiar with this story.

Impacts of Beavers on Forest Communities

Castor canadensis, the North American beaver, is found throughout most of Canada and the United States (fig. 17.15). Beavers have been commercially exploited for their pelts, which has caused population crashes in part of their range, particularly in the southern and central United States. Across North America reintroductions and legislative protections have resulted in a great growth in densities over the last several decades. As you may recognize, beavers aren't quite like most other rodent species, and as a result, they can have pronounced impacts on the structure of communities in which they live.

Beavers fall into a very select grouping of species, generally referred to as **ecosystem engineers** (Jones, Lawton, and Shachak 1994). Ecosystem engineers are species who, by the

Figure 17.15 Beavers can have strong impacts as ecosystem engineers.

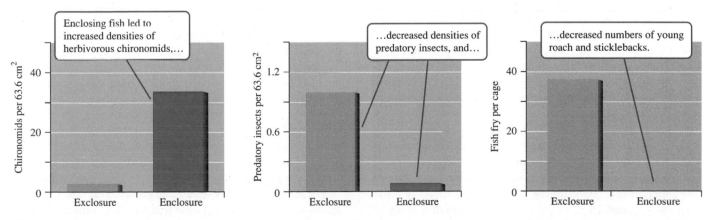

Figure 17.14 Effect of juvenile steelhead and roach on numbers of insects and young (fry) roach and sticklebacks (data from Power 1990).

nature of their activities, maintain and/or create new habitats for themselves and/or other species. It is fair to think of ecosystem engineers as an extreme form of a keystone species. For example, the coral-forming species of chapter 15 are a "poster-child" of ecosystem engineers. Without those species, coral reefs simply would not exist.

Beavers cut down a variety of trees near the edges of streams and other water bodies, forming dams. These dams cause flooding, increasing the amount of riparian area on the landscape. In the resulting ponds, the beavers build lodges. The reasons for this behaviour are not completely clear, though it is thought that the isolation provides some protection from terrestrial predators and increased access to food sources. It is, however, important to recognize that because beavers have effects on natural communities to a much greater extent than would be predicted based upon their relative abundance in a community, this familiar animal also counts as a "keystone species," and thus you are more familiar with these ecological concepts than you may think. In contrast, the species that make up a coral reef are extremely abundant (within their community), and though they are certainly ecosystem engineers, we would not normally also refer to them as keystone species. Jargon aside, what exactly is the impact of beavers on natural communities?

There are two locations of primary impact, the stream and the surrounding terrestrial area. Clearly, putting up a dam, or more likely a series of dams, alters rates of stream flow and drainage, and can alter various aspects of the biogeochemical cycles (Naiman et al 1994). The effects, however, are not consistent from location to location, and instead are dependent upon local issues of water quality, acidity, and level of beaver activity (Rosell et al. 2005). Similarly, because of flooding and alteration of stream flow, there is evidence that stream temperatures can change (Rosell et al. 2005). As we discussed in chapter 5, changes in water temperature can have significant effects on the growth of many aquatic organisms, and thus can alter community structure. I am sure it is no surprise that the activity of beavers causes widespread changes to the aquatic communities in which they reside. What may be less obvious, however, is that beavers can also have strong effects on the terrestrial communities.

Noble Donkor, of the University of Alberta, and John Fryxell, of the University of Guelph, explored the impacts of beaver on the vegetation in Algonquin Provincial Park, Ontario (Donkor and Fryxell 1999). They chose for their study 15 ponds, each less that 2 ha in area, that had one active beaver lodge within it. They laid out several transects extending away from the pond and into the surrounding forest, along which they recorded beaver-cut stumps and the size and identity of woody vegetation.

In total, they found 1,841 tree stems cut by beaver, consisting of 20 plant species. However, 78% of the cut stems belonged to only six species (speckled alder, beaked hazel, red maple, trembling aspen, white birch, and beaked willow). Not surprisingly, the greatest proportion of cuts stem was found near the edge of the pond (fig. 17.16). As a result, there is a sharp herbivory gradient from near the water's edge to the intact forest.

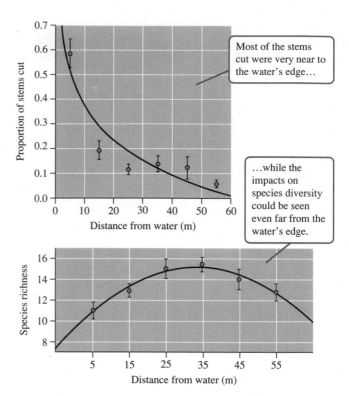

Figure 17.16 The intensity of exploitation and species richness both varied as a function of distance from the edge of a pond containing beavers (data from Donkor and Fryxell 1999).

Donkor and Fryxell found that along this gradient, there was a unimodal relationship between species richness and distance (fig. 17.16), with maximum species diversity at an intermediate distance from the edge of the pond. This should look familiar, as this is exactly the prediction one would make based upon the intermediate disturbance hypothesis and altered competitive interactions. However, the interpretation in this case is not quite as clear. Although certain plant species were most often cut down by beavers, these preferred tree species were also quick to resprout following cutting, and thus were not necessarily underrepresented near the water's edge. Instead, the effects of beaver near the water's edge is likely to increase the abundance of plant species that can tolerate cutting. Deeper into the forest, there is less beaver activity, and thus these areas tend to be dominated by species that are good competitors for light or other resources. Diversity is likely highest at intermediate distances from the water's edge as this is the location where both the cutting-tolerant and competitively dominant species are likely to be found. It is also important to recognize that the beavers are creating soggy conditions for terrestrial plants near the water's edge, and this itself could contribute to reduced growth (or absence) of some species, as those conditions may be outside of their niche requirements. Regardless of the mechanism of effect, the fact that beavers' activity can cause variation in species composition clearly makes them a keystone species in this system.

The legacy of beaver dams extends well beyond the life of the dams themselves. Eventually, all beaver dams will be abandoned, and some time after that they lose structural integrity. When these dams "break" the stored water flows back into the streams, exposing land previously covered by water, initiating forest succession (chapter 18). The impacts of beavers can be seen for decades, even if the individual dams last only a few years.

The Effects of Predation by Birds on Herbivory

Let's move from what is happening at the bottom of the boreal forest to what is appearing at the top. In northern Sweden, Ola Atlegrim (1989) has studied the influence of birds on herbivorous insects and insect-caused plant damage. It appears that insectivorous birds may act as keystones in boreal forests through their effects on populations of herbivorous insects.

Atlegrim studied the food web associated with the bilberry, *Vaccinium myrtillus,* which is a dominant understory shrub in many boreal forests in northern Sweden. The insects that commonly feed on *Vaccinium* include caterpillars of the moth families Geometridae and Tortricidae and the larvae of the Hymenoptera known as sawflies. The geometrid and sawfly larvae feed on the bilberry from exposed positions, while the tortricid larvae bind leaves together with silk to form a shelter within which they feed. Because populations of these larvae can reach high densities, they can do considerable damage to *Vaccinium.* However, Atlegrim observed that larval insect densities peak when many insectivorous birds are feeding insects to their young and posed the following questions: (1) Do birds reduce the density of insect larvae feeding on *Vaccinium?* (2) Do birds have different effects on larvae feeding from exposed versus concealed positions? (3) Does predation by birds reduce larval insect damage to the shoots of *Vaccinium?*

Atlegrim's study sites were located approximately 20 km northwest of Umeå in northern Sweden. He established five study areas in forests ranging from 70 to 120 years old. At each study area, he established 10 study plots 4 m^2 and built a bird exclosure over 5 of them. Exclosures consisted of 40 mm^2 nylon mesh supported by a wooden frame.

Atlegrim took care to ensure that he could attribute any experimental effects to the exclusion of birds. His exclosures excluded birds but allowed small predaceous mammals, such as shrews, and predaceous invertebrates to move freely into and out of the study plots. He also kept track of the densities of these alternative predators by periodically sampling them with pitfall traps. Why was this an important aspect of Atlegrim's study? In the absence of predation by birds, higher densities of herbivorous insects might have attracted higher numbers of other predators, that is, produced a localized numerical response (see chapter 11). Atlegrim also measured the intensity of sunlight within his exclosures and in adjacent control plots. Why was this aspect of the study necessary? If the exclosures created significant shading, physical effects alone (see section II) could have affected the distributions of herbivorous insects. Finally, Atlegrim measured the density of *Vaccinium* shoots to verify similar densities in exclosure and control plots. His measurements showed that levels of light, densities of non-avian predators, and densities of *Vaccinium* shoots were similar on exclosure and control plots.

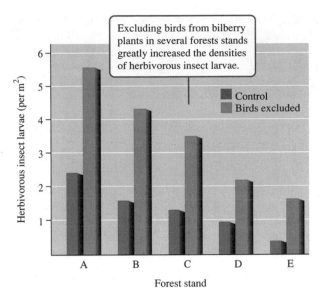

Figure 17.17 Effect of insectivorous birds on herbivorous insect populations on *Vaccinium myrtillus* (data from Atlegrim 1989).

Exclosures increased larval insect density an average of 63% across all study sites (fig. 17.17). So, the answer to Atlegrim's first question is yes. Insectivorous birds reduce the densities of herbivorous insect larvae feeding on *Vaccinium.* However, as Atlegrim predicted, some herbivorous larvae are more vulnerable to insectivorous birds than are others. Sawfly and geometrid larvae, which feed in exposed positions, were significantly higher within exclosures, while the densities of tortricid larvae, which feed in their constructed shelters, showed no effects of bird exclusion. Higher densities of herbivorous insect larvae translated directly into higher levels of damage to *Vaccinium.*

What other piece of information might increase our confidence that the differences between exclosure and control plots were due to bird predation? One of the most significant bits of evidence would be direct observations of birds feeding on the control plots. Atlegrim observed three bird species feeding on control plots: Hazel hen chicks, *Tetrastes bonasia,* great tits, *Parus major,* and pied flycatcher, *Ficedula hypoleuca.*

Insectivorous birds also reduce insect populations and insect damage on plants in midlatitude forests in North America. Robert Marquis and Christopher Whelan (1994) used 3.8 cm white nylon mesh to exclude birds from 30 white oak, *Quercus alba,* saplings at the Tyson Research Center in Eureka, Missouri, during the growing seasons of 1989 and 1990. The bird community at this site includes several dozen species composed of a shifting mix of spring migrants and summer and spring residents.

The researchers sprayed another set of 30 white oak saplings each week with a pyrethroid insecticide. They also handpicked any remaining herbivorous insects from these trees. A third set of white oaks, the control, was not manipulated.

Marquis and Whelan's caged plants were populated by larger numbers of herbivorous insects and experienced significantly greater insect damage (fig. 17.19). These results are consistent with those of Atlegrim's earlier study. Marquis and Whelan also measured the biomass of each of their trees in 1990 and 1991.

Keystone Species, Ecosystem Engineers, and Conservation Biology

In this chapter we have seen how some species are able to alter the structure of natural communities. The potential impacts of keystone species and ecosystem engineers on community structure have been of great interest to conservation biologists for many years, both in terms of conservation efforts and reintroduction of extirpated species. The logic behind such approaches is quite simple: if a "natural" community is maintained through the activities of only a few species, then removal of those species will cause a shift in community structure. As a result, conservation efforts to protect populations of those species should serve to protect the overall structure of the community. Similarly, if human activities have caused the loss of a keystone or engineer within a community, reintroduction of that species should restore critical ecological services and community structure. Right?

Of course, the real world is not nearly that simple. Tony Sinclair, of the University of British Columbia, argues strongly in favour of viewing many large mammals as potential keystone species structuring communities (Sinclair 2003). However, he also acknowledges that there are difficulties in deciding what is, and what is not, a keystone species. For example, exactly how much does a community need to change by the introduction or removal of a species to consider that a critical species? Is 10% enough, 50%, 95%? Further, what do you actually measure? Species richness? Evenness? Biomass production? What trophic levels must be affected for a species to be keystone? For instance, if you add a predator, is it a keystone if that addition causes a decline in prey numbers, or does the effect have to continue on to the plants, decomposers, and soil systems? There are no clear answers to these questions.

The potential advantage of focusing on keystone species in conservation efforts is also supported by Daniel Simberloff (1998). Simberloff argues that many historical approaches to conservation schemes (e.g., using umbrella, flagship, and indicator species—all terms you may have had in other classes) are ineffective and/or not well supported by actual data. Similarly, he argues that a current trend towards "ecosystem management" has dangers in that the management goals are often vague, focusing on processes such as nutrient cycling rather than protection of actual species. Simberlof suggests instead that research should be focused towards identifying keystone species, and groups of species, in natural communities. He readily acknowledges that not all communities will have such members, but in those that do, conservation efforts can be highly focused, and potentially effective.

So, if not all communities have these critical species, what can one do? Further, what evidence can we find from reintro-duction projects to suggest that some of the lofty goals of using keystone species to restore ecological communities may actually be met in communities without keystone species? We will briefly explore two restoration projects without a clearly identified keystone species, restoration of peatlands and *Sphagnum*, and reintroduction of wolves into Yellowstone National Park in the United States.

We begin with an example of an ecosystem engineer. We have already discussed beavers as ecosystem engineers, and reintroductions of beaver are being used in restoration projects throughout Europe. We will instead focus on what is perhaps a less obvious group of organisms, but of equally important potential for restoration, *Sphagnum* mosses. As an ecosystem engineer, *Sphagnum* play a key role in peatlands; however, they should not be considered a keystone species, as they are dominant members of the community. As we saw in chapter 3, peatlands occupy a large proportion of the land base in Canada. Line Rochefort, of the Université Laval, points out that although most peatlands in Canada are in the North, the majority of peatland development is concentrated in the spatially isolated peatlands of southern Canada (Rochefort 2000). While peat moss is used for a variety of human needs, the harvest of peat comes at the loss of critical **ecosystem services**, such as providing a buffer to flooding, filtering ground water, and serving as an interface between terrestrial and atmospheric carbon pools. Following peat mining, restoration projects are generally initiated. Rochefort argues improvement is needed. Specifically, although most mined areas will soon be home to a variety of plant species associated with peatlands, they generally contain only a very low proportion of *Sphagnum* mosses (Rochefort 2000). This moss is critical if one wishes to restore a peatland, as *Sphagnum* mosses are the primary group of mosses that accumulate peat as they age. In other words, it is *Sphagnum* that creates a peatland and it is the ultimate engineer of these systems. Critical to the ability to restore peatlands is going to be the ability to get *Sphagnum* to reestablish in mined areas. Success in reestablishment is going to require a continually improving understanding of the basic ecology of this group of species. Only by seeing the role that *Sphagnum* plays in peatlands can restorations be successful. Unfortunately, successful peatland restorations are well behind relative to the level of peatland mining that occurs in Canada, and throughout the world. We now turn to an example of a program designed to reintroduce a keystone predator.

After 70 years of absence, grey wolves were reintroduced to Yellowstone National Park in the United States in 1995. There were countless reasons justifying this reintroduction, including the argument that bringing back a top predator of this system should restore keystone processes and alter many

Figure 17.18 A wolf on the hunt in Yellowstone National Park.

aspects of the community. More specifically, wolves were expected to alter predation pressures on a dominant herbivore (elk), which in turn will alter plant community organization. In other words, this single species (wolf) is viewed as keystone to the Yellowstone system. It is now over a decade since reintroduction, and data is available to begin to determine whether wolves are in fact keystone in this community.

A team of researchers from the United States and the University of Alberta in Canada followed a number of radio-collared elk in Yellowstone, recording their locations as a function of wolf densities in the area and a number of habitat characteristics (Mao et al. 2005). Mao and her coauthors indicate that elk population sizes did not change much over the course of their study, suggesting that wolves are not having major impacts on the total numbers of these large herbivores. In the summer months, elk primarily occupied areas of low wolf-density, suggesting a behavioural response to predators. In the winter, elk were found in high wolf density areas, indicating the effects of wolves on elk movement are season-dependent. Mao and her coauthors argue that in the summer, food for elk is relatively abundant, and they are able to choose to feed in areas of low predator numbers. In the winter, food is scarce and the luxury to choose to feed in areas without predators does not occur: instead, the elk need to feed wherever they find food. These results lend only limited support to the keystone species idea for wolves. Clearly, if wolves alter where elk feed, this has the potential to alter plant communities. However, because habitat shifts as a function of wolves only occur part of the year, and it doesn't appear that elk numbers were suppressed by wolves, this study does not conclusively show keystone effects. We now turn to another study.

Ripple and Beschta (2006) investigated the effects of wolf reintroduction on the height of a common group of riparian plant species in Yellowstone, willows (*Salix* spp.). Willows are

of particular interest in this system because they serve as browse for elk, and are habitat for a variety of bird species. As a result, a change in *Salix* would be an indication of potential keystone effects of wolves in this system. Ripple and Beschta analyzed a variety of photographs of *Salix* stands prior to wolf reintroduction, and compared them to measured sizes following reintroduction. In upland habitats, wolves had no apparent effects of willow heights, while in lowland sites, the results were quite dramatic. In the river valley populations, nearly all willow stands increased in height following wolf reintroduction, and this was related to a decrease in the frequency of browsing by elk. The impacts of wolves may also extend into other aspects of the food web.

There is some evidence to suggest that wolf activity results in an increase in the amount of carrion available for scavengers, primarily during the winter months (Wilmers et al. 2003). This "temporal subsidy" by the wolves may provide a steadier food supply for the guild of scavengers, which may become more important in the face of climate changes in this system (Wilmers and Getz 2005). However, whether this temporal subsidy actually alters scavenger population sizes has not yet been demonstrated, and is critical to interpreting the importance of these changes in the context of a keystone species.

As we have already discussed, a species is not viewed as keystone in a community if it simply alters some interactions (e.g., removes some prey, is food for some animals), but instead is a keystone if its impacts are large relative to the organism abundance in the system. The research to date suggests that wolves could serve a keystone role in Yellowstone, but is not yet conclusive. Fortunately, the wolves of Yellowstone are quite well established, and continued research by ecologists in this system will be able to provide an answer to whether wolves are important restoration tools that serve keystone roles, or whether desire by people to reintroduce them should be based upon other arguments, independent of any potential cascading effects.

These examples show that the concept of keystone species and ecosystem engineers have implications for the management and restoration of natural areas. However, there are also many examples where the addition of what was perceived to be a keystone species did not actually alter communities. There is a growing realization that some changes to communities may be so severe that "simple" restoration efforts such as a species reintroduction will be insufficient to restore the community. It is important to recognize that even if a species is not found to be keystone or an engineer, it doesn't mean reintroductions are not warranted. Instead, it means that using these concepts as the basis for reintroduction may not be appropriate in all cases. There is much research yet to be done investigating the details of when individual species, may, or may not, alter community structure.

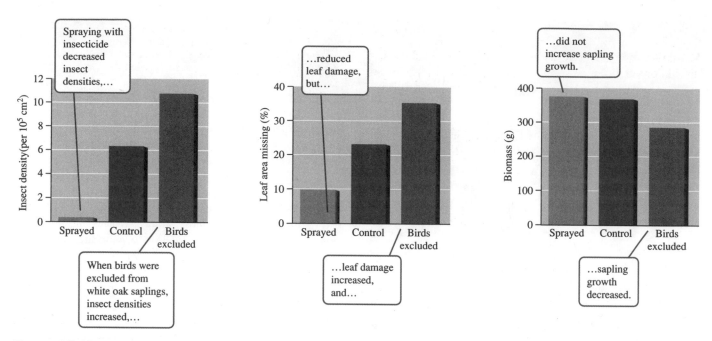

Figure 17.19   Effect of insectivorous birds on herbivorous insect populations, leaf damage, and sapling growth in white oaks (data from Marquis and Whelan 1994).

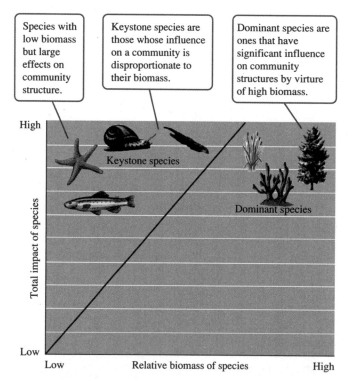

Figure 17.20   What is a keystone species (data from Power et al. 1996)?

They found that the biomasses of sprayed and uncaged white oaks were significantly higher than the biomass of caged white oaks. In other words, the higher densities of herbivorous insects on the trees from which birds were excluded reduced their growth rates. One implication of these results is that insectivorous birds increase the growth rates of temperate forest trees.

Many studies of food webs and keystone species have been done since Robert Paine's classic study of the intertidal food web. The studies have revealed a great deal of biological diversity, which has prompted biologists to ask what characterizes keystone species. This reflection is necessary to avoid the possibility that the term may become so inclusive that it becomes meaningless. The conclusions reached by a conference designed to address this question are summarized in figure 17.20 (Power et al. 1996). Keystone species are those that, despite low biomass, exert strong effects on the structure of the communities they inhabit. As a general rule, keystone species are species whose effects on community structure are disproportionate relative to their abundance in the community. In other words, keystone species are not the dominant members of communities, even if their actions dominate the community. Ecologists also recognize that species don't have to be predators to be keystones, and instead mutualists can also play critical roles in determining community structure. This will all make much more sense when we see what Robert Paine observed in the intertidal zone.

Concept 17.3 Review

1. Paine discovered that intertidal invertebrate communities of higher diversity include a higher proportion of predator species. Did this pattern confirm Paine's predation hypothesis?
2. How can beavers alter the growth of plants they do not eat?
3. What is the difference between a keystone and a dominant species (see figure 17.20)

17.4 Mutualistic Keystones

Mutualists can act as keystone species. While our earlier discussions of keystone species have emphasized the roles of predators as keystone species, many other kinds of organisms can act as keystone species. Returning to the classification of Power and colleagues shown in figure 17.20, the only requirements for keystone status is that the species in question have relatively low biomass in the community and that it has a high impact on community structure. Increasingly, ecologists are discovering that many mutualistic species meet these requirements. One such group are the cleaner fishes on coral reefs.

A Cleaner Fish as a Keystone Species

Many species of fish on coral reefs clean other fish of ectoparasites. This relationship, which involves the cleaner fish and its clients, has been shown to be a true mutualism. One of the most widely distributed cleaner fish in the Indo-Pacific region is the cleaner wrasse, *Labroides dimidiatus*. The feeding activity of cleaner wrasses is intense. Alexandra Grutter of the University of Queensland, Australia, has shown that a single cleaner wrasse can remove and eat 1,200 parasites from client fishes per day. She also performed experiments (Grutter 1999) that documented that fish on reefs without cleaner wrasses harbour approximately four times the number of parasitic isopods as those living on reefs with cleaner wrasses.

What effect might cleaning activity by *L. dimidiatus* have on the diversity of fish on coral reefs? This is the question addressed with a series of field experiments by Redouan Bshary of the University of Cambridge. Bshary studied the effects of cleaner wrasses on reef fish diversity at Ras Mohammed National Park, Egypt (Bshary 2003). The study area consists of a sandy bottom area approximately 400 m from shore dotted with reef patches in water depths from 2 to 6 m. Bshary chose 46 reef patches separated from other patches by at least 5 m of sandy bottom. He identified and counted the fish species present during dives on these reefs and noted the presence or absence of cleaner wrasses on each reef patch. Bshary recorded 29 natural disappearances or appearances of cleaner wrasses during his study. In addition, he performed experimental removals of cleaner wrasses from reefs and introductions of these cleaners to reef patches where there were none.

Bshary followed the responses of the fish community to natural disappearances and experimental removals and natural colonization and experimental introductions. In doing so, he gained insights into the influence of these tiny mutualists on reef fish diversity. Figure 17.21 summarizes the responses of fish communities on reef patches four months following the natural or experimental, addition or removal of cleaner wrasses. Bshary observed a median reduction in fish species richness of approximately 24% where cleaner wrasses disappeared or were removed. Where cleaner wrasses were added, either naturally or experimentally, he observed a median increase in fish species richness of 24%. Bshary's results indicate that the cleaner wrasse acts as a keystone species on the coral reefs of the Red Sea. Mutualists that act as keystone species have also been found on land.

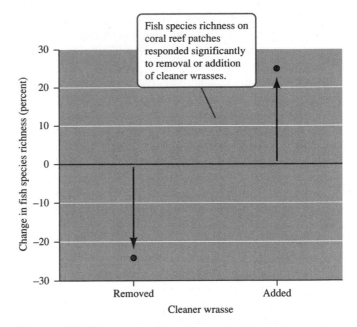

Figure 17.21 Results of experimental and natural removals or additions of cleaner wrasses. *Labroides dimidiatus*, to reef patches in the Red Sea (data from Bshary 2003).

Seed Dispersal Mutualists as Keystone Species

It appears that ants that disperse seeds have a significant influence on the structure of plant communities in the species-rich fynbos of South Africa. Caroline Christian (2001) observed that native ants disperse 30% of the seeds in the shrublands of the fynbos. The plants attract the services of these dispersers with food rewards on the seeds called elaiosomes. However, the Argentine ant, *Linepithema humile* (fig. 17.22), which does not disperse seeds, has invaded these shrublands. Christian documented how the invading Argentine ants have displaced

Figure 17.22 The Argentine ant, *Linepithema humile*, has invaded and disrupted ant communities in many geographic regions. In the fynbos of South Africa, invading Argentine ants are displacing keystone ant species, which threatens the exceptional plant diversity of the fynbos.

(as they have in other regions) many of the native ant species in the fynbos. In addition, she discovered that the native ant species most impacted by Argentine ant invasion are those species most likely to disperse larger seeds.

Seed-dispersing ants are important to the persistence of fynbos plants because they bury seeds in sites where they are safe from seed-eating rodents and from fire. Fires are characteristic of Mediterranean shrublands such as the fynbos, and seeds are the only life stage of many fynbos plants to survive fires. Consequently, ant dispersal is critical to the survival of many plant species. In a comparison of seedling recruitment following fire, Christian found substantial reductions in seedling recruitment by plants producing large seeds in areas invaded by Argentine ants (fig. 17.23). Meanwhile small-seeded plants, whose dispersers are less affected by Argentine ants, showed no reduction in recruitment following fire. Christian's results, like Bshary's, reveal the influence of mutualists acting as keystone species within the communities they occupy. Other studies are revealing the importance of other mutualists, such as pollinators and mycorrhizal fungi, as keystone species.

One of the things you may have noticed in several of the examples we have provided about keystone species, is that not every case was actually a single species! Instead, studies often referred to some group of species, such as insect-eating birds or seed-dispersing ants, as providing ecological services which, if disrupted, can greatly alter natural communities. The issue of whether species, or guilds/functional groups, are most critical for ecosystem function is a topic of much debate amongst ecologists, and we will discuss it in later chapters. We end this chapter instead with a discussion of one more type of keystone species, humans. Humans are nearly everywhere on the planet, and to ignore their impact on community structure would greatly hinder our ecological understanding.

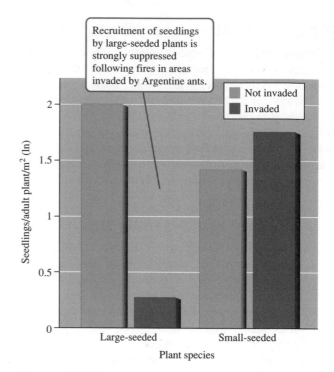

Figure 17.23 A comparison of recruitment of seedlings following fire in areas invaded by Argentine ants and areas not invaded shows the effects of the displacement of native seed-dispersing ants by Argentine ants (data from Christian 2001).

Concept 17.4 Review

1. Bshary studied changes in fish species richness in response to both natural and experimental removals and additions of the cleaner fish *Labroides dimidiatus* (see fig. 17.21). Why did he not just focus on the response of fish species richness to natural additions and removals of the cleaner fish?
2. In many regions, native pollinator insects seem to be declining. Why is this a cause for concern among conservationists and ecologists?

Ecological Tools

Humans as Keystone Species

People have long manipulated food webs both as a consequence of their own feeding activities and by introducing or deleting species from existing webs. In addition, many of these manipulations have focused on keystone species. Consequently, either consciously or unwittingly, people have, themselves, acted as keystone species in communities. In this section we show how critical evaluation of some human activities can provide further information about the function of natural communities.

The Empty Forest: Hunters and Tropical Rain Forest Animal Communities

The current plight of the tropical rain forest is well known. However, Kent Redford (1992) points out that with few exceptions, most studies of human impact on the tropical rain forest have concentrated on direct effects of humans on vegetation, mainly on deforestation. Redford expands our view by examining the effects of humans on animals. The picture that emerges from this analysis is that humans have so reduced the population densities of rain forest animals in many areas that they no longer play their keystone roles in the system, a situation Redford calls "ecologically extinct."

Redford estimated that subsistence hunting, a major source of protein for many rural people, results in an annual death toll of approximately 14 million mammals and 5 million birds and reptiles within the Brazilian Amazon. He estimated further that commercial hunters, seeking skins, meat, and feathers, kill an additional 4 million animals annually. Consequently, the total take by hunters within the Brazilian Amazon is approximately 23 million individual animals. However, this figure underestimates the total number of animal deaths, since many wounded animals escape from hunters only to die. Including those fatally wounded animals that escape, Redford places the annual deaths within the Brazilian Amazon at approximately 60 million animals.

Hunters generally concentrate on a small percentage of larger bird and mammal species, however. For instance, Redford estimated that at Cocha Cashu Biological Station in Manu National Park, located in the Amazon River basin in eastern Peru, hunters concentrate on 9% of the 319 bird species and 18% of the 67 mammal species. Because hunters generally concentrate on the larger species, this small portion of the total species pool makes up about 52% of the total bird biomass and approximately 75% of the total mammalian biomass around Manu National Park (fig. 17.24).

As impressive as all these numbers are, there remains a critical question: Do hunters reduce the local densities of the birds and mammals they hunt? The answer is yes. Redford estimated that moderate to heavy hunting pressure in rain forests reduces mammalian biomass by about 80% to 93% and bird biomass by about 70% to 94%.

There may be cause for concern, however, that goes beyond the losses of these immense numbers of animals. As you might expect, many large rain forest mammals and birds may act as keystone species. If so, their decimation will have effects that ripple through the entire community. The first to suggest a keystone role for the large animals preferred by rain forest hunters was John Terborgh (1988), who presented his hypothesis in a provocative essay titled, "The Big Things That Run the World."

Terborgh's hypothesis has been supported by a variety of studies. He observed that in the absence of pumas and jaguars on Barro Colorado Island, Panama, medium-sized mammal species are over 10 times more abundant than in areas still supporting populations of these large cats. R. Dirzo and A. Miranda (1990) compared two forests in tropical southern Mexico, one in which hunting had eliminated most of the large mammals and one in which most of the large mammals were still present. The comparison was stark. In the absence of large mammals such as peccaries, jaguars, and deer, the researchers found forests carpeted with undamaged plant seedlings and piled with uneaten and rotting fruits and nuts, signs of a changing forest. Such observations prompted Redford to warn, "We must not let a forest full of trees fool us into believing all is well." Tropical rain forest conservation must also include the large, and potentially keystone, animal species that are vulnerable to hunting by humans. However, we must also recognize that importance in a community does not mean a species needs to be big.

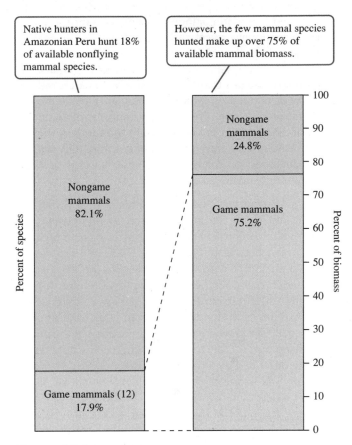

Figure 17.24 Highly selective hunting by Amazonian natives (data from Redford 1992).

Ants and Agriculture: Keystone Predators for Pest Control

In 1982, Stephen Risch and Ronald Carroll published a paper describing how the predaceous fire ant, *Solenopsis geminata*, acts as a keystone predator in the food web of the corn-squash agroecosystem in southern Mexico. While "natural enemies" had been used to control insect pests for some time, Risch and Carroll put these efforts into a community context. They drew conceptual parallels between biological control of insects with natural enemies and studies of the influences of keystone species, citing studies of the influences of herbivores on plant communities and the effects of predators on intertidal communities. In their own experiments, Risch and Carroll demonstrated how predation by *Solenopsis* in the corn-squash agroecosystem reduces the number of arthropods and the arthropod diversity (fig. 17.25). This study showed how *Solenopsis* could act as a keystone species to the benefit of the agriculturist.

The conceptual breakthrough represented by the work of Risch and Carroll is impressive. However, their work had been anticipated, 1,700 years earlier, by farmers in southern China. H. Huang and P. Yang (1987) cite Ji Han, who, in A.D. 304, wrote "Plants and Trees of the Southern Regions" in which he included the following:

The Gan (mandarin orange) is a kind of orange with an exceptionally sweet and delicious taste … In the market, the natives of Jiao-zhi [southeastern China and North Vietnam] sell ants stored in bags of rush mats. The nests are like thin silk. The bags are all attached to twigs and leaves, which, with the ants inside the nests, are for sale. The ants are reddish-yellow in color, bigger than ordinary ants. In the south, if the Gan trees do not have this kind of ant, the fruits will be damaged by many harmful insects and not a single fruit will be perfect.

Now, 17 centuries after the observations of Ji Han, we know this ant as the citrus ant, *Oecophylla smaragdina*. The use of this ant to control herbivorous insects in citrus orchards was unknown outside of China until 1915. In 1915, Walter Swingle, a plant physiologist who worked for the U.S. Department of Agriculture, was sent to China to search for varieties of oranges resistant to citrus canker, a disease that was devastating citrus groves in Florida. While on this trip, Swingle came across a small village where the main occupation of the people was growing ants for sale to orange growers. The ant was the same one described by Ji Han in A.D. 304.

Oecophylla is one of the weaver ants, which use silk to construct a nest by binding leaves and twigs together. These ants spend the night in their nest. During the day, the ants spread out over the home tree as they forage for insects. Farmers place a nest in a tree and then run bamboo strips between trees so that the ants can have access to more than one tree. The ants will eventually build nests in adjacent trees and can colonize an entire orchard.

The ants harvest protein and fats when they gather insects from their home tree, but they have other needs as well. They also need a source of liquid and carbohydrates, and they get these materials by cultivating Homoptera, known as soft-scale insects or mealy bugs, which produce nectar. The ants and soft-scale insects have a mutualistic relationship in which the ants transport the insects from tree to tree and protect them from predators. In return the ants consume the nectar produced by the soft-scale insects. Because of this mutualism with the soft-scale insect, which can itself be a serious pest of citrus, several early agricultural scientists expressed skepticism that *Oecophylla* would be an effective agent for pest control in citrus. They suggested that the use of this ant could produce infestations by soft-scale insects.

Despite these criticisms, all Chinese citrus growers interviewed insisted that *Oecophylla* is effective at pest control and that the damage caused by soft-scale insects is minor. Research done by Yang appears to have solved this apparent contradiction. Comparing orange trees treated with chemical insecticides to those protected by *Oecophylla*, Yang recorded higher numbers of soft-scale insects in the trees tended by ants. However, these higher numbers did not appear to cause serious damage to the orange trees. When Yang inspected the soft-scale insects closely, he found that they were heavily infested with the larvae

of parasitic wasps. He also found that the ants did not reduce populations of lacewing larvae and ladybird beetles, predators that feed on soft-scale insects. Huang and Yang concluded that *Oecophylla* is effective at pest control because while it attacks the principal, larger pests of citrus, it does not reduce populations of other predators that attack the smaller pests of citrus, such as soft-scale insects, aphids, and mites.

The association between *Oecophylla* and citrus trees seems similar to that between ants and acacias (see chapter 15). There is a difference, however. Humans maintain *Oecophylla* as a substantial component of the food web in citrus orchards. Not only have specialized farmers historically cultivated and distributed the ants, *Oecophylla* must also be protected from the winter cold. The ant cannot survive the winter in southeast China in orange trees. Consequently, farmers must generally provide shelter and food for the ants during winter.

The labour and expense of maintaining these ants through the winter may be reduced by mixed plantings of orchard trees. Farmers in Shajian village in the Huaan district of southeast China have successfully maintained *Oecophylla* over the winter in mixed plantings of orange and pomelo trees. During winter the ants are mostly in pomelo trees, which are larger and have thicker foliage than orange trees, characteristics that reduce cooling rates on winter nights. In this situation, farmers do not have to add new nests of *Oecophylla* each spring. Gradually, the ant has become integrated into the mixed citrus and pomelo orchards and requires little special care from the farmers.

The farmers of southeast China have employed *Oecophylla* as a keystone species in a complex citrus-based food web for a long time. However, the results would not be the same with just any ant species. The citrus growers required a species that acts in a particular way. One wonders how long farmers of the region had experimented with this species before Ji Han wrote his account of their activities in A.D. 304.

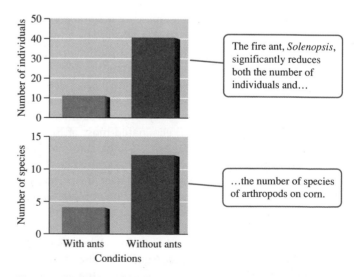

The fire ant, *Solenopsis*, significantly reduces both the number of individuals and…

…the number of species of arthropods on corn.

Figure 17.25   Effect of *Solenopsis geminata* on the arthropod populations on corn (data from Risch and Carroll 1982).

Summary

Community structure will be influenced by a diversity of interactions, all of which may be occurring simultaneously. These ecological processes can interact among themselves, with potentially large consequences for the relative abundances of the component species.

A food web summarizes the feeding relations in a community. The earliest work on food webs concentrated on simplified communities in areas such as the Arctic islands. However, researchers such as Charles Elton (1927) soon found that even these so-called simple communities included very complex feeding relations. Ralph Bird (1930) showed that an added level of complexity exists when members of one community feed upon species primarily found in a different community. This work emphasizes that communities do not have discrete boundaries, and that species connections can be very broad. Missing from most studies of food webs are parasites, pathogens, and decomposers.

Strong competitors can alter community structure. Some communities will contain competitive hierarchies, in which certain species are continually able to suppress the abundance of other species. In such systems, competition can greatly limit species diversity, with the competitively subordinate species being excluded from the community. Paul Keddy combined the ideas of competitive hierarchies and the theory of allocation when he developed the theory of centrifugal organization of species. In this theory, core habitats are occupied by dominant competitors, while poorer competitors will be found in more stressful satellite habitats. The presence of the poorer competitors occurs because they are better able to deal with other stressors in the environment than are the dominant competitors.

The activities of a few keystone species may control the structure of communities. Robert Paine (1966) proposed that the feeding activities of a few species have inordinate influences on community structure. He predicted that some predators may increase species diversity by reducing the probability of competitive exclusion. Manipulative studies of predaceous species have identified many keystone species, including starfish and snails in the marine intertidal zone and fish in rivers. On land, birds exert substantial influences on communities of their arthropod prey. Some keystone species, such as beavers, may also be ecosystem engineers. This designation is given to organisms whose activities result in the construction of a novel habitat. Keystone species are those that, despite low biomass, exert strong effects on the structure of the communities they inhabit.

Mutualists can act as keystone species. Experimental studies have shown that cleaner fish, species that remove parasites from other fish, act as keystone species on coral reefs. Removing cleaner fish produces a decline in reef fish species richness. Ants that disperse plant seeds in the fynbos of South Africa have been shown to have major influences on plant community structure. Where invading ants have displaced the mutualistic dispersing ants, the plant community suffers a decline in species richness following fires. Other mutualistic organisms that may act as keystone species include pollinators and mycorrhizal fungi.

Humans have acted as keystone species in communities. People have long manipulated food webs both as a consequence of their own feeding activities and by introducing or deleting species from existing food webs. In addition, many of these manipulations have been focused on keystone species. Hunters in tropical rain forests have been responsible for removing keystone animal species from large areas of the rain forests of Central and South America. Chinese farmers have used ants as keystone predators to control pests in citrus orchards for over 1,700 years.

Review Questions

1. You could argue that the classical food web of Bear Island included several communities, each with its own food web. What were some of the different communities that Summerhayes and Elton (1923) included in their web? On the other hand, because the Bear Island food web includes significant movement of energy (food) and nutrients between what many ecologists might consider to be separate communities, what does their food web say about the distinctness of what we call communities?

2. What is a keystone species? How does Paine's experiment demonstrate this concept?

3. When Power (1990) excluded predaceous fish from her river sites, the density of herbivorous insect larvae (chironomids) decreased. Use the food web described by Power to explain this response.

4. Atlegrim (1989) and also Marquis and Whelan (1994) showed that birds in high latitudes and temperate forests reduce insect populations. The results of this research suggest that birds act as keystone species in some communities. What else would we need to know about the birds in these communities before we could conclude that they are keystones in the strict sense? (Hint: Consider figure 17.20.)

5. Notice that in the study by Marquis and Whelan (1994) the biomass of uncaged *Q. alba* was as great as that of sprayed individuals. In other words, spraying protected oak seedlings as much as birds did. If spraying can control herbivorous forest insects, why rely on birds to improve tree growth? What advantages does predation by birds have over spraying?

6. Some paleontologists have proposed that overhunting caused the extinction of many large North American mammals at the end of the Pleistocene about 11,000 and 10,000 years ago. The hunters implicated by paleontologists were a newly arrived predatory species, *Homo sapiens*. Offer arguments for and against this hypothesis.

7. All the keystone species work we have discussed in chapter 17 has concerned the influences of animals on the structure of communities. Can other groups of organisms act as keystones? What about parasites and pathogens?

8. According to Paul Keddy's theory of the centrifugal organization of species, dominant species will displace poorer competitors from the "best" habitat in a community. There is evidence this occurs in the wetlands he has studied, at least among vascular plant species. How would you design a study to test whether this theory also applies to animal species?

9. Decomposition and parasitism is generally excluded from discussions of food webs. How might this practice give a biased view towards the relative importance of different ecological processes in structuring communities?

10. What evidence is necessary to make a firm declaration as to whether grey wolves are keystone species in Yellowstone National Park? If they are found not to be keystone, does this mean that there was no justifiable reason to reintroduce them to Yellowstone?

Suggested Readings

Balirwa, J. S., C. A. Chapman, L. C. Chapman, I. G. Cowx, K. Geheb, L. Kaufman, R. H. Lowe-McConnell, O. Seehausen, J. H. Wanink, R. L. Welcomme, and F. Witte. 2003. Biodiversity and fishery sustainability in the Lake Victoria Basin: an unexpected marriage? *BioScience* 53:703–15.

A provocative analysis, suggesting that fishing pressure on Nile perch in Lake Victoria may be a key to preserving surviving remnants of the native fish fauna.

Brown, J. H., T. G. Whitham, S. K. M. Ernest, and C. A. Gehring. 2001. Complex species interactions and the dynamics of ecological systems: long-term experiments. *Science* 93:643–50.

Excellent review of long-term experiments that have revealed some of the complex interactions occurring in biological communities.

Christian, C. E. 2001. Consequences of a biological invasion reveal the importance of mutualism for plant communities. *Nature* 413:635–39.

Fascinating study of how seed dispersal mutualisms play a central role in maintaining the diversity within a species-rich shrubland in South Africa.

Cohen, J. E., T. Jonsson, and S. R. Carpenter. 2003. Ecological community description using the food web, species abundance, and body size. *Proceedings of the National Academy of Sciences of the United States of America* 100:1781–86.

State of the art use of food webs to characterize a biological community.

Power, M. E., D. Tilman, J. A. Estes, B. A. Menge, W. J. Bond, L. S. Mills, G. Daily, J. C. Castilla, J. Lubchenko, and R. T. Paine. 1996. Challenges in the quest for keystones. *BioScience* 46:609–20.

This paper provides a review of the keystone species concept and of the vast body of research related to keystone species. It summarizes the thoughts of some of today's leading ecologists on an important ecological concept.

Terborgh, J. 1988. The big things that run the world: a sequel to E. O. Wilson. *Conservation Biology* 2:402–3.

This paper reviews the influence of humans on populations of large animals in rain forests and the possible consequences to rain forest ecology.

Hairston, N. G., F. E. Smith, L. B. Slobodkin. 1960. Community structure, population control, and competition. *American Naturalist* 94:421–25.

A classic paper describing the possible links between competition, predation, and community organization.

Wilson, S. D. and P. A. Keddy. 1986. Measuring diffuse competition along an environmental gradient—Results from a shoreline plant community. *American Naturalist* 127:862–69.

Excellent field study measuring how the strength of competition can vary within a wetland community.

Chapter *18*

Succession and Stability

Outline

*T*he first recorded visit to Glacier Bay gave no hint of its eventual contributions to our understanding of biological communities and ecosystems. In 1794, Captain George Vancouver visited the inlet to what is today called Glacier Bay, Alaska (fig. 18.1). He could not pass beyond the inlet to the bay, however, because his way was blocked by a mountain of ice. Vancouver and Vancouver (1798) described the scene as follows: "The shores of the continent form two large open bays which were terminated by compact solid mountains of ice, rising perpendicularly from the water's edge, and bounded to the north by a continuation of the united lofty frozen mountains that extend eastward from Mount Fairweather."

In 1879, John Muir explored the coast of Alaska, relying heavily on Vancouver's earlier descriptions. Muir (1915) commented in his journal that Vancouver's descriptions were excellent guides except for the area within Glacier Bay. Where Vancouver had met "mountains of ice," Muir found open water. He and his guides from the Hoona tribe paddled their canoe through Glacier Bay in rain and mist, feeling their way through uncharted territory. They eventually found the glaciers, which Muir estimated had retreated 30 to 40 km up the glacial valley since Vancouver's visit 85 years earlier.

Muir found no forests at the upper portions of the bay. He and his party had to build their campfires with the stumps and trunks of long-dead trees exposed by the retreating glaciers. Muir recognized that this "fossil wood" was a remnant of a forest that had been covered by advancing glaciers centuries earlier. He also saw that plants quickly colonized the areas uncovered by glaciers and that the oldest exposed areas, where Vancouver had met his mountains of ice, already supported forests.

Muir's observations in Glacier Bay were published in 1915 and read the same year by the ecologist William S. Cooper. Encouraged by Muir's descriptions, Cooper visited Glacier Bay in 1916 in what was the beginning of a lifetime of study. Cooper saw Glacier Bay as the ideal laboratory for the study of ecological **succession,** the gradual community change in an area following disturbance, or the creation of new substrate. Glacier Bay was ideal for the study of succession because the history of glacial retreat could be accurately traced back to 1794 and perhaps farther.

Cooper ultimately made four expeditions to Glacier Bay. His work and that of later ecologists produced a detailed picture of succession there. Several species of plants colonize an area during the first 20 years after it is exposed by the retreating glacier. These plants, the first in a successional sequence, form a **pioneer community.** The

Figure 18.1   Glacier Bay, Alaska.

most common members of the pioneer community are horsetail, *Equisetum varietaum,* willow herb, *Epilobium latifolium,* willows, *Salix* sp., cottonwood seedlings, *Populus balsamifera,* mountain avens, *Dryas drummondii,* and Sitka spruce, *Picea sitchensis.*

About 30 years after an area is exposed, the pioneer community gradually grades into a community dominated by mats of *Dryas,* a dwarf shrub. These *Dryas* mats also contain scattered alder, *Alnus crispa, Salix, Populus,* and *Picea.* Then, about 40 years after glacial retreat, the community changes into a shrub-thicket dominated by *Alnus.* Soon after the closure of the *Alnus* thicket, however, *Populus* and *Picea* will grow above it, covering about 50% of the area on sites 50 to 70 years old.

In 75 to 100 years, succession leads to a forest community dominated by *Picea.* Mosses carpet the understory of this spruce forest and here and there grow seedlings of western hemlock, *Tsuga heterophylla,* and mountain hemlock, *Tsuga mertensiana.* Eventually, the population of *Picea* declines and the forests are dominated by *Tsuga.* On landscapes with shallow slopes these hemlock forests eventually give way to muskeg, a landscape of peat bogs and scattered tussock meadows.

Because succession around Glacier Bay occurs on newly exposed geological substrates, not significantly modified by organisms, ecologists refer to this process as **primary succession.** Primary succession also occurs on newly formed volcanic surfaces such as lava flows. In areas where disturbance destroys a community without destroying the soil, the subsequent succession is called **secondary succession.** For instance, secondary succession occurs after agricultural lands are abandoned or after a forest fire.

Succession generally ends with a community whose populations remain stable until disrupted by disturbance. This late successional community is called the **climax community.** The nature of the climax community depends upon environmental circumstances. The communities we discussed in chapter 2—temperate forests, tundra, etc.—were essentially the climax communities for each of the climatic regimes that we considered. Other community types, such as grasslands are referred to as *disclimax communities.* These communities are maintained only through continual disturbances, such as grazing and drought. The climax community around Glacier Bay is determined by the prevailing climate and local topography. On well-drained, steep slopes the climax community is hemlock forest. In poorly drained soil on shallow slopes the climax community is muskeg.

Studies of succession show that communities and ecosystems are not static but constantly change in response to disturbance, environmental change, and their own internal dynamics. In many cases, the general direction of change in community structure and ecosystem processes is predictable, at least over the short term. The patterns of change in community and ecosystem properties during succession and the mechanisms responsible for those changes are subjects covered in chapter 18. We also consider a companion topic, community and ecosystem stability.

Concepts

18.1   **Community changes during succession include increases in species diversity and changes in species composition.**

18.2   **Ecosystem changes during succession include increases in biomass, primary production, respiration, and nutrient retention.**

18.3   **Mechanisms that drive ecological succession include facilitation, tolerance, and inhibition.**

18.4   **Community stability may be due to lack of disturbance or community resistance or resilience in the face of disturbance.**

18.1   Community Changes During Succession

Community changes during succession include increases in species diversity and changes in species composition. Some of the most detailed studies of ecological succession have focused on succession leading to a forest climax. Though primary and secondary forest succession require different amounts of time, the changes in species diversity that occur in each appear remarkably similar.

Primary Succession at Glacier Bay

We return to Glacier Bay to examine successional changes in species diversity and composition reported by William Reiners, Ian Worley, and Donald Lawrence (1971). They worked at sites carefully chosen for similarity in physical features but differing substantially in age. Their eight study sites were below 100 m elevation, were on glacial till, an unstratified and unsorted material deposited by a glacier, and all had moderate slopes. The study sites ranged in age, that is, time since glacial retreat, from 10 to 1,500 years.

Their youngest site, which was approximately 10 years old, supported a pioneer community of scattered *Epilobium, Equisetum,* and *Salix.* Site 2 was about 23 years old and supported a mix of pioneer species and clumps of *Populus* and *Dryas.* Site 3, which was approximately 33 years old, supported a mat of *Dryas* enclosing clumps of *Salix, Populus,* and *Alnus.* Site 4 was 44 years old and was dominated by a mat of *Dryas* with few open patches. Site 5, which was approximately 108 years old, was dominated by a thicket of *Alnus* and *Salix* with enough emergent *Populus* and *Picea* to form a partial canopy. Site 6 was a 200-year-old forest of *Picea.* Using geological methods, Reiners and his colleagues dated site 7 at 500 years and site 8 at 1,500 years. Both sites were located on Pleasant Island, which, because it is located outside the mouth of Glacier Bay, had escaped the most recent glaciation, that had destroyed the forests along the bay. Site 7 was an old forest of *Tsuga* that contained a few *Picea.* Site 8 was a muskeg with scattered lodgepole pines, *Pinus contorta.*

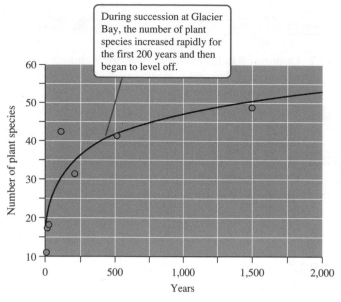

Figure 18.2   Change in plant species richness during primary succession at Glacier Bay, Alaska (data from Reiners, Worley, and Lawrence 1971).

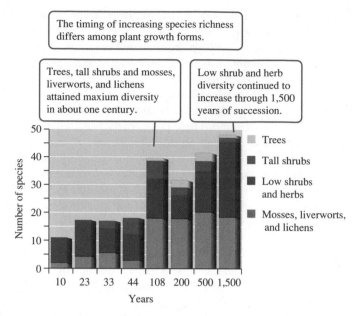

Figure 18.3   Succession of plant growth forms at Glacier Bay, Alaska (data from Reiners, Worley, and Lawrence 1971).

The total number of plant species in the eight study sites increased with plot age. As you can see in figure 18.2, species richness increased rapidly in the early years of succession at Glacier Bay and then more slowly during the later stages, approaching a possible plateau in species richness.

Not all groups of plants increased in diversity throughout succession. Figure 18.3 shows that while the species richness of mosses, liverworts, and lichens reached a plateau after about a century of succession, the diversity of low shrubs and herbs continued to increase throughout succession. In contrast, the diversity of tall shrubs and trees increased until the middle stages of succession and then declined in later stages.

The pattern of increased species richness with stand age that Reiners and his colleagues described for the successional sequence around Glacier Bay is one that we will see several times in the examples that follow. However, the tempo of succession is far different. The late successional climax community at Glacier Bay was 1,500 years old. In the following example of secondary succession, the climax forest community was 150 to 200 years old, approximately one-tenth the age of the climax community studied at Glacier Bay.

Secondary Succession in Boreal Forest

In chapter 2 we saw that boreal forests occupy much of the Northern land base, and are a dominant community-type in Canada. Although we may often think of the boreal as isolated areas of old-forest, the reality is often very different. Aside from the ever-increasing pressures of oil and gas exploration, and forestry and peat extraction, the boreal forest is a dynamic community with frequent disturbances. More specifically, much of the structure of boreal forests and secondary succession is driven by fire.

Fires are common throughout the boreal forest, with lightning strikes a common form of fire initiation. What exactly does

fire do to a forest (fig. 18.4)? The answer to this will depend upon the intensity of the fire, with some fires being relatively minor and affecting only low-lying vegetation, and others being severe and reaching both the tops of the trees and through the accumulated litter on the forest floor to the soil. However, if we ignore the extreme ends of the fire intensity distribution, we can find a few common consequences of fire. First, fire can kill plants, including canopy trees. Death of canopy trees can increase light penetration to the soil floors, allowing the recruitment and growth of smaller trees and seedlings that may have escaped the fire, or were able to quickly colonize (think about light compensation points from chapter 5). Fire effects do not end with their immediate impacts on plant survival. Fire can also cause increases in nutrient availability by the physical breakdown of organic matter, and by stimulating microbial activity. In combination, these factors provide a high-light environment with plenty of available nutrients. It may come as no surprise then that after a fire, recolonization by some plants can occur within a matter of weeks.

But how do plants "know" to colonize a burned area? Many plants possess life-history traits that facilitate regrowth following fire. These fire-tolerant species are widespread throughout the boreal forest. For example, although aspen stems will burn during a fire, the root systems generally survive. Soon after a fire, you will find thousands of young aspen sprouts emerging from these living root systems. This strategy is found in other species as well, such as paper birch, but rarely to the same density that is found with aspen. The strategy of resprouting ensures quick replacement of the shoots following a fire. Other species may not be able to resprout, but fire may trigger seed dispersal or germination. For example, black spruce and jack pine produce seeds inside of cones covered with a thick layer of pitch. The pitch burns off during fire, releasing the seed. In other communities, certain compounds contained

Figure 18.4   Changes in boreal forest composition along a chronosequence. Dates refer to the year of the last fire.

within smoke itself can even serve as a stimulant toward seed germination! The life-history tradeoffs we discussed in chapter 9 are very relevant to understanding the process of succession. Species that invest in large numbers of seeds, which are able to disperse over great distances, are more likely to encounter the "open" environments of a post-burn fire. Following fire it is common to see species such as fireweed and a variety of grasses blanketing the forest floor, until they are shaded out by trees. These species have life-history traits well suited to living in disturbed habitats, but not mature forest. Knowing that some, but not all, species of the boreal forests have adaptations to recover following fire, what do you expect secondary succession in the boreal forest to look like?

Yves Bergeron of the Université de Québec has been studying the secondary succession of southern boreal forests for several decades. The work of Bergeron and his students has provided us with a much clearer understanding of how fire can alter plant community structure in the boreal forest. In one study (Bergeron 2000), we can see a general pattern in species change over time following fire. Bergeron conducted an extensive survey of forest composition in the southern extent of the boreal forest in Quebec, establishing a series of transects and study plots in the forests surrounding Lake Duparquet. These forests contain a mixture of dominant plant species, including jack pine, black and white spruce, balsam poplar, and paper birch. Bergeron wanted to know whether the distribution of these species on the landscape could be explained by fire. In other words, would you tend to find certain types of boreal species in areas that were recently burned and other species in areas that have not been burned for quite some time? Bergeron sampled forest stands that were established after different forest fires, with the most recent occurring in 1964 and the oldest in 1760. The results were quite striking. Bergeron found that prior to the fires there was substantial variation in forest composition, and following fire there was a regular pattern to successional changes over time (fig. 18.5). Soon after fire, forests were dominated by hardwood species, such as aspen, birch, willow, and pin cherry. These species were eventually replaced by white spruce and balsam fir, with white cedar becoming

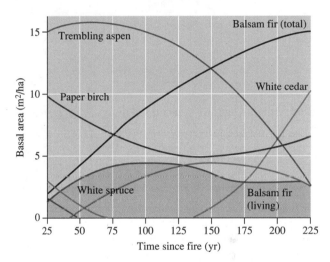

Figure 18.5   Following fire, the composition of the southern boreal forest changes over the course of secondary succession (data from Bergeron 2000).

common even later. Bergeron found that these dynamics were also influenced by periodic outbreaks of spruce budworms, once again emphasizing the point we made in chapter 17 that all communities will be influenced by multiple ecological factors. Despite this complexity, Bergeron was able to paint a nice portrait of secondary succession in the southern boreal forests. His interpretation of this process can help explain the observed heterogeneity in forest types within the boreal, as these areas may be in different stages of the long-term movement towards the local climax community.

Succession in Rocky Intertidal Communities

When we discussed the influence of disturbance on local species diversity in chapter 17, we saw how an intertidal boulder stripped of its cover of attached organisms was soon colonized by algae and barnacles (fig. 18.6). Looking back on that pattern of community change we can now see it as an example

Figure 18.6 Succession in the intertidal zone involves colonization and competition for limited space among species as different as attached marine algae, sea anemones, mussels, and barnacles.

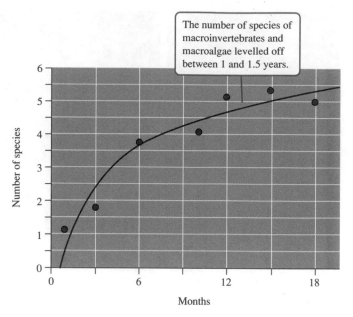

> The number of species of macroinvertebrates and macroalgae levelled off between 1 and 1.5 years.

Figure 18.7 Succession in number of macroinvertebrate and macroalgae species on intertidal boulders (data from Sousa 1979a).

Succession in Stream Communities

Rapid succession has been well documented in Sycamore Creek, Arizona, which has been studied for nearly two decades by Stuart Fisher and his colleagues (1982). Sycamore Creek, a tributary of the Verde River, lies approximately 32 km northeast of Phoenix, Arizona, where it drains approximately 500 km^2 of mountainous desert terrain. Evaporation nearly equals precipitation within the Sycamore Creek catchment, so flows are generally low and often intermittent. However, the creek is subject to frequent flash floods with sufficient power to completely disrupt the community and initiate succession.

Fisher's research team reported on the successional events following one such flood. Intense floods occurred on Sycamore Creek on August 6, 12, and 16, of 1979, with peak flows of 7, 3, and 2 m^3 per second. Floods of this intensity mobilize the stones and sand of the stream, scouring some areas and depositing sediments in others. In the process, most stream organisms are destroyed. The three floods of August 1979 eliminated approximately 98% of algal and invertebrate biomass in Sycamore Creek.

In 63 days following these floods, Fisher and his colleagues observed rapid changes in both the diversity and composition of algae and invertebrates. Patterns among primary producers were especially clear. Two days after the floods, the majority of the stream bottom consisted of bare sand with some patches of diatoms. Five days after the flood, diatoms covered about half the streambed. Within 13 to 22 days, diatoms almost completely covered the stream bottom. Other algae, especially blue-green algae and mats consisting of a mixture of the green alga *Cladophora* and blue-green algae, appeared in significant quantities by day 35. By day 63, the bottom of Sycamore Creek consisted of a patchwork of areas dominated by diatoms, blue-green algae, and mats of *Cladophora* and blue-green algae. The diversity of diatoms and other algae, as measured

of ecological succession. Wayne Sousa (1979a, 1979b) showed that the first species to colonize open space on intertidal boulders were a green alga in the genus *Ulva* and the barnacle *Chthamalus fissus*. The next arrivals were several species of perennial red algae: *Gelidium coulteri, Gigartina leptorhynchos, Rhodoglossum affine,* and *Gigartina canaliculata.* Finally, if there was no disturbance for two to three years, *G. canaliculata* grew over the other species and dominated 60% to 90% of the space.

Sousa explored succession on intertidal boulders with several experiments. In one of them, he followed succession on small boulders that he had cleaned and stabilized. As in forest succession, the number of species increased with time (fig. 18.7). Notice in the figure that the average number of species increased until about 1 to 1.5 years and then levelled off at about five species.

Primary forest succession around Glacier Bay may require about 1,500 years, and secondary forest succession in the boreal forest takes about 200 years. Meanwhile the successional changes described by Sousa occurred within about 1.5 years. In the next example, ecological succession within a desert stream occurs in less than 2 months.

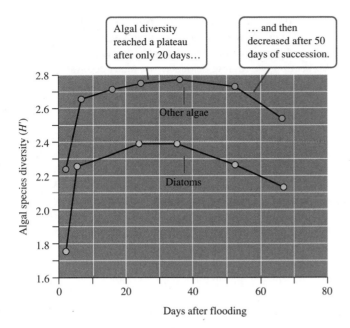

Figure 18.8   Algal species diversity during succession in Sycamore Creek, Arizona (data from Fisher et al. 1982).

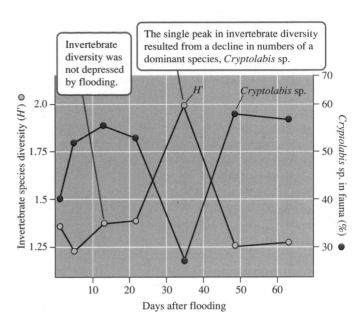

Figure 18.9   Invertebrate species diversity during succession in Sycamore Creek, Arizona (data from Fisher et al. 1982).

by H' (see chapter 16), levelled off after only 5 days and then began to decline after about 50 days (fig. 18.8).

Invertebrate diversity was strongly influenced by a single dominant species of crane fly, family Tipulidae, *Cryptolabis* sp. (fig. 18.9). Large numbers of *Cryptolabis* larvae in Sycamore Creek depressed H' diversity for all collections except for the collection on day 35, when most of the population emerged as adults. Throughout their collections over the 63-day period of the study, the researchers reported that they collected 38 to 43 species of aquatic invertebrates out of a total of 48 species collected during their studies. In other words, most macroinvertebrate species survived the flood.

Where did these invertebrate species find refuge from the devastating floods of August 1979? The invertebrate community of Sycamore Creek is dominated by insects whose adults are terrestrial. During the floods of August, many adult insects were in the aerial stage and the flood passed under them. These aerial adults were the source of most invertebrate recolonization of the flood-devastated Sycamore Creek.

We now move from the flowing waters of the desert stream to the relatively still waters of lakes. Here too we will find predictable patterns of community succession.

Shallow Lake Succession

Lakes experience succession in two principle time scales. Over the short time scale of seasons or years, there will be changes in the composition of species present in response to some disturbance such as flooding, freezing, or introduction of novel species. These are similar in concept to what we have seen in the previous examples of succession in forests and streams. However, lakes also experience succession on a geological time scale. Most lakes, particularly small lakes, eventually disappear. This too is succession and involves predictable changes in species composition as a result of changing conditions in the

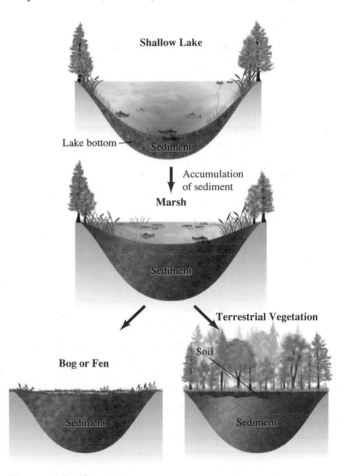

Figure 18.10   Shallow lakes can undergo succession.

lake (fig. 18.10). Driving lake succession is **sedimentation**, the deposition of suspended matter onto the lake bottom.

We begin by imagining a small, shallow lake in the boreal forest. Surrounding the lake will likely be a variety of mosses, cattails, and other plants that can grow in water-logged soils. As this is a shallow lake, there are likely to be substantial amounts of aquatic vegetation even far from the lake edge. Now ask yourself a question: what happens to all of the plant litter surrounding and inside the lake when it falls from the plants? Obviously, much of this will fall into the water and settle onto the bottom of the lake. In these cool regions, decomposition is generally slower than litter accumulations, such that the "bottom" of the lake gradually rises as litter is accumulated across years and decades. These changes eventually result in a conversion of the lake into a marsh-like habitat with standing water surrounding substantial amounts of vegetation. Depending upon the specific conditions (e.g. rate of water flow out of the lake, pH, etc.), continued sedimentation can convert the marsh into a fen or bog (chapter 3) or even into a drier upland forest community. A critical aspect of this form of succession is that it blurs the lines between aquatic and terrestrial systems. High levels of deposition from "terrestrial" vegetation into a shallow lake can cause succession from one to the other. As we have seen many times throughout the book, terms like "aquatic" and "terrestrial" are convenient for scientists to use to describe communities, but they mask the rich complexity of interconnections that actually exist.

It is important to also recognize that not all lakes will undergo this form of long-term succession. Deep lakes are unlikely to have large amounts of vegetation growing throughout the water, and thus relatively little sedimentation occurs. Similarly, lakes with steep, rock-lined boundaries are likely to experience little encroachment by the surrounding terrestrial vegetation, either slowing or preventing succession. Finally, a critical component of lake succession is that sedimentation rates are greater than decomposition rates. If microbial activity is high enough to decompose the litter, or if there is sufficient outflow of water from the lake (carrying sediment), succession is less likely to occur.

As we have just shown, ecological succession involves predictable changes in community structure. As you will see next, succession also leads to predictable changes in ecosystem structure and function.

Concept 18.1 Review

1. What are the primary mechanisms producing the great differences in succession rates in forest, rocky intertidal, and stream communities?
2. How do life-history traits influence whether a species is likely to be found early or late in succession?
3. Why is lake succession likely to occur in shallow lakes with low pH and cool temperatures?

18.2   Ecosystem Changes During Succession

Ecosystem changes during succession include increases in biomass, primary production, respiration, and nutrient retention.   As succession changes the diversity and compo-

sition of communities, ecosystem properties change as well. In the last section, we saw how plant and animal community structure changes during primary and secondary succession. In this section, we review evidence that many ecosystem properties also change during succession. For instance, many properties of soils, such as the nutrient and organic matter content, change during the course of succession.

Ecosystem Changes at Glacier Bay

Stuart Chapin and his colleagues (1994) documented substantial changes in ecosystem structure during succession at Glacier Bay. They focused on four study areas of approximately 2 km² each. Their first site had been deglaciated about 5 to 10 years and was in the pioneer stage. Their second site had been deglaciated 35 to 45 years previously and was dominated by a mat of *Dryas. Dryas* was just beginning to invade this site when it was studied by Reiners' group more than 20 years earlier. The third site had been deglaciated about 60 to 70 years before and was in the alder, *Alnus,* stage. This site was studied by Reiners when it was a young thicket of alder and by Cooper when it was in the pioneer stage. The fourth site studied by Chapin and his colleagues had been deglaciated 200 to 225 years earlier and was a forest of spruce, *Picea,* as it was when studied by Reiners and Cooper.

Chapin and his research team measured changes in several ecosystem characteristics across these study sites. One of the most fundamental characteristics was the quantity of soil. Total soil depth and the depth of all major soil horizons all show significant increases from the pioneer community to the spruce stage (fig. 18.11).

Several other ecologically important soil properties also changed during succession at the Glacier Bay study sites. As figure 18.12 shows, the organic content and moisture concentrations of the soil increased substantially. Over the same successional sequence, soil bulk density and phosphorus concentration decreased.

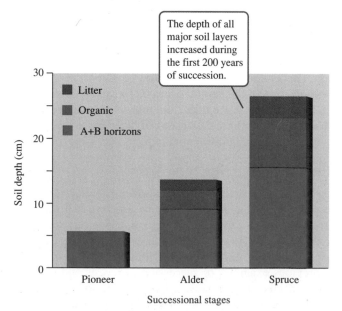

Figure 18.11   Soil building during primary succession at Glacier Bay, Alaska (data from Chapin et al. 1994).

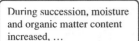

During succession, moisture and organic matter content increased, …

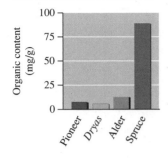
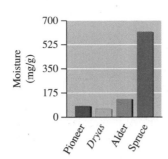

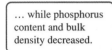

… while phosphorus content and bulk density decreased.

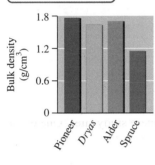
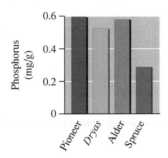

(Pioneer = 0 years ⟶ Spruce = 200+ years)

Figure 18.12 Changes in soil properties during succession at Glacier Bay, Alaska (data from Chapin et al. 1994).

Why are these changes in soil properties important? They demonstrate that succession involves more than just changes in the composition and diversity of species. Changes in soil properties are important because soils are the foundation upon which terrestrial ecosystems are built.

We can also see from these ecological studies that the physical and biological properties of ecosystems are inseparable. Organisms acting upon mineral substrates contribute to the building of soils upon which spruce forests eventually grow around Glacier Bay. Soils, in turn, strongly influence the kinds of organisms that grow in a place.

Four Million Years of Ecosystem Change

The detailed knowledge of ecosystem change that has emerged through studies at Glacier Bay, Alaska, is impressive. However, the sequence of ages represented by the study sites at Glacier Bay, what ecologists call a **chronosequence,** are limited. In 1794, when Captain George Vancouver encountered a wall of ice at the mouth of Glacier Bay, the island of Kauai in the Hawaiian Island chain supported forest ecosystems growing on soils that had developed on lava flows that were over four million years old. The Hawaiian Islands have formed over a hot spot on the Pacific tectonic plate and have been transported on that plate to the northwest, forming a chain of

islands that vary greatly in age. The youngest island in the group is the big island of Hawaii, which is currently growing over the hot spot. The big island is made up of volcanic rocks that vary from fresh lava flows to flows that are approximately 150,000 years old. Meanwhile, the islands to the northwest are sequentially older. As in Glacier Bay, teams of ecologists have probed the chronosequence represented by the Hawaiian Island chain for information on ecosystem development. However, in Hawaii the chronosequence spans not hundreds of years but millions.

Lars Hedin, Peter Vitousek, and Pamela Matson (2003) examined nutrient distributions and losses on a chronosequence of forest ecosystems on the islands of Hawaii, Molokai, and Kauai. The youngest ecosystems, which were on Hawaii, had developed on basaltic lava flows that were 300, 2,100, 20,000, and 150,000 years old. The study site on Molokai had developed on rocks that were 1,400,000 years old and the oldest study site, which was on Kauai, was 4,100,000 years old. All sites currently have an average annual temperature of about 16°C and receive approximately 2,500 mm of precipitation annually. They also all support forest communities dominated by the native tree, *Metrosideros polymorpha.*

Over the chronosequence represented by their six study sites, Hedin, Vitousek, and Matson encountered significant changes in a wide range of soil features. Earlier studies had demonstrated that primary production in the Hawaiian forest ecosystems is limited by nitrogen early in succession and by phosphorus later in succession. Organic matter, which is absent from fresh lava, increased in soils over the first 150,000 years of the chronosequence (fig. 18.13). As we saw, analogous increases in soil organic matter also occur over the course of succession at Glacier Bay (see fig. 18.12). However, in the Hawaiian chronosequence, organic matter was lower at the 1.4 and 4.1 million-year-old sites. Figure 18.13 also shows that changes in soil nitrogen content followed almost precisely the pattern exhibited by soil organic matter.

The pattern of change in the total phosphorus content of soils was remarkably different (fig. 18.14). The total amount of phosphorus in soils showed no obvious pattern of change with site age. However, the forms of phosphorus changed substantially over the chronosequence. Weatherable mineral phosphorus was largely depleted by 20,000 years. Meanwhile the percentage of soil phosphorus in refractory forms, which are not readily available to plants, increased, varying from 68% to 80% of total phosphorus across ecosystems that had developed on lava flows 20,000 years old or older. On these older soils, primary production is limited by phosphorus availability.

Hedin, Vitousek, and Matson found changes in rates of nutrient loss across the chronosequence. Over the course of four million years of ecosystem development, these tropical forest ecosystems show progressively higher rates of nitrogen loss but decreased rates of phosphorus loss (fig. 18.15). In other words, for approximately 2,000 years these ecosystems are highly retentive of nitrogen but as nitrogen content increases in their soils, they begin to lose nitrogen at a higher rate. Most losses are due to leaching to groundwater. In contrast, as phosphorus becomes progressively less available, and eventually

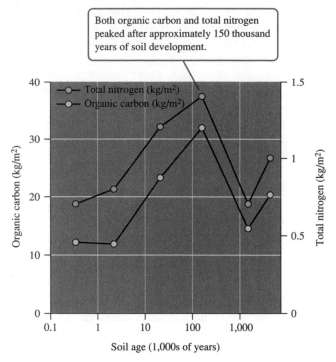

Figure 18.13 Changes in the organic carbon and total nitrogen content of soils developing on Hawaiian lava flows ranging in age from 300 to 4.1 million years old (data from Hedin, Vitousek, and Matson 2003).

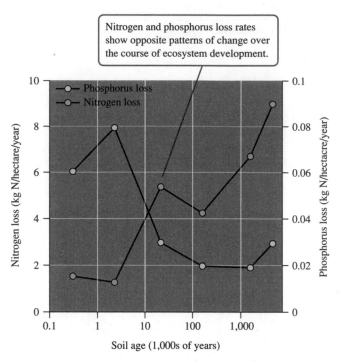

Figure 18.15 Nitrogen and phosphorus loss rates from soils developing on Hawaiian lava flows ranging in age from 300 to 4.1 million years old (data from Hedin, Vitousek, and Matson 2003).

limiting to primary production in these ecosystems, they become more retentive of phosphorus. As we shall see in the next example, intact vegetative cover may play a key role in nutrient retention in forest ecosystems.

Recovery of Nutrient Retention Following Disturbance

Bormann and Likens (1981) monitored a control and an experimental stream catchment for three years prior to an experimental treatment of logging in a New Hampshire Forest. They then cut the forest on their experimental catchment and suppressed regrowth of vegetation with herbicides for three years (Likens et al. 1978). By suppressing vegetative growth, they delayed succession.

When herbicide applications were stopped, succession proceeded and nutrient losses by the forest ecosystem decreased dramatically. As you can see in figure 18.16, the herbicide suppressed vegetative growth on the experimental catchment for at least three consecutive years. It was during this period that the experimental catchment lost large quantities of nutrients, including calcium, potassium, and nitrate.

When herbicide applications stopped in 1969, Likens's group observed simultaneous increases in primary production and decreases in nutrient loss. However, the researchers point out that uptake by vegetation cannot account completely for reduced nutrient loss and that losses of calcium, potassium, and nitrate all peaked during the time when herbicide was still being applied. They suggest that some of the reduced losses during this period can be attributed to reduced amounts of these nutrients in the ecosystem. In other words, nutrient losses were reducing

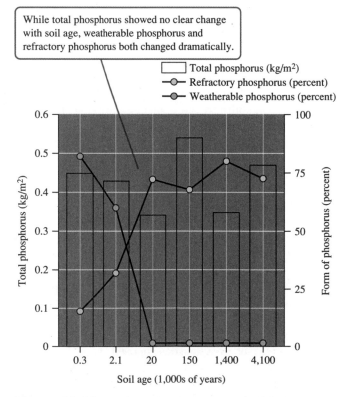

Figure 18.14 Changes in the total phosphorus and percentages of total phosphorus in weatherable and refractory (low availability) forms in soils developing on Hawaiian lava flows ranging in age from 300 to 4.1 million years old (data from Hedin, Vitousek, and Matson 2003).

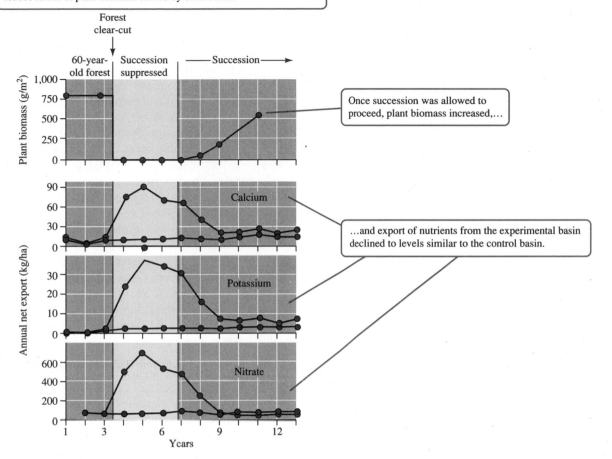

The Hubbard Brook deforestation experiment showed that succession can reduce losses of plant nutrients caused by disturbance.

Once succession was allowed to proceed, plant biomass increased,…

…and export of nutrients from the experimental basin declined to levels similar to the control basin.

Figure 18.16   Succession following deforestation and nutrient retention (data from Likens et al. 1978).

nutrient pools. However, vegetative uptake is clearly implicated since once succession was allowed to occur, nutrient losses from the experimental catchment declined rapidly. Though losses of nitrate returned to predisturbance levels within four years, calcium and potassium losses remained elevated above predisturbance levels even after seven years of forest succession.

A Model of Ecosystem Recovery

As a result of their observations on the Hubbard Brook Experimental Forest, Bormann and Likens proposed a model for recovery of ecosystems from disturbance (fig. 18.17). Their "biomass accumulation model" divides the recovery of a forest ecosystem from disturbance into four phases: (1) a reorganization phase of 10 to 20 years, during which the forest loses biomass and nutrients, despite accumulation of living biomass; (2) an aggradation phase of more than a century, when the ecosystem accumulates biomass, eventually reaching peak biomass; (3) a transition phase, during which biomass declines somewhat from the peak reached during the aggradation phase; and (4) a steady state phase, when biomass fluctuates around a mean level.

How well does the biomass accumulation model represent the process of forest succession? Does a similar sequence of stages occur during succession in other ecosystems? For instance, do ecosystems eventually reach a steady state? The generality of the biomass accumulation model can be tested

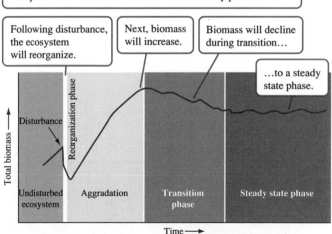

According to the biomass accumulation model, disturbing a forest ecosystem will induce a series of distinct recovery phases.

Following disturbance, the ecosystem will reorganize.

Next, biomass will increase.

Biomass will decline during transition…

…to a steady state phase.

Figure 18.17   The biomass accumulation model of forest succession (data from Bormann and Likens 1981).

on ecosystems, such as Sycamore Creek, Arizona, that undergo rapid succession. Such ecosystems give the ecologist the chance to study multiple successional sequences. As we will see in the following example, the patterns of ecosystem change during succession on Sycamore Creek suggest that several ecosystem features eventually reach a steady state.

Succession and Stream Ecosystem Properties

Patterns similar to those proposed by the biomass accumulation model were recorded by Fisher's research group during just 63 days of postflood succession in Sycamore Creek, Arizona. Algal biomass increased rapidly for the first 13 days following disturbance and then increased more slowly from day 13 to day 63 (fig. 18.18). Sixty-three days after the flood, algal biomass showed clear signs of levelling off. The biomass of invertebrates, the chief animal group in Sycamore Creek, increased rapidly for 22 days following the flood and then, like the algal portion of the ecosystem, began to level off.

Ecosystem metabolic parameters showed even clearer signs of levelling off before the end of the 63-day study (fig. 18.19). Gross primary production (see chapter 19), measured as grams of O_2 produced per square meter per day, increased very rapidly until day 13, increased more slowly between days 13 and 48, and then levelled off between days 48 and 63. Total ecosystem respiration, measured as oxygen consumption per square meter per day, increased quickly for only five days after the flood and then began to level off. Respiration by invertebrates, which at its maximum represented about 20% of total ecosystem respiration, levelled off by day 63.

Nancy Grimm (1987) studied nitrogen dynamics in Sycamore Creek following floods that occurred from 1981 to 1983. As in the earlier studies by Fisher and his colleagues (1982), Grimm found that during succession, algal biomass and whole ecosystem metabolism quickly reached a maximum and then levelled off, as did the quantity of nitrogen in the system.

In addition, however, Grimm examined patterns of nitrogen retention during stream succession. She estimated the nitrogen budget in each of her study reaches by comparing the nitrogen inputs at the upstream end to nitrogen outputs at the downstream end. Each 60 to 120 m study reach began where subsurface flows upwelled to the surface and ended downstream, where water disappeared into the sand. Grimm used the ratio of dissolved inorganic nitrogen entering the study reach in the upwelling zone to the amount leaving at the lower end as a measure of nitrogen retention by the stream ecosystem.

Figure 18.20 shows that in the early stages of succession, approximately equal amounts of dissolved inorganic nitrogen entered and left Grimm's study reaches. What do equal levels of input and output indicate regarding nutrient retention? A balance between input and output means that the ecosystem shows no, or zero, retention. The level of retention increased rapidly during succession, levelling off at nearly 200 mg N per square meter per day, about 28 days after a flood. In other words, the study reach was accumulating 200 mg N per square meter per day. Then, between 28 days and 90 days after the flood, the study reach showed progressively lower retention until it eventually exported a little more dissolved inorganic nitrogen than came in with groundwater.

The results of Grimm's study raise several questions. First, what mechanisms underlie retention? Grimm attributes most retention by the Sycamore Creek ecosystem to uptake by algae and invertebrates, since levels of nitrogen retention are consistent with the rates at which nitrogen was accumulated by algal and animal populations. What causes the stream reaches to eventually export nitrogen? Grimm suggested that at 90 days postflood her study sites may have stopped accumulating biomass or may have even begun to lose biomass. A loss of biomass in the later stages of succession is consistent with the predictions of the Bormann and Likens biomass accumulation model.

The major point here is that succession, which produces changes in species composition and species diversity, also changes the structure and function of ecosystems ranging from forests to streams. However, we are left with a major question concerning this important ecological process. What mechanisms drive succession? Ecologists have proposed that the mechanisms underlying succession may fall into one of three categories. Those mechanisms are the subject of the next section.

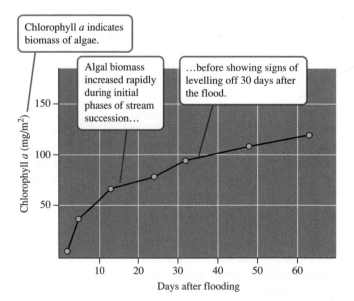

Figure 18.18 Changes in biomass during stream succession (data from Fisher et al. 1982).

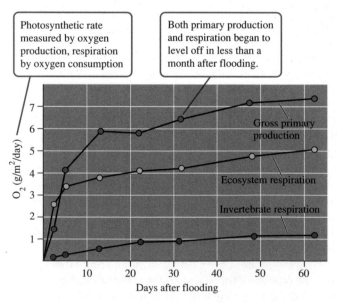

Figure 18.19 Ecosystem processes during succession in Sycamore Creek, Arizona (data from Fisher et al. 1982).

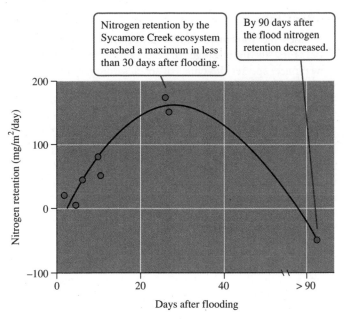

Nitrogen retention by the Sycamore Creek ecosystem reached a maximum in less than 30 days after flooding.

By 90 days after the flood nitrogen retention decreased.

Figure 18.20   Nitrogen retention during stream succession (data from Grimm 1987).

Concept 18.2 Review

1. Why are the changes in soil properties during the course of succession documented by Stuart Chapin and his colleagues ecologically significant?
2. What would equal levels of nitrogen input and output in the stream reaches (sections) studied by Nancy Grimm indicate?
3. How are the biomass accumulation model of Bormann and Likens (see fig. 18.17) and Grimm's observations of changes in nitrogen retention during succession in Sycamore Creek similar?

18.3 Mechanisms of Succession

Mechanisms that drive ecological succession include facilitation, tolerance, and inhibition.   An early model for successional change was proposed by Frederic Clements in 1916. Clements viewed succession as analogous to the development of an organism (1916, 1936), and that the climax community was a kind of *superorganism* (as a point of reference, *Superman* did not appear until 1938, though I do not believe that is what Clements had in mind!). He argued that each wave of species in a successional sequence facilitated the establishment and growth of the next wave. This process of serial replacement would continue until the climax community was established, which, according to Clements, was then able to maintain itself in perpetuity, or at least until a disturbance occurred. Henry Gleason (1926, 1939) opposed this idea, arguing that species are distributed independently of each other, with overlaps in distribution the result of coincidence, not mutual interdependence. Gleason advocated an "individualistic" approach to understanding communities and succession,

arguing that specific conditions and random events could alter the course of succession. By Gleason's model, the outcome of succession wasn't nearly as neat and orderly as that proposed by Clements. Most modern ecologists hold a view more similar to that of Gleason than Clements, though interestingly, many members of the general public seem to fall toward the side of Clements. Ecologists recognize that succession does not always result in the same climax community, even under similar environmental conditions. Instead, substantial research has shown that a variety of processes such as dispersal limitation, influence of herbivores, and simple chance events can have very dramatic impacts on the direction and speed of successional pathways. Though the climax concept is useful in understanding the general concepts of succession, it should not be taken to imply that succession results in a specific community with deterministic distributions and abundances of species. Instead, although there are repeatable patterns in community structure, communities are groups of individuals, rather than a *superorganism* that follows a predictable developmental pathway.

In a seminal paper, Frank Egler was among the first to clearly articulate the contrasting ideas related to succession presented by Gleason and Clements (Egler 1954), and by doing so, Egler ushered in a new wave of research in community ecology. Egler presented two alternatives as to how succession might work in a given location. First was **relay floristics**, which was the name Egler gave to Clements' views of how succession operated (fig. 18.21). In relay floristics, one group of species colonizes an area immediately following disturbance. These pioneer species are then replaced by a second wave of species, and so on until the climax community was reached. A critical point of this model is that each stage facilitates the establishment of the next wave, resulting in very little overlap of species distributions in the different successional stages. As an alternative model Egler presented **initial floristics** (fig. 18.21). In this model you still find that different species are dominant in different time periods following disturbance, but species occurrences can overlap greatly throughout succession. Most important is the idea that many species, even those we associate with late successional communities, may establish immediately following a disturbance. This pattern appears to occur in much of the western boreal forest in Canada. Recent research indicates that white spruce, a species commonly associated with the climax community of the western mixedwood boreal forest, can often establish immediately following fires. The plants can remain as saplings for decades, when they may eventually become dominant species (Peters et al. 2006). Importantly, Peters and his colleagues also show that in some boreal stands, establishment of spruce can occur decades after fire, supporting the idea of delayed regeneration. The fact that the same species of tree can show different patterns of regeneration in nearby forest stands is strong support for Gleason's individualistic concept, and soundly refutes Clements' notion that species replacement is clean and orderly.

Following Egler, Joseph Connell and Ralph Slatyer (1977) provided what remains the unifying concepts for the mechanisms of succession. They presented three models of succession:

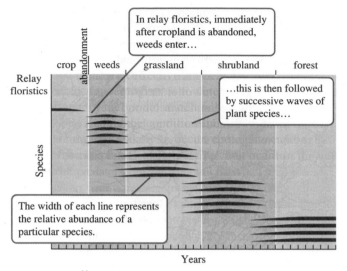

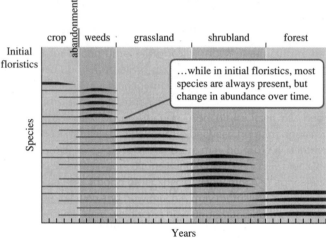

Figure 18.21 (*a*) Relay floristics, and (*b*) initial floristics as presented by Egler (1954).

(1) facilitation, (2) tolerance, and (3) inhibition (fig. 18.22). This classic paper has stimulated substantial research, and we explore the models here.

Facilitation

The **facilitation model** proposes that many species may attempt to colonize newly available space but only certain species, with particular characteristics, are able to establish themselves. These species, capable of colonizing new sites, are called pioneer species. According to the facilitation model, pioneer species modify the environment in such a way that it becomes less suitable for themselves and more suitable for species characteristic of later successional stages. In other words, these early successional species "facilitate" colonization by later successional species. Early successional species disappear as they make the environment less suitable for themselves and more suitable for other species. Replacement of early successional species by later successional species continues in this way until resident species no longer facilitate colonization by other species. This final stage in a chain of facilitations and replacements is the climax community.

Tolerance

How does the **tolerance model** differ from the facilitation model? First, the initial stages of colonization are not limited to a few pioneer species. Juveniles of species dominating at climax can be present from the earliest stages of succession. Second, species colonizing early in succession do not facilitate colonization by species characteristic of later successional stages. They do not modify the environment in a way that makes it more suitable for later successional species. Later successional species are simply those tolerant of environmental conditions created earlier in succession. The climax community is established when the list of tolerant species has been exhausted.

Inhibition

Like the tolerance model, the **inhibition model** assumes that any species that can survive in an area as an adult can colonize the area during the early stages of succession. However, the inhibition model proposes that the early occupants of an area modify the environment in a way that makes the area less suitable for both early and late successional species. Simply, early arrivals inhibit colonization by later arrivals. Later successional species can only invade an area if space is opened up by disturbance of early colonists. In this case, succession culminates in a community made up of long-lived, resistant species. The inhibition model assumes that late successional species come to dominate an area simply because they live a long time and resist damage by physical and biological factors.

Which of these models does the weight of evidence from nature support? As you will see in the following examples, most studies of succession support the facilitation model, the inhibition model, or some combination of the two.

Successional Mechanisms in the Rocky Intertidal Zone

What mechanisms drive succession by algae and barnacles in the intertidal boulder fields studied by Sousa? The alternative mechanisms proposed by Sousa were those of Connell and Slatyer: facilitation, tolerance, and inhibition. Sousa used a series of experiments to test for the occurrence of these alternative mechanisms. He conducted his first experiments on 25 cm^2 plots on concrete blocks placed in the intertidal zone. In this experiment, Sousa explored the influence of *Ulva* on recruitment by later successional red algae by keeping *Ulva* out of four experimental plots and leaving four other control plots undisturbed. This experiment showed that *Ulva* strongly inhibits recruitment by red algae (fig. 18.23).

In a second set of experiments, Sousa studied the effects of the middle successional species *Gigartina leptorhynchos* and *Gelidium* on establishment of the late successional *Gigartina canaliculata*. He selectively removed middle successional species from a set of four experimental plots while simultaneously monitoring another set of four control plots. These experiments were conducted in 100 cm^2 areas on natural substrate, dominated by either *G. leptorhynchos* or *Gelidium*. When Sousa removed these middle successional species, the experimental plots were quickly reinvaded by *Ulva* and eventually by significantly

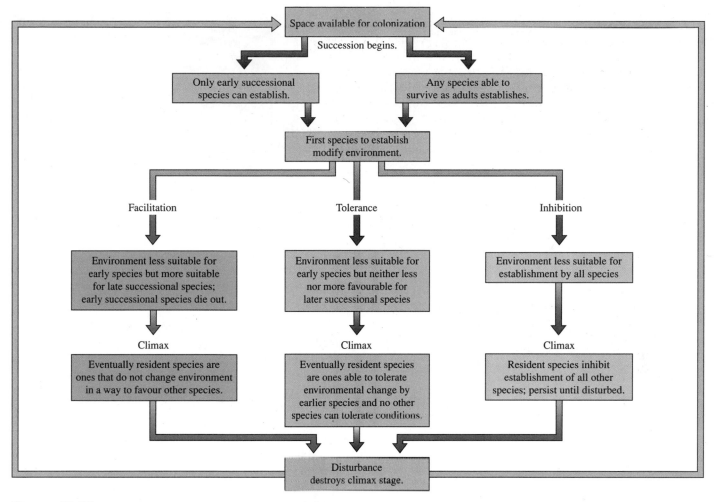

Figure 18.22   Alternative successional mechanisms (data from Connell and Slatyer 1977).

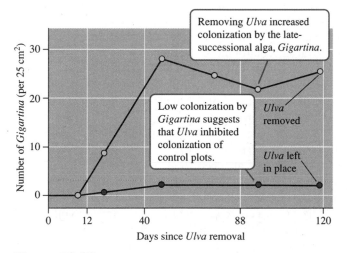

Figure 18.23   Evidence for inhibition of later successional species (data from Sousa 1979a).

higher densities of *G. canaliculata,* the late successional species. The effects of these successional algae support the inhibition model for succession.

The inhibition model of succession proposes that early successional species are more vulnerable to a variety of phys-

ical and biological factors causing mortality. If algal succession in the intertidal boulder fields studied by Sousa follows the inhibition model, then early successional species should be more vulnerable to various sources of mortality.

Sousa addressed the question of relative vulnerability of algal species with several experiments. In one, he studied the relative vulnerability of intertidal algae to physical stress, especially exposure to air, intense sunlight, and drying wind. He studied the vulnerabilities of the five dominant algal species in his study area by tagging 30 individuals of each species and monitoring their survivorship for two months during a period when low tide occurred during the afternoon, when air temperatures are highest. The results of this study show that the early successional species, *Ulva,* had lower survivorship than the middle or late successional species (fig. 18.24).

Sousa also designed several different field and laboratory experiments to explore differential vulnerability to herbivores. The results of all these experiments indicated that the early successional species *Ulva* is more vulnerable to herbivores than later successional species. These results and those of the several other manipulations performed by Sousa support the inhibition model of succession.

Some studies of intertidal succession, however, have demonstrated facilitation. Teresa Turner (1983) pointed out that the

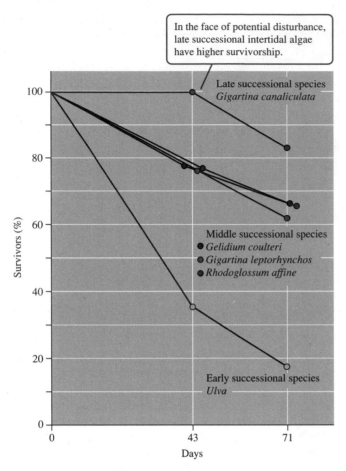

In the face of potential disturbance, late successional intertidal algae have higher survivorship.

Late successional species
Gigartina canaliculata

Middle successional species
● *Gelidium coulteri*
● *Gigartina leptorhynchos*
● *Rhodoglossum affine*

Early successional species
Ulva

Figure 18.24 Survivorship of early, middle, and late successional species (data from Sousa 1979b).

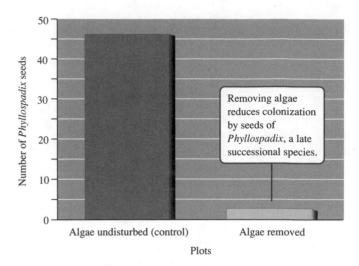

Removing algae reduces colonization by seeds of *Phyllospadix*, a late successional species.

Figure 18.25 Evidence for facilitation of colonization by an intertidal plant, *Phyllospadix scouleri* (data from Turner 1983).

bulk of intertidal studies had supported the inhibition model and that the few studies documenting facilitation had shown that facilitation was not obligate. However, she went on to report a case of obligate facilitation during intertidal succession.

Turner described the successional sequence at her Oregon study site as follows. High waves during winter storms create open space in the lower intertidal zone. In May, these open areas are colonized by *Ulva*, the same early colonist of open areas in Sousa's study area, over 1,000 km south of Turner's study site. *Ulva* is eventually replaced by several middle successional species, especially the red algae *Rhodomela larix, Cryptosiphonia woodii,* and *Odonthalia floccosa.* Through this middle stage, the pattern of succession appears much as that in the intertidal boulder field studied by Sousa. However, in the lower intertidal area studied by Turner, the dominant late successional species was not an alga but a flowering plant, the surfgrass *Phyllospadix scouleri.*

Turner proposed that recruitment of *Phyllospadix* by seeds depends upon the presence of macroscopic algae. The seeds of *Phyllospadix* are large and bear two parallel, barbed projections. These projections hook and hold the seeds to attached algae. From this attached position, the seed germinates, first producing leaves and then roots by which the plant will anchor itself to the underlying rock. Once established, *Phyllospadix* spreads and consolidates space by vegetative growth.

Turner tested whether recruitment by *Phyllospadix* is facilitated by attached algae by clearing eight 0.25 m² plots of all attached algae. She then compared the number of new *Phyllospadix* seeds in these plots with the number in eight nearby control plots. The control plots remained undisturbed with their algal populations intact except that all *Phyllospadix* seeds were removed at the start of the study. Turner's control areas were dominated by the red alga *Rhodomela larix,* a species prominent in the middle successional stages in her study area and to which *Phyllospadix* seeds attach.

Turner set up and manipulated her study plots in September and then checked them the following March, after the period of seed dispersal. Over the fall and winter a brown alga, *Phaeostrophion irregulare,* colonized the removal plots but the bladelike form of this species apparently does not allow attachment by *Phyllospadix* seeds. When Turner checked the removal and control plots, she found a total of 48 seeds, 46 on the control plots (all attached to *Rhodomela*) and 2 on the removal plots (fig. 18.25). Both seeds on the removal plots were attached to two isolated branches of *Rhodomela* that had sprouted from remnant holdfasts.

During three years, Turner systematically searched an area of about 200 m² for *Phyllospadix* seeds and found a total of 298. All were attached to algae. These data support the hypothesis that middle successional algae facilitate recruitment and establishment of *Phyllospadix* and that this facilitation is obligate. As a consequence of Turner's study and others, we can say that facilitation and inhibition occur during intertidal succession. Other research, which we review in the next example, has shown that facilitation and inhibition also occur during forest succession.

Successional Mechanisms in Forests

We now turn from succession in the marine intertidal zone, a place where succession occurs in a matter of a few years, to succession in boreal forests. Forest succession takes hundreds of years to complete and so cannot be observed directly within the period of a typical research project. Therefore, most research on the mechanisms driving succession in forests has focused on the earliest stages.

Mechanisms of Succession in a Boreal Forest

We have already described how succession in boreal forests often results in a transition from hardwood species such as aspen toward dominance by softwood species, such as spruce and fir. Why? We can also think of this issue from an evolutionary perspective. There is certainly no fitness benefit gained by aspen when it is replaced by spruce (rather than its own offspring), so why do aspen plants it "let it happen"? The answer may seem familiar. Specific life-history traits possessed by aspen allow it to perform some ecological processes extremely well (such as recovery following fire), but at the same time, it is unable to perform other ecological processes. Aspen, as it turns out, has seedlings that are shade-intolerant, while spruce has shade-tolerant seedlings (chapter 5). Aspen trees also produce very small seeds (for a tree) able to travel long distances. Following fire, sunlight at the forest floor is very high. Any existing aspen trees will resprout, and high dispersal ability of aspen seeds also means there is a good probability of seeds in the area that will quickly germinate. These seedlings and sprouts grow rapidly, soon casting deep shade onto the forest floor. During this period of rapid aspen (and other pioneer species) growth, there has been increased opportunity for the more poorly dispersed seeds to enter the community. Seeds of spruce and other species are able to germinate and seedlings are able to establish themselves in this shade. Seeds of aspen and other species can not. As a result, beneath the canopy of aspen, you will find young spruce and fir trees, not aspen. In other words, aspen recovery following fire actually results in inhibition of further aspen recruitment. In contrast, the conditions following fire, including felled logs and other dead plants, can facilitate the establishment of the spruce seedlings.

At this point in the growth of the forest, there are two possible events. First, the aspen trees can grow to maturity, and then like all organisms, individual trees will eventually die. What happens in the forest? The small spruce trees have been growing beneath the aspen, and will quickly grow to fill the gap in the canopy made by the death of the aspen. Over time, this can lead to dominance by the softwood tree species. But as we have said before, succession is not inevitable, and communities do not "develop" or "progress." This is very similar to our understanding of evolution. Evolution does not move towards a particular goal (does not optimize traits), but it does result in change. In the boreal system, one clear reminder that succession is not inevitable is the reality that fire can burn the aspen stand well before spruce has become dominant.

If the forest burns again, the floor is once again an excellent place for resprouting and regrowth by the aspen. If spruce seeds are still available, seedlings will once again establish. Depending upon the frequency of fires, regions of the boreal forest may never obtain significant softwood dominance (if fires are frequent), or if fires are rare, the hardwoods will be missing. Because of variation in fire frequency, and because of interspecific differences in life histories, the boreal forest

is a mosaic of different communities, interspersed throughout the landscape. We will discuss more about the role of landscapes in ecology in chapter 21.

As complicated as the dynamics of boreal forest succession may seem, we have yet to discuss one critical issue. What role do the plants themselves have in influencing whether there is a fire? At first, this may seem a ridiculous idea—lightning strikes are the dominant form of fire initiation, and these are driven by weather patterns. In a recent paper by Meg Krawchuk, a graduate student at the University of Alberta, along with her colleagues in Alberta and the Canadian Forest Service in Ontario, Krawchuk has shown that both climate and forest composition can influence the probability of fire initiation in the boreal mixedwoods (Krawchuk et al 2006; fig. 18.26). The research team analyzed an 11-year database of fire histories for 91,000 km^2 of mixedwood forest in central-eastern Alberta. The study area was divided into smaller units of approximately 10,000 ha and one year in spatial and temporal dimensions, called *voxels*. For each voxel, the research team had detailed information on forest composition, meteorological records, and whether any fires occurred. Because of the comprehensive nature of their database, they were then able to construct statistical models that determined the relative contribution of both climate and forest composition on the probability of fire initiation. Their results were quite striking. As expected, fires were more likely to occur in areas that were hotter and drier than those that were cooler and wetter. However, even after accounting for this climate effect, there was a substantial impact of forest composition. Aspen inhibit fire initiation (fig. 18.26), with the probability of fire initiation decreasing as forests move from white or black spruce dominance towards that of aspen. In other words, aspen is inhibiting fires, while spruce are facilitating them.

The result may appear a bit surprising, particularly given that aspen can only successfully recruit following a disturbance! It may not be quite as hard to understand if we instead focus on the spruce. As we discussed previously, their seeds

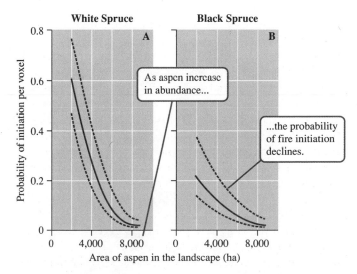

Figure 18.26 The probability of fire initiation changes as a function of forest composition in the boreal mixedwood forest (data from Krawchuk et al. 2006).

will establish soon after a fire, and in many cases cones can not even open unless a fire is present. It may make sense that spruce contains a variety of flammable resins and have a growth structure (fuels near the forest floor) that promotes fire, as fire itself is necessary for spruce to most efficiently complete its life cycle! The end result, however, is that spruce facilitates its own replacement, albeit temporary, by aspen. It is because of patterns like this that most ecologists do not believe in the concept of a single climax community, and instead see communities as dynamic.

In fact, in many communities ecologists do not necessarily view there being even a single climax community, but instead, depending upon local conditions and chance events, there may be **alternative stable states**. Under this model, a single piece of land can persist as alternative types of communities, depending upon some set of factors. This issue will be more fully explored in our discussion of landscape ecology, chapter 21.

Mechanisms of Primary Succession Following Deglaciation

The complex mechanisms underlying succession were well demonstrated by the detailed studies of Chapin's research team (1994). They combined field observations, field experiments, and greenhouse experiments to explore the mechanisms underlying primary succession at Glacier Bay, Alaska. Like Morris and Wood, they found that no single factor or mechanism determines the pattern of primary succession at Glacier Bay, Alaska.

Figure 18.27 summarizes the complex influences of four successional stages on establishment and growth of spruce seedlings. During the pioneer stage, there is some inhibition of spruce germination. Any spruce seedlings that become established, however, have high survivorship but low growth rates. Spruce seedling growth rates and nitrogen supplies are increased somewhat during the *Dryas* stage. However, this facilitation during the *Dryas* stage is offset by poor germination and survivorship, along with increased seed predation and mortality.

Strong facilitation of spruce seedlings first occurs in the alder stage. During this stage, germination and survivorship remain low and seed mortality, root competition, and light competition are significant. However, these inhibitory effects are offset by increased soil organic matter, nitrogen, mycorrhizal activity, and growth rates. The net effect of alder on spruce seedlings is facilitation.

In the spruce stage, the net influence on spruce seedlings is inhibitory. Germination is high during the spruce stage but this is counterbalanced by several inhibitory effects. Growth rates and survivorship are low and nitrogen availability is reduced. In addition, seed predation and mortality, root competition, and light competition are all high.

These results remind us that nature is far more complex and subtle than models such as that proposed by Connell and Slatyer. However, the Connell and Slatyer model challenged ecologists to think more broadly about succession and to go out and conduct field tests of alternative successional mechanisms. Their response produced today's improved understanding of the process of ecological succession.

In this and the previous two sections we have discussed community and ecosystem changes and the mechanisms producing those changes. In the next section, we consider a companion topic: community and ecosystem stability.

Concept 18.3 Review

1. What is the role of disturbance in the Connell and Slatyer succession model?
2. Suppose *Gigartina* had colonized the plots where Sousa had removed *Ulva* and where he had left *Ulva* in place at the same rates. This result would be consistent with which successional model?
3. How does spruce inhibit its own replacement by aspen?

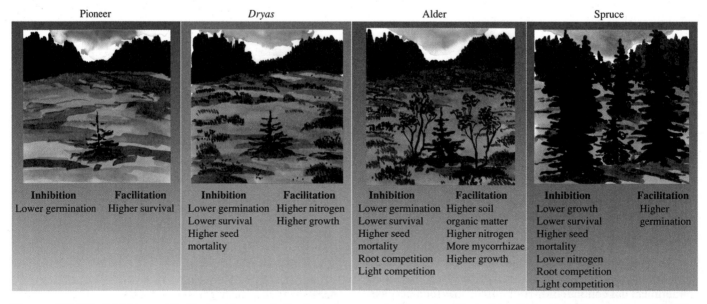

Pioneer	*Dryas*	Alder	Spruce

Inhibition	**Facilitation**	**Inhibition**	**Facilitation**	**Inhibition**	**Facilitation**	**Inhibition**	**Facilitation**
Lower germination	Higher survival	Lower germination	Higher nitrogen	Lower germination	Higher soil	Lower growth	Higher
		Lower survival	Higher growth	Lower survival	organic matter	Lower survival	germination
		Higher seed		Higher seed	Higher nitrogen	Higher seed	
		mortality		mortality	More mycorrhizae	mortality	
				Root competition	Higher growth	Lower nitrogen	
				Light competition		Root competition	
						Light competition	

Figure 18.27 Inhibition and facilitation of spruce during the major successional stages at Glacier Bay, Alaska (data from Chapin et al. 1994).

Community and Ecosystem Stability

Community stability may be due to lack of disturbance or community resistance or resilience in the face of disturbance.

Some Definitions

The simplest definition of **stability** is the absence of change. A community or ecosystem may be stable for a variety of reasons. One reason may be that there has been no disturbance. For instance, the benthic communities of the deep sea may remain stable over long periods of time because of constant physical conditions. The type of stability resulting from an absence of disturbance, if it exists, is not particularly interesting to ecologists.

Ecologists are more interested in how communities and ecosystems may remain stable even when exposed to potential disturbance. Consequently ecologists generally define stability as the persistence of a community or ecosystem in the face of disturbance. Stability may result from two very different characteristics. **Resistance** is the ability of a community or ecosystem to maintain structure and/or function in the face of potential disturbance. However, stability may also result from the ability of a community to return to its original structure after a disturbance. The ability to bounce back after disturbance is called **resilience.** A resilient community or ecosystem may be completely disrupted by disturbance but quickly return to its former state.

What causes communities and ecosystems to be resilient? The phenomenon of resilience takes us back to succession. Remember that we defined succession as the gradual change in plant and animal communities in an area following disturbance or the creation of new substrate. It is succession that restores a community disrupted by disturbance. Succession is the basis for resilience.

Ecologists ask many questions about stability. Are some communities and ecosystems more resistant than others? What factors determine differences in resistance among communities and ecosystems? Are some ecosystems and communities more resilient than others? What factors determine the rate of recovery of community structure and ecosystem processes following disturbance? However, few studies have been conducted at scales appropriate to address these questions. One of the main problems faced by ecologists interested in community and ecosystem stability is the need to conduct detailed studies over a long period of time. There are a few studies that meet this requirement; one of them is the Park Grass Experiment.

Lessons from the Park Grass Experiment

The Park Grass Experiment is the prototype of all long-term experimental studies in ecology. It was started at the Rothamsted Experimental Station in Hertfordshire, England, between 1856 and 1872. The purpose of the experiment was to study the effects of several fertilizer treatments on the yield and structure of a hay meadow community. Because the Park Grass Experiment has continued without interruption for nearly one and a half centuries, it provides one of the most valuable records of long-term community dynamics. That record provides some unique insights into the nature of community stability.

Jonathan Silvertown (1987) used data from the Park Grass Experiment to respond to the suggestion that existing studies do not conclusively demonstrate that any ecological community is stable. Silvertown pointed out that the Park Grass Experiment is one of the few studies of terrestrial communities that have been carried out in sufficient detail and over sufficient time to provide a test of stability that meets the rigorous requirements suggested by Connell and Sousa.

The composition of the plant community at the Park Grass Experiment has been monitored since 1862. This record reveals at least one level of stability. Over this period, virtually no new species have colonized the meadow. Changes in the community have occurred as a consequence of increases or decreases in species already present in the meadow at the beginning of the experiment.

Silvertown used variation in community composition as a measure of stability. He represented composition as the proportion of the community consisting of grasses, legumes, or other species. The analysis of composition was restricted to the period from 1910 to 1948 to avoid the early period of the experiment when the meadow community was adjusting to the various fertilizer treatments. Figure 18.28 shows the relative proportions of grasses, legumes, and other plants on plots receiving three different treatments: plot 3, no fertilizer; plot 7, P, K, Na, and Mg; and plot 14, N, P, K, Na, and Mg. The differences in vegetation on the three plots were mostly produced by the different fertilizer treatments and developed early in the Park Grass Experiment.

The proportion of grasses, legumes, and other plants in the study plots varied from year to year, mainly in response to variation in precipitation. Despite this annual variation, figure 18.28 indicates that the proportions of three plant groups remained remarkably similar over the interval of the study. A quantitative analysis of trends in biomass revealed no significant changes in the biomass of the three plant groups in plots 3 and 7 and only a minor, but statistically significant, decrease in the biomass of grasses on plot 14. In other words, the data presented in figure 18.28 show remarkable stability in the proportion of grasses, legumes, and other species.

Does the stability of Silvertown's three major groups of plants in the Park Grass Experiment hold up if we examine community structure at the species level? It turns out that while the proportions of grasses, legumes, and other species remained fairly constant, populations of individual species changed substantially. Mike Dodd and his colleagues (1995) used census data from 1920 to 1979 to examine plant population trends. The result of their analysis showed that some species increased in abundance, some decreased, some showed no trend, while others increased and then decreased (fig. 18.29).

The contrasting results obtained by Silvertown and by Dodd's project suggest that whether a community or ecosystem appears stable may depend upon how we view it. At a very coarse level of resolution, the Park Grass community has remained absolutely stable. It was a meadow community when the Park Grass Experiment began in 1856 and it remains so today. When Silvertown increased the resolution to distinguish

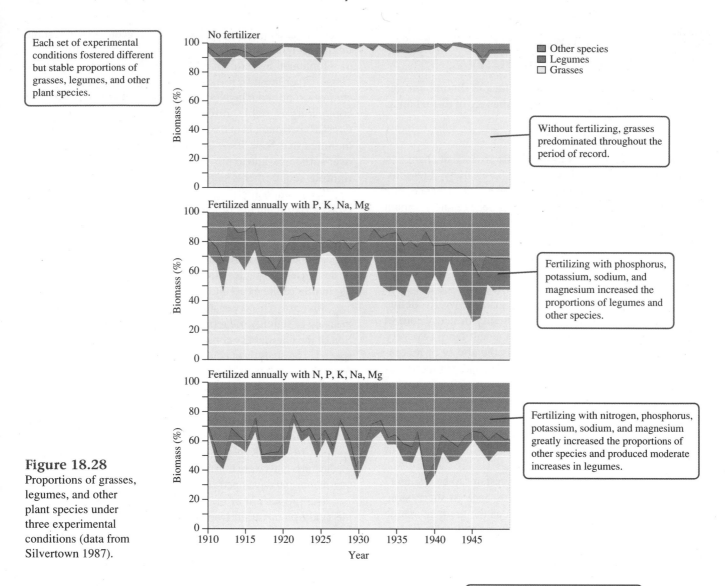

Each set of experimental conditions fostered different but stable proportions of grasses, legumes, and other plant species.

Without fertilizing, grasses predominated throughout the period of record.

Fertilizing with phosphorus, potassium, sodium, and magnesium increased the proportions of legumes and other species.

Fertilizing with nitrogen, phosphorus, potassium, sodium, and magnesium greatly increased the proportions of other species and produced moderate increases in legumes.

Figure 18.28
Proportions of grasses, legumes, and other plant species under three experimental conditions (data from Silvertown 1987).

between grasses, legumes, and other species, the community again appeared stable. However, when Dodd and his colleagues increased the resolution still further and examined trends in the abundances of individual species, the Park Grass community no longer appeared stable.

Are there stable natural communities? The answer to this question may depend upon how you make your measurements. The ecologist interested in addressing any question concerning community stability is faced with several practical problems. Generally, an adequate study requires a great deal of time, which limits the possibility of replication. One solution to this problem is to study communities and ecosystems, such as Sycamore Creek, Arizona, that undergo more frequent disturbance and show relatively rapid recovery. These systems offer the opportunity to compare recoveries from multiple disturbances.

Replicate Disturbances and Desert Stream Stability

Numerous studies of disturbance and recovery in Sycamore Creek, Arizona, have produced a highly detailed picture of community,

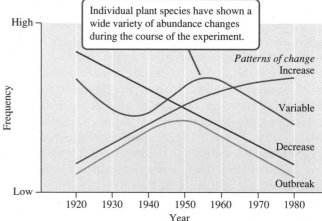

Individual plant species have shown a wide variety of abundance changes during the course of the experiment.

Figure 18.29 Patterns of species abundance during 60 years of the Park Grass Experiment (data from Dodd et al. 1995).

ecosystem, and population responses. This detailed picture suggests that ecologists have just begun to probe the subtleties of ecological stability. For instance, one study shows that resistance in the spatial structure of the Sycamore Creek ecosystem

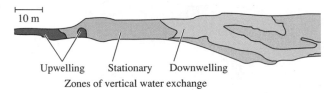

Figure 18.30   Patterns of upwelling and downwelling in a reach of Sycamore Creek, Arizona (data from Valett et al. 1994).

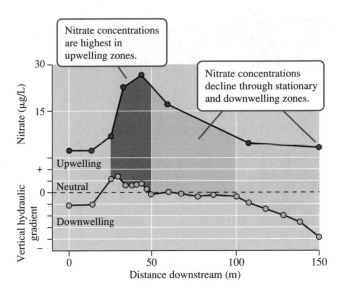

Figure 18.31   Relationship of nitrate to vertical hydraulic gradient in Sycamore Creek, Arizona (data from Valett et al. 1994).

underlies spatial variation in ecosystem resilience. Maury Valett and his colleagues (1994) studied the interactions between surface and subsurface waters in Sycamore Creek to study the influence of these linkages on ecosystem resilience. They tested the hypothesis that ecosystem resilience is higher where hydrologic linkages between the surface and subsurface water increase the supply of nitrogen. They proposed a controlling role for nitrogen because it is the nutrient that limits primary production in Sycamore Creek.

Valett and his colleagues intensely studied two stream sections at middle elevations in the 500 km² Sycamore Creek catchment. They measured the flow of water between the surface and subsurface along these reaches with devices called *piezometers.* Piezometers can be used to measure the vertical hydraulic gradient, which indicates the direction of flow between surface water and water flowing through the sediments of a streambed. Positive vertical hydraulic gradients indicate flow from the streambed to the surface in areas called upwelling zones. Negative vertical hydraulic gradients indicate flow from the surface to the streambed, which occurs in downwelling zones. Zero vertical hydraulic gradients indicate no net exchange between surface waters and water flowing within the sediments. Areas with zero vertical hydraulic gradients are called stationary zones.

Valett and his colleagues measured vertical hydraulic gradient along the lengths of both study sections, producing hydrologic maps for both. The upper end of each study reach was an upwelling zone. The middle reaches were stationary zones and the lower reaches were downwelling zones. Figure 18.30 shows the distributions of these zones across one of the study reaches.

The concentration of nitrate in surface water in the two study reaches varies directly with vertical hydraulic gradient (fig. 18.31). Upwelling zones, which are fed by nitrate-rich waters upwelling from the sediments, have the highest concentrations of nitrate. Nitrate concentrations gradually decline with distance downstream through the stationary and downwelling zones.

The higher concentrations of nitrate in the upper reaches of each study section are associated with higher algal production. Algal biomass accumulates at a higher rate in upwelling zones compared to downwelling zones. Valett and his colleagues used rate of algal biomass accumulation as a measure of rate of recovery from disturbance. Because the rate at which algal biomass accumulates in upwelling zones is so much higher than in downwelling zones, they concluded that the rate of ecosystem recovery is higher in upwelling zones. This pattern supports their hypothesis that algal communities in upwelling zones are more resilient.

The team also found that while flash floods devastated the biotic community, the spatial arrangement of upwelling, stationary, and downwelling zones remained stable. In other words, this aspect of the spatial structure of the Sycamore Creek ecosystem is highly resistant to flash flooding. The location of upwelling, stationary, and downwelling zones remained stable in the face of numerous intense floods.

The spatial stability of the Sycamore Creek ecosystem in the face of potential disturbance is an example of ecosystem resistance. However, what is the source of this stable spatial structure? This spatial stability can be explained by considering geomorphology, especially the distribution of bedrock. Subsurface water is forced to the surface in areas where bedrock lies close to the surface. Upwelling zones in Sycamore Creek are located in such areas, and since flooding does not move bedrock, the locations of upwelling zones are stable. Therefore, this aspect of ecosystem stability is controlled by landscape structure. Consequently, the ecologist trying to understand the organization and dynamics of the Sycamore Creek ecosystem must consider the structure of the surrounding landscape. Landscape ecology is the subject of chapter 21.

Concept 18.4 Review

1. What causes community resilience?
2. How might taxonomic resolution—that is, how precisely we identify organisms—influence an assessment of community stability?
3. Is the index of resilience used by Valett and his colleagues consistent with the biomass accumulation model of Bormann and Likens?

Ecology In Action

Using Disturbances for Conservation

In the public, and among researchers, there are a variety of issues that often stimulate controversy. We have discussed several of these throughout the text, including issues related to fisheries, the Species at Risk Act, and impacts of hunting on evolution. Here we discuss another, the incorporation of disturbances into conservation programs. The goal of this section is not to suggest all uses of disturbances are appropriate in all conservation programs. Instead, our intention is to show you how the basic information you have learned about succession has direct consequences for conservation.

Like ecologists, land managers have historically viewed communities as static discrete entities. Each park was seen as an island, rather than a piece connected to a larger whole, and one that can itself change through time. At the core of this philosophical approach to communities has been the tendency to encourage the preservation of "pristine wilderness," areas free from any disturbances (Gillson and Willis 2004). In this mindset, natural communities were to be protected from disturbances such as logging, grazing, and fire (Hobbs and Huenneke 1992). However, as we have seen in this chapter communities are naturally dynamic, with substantial variation in species composition over space and time. If this is true for most communities, and currently ecological thought believes it to be so, then the idea of trying to "protect" a community from change is at odds with basic ecological understanding.

In a nice summary of paleoecological work, Gillson and Willis (2004) are able to show that there have been interactions between humans and the environments in which they live for thousands of years, and these interactions are partially responsible for landscape we currently see, and are trying to protect. A significant question emerges: if humans have caused a certain disturbance (e.g., sheep grazing in Europe) for thousands of years, what is "natural"; the continuation of this grazing or its cessation? In other words, the landscape one sees now, shaped by disturbance, would not be the same one seen if you remove grazing (think succession!). Which landscape is the one we should preserve? This question is critical to governmental policy. For example, several governments in Europe pay landowners and occupants to regularly mow or graze grasslands, preventing succession to a forest community. Why? Because these fields have been covered with grasslands for thousands of years of human occupation, and the governments have chosen to preserve the historic human-maintained landscape, rather than a landscape without human intervention (that hasn't been seen for many centuries).

It is issues like these that are shaking the foundations of many common practices in conservation biology. Should you manage a reserve to maintain the diversity of a single area, or of greater diversity on the landscape? As a reflection of this shifting mindset, fires are now routinely set in many of the National Parks of Canada (fig. 18.32), not to preserve a single community, but instead to protect a *disturbance regime*. This, in turn, will result in the desired diversity of communities. For example, an aggressive anti-fire program over the last several decades has resulted in tree encroachment into alpine meadows, putting these habitats at risk. By reintroducing fire to these systems, park managers hope to restore these unique habitats.

There are few places where controversies regarding using disturbances as a conservation tool rage as strongly as they do in grasslands. As we have discussed, grasslands are a generally unstable habitat, often changing to forest or shrubland in the absence of disturbances. We generally view some com-

Ecological Tools

Using Repeat Photography to Detect Long-Term Change

While some graduate students look over their shoulders, Raymond Turner and Julio Betancourt of the U.S. Geological Survey carefully examine a photograph of a desert landscape taken about 100 years earlier. Their goal is to take another photograph of the same scene to document long-term change in the plant community. To do so they must return to the same location and take a photograph from exactly the same spot.

The larger landmarks such as hills and ridges will help them find the general location, but they need finer-scale reference points to locate the exact spot. Turner finally indicates a small boulder about 30 cm in diameter in the foreground, saying, "This should get us close and those small junipers will help orient the cameras." Betancourt agrees. The students are incredulous that someone should think that they can find a small boulder and two small trees after a century. However, long practice at repeat photography has taught Turner what can be found after a century in the arid lands of the American Southwest.

Figure 18.32   A controlled fire being set as part of ecosystem management in Jasper National Park.

bination of fire, drought, and grazing as necessary to maintain grassland habitats for extended periods of time. What is a land manager supposed to do if they have been charged with the goal of "protecting" a grassland? Clearly they can not alter the frequency of droughts. As we have already seen, fire can be used, under some conditions. Fire is less often a viable tool if the land being managed is near either private land and houses, or near major civic infrastructure (e.g., highways, bridges). The large native herbivores, such as bison, have been fairly efficiently removed from the grasslands of North America. The question that then faces the land manager is "Do I allow cattle to graze on this conservation land?" What do you think should happen? Is it justified to bring in an alien

species (domesticated cattle) in an attempt to preserve a native habitat (grasslands)? If so, who gets to decide how many cattle and when they graze, the conservation organization or the ranchers that own the herd? Should the ranchers be paying for the right to graze, or instead should the conservation organization be paying to have their land grazed? These questions are not trivial, and need to be resolved, as it is clear that the effects of herbivores on plant diversity and community structure can vary as a function of the types of herbivore and site conditions (Olff and Ritchie 1998).

Some ecologists are taking the issue of "what is natural" even further. Josh Donlan and colleagues have recently proposed "re-wilding" North America (Donlan et al. 2005). Donlan argues that humans have been, in part, responsible for the loss of a diverse mega-fauna that existed in North America 13,000 years ago. At that time there were species of camels, cheetahs, elephants, and lions throughout the Great Plains. Donlan argues that these species played critical roles in the ecology of these systems (think keystone species and ecosystem engineers; chapter 17). By reintroducing their extant relatives (from Africa and Asia), they propose to reinstate the "natural" disturbance regime while also providing a new home to species that are likely to go extinct throughout parts of Asia and Africa. Needless to say, this proposal is controversial.

Hopefully, the points we have raised here have forced you to rethink some assumptions regarding the preservation of natural areas. If the plants and animals are always changing, can one ever succeed in preserving a single community without controlled disturbances? Clearly, the next generation of ecologists will be pivotal in further integrating current ecological understanding into the preservation of natural areas.

A field trip later takes the group to the general area of the site. After a careful search, Betancourt finds the remains of the two junipers. They have died sometime during the last half century. Next, Turner finds the small boulder. They use a few more landmarks to orient the camera and then position it within about 1 m of the spot from which the century-old photo was taken.

Using techniques such as these, Ray Turner and his colleagues have produced a very useful photographic record of vegetation changes from throughout the southwestern United States and northwestern Mexico. For instance, a series of repeat photographs beginning in 1907 document substantial vegetation change in MacDougal Crater in northern Sonora, Mexico (Turner 1990). The crater is about 137 m deep and was formed by a volcanic eruption about 200,000 years ago.

MacDougal Crater is protected by its steep walls from livestock and other human impacts. This protection removes the possibility that observed changes in vegetation might be the result of human influences.

Figure 18.33 shows a series of photographs taken of MacDougal Crater from 1907 to 1984. While most changes depicted by these photographs are subtle, there is one obvious change in the lower left corner, the location of a population of saguaro cactus, *Carnegiea gigantea*. The saguaro, which appear as small stick figures in the photo, increase in number between the 1907 photograph and the 1959 photograph. Though difficult to see with the naked eye, the saguaros are clearly visible with a magnifying glass. Get a magnifying glass and compare the numbers of *Carnegiea* in the 1907 and 1959 photographs.

Figure 18.33 Detecting change in plant populations using repeat photography: (*a*) MacDougal Crater, Sonora, Mexico, in 1907, (*b*) in 1959, (*c*) in 1972, and (*d*) in 1984.

Figure 18.34 Details of plant population biology from repeat photography: (*a*) saguaro cactus in MacDougal Crater, Sonora, Mexico, in 1959, (*b*) same scene in 1984, and (*c*) in 1998. By 1998, the two cactus in the foreground of the 1959 photo had died and fallen.

Close-up photos reveal even more detail. Figure 18.34 shows photographs taken in 1959, 1984, and 1998. The growing conditions were so poor in 1959 that the live saguaro in the photograph formed permanent constrictions on its stems that are still visible in the 1984 photograph. This saguaro died between 1984 and 1998. The dead shrubs in the 1984 photo-graph are the remains of creosote bushes, *Larrea tridentata*, that apparently died in response to the same drought that formed the constrictions on the saguaro stems.

Using repeat photographs, Turner was able to quantify changes in the plant community of MacDougal Crater. One of the changes he documented was a decrease in the population of *Larrea* and an increase in the population of saguaros (fig. 18.35). From 1907 to 1986 the number of *Larrea* in Turner's study area decreased from 103 to 48. Over the same interval, the number of saguaros increased from 38 to 159 in 1972 and then declined to 140 by 1986.

Some of the most important questions asked by ecologists concern changes in the distribution and abundance of organisms. Repeat photography is an easily overlooked tool that is helping to document changes in plant distribution and abundance during the past century.

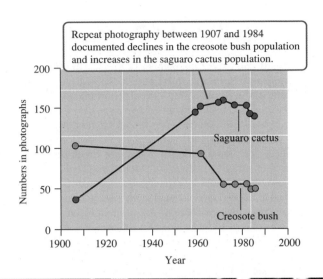

Figure 18.35 Changes in populations of creosote bushes and saguaro cactus determined by repeat photography (data from Turner 1990).

Summary

Succession is the gradual change in plant and animal communities in an area following disturbance or the creation of new substrate. *Primary succession* occurs on newly exposed geological substrates not significantly modified by organisms. *Secondary succession* occurs in areas where disturbance destroys a community without destroying the soil. Succession generally ends with a climax community whose populations remain stable until disrupted by disturbance.

Community changes during succession include increases in species diversity and changes in species composition. Primary forest succession around Glacier Bay may require about 1,500 years, while secondary forest succession on the Piedmont Plateau takes about 150 years. Meanwhile, succession in the boreal forest requires 100 to 200 years and succession within a desert stream occurs in less than two months. Over even longer time periods, some lakes will undergo succession, becoming fens, bogs, or forest. Despite the great differences in the time required, all these successional sequences show increased species diversity over time.

Ecosystem changes during succession include increases in biomass, primary production, respiration, and nutrient retention. Succession at Glacier Bay produces changes in several ecosystem properties, including increased soil depth, organic content, and moisture. Over the same successional sequence, several soil properties show decreases, including soil bulk density and phosphorus concentration. During ecosystem development on lava flows in Hawaii, organic matter and nitrogen content of soils increased over the first 150,000 years and then declined by 1.4 and 4.1 million years. Weatherable mineral phosphorus in soils was largely depleted on lava flows 20,000 years old. The percentage of soil phosphorus in refractory form made up the majority of phosphorus on lava flows 20,000 years old or older. Nitrogen losses from these ecosystems increased over time, while phosphorus losses decreased. Succession at the Hubbard Brook Experimental Forest increased nutrient retention by the forest ecosystem. Several ecosystem properties change predictably during succession in Sycamore Creek, Arizona, including biomass, primary production, respiration, and nitrogen retention.

Mechanisms that drive ecological succession include facilitation, tolerance, and inhibition. Most studies of succession support the facilitation model, the inhibition model, or some combination of the two. Both facilitation and inhibition occur during intertidal succession. Facilitation and inhibition also occur during secondary and primary forest succession.

Community stability may be due to lack of disturbance or community resistance or resilience in the face of disturbance. Ecologists generally define stability as the persistence of a community or ecosystem in the face of disturbance. Resistance is the ability of a community or ecosystem to maintain structure and/or function in the face of potential disturbance. The ability to bounce back after disturbance is called resilience. A resilient community or ecosystem may be completely disrupted by disturbance but quickly return to its former state. Studies of the Park Grass Experiment suggest that our perception of stability is affected by the scale of measurement. Studies in Sycamore Creek indicate that resilience is sometimes influenced by resource availability and that resistance may result from landscape-level phenomena. Some areas likely form alternative stable states depending upon the disturbance regime.

Repeat photography can be used to detect long-term ecological change. Most successional sequences and most community and ecosystem responses to climatic change take place over very long periods of time. Repeat photography has become a valuable tool to help ecologists study these long-term changes.

Review Questions

1. Would you expect the number of species to remain indefinitely at the level shown in figure 18.7? Space on large stable boulders in Sousa's study site are dominated by the algal *G. canaliculata* and support 2.3 to 3.5 species, not the 5 shown in figure 18.7. Explain. (Hint: How long did Sousa follow his study boulders?)

2. The successional studies in Sycamore Creek produced patterns of variation in diversity that differed significantly from those observed during primary succession at Glacier Bay or algal and barnacle succession in the intertidal zone. What may have been responsible for these different results? How might have differences in the longevity of species contributed to the different patterns observed by researchers? (Hint: Think about what we might observe in the other communities if they were studied for a longer period of time.)

3. In most studies of forest succession, researchers study succession by comparing sites of various ages. This approach is called a "space for time substitution." What are some major assumptions of a space for time substitution? How else could you study boreal forest succession?

4. The rapid succession shown by the Sycamore Creek ecosystem is impressive. How might natural selection influence the life cycles of the organisms living in Sycamore Creek? Imagine a creek that floods about twice per century. How quickly would you expect the community and ecosystem to recover following one of these rare floods? Explain your answer in terms of natural selection by flooding on the life cycles of organisms.

5. In the studies of mechanisms underlying succession, ecologists have found a great deal of evidence for both facilitation and inhibition. However, they have found little evidence for the tolerance model. Explain this lack of support for the tolerance model.

6. Ecological succession has been compared to the development of an organism and the climax community to a kind of super-organism. Which of the following graphs showing hypothetical distributions of species along an environmental gradient supports the superorganismic view of communities? How does the other graph support the individualistic view of species held by Gleason? (*A*, *B*, *C*, and *D* represent the distributions of species along an environmental gradient.)

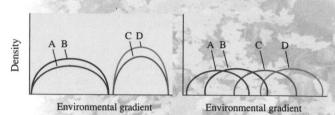

7. Species have come and gone in response to changing global climates during the history of the earth. Some of the mass extinctions of the past have resulted in the deaths of over 90% of existing species. What do these biological changes suggest about the long-term stability of the species composition of climax communities?

8. Succession seems to lead to predictable changes in community and ecosystem structure. Predict the characteristics of a frequently disturbed community/ecosystem versus a largely undisturbed community/ecosystem. What do your predictions suggest about a future biosphere increasingly disturbed by a growing human population? How does the intermediate disturbance hypothesis (see chapter 17) figure into your answer?

9. Describe the successional pathway of the boreal forest. Is there a climax community that is stable?

10. In lake succession, shallow lakes can be converted into bogs/fens or a drier terrestrial habitat such as a forest. What factors do you think are likely to influence the direction of succession for a given body of water?

Suggested Readings

Bruno, J. F., J. J. Stachowicz, and M. D. Bertness. 2003. Inclusion of facilitation into ecological theory. *Trends in Ecology & Evolution* 18:119–25.

In this article, Bruno, Stachowicz, and Bertness present a strong case for the influence of facilitation as a major factor influencing community structure.

Chadwick, O. A., L. A. Derry, P. M. Vitousek, B. J. Huebert, and L. O. Hedin. 1999. Changes in sources of nutrients during four million years of ecosystem development. *Nature* 397:491–97.

Fascinating study of the long-term shift in Hawaiian forest ecosystems from nitrogen limitation to phosphorus limitation. The researchers document dependence of the older ecosystems on wind-transported phosphorus in marine aerosols and in dust from central Asia.

Crews, T. E., L. M. Kurina, and P. M. Vitousek. 2001. Organic matter and nitrogen accumulation and nitrogen fixation during early ecosystem development in Hawaii. *Biogeochemistry* 52:259–79.

The authors document substantial change in ecosystem properties during the course of succession on 10-, 52-, and 142-year old lava flows. The paper provides an interesting comparison to succession at Glacier Bay, Alaska.

Flory, E. A. and A. M. Milner. 2000. Macroinvertebrate community succession in Wolf Point Creek, Glacier Bay National Park, Alaska. *Freshwater Biology* 44:465–80.

This study describes nearly 16 years of change in the benthic invertebrate community of a creek created by a receding glacier. The pace of succession is in marked contrast to that in Sycamore Creek, Arizona.

Attwill, P. M. 1994. The disturbance of forest ecosystems. The ecological basis for conservation management. *Forest Ecology and Management.* 63:247–300

A nice overview of disturbances common to North American forests.

Chapter 19

Primary Production and Energy Flow

*T*he interactions between organisms and their environments are fuelled by complex fluxes and transformations of energy. Sunlight shines down on the canopy of a forest—some is reflected, some is converted to heat energy, and some is absorbed by chlorophyll. Infrared radiation is absorbed by the molecules in organisms, soil, and water, increasing their kinetic state and raising the temperature of the forest. Forest temperature affects the rate of biochemical reactions and transpiration by forest vegetation.

Forest plants use photosynthetically active solar radiation, or PAR (see chapter 7), to synthesize sugars. The plants use some of this fixed energy to meet their own energy needs. Some fixed energy goes directly into plant growth: to produce new leaves, to lengthen the tendrils of vines, to grow new root hairs, and so forth. Some fixed energy is stored as nonstructural carbohydrates, which act as energy stores in roots, seeds, or fruits. Photosynthesis may increase forest biomass.

A portion of the energy fixed by forest vegetation is consumed by herbivores, some is consumed by detritivores, and some ends up as soil organic matter. Energy fixed by forest vegetation powers bird flight through the forest canopy and fuels the muscle contractions of earthworms as they burrow through the forest soil. The forest vegetation is sunlight transformed, as are all the associated bacteria, fungi, and animals and all their activities (fig. 19.1).

We can view a forest as a system that absorbs, transforms, and stores energy. In this view, physical, chemical, and biological structures and processes are inseparable. When we look at a forest (or stream or coral reef) in this way we view it as an ecosystem. An ecosystem is a biological community plus all of the abiotic factors influencing that community. The term *ecosystem* and its definition were first proposed in 1935 by the British ecologist Arthur Tansley. Sometime during his exploration of nature, he realized the importance of considering organisms and their environment as an integrated system. Tansley wrote: "Though the organisms may claim our primary interest, . . . we cannot separate them from their special environment, with which they form one physical system. It is the [eco]systems

Figure 19.1 In most ecosystems, sunlight provides the ultimate source of energy to power all biological activity, including the huddling of these ground squirrels and the plants in which they rest.

so formed which, from the point of view of the ecologist, are the basic units of nature on the face of the earth."

Ecosystem ecologists study the flows of energy, water, and nutrients in ecosystems and, as suggested by Tansley, pay as much attention to physical and chemical processes as they do to biological ones. Some fundamental areas of interest for ecosystem ecologists are primary production, energy flow, and nutrient cycling. We will discuss the first two topics in chapter 19 and nutrient cycling in chapter 20.

We saw in chapter 7 how the photosynthetic machinery of plants uses solar energy to synthesize sugars. In chapter 7 we considered photosynthesis from the perspective of the individual plant. Here we step back from the biochemical and physiological details of photosynthesis and back even from the individual organism to look at photosynthesis at the level of the whole ecosystem.

Primary production is the fixation of energy by autotrophs in an ecosystem. The **rate of primary production** is the amount of energy fixed over some interval of time. Ecosystem ecologists distinguish between gross and net primary production. **Gross primary production** is the total amount of energy fixed by all the autotrophs in the ecosystem. **Net primary production (NPP)** is the amount of energy left over after autotrophs have met their own energetic needs. Net primary production is gross primary production minus respiration by primary producers; it is the amount of energy available to the consumers in an ecosystem. Ecologists have measured primary production in a variety of ways but mainly as the rate of carbon uptake by primary producers or by the amount of biomass or oxygen produced.

We discussed feeding biology from a variety of perspectives in previous chapters. In chapter 7, we examined the biology of herbivores, detritivores, and carnivores. In chapters 14 and 15, we discussed the ecology of exploitation, and in chapter 17, we used food webs as a means of representing the trophic structure of communities. Ecosystem ecologists are also concerned with trophic structure but have taken a different approach than population and community ecologists.

Ecosystem ecologists have simplified the trophic structure of ecosystems by arranging species into trophic levels based on the predominant source of their nutrition. A **trophic level** is a position in a food web and is determined by the number of transfers of energy from primary producers to that level. Primary producers occupy the first trophic level in ecosystems since they convert inorganic forms of energy, principally light, into biomass. Herbivores are often called primary consumers and occupy the second trophic level. Carnivores are called secondary consumers and occupy the third trophic level. Carnivores that feed on other carnivores occupy a fourth trophic level. Since each trophic level may contain several species, in some cases hundreds, an ecosystem perspective simplifies trophic structure. Consuming members of all trophic levels are the parasites and detritivores.

Primary production, the conversion of inorganic forms of energy into organic forms, is a key *ecosystem process*. All consumer organisms, including humans, depend upon primary production for their existence. Because of its importance and because rates of primary production vary substantially from one ecosystem to another, ecosystem ecologists study the factors controlling rates of primary production in ecosystems.

Patterns of natural variation in primary production provide clues to the environmental factors that control this key ecosystem process. Experiments test the importance of those controls. In chapter 19, we discuss the major patterns of variation in primary production in terrestrial and aquatic ecosystems and key experiments designed to determine the mechanisms producing those patterns. In the last sections of chapter 19, we examine patterns of energy flow through ecosystems.

Concepts

19.1 Terrestrial primary production is generally limited by temperature and moisture.

19.2 Aquatic primary production is generally limited by nutrient availability.

19.3 A variety of species can influence rates of primary production in aquatic and terrestrial ecosystems.

19.4 Energy losses limit the number of trophic levels in ecosystems.

19.1   Patterns of Terrestrial Primary Production

Terrestrial primary production is generally limited by temperature and moisture.   As we surveyed the major terrestrial biomes in chapter 2, you probably got a sense of the geographic variation in rates of primary production. Perhaps you also developed a feeling for the major environmental correlates with that variation. The variables most highly correlated with variation in terrestrial primary production are *temperature* and *moisture*. Highest rates of terrestrial primary production occur under warm, moist conditions.

The importance of temperature and moisture to net primary productivity can clearly be seen in a map of primary productivity across Canada (fig. 19.2). This map was developed by Jing Chen and colleagues from the Canada Centre of Remote Sensing based at the University of Toronto (Liu et al. 2002). Across the entire country, NPP was 1.22 gigatonnes of carbon (Gt C) per year. However, this production was highly variable, with 78% of this production occurring in the boreal forest, even though these forests only occupy 40% of the land base in Canada. Not too surprisingly, productivity is very low in the northern part of Canada, as well as along the Rocky Mountain and Pacific Coast mountain ranges in Alberta and British Columbia. This should not be surprising, as mountain peaks and high latitudes are quite cold, which clearly limits plant growth. However, there is another large area of low productivity found primarily in southern Alberta and Saskatchewan. This is the northern extent of the Great Plains, and summer temperatures regularly exceed 30°C. Primary production here is limited by low soil moisture, not temperatures.

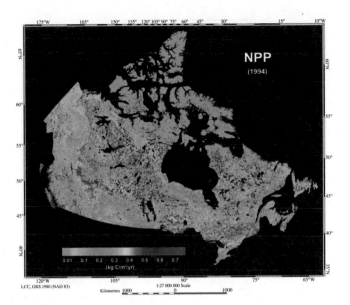

Figure 19.2   Estimated (terrestrial) net primary productivity across Canada.

Actual Evapotranspiration and Terrestrial Primary Production

Michael Rosenzweig (1968) estimated the influence of moisture and temperature on rates of primary production by plotting the relationship between annual net primary production and annual actual evapotranspiration. Annual **actual evapotranspiration (AET)** is the total amount of water that evaporates and transpires off a landscape during the course of a year and is measured in millimeters of water per year. The AET process is affected by both temperature and precipitation. The ecosystems showing the highest levels of primary production are those that are warm and receive large amounts of precipitation. Conversely, ecosystems show low levels of AET either because they receive little precipitation, are very cold, or both. For instance, both hot deserts and tundra exhibit low levels of AET.

Figure 19.3 shows Rosenzweig's plot of the positive relationship between net primary production and AET. Tropical forests show the highest levels of net primary production and AET. At the other end of the spectrum, hot, dry deserts and cold, dry tundra show the lowest levels. Intermediate levels occur in temperate forests, temperate grasslands, woodlands, and high-elevation forests. Figure 19.3 shows that AET accounts for a significant proportion of the variation in annual net primary production among terrestrial ecosystems.

Rosenzweig's analysis attempts to explain variation in primary production across the whole spectrum of terrestrial ecosystems. What controls variation in primary production within similar ecosystems? O. E. Sala and his colleagues (1988) at Colorado State University explored the factors controlling primary production in the central grassland region of the United States. Their study was based on data collected by the U.S. Department of Agriculture Soil Conservation Service at 9,498 sites. To make this large data set more manageable, the researchers grouped the sites into 100 representative study areas.

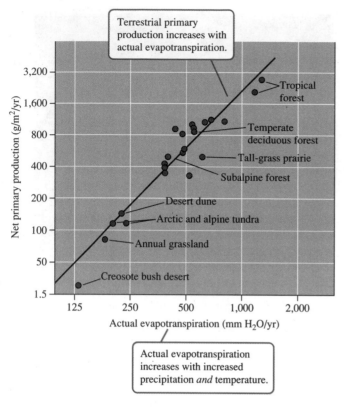

Figure 19.3 Relationship between actual evapotranspiration and net above-ground primary production in a series of terrestrial ecosystems (data from Rosenzweig 1968).

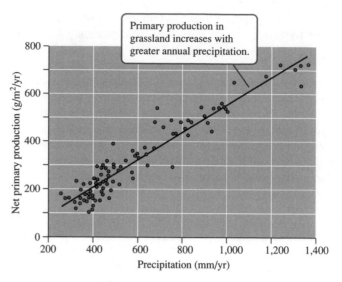

Figure 19.4 Influence of annual precipitation on net above-ground primary production in grasslands of central North America (data from Sala et al. 1988).

The study areas extended from Mississippi and Arkansas in the east to New Mexico and Montana in the west and from North Dakota to southern Texas. Primary production was highest in the eastern grassland study areas and lowest in the western study areas. This east–west variation corresponds to the westward changes from tall-grass prairie to short-grass prairie that we reviewed in chapter 2. Sala and his colleagues found that this east–west variation in primary production among grassland ecosystems correlated significantly with the amount of rainfall (fig. 19.4).

Compare the plot by Sala and his colleagues (fig. 19.4) with the one constructed by Rosenzweig (fig. 19.3). How are they similar? How are they different? Both graphs have primary production plotted on the vertical axis as a dependent variable. However, while the Rosenzweig plot includes ecosystems ranging from tundra to tropical rain forest, the plot by Sala and his colleagues includes grasslands only. In addition, different variables are plotted on the horizontal axes of the two graphs. While Rosenzweig plotted actual evapotranspiration, which depends upon temperature and precipitation, Sala and his colleagues plotted precipitation only. They found that including temperature in their analysis did not improve their ability to predict net primary production. Why do you think precipitation alone was sufficient to account for most of the variation in grassland production? A likely reason is that warm temperatures occur during the growing season at all of the study areas included by Sala and his colleagues. In contrast, Rosenzweig's study areas vary widely in growing season temperature.

These researchers found strong correlations between AET or precipitation and rates of terrestrial primary production. However, their models did not completely explain the variation in primary production among the study ecosystems. For instance, in figure 19.3, ecosystems with annual AET levels of 500 to 600 mm of water showed annual rates of primary production ranging from 300 to 1,000 g per square meter. In figure 19.4, grassland ecosystems receiving 400 mm of annual precipitation had annual rates of primary production ranging from about 100 to 250 g per square meter. These differences in primary production challenge ecologists for an explanation.

Soil Fertility and Terrestrial Primary Production

Significant variation in terrestrial primary production can be explained by differences in soil fertility. Farmers have long known that adding fertilizers to soil can increase agricultural production. However, it was not until the nineteenth century that scientists began to quantify the influence of specific nutrients, such as nitrogen (N) or phosphorus (P), on rates of primary production. Justus Liebig (1840) pointed out that nutrient supplies often limit plant growth. He also suggested that nutrient limitation to plant growth could be traced to a single limiting nutrient. This hypothetical control of primary production by a single nutrient was later called "Liebig's Law of the Minimum." We now know that Liebig's perspective was too simplistic. Usually several factors, including a number of nutrients, simultaneously affect levels of terrestrial primary production. However, his work led the way to a concept that remains true today; variation in soil fertility can significantly affect rates of terrestrial primary production.

Liebig's work, and most practical experience prior to Liebig, concerned the productivity of agricultural ecosystems. Do nutrients influence rates of primary production in other ecosystems, such as the tundra or deserts, where human

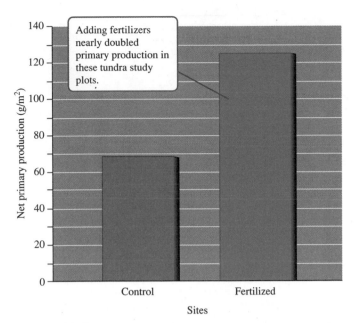

Figure 19.5   Effect of addition of nitrogen, phosphorus, and potassium on net above ground primary production in arctic tundra (data from Shaver and Chapin 1986).

manipulation has been less prominent? Ecologists have demonstrated the significant influence of nutrients on terrestrial primary production through numerous experiments involving addition of nutrients to natural ecosystems.

Ecologists have increased primary production by adding nutrients to a wide variety of terrestrial ecosystems, including arctic tundra, alpine tundra, grasslands, deserts, and forests. For instance, Gaius Shaver and Stuart Chapin (1986) studied the potential for nutrient limitation in arctic tundra. They added commercial fertilizer containing nitrogen, phosphorus, and potassium to several tundra ecosystems in Alaska. They made a single application of fertilizer to half of their experimental plots and two applications to the remaining experimental plots.

Shaver and Chapin measured net primary production at their control and experimental sites two to four years after the first nutrient additions. Nutrient additions increased net primary production (by 23%–300%) at all of the study sites. The response to fertilization was substantial and clear at most study sites. Four years after the initial application of fertilizer, net primary production on Kuparuk Ridge was twice as high on the fertilized plots compared to the unfertilized control plots (fig. 19.5).

You may recall from chapter 14 that a large number of Canadian researchers conducted a large-scale experiment manipulating resources, prey, and predators in an attempt to understand the linkages between plants, hares, and lynx in the Yukon. As part of this study, Roy Turkington, from the University of British Columbia, along with researchers from the University of Alberta, Nova Scotia Agricultural College, University of Toronto, and University of Sussex analyzed the response of the boreal vegetation to long-term nutrient additions (Turkington et al. 1998). The research team added fertilizer to two large (1 km²) plots, and monitored plant growth in these, and two control plots, for six years. Fertilizer was added each year, always including nitrogen, and in some years P and

Species	Variable	Magnitude
Cryptogams		
Lichens	percent cover	−26%
Moss	percent cover	−25%
Herbaceous species		
Achillea millefolium	percent cover	+22%
	biomass	+33%
Anemone parviflora	percent cover	−124%
Epilobium angustifolium	percent cover	+176%
	biomass	+96%
Festuca altaica	percent cover	+173%
Lupinus arcticus	percent cover	−119%
	biomass	no change
Mertensia paniculata	percent cover	+192%
	biomass	+224%
Solidago multiradiata	percent cover	+66%
All species	percent cover	+18%
Dwarf shrubs		
Arctostaphylos uva-ursi	percent cover	−41%
Linnaea borealis	percent cover	−54%
Shrubs		
Betula glandulosa	percent cover	+37%
	biomass	no change
Salix glauca	growth rate	+146%
	biomass	no change
Trees		
Picea glauca	twig growth	+15–50%
	cone crop	no change
	seed fall	no change

Figure 19.6   Addition of mineral nutrients to the boreal forest can have different effects on different plant species (data from Turkington et al. 1998).

K were also added. The response they found varied more than what we saw on Kuparuk Ridge.

One of the great strengths of the Turkington study is that they did not just measure total production in the plots, but instead measured each of the major plant groups separately. By doing this, they found a rather interesting story (fig. 19.6). Overall, the biomass of the system increased, indicating nutrient limitation of primary production. However, the exact effects varied among the different plant types. The fast growing herbaceous species responded very quickly, while effects on tree growth only became apparent later in the study. Additionally, several plant species actually showed a reduction in growth due to fertilization. How is this possible if the boreal forest is nutrient limited? The answer is very straightforward: not all plants are equally limited by nutrients, and instead there exists a set of species that have life-histories adapted to stress tolerance (chapter 9). Under low nutrient conditions these plants will do just fine. However, by adding nutrients, the stress has been removed, and now the faster growing and more competitively dominant species are able to take over. In other words, even though an ecosystem may be nutrient limited, this does not mean that all species increase in growth if nutrients are added.

Experiments such as these have shown that despite the major influence of temperature and moisture on rates of primary production in terrestrial ecosystems, variation in nutrient availability can also have measurable influence. As we shall see in the next section, nutrient availability is the main factor limiting primary production in aquatic ecosystems.

Concept 19.1 Review

1. Why was precipitation alone, without temperature, sufficient to account for most of the variation in grassland net primary production across central North America?
2. How are the desert dune ecosystem and the arctic and alpine tundra ecosystems indicated in figure 19.3 the same?
3. Why do different species respond differently to nutrient addition, even if the net primary production is nutrient limited?

19.2 Patterns of Aquatic Primary Production

Aquatic primary production is generally limited by nutrient availability. Limnologists and oceanographers have measured rates of primary production and nutrient concentrations in many lakes and at many coastal and oceanic study sites. These studies have produced one of the best documented patterns in the biosphere: the positive relationship between nutrient availability and rate of primary production in aquatic ecosystems.

Patterns and Models

A quantitative relationship between phosphorus, an essential plant nutrient, and phytoplankton biomass was first described for a series of lakes in Japan (Hogetsu and Ichimura 1954, Ichimura 1956, Sakamoto 1966). The ecologists studying this relationship found a remarkably good correspondence between total phosphorus and phytoplankton biomass.

Soon after the ecologists from Japan studied this relationship, there emerged two Canadian researchers who further explored nutrient controls on aquatic productivity. Peter Dillon, now an industrial research chairholder at Trent University, and Frank Rigler, formerly of University of Toronto. Rigler was an exceptionally influential person in the field of aquatic ecology, and today the Society of Canadian Limnologists has named its highest award, the Frank H. Rigler Award, in his honour. Since his work with Rigler, Dillon has continued to study nutrient issues in lakes, influencing governmental policy through sound ecological studies. Dillon and Rigler (1974) described a similar positive relationship between phosphorus and phytoplankton biomass for lake ecosystems throughout the Northern Hemisphere (fig. 19.7). Remarkably, the slopes of the lines describing the relationship between phosphorus and phytoplankton biomass for the Japanese and Canadian lakes were nearly identical.

The data from Japan and North America strongly support the hypothesis that nutrients, particularly phosphorus, control phytoplankton biomass in lake ecosystems. However, what is

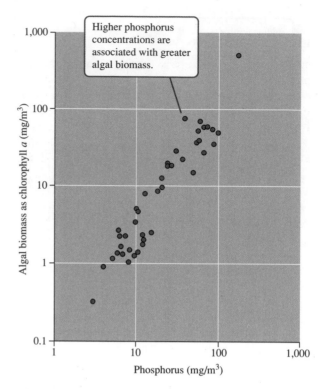

Figure 19.7 Relationship between phosphorus concentration and algal biomass in north temperate lakes (data from Dillon and Rigler 1974).

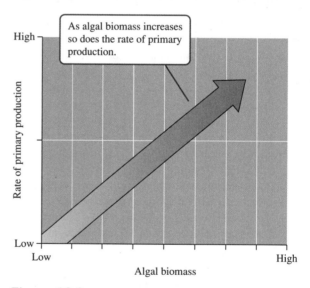

Figure 19.8 Relationship between algal biomass and rate of primary production in temperate zone lakes (data from Smith 1979).

the relationship between phytoplankton biomass and the rate of primary production? This relationship was explored by Val Smith (1979) for 49 lakes of the north temperate zone. The data from these lakes showed a strong positive correlation between chlorophyll concentrations and photosynthetic rates (fig. 19.8). Smith also examined the relationship between total phosphorus concentration and photosynthetic rate directly. Aquatic ecologists have extended these correlational studies of the relationship between nutrient availability and primary production by manipulating nutrient availability in entire lake ecosystems.

Whole Lake Experiments on Primary Production

In chapter 1 we introduced some experiments on primary production conducted at the Experimental Lakes Area. Here we provide more information about the groundbreaking work by the team of ELA researchers. The Experimental Lakes Area was founded in northwestern Ontario, Canada, in 1968, as a place in which aquatic ecologists could manipulate whole lake ecosystems (Mills and Schindler 1987, Findlay and Kasian 1987). For instance, ecologists manipulated nutrient availability in a lake called Lake 226. They used a vinyl curtain to divide Lake 226 into two 8 ha basins each containing about 500,000 m³ of water. Each subbasin of Lake 226 was fertilized from 1973 to 1980. The researchers added a mixture of carbon in the form of sucrose and nitrate to one basin and carbon, nitrate, and phosphate to the other basin. They stopped fertilizing the lakes after 1980 and then studied the recovery of the Lake 226 ecosystem from 1981 to 1983.

Both sides of Lake 226 responded significantly to nutrient additions, however the side that received phosphorus showed a much more dramatic increase on phytoplankton growth (fig. 1.5). Prior to the manipulation, Lake 226 supported about the same biomass of phytoplankton as two reference lakes (fig. 19.9). However, when experimenters began adding nutrients, the phytoplankton biomass in Lake 226 quickly surpassed that in the reference lakes. Phytoplankton biomass remained elevated in Lake 226 until the experimenters stopped adding fertilizer at the end of 1980. Then, from 1981 to 1983 the phytoplankton biomass in Lake 226 declined significantly.

Correlations between phosphorus concentrations and primary productivity, as well as whole-lake experimental manipulation, support the generalization that nutrient availability controls primary productivity in freshwater ecosystems. Now, let's examine the evidence for this relationship in marine ecosystems.

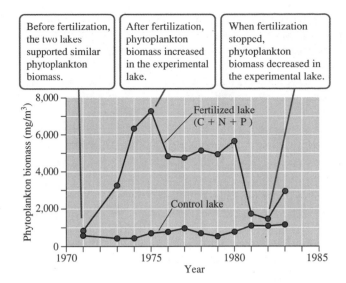

Figure 19.9 A whole lake experiment shows the effect of nutrient additions on average phytoplankton biomass (data from Findlay and Kasian 1987).

Global Patterns of Marine Primary Production

The geographic distribution of net primary production in the sea indicates a positive influence of nutrient availability on rates of primary production. The highest rates of primary production by marine phytoplankton are generally concentrated in areas with higher levels of nutrient availability (fig. 19.10). The highest rates of primary production are concentrated along the margins of continents over continental shelves and in areas of upwelling. Along continental margins, nutrients are renewed by runoff from the land and by biological or physical disturbance of bottom sediments. As we saw in chapter 3, the upwelling that brings nutrient-laden water from the depths to the surface is

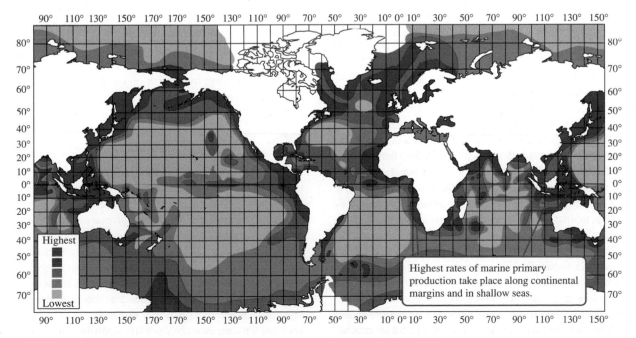

Figure 19.10 Geographic variation in marine primary production (data from F.A.O. 1972).

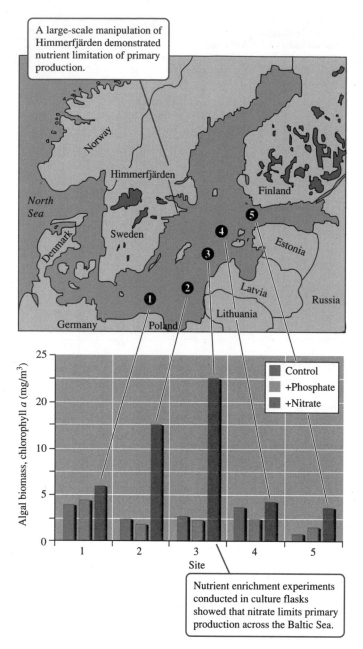

A large-scale manipulation of Himmerfjärden demonstrated nutrient limitation of primary production.

Nutrient enrichment experiments conducted in culture flasks showed that nitrate limits primary production across the Baltic Sea.

Figure 19.11 Nitrate control of primary production in the Baltic Sea (data from Granéli et al. 1990).

lake manipulations at the Experimental Lakes Area (e.g., Schindler 1990). However, in one experiment, researchers were able to alter the nutrient inputs and concentrations in Himmerfjärden, Sweden, a brackish water coastal inlet of the Baltic Sea with a surface area of 195 km^2 (see fig. 19.11; Glunélie et al. 1990). (For comparison, the lake subbasins manipulated in the whole lake experiments were < 0.1 km^2.) The researchers combined this large-scale manipulation with small-scale culture flask experiments, providing critical data for understanding nutrient controls of production in a marine system. The results of this manipulative experiment indicate that nitrogen limitation of primary production can shift to phosphorus limitation by altering nitrogen:phosphorus ratios. Increasing additions of phosphorus to Himmerfjärden reinforced nitrogen limitation, while decreasing phosphorus additions and increasing nitrogen additions led to increased phosphorus limitation.

Dillon and Rigler suggested that limnologists pay attention to the scatter of points around lines showing a relationship between nutrient concentrations and phytoplankton biomass (F.A.O. 1972). We call that scatter of points residual variation (see appendix A). Residual variation is that proportion of variation not explained by the independent variable, in this case, by nutrient concentration. Dillon and Rigler suggested that environmental factors besides nutrient availability significantly influence phytoplankton biomass. One of those factors is the intensity of predation on the zooplankton that feed on phytoplankton. As we shall see in the next section, consumers can influence rates of primary production in both terrestrial and aquatic ecosystems.

Concept 19.2 Review

1. Suppose that when you add nitrogen to one half of a lake, you observe no change in phytoplankton biomass but when you add phosphorus to the other half of the lake, phytoplankton biomass more than doubles. What is the most likely explanation of your results?
2. Suppose you fertilize a region of an ocean with nitrogen only, another region with phosphorus only, and a third region with nitrogen plus phosphorus and observe no change in phytoplankton biomass. What is the most likely explanation of your results?

19.3 Biotic Influences

A variety of species can influence rates of primary production in aquatic and terrestrial ecosystems. In the first section of chapter 19, we emphasized the effects of physical and chemical factors on rates of primary production. More recently, ecologists have discovered that primary production is also affected by a diversity of species interactions as well. Ecologists refer to the influences of physical and chemical factors, such as temperature and nutrients, on ecosystems as **bottom-up controls.** The influences of consumers on ecosystems are known as **top-down controls.** In the previous two sections we discussed bottom-up controls on rates of primary production. Here we discuss top-down control.

concentrated along the west coasts of continents and around the continent of Antarctica, areas that appear dark red on figure 19.10, indicating high to very high rates of primary production.

Meanwhile, the central portions of the major oceans show low levels of nutrient availability and low rates of primary production. The main source of nutrient renewal in the surface waters of the open ocean is vertical mixing. Vertical mixing is generally blocked in open tropical oceans by a permanent thermocline. Consequently, the surface waters of open tropical oceans contain very low concentrations of nutrients and show some of the lowest rates of marine primary production.

What is the experimental evidence for nutrient limitation of marine primary production? There have been no experiments done in the marine environment that are equivalent to the whole

Piscivores, Planktivores, and Lake Primary Production

Stephen Carpenter, James Kitchell, and James Hodgson (1985) proposed that while nutrient inputs determine the potential rate of primary production in a lake, piscivorous and planktivorous fish can cause significant deviations from potential primary production. In support of their hypothesis, Carpenter and his colleagues (1991) cited a negative correlation between zooplankton size, an indication of grazing intensity, and primary production.

Carpenter and Kitchell (1988) proposed that the influences of consumers on lake primary production can extend to other levels throughout food webs. Since they visualized the effects of consumers coming from the top of food webs to the base, they called these effects on ecosystem properties "trophic cascades." The trophic cascade hypothesis (fig. 19.12) is very similar to the keystone species hypothesis (see chapter 17). However, notice that the trophic cascade model is focused on the effects of consumers on ecosystem processes, such as primary production, and not on their effects on species diversity.

Carpenter and Kitchell (1993) interpreted the trophic cascade in their study lakes as follows: Piscivores, such as largemouth bass, feed on planktivorous fish and invertebrates. Because of their influence on planktivorous fish, largemouth bass indirectly affect populations of zooplankton. By reducing populations of planktivorous fish, largemouth bass reduce feeding pressure on zooplankton and zooplankton populations. Large-bodied zooplankton, the preferred prey of size-selective planktivorous fish (see chapter 7), soon dominate the zooplankton community. A dense population of large zooplankton reduces phytoplankton biomass and the rate of primary production. This interpretation of the trophic cascade is consistent with the negative correlation between zooplankton body size and primary production reported by Carpenter and his research team. This hypothesis is summarized in figure 19.13.

Carpenter and Kitchell tested their trophic cascade model by manipulating the fish communities in two lakes and using a third lake as a control. Figure 19.14 shows the overall design of their experiment. Two of the lakes contained substantial populations of largemouth bass. A third lake had no bass, due to occasional winterkill, but contained an abundance of planktivorous minnows. The researchers removed 90% of the largemouth bass from one experimental lake and put them into the other. They simultaneously removed 90% of the planktivorous minnows from the second lake and introduced them to the first. They left a reference lake unmanipulated as a control.

The responses of the study lakes to the experimental manipulations support the trophic cascade hypothesis (fig. 19.14). Reducing the planktivorous fish population led to reduced rates of primary production. In the absence of planktivorous minnows, the predaceous invertebrate *Chaoborus* became more numerous. *Chaoborus* fed heavily upon the smaller herbivorous zooplankton, and the herbivorous zooplankton assemblage shifted in dominance from small to large species. In the presence of abundant, large herbivorous zooplankton, phytoplankton biomass and rate of primary production declined.

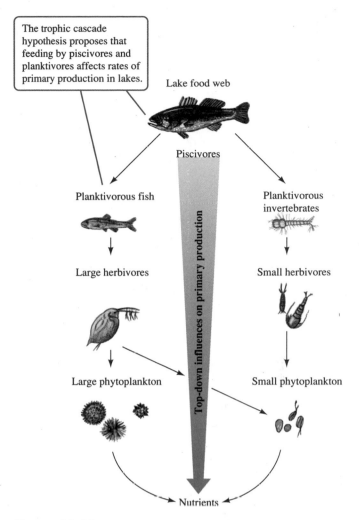

The trophic cascade hypothesis proposes that feeding by piscivores and planktivores affects rates of primary production in lakes.

Lake food web

Piscivores

Planktivorous fish

Planktivorous invertebrates

Large herbivores

Small herbivores

Large phytoplankton

Small phytoplankton

Top-down influences on primary production

Nutrients

Figure 19.12   The trophic cascade hypothesis.

Adding planktivorous minnows produced a complex ecological response. Increasing the planktivorous fish population led to increased rates of primary production. However, though the researchers increased the population of planktivorous fish in this experimental lake, they did so in an unintended way. Despite the best efforts of the researchers, a few bass remained. So, by introducing a large number of minnows they basically fed the remaining bass. An increased food supply combined with reduced population density induced a strong numerical response by the bass population (see chapter 11). The manipulation increased the reproductive rate of the remaining largemouth bass 50-fold, producing an abundance of young largemouth bass that feed voraciously on zooplankton.

The lake ecosystem responded to the increased biomass of planktivorous fish (young largemouth bass) as predicted at the outset of the experiment. The biomass of zooplankton decreased sharply, the average size of herbivorous zooplankton decreased, and phytoplankton biomass and primary production increased.

The results of these whole-lake experiments show that the trophic activities of a few species can have large effects on ecosystem processes. However, the majority of trophic cascades described by ecologists have been in aquatic ecosystems with

Figure 19.13 Predicted effects of piscivores on planktivore, herbivore, and phytoplankton biomass and production (data from Carpenter, Kitchell, and Hodgson 1985).

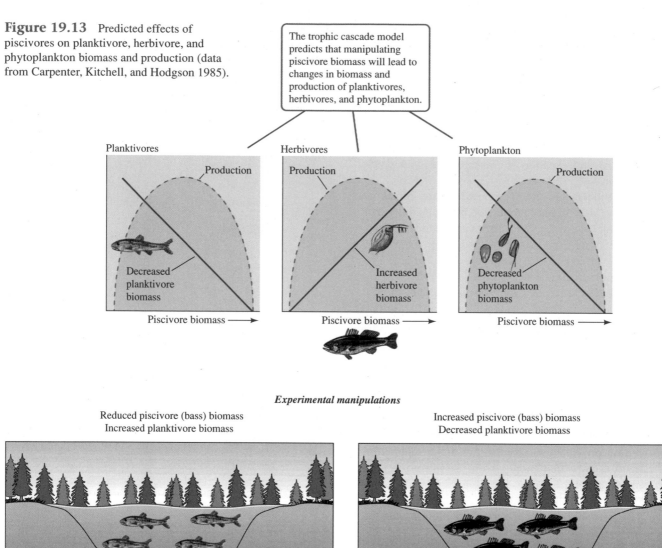

The trophic cascade model predicts that manipulating piscivore biomass will lead to changes in biomass and production of planktivores, herbivores, and phytoplankton.

Planktivores

Production

Decreased planktivore biomass

Piscivore biomass →

Herbivores

Production

Increased herbivore biomass

Piscivore biomass →

Phytoplankton

Production

Decreased phytoplankton biomass

Piscivore biomass →

Experimental manipulations

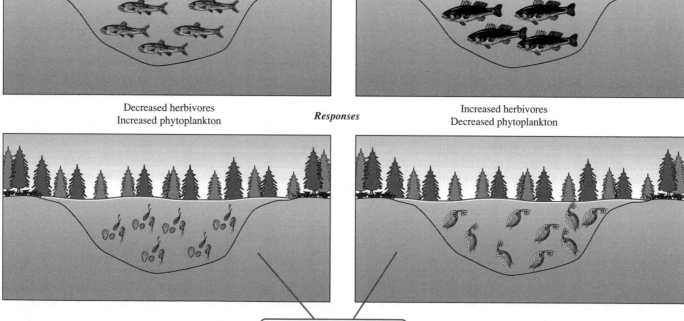

Reduced piscivore (bass) biomass
Increased planktivore biomass

Increased piscivore (bass) biomass
Decreased planktivore biomass

Decreased herbivores
Increased phytoplankton

Responses

Increased herbivores
Decreased phytoplankton

The responses of herbivores and phytoplankton to manipulations of piscivore and planktivore biomass support the trophic cascade model.

Figure 19.14 Experimental manipulations of ponds and responses.

algae as primary producers. This pattern prompted Donald Strong (1992) to ask, "Are trophic cascades all wet?" Strong suggested that trophic cascades most likely occur in ecosystems of lower species diversity and reduced spatial and temporal complexity. These are characteristics of many aquatic ecosystems. Despite these restrictions, consumers have significant effects on rates of primary production in some terrestrial ecosystems; one of those is the Serengeti grassland ecosystem.

Grazing by Large Mammals and Primary Production on the Serengeti

The Serengeti-Mara, a 25,000 km² grassland ecosystem that straddles the border between Tanzania and Kenya, is one of the last ecosystems on earth where great numbers of large mammals still roam freely. Sam McNaughton (1985) reported estimated densities of the major grazers in the Serengeti that included 1.4 million wildebeest, *Connochaetes taurinus albujubatus,* 600,000 Thomson's gazelle, *Gazella thomsonii,* 200,000 zebra, *Equus burchelli,* 52,000 buffalo, *Syncerus caffer,* 60,000 topi, *Damaliscus korrigum,* and large numbers of 20 additional grazing mammals. McNaughton estimated that these grazers consume an average of 66% of the annual above ground primary production on the Serengeti. In light of this estimate, the potential for consumer influences on primary production seems very high.

Over two decades of research on the Serengeti ecosystem in Tanzania led McNaughton to appreciate the complex interrelations of abiotic and biotic factors there. For instance, both soil fertility and rainfall stimulate plant production and the distributions of grazing mammals. However, grazing mammals also affect water balance, soil fertility, and plant production.

As you might predict, the rate of primary production on the Serengeti is positively correlated with the quantity of rainfall. However, McNaughton (1976) also found that grazing can increase above ground primary production. Similar to the methods used by Jefferies in chapter 15, McNaughton fenced in some areas in the western Serengeti to explore the influence of herbivores on production. The migrating wildebeest that flooded into the study site grazed intensively for four days, consuming approximately 85% of plant biomass. During the month after the wildebeest left the study area, biomass within the enclosures decreased, while the biomass of vegetation outside the enclosures increased (fig. 19.15). Similar to the geese in arctic wetlands, these mammals caused compensatory growth of many grass species. Compensatory growth was likely caused by reduced self-shading, and improved water balance due to reduced leaf area and reduced respiration. Compensatory growth was highest at intermediate grazing intensities (fig. 19.16). Apparently, light grazing is insufficient to produce compensatory growth and very heavy grazing reduces the capacity of the plant to recover.

What McNaughton and his colleagues described is essentially a trophic cascade in a terrestrial environment where the feeding activities of consumers have a major influence on ecosystem properties. The Serengeti is now an exceptional terrestrial ecosystem but it was not always so. As we saw in chapter 2, the extensive grasslands of North America and Eurasia were also once populated by vast herds of mammalian grazers. Historians estimate that the population of North American bison in the middle of the nineteenth century numbered up to 60 million. Such a dense concentration of grazers must have had significant influences upon the grassland ecosystems of which they were part. It appears that terrestrial consumers, as well as the aquatic ones studied by Carpenter and Kitchell, can have important influences on primary production.

As important as consumers are in affecting the production of some communities, exploitation is not the only type of species interaction that can alter primary production.

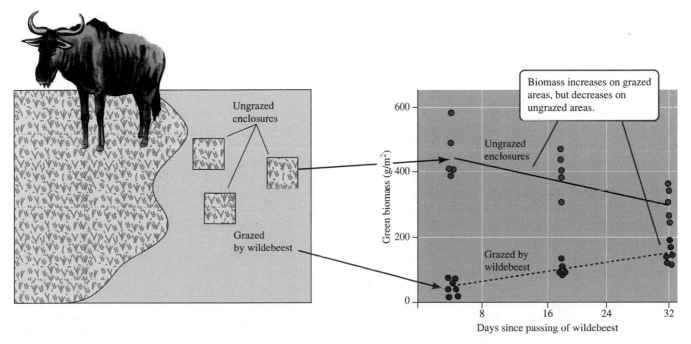

Figure 19.15   Growth response by grasses grazed by wildebeest (data from McNaughton 1976).

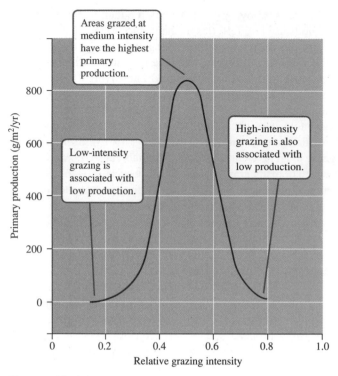

Figure 19.16 Grazing intensity and primary production of Serengeti grassland (data from McNaughton 1985).

Impacts of Biodiversity

Globally, there is significant concern about the rapid rate of biodiversity loss, often associated with human disturbances. This concern is on a variety of dimensions, including aesthetic, moral, and even functional grounds. It is this latter issue, the impact of loss of biodiversity on the functioning of ecosystems, that we will discuss here.

What exactly is an ecosystem function? It is some process that is performed by the ecosystem, such as biomass production, nutrient cycling, or carbon sequestration. Ecosystem function does not imply intent by the ecosystem; instead the function is a natural byproduct of ecological and biogeochemical interactions within the ecosystem. Some of these ecosystem functions will directly impact humans. For example, if a large wetland along a coastal region buffers tidal surges, then the loss of that ecosystem service (tidal dissipation) costs humans through risk of personal and property damage. A grassland that produces substantial amounts of plant matter has the potential to be more economically viable for a rancher than one that produces little. In other words, the ecological services provided by ecosystems directly alter the economic well-being and personal safety of humans. As a result, there is substantial interest in understanding what factors control the efficiency of ecosystem services, so that some processes can be protected or even augmented to enhance or restore the delivery of these services.

As you have seen already in this chapter, the abiotic environment, such as nutrient and water inputs, can alter primary production of terrestrial and aquatic systems. In other words, this type of ecosystem service is partially controlled by nutrient inputs. You also have seen that animals feeding upon the primary producers can cause shifts in primary production. Here we will discuss a third influence on primary production, the species diversity of the community.

The idea that species diversity can increase primary production has a long history in ecology. There are three main mechanisms proposed to explain how biodiversity could enhance productivity. The first, complementarity, comes from niche theory. The basic logic is that production will be highest in a community in which all resources are most fully being exploited. So, in a terrestrial community this would mean that production should be highest when roots fully exploit the soil environment, and shoots the light environment. If a single species has a single niche, then one might expect it only to be able to exploit a fraction of the potential "niche space." However, if you have another species, with a different set of niche requirement (perhaps it can exploit deeper soil), then more of the niche space in the community gets exploited, and production should increase. This can continue as you add species, until you get a predicted levelling off of production once all niche space (and resources) is exploited. A second mechanism of diversity effects is facilitation. In this model, some species enhance the growth of others, perhaps by reducing soil salinity or modifying the thermal environment. The third possible effect of biodiversity on function is called the sampling effect. This idea is based upon the assumption that the function of communities that have low species evenness (chapter 16) are going to be driven by the activity of the dominant species. In other words, what might influence production is not increased growth of rare plants, but instead very slight increase in growth of the dominants. In the sampling effect model, diverse communities are more likely to contain plants that have the greatest potential for higher growth than species-poor communities. Thus "sampling" isn't a benefit of diversity itself, as much as increased odds of having the most productive species. These three mechanisms are not exclusionary, and instead can co-occur.

In recent years, there has been an explosion of research activity trying to move beyond explaining how biodiversity *might* influence ecosystem function, and instead testing whether it *does* have a biologically meaningful impact. These experiments have taken place in the computer lab, greenhouse, and in the field. The standard experimental design is to grow "synthetic communities," which consist of a certain number of species (fig. 19.17). Different treatment would have different numbers of species, perhaps ranging from 1 to 16 within a single experiment. After some period of time, the researchers would measure ecosystem function in the plots, and use a regression or other analysis to determine whether there is a positive relationship between plant diversity and ecosystem function.

As a sign of the increased importance this topic has gained over the years, there were less than 5 experiments investigating biodiversity–ecosystem function relationships in 1995, and about 40 just 10 years later in 2004. Patricia Balvanera and colleagues have synthesized the findings from 103 studies, allowing us to draw some general conclusions (Balvanera et al. 2006).

Across the studies they sampled, increased plant diversity caused a significant increase in primary production (fig. 19.18). The effects of plant diversity manipulation were not

Figure 19.17 Aerial and close-up views of a large biodiversity experiment in Cedar Creek, Minnesota. Each of the 342 plots is 13 × 13 m in size, with measurements taken only on the innermost 9 × 9 m.

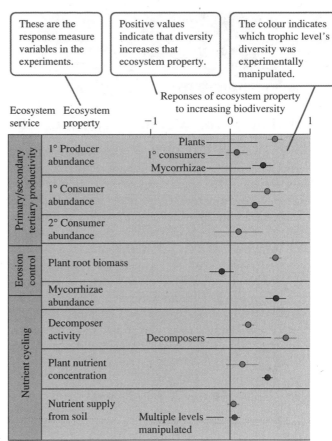

These are the response measure variables in the experiments.

Positive values indicate that diversity increases that ecosystem property.

The colour indicates which trophic level's diversity was experimentally manipulated.

Figure 19.18 Changes in species diversity can impact a number of ecosystem processes (data from Balvanera et al. 2006).

limited to the plants. Increased plant diversity also caused an increase in herbivore biomass (insects) in most studies in which it was measured. In other words, plant diversity causes a trophic cascade. These effects are smaller at higher trophic levels, to the point where predator biomass was generally unaffected by plant diversity (fig. 19.18). These findings are a clear indication that aspects of the community itself, such as plant species diversity, impact the functioning of the local community. It is also important to note that not all members of the community have the same effects on every ecosystem process. For instance, manipulating the diversity of the herbivores, rather than the plants, has no impact on primary production (fig. 19.18). In contrast, manipulating the diversity of mycorrhizal fungi has nearly as large an impact on primary production as does manipulating the plants directly! These findings are a clear example that ecosystem processes impact, and are impacted by, a diversity of ecological interactions. Understanding which of these will be functionally important requires a clear understanding of ecology.

What mechanisms likely cause the observed biodiversity–production relationships? It is not completely clear, and substantially more research is needed. One particularly interesting result is that soil nutrient levels generally do not change as a function of plant biodiversity. This result does not support the complementarity hypothesis, which predicts that more diverse communities should more efficiently use the available

resources, and thus deplete soil nutrient levels relative to a species-poor community. Instead, there was evidence that plant diversity increased the activity of decomposers, which could in turn result in increased nutrient inputs. In other words, one possibility is that increased plant diversity results in increased production through facilitation of another ecosystem service, decomposition!

As we have seen, primary production can be influenced by processes both internal and external to the community. Many factors also influence how energy will move from one trophic level to another. In the next section we will ask the question, "what limits the number of trophic levels in an ecosystem, and why do ecosystems differ in the number of levels they contain?"

Concept 19.3 Review

1. Since increased phytoplankton biomass decreases water clarity in lakes, how should fishing pressure on the bass population in a lake ecosystem, such as that pictured in figure 19.12, impact water clarity?
2. Why is it more difficult to obtain evidence for trophic cascades in terrestrial ecosystems, as opposed to lakes?
3. Why can plant diversity increase both primary and secondary productivity?

Ecology In Action

Interactions Across Community Boundaries

In chapter 18 we observed that there is growing acceptance that communities are not static entities, but instead are constantly in a state of flux due to natural and human-induced disturbances. More progressive conservation programs generally try to incorporate some aspect of disturbance into the management plan. Here we will explore a related topic. The factors that influence the growth and ecosystem dynamics of a particular community (e.g., forest, lake, etc.) include not only those factors internal to the community that we have discussed (biodiversity, consumers), but also can include processes in the surrounding communities. There is an increasing realization that to preserve a particular community will require an understanding of nutrient inputs from the surrounding area, as changes in primary production can have cascading effects on competitive interactions, herbivory, and community structure.

Many communities receive **allochthonous** inputs of nutrients and biomass. Allochthonous inputs are derived/created within a community external to the one in which they are eventually deposited. For example, the nutrients and energy contained in leaves that fall from trees into a stream are an allochthonous input into the stream ecosystem. Thomas Reimchen and his colleagues and students at the University of Victoria have been studying the role that bears feeding upon salmon has on the primary production of coastal forests (fig. 19.19).

Coastal forests tend to be nitrogen-limited, and thus they are likely very sensitive to any additions of nitrogen into the system. Large numbers of salmon spawn in the rivers throughout coastal British Columbia, and enormous quantities of these fish are eaten by bears, wolves, and other animals. Let's look at this interaction from an ecosystem perspective. You have fish that leave the streams at a very small size and move into the ocean.

(b)

(a)

Figure 19.19   (*a*) Feeding by bear on salmon results in large allochthonous inputs of nutrients into (*b*) the forest surrounding salmon spawning grounds.

There, they live for many years, growing to large size. The resources they use for this growth come from the marine environment. They then move back into freshwater, where they either are consumed by terrestrial animals, or die in the streams. In either case, many of the nutrients they carried with them from the ocean are released onto land (as bear feces and urine, or decomposing fish carcasses), on the stream edges (for fish that die in the stream), or they are swept with the currents into the ocean. In other words, the exploitative interaction between bear and salmon causes an allochthonous input of nutrients into coastal forests. Reimchen and his group have been working to determine whether such nutrient inputs alter primary production of the forests.

As you will see in the Ecological Tools section of this chapter, ecologists are able to use stable isotope analyses to determine the source of different nutrients in different trophic levels. We will not go into the details here, but instead it's sufficient to understand that animal tissue that comes from marine habitats contains a higher percentage of ^{15}N than similar tissue from terrestrial habitats. As a result, if plants near the water's edge "consume" the nitrogen that comes from the ocean, rather than the nitrogen that is found on land, they should have more ^{15}N in their leaves than plants that do not have access to this marine-derived nitrogen source (MDN). Reimchen and his colleagues (Mathewson et al. 2003) were able to test whether this was true by comparing ^{15}N levels of several riparian plant species collected in different positions along a stream, in each of two watersheds. Specifically, they recognized that some waterfalls are impenetrable barriers to salmon, such that plants below the waterfall would have access to MDN, while those above would not. When they looked at the plant tissues, they found their hunch was correct; most species tested had significantly more ^{15}N below the waterfall than above it (fig. 19.20). More importantly, Reimchen and his colleagues found that in most samples, more than 30% of the nitrogen in the plant tissues came from the ocean! To put it mildly, this is strong evidence that the bear-salmon interaction can have strong impacts on nutrient inputs. But does it actually alter the composition and production of these forests? Again, Mathewson and colleagues (2003) have data suggesting yes, it is important. Plants generally associated with low-N soils were much more abundant above the waterfalls, while plants associated with high-N soils were much more abundant below

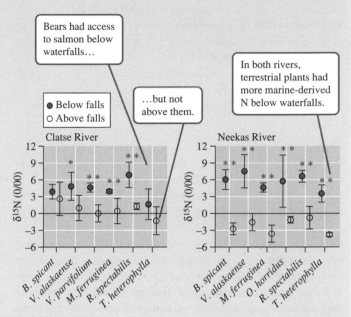

Figure 19.20 ^{15}N concentrations were higher for most plants species when they had access to marine-derived nitrogen (data from Reimchen et al. 2003).

the falls. This is initial evidence to suggest that not only do salmon alter nitrogen levels, they can alter the outcome of interactions among plant species!

The idea that fish can influence plant competition and forest community composition has significant implications for any conservation program of the coastal forests. It suggests that if you want to preserve the forest, you also need to protect the fish that feed the forest. Without the large number of salmon that die each year and serve as fertilizer for the riparian forest, there will most certainly be a shift in plant species composition, and a loss of the ecosystem we are trying to preserve. Realization of this concept serves as the foundation of ecosystem-based management, where the goal is to protect an entire set of interactions, rather than specific communities. A recent success story is the Great Bear Rainforest, a newly protected, five-million acre expanse of coastal rainforest along the coast of British Columbia and Alaska. An understanding of the basic ecological principles occurring in nature serves as the foundation for such an ambitious conservation program.

Energy losses limit the number of trophic levels in ecosystems.   We began chapter 19 with a partial and highly qualitative energy budget for a forest: Sunlight shines down on the canopy of a forest—some is reflected, some is converted to heat energy, and some is absorbed by chlorophyll. The energy budgets of ecosystems reveal that with each transfer or conversion of energy, some energy is lost. To verify that these losses have the potential to limit the number of trophic levels in ecosystems, we need to quantify the flow of energy through ecosystems. One of the very first ecologists to quantify the flux of energy through ecosystems was Raymond Lindeman.

A Trophic Dynamic View of Ecosystems

Raymond Lindeman (1942) published a revolutionary paper with the provocative title, "The Trophic-Dynamic Aspect of Ecology." In this paper, Lindeman articulated a view of ecosystems centred on energy fixation, storage, and flows that remains influential to this day. Like Tansley before him, Lindeman pointed out the difficulty and artificiality of separating organisms from their environment and promoted an ecosystem view of nature. Lindeman concluded that the ecosystem concept is fundamental to the study of **trophic dynamics,** which he defined as the transfer of energy from one part of an ecosystem to another.

Lindeman suggested grouping organisms within an ecosystem into trophic levels: primary producers, primary consumers, secondary consumers, tertiary consumers, and so forth. In this scheme, each trophic level feeds on the one immediately below it. Energy enters the ecosystem as primary producers engage in photosynthesis and convert solar energy into biomass. As energy is transferred from one trophic level to another, energy is lost due to limited assimilation, respiration by consumers, and heat production. As a result of these losses, the quantity of energy in an ecosystem decreases with each successive trophic level, forming a pyramid-shaped distribution of energy among trophic levels. Lindeman called these trophic pyramids "Eltonian pyramids," since Charles Elton (1927) was the first to propose that the distribution of energy among trophic levels is shaped like a pyramid.

Figure 19.21 shows the distribution of annual primary production among trophic levels in Cedar Bog Lake and in Lake Mendota, Wisconsin. Energy losses at each trophic level determine the trophic structure of these two ecosystems. As predicted by Elton, the distribution of energy across trophic levels in both lakes is shaped like a pyramid. As suggested at the beginning of this section, the number of trophic levels is limited in both lakes. Lake Mendota includes four trophic levels, while Cedar Bog Lake includes just three.

Following Lindeman's pioneering work, many other ecologists studied energy flow within ecosystems. One of the most comprehensive of these later studies focused on the Hubbard Brook Experimental Forest in New Hampshire.

Energy Flow in a Temperate Deciduous Forest

James Gosz and his colleagues (1978) studied energy flow in the Hubbard Brook Experimental Forest, which is managed for research by the U.S. Forest Service. They concentrated their efforts on a stream catchment called watershed 6, which was left undisturbed so it could serve as a control for experimental studies on other stream catchments. The energy flow in the Hubbard Brook Experimental Forest was quantified as kilocalories (kcal) per square meter per year. The results of the analysis are shown in figure 19.22.

First let's examine the distribution of organic matter among the major components of the Hubbard Brook ecosystem. The largest single pool of energy in the forest, 122,442 kcal/m^2, occurred as dead organic matter. Most of the dead organic matter, 88,120 kcal/m^2, was organic matter in the upper 36 cm of soil. The remainder, 34,322 kcal/m^2, occurred as plant litter on the forest floor. Total living-plant biomass amounted to 71,420 kcal/m^2, of which 59,696 kcal/m^2 was stored in above-ground biomass and 11,724 kcal/m^2 as below-ground biomass.

The total standing stock of energy occurring as dead organic matter and living plant biomass was 193,862 kcal/m^2. This estimate by Gosz and his colleagues dwarfs the energy stored in all

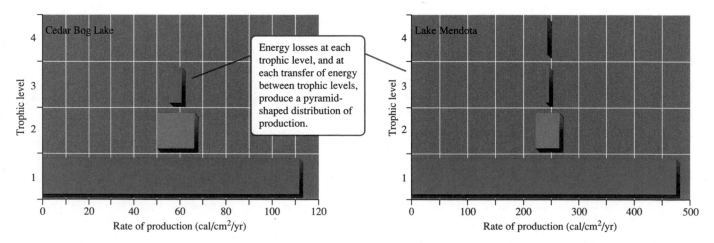

Figure 19.21   Annual production by trophic level in two lakes (data from Lindeman 1942).

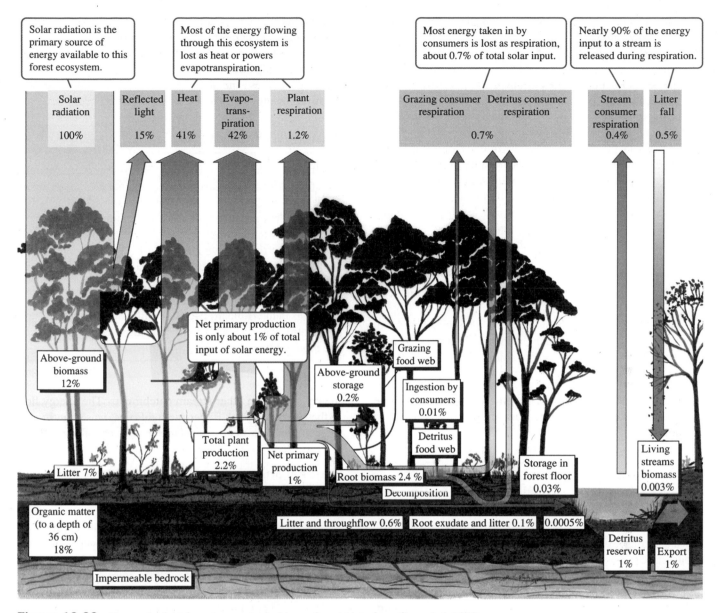

Figure 19.22 Energy budget for a temperate deciduous forest (data from Gosz et al. 1978).

other portions of the ecosystem. For instance, the energetic content of a caterpillar population during a severe population outbreak amounted to only 160 kcal/m². However, even this amount far exceeds the total energetic content of all vertebrate biomass. The researchers estimated that the total energetic content of the most numerous vertebrates, including chipmunks, mice, shrews, salamanders, and birds, amounted to less than 1 kcal/m². In other words, in an ecosystem, animals make up an amazingly small fraction of the biomass. The study of energy movement in ecosystems is often the same as the study of the plants. Now that we have inventoried the major standing stocks of energy, let's look at energy flow through the Hubbard Brook Forest.

The main source of energy for the ecosystem is solar radiation. The total input of solar energy to the study area during the growing season was estimated to be 480,000 kcal/m² (expressed as 100% in fig. 19.22). Of this total energy input, 15% was reflected, 41% was converted to heat, and 42% was absorbed

during evapotranspiration. About 2.2% of the solar input was fixed by plants as gross primary production. Plant respiration accounted for 1.2%, leaving about 1% as net primary production. In other words, only about 1% of the solar input to the Hubbard Brook ecosystem was available to the herbivores and detritivores that made up the second trophic level.

About 1,199 kcal/m² of net primary production in the Hubbard Brook Forest went into plant growth. Herbivores consumed only about 41 kcal/m², approximately 1% of net primary production. Most of the energy available to consumers, approximately 3,037 kcal/m², occurred as surface litter fall. About 150 kcal/m² of the litter fall was stored as organic matter on the forest floor. The remainder was used by consumers. An additional source of detritus, amounting to 437 kcal/m², occurred below ground as root exudate and litter. Most of the energy consumed by grazers and detritivores, approximately 3,353 kcal/m², was lost as consumer respiration.

Now let's go back to the concept that started this section: Energy losses limit the number of trophic levels in ecosystems. The energy budget carefully constructed by Gosz and his colleagues gives us a basis for understanding this concept. Net primary production in the Hubbard Brook Forest ecosystem was less than 1% of the input of solar energy. In other words, over 99% of the solar energy available to the Hubbard Brook was unavailable for use by a second trophic level. Of the net primary production available to consumers, approximately 96% is lost as consumer respiration. This leaves very little for a third trophic level. It is such losses with each transfer of energy in a food chain that limit the number of trophic levels. As these losses between trophic levels accumulate, eventually there is insufficient energy left over to support a viable population at a higher trophic level.

The top predator on the African savanna is the lion. We might imagine predators fierce enough to prey on lions, but the energetics of energy conversion and transfer within ecosystems would preclude such a predator.

We can see from the studies of Gosz and his colleagues and others that ecosystems depend upon an outside input of energy.

Ecosystems store some energy in the form of dead organic matter and biomass, but most energy flows through. As we shall see in chapter 20, however, ecosystems recycle elements such as nitrogen and sulphur. In the Ecological Tools section we review how forms of these and other elements can be used as a tool to determine the trophic structure of ecosystems.

Concept 19.4 Review

1. If we assume that the Hubbard Brook forest ecosystem studied by James Gosz and colleagues is subject to a trophic cascade (top-down control), can we explain why herbivores consume such a small amount of plant net primary production?
2. What are the relative amounts of net primary production consumed by herbivores versus plant litter-feeders (detritivores) living on the forest floor?
3. Could the relative low rates of consumption by herbivores in the Hubbard Brook be influenced by bottom-up controls by plants? If so, what might be the nature of those controls?

Ecological Tools

Using Stable Isotope Analysis to Trace Energy Flow Through Ecosystems

How do ecologists study the flow of energy through ecosystems? First, they identify the organisms that make up the biological part of the ecosystem. Then, they determine the feeding habits of consumers. They may identify consumers down to species or assign them broader taxonomic categories. Next, they assign organisms to trophic levels and determine (1) the biomass of each trophic level, (2) the rate of energy or food intake by each trophic level, (3) the rate of energy assimilation, (4) the rate of respiration, and (5) rates of loss of energy to predators, parasites, etc. Finally, ecologists combine their information on individual trophic levels to construct a trophic pyramid such as that constructed by Lindeman (see fig.19.21) or an energy flow diagram such as that by Gosz and his colleagues (see fig. 19.22).

One of the fundamental steps in constructing a trophic pyramid or energy flow diagram is assigning organisms to trophic levels. While this task may sound easy, for most organisms, it is not. Most assignments are based on studies of feeding habits. If food items are easily identified and feeding habits are well studied and do not change significantly over time or from place to place, you may accurately identify feeding relations and assign organisms to trophic levels. However, if feeding habits are variable or if food items are difficult to identify, it may be difficult to assign organisms accurately to a particular trophic level. One of the most useful tools for making such assignments is stable isotope analysis (see chapter 6).

Seasonal Shifts in the Diet of the Arctic Fox

In this book we have presented food webs as static descriptions of the natural communities. However, life isn't a cartoon, and the composition of an individual's diet varies greatly over the course of a year. The reasons for this are obvious: different food items become available at different times of year due to phenological patterns in plant growth, animal migration, and activity. Stable isotopes can serve as a useful tool for deciphering the actual complexity of food webs.

James Roth has been studying the feeding behaviour of the animals near Churchill, Manitoba, for nearly a decade. Arctic foxes, *Alopex lagopus*, are a common carnivore of the area with a potentially broad diet. The foxes are known to eat lemmings, bird eggs, and birds. However, some of these food items are available primarily during the summer, while the foxes are year-round residents of the north (chapter 5). Additionally, lemmings have notoriously large population booms and busts, and they will not always be available in high numbers as a food item. It has been hypothesized that in the winter the foxes can walk along the sea ice and scavenge seal meat from polar bear kill sites. Roth used a stable isotope approach to study seasonal shifts in the diets of the foxes (Roth 2002).

To measure seasonal shifts in diet, Roth needed samples from the foxes that would reflect short-term, rather than long-term diet composition. In other words, he needed some animal tissue that grows rapidly. The Arctic foxes molt twice each year, and thus Roth was able to make the reasonable assumption that the dark brown hair produced at the start of spring would have the isotopic composition of their winter food, and the white hair produced at the start of winter would reflect their summer diet. Roth then took samples of fox hair over three years, as well as samples of the eggs of Canada geese, caribou, lemmings, and other possible food sources. Roth measured $^{13}C/^{12}C$ ratios for all samples.

There was a substantial shift in $^{13}C/^{12}C$ ratios across seasons (fig. 19.23), with substantially more ^{13}C in the winter diet than summer diet. This shift is consistent with a shift towards more marine-based food items in winter, as these animals tend to be enriched in ^{13}C relative to terrestrial animals. In a mark-recapture study, Roth found that the lemming population went from approximately 13 animals per ha in 1994 to less than 4 animals per ha in 1995, 1996, 1997. Using a variety of analytical methods, Roth was able to estimate that when lemmings were abundant, marine food sources represented only about 17% of the foxes' diet. Immediately after the lemming population crash, marine food, such as leftovers scavenged from polar bear kills, represented over 40% of the foxes' diet.

This study is a great example of how stable isotopes allow ecologists to study complex phenomena, such as the relative contribution of different food items to the diet of animals. The results also have important implications for the future of the arctic fox. Due to rapid global warming in the North (chapter 23), sea ice is forming later and breaking up earlier than it has over the last several decades. The impacts of this will most immediately be felt by polar bear populations, as their hunting grounds become less available. If this change results in decreasing number of polar bears, and polar bear kill sites, it could mean a great reduction in a winter food source for the arctic fox.

Using Stable Isotopes to Identify Sources of Energy in a Salt Marsh

The main energy source in a salt marsh in eastern North America is primary production by the salt marsh grass *Spartina*, most of which is consumed as detritus. The detritus of *Spartina* is carried into tidal creeks at high tide, where it is consumed by a variety of organisms, including crabs, oysters, and mussels. However, *Spartina* is not the only potential source of food for these organisms. The waters of the salt marsh also contain organic matter from upland plants and carry phytoplankton. How much might these other food sources contribute to energy flow through the salt marsh ecosystem?

Bruce Peterson, Robert Howarth, and Robert Garritt (1985) used stable isotopes to determine the relative contributions of *Spartina*, phytoplankton, and upland plants to the nutrition of the ribbed mussel, *Geukinsia demissa*, a dominant filter-feeding species in New England salt marshes. The researchers pointed out that determining the trophic structure of salt marshes is difficult because detritus from different sources is difficult to identify visually, because there are several potential sources of detritus, and because organisms may frequently change their feeding habits. It is difficult to accurately quantify the relative contributions of alternative energy sources to a species like *Geukinsia* using traditional methods. Those methods will also probably miss transient dietary switches entirely.

As a solution for these problems, Peterson and his colleagues used the ratios of stable isotopes of carbon, nitrogen, and sulphur to assess the relative contributions of alternative food sources to the nutrition of the mussel. They used the stable

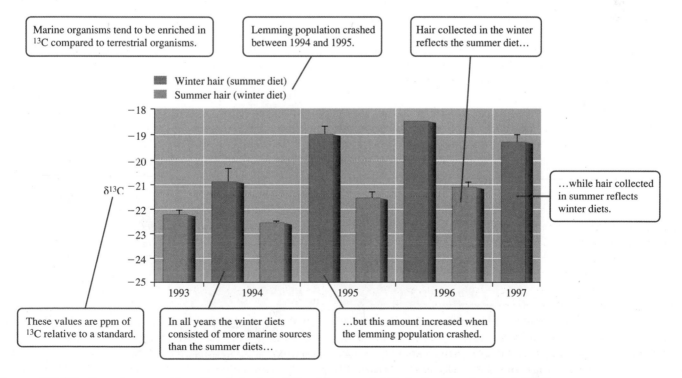

Figure 19.23   Isotopic composition of arctic fox hair shifts with seasonal shifts in diet (data from Roth 2002).

isotopes of these three elements because their ratios are different in phytoplankton, upland C_3 plants (see chapter 7), and *Spartina*, a C_4 grass (fig. 19.24). Upland plants, with a $\delta^{13}C = -28.6\ ^0/_{00}$, are the most depleted of ^{13}C, while *Spartina*, with a $\delta^{13}C = -13.1\ ^0/_{00}$, is the least depleted. Stable isotopes of sulphur and nitrogen are also distributed differently among these potential energy sources. For instance, *Spartina*, with a $\delta^{34}S = -2.4\ ^0/_{00}$, has the lowest relative concentration of ^{34}S, while plankton, with a $\delta^{34}S = +18.8\ ^0/_{00}$, has the highest concentration of ^{34}S.

Because of these differences in isotopic concentrations, the researchers were able to identify the relative contributions of potential food sources to the diet of the mussel (fig. 19.25). Their analyses showed that *Geukinsia* gets most of its energy from plankton and *Spartina* but that the relative contributions of these two food sources depends upon location. In the interior of the marsh, the mussel feeds mainly on *Spartina*, while near the mouth of the marsh it depends mainly on plankton. This is an example of how analyses of stable isotopes can provide us with a window to the otherwise hidden biology of species.

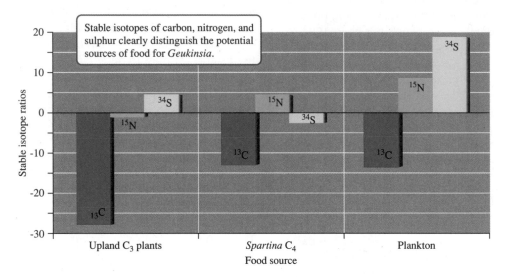

Figure 19.24   Isotopic content of potential food sources for the ribbed mussel, *Geukinsia demissa*, in a New England salt marsh (data from Peterson, Howarth, and Garritt 1985).

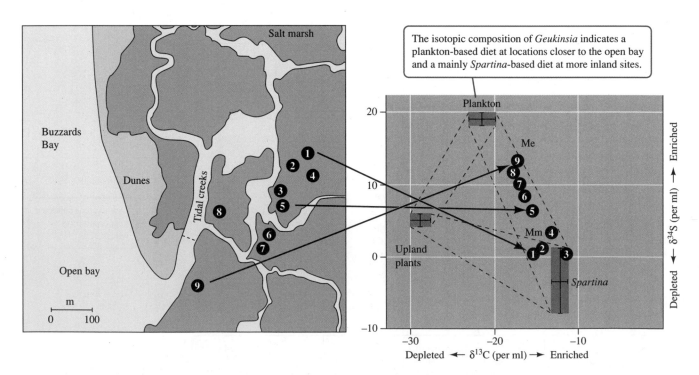

Figure 19.25   Variation in isotopic composition of ribbed mussels, *Geukinsia demissa*, by distance inland in a New England salt marsh (data from Peterson, Howarth, and Garritt 1985).

Summary

We can view a forest, a stream, or an ocean as a system that absorbs, transforms, and stores energy. In this view, physical, chemical, and biological structures and processes are inseparable. When we look at natural systems in this way we view them as ecosystems. An *ecosystem* is a biological community plus all of the abiotic factors influencing that community.

Primary production, the fixation of energy by autotrophs, is one of the most important ecosystem processes. The rate of primary production is the amount of energy fixed over some interval of time. Gross primary production is the total amount of energy fixed by all the autotrophs in the ecosystem. Net primary production is the amount of energy left over after autotrophs have met their own energetic needs.

Terrestrial primary production is generally limited by temperature and moisture. The variables most highly correlated with variation in terrestrial primary production are temperature and moisture. Highest rates of terrestrial primary production occur under warm, moist conditions. Temperature and moisture conditions can be combined in a single measure called annual actual evapotranspiration, or AET, which is the total amount of water that evaporates and transpires off a landscape during the course of a year. Annual AET is positively correlated with net primary production in terrestrial ecosystems. However, significant variation in terrestrial primary production results from differences in soil fertility.

Aquatic primary production is generally limited by nutrient availability. One of the best documented patterns in the biosphere is the positive relationship between nutrient availability and rate of primary production in aquatic ecosystems. Phosphorus concentration usually limits rates of primary production in freshwater ecosystems, while nitrogen concentration usually limits rates of marine primary production.

A variety of species can influence rates of primary production in aquatic and terrestrial ecosystems. Trophic cascades can occur in terrestrial and aquatic ecosystems. Piscivorous fish can indirectly reduce rates of primary production in lakes by reducing the density of plankton-feeding fish, leading to increased densities of herbivorous zooplankton, and decreased densities of phytoplankton. Intense grazing in the Serengeti can lead to compensatory growth by plants. Species diversity of plants or mycorrhizal fungi can enhance primary productivity. These effects may also cascade up the food chain, increasing herbivore biomass.

Energy losses limit the number of trophic levels in ecosystems. Ecosystem ecologists have simplified the trophic structure of ecosystems by arranging species into trophic levels based upon the predominant source of their nutrition. A trophic level is determined by the number of transfers of energy from primary producers to that level. As energy is transferred from one trophic level to another, energy is lost due to limited assimilation, respiration by consumers, and heat production. As a result of these losses, the quantity of energy in an ecosystem decreases with each successive trophic level, forming a pyramid-shaped distribution of energy among trophic levels. As losses between trophic levels accumulate, eventually there is insufficient energy to support a viable population at a higher trophic level.

Stable isotope analysis can be used to trace the flow of energy through ecosystems. The ratios of different stable isotopes of important elements such as nitrogen and carbon are generally different in different parts of ecosystems. As a consequence, ecologists can use isotopic ratios to study the trophic structure and energy flow through ecosystems.

Review Questions

1. Population, community, and ecosystem ecologists study structure and process. However, they focus on different natural characteristics. Contrast the important structures and processes in a forest from the perspectives of population, community, and ecosystem ecologists.

2. M. Huston (1994b) pointed out that the well-documented pattern of increasing annual primary production from the poles to the equator is strongly influenced by the longer growing season at low latitudes. The following data are from table 14.10 in Huston. The data cited by Huston are from Whittaker and Likens (1975).

Forest Type	Annual NPP (t/ha/yr)	Length of Growing Season (months)	Monthly NPP (t/ha/mo)
Boreal forest	8	3	2.7
Temperate forest	13	6	?
Tropical forest	20	12	?

Complete the missing data to compare the *monthly* production of boreal, temperate, and tropical forests. How does this short-term perspective of primary production in high-, middle-, and low-latitude forests compare to an annual perspective? How does the short-term perspective change our perception of tropical versus high-latitude forests?

3. Many migratory birds spend approximately half the year in temperate forests during the warm breeding season and the other half of the year in tropical forest. Given the analyses you made in question 2, which forest appears to be more productive from the perspective of these migratory birds?

4. Turkington and colleagues (1998) found that although forests increased in primary productivity in response to fertilization, there was substantial variation among species. What do these differences in response say about using the responses of individual species to predict responses at the ecosystem level? What about the reverse—can we predict the responses of individual species or growth forms from ecosystem-level responses?

5. Compare the pictures of trophic structure that emerged from our discussions of food webs in chapter 18 with those in chapter 19. What are the strengths of each perspective? What are their limitations?

6. Some researchers do not believe the sampling effect is a meaningful benefit of diversity. Do you? Explain.

7. Suppose you are studying a community of small mammals that lives on the boundary between a riverside forest and a semidesert grassland. One of your concerns is to discover the relative contributions of the grassland and the forest to the nutrition of small mammals living between the two ecosystems. Design a research program to find out.

8. Most of the energy that flows through a forest ecosystem flows through detritus-based food chains, and the detritus consists mainly of dead plant tissues (e.g., leaves and wood). In contrast, most of the energy flowing through a pelagic marine or freshwater ecosystem flows through grazing food chains with phytoplankton constituting the major primary producers. Ecologists have determined that on average, a calorie or joule of energy takes only several days to pass through the pelagic ecosystem but a quarter of a century to pass through the forest ecosystem. Explain.

9. In chapter 18, we examined the influences of keystone species on the structure of communities. In chapter 19 we reviewed trophic cascades. Discuss the similarities and differences between these two concepts. Compare the measurements and methods of ecologists studying keystone species versus those studying trophic cascades.

10. Are top-down or bottom-up processes more important in controlling primary production? Design an experiment to test your hypothesis.

Suggested Readings

Carpenter, S. R. and J. F. Kitchell. 1993. *The Trophic Cascade in Lakes*. Cambridge, England: Cambridge University Press.

An engaging synthesis of the authors' work on trophic cascades. The book outlines one of the pioneering large-scale experiments in ecology.

Codispoti, L. A. 1997. The limits to growth. *Nature* 387:237–38.

Falkowski, P. G. 1997. Evolution of the nitrogen cycle and its influence on the biological sequestration of CO_2 in the ocean. *Nature* 387:272–75.

This pair of papers reviews the evidence for nitrogen, phosphorus, and iron limitation of marine primary production on short and long timescales.

Meserve, P. L., D. A. Kelt, W. B. Milstead, and J. R. Gutiérrez. 2003. Thirteen years of shifting top-down and bottom-up control. *BioScience* 53:633–46.

This long-term study of a terrestrial ecosystem in Chile documents a shifting influence of top-down and bottom-up control of community structure that depends on large-scale climate dynamics.

Polis, G. A., A. L. W. Sears, G. R. Huxel, D. R. Strong, and J. Maron. 2000. When is a trophic cascade a trophic cascade? *Trends in Ecology & Evolution* 15:473–75.

This is a thought-provoking call for consistency in the way ecologists use the term "trophic cascade."

Schmitz, O. J., P. A. Hamback, and A. P. Beckerman. 2000. Trophic cascades in terrestrial systems: a review of the effects of carnivore removals on plants. *American Naturalist* 155:141–53.

A review that supports the applicability of the trophic cascade hypothesis to terrestrial as well as aquatic systems.

Sinclair, A. R. E., S. Mduma, and J. S. Brashares. 2003. Patterns of predation in a diverse predator-prey system. *Nature* 425:288–90.

Terborgh, J., K. Feeley, M. Silman, P. Nuñez, and B. Balukjian. 2006. Vegetation dynamics of predator-free land-bridge islands. *Journal of Ecology* 94:253–63.

These two studies take advantage of exceptional situations to investigate the potential for trophic cascades in two tropical ecosystems. The first shows the potential for a trophic cascade on the Serengeti by demonstrating that predators control the abundance of several species of mammalian herbivores, while the second documents a trophic cascade in a South American tropical forest.

Knight, T. M, M. W. McCoy, J. M. Chase, K. A. McCoy, and R. D. Holt. 2005. Trophic cascades across ecosystems. *Nature*. 437:880–83.

A fascinating study showing how predation on larval dragonflies can have a cascade of effects, eventually altering plant pollination.

Chapter 20

Nutrient Cycling and Retention

Outline

xchanges of nutrients between organisms and their environment is one of the essential aspects of ecosystem function. A diatom living in the surface waters of a lake absorbs an ion of phosphate from the surrounding water. It incorporates the phosphate into some of its DNA as it replicates its chromosomes during cell division. A few hours later, one of the diatom's daughter cells is eaten by a cladoceran, an algae-feeding member of the zooplankton. The cladoceran incorporates the phosphate into a molecule of ATP. The cladoceran lives two days more and then is eaten by a planktivorous minnow. Within the minnow, the phosphate is combined with a lipid to form a phospholipid molecule in the cell membrane of one of the minnow's neural cells. A few weeks later, the minnow is eaten by a northern pike and the phosphate is incorporated into part of the pike's skeleton. During the following winter, the pike dies and its tissues are attacked by bacteria and fungi that gradually decompose the pike, including its skeleton. During decomposition, the phosphate is dissolved in the surrounding water. The following spring the very same ion of phosphate is taken up by another diatom, completing its cycle through the lake ecosystem (fig. 20.1).

In chapter 19, we saw that energy makes a one-way trip through ecosystems. In contrast, elements such as phosphorus (P), carbon (C), nitrogen (N), potassium (K), and iron (Fe) are used over and over. Elements that are required for the development, maintenance, and reproduction of organisms are called *nutrients*. Ecologists refer to the use, transformation, movement, and reuse of nutrients in ecosystems as **nutrient cycling.** Because of the physiological importance of nutrients, their relative scarcity, and their influence on rates of primary production, nutrient cycling is one of the most significant ecosystem processes studied by ecologists. Three nutrient cycles play especially prominent roles: the *phosphorus cycle,* the *nitrogen cycle,* and the *carbon cycle.* In the next few pages we review the major features of each of these cycles.

The Phosphorus Cycle

Phosphorus is essential to the energetics, genetics, and structure of living systems. For instance, phosphorus forms part of the ATP, RNA, DNA, and phospholipid molecules. While of great biological importance, phosphorus is not very abundant in the biosphere. Consequently, phosphorus cycling has received a great deal of attention from ecosystem ecologists.

In contrast to carbon and nitrogen, the global phosphorus cycle does not include a substantial atmospheric pool (fig. 20.2). The largest quantities of phosphorus occur in mineral deposits and marine sediments. Sedimentary rocks that are especially rich in phosphorus are mined for fertilizer and applied to agricultural soils. Soil may contain substantial quantities of phosphorus. However, much of the phosphorus in soils occurs in chemical forms not directly available to plants.

Phosphorus is slowly released to terrestrial and aquatic ecosystems through the weathering of rocks. As phosphorus is released from mineral deposits, it is absorbed by plants and recycled within ecosystems. However, much phosphorus is washed into rivers and eventually finds its way to the oceans, where it will remain in dissolved form until eventually finding its way to the ocean sediments. Ocean sediments will be eventually transformed into phosphate-bearing sedimentary rocks that through geological uplift can form new land. William Schlesinger (1991) points out that the phosphorus released by the weathering of sedimentary rocks has made at least one passage through the global phosphorus cycle.

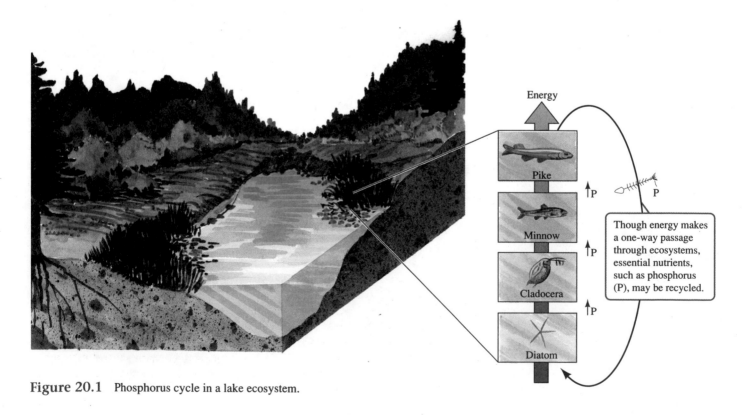

Figure 20.1   Phosphorus cycle in a lake ecosystem.

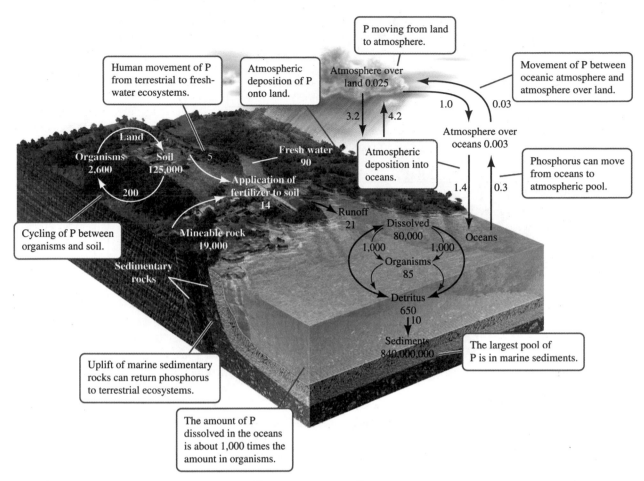

Figure 20.2 The phosphorus cycle. Numbers are 10^{12} g P or fluxes as 10^{12} g P per year (data from Schlesinger 1991, after Richey 1983, Meybeck 1982, Graham and Duce 1979).

The Nitrogen Cycle

Nitrogen is important to the structure and functioning of organisms. It forms part of key biomolecules such as amino acids, nucleic acids, and the porphyrin rings of chlorophyll and hemoglobin. In addition, as we saw in chapter 19, nitrogen supplies may limit rates of primary production in marine and terrestrial environments. Because of its importance and relative scarcity, nitrogen has drawn a great deal of attention from ecosystem ecologists.

Two critical aspects of the nitrogen cycle are **mineralization** and **immobilization**. Mineralization is the conversion of organic forms of nitrogen (e.g., proteins) into mineral forms (e.g., ammonia and nitrate). Immobilization is the reverse process, the conversion of mineral forms of nitrogen into organic forms. Because mineral nitrogen is often limiting plant growth, the balance between these processes can greatly alter productivity. As you will see next, microbes play a central role in nitrogen cycling.

Like the carbon cycle, the nitrogen cycle also includes a major atmospheric pool in the form of molecular nitrogen, N_2 (fig. 20.3). However, only a few organisms can use this atmospheric supply of molecular nitrogen directly. These organisms, called nitrogen fixers, include (1) the cyanobacteria, or blue-green algae, of freshwater, marine, and soil environments,

(2) free-living soil bacteria, (3) bacteria associated with the roots of leguminous plants, and (4) actinomycetes bacteria, associated with the roots of alders, *Alnus,* and several other species of woody plants.

Because of the strong triple bonds between the two nitrogen atoms in the N_2 molecule, nitrogen fixation is an energy-demanding process. During nitrogen fixation, N_2 is reduced to ammonia, NH_3. Nitrogen fixation takes place under aerobic conditions in terrestrial and aquatic environments, where nitrogen-fixing species oxidize sugars to obtain the required energy. Nitrogen fixation also occurs as a physical process associated with the high pressures and energy generated by lightning. Ecologists propose that all of the nitrogen cycling within ecosystems ultimately entered these cycles through nitrogen fixation by organisms or lightning. There is a relatively large pool of nitrogen cycled in the biosphere but only a small entryway through nitrogen fixation.

Once nitrogen is fixed by nitrogen-fixing organisms, it becomes available to other organisms within an ecosystem. Upon the death of an organism, the nitrogen in its tissues can be released by fungi and bacteria involved in the decomposition process. These fungi and bacteria release nitrogen as ammonium, NH_4^+, a process called **ammonification**. Ammonium may be converted to nitrate, NO_3^-, by other bacteria in a

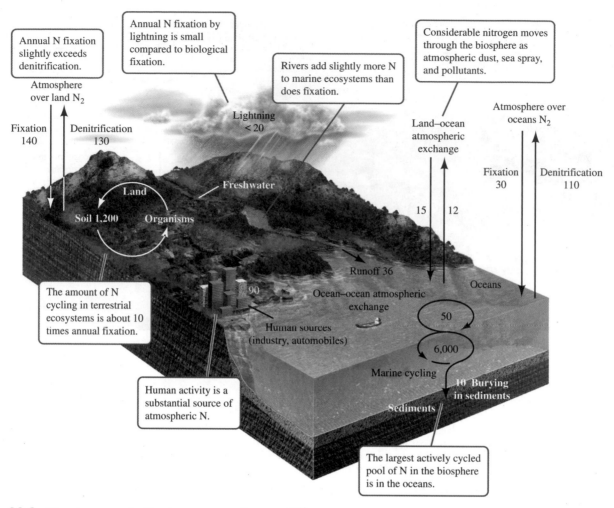

Figure 20.3 The nitrogen cycle. Numbers represent fluxes as 10^{12} g N per year (data from Schlesinger 1991, after Söderlund and Rosswall 1982).

process called **nitrification**. Ammonium and nitrate can be used directly by some bacteria, fungi, or plants. The nitrogen in dead organic matter can also be used directly by some mycorrhizal fungi, which can be passed on to plants. The nitrogen in bacterial, fungal, and plant biomass may pass on to populations of animal consumers or back to the pool of dead organic matter, where it will be recycled again.

Nitrogen may exit the organic matter pool of an ecosystem through denitrification. **Denitrification** is an energy-yielding process that occurs under anaerobic conditions and converts nitrate to molecular nitrogen, N_2. The molecular nitrogen produced by denitrifying bacteria moves into the atmosphere and can only reenter the organic matter pool through nitrogen fixation. The mean residence time of fixed nitrogen in the biosphere is about 625 years. Ecologists estimate that the mean residence time of phosphorus in the biosphere is on the order of thousands of years.

The Carbon Cycle

Carbon is an essential part of all organic molecules, and, as constituents of the atmosphere, carbon compounds such as carbon dioxide, CO_2, and methane, CH_4, substantially influ-

ence global climate. This connection between atmospheric carbon and climate has drawn all nations of the planet into discussions of the ecology of carbon cycling.

Carbon moves between organisms and the atmosphere as a consequence of two reciprocal biological processes: photosynthesis and respiration (fig. 20.4). Photosynthesis removes CO_2 from the atmosphere, while respiration by primary producers and consumers, including decomposers, returns carbon to the atmosphere in the form of CO_2. In aquatic ecosystems, CO_2 must first dissolve in water before being used by aquatic primary producers. Once dissolved in water, CO_2 enters a chemical equilibrium with bicarbonate, HCO_3^-, and carbonate, CO_3^-. Carbonate may precipitate out of solution as calcium carbonate and may be buried in ocean sediments.

While some carbon cycles rapidly between organisms and the atmosphere, some remains sequestered in relatively unavailable forms for long periods of time. Carbon in soils, peat, fossil fuels, and carbonate rock would generally take a long time to return to the atmosphere. However, fossil fuels have become a major source of atmospheric CO_2 as humans have tapped into fossil fuel supplies to provide energy.

Ecosystem ecologists study the factors controlling the movement, storage, and conservation of nutrients within

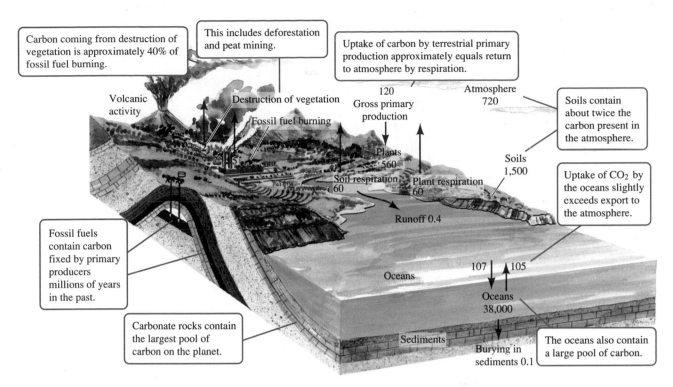

Figure 20.4 The carbon cycle. Numbers are storage as 10^{15} g or fluxes as 10^{15} g per year (data from Schlesinger 1991).

ecosystems. You can see broad outlines of these processes in figures 20.2, 20.3, and 20.4. However, much remains to be learned, especially concerning the factors controlling rates of nutrient exchange within and between ecosystems. Nutrient exchange is substantially affected by the process of decomposition, which we will discuss below.

Concepts

20.1 Decomposition rate is influenced by temperature, moisture, and chemical composition of litter and the environment.

20.2 Plants and animals can modify the distribution and cycling of nutrients in ecosystems.

20.3 Disturbance increases nutrient loss from ecosystems.

20.1   Rates of Decomposition

Decomposition rate is influenced by temperature, moisture, and chemical composition of litter and the environment. The rate at which nutrients, such as nitrogen and phosphorus, are made available to the primary producers of terrestrial ecosystems is determined largely by the rate at which nutrient supplies are converted from organic to inorganic forms (mineralization). Mineralization takes place principally during **decomposition,** which is the breakdown of organic matter accompanied by the release of carbon dioxide. Consequently, ecologists consider decomposition a key ecosystem process.

The rate of decomposition in ecosystems is influenced by temperature, moisture, and the chemical composition of both plant litter and the environment. The chemical characteristics of plant litter that influence decomposition rates include nitrogen concentration, phosphorus concentration, carbon:nitrogen ratio, and lignin content. Ecologists have studied how several of these variables affect rates of leaf decomposition in Mediterranean ecosystems.

Decomposition in Two Mediterranean Woodland Ecosystems

Antonio Gallardo and José Merino (1993) studied how chemical and physical factors affect rates of decomposition of leaf litter in two Mediterranean woodland ecosystems in southwestern Spain. The mean annual temperature at the two sites differs by only 0.5°C, from 16.7°C at Doñana versus 16.2°C at Monte La Sauceda. Both study sites experience Mediterranean climates with wet winters and dry summers (see chapter 2). However, they differ significantly in average annual rainfall. While Doñana Biological Reserve receives about 500 mm of rain annually, Monte La Sauceda receives about 1,600 mm. This difference in precipitation results from a difference in elevation. The study site at the Doñana Biological Reserve is located at approximately 20 m elevation, while the elevation at La Sauceda is 432 m. These two sites were ideally suited to study the effects of moisture on rates of decomposition.

Gallardo and Merino also explored the effects of litter chemistry on decomposition by including leaves from nine species of native trees and shrubs that differed significantly in chemical composition. Chemical differences among leaves included differences in concentrations of tannins, lignin, nitrogen, and

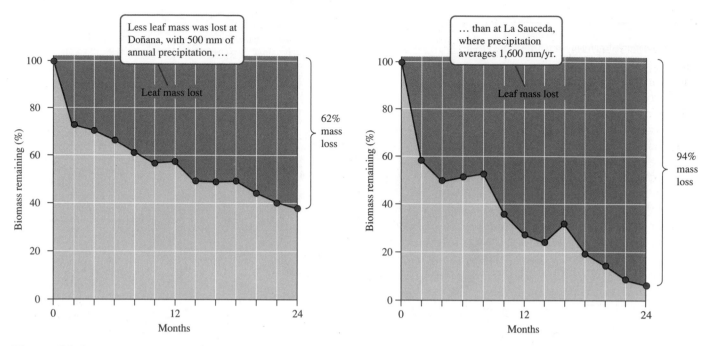

Figure 20.5 Decomposition of *Fraxinus angustifolia* leaves at wetter and drier sites (data from Gallardo and Merino 1993).

phosphorus. You may remember from chapter 2 that many of the native plants from areas with a Mediterranean climate produce tough or sclerophylous leaves. Gallardo and Merino also explored the influence of leaf toughness on decomposition rate.

Approximately 2 g of air-dried leaves from each of the study species was put into several nylon mesh "litter bags" and placed at the Doñana Biological Reserve and at Monte La Sauceda. The litter bags had a mesh size of 1 mm—small enough to reduce the loss of small leaves, yet large enough to permit aerobic microbial activity and entry of small soil invertebrates. Every two months, for two years Gallardo and Merino retrieved litter bags from each study site.

In the laboratory, the researchers measured the mass of leaf tissue remaining in each of 6 to 10 replicate litter bags for each leaf species. Figure 20.5 shows that the amount of leaf mass lost by ash leaves, *Fraxinus angustifolia,* was much higher at Monte La Sauceda. This higher decomposition rate probably reflects the higher precipitation at that site.

Though all types of leaves decomposed faster at Monte La Sauceda, differences in decomposition rates among leaf species were similar at the two sites. For instance, the leaves of ash, *Fraxinus,* showed the greatest mass loss at both study sites, while the oak, *Quercus lusitanica,* showed the lowest mass loss at both study sites. Differences in mass loss by the nine plant species reflected differences in the physical and chemical characteristics of their leaves. Gallardo and Merino found that the best predictor of mass loss at the Doñana site was the ratio of toughness to nitrogen content, toughness/%N, and that mass loss was a power function of this ratio:

$$mass = 545[toughness/N]^{-0.38}$$

This is the equation for the line shown in figure 20.6. This equation indicates that tougher leaves with lower concentrations of nitrogen decomposed at a lower rate.

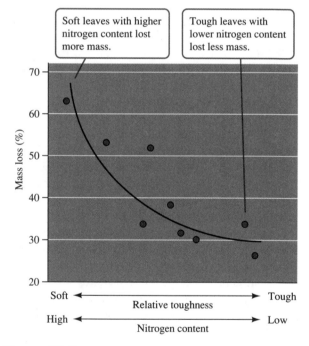

Figure 20.6 Influence of leaf toughness and nitrogen content on decomposition (data from Gallardo and Merino 1993).

The greater mass losses at Monte La Sauceda demonstrate a positive influence of moisture on rates of decomposition, while differences in decomposition rates among leaf species show the influences of chemical composition on decomposition. Even toughness, which is a physical property, is a consequence of chemical composition, especially the concentration of lignin. As we will see in the next example, the ratio of lignin concentration to nitrogen content in leaves is also highly correlated with decomposition rates in temperate forest ecosystems.

Decomposition in Forest Ecosystems

Jerry Melillo, John Aber, and John Muratore (1982) used litter bags to study leaf decomposition in a temperate forest in New Hampshire. Their study species were beech, *Fagus grandifolia;* sugar maple, *Acer saccharum;* paper birch, *Betula papyrifera;* red maple, *Acer rubrum;* white ash, *Fraxinus americana;* and pin cherry, *Prunus pennsylvanica*. They also compared their results with decomposition of leaves from white pine, chestnut oak, white oak, red maple, and flowering dogwood in a temperate forest in North Carolina.

In both the New Hampshire and North Carolina forests, the researchers found a negative correlation between the leaf mass remaining after one year of decomposition and the ratio of lignin to nitrogen concentrations in leaves, % lignin:% N. In other words, leaves with higher lignin:nitrogen ratios lost less mass during the year-long study. As you can see in figure 20.7, the amount of leaf mass remaining was lower at the North Carolina site than at the New Hampshire site. What factors were responsible for these higher rates of decomposition at the North Carolina site? Melillo and his colleagues suggested that higher nitrogen availability in the soils at the North Carolina site may contribute to the higher rates of decomposition observed there. However, higher temperatures at the North Carolina site may also contribute to higher decomposition rates.

Studies in both temperate and Mediterranean regions suggest that rates of decomposition are positively correlated with temperature and moisture. Can we combine these two factors into one? In chapter 19, we reviewed how ecologists studying the effect of climate on terrestrial primary production combined temperature and precipitation into a single measure called actual evapotranspiration, or AET. Vernon Meentemeyer (1978) analyzed the relationship between AET and decomposition and found a significant positive relationship.

If decomposition rates increase with increased evapotranspiration, how would you expect rates of decomposition in tropical and temperate ecosystems to compare? As you probably predicted, rates of decomposition are generally higher in tropical ecosystems. The average annual mass loss in tropical forests shown in figure 20.8 is 120%, or three times the average rate measured in temperate forests. These higher rates probably reflect the effects of higher AET in tropical forests and indicate complete decomposition in less than a year.

Soil nutrient content has also been shown to have a strong positive effect on rates of nutrient cycling in tropical forests. Three forest ecologists, Masaaki Takyu, Shin-Ichiro Aiba, and Kanehiro Kitayama, took advantage of natural variation in nutrient content on different geologic formations and different topographic situations to explore the factors influencing tropical rain forest functioning in Borneo (Takyu, Aiba, and Kitayama 2003). Takyu, Aiba, and Kitayama established research sites on ridges, which tend to have soils with lower nutrient content, and lower slopes, where nutrient content is higher, on three different rock types. The younger Quaternary sedimentary rock in their study area was approximately 30,000 to 40,000 years old and soils developing on these rocks tended to have higher nutrient content compared to soils on the other rock

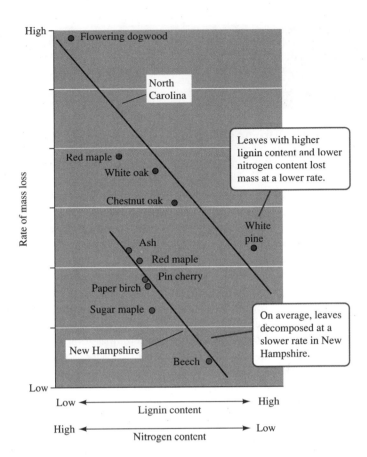

Figure 20.7   Influence of lignin and nitrogen content of leaves on decomposition (data from Melillo, Aber, and Muratore 1982).

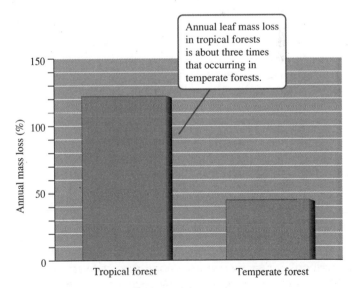

Figure 20.8   Decomposition in tropical and temperate forests (data from Anderson and Swift 1983).

types in the study, especially on lower slopes (fig. 20.9). Two older rock types were both approximately 40 million years old. One, a Tertiary sedimentary rock, supported soils that were considerably more fertile than the other, a Tertiary ultrabasic rock.

Ecology In Action

Why Decomposition Can Change the World

In chapters 19 and 20 we have provided a foundation for understanding the most basic ecosystem functions: primary production and nutrient cycling. We have discussed how these ecosystem services can be altered by human activities, by the abiotic environment, and by interactions within the ecosystems themselves. The question I am sure that many of you are asking is, so what? Although nutrient cycling is widely recognized by ecological researchers as one of the most critical aspects of ecosystem ecology, and that alteration of the rates of decomposition can have cascading effects altering a variety of other ecological interactions and patterns of diversity, this message is not often clearly transmitted to undergraduate students and the general population. Instead, decomposition is often viewed as among the dullest of subjects: studying things we can't see eating things that are dead. Why on earth would anyone want to devote their life to the study of the rate at which dead leaves and roots turn into CO_2 and other molecules? The answer, quite simply, is that changes in decomposition will more directly and indirectly alter processes humans care about (such as climate change and biomass production) than nearly any other ecological process you will find in this book. Certainly, studying bear and elk in a national park is a great life, and understanding the ecology of these organisms is a worthwhile endeavor. However, a 10% increase or decrease in predation rates or population sizes isn't going to have much global impact. A 10% increase in decomposition will.

The issue to which we are referring is the potential for altered rates of decomposition in the arctic and sub-arctic regions of the world. As we saw in chapters 2 and 3, northern regions are home to large expanses of peatlands and deep organic soils. Additionally, these regions represent a large portion of the land mass on the planet. These areas are also quite cold for much of the year, and in many areas deep layers of permafrost keep the layers of the ground frozen year round (fig. 20.10). What actually is frozen in the north? Is it simply clay, sand, and other layers of mineral soil? No. Although soil particles are certainly frozen, much of the permafrost contains organic matter—dead plants, animals, bacteria, and fungi. Put another way, the north is home to an enormous reservoir of frozen carbon, which could potentially be liberated into the atmosphere with a bit of liquid water and some warming. Let's try to put this into a larger perspective.

Between 20%–60% of the carbon stored in the soil in the world is found in the northern regions, including the boreal forest and arctic tundra. This volume of C is roughly 10–100

Figure 20.10   Permafrost is found in much of Northern Canada

times the amount of C released each year through deforestation and the burning of fossil fuels (Hobbie et al. 2000). Because of the magnitude of carbon stored in these soils, even a small change in decomposition rates has the potential to greatly alter the amount of carbon entering the atmosphere. As you certainly are aware, and as we will discuss in chapter 23, increases in the amount of CO_2 in the atmosphere can further enhance global temperatures. And so if decomposition rates in the arctic increase due to increased temperatures, this could increase atmospheric warming, which in turn would further enhance decomposition rates. In other words, the effects of temperature on decomposition rates are of global importance. But as you might imagine, the story isn't quite this simple.

What are the impacts of temperature on decomposition in the North? The answer to this question is complicated.

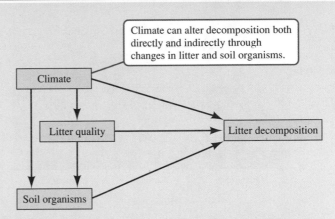

Figure 20.12 in diagram: "Climate can alter decomposition both directly and indirectly through changes in litter and soil organisms."

Climate → Litter quality → Litter decomposition; Climate → Soil organisms; Litter quality → Soil organisms → Litter decomposition; Climate → Litter decomposition

Figure 20.12 Climate, litter chemistry, and soil organisms will all interact to affect rates of decomposition (data from Aerts 2006).

Figure 20.11 Open-top chambers, such as the one pictured above in a polar desert on Ellesmere Island, are commonly used to study the effects of warming on ecological processes.

Although we often view the arctic as a homogeneous expanse of land, the reality is quite different. There are numerous community types in the north, including salt-marshes, dry grasslands, peatlands, and forested areas. The plants of different community types differ in tissue composition, and, importantly, in the effects of increased temperature on decomposition rates (Shaver et al. 2006). In general, it is thought that the wetter areas will show the greatest increase in decomposition in response to increased temperatures (Shaver et al. 2006; Aerts 2006). In contrast, it is thought that in the drier regions of the North it is soil moisture, rather than soil temperature, that limits decomposition rates. However, there is much variation among studies in the actual change in decomposition that has occurred, and some of this variation appears due to different types of experimental treatments being imposed (Aerts 2006; fig. 20.11). Some data even suggests that increased decomposition associated with warming may result in increased N-mineralization, essentially fertilizing parts of the arctic. This in turn may stimulate plant growth, resulting in increased, rather than decreased, storage of C in the soil! It is too early to say for certain what the direct effect of altered temperature will be on decomposition rates, though there is grave concern among many researchers.

A second complication is that even if increased temperature has a minimal effect on the rate of decomposition of the unfrozen parts of soil, it could greatly impact global carbon cycles if it causes a partial thawing of the permafrost. There already exists substantial evidence that this is occurring throughout much of the high Arctic (Serreze et al. 2000). As a consequence of this thawing, more organic matter is being decomposed, even though the rate of decomposition is constant. Again, the impact on global carbon cycles will depend upon whether the increase in nitrogen that also occurs is enough to stimulate plant growth.

The effects of temperature on decomposition are not limited to direct impacts due to increased temperatures. Instead, decomposition rates can be altered also through changes in litter composition and changes in the soil fauna (fig. 20.12). In particular, *Sphagnum* mosses have very low decomposition rates, and may even reduce decomposition of the surrounding vegetation (Aerts 2006). Although long-term studies are few in number, those that have occurred suggest that moss abundances decrease under warming (Aerts 2006), supporting the idea that warming can enhance decomposition through a shift in plant composition and litter quality. As we discussed in chapter 2, the functional ecology and description of soil fauna communities is very poorly understood, and this lack of information is even more pronounced in northern systems.

As you can see here, the functional consequences of warming on soil communities are unknown, and major discoveries wait for the next generation of ecologists. That is, of course, if they are willing to take on the challenge of working (with organisms they can't see that eat dead things), on questions whose answers could change the world.

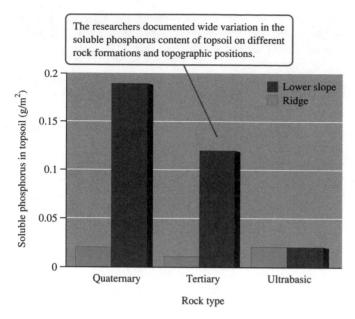

Figure 20.9 Concentrations of soluble phosphorus in topsoils formed on three rock types and at two topographic positions in Borneo (data from Takyu, Aiba, and Kitayama 2003).

Takyu, Aiba, and Kitayama's study clearly demonstrated the influence of soil fertility on rates of decomposition and nutrient cycling. Because all study sites were at approximately the same elevation and all were on south-facing aspects, the research team was able to isolate the influences of geologic conditions, especially soil characteristics. Takyu, Aiba, and Kitayama found higher rates of above-ground net primary production, higher rates of litter fall, and higher rates of decomposition on sites with higher concentrations of soluble phosphorus in topsoil, particularly on soils formed on the lower slopes of Quaternary and Tertiary rock formations. These results show that while climate may have a primary influence on decomposition rates, within climatic regions nutrient availability has an ecologically significant effect on decomposition and nutrient cycling rates.

In summary, decomposition in terrestrial ecosystems is influenced by moisture, temperature, soil fertility, and the chemical composition of litter, especially the concentrations of nitrogen and lignin. With the obvious exception of moisture, these factors also influence decomposition rates in aquatic ecosystems, which we examine next.

Decomposition in Aquatic Ecosystems

Jack Webster and Fred Benfield (1986) reviewed what was known about the decomposition of plant tissues in freshwater ecosystems. Among the most important variables that emerged from their analysis were leaf species, temperature, and nutrient concentrations in the aquatic ecosystem.

Webster and Benfield summarized the rates of leaf breakdown for 596 types of woody and nonwoody plants decaying in aquatic ecosystems and found that the average daily breakdown rate varied more than tenfold. As in terrestrial ecosystems, the chemical composition of litter significantly influences rates of decomposition in aquatic ecosystems.

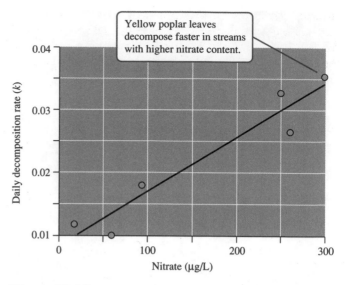

Figure 20.13 Stream nitrate and decomposition of *Liriodendron* leaves (data from Suberkropp and Chauvet 1995).

The nutrient content of stream water can also influence rates of decomposition. Keller Suberkropp and Eric Chauvet (1995) studied how water chemistry affects rates of leaf decomposition, using the leaves of yellow poplar, *Liriodendron tulipifera*. They placed the leaves in several temperate zone streams differing in water chemistry. The leaves in their litter bags decayed as an exponential function of time, following the relationship:

$$m_t = m_0 e^{-kt}$$

where:

m_t is the mass of leaves at time t

m_0 is the initial mass of leaves

e is the base of the natural logarithms

t is time in days

k is the daily rate of mass loss

We can use the constant k as an index of decay rate under particular environmental conditions. Suberkropp and Chauvet found that k varied significantly among their study streams. It turned out that leaves decayed faster, that is, had higher k, in streams with higher concentrations of nitrates (fig. 20.13). This result is consistent with the suggestion by Melillo's research team that higher rates of decomposition at one of their study sites was due to higher availability of soil nitrogen. Similar results were found in streams draining a tropical forest. Amy Rosemond and colleagues (2002) found leaf decomposition rate increased markedly as phosphorus concentration increased to about 20 μg per liter, after which decomposition rate levelled off.

As in terrestrial ecosystems, litter chemistry and nutrient availability in the environment affect decomposition rates in aquatic ecosystems. These impacts of litter composition on water chemistry are found in all aquatic systems, including lakes, streams, bogs, and oceans. The patterns discussed in this section emphasize the role played by the physical and chemical environment in the process of decomposition. As we shall see in the next section, animals and plants can also significantly affect the nutrient dynamics of ecosystems.

Concept 20.1 Review

1. During the past 30 years, thousands of papers have been published on decomposition within ecosystems. Why have ecologists spent so much time studying decomposition?
2. Why does litter chemistry alter decomposition rates?

20.2 Organisms and Nutrients

Plants and animals can modify the distribution and cycling of nutrients in ecosystems. In chapters 17 and 18 we discussed how interactions among organisms can cause changes to community structure. These ecological interactions also can impact nutrient cycling within ecosystems. One of the great realizations in ecosystem ecology over the last several decades has been that although the same ecological processes occur in terrestrial and aquatic habitats (e.g., decomposition, herbivory, predation), there are consistent difference in the patterns of nutrient cycling between these ecosystems. Jonathan Shurin, of the University of British Columbia, has summarized many of the critical differences in nutrient cycling between aquatic and terrestrial habitats (Shurin et al. 2006).

Shurin points out, and as we saw in chapter 19, there is strong evidence for top-down control of productivity in aquatic systems, while terrestrial systems are primarily controlled by bottom-up processes. However, there are a number of other general differences in the trophic structure and distribution of nutrients among terrestrial and aquatic systems (fig. 20.14). For example, aquatic systems tend to have a greater proportion of autotrophs being consumed by herbivores than by detritivores when compared to terrestrial systems. A consequence of this is that these systems tend to have a lower proportion of carbon and nutrients stored in detritus and detritivores than in terrestrial systems. Shurin and colleagues (2006) suggest that driving these differences among aquatic and terrestrial ecosystems are fundamental differences in life-history, morphology, and chemistry between phytoplankton and terrestrial plants. In general, phytoplankton appear less well-defended than terrestrial plants (chapter 15), resulting in higher consumption rates of phytoplankton by zooplankton than of terrestrial plants by herbivores. Additionally, growth rates of phytoplankton are generally much higher than terrestrial plants, facilitating rapid nutrient cycling.

Overall, it is clear that species interactions, life-histories, organismal and environmental chemistry can all interact to influence nutrient cycling within an ecosystem. This should serve as a reminder that although we have divided this book into different sections, this does not mean that ideas presented in the first few chapters are not relevant to our discussion here! We now move away from general differences that occur among ecosystems, and present a few specific examples of how organisms can influence the distribution and dynamics of nutrients within ecosystems.

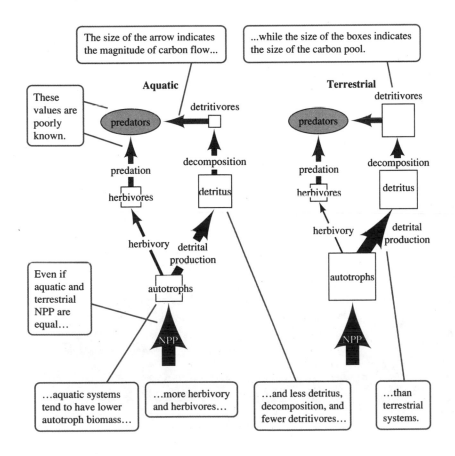

Figure 20.14 General differences in food webs and carbon flow among terrestrial and aquatic ecosystems (adapted from Shurin et al. 2006).

Nutrient Cycling in Streams

Before we consider how stream animals influence the dynamics of nutrient turnover in streams, we have to consider some special features of this ecosystem. As we saw in chapter 3, the most distinctive feature of stream and river ecosystems is water flow. Jack Webster (1975) was the first to point out that because nutrients in streams are subject to downstream transport, there is little nutrient cycling in one place. Water currents move nutrients downstream. Webster suggested that rather than a stationary cycle, stream nutrient dynamics are better represented by a spiral. He coined the term **nutrient spiralling** to describe stream nutrient dynamics (fig. 20.15).

As an atom of a nutrient completes a cycle within a stream, it may pass through several ecosystem components such as an algal cell, an invertebrate, a fish, or a detrital fragment. Each of these ecosystem components may be displaced downstream by current and therefore contribute to nutrient spiraling. The length of stream required for an atom of a nutrient to complete a cycle is called the **spiralling length.** Spiralling length is related to the rate of nutrient cycling and average velocity of nutrient movement downstream. Denis Newbold and his colleagues (1983) represented spiralling length, S, as:

$$S = VT$$

where V is the average velocity at which a nutrient atom moves downstream and T is the average time for a nutrient atom to complete a cycle. If velocity, V, is low and the time to complete a nutrient cycle, T, is short, nutrient spiralling length is short. Where spiralling lengths are short, a particular nutrient atom may be used many times before it is washed out of a stream system.

The tendency of an ecosystem to retain nutrients is called **nutrient retentiveness.** In stream ecosystems, retentiveness is inversely related to spiralling length. Short spiralling lengths are equated with high retentiveness and long spiralling lengths with low retentiveness. Any factors that influence spiralling length affect nutrient retention by stream ecosystems.

Stream Invertebrates and Spiralling Length

Nancy Grimm (1988) showed that aquatic macroinvertebrates significantly increase the rate of nitrogen cycling in Sycamore Creek, Arizona. Streams in the arid American Southwest support high levels of macroinvertebrate biomass. Grimm estimated invertebrate population densities as high as 110,000 individuals per square meter and dry biomass as high as 9.62 g per square meter. More than 80% of macroinvertebrate biomass in Sycamore Creek was made up of species that feed on small organic particles, a feeding group that stream ecologists call *collector-gatherers*. The collector-gatherers of Sycamore Creek are dominated by two families of mayflies, Baetidae and Tricorythidae, and one family of Diptera, Chironomidae.

Grimm quantified the influence of macroinvertebrates on the nitrogen dynamics in the creek, where primary production is limited by nitrogen availability. She developed nitrogen budgets for stream invertebrates, mainly insect larvae and snails, by quantifying their rates of nitrogen ingestion, egestion (defecation), excretion, and accumulation during growth. By combining these rates with her estimates of macroinvertebrate biomass, Grimm was able to estimate the contribution of macroinvertebrates to the nutrient dynamics of the Sycamore Creek ecosystem.

Her measurements indicated that macroinvertebrates could play an important role in nutrient spiralling. To determine whether they play such a role, what information do we need? We need to know how much of the available nitrogen they ingest. If invertebrates ingest a large proportion of the nitrogen pool, then their influences on nitrogen spiralling may be substantial. Grimm measured the nutrient retention of Sycamore Creek as the daily difference between nitrogen inputs and outputs in her study area. These measurements showed an average rate of retention of nitrogen as 250 mg per square meter per day.

Grimm set this rate of retention as 100% and then expressed her estimates of flux rates as a percentage of this total (fig. 20.16).

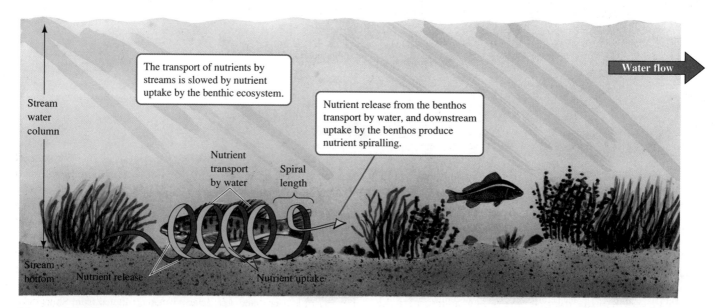

Figure 20.15   Nutrient spiralling in streams.

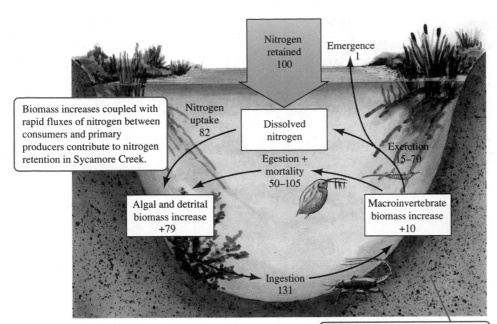

Biomass increases coupled with rapid fluxes of nitrogen between consumers and primary producers contribute to nitrogen retention in Sycamore Creek.

Though macroinvertebrate biomass includes only 10% retained nitrogen, they ingest a large proportion of available nitrogen.

Figure 20.16 Nitrogen fluxes in Sycamore Creek, Arizona (data from Grimm 1988).

Nitrogen ingestion rates by macroinvertebrates averaged about 131%. How can ingestion rates be greater than 100%? What this means is that the collector-gatherers in the study stream reingest nitrogen in their feces. This is a well-known habit of detritivores, many of which gain more nutritional value from their food by processing it more than once.

Grimm suggests that rapid recycling of nitrogen by macroinvertebrates may increase primary production in Sycamore Creek. Stream macroinvertebrates excreted and recycled 15% to 70% of the nitrogen pool as ammonia. By their high rates of feeding on the particulate nitrogen pool and their high rates of excretion of ammonia, the macroinvertebrates of the creek reduce the T in the equation for spiral length, $S = VT$. This effect coupled with the 10% of nitrogen tied up in macroinvertebrate biomass, which reduces V, reduces the nitrogen spiral length and increases the nutrient retentiveness of Sycamore Creek.

Animals and Nutrient Cycling in Terrestrial Ecosystems

As we saw in chapter 16, burrowing animals, such as ground squirrels and pocket gophers, affect local plant diversity. These burrowers also alter the distribution and abundance of nitrogen within their ecosystems.

Pocket gophers can significantly affect their ecosystems because, as we discussed in chapter 16, their mounds may cover as much as 25% to 30% of the ground surface. This deposition represents a massive reorganization of soils and a substantial energy investment, since the cost of burrowing is 360 to 3,400 times that of above-ground movements. Estimates of the amount of soil deposited in mounds by gophers range from 10,000 to 85,000 kg per hectare per year.

Nancy Huntly and Richard Inouye (1988) found that pocket gophers altered the nitrogen cycle at the Cedar Creek Natural

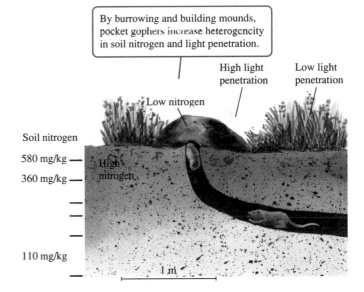

By burrowing and building mounds, pocket gophers increase heterogeneity in soil nitrogen and light penetration.

Figure 20.17 Pocket gophers and ecosystem structure (data from Huntly and Inouye 1988).

History Area in Minnesota by bringing nitrogen-poor subsoil to the surface (fig. 20.17). The result was greater horizontal heterogeneity in nitrogen availability and greater heterogeneity in light penetration. These effects on the nitrogen cycle in prairie ecosystems help explain some of the positive influences that pocket gophers have on plant diversity.

April Whicker and James Detling (1988) found that the feeding activities of prairie dogs also influence the distribution of nutrients within prairie ecosystems. This should not be surprising since these researchers estimate that prairie dogs consume or waste 60% to 80% of the net annual production from

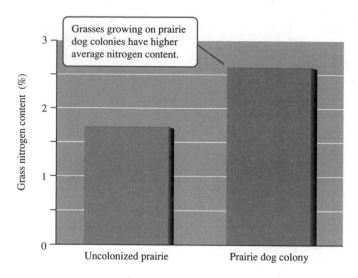

Figure 20.18 Early season nitrogen content of grasses growing on uncolonized prairie and on a young prairie dog colony (data from Whicker and Detling 1988).

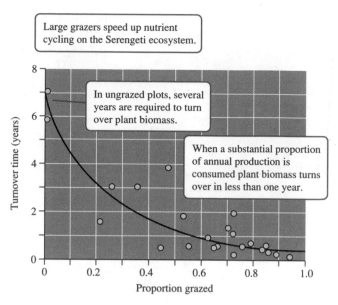

Figure 20.19 Effect of grazing on time required for turnover of plant biomass on the Serengeti ecosystem (data from McNaughton, Ruess, and Seagle 1988).

the grass-dominated areas around their colonies. One result of this heavy grazing is that above-ground biomass is reduced by 33% to 67% and the young grass tissue that remains is higher in nitrogen content (fig. 20.18). This higher nitrogen content may influence the behaviour of bison, which spend a disproportionate amount of their time grazing near prairie dog colonies.

Bison and other large herbivorous mammals, such as moose and African buffalo, may also influence the cycling of nutrients within terrestrial ecosystems. Sam McNaughton and his colleagues (1988) report a positive relationship between grazing intensity and the rate of turnover of plant biomass in the Serengeti Plain of eastern Africa. Figure 20.19 suggests that increased grazing increases the rate of nutrient cycling. Without grazing, nutrient cycling occurs more slowly through decomposition and through the feeding of small herbivores.

Steve Côte and colleagues at the Université Laval (Côte et al. 2004) have surveyed the literature and suggest that deer may have similar effects in the forests of North America. At the heart of this is broad recognition that deer populations have increased rapidly for several decades throughout much of North America, reaching densities as high as 10/km^2 throughout the temperate forests (chapter 2). The causes of this population boom are numerous, ranging from reforestation on abandoned farmland, increased forage availability, and reduced predation by hunters and natural predators (Côte et al. 2004). Many forests are now experiencing an intensity of grazing that was not common in the evolutionary history of the species of these communities. As a result, many of the seedlings of the common canopy tree species, such as oak and maple, are poorly defended against high levels of predation. In areas of high deer density, prolonged predation appears to be shifting the community towards species that are less palatable, such as conifers and ferns (Côte et al. 2004). This makes perfect sense given our understanding of natural selection, life-histories, and the intermediate disturbance hypothesis. What is less obvious, but potentially of greater long-term effect, is what may be happening in the soil.

Although deer impacts on nutrient cycling are not as well studied as are the pocket gopher and Serengeti examples we have already discussed, there is accumulating evidence that deer can alter ecosystem processes. Côte and colleagues (2004) have found evidence that deer browsing can reduce the frequency of ectomycorrhizal infections among dominant trees, which could have negative implications for nutrient uptake. Additionally, intense grazing causes dominance of plant species that have substantial morphological and chemical defenses. These species produce litter of lower quality than the former dominant plants, and thus rates of decomposition are reduced. As a result, previously dominant plants seem hurt both through reduced nitrogen availability due to reduced decomposition, as well as decreased foraging ability due to reduced mycorrhizae.

As you will see below, shifts in community composition can often cause changes in nutrient cycling and ecosystem dynamics.

Plants and the Nutrient Dynamics of Ecosystems

Plants are not simply the passive recipients of influences from the physical environment or from animals and microbes. Introduced plant species show clearly how plants modify ecosystems. We begin in Saskatchewan.

An Introduced Grass on the Great Plains

Scott Wilson and his graduate student Janice Christian have studied the relationship between an introduced grass and nutrient cycling in Grasslands National Park (Christian and Wilson, 1999). Grasslands National Park lies just north of the border between Saskatchewan and Montana, and is a northern extension of the Great Plains (chapter 2). The natural vegetation is mixed-grass prairie (fig. 20.20), dominated by species

Figure 20.20   Stands of crested wheatgrass occur across much of the Great Plains of North America.

such as blue grama grass (*Bouteloua gracilis*) and needle-and-thread grass (*Stipa comata*). However, much of the Great Plains has been converted to agriculture (chapter 23), or has been "improved" through the widespread planting of "tame" grass species, with the goal of increasing forage production and/or extending the grazing season for cattle. One widely used forage species is *Agropyron cristatum*, crested wheatgrass. This species has been planted in the Great Plains since the 1930s and currently is found on over 6,000,000 ha (Christian and Wilson 1999). This species has been of enormous economic importance to western North America, and is widely credited with making ranching economically viable throughout much of the region. As a sign of its economic importance, new cultivars of crested wheatgrass are currently being bred, and it continues to be planted in many provinces and states. At the same time, however, there is growing concern that this species has many qualities that can alter a variety of ecological services and negatively impact native species diversity. Because this species may be an example of conflict between economic gain and ecological sustainability, the designation of crested wheatgrass as a "weed" or "invasive species" is contentious. In such situations, strong science is a good foundation from which social policy can be built. As an important step, Christian and Wilson (1999) explored the impact of crested wheatgrass on nutrient cycling.

First, they needed to find areas of land that had similar histories, but differed only in whether they were seeded with crested wheatgrass, or were left to recover as native prairie. Fortunately, there exist good aerial records of much of the prairies, and they found 10 suitable sites within what is now Grasslands National Park. Each location was farmed from between approximately 1920 and 1950, at which point the farms were abandoned. Five of the sites were sown with crested wheatgrass, while the other five were left to undergo natural recovery. Christian and Wilson also identified five more sites that contained undisturbed prairie (never cultivated). They then went into these 15 sites and measured plant species composition, %C and %N content of the plants and soil, and a variety of other measures of nutrient availability.

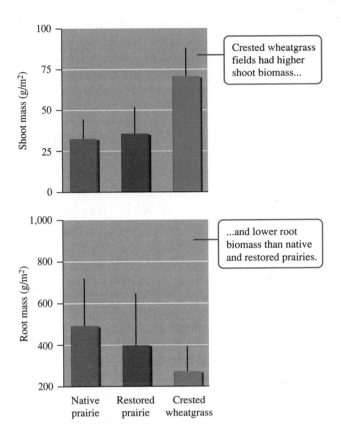

Figure 20.21   Root and shoot biomass taken at the end of the growing season in August varied as a function of land-use history (data from Christian and Wilson 1999).

The undisturbed and recovered native prairie sites did not differ in the abundance of the dominant native grasses. However, native grasses were either significantly less abundant, or absent, from the crested wheatgrass sites. Similarly, plant species richness did not differ among the undisturbed and recovered prairie sites, but was significantly lower in the crested wheatgrass sites. These findings indicate that the sowing of this introduced species causes significant changes to the composition of the plant community. What is less visually obvious is that the effects on nutrient cycling were just as strong.

Wheatgrass stands had higher shoot biomass and lower root biomass than did the two native stands (fig. 20.21). In other words, in wheatgrass sites much more of the plant growth was above ground relative to native prairie. This is obviously desired (at least for the short-term) in terms of forage production for cattle, but is negatively associated with some soil nutrient measures. Most dramatically, though there was no difference between recovered and undisturbed prairies, the crested wheatgrass stands had about 25% less C and N in the soil. The lower N content has significant implications for the long-term fertility of these systems. The impacts of the lower soil C are more immediately dramatic. Due to the large spatial extent over which crested wheatgrass is planted across North America, Christian and Wilson (1999) estimate that the planting of this species left between $3.3 \times 10^{14} - 4.8 \times 10^{14}$ g of C in the atmosphere that would otherwise have been stored beneath native grasses.

This study shows quite clearly how a single species can dramatically alter ecosystem process, with potential global implications. The introduction of exotic plants to ecosystems may be considered one type of disturbance. In the next section, we review how other disturbances increase rates of nutrient loss from ecosystems.

Concept 20.2 Review

1. The Great Plains of North America have experienced many changes over the last 200 years. How have the extermination of wild bison and the introduction of crested wheatgrass likely influenced nutrient cycling?
2. How can differences in the intensity of herbivory cause differences in nutrient cycling between terrestrial and aquatic ecosystems?
3. How does spiralling length influence the nutrient retentiveness of a stream?

20.3 Disturbance and Nutrients

Disturbance increases nutrient loss from ecosystems. In the previous section we saw how macroinvertebrates may increase nutrient retention by stream ecosystems. In this section, we consider evidence that disturbance reduces nutrient retention.

Disturbance and Nutrient Loss from the Hubbard Brook Experimental Forest

We have now discussed several times the classic study by Gene Likens and Herbert Bormann and their colleagues (1970) that demonstrated biological influences on nutrient loss from forested ecosystems. By clear-cutting the forest on one of their study basins these researchers revealed the role of vegetation in regulating nutrient losses from a temperate forest ecosystem.

The increased rates of nutrient loss following forest cutting were dramatic. The connection between forest cutting and increased nutrient output is shown clearly by plotting nutrient concentrations in the streams draining experimental and control stream basins. Figure 20.22 shows the highly significant increases in nitrate losses following deforestation.

What message can we take away from this pioneering experiment? The important point is that vegetation in the northern hardwoods ecosystem significantly affects rates of nutrient loss by the ecosystem. When Likens and Bormann cut the forest, they removed those biological controls. Similar controls have been demonstrated in other ecosystems.

Peter Vitousek and his colleagues (1979, 1982) studied the effects of disturbance and environmental conditions on rates of nitrogen loss from forest ecosystems. Their study sites included 8 deciduous forests and 11 coniferous forests growing in conditions ranging from acidic to neutral soils, and from wet climates in Washington and Oregon to a dry site in New Mexico. The study also included cold subalpine forests in New Hampshire, New Mexico, and Washington. A major goal of the research team was to identify the factors increasing the risk of nitrogen loss in response to disturbance. Including forests from a wide range of environmental conditions provided the potential to identify the site-specific factors that may promote either loss or retention of nitrogen in the face of disturbance.

Vitousek and his colleagues emphasized nitrogen losses for several reasons. First, as we saw in chapter 19, nitrogen can limit the rate of primary production in terrestrial ecosystems. In addition, as we saw in the experiments of Likens and Bormann, losses of nitrogen are often greater than losses of other nutrients.

Vitousek and his team created "trenched" plots by digging trenches 1 m deep around several 1 m² plots and lining the trenches with plastic to prevent the regrowth of tree roots into the study plots. The researchers also cut any plants within the plots and kept them free of vegetation throughout the

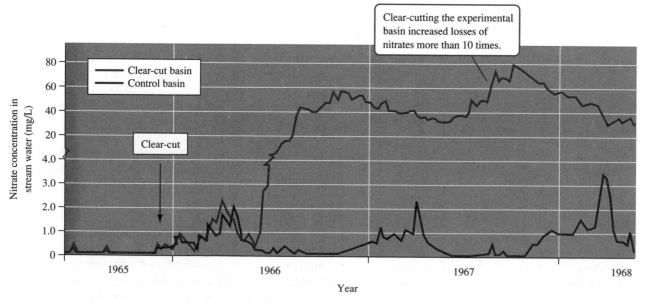

Figure 20.22   Deforestation and nitrate loss from a deciduous forest ecosystem (data from Likens et al. 1970).

study by weeding periodically. They studied the responses of the study plots to trenching by sampling soil water for nitrogen. Any nitrogen occurring in soil water represented potential loss of nitrogen from the forest ecosystem to groundwater, which might eventually find its way to stream water.

What were the similarities and differences between the experiment by Vitousek and his colleagues and that by Likens and Bormann? A major difference was that the trenching experiment was conducted on a small scale and did not disturb the forest canopy. An intact canopy kept the input of solar energy to the forest floor constant. Therefore temperature changes were minimized. Two similarities were that both experiments stopped most uptake of nutrients by plants and both increased the concentrations of nitrate in soil water.

Vitousek and his team found that trenching increased the concentrations of nitrate in soil water up to 1,000 times but that the amount of nitrate in soil water varied greatly from one forest to another. The lowest losses of nitrate occurred in the dry forest site in New Mexico and in the cold alpine environments of New Mexico and Washington. Generally, nitrate losses were greatest at the sites with combinations of temperature and moisture that promoted rapid decomposition.

What do these results suggest about the role of vegetation in preventing losses of nitrogen from forest ecosystems? Over the short term, at least, uptake by vegetation is most important in ecosystems with fertile soils and warm, moist conditions during the growing season. Since these are conditions that would promote high rates of plant growth, trees at these sites should be able to rapidly reestablish control of nitrogen loss following disturbance.

Now let's consider how disturbance affects nutrient losses from stream ecosystems, where nutrient loss appears to be highly episodic and associated with disturbance during flooding.

Flooding and Nutrient Export by Streams

How do the nutrient dynamics of stream ecosystems respond to variations in streamflow? Judy Meyer and Gene Likens (1979) examined the long-term dynamics of phosphorus in Bear Brook, a stream ecosystem in the Hubbard Brook Experimental Forest. They found that during periods of average flow, the ratio of annual phosphorus inputs to exports varied from 0.56 to 1.6 and that the balance depended upon stream discharge. Meyer and Likens found that exports were highly episodic and associated with periods of high flow.

How did Meyer and Likens determine the phosphorus dynamics of Bear Brook ecosystem? They measured the geological and meteorological inputs and the geological exports of phosphorus in the stream, which they divided into three size fractions: (1) dissolved phosphorus, < 0.45 μm, (2) phosphorus associated with fine particles, 0.45 μm to 1 mm, and (3) phosphorus associated with coarse particles, > 1 mm.

Meyer and Likens inventoried the movement and storage of phosphorus in the Bear Brook ecosystem. They measured the inputs of dissolved phosphorus at 12 seeps (areas of groundwater input) along the length of the stream. They also measured

meteorological inputs, which included precipitation and forest litter falling or blowing into the stream. The only significant export of phosphorus in the ecosystem was transport with streamflow. The researchers measured the amount of particulate matter transported by the Bear Brook ecosystem by collecting the organic matter deposited behind the weir (a small dam used to measure streamflow) on the stream and by collecting organic matter captured by nets set at seven sites. They estimated the amount of organic matter stored by removing all the organic matter in 42 randomly located 1 m² areas of stream bottom.

During 1974 to 1975, Meyer and Likens estimated an almost exact balance between inputs and exports of phosphorus, with approximately 1,250 mg of phosphorus per square meter of input and approximately 1,300 mg of phosphorus per square meter of output. Despite a balance between input and output, their data indicated significant transformation of phosphorus-size fractions. Phosphorus inputs to Bear Brook were almost evenly divided between dissolved (28%), fine particulate (37%), and coarse particulate (35%) fractions. However, 62% of exports were fine particulates. Clearly physical and biological processes converted dissolved and coarse particulate forms of phosphorus into fine particulate forms.

Meyer and Likens used their estimates to reconstruct the long-term phosphorus dynamics of Bear Brook. During 1974 to 1975, the ratio of phosphorus export to input was almost exactly one (1.04). However, the Meyer and Likens model of phosphorus dynamics indicated considerable year-to-year variation in this ratio during the period from 1963 to 1975, which included the wettest and driest years in the 20-year precipitation record for the area. The predicted ratio of output to input over this interval was highly correlated with annual streamflow. The ratio ranged from 0.56 in the driest year to 1.6 in the wettest year (fig. 20.23). In other words, during the driest year only 56% of phosphorus inputs were exported, while during the wettest year exports amounted to 160% of

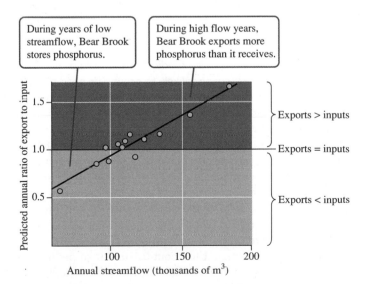

Figure 20.23 Annual streamflow and ratio of phosphorus export to input in Bear Brook, New Hampshire (data from Meyer and Likens 1979).

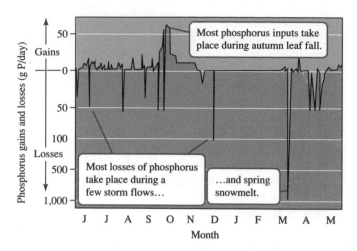

Figure 20.24   Daily gains and losses of phosphorus (P) by the Bear Brook ecosystem from 1974 to 1975 (data from Meyer and Likens 1979).

inputs. In wet years the stream ecosystem's standing stocks of phosphorus were reduced by high levels of export.

The patterns of inputs and exports of phosphorus from Bear Brook were highly pulsed during Meyer and Likens' study (fig. 20.24). They estimated that from 1974 to 1975, 48% of total annual input of phosphorus to Bear Brook entered during 10 days and that 67% of exports left the ecosystem during 10 days. The annual peak in phosphorus input was associated with

autumn leaf fall, and an annual pulse of export was associated with spring snowmelt. Most phosphorus export, however, was irregular because it was driven by flooding caused by intense storms that may occur during any month of the year. If we consider floods as a source of disturbance, the behaviour of stream ecosystems is consistent with the generalization that disturbance increases the loss of nutrients from ecosystems.

Aquatic ecologists study the nutrient dynamics of aquatic ecosystems like Bear Brook because, as we saw in chapter 19, nutrient availability is a key regulator of aquatic primary production. As we shall see in the Ecological Tools section, nutrient enrichment of ecosystems by human activity is a worldwide problem.

Concept 20.3 Review

1. What major conclusion we can draw from the pioneering experiment by Likens and Bormann?
2. What were the similarities and differences between the experiments by Vitousek and his colleagues and that of Likens and Bormann?
3. Flood control on streams and rivers has often been cited as a potential threat to populations of aquatic animals and riparian trees that require flooding for reproduction. How might flow regulation also alter stream ecosystem nutrient dynamics?

Ecological Tools

Altering Aquatic and Terrestrial Ecosystems

So far in the text, our discussion of research tools has focused on aspects of physiology, differences among species, or aspects of communities. Here we discuss how understanding the process of nutrient cycling can allow ecologists to make predictions about what changes in communities or ecosystem functions we may expect in the future. By knowing the mechanisms of ecosystem function, ecologists can make predications, and hopefully help mitigate any negative changes likely to occur. The need for such a predictive approach comes from the rate at which humans are altering the historical rules of nutrient cycles across the planet.

Human activity increasingly affects the nutrient cycles of ecosystems. Agriculture and forestry may remove nutrients from ecosystems. However, increasingly, human activity enriches ecosystems with nutrients, especially with nitrogen (see chapter 23) and phosphorus. The main source of nitrogen enrichment is air pollution due to burning of fossil fuels and intensive applications of fertilizer by farmers. In the temperate coastal forests of southern Chile, far from urban and industrial centres, inputs of nitrogen amount to about 0.1 to 1.0 kg per hectare per year. In contrast, in the Netherlands, with its high population density and intense agriculture, precipitation adds nitrogen to forest ecosystems at rates up to 60 kg per hectare per year.

Humans are also a major source of nutrient input to aquatic ecosystems. Benjamin Peierls and his colleagues (1991) examined the relationship of human population density within river basins and nitrate concentration and export by 42 major rivers. These rivers, which deliver approximately 37% of the total freshwater flow to the oceans, support human population densities ranging from 1 to 1,000 individuals per square kilometer.

Peierls noted that while the concentration and export of nitrate by rivers is affected by complex biotic, abiotic, and anthropogenic factors, a single variable, human population density, explains most of the variation in nitrate concentration and export (fig. 20.25). The most probable sources of nitrate enrichment of river ecosystems are sewage disposal, atmospheric deposition, agriculture, and deforestation, all of which generally increase with increased human population density.

Human disturbance also increases export of phosphorus from aquatic catchments. There is a significant relationship between land use and export of phosphorus from catchments in southern Ontario. Conversion of forest to agriculture approximately quadruples phosphorus export. Meanwhile, phosphorus exports from urban catchments are nearly two times higher than exports from agricultural catchments and approximately nine times exports from forested catchments (fig. 20.26).

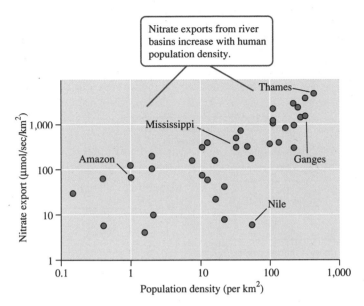

Figure 20.25 Human population density and nitrate export from river basins (data from Peierls et al. 1991).

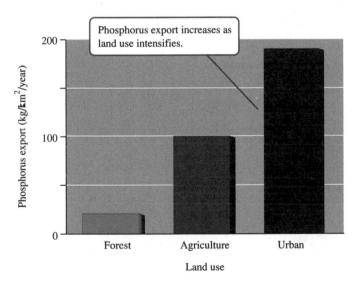

Figure 20.26 Land use and phosphorus export from stream basins (data from Reckhow and Simpson 1980).

What are the ecological effects of increased nutrient inputs to ecosystems? One of the most obvious negative consequences is the impoverishment of biological communities. As we saw in chapter 16, terrestrial and aquatic ecosystems enriched with nutrients generally support a lower diversity of primary producers. As nutrients become abundant, light may be left as the single limiting resource. In the absence of disturbance, the nutrient-enriched community is eventually dominated by the best competitors for light. This hypothesis is supported by the fertilization experiments at Rothamsted, England (chapter 16).

Nutrient enrichment of ecosystems, particularly with nitrogen, may also be causing massive local extinctions of fungi. John Jaenike (1991) cites declines in mushroom species diversity of 40% to 80% in Germany, Austria, the Netherlands, and the Czech Republic. Similar declines may also be occurring in North America, but the fungi of North America have not been studied carefully enough to make an assessment. Jaenike suggests that the most significantly affected fungi are the ectomycorrhizal species that form associations with trees. It appears that fertilization is somehow interfering with the mutualistic relationship between trees and their mycorrhizal associates. This hypothesis is consistent with the studies of Nancy Johnson (1993) (see chapter 15), which suggested that fertilization alters the mutualistic relationship between plants and mycorrhizal fungi. The loss of mycorrhizal fungi may threaten the long-term survival of entire forest ecosystems.

The main factors affecting phosphorus concentration in lakes include geology, land use, precipitation, hydrologic budget, lake morphometry, and human population density. Using these factors, researchers have been able to predict the phosphorus concentrations of lakes with reasonable accuracy (fig. 20.27).

How can a model that predicts phosphorus concentration be useful to land managers? Remember that phosphorus concentration translates directly into lake trophic status, which, in turn, influences the lake's suitability for a variety of human uses. With such a model, the land manager can predict the potential impact of changes in land use or urbanization within a lake basin and determine whether a significant change in lake trophic status is likely. These quantitative predictions by the nutrient loading model can be used to make land management decisions. David Schindler (1987) suggested that the worldwide use of these loading models to manage phosphorus inputs into aquatic ecosystems is one of the best examples of how ecological knowledge has been used to solve an environmental problem.

In summary, we know that there is a direct connection between human activity and nutrient enrichment of ecosystems and that nutrient enrichment has a number of negative consequences. How have land managers addressed this significant and complex problem? One of the most successful tools available to land managers has been the nutrient loading model (Peters 1991), especially models that predict the concentration of phosphorus in lakes. As we saw in chapter 19, phosphorus usually limits primary production in freshwater lakes. High concentrations of phosphorus produce eutrophic conditions, including algal blooms, reduced water clarity, and lowered dissolved oxygen. These effects generally reduce the esthetic quality of lakes and restrict their suitability for recreation.

Nutrient loading models are the basis for management of lake basins around the world. Land managers have used nutrient loading models to regulate the level of human activity in lake basins, particularly the development of summer cottages, to forestall the negative impacts of eutrophication.

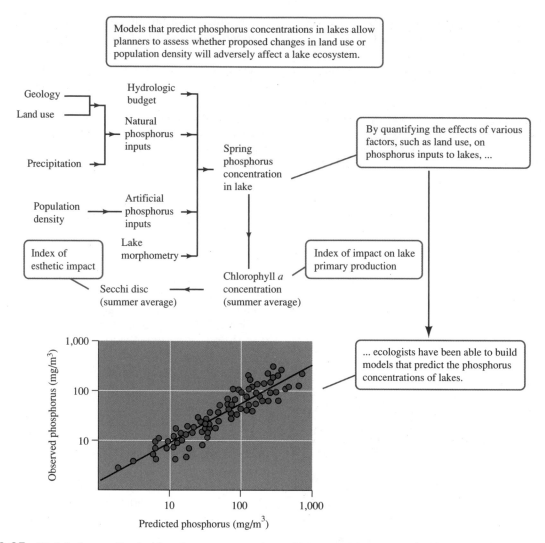

Figure 20.27 Models that predict the phosphorus concentrations of lakes (data from Dillon and Rigler 1975, Peters 1991).

Summary

The elements organisms require for development, maintenance, and reproduction are called *nutrients*. Ecologists refer to the use, transformation, movement, and reuse of nutrients in ecosystems as *nutrient cycling*. Nutrient cycling is one of the most ecologically significant processes studied by ecosystem ecologists. The *carbon, nitrogen,* and *phosphorus cycles* have played especially prominent roles in studies of nutrient cycling.

Decomposition rate is influenced by temperature, moisture, and chemical composition of litter and the environment. The rate of decomposition affects the rate at which nutrients, such as nitrogen and phosphorus, are made available to primary producers. Rates of decomposition in terrestrial ecosystems are higher under warm, moist conditions. The rate of decomposition in terrestrial ecosystems increases with nitrogen content and decreases with the lignin content of litter. The chemical composition of litter and the availability of nutrients in the surrounding environment also influence rates of decomposition in aquatic ecosystems.

Plants and animals can modify the distribution and cycling of nutrients in ecosystems. Aquatic and terrestrial systems have significant differences in their nutrient cycles. The dynamics of nutrients in streams are best represented by a spiral rather than a cycle. The length of stream required for an atom of a nutrient to complete a cycle is called the spiralling length. Stream macroinvertebrates can substantially reduce spiralling length of nutrients in stream ecosystems. Animals can also alter the distribution and rate of nutrient cycling in terrestrial ecosystems. Plants can cause increases or decreases to soil N and C, depending upon species-specific traits.

Disturbance increases nutrient loss from ecosystems. Vegetation exerts substantial control on nutrient retention by terrestrial ecosystems. Vegetative controls on nutrient loss from forest ecosystems appear to be most important in environments that are warm and moist during the growing season. Vegetative controls appear to be less important in cold and/or dry environments. Nutrient loss by stream ecosystems is highly pulsed and associated with disturbance by flooding.

Nutrient enrichment by humans is altering aquatic and terrestrial ecosystems. Nitrate concentration and export by the earth's major rivers correlate directly with human population density. Human disturbance also increases export of phosphorus from aquatic catchments. Nutrient enrichment appears to be reducing the diversity of plants and fungi in terrestrial ecosystems. Land managers around the world use nutrient loading models to predict and manage the impact of land use on aquatic ecosystems.

Review Questions

1. Of all the naturally occurring elements in the biosphere, why have the cycles of carbon, nitrogen, and phosphorus been so intensively studied by ecologists? (Hint: Think about the kinds of organic molecules of which these elements are constituents. Also think back to our discussions, in chapter 19, of the influences of nitrogen and phosphorus on rates of primary production.)

2. Parmenter and Lamarra (1991) studied decomposition of fish and waterfowl carrion in a freshwater marsh. During the course of their studies they found that the soft tissues of both fish and waterfowl decomposed faster than the most rapidly decomposing plant tissues. Explain the rapid decomposition of these animal carcasses.

3. Review figure 19.3, in which Rosenzweig (1968) plotted the relationship between actual evapotranspiration and net primary production. How do you think that decomposition rates change across the same ecosystems? Using what you learned in chapter 20, design an experiment to test your hypothesis.

4. Melillo, Aber, and Muratore (1982) suggested that soil fertility may influence the rate of decomposition in terrestrial ecosystems. Design an experiment to test this hypothesis. If you test for the effects of soil fertility, how will you control for the influences of temperature, moisture, and litter chemistry?

5. Many rivers around the world have been straightened and deepened to improve conditions for navigation. Side effects of these changes include increased average water velocity and decreased movement of water into shallow riverside environments such as eddies and marginal wetlands. What are the probable influences of these changes on nutrient spiralling length? Use the model of Newbold et al. (1983) in your discussion.

6. Likens and Bormann (1995) found that vegetation substantially influences the rate of nutrient loss from small stream catchments in the northern hardwood forest ecosystem. How do vegetative biomass and rates of primary production in these forests affect their capacity to regulate nutrient loss? How much do you think vegetation affects nutrient movements in desert ecosystems?

7. McNaughton, Ruess, and Seagle (1988) proposed that grazing by large mammals increases the rate of nitrogen cycling on the savannas of East Africa. Explain how passing through a large mammal could increase the rate of breakdown of plant biomass. In chapter 19 we also saw how grazing mammals may increase the rate of primary production on the savanna. How might the disappearance of the large mammals of East Africa affect ecosystem processes on the savanna?

8. If rates of decomposition are higher in ecosystems with higher nutrient availability, how should nutrient enrichment affect rates of decomposition? Because of its effects on fungal diversity, could nutrient enrichment of ecosystems affect rates of decomposition differently over the short term versus the long term?

9. Christian and Wilson (1999) have shown how the introduction of crested wheatgrass, *Agropyron cristatum*, can dramatically alter the appearance and function of the mixed-grass prairie. They found that the introduced plant was associated with both a decrease in soil N and a decrease in species richness. What do you think are the causal linkages between native plants, crested wheatgrass, and soil fertility? In other words, did the drop in soil N cause a loss of diversity? Vice versa? Something else?

10. Atmospheric warming may cause increases, or decreases, to decomposition in the arctic. A shift in either direction has the potential to greatly alter the atmospheric concentration of CO_2, which can further alter global temperatures. However, the science is not conclusive on what direction of effect will occur. What do you believe is the role of the scientist in public debate on this issue? More generally, should a scientist speak out on environmental issues? If so, when?

Suggested Readings

Augustine, D. J. and D. A. Frank. 2001. Effects of migratory grazers on spatial heterogeneity of soil nitrogen properties in a grassland ecosystem. *Ecology* 82: 3149–62.

This study demonstrates the influence of native grazers on the distribution of soil nitrogen at small to large scales.

Fisk, M. C., D. R. Zak, and T. R. Crow. 2002. Nitrogen storage and cycling in old- and second-growth hardwood forests. *Ecology* 83: 73–87.

A very detailed comparison of nitrogen fluxes in second-growth and old-growth temperate deciduous forests, which reveals a great deal of complexity and no simple contrast between forests of different ages.

Hattenschwiler, S., A. V. Tiunov, and S. Scheu. 2005. Biodiversity and litter decomposition in terrestrial ecosystems. *Annual Review of Ecology Evolution and Systematics* 36:191–218.

This comprehensive review outlines what is known concerning the complex relationship between biodiversity and decomposition in terrestrial ecosystems.

Jonsson, M. and B. Malmqvist. 2003. Mechanisms behind positive diversity effects on ecosystem functioning: testing the facilitation and interference hypotheses. *Oecologia* 134:554–59.

This experimental study demonstrates the mechanisms underlying the positive relationship between diversity of detritivores and leaf processing rates.

Likens, G. E. and F. H. Bormann. 1995. *Biogeochemistry of a Forested Ecosystem.* 2d ed. New York: Springer-Verlag.

A 32-year record of the structure and dynamics of the Hubbard Brook ecosystem—a worthwhile companion and update to the original papers reporting on the Hubbard Brook experiment.

McCulley, R. L., I. C. Burke, J. A. Nelson, W. K. Lauenroth, A. K. Knapp, and E. F. Kelly. 2005. Regional patterns in carbon cycling across the Great Plains of North America. *Ecosystems* 8:106–21.

A detailed study of carbon flux across the Great Plains that examines how precipitation influences decomposition rates along with above-ground net primary production, below-ground net primary production, and soil respiration.

Perakis, S. S. and L. O. Hedin. 2001. Fluxes and fates of nitrogen in soil of an unpolluted old-growth temperate forest, southern Chile. *Ecology* 82:2245–60.

Fascinating work on one of the rarest ecosystem types on earth: an unpolluted, old-growth temperate forest. The work documents the exceptional retentiveness of old-growth temperate forests.

Raich, J. W., A. E. Russell, K. Kitayama, W. J. Parton, and P. M. Vitousek. 2006. Temperature influences carbon accumulation in moist tropical forests. *Ecology* 87:76–77.

The authors explore the relationship between temperature, net primary production, decomposition, and carbon storage in moist tropical forests on three continents, finding consistent patterns that will be relevant to global carbon management in a warming climate.

LARGE-SCALE ECOLOGY

Many ecological processes occur at scales much larger than individual ecosystems, and many patterns of diversity emerge only if we step back and look at natural systems from a great distance. In this final section, we explore the mechanisms and consequences of interactions at scales much greater than individuals, populations, communities, or even ecosystems. Here we explore the ecology of landscapes (chapter 21), geographic regions (chapter 22), and global patterns (chapter 23).

Landscape Ecology

*I*n every region on earth and at every stage in history, human survival has required a basic understanding of landscapes. In contemporary ecology, a **landscape** is a heterogeneous area consisting of distinctive patches—which landscape ecologists refer to as **landscape elements**—organized into a mosaic-like pattern. The elements of a mountain landscape may include forests, meadows, bogs, and streams, while those in an urban landscape include parks, industrial districts, and residential areas.

While our distant ancestors did not articulate a formal definition of landscape, their lives and livelihoods clearly reflect their understanding of landscape structure and process. Hunters and gatherers were familiar with variation across the landscapes in which they lived. They learned where to find plants useful as food or medicines, and where to find game animals, including where the animals hid, fed, watered, and how they moved with the seasons. Later, pastoralists learned how to locate forage for livestock, how the most productive pastures changed with the seasons and between years of drought and years with ample rain, and where in the landscape predators and other dangers were likely to be encountered (fig. 21.1). Settled agriculturalists learned which areas were most suitable for planting row crops, which were best for orchards and vineyards, and how to work and shape the land to guide the movement of water and avoid soil losses (fig. 21.2). The establishment of cities required managing the movements of food, waste, and water between the urban centre and the surrounding agricultural and wild lands.

With mounting environmental pressures from human populations, the need for understanding landscapes has grown, and that need has created the modern science of landscape ecology. Jianguo Wu and Richard Hobbs (2006), of Arizona State University and Murdoch University, Australia, respectively, point out that the precise meaning of the term "landscape ecology," first coined by the German geographer Carl Troll (1939), is still debated among landscape ecologists. However, drawing from its many definitions, Wu and Hobbs identify a thematic thread uniting the discipline and on that basis define *landscape ecology* as the study of the relationship between spatial pattern and ecological processes over a range of scales. Though most landscape ecologists have worked at larger spatial scales, the concepts of landscape ecology have been applied to spatial patterns and ecological processes ranging from those relevant to ground beetles moving across a few metres of grassland (Wiens, Schooley, and Weeks 1997) to very large regional scales measured in thousands of square kilometres. Also, while the concepts of landscape ecology were first developed in terrestrial settings, they can be applied in aquatic environments as well.

Three facets of landscape ecology distinguish it from the other subdisciplines of ecology presented in this text. The first is that landscape ecology is generally highly interdisciplinary. Gunther Tress, Bärbel Tress, and Gary Fry (2005) point out that **interdisciplinary research** involves researchers from multiple disciplines working closely to produce an understanding that integrates across disciplines. Interdisciplinary research can include several scientific disciplines or extend beyond the boundaries of the natural sciences into the social sciences and humanities. The second characteristic distinguishing landscape

Figure 21.1 Managing large bands of grazing animals requires detailed knowledge of local landscapes, especially the locations of good forage, water, and shelter.

Figure 21.2 Successful agriculturalists must have a basic understanding of landscape structure and process. These terraced rice fields in China are the result of human engineering of the landscape to retain water and prevent erosion.

ecology from other subdisciplines is that it has included humans, and human influences on landscapes, since its beginnings. As a consequence, landscape ecology often plays a central role where ecologists attempt to restore degraded landscapes. Third, and perhaps most central to the discipline, landscape ecology focuses on understanding the extent, origin, and ecological consequences of spatial heterogeneity across multiple spatial scales.

The full scope of landscape ecology cannot be covered in a single chapter. However, we will sample the discipline by reviewing some studies concerning core areas of landscape ecology. In earlier chapters we discussed structure, process, and change within the context of populations, communities, and ecosystems. In chapter 21 we revisit structure, process, and change within the context of landscapes.

Concepts

21.1 **Landscape structure includes the size, shape, composition, number, and position of patches, or landscape elements, in a landscape.**

21.2 **Landscape structure influences processes such as the flow of energy, materials, and species distributions across a landscape.**

21.3 **Landscapes are structured and change in response to geological processes, climate, activities of organisms, and fire.**

21.1   Landscape Structure

Landscape structure includes the size, shape, composition, number, and position of patches, or landscape elements, in a landscape.   Much of ecology focuses on studies of structure and process; landscape ecology is no exception. We are all familiar with the structure, or anatomy, of organisms. In chapters 10–12 we discussed the structure of populations, and in chapters 16 to 20 we considered the structure of communities and ecosystems. What constitutes landscape structure? **Landscape structure** consists mainly of the size, shape, composition, number, and position of patches, or landscape elements, within a landscape. As you look across a landscape you can usually recognize its constituent ecosystems as distinctive patches, which might consist of woods, fields, ponds, marshes, or towns. Landscape ecologists define a **patch** as a relatively homogeneous area that differs from its surroundings, for example, an area of forest surrounded by agricultural fields. The patches within a landscape form the mosaic that we call landscape structure. The background in this mosaic is called the **matrix,** which is the element within the landscape that is the most spatially continuous.

Most questions in landscape ecology require that ecologists quantify landscape structure. The following examples show how this has been done on some landscapes and how some aspects of landscape structure are not obvious without quantification.

The Structure of Six Landscapes in Ohio

In 1981, G. Bowen and R. Burgess published a quantitative analysis of several Ohio landscapes. These landscapes consisted of forest patches surrounded by other types of ecosystems. Six of the 10 km by 10 km areas analyzed are shown in figure 21.3. If you look carefully at this figure you see that the landscapes, which are named after nearby towns, differ considerably in total forest cover, the number of forest patches, the average area of patches, and the shapes of patches. Some of the landscapes are well forested, and others are not. Some contain only small patches of forest, while others include some large patches. In some landscapes, the forest patches are long and narrow, while in others they are much wider. These general differences are clear enough, but we would find it difficult to give more precise descriptions unless we quantified our impressions.

First, let's consider total forest cover. Forest cover varies substantially among the six landscapes. The Concord landscape, with 2.7% forest cover, is the least forested. At the other extreme, forest patches cover 43.6% of the Washington landscape. Differences between these extremes are clear, but what about some of the less obvious differences. Compare the Monroe and Somerset landscapes (fig. 21.3) and try to estimate which is more forested and by how much. Somerset may appear to have greater forest cover, but how much more? You may be surprised to discover that Somerset, with 22.7% forest cover, has twice the forest cover of the Monroe landscape, which includes just 11.8% forest cover (fig. 21.4). This substantial difference could mean the difference between persistence and local extinction for some forest species.

Now let's examine the size of forest patches in each of the landscapes. Again, the median area of forest patches differs significantly across the landscapes. The smallest median areas are in the Monroe landscape, 3.6 ha, and the Concord landscape, 4.1 ha. The Washington landscape has the largest median patch area.

Now, look back at figure 21.3 and try to estimate which of the landscapes contains the greatest number, or highest density, of forest patches. The Somerset landscape, with 244 forest patches, has the highest patch density, and the Monroe landscape, with 180 patches, has the next highest density of forest patches. Obviously, the Concord landscape has the lowest density of forest patches, with only 46. The Boston landscape, with 86 forest patches, contains the next lowest density of forest patches.

Now let's look at a more subtle feature of landscape structure, patch shape. Bowen and Burgess quantified patch shape by the ratio of patch perimeter to the perimeter (circumference) of a circle with an area equal to that of the patch. Their formula was:

$$S = \frac{P}{2\sqrt{\pi A}}$$

where:

S = patch shape

P = patch perimeter

A = patch area

Quantifying landscape structure may reveal relationships not apparent visually. Compare your impression of the landscapes shown here to quantitative representations of some attributes presented in figures 21.4 and 21.5.

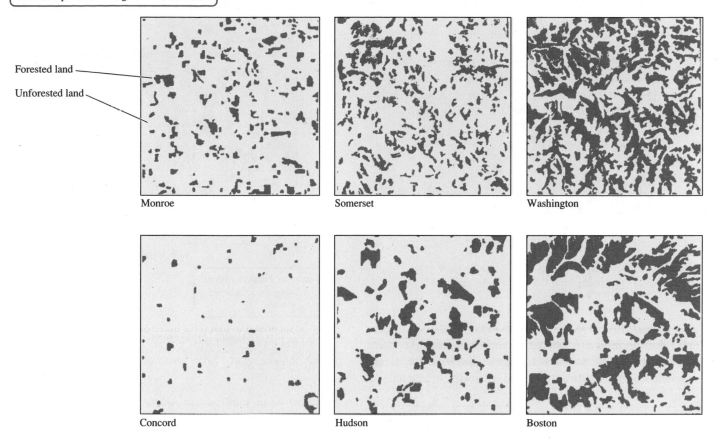

Forested land

Unforested land

Monroe

Somerset

Washington

Concord

Hudson

Boston

Figure 21.3   Forest fragments, shown as dark green, in six landscapes in Ohio (data from Bowen and Burgess 1981).

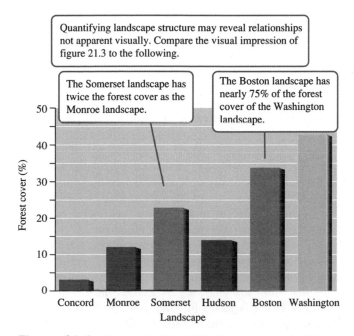

Quantifying landscape structure may reveal relationships not apparent visually. Compare the visual impression of figure 21.3 to the following.

The Somerset landscape has twice the forest cover as the Monroe landscape.

The Boston landscape has nearly 75% of the forest cover of the Washington landscape.

Figure 21.4   Percent forest cover in six landscapes in Ohio (data from Bowen and Burgess 1981).

How do you translate differences in the value of this index into shape? If S is about equal to one, the patch is approximately circular. Increasing values of S indicate less circular patch shapes. High values of S generally indicate elongate patches and a long perimeter relative to area. The issue of patch shape is particularly important as elongate shapes will have more edge relative to circular patches. This in turn means greater potential influence of the adjacent ecosystems on the dynamics within the forest patch.

Bowen and Burgess calculated the shapes, S, for the forest patches in each of their landscapes and then determined the median shape for each (fig. 21.5). The Concord landscape, with a median S of 1.16, contains the most circular patches of the six landscapes. The Washington landscape, with a median S of 1.6, contains the least circular patches. As we shall see in the next example, landscape ecologists have developed methods for representing landscape structure that go well beyond the classical methods used by Bowen and Burgess.

Until recently, geometry, which means "earth measurement," could only offer rough approximations of complex landscape structure. Today, an area of mathematics called *fractal geometry* can be used to quantify the structure of complex

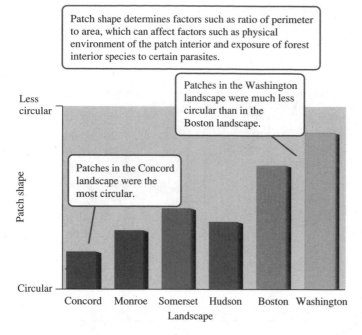

Figure 21.5 Relative shapes of forest patches in six landscapes in Ohio (data from Bowen and Burgess 1981).

natural shapes. Fractal geometry was developed by Benoit Mandelbrot (1982) to provide a method for describing the dimensions of natural objects as diverse as ferns, snowflakes, root systems, and patches in a landscape. Fractal geometry offers unique insights into the structure of nature.

The Fractal Geometry of Landscapes

During the development of fractal geometry, Mandelbrot asked a deceptively simple question: "How long is the coast of Great Britain?" This is analogous to estimating the perimeter of a patch in a landscape. Think about this question. At first, you might expect there to be only one, exact answer. For simple shapes with smooth outlines such as squares and circles, the assumption of a single answer is approximately correct. However, an estimate of the perimeter of a complex shape often depends upon the size of the measuring device. In other words, if you measure the coastline of Great Britain, you will find that your measurement depends upon the size of the ruler you use. If you were to step off the perimeter of Great Britain in 1 km lengths, which is like using a ruler 1 km long, you would get a smaller estimate than if you made your measurements with a 100 m ruler. If you measured the coastline with a 10 cm ruler you would get an even larger estimate of the perimeter. The reason that a larger ruler gives a smaller estimate is that the large ruler misses many of the nooks and crannies along the coast. These smaller features show up in estimates made with smaller rulers.

Mandelbrot's answer to his question about the British coastline was, "Coastline length depends on the scale at which it is measured!" We can see the ecological significance of this finding by considering some of its consequences to organisms. Bruce Milne (1993) measured the coastline of Admiralty Island

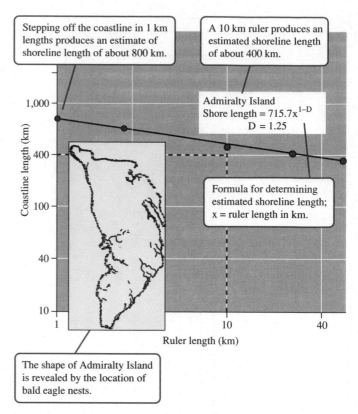

Figure 21.6 Relationship between ruler length and the measured length of the coastline of Admiralty Island, Alaska (data from Milne 1993).

off the coast of southeastern Alaska. He made his measurements from the perspective of two very different animal residents of the island, bald eagles and barnacles.

Milne considered how the measured length of Admiralty Island's coastline depends upon the length of the measuring device. Figure 21.6 plots ruler length on the horizontal axis and estimated length of coastline on the vertical axis. The straight line that joins the dots slopes downward to the right. As Mandelbrot suggested, the estimated coastline length decreases as ruler length increases.

Now, what "ruler" are bald eagles and barnacles using? The distribution of eagle nests around Admiralty Island are about 0.782 km apart. This measurement of internest distance gives us an estimate of the length of coastline required by a bald eagle territory on the island. In contrast, barnacles range from 1 to a few centimetres in basal diameter and they are sedentary. Barnacles only need a small area of solid surface to attach themselves and are often packed side by side along a rocky shore. Milne estimated that an individual barnacle requires about 2 cm (0.00002 km) of coastline.

Milne assumed that the eagles are, in effect, using a ruler 0.782 km long to step off the perimeter of the island and that barnacles use a ruler 0.00002 km long. Milne's analysis estimates that from the eagle's perspective, the perimeter of Admiralty Island is just a bit over 760 km. However, to a barnacle stepping off the coastline with its tiny ruler, the perimeter is over 11,000 km! Any of us would probably have assumed that the barnacle population "sees" a lot more of the spatial complexity around Admiralty Island. However, without Mandelbrot's fractal geometry, it would be difficult to predict that the difference in island perimeter for eagles and barnacles would be as great as 760 versus 11,000 km. At the conclusion of his analysis, Milne challenges us to imagine how long the coastline of Admiralty Island must be from the perspective of crude oil molecules. This is the length of coastline that determines the cost of a thorough cleanup after oil spills like that of the *Exxon Valdez*.

As in other areas of science, describing aspects of landscape structure, such as the length of the coastline of Admiralty Island or the size, shape, and number of forest patches in Ohio landscapes, is not an end in itself. Landscape ecologists study landscape structure because it influences landscape processes and change. These are the next topics in the following sections.

Concept 21.1 Review

1. In the landscapes shown in figure 21.3, what is patch and what is matrix?
2. Why can the length of an object, such as a coastline, depend upon the scale of measurement?

21.2   Landscape Processes

Landscape structure influences processes such as the flow of energy, materials, and species distributions between the ecosystems within a landscape.   Landscape ecologists study how the size, shape, composition, number, and position of ecosystems in the landscape affect **landscape processes.** Though less familiar than physiological and ecosystem processes, landscape processes are responsible for many important ecological phenomena.

Lenore Fahrig, of Carleton University, has written extensively on landscape ecology, and what this level of ecological study can provide that is unique from the other topics more commonly associated with ecology (e.g., population growth, distributions, etc.). At the most basic level, if a goal of ecology is to understand where species are, and why, then it is important to understand all the mechanisms that govern these patterns. Fahrig (2005) has presented a conceptual diagram of how landscape processes can be integrated into ecological theory (fig. 21.7). While the model appears simple, it illustrates the central role that landscape structure may have on the outcomes of a number of other ecological patterns and processes. In this model, changes in abiotic factors will have differential impacts on biotic factors as a function of landscape structure (fig. 21.7). This adds a level of complexity that was missing from our discussions of ecosystem ecology in chapters 19 and 20. As we will see in the following examples, landscape structure affects ecologically important processes such as the movement of organisms, local population density, extinction of local populations, and the chemical composition of lakes.

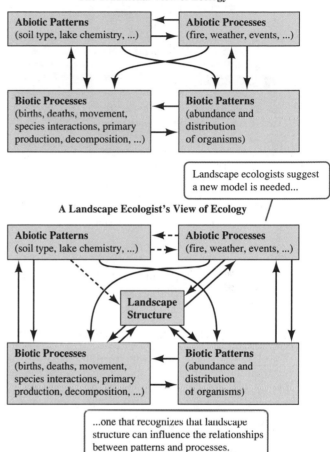

Figure 21.7   Studies in landscape ecology indicate that interactions between biotic and abiotic processes are dependent upon landscape structure (data from Fahrig 2005).

Landscape Structure and the Movement of Small Animals

Landscape ecologists have proposed that landscape structure, especially the size, number, and isolation of habitat patches, can influence the movement of organisms between potentially suitable habitats.

Human activity often produces habitat fragmentation, which occurs where a road cuts through a forest, a housing development eliminates an area of shrubland, or tracts of forest are cut for timber. Because habitat fragmentation is increasing, ecologists study how landscape structure affects the movements of organisms, movements that might mean the difference between population persistence and local extinction.

James Diffendorfer, Michael Gaines, and Robert Holt (1995) studied how patch size affects the movements of three small mammal species: cotton rats, *Sigmodon hispidus,* prairie voles, *Microtus ochrogaster,* and deer mice, *Peromyscus maniculatus.* They divided a 12 ha prairie landscape in Kansas into

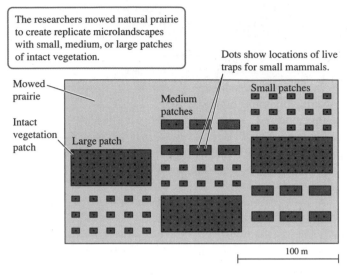

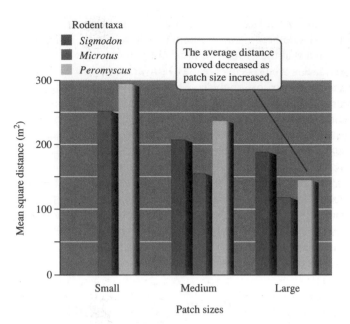

Figure 21.8 Experimental landscape for the study of small mammal movements (data from Diffendorfer, Gaines, and Holt 1995).

eight 5,000 m² areas. The prairie vegetation was mowed to maintain three patterns of fragmentation (fig. 21.8). The least fragmented areas consisted of large, 50 m by 100 m patches. The areas with medium fragmentation each contained 6 medium 12 m by 24 m patches. The most fragmented landscapes contained 10 or 15 small 4 m by 8 m patches.

The researchers predicted that animals would move farther in the more fragmented landscapes consisting of small habitat patches. In fragmented landscapes, individuals must move farther to find mates, food, and cover. They also predicted that animals would stay longer in the more isolated patches within fragmented landscapes. Consequently, the proportion of animals moving would decrease with habitat fragmentation.

The rodent populations were monitored on the study site by trapping them with live traps twice each month from August 1984 to May 1992. When trapped for the first time, the sex of each individual was determined and the animal was fitted with an ear tag with a unique number. The researchers also weighed, recorded the location of, and checked the reproductive condition of each animal trapped. Over the course of their eight-year study, Diffendorfer, Gaines, and Holt amassed a data set consisting of 23,185 captures. They used these data to construct movement histories for individual animals to test their predictions. They expressed movements as *mean square distances,* a measurement that estimates the size of an individual's home range. A home range is the area that an animal occupies on a daily basis.

The behaviour of two of the three study species supports the hypothesis that small mammals move farther in more fragmented landscapes. As predicted, *Peromyscus* and *Microtus,* living in small patches, moved farther than individuals living in medium or large patches (fig. 21.9). However, the movements of *Sigmodon* in medium and large patches did not differ significantly.

The proportion of *Sigmodon, Microtus,* and *Peromyscus* moving within the 5,000 m² experimental areas supported the hypothesis that animal movements decrease with habitat fragmentation (fig. 21.9). A larger proportion of *Sigmodon* moved within large patch areas than moved within areas with medium

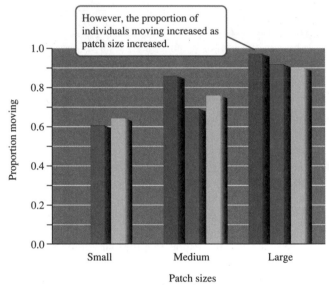

Figure 21.9 Influence of patch size on small mammal movements within experimental landscapes (data from Diffendorfer, Gaines, and Holt 1995).

patches. Because few *Sigmodon* were captured within small patch areas, their movements within these areas could not be analyzed. A larger proportion of *Microtus* and *Peromyscus* moved within large and medium patches than moved within small patches.

In summary, this experiment shows a predictable relationship between landscape structure and the movement of organisms across landscapes. As the following example shows, these results are not necessarily universal.

The Relative Importance of Landscape Structure on Organisms

Recently, Charles Krebs, of the University of British Columbia, has suggested that relative to disciplines such as behavioural ecology, population biology, and experimental biology, landscape ecology has not made great advances in the last 100 years (Krebs 2006). This point is certainly going to raise the eyebrows of some researchers, but it is representative of a fairly common feeling that landscape ecology, much like the study of mutualisms (chapter 15), has not become fully integrated into the broader ecological community. In this section we describe a few studies that have attempted to place the effects of landscape structure into the broader context of other ecological drivers. We begin with an experiment in the boreal forests of Alberta.

Fragmentation Effects of Boreal Birds

In 1997 three researchers published a landmark study on the role of fragmentation on birds in the boreal forest (Schmiegelow et al. 1997). The team consisted of Fiona Schmiegelow, formerly of the University of British Columbia and now at the University of Alberta, Craig Machtans, now with the Canadian Wildlife Service, and Susan Hannon, a professor at the University of Alberta. The basic idea was similar to that of the study by Diffendorfer and colleagues: they wanted to understand how landscape structure could alter the biology of a group of organisms. The central difference between these studies is that of scale. While Diffendorfer and colleagues created patches that ranged from 0.0032 to 0.50 ha in size, Schmiegelow and colleagues created patches that ranged from 1 to 100 ha in size (fig. 21.10). Additionally, Diffendorfer and colleagues focused on the response of 3 species, while Schmiegelow and her colleagues followed the responses of 59 species.

These differences in scale are not trivial, and instead reflect the biology of the system and organisms with which Schmiegelow, Machtans, and Hannon work. The study site was in the boreal mixedwood forest of northern Alberta. Dominant vegetation includes aspen, poplar, and spruce and the forest is home to many resident and transient bird species. The boreal forest throughout Canada is home to a large forestry industry, and Alberta is no exception. Forestry activity often results in a landscape of large and small forest fragments separated by areas of clear-cutting. Some of these fragments will be iso-lated from intact forest, while other fragments will be connected through thin belts of forest, often along the edges of rivers. A great strength of this study is that the authors set out to recreate the environment that organisms were likely to encounter in the real world, and test whether this scale of fragmentation and isolation influenced boreal bird species. In other words, Schmiegelow and her colleagues chose a spatial scale for study that was relevant to the disturbance regime that is being imposed on the boreal forest through human activity, and thus their results are of great potential importance for understanding the ecological effects of logging on boreal birds, and for developing possible strategies of mitigation.

The experimental design was straightforward, at least on paper (fig. 21.10). The research team created fragments that varied in size from small (1 ha) to large (100 ha). Fragments also varied by being connected to a forested riparian buffer, or being isolated and surrounded on all sides by clear-cutting. There was not enough room in the area to include the treatment of a 100 ha patch connected to the riparian habitat. This is one example of how implementation of an experimental design at this scale is challenging. The team made it even more difficult, but better scientifically, by using three replicates of each treatment, leading one to ask a simple question: how do three ecologists actually create an experiment on this scale? The answer was to collaborate with the Alberta Forest Service and forestry companies. The foresters were able to perform the logging necessary to create the experiment, while the ecologists were able to study the effects. Another great strength of this experiment is that it shows that industry and university biologists can work together to create outstanding science on a scale that is biologically meaningful to the organisms of interest. Because of this collaboration between industry and the research team, they were also able to measure the plants and birds in the sites the year before fragmentation occurred. In other words, because they worked with those logging the area, they were able to influence the timing and structure of the logging activity, rather than relying on a correlative study after logging had taken place. So what did they find?

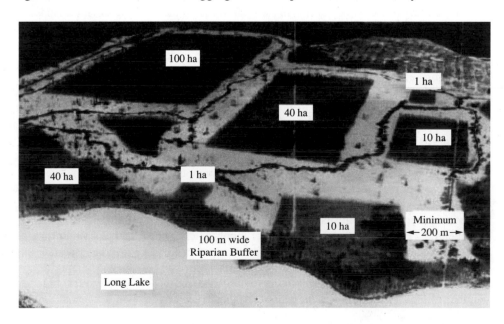

Figure 21.10   Aerial view of some of the plots in a large-scale experiment testing the effects of fragmentation on the structure of boreal bird communities (Schmiegelow et al. 1997).

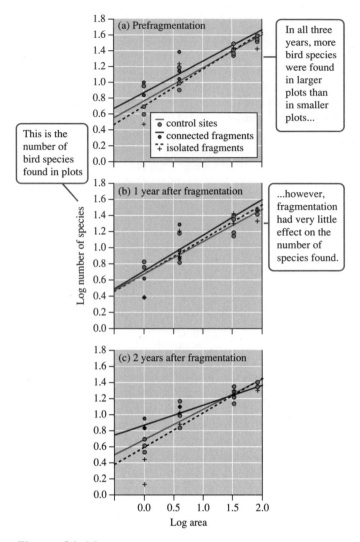

Figure 21.11 The relationship between bird community species richness and area in a large manipulative study in northern Alberta (date from Schmiegelow et al. 1997).

In total, they recorded 21,340 records of 59 bird species over three years in their study area. This is a remarkable sample size. As was expected, more species were found in larger patches, though the relationship between species richness and area was not influenced by whether patches were connected or isolated (fig. 21.11). Although species richness was roughly similar among treatments, the small isolated fragments changed in overall species composition during the experiment more than the larger and connected fragments. In other words, the bird communities were more dynamic in the small isolated patches. These patches tended to lose species that were resident species commonly found in older forests, and accumulated more transient species. Immediately following fragmentation, isolated patches had increased numbers of birds relative to the connected fragments and controls, though these effects largely disappeared by the second year of the experiment. After two years, there was some evidence that neotropical migrants and resident species were less abundant in fragmented forests than the controls, though this pattern was not found for short-distance migratory species. In general, species that prefer old

forests decreased in abundance following fragmentation, and species that prefer younger forests increased in abundance.

Overall, Schmiegelow and her colleagues observed some significant effects of fragmentation and isolation on the bird community. However, given the severity and scale of the experimental treatments, the absolute magnitude of the effects was small. The authors conclude that the breeding bird community in this boreal forest is relatively resilient to a severe disturbance, at least over the time scale of this study. At the same time, they recognize that even if the community as a whole does not seem affected by changes in landscape structure, some groups of birds clearly were.

The work by Schmiegelow and her colleagues provides a strong contrast to the results of Diffendorfer and his colleagues. At a minimum, these result show that fragmentation is not necessarily a problem for all species. Instead, some groups of organisms with specific life-history traits will be strongly affected, while other organisms will not. By demonstrating this link between life-history and the impacts of fragmentation, this study provides a critical first step in integrating landscape ecology into the larger body of ecological theory. We now turn to a model created to explore the relative effects of fragmentation versus those of habitat loss.

Fragmentation and Habitat Loss

We once again turn to work by Lenore Fahrig (1997), and show how the use of models can be an important tool in understanding the effects of one ecological process relative to other processes. For example, Schmiegelow and colleagues concluded that although there were significant effects of fragmentation, the magnitude—its potential importance—was low. Fahrig approached a similar issue from a modelling perspective. She recognized that fragmentation of a habitat has two important aspects: habitat loss and altered landscape structure. There is no doubt that the spatial pattern of fragments might alter the biological processes of the organisms in the landscape, but are these effects strong relative to the effects of habitat loss itself?

To test this, she constructed a simulation containing a number of virtual landscapes, independently varying both the *amount* and degree of *fragmentation* of "breeding habitat" for her virtual organisms. She then added a variety of rules to the landscape, such as the idea that if one organism is already in a given location, another organism can not also breed there. She then followed the population dynamics of the population, and recorded if and when the populations went extinct on the landscape.

Her results were striking. In her 2,000 simulations, decreasing habitat amounts greatly increased the risk of extinction, while increasing fragmentation only had an effect when remaining habitat cover was below 20% (fig. 21.12). In other words, across all possible landscapes, fragmentation was a minor influence for her populations; but in landscapes with very little cover, fragmentation became important. These results provide strong theoretical support for the idea that fragmentation will be important in some, but not all landscapes. In terms of management directives, protection of habitat would seem to be of greater urgency to reduce extinction risks than focusing on the spatial arrangement of the habitat. However, if habitat

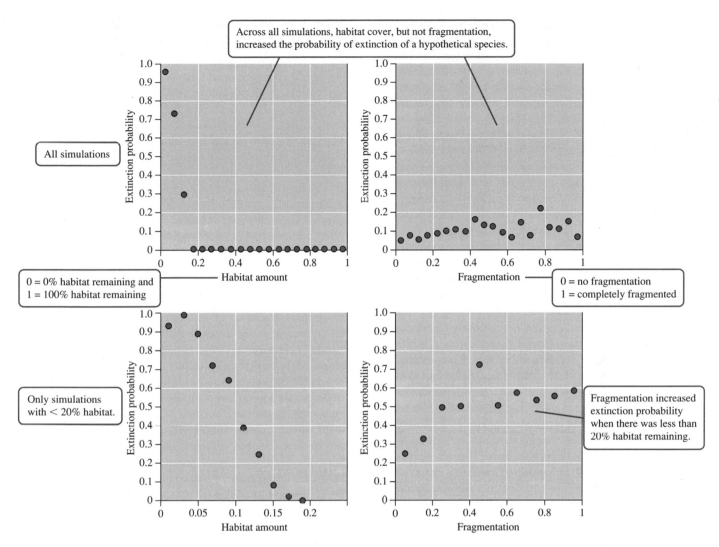

Figure 21.12 Relative effects of habitat loss and fragmentation of the probability of extinction on a virtual landscape (data from Fahrig 1997).

loss is already severe, then the arrangement of the habitat is likely something worth worrying about.

Fragmentation and Population Dynamics

Marc-André Villard, a former postdoctoral researcher who worked with Susan Hannon (whose work is described above), and now of the Université de Moncton, has also studied the role of landscape structure on the persistence of natural populations. Along with Marc Mazerolle, Villard conducted a review of the literature to determine whether including information about landscape structure improves one's ability to explain patterns of species abundances and distributions (Mazerolle and Villard 1999). They were able to find 61 empirical studies, including papers on invertebrates, amphibians, reptiles, mammals, and birds. In fact, a full 36% of the studies that they found were focused on birds! Clearly there has been a taxonomic bias in the study of fragmentation. Across all taxa, aspects of the local patch, (size, age, plant community composition, etc.) influenced species presence and abundance in over 90% of the studies. In contrast, landscape variables (total cover and configuration) were significant in only 59% of the studies. Local factors were significant for all

taxa, while the effects of landscape factors varied greatly. Only 20% of the studies on invertebrates showed an effect of landscape, in contrast to nearly 80% of the studies on vertebrates. Clearly the effects of landscape will not be the same for all species that occupy that landscape.

In this section we have shown how current research is moving beyond the stage of just documenting an effect of landscape on some biological process, and is now focused on understanding how these effects interact with other ecological processes. This is a major step in the development of this subdiscipline of ecology, and is likely setting the stage for major breakthroughs over the next 100 years. Next we explore another topic of much interest, habitat corridors.

Habitat Corridors and Movement of Organisms

If fragmentation and isolation of patches can negatively impact the population dynamics of some species, a logical conservation goal would be to connect patches, using **corridors**, thereby reducing patch isolation. Corridors are generally some sort of strip of habitat connecting patches across a landscape. This idea is so inherently attractive that it serves as a cornerstone in conservation biology, and is widely promoted by environmental lobbying groups. However, the success of corridors has not matched the hope, despite their being extensively used throughout the world. Here we will discuss the science behind corridors.

The Trans-Canada Highway is a corridor that facilitates animal (human) movement. This strip of asphalt allows us to travel quickly between widely dispersed ecosystems. However, this corridor is also a barrier to the movement of many other species (see the Ecology In Action section in this chapter). The point here is that a corridor to one species may be a barrier to another, and this poses challenges to conservation biologists. Corridors may also facilitate the movement of parasites and diseases of the species of conservation interest, highlighting the point that corridors have the potential to affect the biology of more species than the target of any conservation program. Perhaps before worrying about barriers and disease, it is important to ask an even more basic question: do animals actually use corridors?

The most current understanding of the use of corridors is provided by a review written by Cheryl-Lesley Chetkiewicz, Colleen St. Clair, and Mark Boyce (Chetkiewicz et al. 2006), all from the University of Alberta. Some of these names may be familiar. St. Clair's work on using animal behaviour to move elk out of the Banff town site was discussed in chapter 8. The work of Boyce, a population ecologist, will be discussed in more depth later in this chapter in the Ecological Tools section. This comprehensive review was initiated by Chetkiewicz while she was a Ph.D. student working with Boyce. The science behind corridors is a blending of landscape ecology, behavioural ecology, and population biology, and thus this research team was well positioned to review the field.

As a sign of the importance of corridors to ecology and conservation biology, over 700 scientific papers discussing corridors have been published. However, very few of these demonstrate that corridors actually enhance animal movement, as opposed to just providing additional habitat. Chetkiewicz and colleagues argue that the lack of detailed information linking corridors to behavioural ecology and animal movement reduces the ability to design effective corridors, limiting their potential usefulness. In other words, if some aspect of the landscape (e.g., predator densities) will prevent a target animal from entering a corridor in a certain location, then there is little economic or ecological value in putting a corridor in that location. Instead, it makes more sense to know what habitats an organism is likely to use, and then establish corridors in those areas. These ideas are very similar to what we found in the prior section, discussing the impacts of landscape structure on populations: the effects of the landscape (or corridors) will be dependent upon interactions between landscape structure, species-specific traits, and other ecological processes such as competition and predation. It is clear that much more research linking behavioural, population, and landscape ecology is needed.

Well, so what does determine where an animal moves? The tools that ecologists use to gain this information are discussed in the Ecological Tools section of this chapter. But first, we need to discuss the relationship between landscape structure and animal movement and the development of ecological patterns.

The Role of the Matrix in Influencing Animal Movement

First, this has nothing to do with Keanu Reeves or the Wachowski brothers. In the context of landscape ecology, matrix refers to the dominant, connected ecosystem on a landscape. For example, imagine a landscape that consists primarily of agricultural fields with an occasional patch of forest. In this example, the agricultural ecosystem will be the matrix. Now imagine a heavily forested area, with a single patch of agriculture on the landscape. Now it is the forest that is the matrix.

So far in this chapter we have shown that, sometimes, landscape structure can influence a variety of ecological processes, through fragmentation, isolation, and total habitat abundance. What is missing so far, and what helps differentiate landscape ecology from the study of metapopulations (chapter 10), is recognition that the identity of the matrix itself may alter biological processes. In some cases, the matrix may be completely inhospitable for a given species, while other potential matrix ecosystems may be completely permeable. As a result, the identity of the matrix has the potential to enhance, or mitigate, the effects of isolation and fragmentation. To explain this, we first turn to an example in damselflies.

Philip Taylor, of Acadia University, and a former M.Sc. student, Ian Jonsen, were interested in understanding how movement by damselflies could be altered by changes in landscape structure (Jonsen and Taylor 2000). The researchers used two species, *Calopteryx aequabilis* and *Calopteryx maculata*, both of which are able to utilize both stream and forested habitats. The experiment was conducted in the Annapolis Valley of Nova Scotia. Six field sites were identified, all of which contained a stream running through surrounding matrix vegetation. What differed among sites, however, was the identity of the matrix vegetation. In forested landscapes, the stream flowed through continuous forest; in non-forested landscapes, the stream flowed through pastures with minimal forest; and in the partially forested landscapes, the stream flowed through a mixture of pasture and forest—landscapes without a single clear matrix. Jonsen and Taylor captured a number of damselflies from each field site, moved them to streams in one of the six field sites, and measured animal movement and whether the animals left the stream habitat. A rather elegant aspect of this design is that they released all animals within the stream habitat in all landscapes. As a result, they can be certain that if an animal left the stream habitat, it was due to the surrounding vegetation (the matrix) and not due to any differences among the release sites themselves.

In total, they were able to release and follow 115 damselflies during their study. For both species, the probability of leaving the stream habitat was strongly influenced by the identity of the surrounding vegetation (fig. 21.13). Both species stayed on the stream when surrounded by a non-forested landscape, though they left the stream when forest was present. Interestingly, one species was most likely to leave when the landscape was completely forested, and the other would leave when only partially forested. This is an important result, indicating how the matrix vegetation will have different effects on different species, even sympatric congeners!

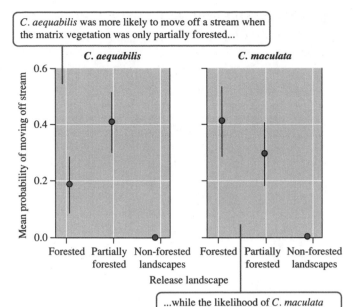

C. *aequabilis* was more likely to move off a stream when the matrix vegetation was only partially forested...

...while the likelihood of C. *maculata* decreased with decreasing forest cover.

Figure 21.13 Movement of damselflies is influenced by the surrounding landscape (data from Jonsen and Taylor 2000).

Matrix effects have also been found in other species. For example, in the boreal mixedwoods, ovenbirds and the white-throated sparrow differ in their responses to different types of matrix vegetation (Gobeil and Villard 2002). In this study, the researchers translocated birds and measured the time it took them to return to their territories as a function of the landscape structure (agricultural, harvested forest, natural forest). For the sparrow, the natural forest landscape was the least penetrable, while that landscape was the most penetrable for the ovenbird. As in the prior study, the effects of matrix vegetation and landscape structure will differ among species.

Studies like those presented here are allowing landscape ecologists not only to describe the patterns they observe in a landscape, but to also understand the ecological mechanisms that cause those patterns. This, in turn, is a critical step towards being able to use ecological knowledge to successfully manage conservation networks and design appropriate (and used) habitat corridors. We now turn our attention away from interactions between landscape structure and animal behaviour, and focus on how landscapes can alter a variety of characteristics of ecosystems themselves.

Landscape Position and Lake Chemistry

Katherine Webster and her colleagues (1996) at the Center for Limnology at the University of Wisconsin and the U.S. Geological Survey explored how the position of a lake in a landscape affects its chemical responses to drought. Drought can affect a wide range of lake ecosystem properties, including nutrient cycling and the concentrations of dissolved ions. However, all lakes do not respond in the same way to drought. For instance, while drought increased the concentration of dissolved substances in Lake 239 at the Experimental Lakes Area in Ontario, it decreased them in Nevins Lake, Michigan.

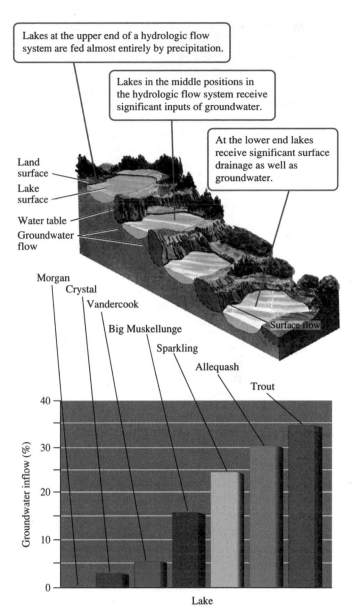

Lakes at the upper end of a hydrologic flow system are fed almost entirely by precipitation.

Lakes in the middle positions in the hydrologic flow system receive significant inputs of groundwater.

At the lower end lakes receive significant surface drainage as well as groundwater.

Figure 21.14 Lake position in the landscape and proportion of water received as groundwater (data from Webster et al. 1996).

Webster and her colleagues set out to determine whether the contrasting chemical responses of lakes to drought can be explained by the position of the lake in the landscape. They worked in northern Wisconsin, where they defined the landscape position of a lake as its location within a hydrologic flow system. The team quantified the position of a lake within a hydrologic flow system as the proportion of total water inflow supplied by groundwater.

The sources of water for a lake are precipitation, surface water, and groundwater flow. Different lakes receive different proportions of their water from these sources, and these proportions depend upon a lake's position in the landscape. Figure 21.14 shows a series of lakes along a hydrologic flow system in northern Wisconsin. Morgan Lake, which receives the bulk of its water from precipitation, occupies the upper end of this continuum. Lakes such as this one occupy high points in the

Linear Disturbances Across the Landscape

Viewed from above, it is clear that a variety of human activities have divided the landscape with sharp, linear disturbances (fig. 21.15). For example, the Trans-Canada Highway cuts a line through the centre of Banff National Park, not to mention the railroads, gas lines, and small access roads that are throughout the Park. Across the country, gas development is serving as a major source of revenue. To explore gas fields, and to transport natural gas across land, requires the construction of long linear disturbances, such as seismic lines. Forestry activity creates a variety of disturbances, from large clear-cut areas to the even more numerous large and small roads used to move equipment and timber. Even recreational use by humans, through the creation of snowmobile, ATV, motorbike, bicycle, and hiking trails, creates linear disturbances. All of these disturbances become part of the landscape for the organisms that live within these ecosystems. We all recognize that some human activities will have direct consequences for natural populations (e.g., habitat loss, hunting, etc.). Conservation biologists are becoming increasingly interested in understanding what impacts the alteration of landscape structure, through the construction of linear disturbances, has on natural populations. This issue is likely to increase in importance as both human populations and rates of natural resource use increase. Here we discuss just one type of linear disturbance, roads.

In a review of the ecological impacts of roads, Richard Forman and Lauren Alexander (Forman and Alexander 1998)

Figure 21.15   Gas pipelines cut across much of the boreal forest.

indicate that the United States alone has about 6.2 million km of roads, 10% of which are in National Forests, and only 1% are interstate highways. Clearly, the impact of roads on animals has the potential to be of importance across a very large area. They estimate that over 1,000,000 vertebrates are killed per day on roads in the United States, a number much higher than mortality due to hunting. Of greater concern, however, is the effect roads may have on the rest of the animal populations, potentially serving as barriers to the movement of genes or individuals, as well as reducing the amount of suitable habitat in a landscape. For example, Simon Dyer and Stan

hydrologic flow system and are called "hydrologically mounded" lakes. These lakes are sources of water for the rest of the hydrologic flow system. Crystal Lake and Sparkling Lake, which occupy intermediate positions within the hydrologic flow system and receive significant inflows of groundwater, are "groundwater flow through" lakes. Finally, at the lower end of the flow system, are the "drainage" lakes that receive significant surface drainage as well as groundwater drainage.

The important point here is that the positions of these lakes in the landscape determine the proportion of water they receive as groundwater. Webster and her colleagues estimated that Morgan Lake receives no groundwater inflow, while Trout Lake, at the lower end of the hydrologic flow system, receives 35% of its inflow as groundwater. The main source of water for a lake determines its response to drought.

The responses of these seven lakes to a drought were studied from 1986 to 1990. As you might expect, the levels of the lakes dropped during this four-year drought. However,

the amount of drop in lake level was related to a lake's position in the landscape. The level of Morgan Lake, at the upper end of the hydrologic flow system, dropped 0.7 m, while the levels of Vandercook, Big Muskellunge, Crystal, and Sparkling Lakes, in the middle of the hydrologic flow system, dropped 0.9 to 1.0 m. Meanwhile, the levels of Trout and Allequash Lakes, the two drainage lakes at the lower end of the hydrologic flow system, dropped very little.

Landscape position also significantly influenced a lake's chemical responses to the drought. The *concentrations* of dissolved ions such as calcium (Ca^{2+}) and magnesium (Mg^{2+}) increased in the majority of the lakes. However, the increase in ion concentration was highest at the upper and lower ends of the hydrologic flow system. Meanwhile, the combined *mass* of Ca^{2+} and Mg^{2+} increased in the three lakes at the lower end but did not change in Morgan Lake, at the upper end of the flow system, and either decreased or did not change in the lakes occupying the middle portions of the hydrologic flow system.

Boutin from the University of Alberta, along with Jack O'Neill and Shawn Wasel from a forestry company, found that the threatened woodland caribou crossed roads with moderate vehicle traffic six times less frequently than would be expected by chance (Dyer et al. 2002). Road avoidance behaviours effectively increase the isolation of patches, not due to distances, but due to a behavioural shift in the animals. Once again, this issue emphasizes the need to link animal behaviour, landscape structure, and population biology in any successful conservation program.

One example of how these disciplines can be integrated to enhance conservation efforts comes from Anthony Clevenger from Parks Canada and Nigel Waltho from York University (Clevenger and Waltho 2005). Clevenger and Waltho explored the effectiveness of different wildlife crossing structures in Banff National Park (fig. 21.16). Crossing structures have been incorporated into road development across the world, with the hope that animals will use the structures, thereby reducing mortalities due to collisions as well as increasing permeability of the landscape. Clevenger and Waltho point out that although crossings are now widespread, there is a paucity of data collected measuring whether they are actually used, and whether they result in the desired conservation goals. They decided to test the effectiveness of different crossing designs along the Trans-Canada Highway in Banff, a road that carried an average of nearly 15,000 vehicles per day in 1999. The designs used included both under- and overpasses, with construction materials ranging from concrete to metal. Over the course of 34 months, they recorded 4,209

Figure 21.16 Structures built across the Trans-Canada Highway in Banff reduce road mortality of wildlife.

uses (by identifying tracks) by large mammals, including wolves, cougars, black bears, grizzly bears, deer, elk, and humans (8%). Not surprisingly, they found that use differed among species, and the species responded differently to different structures and location of the crossings in the landscape. The information they have provided will be of great value for future ecologists as they develop new crossings for the protection of these animals in Banff, and elsewhere.

The researchers concluded that the increased mass of Ca^{2+} and Mg^{2+} seen at the lower end of the hydrologic flow system was due to an increased proportion of inflows from groundwater and surface water, sources rich in Ca^{2+} and Mg^{2+}. The declines in mass of Ca^{2+} and Mg^{2+} in Big Muskellunge Lake are likely due to reduced inflow of ion-rich groundwater. The stability of Ca^{2+} and Mg^{2+} mass in Morgan Lake was attributed to its isolation from the groundwater flow system. Morgan Lake receives almost no groundwater even during wet periods. Regardless of the mechanisms, the chemical responses of these lakes to the drought were related to their positions in the landscape.

In the first section of this chapter, we reviewed the concept of landscape structure. In this section, we explored the connection between landscape structure and landscape processes. But what creates landscape structure? Landscape structure, like the structure of populations, communities, and ecosystems, changes in response to an interplay between dynamic processes. We explore the sources of landscape structure and change below.

Concept 21.2 Review

1. Why might the effects of fragmentation on animal populations be greatest when habitat abundance is low?
2. What information is needed by ecologists to determine whether a corridor is effective at enhancing the movement and population sustainability of a particular species?
3. How can large-scale experiments be used to address questions in landscape ecology?

21.3 Origins of Landscape Structure and Change

Landscapes are structured and change in response to geological processes, climate, activities of organisms, and fire. What creates the patchiness we see in landscapes? Many forces combine in numerous ways to produce the patchiness that we call landscape structure. In this section, we review examples of how geological processes, climate, organisms, and fire contribute to landscape structure.

Geological Processes, Climate, and Landscape Structure

The geological features produced by processes such as volcanism, sedimentation, and erosion provide a primary source of landscape structure. For instance, the alluvial deposits along a river valley provide growing conditions different from those on thin, well-drained soils on nearby hills. A volcanic cinder cone in the middle of a sandy plain offers different environmental conditions than the surrounding plain. Distinctive ecosystems may develop on each of these geological surfaces, creating patchiness in the landscape. In the following example, we shall see how glaciers have contributed to the vegetative patchiness found in much of Canada and other countries of mid-to-high latitudes.

Glaciations and Vegetation Mosaics in Northern North America

Around 20,000 years ago, most of what is now Canada and the northern United States was covered by glaciers. The landscape that we see now is largely a result of the behaviour of ice and snow, creating a mosaic of soil conditions, landforms, and the substrate that forms today's ecosystems. Twenty-thousand years is hardly a blink of the eye in terms of geological time; however, the impact of glaciers in moving rocks and scouring the land more than compensates for their ephemeral nature. We begin with a brief overview of the rise and fall of glaciers. Evelyn Pielou, who we first encountered in chapter 16, has provided a most readable account of the role glaciation has played in structuring the landscape around us (Pielou 1991).

Earth's climate is subject to a variety of naturally occurring cycles (chapter 23), as well as newer impacts of human activities. Over the last many millions of years, we have had periods of **glacial ages**, within which occur **glaciations**.

Glacial ages can last millions of years, within which are approximately 100,000-year cycles that include very cold periods lasting between 60,000 and 90,000 years (glaciations), and warmer periods lasting 10,000–40,000 years (**interglacials**). We are currently living within an interglacial period of a glacial age. The last glaciation was the Wisconsin, and it reached its peak 20,000 years ago (fig. 21.17*b*). During the current interglacial period, only remnants of glaciers remain (fig. 21.17*a*), and in their place is our landscape, which was formed as the plants migrated out from areas not covered in ice.

The effects of glaciers on the physical structure of landscapes are dramatic, and can been seen all around much of Canada (fig. 21.18). Glaciers have an unrivalled ability to move soil and rock over great distances, literally reshaping the landscape. As a glacier moves forward, it carries with it large volumes of rock, scouring the landscape. More erosion occurs when rocks are ripped out of the earth as water enters cracks in the surrounding material and freezes, further widening the cracks and weakening the rock's structure. When alpine glaciers flow down valleys in mountains, they cause a U-shaped cross-section in the valley, in contrast to the familiar V-shape of valleys created by streams. Throughout a valley created by glaciers will be **talus**, great rock piles pushed aside and left behind by glaciers. Continental glaciers also leave a variety of signatures in the landscape. When the glaciers retreat, they leave behind large masses of **till**, unsorted material that includes clays, rocks, and boulders. When the till is piled up by either being pushed to the side or left behind with glacial retreat, they form **moraines**. Marking the furthest extent of glaciers are terminal moraines, formed by the materials being pushed forward. When a glacier passes over a moraine left by a prior glacier, it can be reshaped into **drumlins**, a hill (or series of hills) drained by streams. When much debris flows out of streams fed by glaciers, long narrow ridges called **eskers** can be formed. When an ice block becomes detached from the glacier, melting in place, a depression is formed called a **kettle**. As depressions generally fill with water, kettle lakes dot landscapes carved by glaciers.

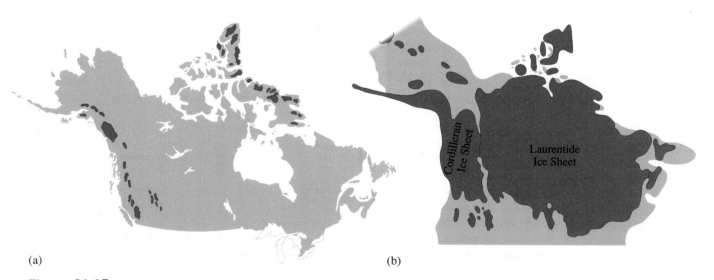

(a)   (b)

Figure 21.17   Distribution of glaciers in North America (*a*) in the late twentieth century, and (*b*) 18,000 years ago (data from Pielou 1991).

Figure 21.18 Impacts of glaciers on landscapes can be seen as (*a*) a U-shaped valley in Labrador, (*b*) a drumlin field in Manitoba, (*c*) eskers in Québec, and (*d*) a till plain in the Northwest Territories.

These physical structures are common throughout Canada and a close look while biking across the Canadian Shield will reveal the impacts of glaciers on the shape of a landscape. The story of the landscape does not end with glacial melting, instead, for the plants and animal, it just begins.

Glacial retreat reveals a bare rocky substrate. No soil, no seedbank, no plants. Very quickly, however, seeds and spores arrive and new plants grow. We have seen evidence for these plant migrations throughout the text, such as the work of Margaret Davies (chapter 1). But where exactly do these migrating plants come from? Some of these seeds come from **glacial refugia**, areas that through a variety of interactions between geology and climate were never glaciated, while others come from populations that were south of the terminal extent of the glaciers (fig. 21.19). A special type of refugia is the **nunatak**, mountain peaks that were surrounded, but not covered, by continental glaciers. Of course, not all mountains served as refugia, and instead many are (and were) home to a number of alpine glaciers that also carve a landscape into the rock.

What the colonizing plants encountered following the melt was a very diverse landscape. In some areas there was nothing but large rocks, a substrate nearly impossible to get roots into.

Others areas had fine glacial till, facilitating root growth. These geological differences persist to this day, and a great variety of ecosystems can be found within a short distance along moraines, eskers, and kettles. The spatial arrangements of these different ecosystems are caused by interactions between species-specific traits of the colonizing plants and the changes to the landscape caused by the power of glaciers.

The effects of glaciers are most visibly obvious through their direct influence on the shape of the land on which they rested. However, their true impact can be global in scale. Global sea levels rise and fall with glaciers. As we saw in chapter 3, large volumes of water are stored in glaciers. When glaciers melt, much of that water ends up in the ocean, contributing to a rise in sea levels. The effects of rising sea levels are obvious, and highlight the ephemeral (on a geological time scale) nature of mangrove islands and coral atolls (chapter 3). However, we can also imagine back to when much of the water currently found in the oceans was stored as ice across much of North America. During these periods of lower sea levels, many now isolated islands were connected by "land-bridges." These connections served as corridors for the movement of numerous species, allowing the colonization of new habitats.

Figure 21.19 These cypress hills in Alberta and Saskatchewan were the northern-most location that remained south of the glacial advance in North America. As a result, this area is home to unique vegetation and likely played a critical role in seed production and dispersal following the melt.

While geological processes and climate set the basic template for landscape structure, we show next how the activities or organisms can be an additional source of landscape structure and change.

Organisms and Landscape Structure

Organisms of all sorts, including people, influence the structure of landscapes. Many studies of landscape change have focused on the conversion of forest to agricultural landscapes. In North America, an often-cited example of this sort of landscape change is that of Cadiz Township, Green County, Wisconsin (Curtis 1956). In 1831, approximately 93.5% of Cadiz Township was forested. By 1882 the percentage of forested land had decreased to 27% and by 1902 forest cover had fallen to less than 9%. Between 1902 and 1950 the total area of forest decreased again to 3.4%. Similar changes in landscape structure have been observed throughout the midwestern region of the United States. However, in some other forested regions of North America and Europe, the pattern of recent landscape change has been different.

In eastern North America, many abandoned farms have reverted to forest and in these landscapes forest cover has increased. Recent increases in forest cover have also been observed in some parts of northern Europe. One such area is the Veluwe region in the central Netherlands. Maureen Hulshoff (1995) reviewed the landscape changes that have occurred in the Veluwe region during the past 1,200 years. The Veluwe landscape was originally dominated by a mixed deciduous forest. Then, from A.D. 800 to 1100, people gradually occupied the area and cut the forest. Consequently, forests were gradually converted to heathlands, which are landscapes dominated by low shrubs and used for livestock foraging. Later, small areas of cropland were interspersed with the extensive heathlands. During the tenth and eleventh centuries some areas were devegetated completely and converted to areas of drifting sand. The problem of drifting sand

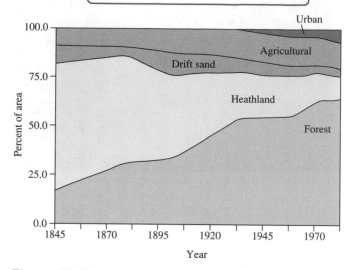

The most substantial change in this landscape in the Netherlands was a shift from predominantly heathland to predominantly forest.

Figure 21.20 Change in a Dutch landscape (data from Hulshoff 1995).

continued to increase until the end of the nineteenth century, when the Dutch government began planting pine plantations on the Veluwe landscape, a practice that continued into the twentieth century.

Figure 21.20 shows the changes in the composition of the Veluwe landscape from 1845 to 1982. The greatest change over this period was a shift in dominance from heathlands to forests. In 1845, heathlands made up 66% of the landscape, while forests constituted 17%. By 1982, coverage by heathlands had fallen to 12% of the landscape and forest coverage had risen to 64%. The figure also shows modest but ecologically significant changes in the other landscape elements. The area of drift sand reached a peak in 1898 and then dropped and held steady at 3% to 4% from 1957 to 1982. Urban areas established a significant presence beginning in 1957. Finally, coverage by agricultural areas has varied from 9% to 16% over the study interval, the least variation shown by any of the landscape elements.

As total coverage by forest and heathlands changed within the Veluwe landscape, the number and average area of forest and heath patches also changed. These changes indicate increasing fragmentation of heathlands and decreasing fragmentation of forests. For instance, between 1845 and 1982, the number of forest patches declined, while the average area of forest patches increased. During this period, the number of heath patches increased until 1957. Between 1957 and 1982, the number of heath patches decreased as some patches were eliminated. The average area of heath patches decreased rapidly between 1845 and 1931 and then remained approximately stable from 1931 to 1982.

During the period that Cadiz Township in Wisconsin was losing forest cover, this landscape element was increasing in the Veluwe district of the Netherlands. These two examples show how human activity has changed landscape structure. However, what forces drive human influences on landscapes? In both Cadiz Township and the Veluwe landscape, the driving forces were economic. A developing agricultural economy converted Cadiz Township from forest to farmland. The Veluwe landscape was converted from heathland to forest as the local sheep-raising economy collapsed in response to the introduction of synthetic fertilizers and inexpensive wool from Australia.

As we enter the twenty-first century, economically motivated human activity continues to change the structure of landscapes all over the globe. We examine current trends in land cover at the global scale in chapter 23. Before we do that, however, let's examine the effects of some other species on landscape structure.

In chapters 17 and 18 we discussed keystone species and ecosystem engineers. As you may remember, beaver activity can change the course of streams, create ponds, and alter forest structure. Using the terms from this chapter, we now explore in more depth how beavers create and modify landscape structure.

The influences of beavers on landscape structure once shaped the face of entire continents. At one time, beavers modified nearly all the temperate stream valleys in the Northern Hemisphere. The range of beavers in North America extended from arctic tundra to the Chihuahuan and Sonoran Deserts of northern Mexico, a range of approximately 15 million km². Before European colonization, the North American beaver population numbered 60 to 400 million individuals. However, fur trappers eliminated beavers from much of their historical range and nearly drove them to extinction. With protection, North American beaver populations are recovering and large areas once again show the influence of beavers on landscape structure.

Carol Johnston and Robert Naiman and their colleagues have carefully documented the substantial effects of beavers on landscape structure (e.g., Naiman et al. 1994). Much of their work has focused on the effects of beavers on the 298 km² Kabetogama Peninsula in Voyageurs National Park, Minnesota. Following their near extermination, beavers reinvaded the Kabetogama Peninsula beginning about 1925. From 1927 to 1988 the number of beaver ponds on the peninsula increased from 64 to 834, a change in pond density from 0.2 to 3.0 per square kilometre. Over this 63-year period, the area of new ecosystems created by beavers, including beaver ponds, wet meadows, and moist meadows, increased from 200 ha, about 1% of the peninsula, to 2,661 ha, about 13% of the peninsula. Foraging by beavers altered another 12% to 15% of upland areas.

Beaver activity has changed the Kabetogama Peninsula from a landscape dominated by boreal forest to a complex mosaic of ecosystems. Figure 21.21 shows how beavers have changed a 45 km² catchment on the peninsula. Between 1940 and 1986, beavers increased landscape complexity within this catchment. Similar changes have occurred over nearly the entire peninsula.

Naiman and his colleagues quantified the effects of beaver over 214 km², or 72%, of the Kabetogama Peninsula. Within this area, there are about 2,763 ha of low-lying area that can be impounded by beavers. In 1927, the majority of the landscape, 2,563 ha, was dominated by forest. In 1927,

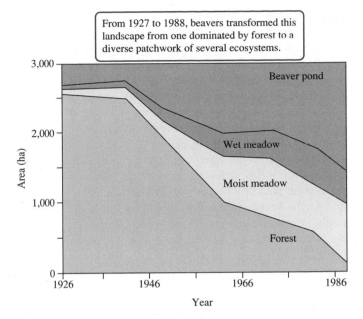

Figure 21.21 Beaver-caused landscape changes on the Kabetogama Peninsula, Minnesota (data from Naiman et al. 1994).

moist meadow, wet meadow, and pond ecosystems covered only 200 ha. By 1988, moist meadows, wet meadows, and beaver ponds covered over 2,600 ha and boreal forest was limited to 102 ha. Between 1927 and 1988, beavers transformed most of the landscape.

The changes in landscape structure induced by beavers substantially alter landscape processes such as nutrient retention. Beaver activity between 1927 and 1988 increased the quantity of most major ions and nutrients in the areas affected by impoundments. The total quantity of nitrogen increased by 72%, while the amounts of phosphorus and potassium increased by 43% and 20%, respectively. The quantities of calcium, magnesium, iron, and sulfate stored in the landscape were increased by even greater amounts.

Naiman and his colleagues offer three possible explanations for increased ion and nutrient storage in this landscape: (1) beaver ponds and their associated meadows may trap materials eroding from the surrounding landscape, (2) the rising waters of the beaver ponds may have captured nutrients formerly held in forest vegetation, and (3) the habitats created by beavers may have altered biogeochemical processes in a way that promotes nutrient retention. Whatever the precise mechanisms, beaver activity has substantially altered landscape structure and processes on the Kabetogama Peninsula.

Fire and the Structure of a Mediterranean Landscape

Fire contributes to the structure of landscapes ranging from tropical savanna to boreal forest. However, fire plays a particularly prominent role in regions with a Mediterranean climate. As we saw in chapter 2, terrestrial ecosystems in regions with Mediterranean climates, which support Mediterranean woodlands and shrublands, are subject to frequent burning. Hot, dry summers combined with vegetation rich in essential oils create ideal conditions for fires, which can be easily ignited by lightning or humans. In regions with a Mediterranean climate, fire is responsible for a great deal of landscape structure and change.

Richard Minnich (1983) used satellite photos to reconstruct the fire history of southern California and northern Baja California, Mexico, from 1971 to 1980, and found that the landscapes of both areas consist of a patchwork of new and old burns. Though these regions experience similar Mediterranean climates and support similar natural vegetation, their fire histories diverged significantly in the early twentieth century. For centuries, lightning-caused fires burned, sometimes for months, until they burned out naturally. In addition, Spanish and Anglo-American residents would set fire to the land routinely to improve grazing for cattle and sheep. Then, early in the twentieth century, various government agencies in southern California began to suppress fires to protect property within an increasingly urbanized landscape.

Minnich proposed that the different fire histories of southern California and northern Baja California might produce landscapes of different structure. He suggested that fire suppression allowed more biomass to accumulate and set the stage for large, uncontrollable fires. His specific hypothesis was that the average area burned by wildfires would be greater in southern California.

Minnich tested his hypothesis using satellite images taken from 1972 to 1980 (fig. 21.22). He found that between 1972 and 1980 the total area burned in the two regions was fairly similar (fig. 21.23). However, the size of burns differed significantly between the two regions. The frequency of small burns below 1,000 ha was higher in northern Baja California, while large burns above 3,000 ha were more frequent in southern California. Consequently, median burn size in southern California, 3,500 ha, was over twice that observed in Baja California, 1,600 ha (fig. 21.23).

Figure 21.22 Areas of Mediterranean shrubland in southern California periodically burn over large areas, destroying human habitations in the process.

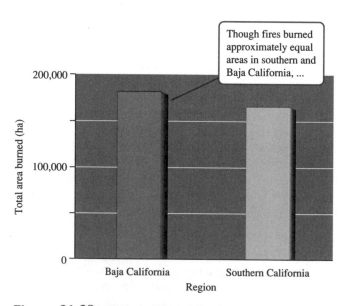

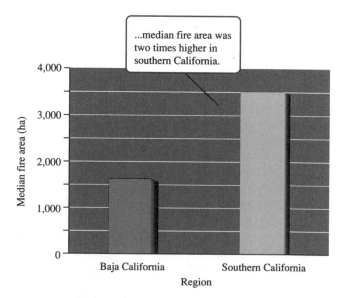

Figure 21.23 Characteristics of fires in the Mediterranean landscapes of southern and Baja California from 1972 to 1980 (data from Minnich 1983).

These results are consistent with Minnich's hypothesis, but do they show conclusively that differences in fire management in southern California and Baja California have produced a difference in burn area? Other factors may contribute to the observed differences in the fire mosaic, including climatic differences, differences in age structure of vegetation, and topographic differences. The exploration of fire's influence on the structure of Mediterranean landscapes continues.

In this section, we have seen how geological processes, climate, the activities of organisms, and fire can contribute to landscape structure and change. In the next section we explore how ecologists are able to assess the impacts of the landscape features on animal populations.

Concept 21.3 Review

1. What similarities are shared between beavers and glaciers in constructing the shape of a landscape?
2. Do the patterns described by Minnich (fig. 21.23) conclusively show that the differences in burn area in the two regions are the result of different fire management practices?
3. What are some common means by which humans modify landscape structure?

Ecological Tools

Linking Population, Behavioural, and Landscape Ecology

How much change to the landscape is too much to sustain natural populations of animals? What areas of the landscape are used by species of concern and thus are a high conservation priority? What areas on the landscape are rarely used, and thus industrial development may have a less negative impact if located there? These are critical questions in ecology and conservation biology. In the last several years, there has been a growing appreciation that animal behaviour and landscapes are intimately tied. To begin to provide answers to the questions above, ecologists must work across disciplines, and truly understand the systems in which they work. The rapid increase in available computing power has facilitated research, allowing the construction of detailed models predicting which ecological parameters are, or are not, likely to influence animal populations on the landscape. In this section, we will explore how ecologists are working at blending population, landscape, and behavioural ecology, with important consequences for management and conservation of natural resources.

Using Thresholds to Estimate Risk

There is significant societal pressure to "develop" natural areas. Development can take a variety of forms, including oil and gas exploration, construction of residential areas, forestry, agriculture, water extraction, dams, and road construction. As we have seen in this chapter, every activity that occurs changes the structure of the landscape. In some cases, these changes have no meaningful consequence for the long-term sustainability of natural populations. In other cases, these changes may cause the collapse of a population. Assuming politicians value land-use planning that protects both economic interests and ecological sustainability, it is critical that ecologists provide tools that help identify risk. The key question becomes: how much habitat loss and change in landscape structure is too much?

The answer to this depends upon whether the effects of habitat loss and changes to landscape structure have propor-

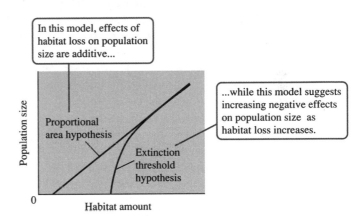

In this model, effects of habitat loss on population size are additive...

...while this model suggests increasing negative effects on population size as habitat loss increases.

Population size

Proportional area hypothesis

Extinction threshold hypothesis

0   Habitat amount

Figure 21.24   Two possible relationships between habitat abundance and population sizes (Fahrig 2003).

tional or disproportional effects on populations (fig. 21.24). Lenore Fahrig, whom we have highlighted before, has written a review exploring the impacts of fragmentation and habitat loss on populations (Fahrig 2003). She has found that the majority of theoretical studies suggest that the relationship between habitat amount and population sizes will be nonlinear. If this is true, it means that at some amount of habitat, well above zero, a population will go extinct (fig. 21.24). Fahrig suggests that habitat fragmentation can alter the exact location of this threshold, though empirical data is sparse. Regardless of the data available right now, thresholds are one tool that may allow a researcher to predict at what point development may switch a landscape from one that can support sustainable populations (or the organisms of interest) to one that can not.

These ideas form the basis of **conservation thresholds**, points at which habitat loss and fragmentation cause populations to tip from sustainable to extinct. Ecologists are charged with finding those tipping points before they are reached. If these thresholds can be identified, then they can be incorporated into a regional land-use plan, ensuring adequate areas are left undeveloped, while also allowing for development in areas that are redundant in terms of population sustainability.

This approach recognizes that different citizens value different things (development, wilderness, sustainability), and the threshold approach holds promise by setting the point at which balanced land uses are no longer viable. We turn to New Brunswick for an example.

Marc-André Villard and a former graduate student, Jean-Sébastien Guénette, of the Université de Moncton, explore whether thresholds can be a useful concept for conservation planning of forest bird species (Guénette and Villard 2005). The researchers conducted their study in a 1,891 km² managed forest in northwestern New Brunswick. About 27% of the landscape consists of hills covered with forests dominated by sugar maples and American beech. In the valleys and on hilltops there also exists coniferous (20%) and mixedwood forests (13%). The remaining area consists of forest plantations (spruce), roads, and water. The dominant human land-use in this area is logging. The deciduous stands are logged by removing subsets of a stand (approximately 20%–40% volume in a process called "single-tree selection") every 20–50 years. The coniferous forests are clear-cut, with tree-planting crews hired to (generally) plant monocultures of seedlings in their place. Guénette and Villard wanted to understand how forest birds (songbirds and woodpeckers) responded to this diverse landscape and these disturbance regimes.

To measure bird communities, they laid out 5–10 sampling stations in each of 43 sites. The sites were located using a stratified, systematic design (chapter 16), ensuring that they sampled all ecosystem types on the landscape. In each of three summers, they went to the sampling stations and recorded the presence of birds. They did this by arriving very early in the day and identifying any bird they saw during a 15-minute interval. During 5 of the 15 minutes, they played a recording of a Black-capped Chickadee mobbing call. Many bird species respond to these calls, which makes them easier to detect. In addition to the detailed data on birds, the researchers also sampled the plant community composition at each station. They measured at total of 23 plant variables such as canopy height, groundcover, and sapling densities.

The more complicated aspects of the study came at the time of statistical analyses. Quite simply, Guénette and Villard had an enormous dataset. They had measures of all bird species across the landscape, along with information on land-use practices, and 23 measures of the vegetation. The first step was to use a statistical procedure called *ordination* (see appendix A) to collapse the vegetation data into few dimensions. A strength of ordination techniques is that they allow an ecologist to take a complicated and multidimensional data set (such as that Guénette and Villard had compiled) and collapse many variables into just a few dimensions. Ordinations work by creating new variables that represent trends in groups of variables. In the resulting ordination diagram (fig. 21.25), each data point represents a single sampling station. In the Guénette and Villard study, data points that are close together represent areas that were similar in the vegetation measures taken. Knowing that, you can see that the plant communities differ among harvest treatment types (fig. 21.25). Addition-

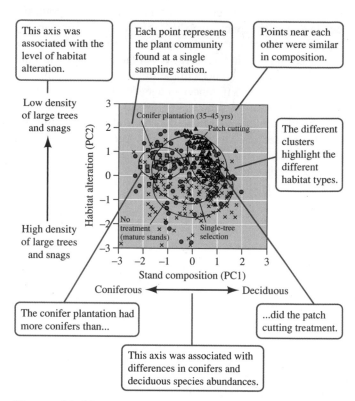

Figure 21.25 Results of an ordination describing variation in the local vegetation among 390 sampling stations (data from Guénette and Villard 2005).

ally, when they looked at what variables were correlated with each axis, they found that the x-axis was driven primarily by species composition, and the y-axis by variables related to harvest. The critical tests of the study are then to determine how bird distributions were correlated with this y-axis, the measure of habitat alteration.

Of the 42 bird species that were regularly found at the stations, 25 were significantly associated with the degree of habitat alteration (y-axis in figure 21.25). Of these, eight species were "sensitive," decreasing in abundance with increasing alteration even after controlling for differences in plant species composition. Another seven species had a positive relationship with habitat alteration, even after accounting for differences in plant species composition. Why would a species respond positively to logging? Birds, like all taxonomic groups, consist of species with diverse life-history strategies (chapter 9). The environment of high resources and rapid growth following logging is clearly suitable for a suite of colonizing bird species. Returning to the sensitive species, was there evidence of a threshold?

As you might expect, the answer depends to some extent on which species is being looked at (fig. 21.26). The ovenbird, golden-crowned kinglet, and winter wren show clear non-linearity it the relationship between occurrence and habitat alteration, while the Blackburnian warbler does not. The models suggested that one should only find all the sensitive species when canopy closure was about 70%, or there were at least 80 large trees/ha. Going below either of these thresholds increased the probability of losing at least one species. Which

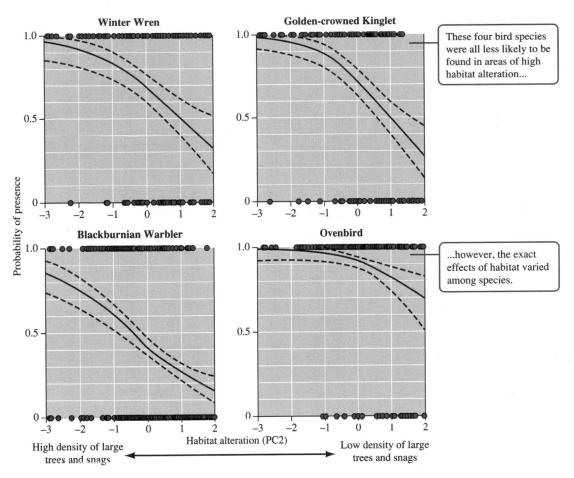

Figure 21.26 The results of the ordination presented in figure 21.25 are used here to help predict the occurrence of four bird species (data from Guénette and Villard 2005).

species would be lost depends on species-specific traits and which forest type is being studied. Knowing that thresholds exist, at least for these species, provides land managers with the information they need to develop a management plan that allows for the long-term sustainability of populations.

As effective as conservation thresholds may be, they are not the only method available to ecologists and conservation biologists. Next we explore another method, resource selection functions.

Using Resource Selection Functions to Link Movement to the Landscape

As we have seen, thresholds can be a valuable tool in helping ecologists and land managers understand the point at which development is likely to cause collapse of natural populations. There exists a complementary approach that is also proving to be critical to the development of scientifically sound management strategies. This approach, resource selection functions (RSF), also blends measures of the local environment, landscape, and animal behaviour in models that allow researchers to describe (and predict) where animals will be found on the landscape. As we have discussed previously in the chapter, this information is critical to the development of corridors that actually serve as corridors. Only by knowing

what habitat animals will actually use can one hope to be successful in having functional links between isolated fragments.

Mark Boyce, of the University of Alberta, has been a leading advocate for greater use of resource selection functions in ecology. Boyce argues that the basis of RSFs is very straightforward: if one wants to know the distribution and abundance of species on a landscape, then it makes sense to know the distribution of resources on the landscape (Boyce and McDonald 1999). The mathematics behind RSF are beyond the scope of this textbook, but the output from the models they produce is very understandable. If a model determines that some factor, such as elk density, is associated with the probably of some other factor, such as the presences of wolves, then the model will generate a probability function. In this case, the RSF would represent the probability of finding a wolf as a function of elk density. To develop this model requires locating large numbers of individuals of the species of concern through one of the methods previously discussed in chapter 10 (e.g. radiotelemetry, trapping, etc.). At the same time, the researchers would measure all aspects of their locations. Additional data would be collected about locations that the animals were not found in. The factors measured could include abiotic conditions, abundance of predators and prey, vegetation and habitat complexity, and any other factor thought to influence the ecology of that particular species.

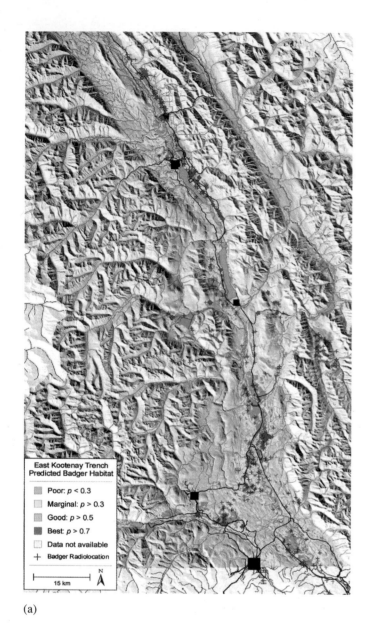

(a)

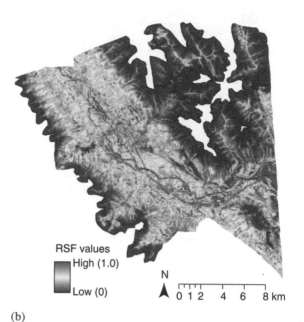

(b)

Figure 21.27 RSF predict the preferred and avoided habitat for (*a*) badgers in the east Kootenays of British Columbia (Apps et al. 2002), and (*b*) grizzly bears around Canmore, Alberta (Chetkiewicz et al. 2006).

A statistical model would then be constructed that relates the location of animals to these landscape and environmental measures. Those factors found to be of minimal explanatory power are usually discarded, resulting in a model that identifies what are likely the most important factors influencing the dis-

tribution of the animals on this particular landscape. Perhaps in this case that would include elk density, snow depth, and slope. What is particularly attractive about RSF is that these functions can all be combined on a map of the landscape, showing exactly where animals are most likely to occur (fig. 21.27). The maps that are developed are then very helpful guides for land managers, allowing them to visually understand which habitats on the landscape are preferred by the species of concern. This approach is rapidly spreading throughout western Canada, including the large national parks of Jasper and Banff.

RSFs, like thresholds, show that ecologists are developing the research tools that are critical to understanding the factors that drive species distributions and abundances. At the core of the models is the realization that there will not be a single factor that is most important, but instead a suite of processes and conditions will influence the distribution of the species of concern.

Summary

A landscape is a heterogeneous area composed of several ecosystems. The ecosystems making up a landscape generally form a mosaic of visually distinctive patches. These patches are called *landscape elements. Landscape ecology* is the study of landscape structure and processes.

Landscape structure includes the size, shape, composition, number, and position of patches, or landscape elements, in a landscape. Most questions in landscape ecology require that ecologists quantify landscape structure. Until recently, however, geometry, which means "earth measurement," could offer only rough approximations of complex landscape structure. Today, an area of mathematics called fractal geometry can be used to quantify the structure of complex natural shapes. One of the findings of fractal geometry is that the length of the perimeter of complex shapes depends upon the size of the device used to measure the perimeter. One implication of this result is that organisms of different sizes may use the environment in very different ways.

Landscape structure influences processes such as the flow of energy, materials, and species distributions between the ecosystems within a landscape. Landscape ecologists have proposed that landscape structure, especially the size, number, and isolation of habitat patches, can interact with other ecological processes such as competition, predation, and behaviour, to influence populations and communities. Studies of the movements of small mammals in a prairie landscape show that a smaller proportion of individuals moves in more fragmented landscape but that the individuals that do move will move farther. Not all studies of landscape structure suggest biologically meaningful effects on natural populations. Fragmentation of the boreal forest appears to have only minor effects on the species composition of boreal bird communities. However, some species responded quite strongly, indicating that landscape structure can interact with species-specific traits. Habitat loss and local processes such as habitat quality appear to have stronger impacts on most species than landscape structure. However, some species, particularly large mobile species, appear to be strongly affected by changes in landscape structure. Habitat corridors may reduce the negative effects of fragmentation and patch isolation for some species; however, there is little empirical data indicating current practices in corridor design result in the desired conservation goals. Not all ecosystems on a landscape are equally permeable to animal movement, and thus the contrast between a patch and the surrounding matrix ecosystem can serve as another factor altering animal movement. The source of water for lakes in a Wisconsin lake district is determined by their positions in the landscape, which in turn determine their hydrologic and chemical responses to drought.

Landscapes are structured and change in response to geological processes, climate, activities of organisms, and fire. Geological features produced by processes such as volcanism, sedimentation, and erosion interact with climate to provide a primary source of landscape structure. Repeated glaciations in North America have created much of the landscape that is currently found in Canada. We are currently living in an interglacial period, with the last glaciation reaching a peak approximately 20,000 years ago. Glacial movement causes scouring and translocation of substantial amount of soil, creating a topologically diverse landscape. The resulting variation in soil textures influences the distribution of plant species and ecosystems. While geological processes and climate set the basic template for landscape structure, the activities of organisms, from plants to elephants, can be an additional source of landscape structure and change. Economically motivated human activity changes the structure of landscapes all over the globe. Beavers can quickly change landscape structure and processes over large regions. Fire contributes to the structure of landscapes ranging from tropical savanna to boreal forest. However, fire plays a particularly prominent role in regions with a Mediterranean climate.

Society requires scientific knowledge about the ecological impacts of landscape development. Providing answers requires a coordinated approach among landscape, population, and behavioural ecologists. Ecologists are currently using threshold models to understand the potential impacts of habitat loss on the distribution of forest bird species. These models require the use of ordination, a statistical procedure that reduces the dimensionality of ecological data sets. Resource selection functions can be used to predict habitats of high and low "value" for focal species. These approaches are critical to the development of successful corridors, conservation programs, and finding actual balances between development and species protection.

Review Questions

1. How does landscape ecology differ from ecosystem and community ecology? What questions might an ecosystem ecologist ask about a forest? What questions might a community ecologist ask about the same forest? Now, what kinds of questions would a landscape ecologist ask about a forested landscape?

2. How should the *area* of forest patches in an agricultural landscape affect the proportion of bird species in a community that are associated with forest edge habitats? How should patch area affect the presence of birds associated with forest interiors?

3. In the figure to the right, the green areas represent forest fragments surrounded by agriculture. Landscapes 1 and 2 contain the same total forest area. Will landscape 1 or 2 contain more forest interior species? Explain.

Landscape 1

Landscape 2

4. How might the *shapes* of forest patches in a landscape affect the proportion of birds in the community associated with forest edge habitat? How might patch shape affect the presence of birds associated with forest interior?

5. Consider the following options for preserving patches of riverside forest. Again, the two landscapes below contain the same total area of forest but the patches in the two landscapes differ in shape. Which of the two would be most dominated by forest edge species?

Landscape 1

Landscape 2

6. In this chapter, we have presented evidence that landscape structure can influence population growth. In Section III we presented the idea that some populations exist as metapopulations. Describe the similarities and the differences between landscape ecology and metapopulations. Do aspects of the landscape necessarily influence metapopulation dynamics?

7. How do the positions of patches in a landscape affect the movement of individuals among habitat patches and among portions of a metapopulation? Again, consider the hypothetical landscapes shown in question 5. Which of the two landscapes would promote the highest rate of movement of individuals between forest patches? Can you think of any circumstances in which it might be desirable to reduce the movement of individuals across a landscape? (Hint: Think of the potential threat of pathogens that are spread mainly by direct contact between individuals within a population.)

8. Use fractal geometry and the niche concept to explain why the canopy of a forest should accommodate more species of predaceous insects than insectivorous birds. Assume that the numbers of bird and predaceous insect species are limited by competition.

9. Several of the studies we have discussed in this chapter find few effects of landscape structure on some natural populations. Other species, however, respond very strongly to changes in landscape structure. What aspects of an organism's life-history are likely to determine whether or not a species responds? What types of shifts in landscape structure are most likely to cause biological effects?

10. How do the activities of animals affect landscape heterogeneity? You might use either beaver or human activity as your model. What parallels can you think of between the influence of animal activity on landscape heterogeneity and the intermediate disturbance hypothesis? Which is concerned with the effect of disturbance on species diversity?

Suggested Readings

Berggren, Å, B. Birath, and O. Kindvall. 2002. Effect of corridors and habitat edges on dispersal behavior, movement rates, and movement angles in Roesel's bush-cricket (*Metrioptera roeseli*). *Conservation Biology* 16:1562–69.

Berggren, Å, A. Carlson, and O. Kindvall. 2001. The effect of landscape composition on colonization success, growth rate and dispersal in introduced bush-crickets *Metrioptera roeseli*. *Journal of Animal Ecology* 70:663–70.

These two studies give a highly detailed assessment of how landscape structure, particularly corridors, affect behaviour and population persistance. The studies span several years and employ a small arthropod as a model, experimental organism.

Bayley, P. B. 1995. Understanding large river floodplain ecosystems. *Bio Science* 45:153–58.

An excellent introduction to the structure and dynamics of riverine landscapes.

Dunford, W. and K. Freemark. 2004. Matrix matters: effects of surrounding land uses on forest birds near Ottawa, Canada. *Landscape Ecology* 20:497–511.

Dunford and Freemark document the influence that land use in the matrix surrounding a forest patch has on bird abundance and species richness.

Ellis, A. M., et al. 2005. Loss of foundation species: consequences for the structure and dynamics of forested ecosystems. *Frontiers in Ecology and the Environment* 9:479–86.

This paper summarizes the major changes that are occurring in forested landscapes as a consequence of the loss of foundation species. It also clarifies the history and meaning of the term "foundation species."

Johnson, C. J., M.S. Boyce, R. L. Case, H. D. Cluft, R. J. Gav, A. Gunn, and R. Mulders. 2005. Cumulative affects of human developments on acrtic wildlife. *Wildlife Monographs* (160): 1–36.

This study uses resource section functions to explore impacts of development on a number of arctic mammals.

Tewksbury, J. J., D. J. Levey, N. M. Haddad, S. Sargent, J. L. Orrock, A. Weldon, B. J. Danielson, J. Brinderhoff, E. I. Damschen, and P. Townsend. 2002. Corridors affect plants, animals and their interactions in fragmented landscapes. *Proceedings of the National Academy of Sciences of the United States of America* 99:12923–12926.

An experimental study that goes beyond the usual focus to show the positive effects of corridors on critical species interactions.

Wu, J. and R. Hobbs. 2002. Key issues and research priorities in landscape ecology: an idiosyncratic synthesis. *Landscape Ecology* 17:355–65.

An excellent summary and synthesis of the central issues and research priorities within the field of landscape ecology.

Chapter 22

Geographic Ecology

Outline

Geographic ecology began on June 5, 1799, as Alexander von Humboldt and Aimé Bonpland sailed out of the port of Coruña in northwest Spain. Their small Spanish ship managed to slip past a British naval blockade and sail on, first to the Canary Islands and then to South America. Humboldt was a Prussian engineer and scientist and Bonpland was a French botanist. Humboldt came equipped with the finest scientific instruments of the time and was prepared to systematically survey the lands that he and Bonpland would visit. He wrote a letter to a friend a few hours before his ship left port outlining his purpose for the expedition: "I shall try to find out how the forces of nature interreact upon one another and *how the geographic environment influences plant and animal life* [emphasis added]."

Humboldt and Bonpland carried passports issued by the court of King Carlos IV of Spain, giving them permission to conduct scientific studies throughout the Spanish Empire, which then stretched from California to Texas in North America and south to the tip of South America. They had complete access to a vast area of the earth's surface that was essentially unexplored scientifically, and they put that access to productive use. Because their discoveries were so numerous and their explorations so thorough, Simón Bolívar, the liberator of most of Spanish America, referred to Humboldt as "the discoverer of the New World."

Humboldt's expedition was one of the most ambitious scientific explorations of the age. During the course of their expedition Humboldt and Bonpland travelled nearly 10,000 km through South and North America. They travelled on foot, by canoe, or on horseback, visiting latitudes ranging between 12° S and 52° N. They also climbed to nearly 5,900 m on the slopes of Chimborazo; the highest ascent by anyone in history up to that time (fig. 22.1).

The physical feats of their expedition, however, never took precedence over their scientific purpose. For instance, on their climb of Chimborazo, they faced the uncertain dangers of high altitude. Yet, as blood oozed from their lips and gums, Humboldt and Bonpland recorded the altitudinal distributions of plants and animals. Later, Humboldt organized their observations of climate

and plant distributions into ingenious visual representations of plant geography. What he did not accomplish, he inspired others to. One of those inspired to follow in Humboldt's footsteps was Charles Darwin. Darwin said that his reading of Humboldt's expedition to South America set the course of his whole life.

Robert H. MacArthur (1972) defined geographic ecology as the "search for patterns of plant and animal life that can be put on a map." MacArthur's map might include an archipelago of islands, a region, or a series of continents. Somewhere above the level of local community and ecosystem ecology and even above the level of landscapes is the realm of *geographic ecology*. Though geographic ecology began long before MacArthur, with explorers such as Humboldt, Darwin, and Wallace, MacArthur put an indelible quantitative stamp on the field when he and E. O. Wilson published their first models of island biogeography.

The development of geographic ecology continues as new generations of scientists equipped with a diversity of tools, both ancient and modern, search for the elusive patterns that can be put on maps. The breadth of geographic ecology is as vast as its subject. Consequently, we concentrate our discussions in chapter 22 on just a few aspects of the field: island biogeography, latitudinal patterns of species diversity, and the influences of large-scale regional and historical processes on biological diversity.

Concepts

22.1 On islands and habitat patches on continents, species richness increases with area and decreases with isolation.

22.2 Species richness on islands can be modelled as a dynamic balance between immigration and extinction of species.

22.3 Species richness generally increases from middle and high latitudes to the equator.

22.4 Long-term historical and regional processes significantly influence the structure of biotas and ecosystems.

22.1 Area, Isolation, and Species Richness

On islands and habitat patches on continents, species richness increases with area and decreases with isolation.

Sampling Area and Number of Species

A quantitative relationship between area and number of species was first developed by Olof Arrhenius (1921), a pioneer in the area of geographic ecology. Arrhenius made his observations on islands near Stockholm, Sweden, where he worked within several plant communities that he identified by names such as *herb–Pinus wood and shore association*. He counted the number of species within areas of various sizes and then

Figure 22.1   On the slopes of Chimborazo, a 6,310 m high volcanic peak in the Andes Mountains of Ecuador, Alexander von Humboldt and Aimé Bonpland meticulously recorded the altitudinal distributions of plants.

developed a mathematical description of the relationship between area sampled and number of plant species. However, Arrhenius worked at scales much smaller than the geographic focus of chapter 22. To see the first quantitative work on geographic patterns, we have to move to a later time.

Island Area and Species Richness

David Currie, of the University of Ottawa, and his graduate student, Attila Kalmar, examined the relationship between island area and bird species (Kalmar and Currie 2006). They compiled data on 346 marine islands scattered throughout the globe. Islands included in the database varied in size from 0.1 km² to 800,000 km², and were found in all major climatic regions on the planet. They then searched through field guides, checklists, and specialized journals to compile lists of the breeding bird species found on each of the islands. Across all islands, there was a clear relationship between island area and the number of bird species found (fig. 22.2a). The large dataset also shows that some islands have substantially lower diversity for their size than would be expected. Kalmar and Currie suggest that island area results in an upper bound to diversity, while other factors such as extreme temperatures and precipitation can suppress diversity on the island. The relationship between island area and number of species is not just a property of bird assemblages. Sven Nilsson, Jan Bengtsson, and Stefan Ås (1988) explored patterns of species richness among woody plants, carabid beetles, and land snails on 17 islands in Lake Mälaren, Sweden. The islands ranged in area from 0.6 to 75 ha and were all forested. The researchers were careful to choose islands that showed few or no signs of human disturbance. One of the results of their study was that island area was the best single predictor of species richness in all three groups of organisms. Figure 22.2b shows the relationship found between island area and number of carabid beetles.

When most of us think of islands, the picture that generally comes to mind is a small bit of land in the middle of an ocean. However, many habitats on continents are so isolated that they can be considered as islands.

Habitat Patches on Continents: Mountain Islands

The many isolated mountain ranges that extend across the Great Basin and southwestern regions of North America are now continental islands. During the late Pleistocene, 11,000 to 15,000 years ago, forest and woodland habitats extended unbroken from the Rocky Mountains to the Sierra Nevada in California. Then as the Pleistocene ended and the climate warmed, forest and alpine habitats contracted to the tops of the high mountains scattered across the American Southwest. As montane habitats retreated to higher elevations, woodland, shrubland, grassland, or desert scrub vegetation invaded the lower elevations. As a consequence of these changes, once-continuous forest and alpine vegetation was converted to a series of islandlike habitat patches associated with mountains and therefore called *montane*.

As montane vegetation contracted to mountaintops, montane animals followed. Mark Lomolino, James H. Brown,

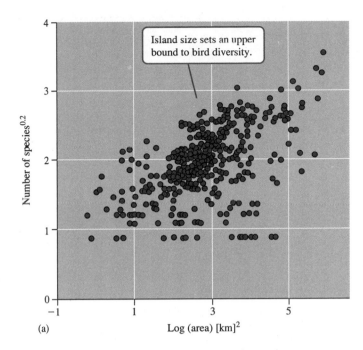

(a)

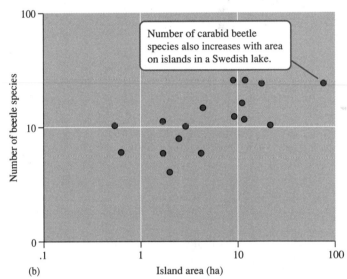

(b)

Figure 22.2 Relationship between island area and number of species (data from Kalmar and Currie 2006; Nilsson, Bengtsson, and Ås 1988).

and Russell Davis (1989) studied the diversity of montane mammals on isolated mountains in the American Southwest. They focused on the distributions of 26 species of nonflying forest mammals that occur on 27 montane islands. They chose mountain ranges that had been studied thoroughly enough so that their mammal faunas were well known. The list of species, which included shrews, ermine, squirrels, chipmunks, and voles, was limited to species that show a strong association with montane environments.

The team found that montane mammal richness was positively correlated with habitat area. As figure 22.3 shows, the area of the 27 montane islands ranged from less than 7 km² to over 10,000 km², while the number of montane mammals on them ranged from 1 to 16.

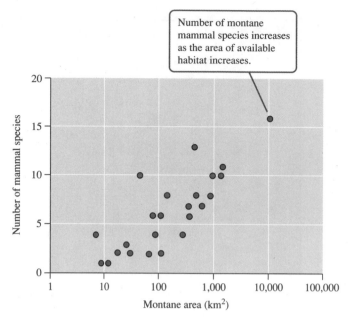

Figure 22.3 Area of montane habitat and number of montane mammal species on isolated mountain ranges in the American Southwest (data from Lomolino, Brown, and Davis 1989).

Lakes as Islands

Lakes can also be considered as habitat islands—aquatic environments isolated from other aquatic environments by land. However, lakes differ widely in their degree of isolation. Seepage lakes, which receive no surface drainage, are completely isolated, while drainage lakes, which have stream inlets and/or outlets, are less isolated (see chapter 21).

Bill Tonn, now of the University of Alberta, and John Magnuson of the University of Wisconsin (1982) studied patterns of species composition and richness among fish inhabiting lakes in northern Wisconsin. They focused their research on 18 lakes in the Northern Highlands Lake District of Wisconsin and Michigan. The study was conducted in Vilas County, Wisconsin, which includes over 1,300 lakes (fig. 22.4). With so many lakes at their disposal, Tonn and

Magnuson could match lakes carefully for a variety of characteristics. All 18 study lakes had similar bottom substrates and similar maximum depths. However, the lakes spanned a considerable range of surface area (2.4–89.8 ha). Ten of the lakes were drainage lakes or spring fed and eight lakes were seepage lakes. Eight lakes had a history of low oxygen content during winter.

Tonn and Magnuson collected a total of 23 species, 22 in summer and 18 in winter. If we combine their winter and summer collections on each lake and plot total species richness against area, there is a significant positive relationship (fig. 22.4). Once again, we see that the number of species increases with the area of an insular environment. However, these researchers worked with a single lake district. Is there a relationship between lake area and diversity when lakes from several regions are included in the analysis?

Clyde Barbour and James H. Brown (1974) studied patterns of species richness across a worldwide sample of 70 lakes. The lakes in their sample ranged in area from 0.8 to 436,000 km^2, while the number of fish species ranged from 5 to 245. Barbour and Brown also found a positive relationship between area and fish species richness.

Island Isolation and Species Richness

There is often a negative relationship between the isolation of an island and the number of species it supports. However, because organisms differ substantially in dispersal rates, an island that is very isolated for one group of organisms may be completely accessible to another group.

Marine Islands

We now return to the study of Kalmar and Currie (2006), who explored patterns of diversity among marine islands distributed across the planet. Because the researchers knew the location of each island (fig. 22.5a), they were able to measure the linear distance between the island and the nearest continental shore. The relationship between isolation and bird species richness is clear: the more isolated the island, the fewer bird species that will be found (fig. 22.5b).

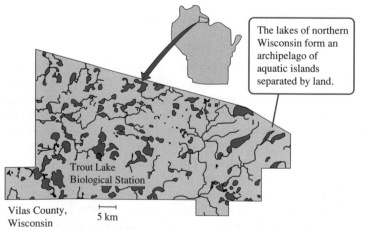

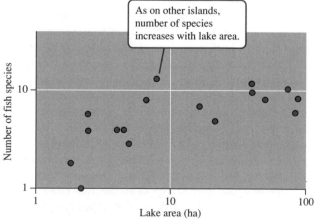

Figure 22.4 Lake area and number of fish species in lakes of northern Wisconsin (data from Tonn and Magnuson 1982).

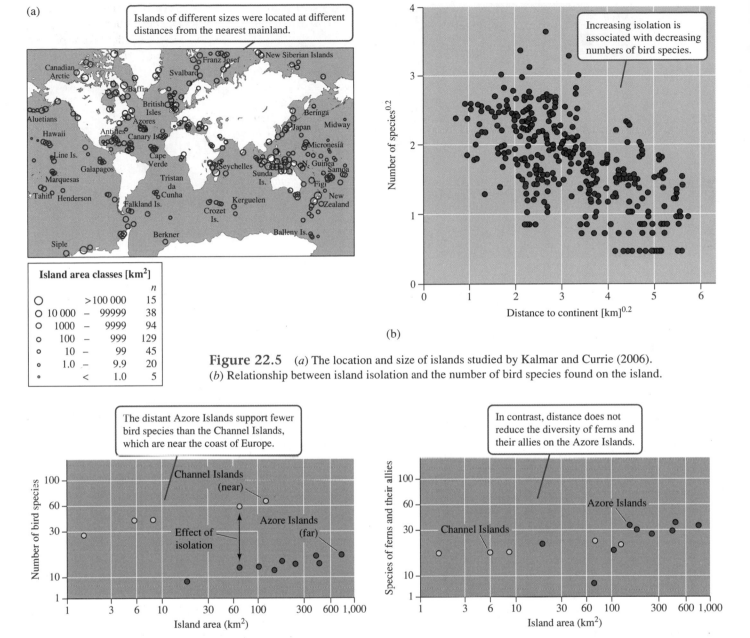

Figure 22.5 (*a*) The location and size of islands studied by Kalmar and Currie (2006). (*b*) Relationship between island isolation and the number of bird species found on the island.

Figure 22.6 Influence of isolation on diversity of birds and ferns and their allies on the Channel and Azore Islands (data from Williamson 1981).

Comparative studies of diversity patterns on islands remind us that different organisms have markedly different dispersal abilities. Mark Williamson (1981) summarized the data for the relationship between island area and species richness for various groups of organisms inhabiting the Azore and Channel Islands. The Azore Islands lie approximately 1,600 km west of the Iberian Peninsula, while the Channel Islands are very near the coast of France. While vastly different in distance from mainland areas, both island groups experience moist temperate climates and have biotas that are of European origin. Consequently, a comparison of their biotas should reveal the potential influence of isolation on diversity.

Figure 22.6 shows Williamson's summary of species area relationships for ferns and fernlike plants (pteridophytes) and

land- and water-breeding birds. Both groups of organisms show a positive relationship between island area and diversity on both the Channel and Azore Islands. However, while birds show a clear influence of isolation on diversity, pteridophytes do not. Notice that bird species richness is lower on Azore Islands compared to Channel Islands of similar size. Meanwhile, pteridophyte diversity is similar on islands of comparable size in the two island groups.

These differences in pattern show that the 1,600 km of ocean between the Azore Islands and the European mainland reduces the diversity of birds but not pteridophytes. These differences in the effect of isolation reflect differences in the dispersal rates of these organisms. While land birds must fly across water barriers, pteridophytes produce large quantities

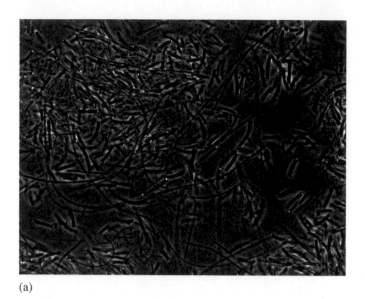

(a)

(b)

Figure 22.7 Cyanobacteria of the (a) genus *Synechococcus* form (b) mats that line hot springs around the world.

of light spores that are easily dispersed by wind. One species of pteridophyte, bracken fern, has naturally established populations throughout the globe, including New Guinea, Britain, Hawaii, and New Mexico. When we consider the potential effects of isolation on diversity, we must also consider the dispersal capabilities of the study organisms.

Isolation of a Thermophilic Cyanobacteria

Studies of geographic isolation generally focus on plants, mammals, birds, and other relatively large taxa. Part of this bias comes from the general bias towards the study of larger organisms that we have discussed throughout the book. Another aspect comes from a long-standing assumption that free-living microbes are widely distributed, and thus unlikely to show effects of isolation on patterns of population and community structure. There is substantial support for this idea, with numerous examples of widespread distributions of bacteria on land and in the water. However, as Thane Papke, from Dalhousie University, and his colleagues show, some microbes show effects of geographic isolation.

In locations throughout the world, springs can be heated by a variety of sources (geothermal heat, magma, etc), causing what are commonly referred to as "hot springs." We may be most familiar with the hot springs found in the Rocky Mountains, a prime destination for visitors of Banff, Jasper, and other parks. Or we may think of Old Faithful Geyser in Yellowstone National Park in the United States. Environmental conditions in hot springs can be extreme, with some hot springs having water temperatures near boiling point (or even above in the case of a geyser). Even the cooler hot springs will be elevated in temperature compared to the surrounding (non-hot) springs. It may come as no surprise that hot springs are home to a number of thermophilic bacteria. These microbes have very narrow niche requirements, and many species are unable to live outside of hot springs. As a result, these bacteria living in hot springs scattered across the world are similar to birds or mammals that can only

live on mountaintops or other isolated habitats. Therefore, if isolation from other habitats can cause shifts in community structure, there should be variation in the composition of the microbial populations found in hot springs across the planet.

Prior work has indicated that one genus of cyanobacteria, *Synechococcus* (Fig. 22.7), is particularly diverse, and this group was the focus for Papke and his colleagues (Papke et al. 2003). As we discussed in chapter 4, the definition of "species" is complicated, and the biological species concept simply does not apply to the microbial world. Instead, researchers measure diversity by determining the number of genetically distinct clones they find within some sample. Papke and colleagues were able to isolate clones from numerous hot springs in North America, Japan, New Zealand, and Italy. Because they sampled multiple hot springs in different regions within each of these widely separated geographic locations, there were able to explore variation in species composition of this group of cyanobacteria. If geographic isolation is not important, one would expect to find most clones of *Synechococcus* even in widely separated locations.

Across their samples, there was clear evidence for geographical isolation. This isolation occurred at the largest scale, such as North America vs. Japan, as well as finer scales, such as variation among hot springs within North America. Importantly, the variation among locations could not be explained by variations in the chemical properties of the hot springs. Instead, hot springs with similar chemical properties contained different species assemblages if they were isolated from each other. These results show that geographical isolation can impact even the smallest of organisms, such as these cyanobacteria. The study of geographic ecology of microbes remains in its infancy, with substantial surprises yet to be uncovered.

In the next section, we take a dynamic, rather than static, view of island diversity. This will serve as the foundation for one of the most influential theories in ecology, the equilibrium model of island biogeography.

Concept 22.1 Review

1. In chapter 21 we discussed how species number decreases with increasing habitat loss. Drawing from the information in this section, provide an explanation for that pattern.
2. In Figure 22.2*a*, island size appears to set a maximal, rather than minimal, boundary for bird diversity. Why?

22.2 The Equilibrium Model of Island Biogeography

Species richness on islands can be modelled as a dynamic balance between immigration and extinction of species. The examples we just reviewed show clear relationships between species richness and island area and isolation. When confronted with such a pattern, scientists look for explanatory mechanisms. What mechanisms might increase species richness on large islands and reduce richness on small and isolated islands? MacArthur and Wilson (1963, 1967) proposed a model that explained patterns of species diversity on islands as the result of a balance between rates of immigration and extinction (fig. 22.8). This model is called the **equilibrium model of island biogeography**.

Figure 22.8 shows that the model presents rates of immigration and extinction as a function of numbers of species on islands. How might rates of immigration and extinction be influenced by the numbers of species on an island? To answer this question, we need to understand what MacArthur and Wilson meant by rates of immigration and extinction. They defined the *rate of immigration* as the rate of arrival of *new* species on an island. *Rate of extinction* was the rate at which species went extinct on the island. MacArthur and Wilson reasoned that rates of immigration would be highest on a new island with no organisms, since every species that arrived at the island would be new. Then as species began to accumulate on an island, the rate of immigration would decline since fewer and fewer arrivals would be new species. They called the point at which the immigration line touches the horizontal axis *P* because it is the point representing the entire "pool" of species that might immigrate to the island.

How might numbers of species on an island affect the rate of extinction? MacArthur and Wilson predicted that the rate of extinction would rise with increasing numbers of species on an island for three reasons: (1) the presence of more species creates a larger pool of potential extinctions, (2) as the number of species on an island increases, the population size of each might diminish, increasing risk of extinction, and (3) as the number of species on an island increases, the potential for competitive interactions between species will increase.

Since the immigration line falls and the extinction line rises as number of species increases, the two lines must cross as shown in figure 22.8. What is the significance of the point where the two lines cross? The point where the two lines cross predicts the number of species that will occur on an island. Thus, the equilibrium model represents the diversity of species on islands as the result of a dynamic balance between immigration and extinction.

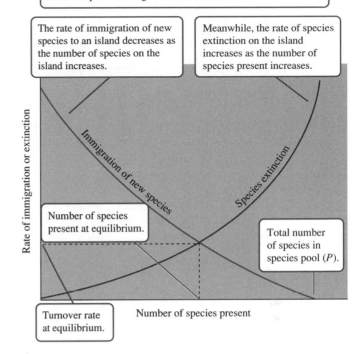

According to the equilibrium model of island biogeography, the number of species on an island is determined by a balance between species immigration and extinction.

The rate of immigration of new species to an island decreases as the number of species on the island increases.

Meanwhile, the rate of species extinction on the island increases as the number of species present increases.

Immigration of new species

Species extinction

Rate of immigration or extinction

Number of species present at equilibrium.

Total number of species in species pool (*P*).

Turnover rate at equilibrium.

Number of species present

Figure 22.8 Equilibrium model of island biogeography (data from MacArthur and Wilson 1963).

MacArthur and Wilson used the equilibrium model to predict how island size and isolation should affect rates of immigration and extinction. They proposed that the rate of immigration is mainly determined by an island's distance from a source of immigrants; for example, the distance of an oceanic island from a mainland. They proposed that rates of extinction on islands would be determined mainly by island size. These predictions are represented in figure 22.9. Notice that the figure predicts that large, near islands will support the greatest number of species, while small, far islands will support the lowest number of species. The model predicts that small, near islands and large, far islands will support intermediate numbers of species.

The predictions of the equilibrium model of island biogeography are consistent with the patterns of island diversity reviewed in the previous section. Large islands hold more species than small islands, and islands near sources of immigrants hold more species than islands far from sources of immigrants. We should expect the equilibrium model to be consistent with known variation in species richness across islands since MacArthur and Wilson designed their model to explain the known patterns. Did the equilibrium model make any new predictions? The main new predictions were (1) that island diversity is the outcome of a highly dynamic balance between immigration and extinction and (2) that the rates of immigration and extinction are determined mainly by the isolation and area of islands. In other words, the equilibrium model predicts that the species composition on islands is not static but changes over time. Ecologists call this change in species composition **species turnover.**

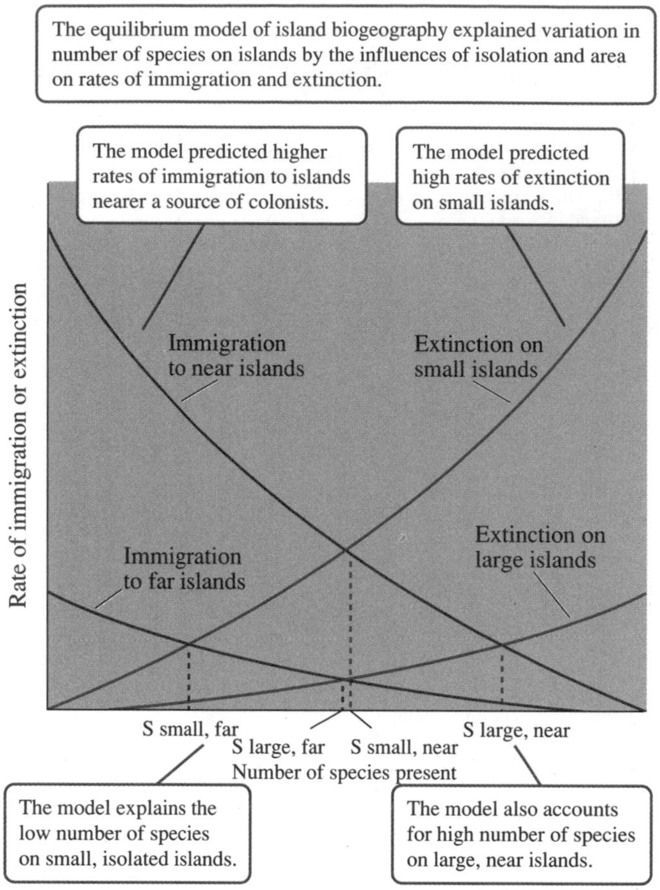
The equilibrium model of island biogeography explained variation in number of species on islands by the influences of isolation and area on rates of immigration and extinction.
The model predicted higher rates of immigration to islands nearer a source of colonists.
The model predicted high rates of extinction on small islands.
Immigration to near islands
Extinction on small islands
Extinction on large islands
Immigration to far islands
Rate of immigration or extinction
S small, far
S large, far
S small, near
S large, near
Number of species present
The model explains the low number of species on small, isolated islands.
The model also accounts for high number of species on large, near islands.

Figure 22.9 Island distance and area and rates of immigration and extinction (data from MacArthur and Wilson 1963).

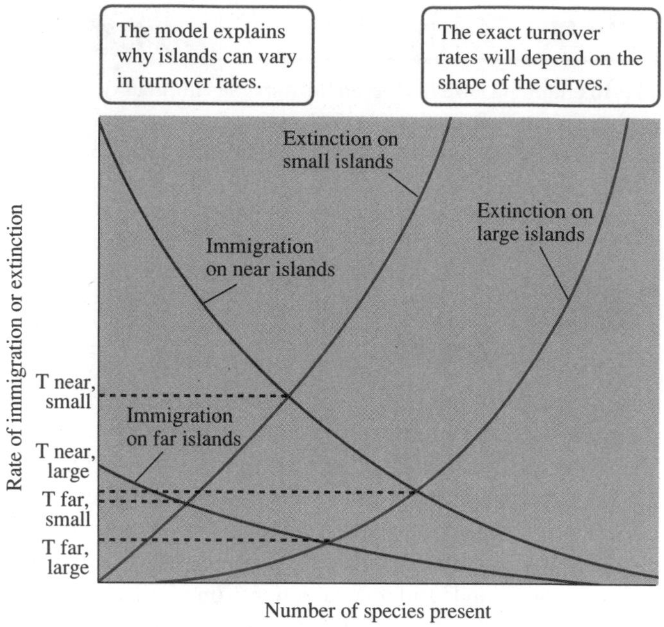
The model explains why islands can vary in turnover rates.
The exact turnover rates will depend on the shape of the curves.
Extinction on small islands
Extinction on large islands
Immigration on near islands
Immigration on far islands
Rate of immigration or extinction
T near, small
T near, large
T far, small
T far, large
Number of species present

Figure 22.10 Island distance and size influence species turnover rates (from MacArthur and Wilson 1963).

Species Turnover on Islands

In the equilibrium model of island biogeography, the equilibrium number of species predicted to be found on an island is determined by the value of species richness (x-axis) where immigration and extinction rates intersect (fig. 22.9). However, another critical prediction of this theory is that distance from mainland and island size will influence the rate of species turnover on the island. In other words, on some islands species will be predicted to persist for long periods, while the same species are predicted to persist only briefly on other islands. Using this model, how can we predict which islands will have higher, or lower, turnover rates? The answer lies in taking a close look at the y-axis, the one that describes immigration and extinction rates. Just as the value of the x-axis at equilibrium indicates the equilibrium species richness, the value of the y-axis at equilibrium indicates the equilibrium turnover rate. You can see in figure 20.10 that turnover rates are predicted to be highest on small, near islands, and lowest and large, far islands. These conditions are different for where we predict the highest, and lowest, number of species. It may seem paradoxical to talk about species turnover at equilibrium. However, it is important to remember that this model of biogeography predicts solely the number of species and rate of change, not the identity of the species on the island. Based upon this model, do you think that species composition is likely to be at equilibrium on any island? As you will see below, species turnover on islands is much more than a theoretical concept.

Turnover of bird species was demonstrated on the California Channel Islands by Jared Diamond (1969). Diamond surveyed the birds of the nine California Channel Islands in 1968, approximately 50 years after an earlier survey by A. B. Howell. The islands range in area from less than 3 to 249 km^2 and lie 12 to 61 km from the coast of southern California (fig. 22.11). Howell had thoroughly censused all of the islands except for San Miguel and Santa Rosa Islands, where he had difficulty getting permission to do bird surveys. In his later study, Diamond had full access to all the islands and was able to survey all land and water birds.

The results of Diamond's study support the equilibrium model of island biogeography. The number of bird species inhabiting the California Channel Islands remained almost constant over the 50 years between the two censuses. However, this stability in numbers of species was the result of an approximately equal number of immigrations and extinctions on each of the islands (fig. 22.11). Diamond's study is an excellent example of how theory can guide field ecology. He discovered the dynamics underlying the diversity of birds on the California Channel Islands because he went out to test the MacArthur-Wilson equilibrium model of island biogeography. Additional insights into this model have been provided by experiments.

Experimental Island Biogeography

As Diamond conducted his surveys of the California Channel Islands, Daniel Simberloff and Edward O. Wilson were engaged in experimental studies of mangrove islands in the Florida Keys (Wilson and Simberloff 1969, Simberloff and Wilson 1969). The Florida Keys support very large stands of mangroves, which are dominated by the red mangrove, *Rhizophora mangle*. Many of

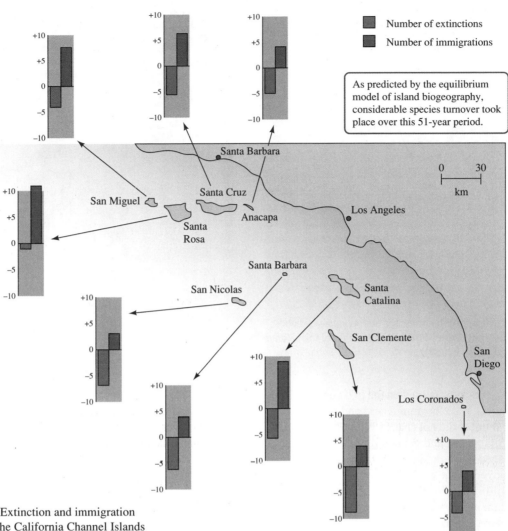

Figure 22.11 Extinction and immigration of bird species on the California Channel Islands between 1917 and 1968 (data from Diamond 1969).

these stands occur as small islands that lie hundreds of meters from the nearest large patch of mangroves (fig. 22.12). Simberloff and Wilson chose eight of these small mangrove islands for their experimental study. Their study islands were roughly circular and varied from 11 to 18 m in diameter and 5 to 10 m in height. The distance of islands from large areas of mangroves that could act as a source of colonists varied from 2 to 1,188 m.

The main fauna inhabiting the small mangrove islands of the Florida Keys are arthropods, chiefly insects. Simberloff and Wilson estimated that of the approximately 4,000 species of insects in the Florida Keys, about 500 species inhabit mangroves. Of these 500 species, about 75 commonly live on small mangrove islands. In addition to insects, the mangroves supported 15 species of spiders and other arthropods. The number of insect species on the experimental islands averaged 20 to 40 and the number of spider species ranged from 2 to 10.

Simberloff and Wilson chose two of the islands to act as controls and designated the six others as experimental islands. They carefully surveyed all the islands prior to defaunating the experimental islands. The islands were defaunated by enclosing them with a tent and then fumigating with methyl bromide. Fumigating was done at night to avoid heat damage to the man-

Figure 22.12 The mangrove islands in the Florida Keys, which number in the thousands, are convenient places to test the equilibrium model of island biogeography.

grove trees. Simberloff and Wilson examined the trees immediately after fumigating and found that, with the possible exception of some wood-boring insect larvae, all arthropods had been killed. They followed recolonization by periodically censusing the arthropods on each island for approximately one year.

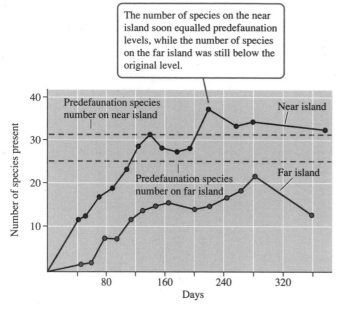

Figure 22.13 Colonization curves for two mangrove islands that were "near" and "far" from sources of potential colonists (data from Simberloff and Wilson 1969).

The number of species recorded on the two control islands was virtually identical at the beginning and end of the experiment. Though the number did not change significantly over the period of study, Simberloff and Wilson reported that species composition changed considerably. In other words, there had been species turnover on the control islands, a result consistent with the equilibrium model of island biogeography.

The equilibrium model was also supported by the recolonization studies of the experimental islands. Following defaunation, the number of arthropod species increased on all of the islands. All the islands, except the farthest island, eventually supported about the same number of species as they did prior to defaunation (fig. 22.13). Again, however, the composition of arthropods on the islands was substantially different, indicating species turnover. Species turnover is also indicated by the colonization histories of individual islands, which include many examples of species appearing and then disappearing from the community.

Island colonization can be followed either by removing the organisms from existing islands, as Simberloff and Wilson did when they defaunated their mangrove islands, or by creating new islands. Many new islands formed in a large lake in southern Sweden when the level of the lake was dropped at the end of the nineteenth century. Fortunately, some biologists recognized the rare opportunity offered by the new islands and studied their colonization by plants. These studies have continued for a century.

Colonization of New Islands by Plants

The site of this long-term study is Lake Hjälmaren, which covers about 478 km² in Sweden (fig. 22.14). The level of Lake Hjälmaren was lowered 1.3 m between 1882 and 1886 and exposed many new islands. The first plant surveys of the new

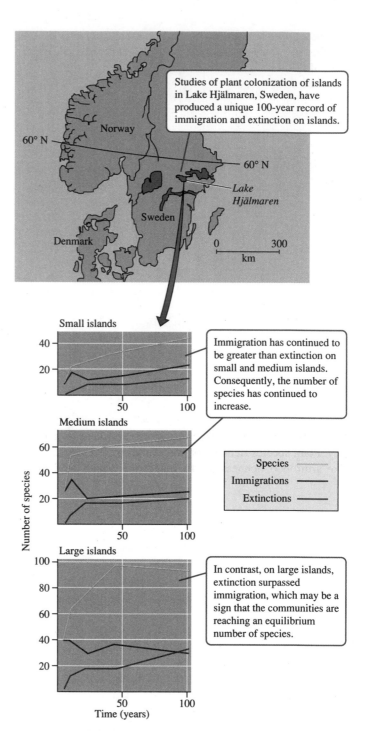

Figure 22.14 Species number, immigration, and extinction on 30 islands in Lake Hjälmaren, Sweden (data from Rydin and Borgegård 1988).

islands were conducted in 1886, and the islands were surveyed again in 1892, from 1903 to 1904, from 1927 to 1928, and from 1984 to 1985. Håkan Rydin and Sven-Olov Borgegård (1988) summarized the earlier surveys of these new islands and conducted their own surveys in 1985. The result was a unique long-term record of the colonization of 40 islands.

The study islands vary in area from 65 m² to over 25,000 m² and support a limited diversity of plants. Rydin and Borgegård estimated that approximately 700 species of plants occur around Lake Hjälmaren. Of these 700 plant species, the number recorded on individual islands during the first century of their existence varied from 0 to 127. As expected, this variation in species richness correlated positively with island area over the entire history of the islands and accounted for 44% to 85% of the variation in species richness among islands. Measures of island isolation accounted for 4% to 10% of the variation in plant species richness among islands through the 1903–04 census. Island isolation did not account for significant variation in species richness among islands in subsequent censuses.

Rydin and Borgegård used the censuses of 30 islands to estimate rates of plant immigration and extinction (fig. 22.14). The historical record documents many immigrations and extinctions. There has been a slight excess of immigrations over extinctions on small- and medium-sized islands during the entire 100 years of record. What do these higher rates of immigration indicate? They show that small and medium islands continue to accumulate species. In contrast, large islands attained approximately equal rates of immigration and extinction sometime between 1928 and 1985. Over this period, approximately 30 plants became extinct on each large island and another 30 new species arrived. In other words, it appears that the number of species may have reached equilibrium on large islands.

The observed patterns of colonization were consistent with the predictions of the equilibrium model of island biogeography. Plant species richness on the islands of Lake Hjälmaren, like arthropod richness on the mangrove islands studied by Simberloff and Wilson, appears to be maintained by a dynamic interplay between immigration and local extinction. Many studies support the basic predictions of the equilibrium model of island biogeography. However, many questions remain.

For instance, why do larger islands support more species? Is the greater species richness on large islands due to a direct effect of area or do large islands support higher species richness because they include a greater diversity of habitats? Rydin and Borgegård found that measures of habitat diversity on the study islands accounted for only 1% to 2% of the variation in plant species richness. However, they point out that while some large islands with few habitats support low numbers of plant species, some small islands, with diverse habitats, support higher species richness than would be expected on the basis of area alone. The researchers point out that it is very difficult to separate the effects of habitat diversity from the effects of area. As we shall see in the next example, there is at least one experiment that came close to demonstrating that species richness on islands can be directly affected by area.

Manipulating Island Area

Daniel Simberloff (1976) tested the effect of island area on species richness experimentally. He surveyed the arthropods inhabiting nine mangrove islands that ranged in area from 262 to 1,263 m². The distance of these islands from large areas of mangrove forest ranged from 2 to 432 m. The islands were up to five times the size of the mangrove islands fumigated by Simberloff and Wilson in their earlier study of recolonization and so contained a larger number of arthropod species.

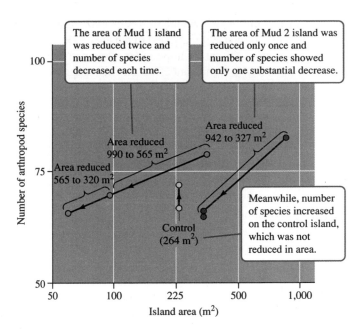

Figure 22.15   Effect of reducing mangrove island area on number of arthropod species (data from Simberloff 1976).

Simberloff kept one island as a control, while reducing the area of the eight other islands by 32% to 76%. Island area was reduced during low tide by removing whole sections of the islands. Workers cut mangroves off below the high tide level and loaded the cut trees and branches on a barge. They then moved the cut material away from the island, where they sank it into deeper water (green mangrove wood sinks). Simberloff reduced the area of four experimental islands twice and the area of the other four experimental islands once only.

The results of Simberloff's experiment show a positive relationship between area and species richness. In all cases where island area was reduced, species richness decreased (fig. 22.15). Meanwhile, species richness on the control island, which was not changed in area, increased slightly. Additional insights are offered by the contrasting histories of islands whose areas were reduced once and those whose areas were reduced twice. For instance, the area of Mud 2 island was reduced from 942 to 327 m² and the richness of its arthropod fauna fell from 79 to 62 species. The area of Mud 2 was not reduced further, and its arthropod richness remained almost constant. Meanwhile, the islands whose area was reduced twice lost species with each reduction in area. Simberloff's results showed that area itself, without increased habitat heterogeneity, has a positive influence on species richness.

Island Biogeography Update

The equilibrium theory of island biogeography has had a major influence on the disciplines of biogeography and ecology. However, much has been discovered in the 40 years since MacArthur and Wilson proposed their theory. For instance, James Brown and Astrid Kodric-Brown (1977) showed how higher rates of immigration to near islands can reduce extinction rates. As a consequence, we now know that, contrary to the original MacArthur-Wilson model, island distance from sources of colonists can influence rates of extinction. Similarly, Mark Lomolino (1990) also extended the original model when he proposed the target hypothesis, demonstrating that island area can have a significant effect on rates of immigration to islands. Brown and Lomolino (2000) pointed out that we have also discovered that species richness is not in equilibrium on many islands. In addition, we now know that species richness on islands is affected by differences among species groups in their speciation, colonization, and extinction rates. And perhaps most significantly, area and isolation are only two of several environmental factors that affect species richness on islands. Brown and Lomolino suggest that we may be on the eve of another revolution in theories that will replace the MacArthur-Wilson model. If so, it will be the result of research largely inspired by their theory as well as by our fascination for the islands themselves.

Experiments on islands such as those of Simberloff and Wilson demonstrate the value of an experimental approach to answering ecological questions. However, there are important ecological patterns that occur over such large scales that experiments are virtually impossible. The ecologists who study these large-scale patterns must rely on other approaches. In the next section, we discuss one of these important large-scale patterns, latitudinal variation in species richness.

Concept 22.2 Review

1. Why are virtually all estimates of immigration and extinction rates on islands underestimates of the true rates?
2. What result would have been grounds for Diamond to reject the equilibrium model of island biogeography based on his studies of the California Channel Islands?
3. In the course of studies by Simberloff and Wilson (1969) and Simberloff (1976), several mangrove islands were defaunated and several were partially destroyed to reduce island area. Do such experiments raise ethical issues?

22.3 Latitudinal Gradients in Species Richness

Species richness generally increases from middle and high latitudes to the equator.   Most groups of organisms are more species-rich in the tropics. This well-known increase in species richness toward the equator became apparent by the middle of the eighteenth century as taxonomists, led by Carolus Linnaeus, described tropical species sent back to Europe by explorers. These explorers and later naturalists, such as Humboldt, Darwin, and Wallace, described overwhelming biological diversity in the tropics. Today, two and a half centuries later, we are still trying to catalogue this diversity and do not even know within an order of magnitude its full extent.

Figures 22.16 and 22.17 show examples of how plant species richness (Reid and Miller 1989) and bird species richness (Dobzhansky 1950) decrease toward the poles. Despite some exceptions to the equatorial peak in species diversity (fig. 22.18), the pattern of increased numbers of species in

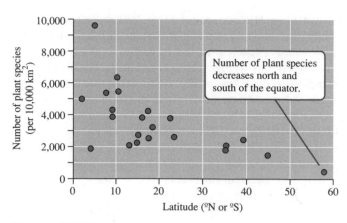

Figure 22.16   Variation in number of vascular plant species with latitude in the Western Hemisphere (data from Reid and Miller 1989).

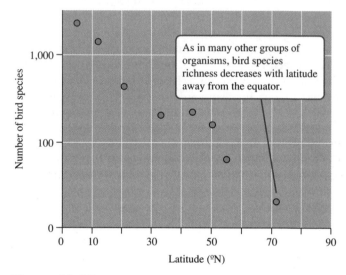

Figure 22.17   Latitudinal variation in number of bird species from Central to North America (data from Dobzhansky 1950).

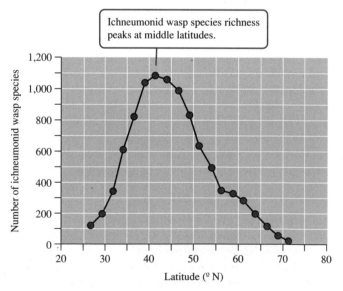

Figure 22.18   An exception to the general decline in species number with latitude: latitudinal variation in ichneumonid wasp species richness (data from Janzen 1981).

the tropics is pervasive and dramatic. This pattern challenges ecologists for an explanation. Many mechanisms have been proposed to explain latitudinal gradients in species richness. James H. Brown (1988) grouped the hypotheses proposed to explain geographic gradients in species richness into six categories.

Time Since Perturbation

The *time since perturbation hypothesis* proposes that there are more species in the tropics because the tropics are older and they are disturbed less frequently. That is, more species occur in the tropics because (1) there has been more time for speciation and (2) less frequent perturbation reduces extinction rates. The proponents of this hypothesis assume that the tropics have remained relatively stable while middle and high latitudes have been repeatedly disrupted by the advance and retreat of glaciers. However, in chapter 16 we saw that intermediate levels of disturbance may increase local diversity. In counterpoint to this hypothesis, Joseph Connell (1978) proposed that the extraordinary diversity of tropical rain forests and coral reefs is maintained by frequent disturbance.

Productivity

The authors of the *productivity hypothesis* observe that two of the most diverse environments on earth, coral reefs and tropical rain forests, are also extraordinarily productive. This hypothesis proposes that high productivity contributes to high species richness. It assumes that with more energy to divide among organisms, specialized consumers will have larger populations. Since larger populations generally have lower probabilities of extinction than smaller populations, extinction rates should be lower in more productive environments. However, Brown points out that this hypothesis must somehow explain the reduction in species diversity that accompanies nutrient enrichment and increased primary production (see chapter 16).

Environmental Heterogeneity

The *environmental heterogeneity hypothesis* proposes that the tropics contain more species because they are more heterogeneous than temperate regions. Daniel Janzen (1967) and George Stevens (1989) pointed out that, compared to high-latitude species, most tropical species occur in far fewer environments along altitudinal and latitudinal gradients.

Michael Rosenzweig (1992), however, cautioned that we cannot consider habitat structure independently of the organisms living in a region. Species within more diverse communities tend to subdivide the environment more finely. Consequently, species diversity and habitat heterogeneity are not necessarily independent factors. For instance, when G.W. Cox and Robert Ricklefs (1977) estimated the number of habitats used by birds in Panama versus four Caribbean islands, they found an inverse relationship between numbers of species and the number of habitats used by the birds. In other words, birds appeared to restrict their habitat use in the presence of more species.

Favourableness

The *favourableness hypothesis* proposes that the tropics provide a more favourable environment than do high latitudes. As we saw in chapter 2, the variation in temperature in high-latitude environments is much greater than in tropical environments. Biologists have proposed that the correspondence between low diversity and the physical variability of high latitudes is no accident. While many species are well adapted to physically harsh conditions, most species on earth are not. Biologists have proposed that physically extreme environments restrict the diversity of organisms. Brown also pointed out that many of the most physically extreme environments are small and isolated. As we saw when we discussed island biogeography, small habitat area and isolation are correlated with reduced species richness.

Niche Breadths and Interspecific Interactions

Biologists have tried to explain latitudinal gradients in species diversity with several hypotheses concerning relative niche breadths and interspecific interactions. Their hypotheses have included:

1. Tropical species are limited more by biological factors than by physical factors.
2. Tropical species are affected more by interspecific interactions than by intraspecific interactions.
3. The niches of tropical species overlap more than those of higher-latitude species and so tropical species compete more intensively.
4. Tropical species are more specialized, that is, have narrower niches, and so compete less intensively than species at higher latitudes.
5. Tropical species are more subject to controls by predators, parasites, and pathogens.
6. Compared to temperate species, tropical species are involved in more mutualistic interactions.

Brown suggested that these hypotheses present the ecologist with a number of difficulties. Notice that some of these hypotheses are contradictory. In addition, they are difficult to test and do not address the primary differences between the tropics and higher latitudes. For instance, even if the niches of tropical species differ consistently from those of species at higher latitudes, we must determine the causes of those differences. Brown suggests that biological processes such as competition and predation must play a secondary role in determining species diversity gradients. He proposes that the ultimate causes of geographic gradients in species richness must be physical differences between the tropics and higher latitudes. The following hypothesis uses differences in physical settings to explain latitudinal patterns of diversity.

Differences in Speciation and Extinction Rates

Ultimately the number of species in a particular area reflects the rate at which new species have been added to the species pool minus the rate at which they have disappeared. Species are added to species pools by either immigration or speciation. However, Rosenzweig (1992) proposed that when we consider the diversity of whole biogeographic provinces, immigration can be largely discounted and speciation will be the primary source of new species. Species are removed from species pools by extinction. So, tropical species richness is greater than at higher latitudes because the tropics have experienced higher rates of speciation and/or lower rates of extinction. However, Brown would remind us here that we need to determine the physical mechanisms that produce differences in speciation and extinction rates in tropical versus higher latitudes.

Area and Latitudinal Gradients in Species Richness

John Terborgh (1973) and Michael Rosenzweig (1992) proposed that the greater species richness of the tropics can be explained by the greater area covered by tropical regions. It may not be immediately apparent that the tropics, which mainly occupy the area between the tropics of Cancer and Capricorn, include a greater area of both land and water than do higher latitudes. The reason for this is that the typical world map is based upon the *Mercator Projection,* a projection that increases the apparent area at high latitudes. However, if you look at a world globe you will immediately see that the tropical areas of the earth constitute a vast area.

Is there a greater land surface area in the tropics? Rosenzweig quantified the amount of land surface area in various latitudinal zones using a computer map of the earth. He divided the globe into tropical (± 26° of latitude), subtropical (26°–36°), temperate (36°–46°), boreal (46°–56°), and tundra (> 56°). He then measured the area of land within these latitudinal zones and found that the area of land within the tropics far exceeds that of other areas (fig. 22.19).

Not only is there more land (and water) at tropical latitudes, but in addition, temperatures are more uniform across

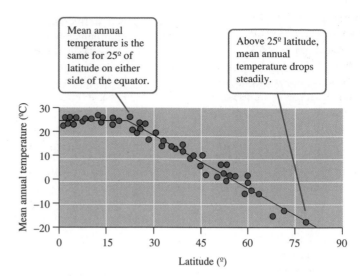

Figure 22.20   Mean annual temperature by latitude (data from Rosenzweig 1992, after Terborgh 1973).

this tropical belt. This pattern was put in the context of geographic ecology by Terborgh, who plotted mean annual temperatures against latitude. As figure 22.20 shows, there is little difference in mean annual temperatures between about 0° and 25° latitude. Because this temperature pattern occurs both north and south of the equator, mean annual temperature changes little over about 50° of latitude within the tropics. However, above 25° latitude, mean annual temperature declines linearly with latitude. What is the biological significance of this latitudinal pattern of temperature variation? One implication is that tropical organisms can disperse over large areas and not meet with significant changes in temperature.

How do patterns of temperature variation affect rates of speciation and extinction? Rosenzweig proposed that the larger area of tropical regions should reduce extinction rates in two ways. First, large, physically similar areas will allow tropical species to be distributed over a larger area. Within these larger areas, there should be more refuges in which to survive environmental disturbances. Because of their larger range, tropical species should also have greater total population sizes. Larger populations are less likely to become extinct.

Rosenzweig also proposed that larger species ranges should increase rates of allopatric speciation. He reasoned that geographic barriers, such as mountain ranges or deep canyons, are more likely to form within large species ranges than within small species ranges. Therefore, since geographic isolation initiates allopatric speciation, speciation rates are likely to be higher in tropical regions.

Earlier in chapter 22, we saw that species richness increases with island area. However, do larger continents also harbour more species? We explore this question in the following example.

Continental Area and Species Richness

Karl Flessa (1975, 1981) was the first to examine the relationship between continental area and species richness. He found a strong positive relationship between mammalian richness and the area of continents, large islands, and island groups. Flessa

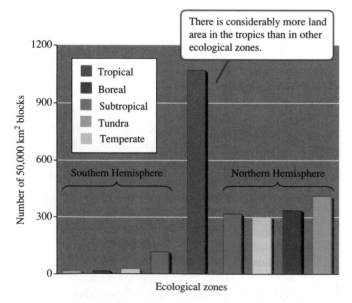

Figure 22.19   Land area in five latitudinal biomes (data from Rosenzweig 1992).

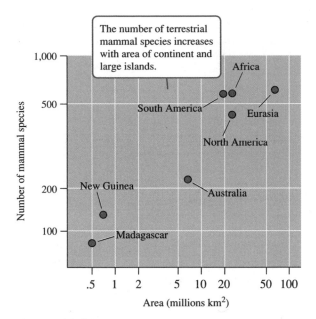

Figure 22.21 Relationship between area of continents and large islands and number of nonflying terrestrial mammals (data from Brown 1986).

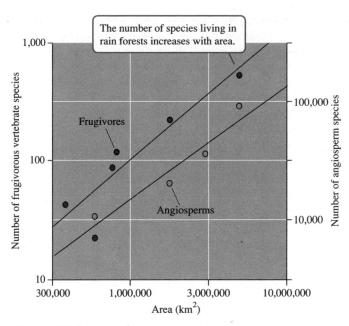

Figure 22.22 Rain forest area, from Australia to Amazonia, and numbers of flowering plant (angiosperm) species and number of fruit-eating (frugivorous) vertebrate species (data from Rosenzweig 1992).

found a significant positive relationship whether his index of mammalian richness was total number of orders, families, or genera. James H. Brown (1986) performed an analysis similar to Flessa's; however, he restricted his analysis to the five major continents plus two large tropical islands, Madagascar and New Guinea. Brown also excluded flying mammals and analyzed patterns of mammalian diversity at the level of genera and species. Like Flessa, Brown found a strong positive relationship between mammalian richness and area (fig. 22.21). Madagascar, with the smallest land area, supports the lowest mammalian richness. Eurasia, with the largest land area, supports the greatest mammalian diversity. The continents of Australia, South America, North America, and Africa, with intermediate areas, contain intermediate levels of mammalian richness.

What do these analyses by Flessa and Brown have to do with higher tropical species richness? Rosenzweig proposed that the greater area of the tropics (see fig. 22.19) is a primary cause of the higher diversity. If differences in area produce differences in species richness, then we should see a positive relationship between continental area and species richness. Flessa and Brown have shown such a relationship. Now, let's go back to the tropics.

Do tropical regions with different areas differ in species richness? If Rosenzweig's explanation for the greater tropical diversity is correct, tropical regions of different areas should support different levels of biological diversity. Rosenzweig examined patterns of diversity among fruit-eating mammals and plants in tropical rain forests ranging from Australia to Amazonia. The result was a strong positive relationship between area and diversity, a result that supports the area hypothesis (fig. 22.22). The smallest area of tropical rain forest, Australia, contains the smallest number of fruit-eating mammal and plant species. Amazonia, with the largest rain forest area, contains the greatest number of fruit-eating mammal and plant species.

In summary, many factors may contribute to higher tropical species richness, including (1) time since perturbation, (2) productivity, (3) environmental heterogeneity, (4) favourableness, (5) niche breadths and interspecific interactions, and (6) differences in speciation and extinction rates. However, several lines of evidence support the hypothesis that differences in surface area play a primary role in determining latitudinal gradients in species richness. Can we conclude that we fully understand the mechanisms underlying latitudinal gradients in diversity? Brown concluded that while we are close to understanding the mechanisms controlling variation in species richness across islands, "The distributions of species and higher taxa within continents are more complex and for the most part remain to be deciphered." We must remember that many taxa do not show this same increased diversity near the equator. Why? As we shall see in the next section, some of that unexplained complexity is due to historical and regional differences between the continents.

Concept 22.3 Review

1. Why is there no one factor that seems to explain latitudinal gradients in species diversity?
2. What major pattern do patterns of island diversity and continental diversity have in common?

22.4 Historical and Regional Influences

Long-term historical and regional processes significantly influence the structure of biotas and ecosystems. Area and isolation explain much of the variation in species diversity

and composition across islands. Area appears to account for much of the variation in biological diversity across continents. Additional variation in local diversity appears to be due to differences in habitat heterogeneity, disturbance, predation, and successional age of the local community, factors that we discussed in chapters 16, 17, and 18. However, as the following examples show, these factors are not adequate to explain many geographic differences in biological diversity and community organization. Robert Ricklefs (1987) pointed out that in many cases, unique historical and geographic factors appear to have produced significant regional differences in species richness.

We will first explore the relationship between the diversity found in a given community and the diversity of the surrounding region. We will then discuss a few specific mechanisms by which regional processes can cause unusual patterns of diversity.

Patterns of Local and Regional Diversity

What determines the number of species that are found in a given location? In this chapter we have already discussed how this could influenced by area and isolation. In prior chapters we have also described how competition, herbivory, and a variety of local processes can alter community structure. One factor we have not yet considered is the relatively straightforward idea that the number of species found in a community must be no greater than the regional species pool. Only species which are present somewhere in the region could possibly be found in any particular community, and thus the size of the species pool serves as an upper bound of local diversity. Therefore, as regional diversity increases, local diversity increases too. Or does it? We have seen before that the presence of competitive dominant species may actually exclude other species from entering a community. Similarly, abiotic stress or herbivory could be so extreme in a given community that only a few, specially adapted species may persist, regardless of how many species are in the region. Similar statements could be made about all the ecological processes we discussed in Section IV of the book. In short, even if there were an unlimited number of species in the regional pool, local processes might limit the number of species found in any particular community. These contrasting predictions can be summarized in a graph describing the hypothetical relationships between local and regional species richness (fig. 22.23). In both models, a line with a slope of 1 represents the theoretical maximum. In model I there is a linear relationship between local and regional diversity. Such a relationship indicates that local diversity is a constant fraction of regional diversity. In model II there is species saturation at high levels of regional diversity. This model predicts that there is only a set amount of "niche-space" within a community, and thus species exclusion occurs through local processes. What does the data suggest?

Ronald Karlson, Howard Cornell, and Terence Hughes have provided one of the most comprehensive tests of this question (Karlson et al. 2004). They sampled the diversity of corals around 15 islands that were spread across five Indo-Pacific regions (fig. 22.24). In total, these locations represented a 10,000 km gradient, and represented a truly ambitious research

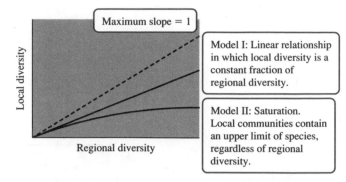

Figure 22.23 Hypothetical relationships between local and regional diversity.

Figure 22.24 A rich diversity of life lives in and among coral reefs.

project. In each location, they measured coral diversity in three habitat types: reef flats that were 5–10 m inshore of breaking waves; reef crests that were seaward of breaking waves and at a depth of 1–2 m; and reef slopes which were also seaward of breaking waves but at a depth of 6–7 m. Through extensive dives below the water's surface, they sampled a total

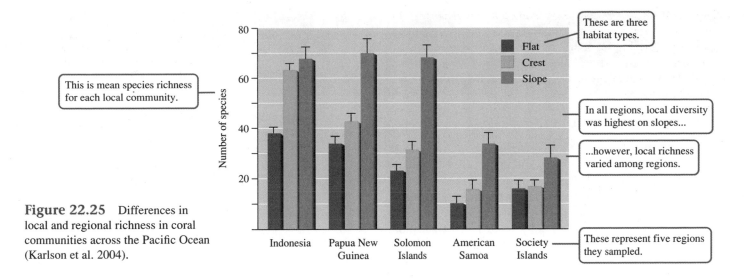

Figure 22.25 Differences in local and regional richness in coral communities across the Pacific Ocean (Karlson et al. 2004).

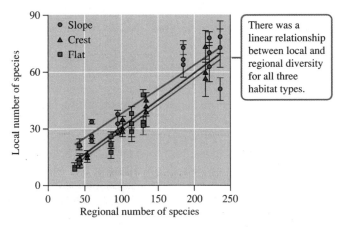

Figure 22.26 Relationship between local and regional diversity of coral communities in the Pacific Ocean (Karlson et al. 2004).

of 41,710 coral colonies. There were clear differences in diversity among the five regions and three habitats they sampled (fig. 22.25). Reef flats consistently had the lowest diversity, and reef slopes the highest in nearly all regions. When they compared local and regional diversity, they found a clear linear relationship for all three habitats (fig 22.26), supporting model I. Karlson and his colleagues are not the only ones to find support for a regional effect on local diversity. A group of researchers from the United States and Canada found similar results for a number of groups of zooplankton in lakes throughout North America (Shurin et al. 2000).

Why does regional richness increase local dispersal? One likely mechanism is **dispersal limitation**. This idea suggests that many species in a region are capable of living in more communities; however they simply have not successfully dispersed into those areas. As we see next, there can be a variety of other influences of the region on local patterns of diversity.

Exceptional Patterns of Diversity

There are major differences in species richness that cannot be explained by differences in area. For instance, consider the regions with Mediterranean climates that we discussed in chapter 2, which support Mediterranean woodlands and shrublands. Such regions include the Cape region of South Africa (90,000 km^2), southwestern Australia (320,000 km^2), and the California Floristic Province (324,000 km^2). These regions have similar climates but differ significantly in area. Which of these areas should contain the greatest number of species? The positive relationship between area and species richness that we have seen repeatedly earlier in chapter 22 leads us to predict that southwestern Australia and the California Floristic Province, with more than three times the area of the Cape region of South Africa, will contain the greatest biological diversity. Southwestern Australia and the California Floristic Province have the same area and approximately the same number of species. However, as figure 22.27 shows, the Cape region, the smallest area, contains more than twice the number of plant species as the other two regions.

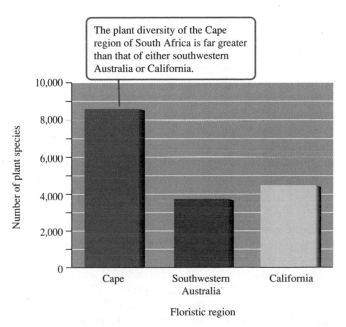

Figure 22.27 Number of plant species living in three regions with Mediterranean climates (data from Bond and Goldblatt 1984).

Ecology In Action

Biodiversity Hotspots

Species are not distributed evenly across the globe; instead, biodiversity is concentrated into specific areas of the planet known as *biodiversity hotspots*. The realization that biodiversity is clustered into these hotspots across the planet is important for a variety of reasons. First, it is an intriguing ecological pattern that is certainly worthy of explanation. Second, the concentration of biodiversity across the planet suggests that loss of certain habitats and areas to development will result in a greater ecological cost than similar development in other areas. In other words, by identifying biodiversity hotspots, ecologists may provide ecological triage, identifying those areas that are most urgently in need of treatment and repair.

As we discussed in chapter 10 there are different types of rarity for species, with different consequences for conservation. Of particular concern are the species that have a very narrow range, and are endemic to a very small area. Even small amounts of development can threaten these species, if it were to occur in their relatively restricted habitat.

One concern about the hotspot approach to identifying areas of critical conservation need has been that high levels of species richness do not necessarily equate to high levels of rare and endemic species. Instead, it is possible that areas are particularly diverse due to large numbers of cosmopolitan species, ones not likely in need of protection. Jeremy Kerr, of York University, has analyzed this issue for several taxa. He has found that patterns of richness were generally correlated with patterns of endemism, supporting the hotspot approach (Kerr 1997). However, he also found that the location of biodiversity hotspots varied among taxa, and protection of area for one group of species could not be assumed to provide an umbrella that would reach over and cover other taxa. Instead, each taxonomic group is likely going to have its own locations in most critical need of protection.

Norman Myers and colleagues have produced one of the more comprehensive studies identifying terrestrial biodiversity hotspots (Myers et al. 2000). They focused specifically on endemic plants, mammals, birds, reptiles, and amphibians. They state that because plants are "essential to virtually all forms of animal life," an area could only qualify as a hotspot if it contained a minimum of 0.5% of the world's plant species as endemics (this equates to 1,500 of the 300,000 known spe-

Figure 22.28   Identified terrestrial biodiversity hotspots around the planet (data from Myers et al. 2000).

cies). Only if a location met these criteria would information regarding endemic vertebrates be added for comparison. The research team did not include invertebrates in this analysis primarily because a large proportion of invertebrate diversity remains undescribed by science, and thus accurate information is lacking. An area only made the final cut for inclusion as a hotspot if it was under significant threat of development, with at least 70% or more of the vegetation lost. This criteria was added to allow this list to identify areas in need of urgent protection, rather than simply a map of diversity patterns.

In total, Myers et al. (2000) identified 25 hotspots around the globe (fig. 22.28). These areas represent only 1.4% of planet's land base, yet contain 44% of the known plant species. In total, 88% of the primary vegetation in these areas has already been lost to development. It should come as no surprise that a majority of these sites are in tropical areas, where diversity is high and pressure to develop the land is strong. Figure 22.29 shows that these hotspots vary in terms of biodiversity and habitat threat. For example, the top five hotspots contain 20% of all plant and 16% of all vertebrate species and yet only occupy 0.4% of the earth's surface. Clearly, not all areas on the planet are ecologically equivalent, nor of equal conservation priority.

Diversity hotspots can be identified in marine systems as well. By definition, these can not be exactly the same place as the terrestrial hotspots. However, if these areas were in close proximity to one another, such as marine areas immediately offshore a terrestrial hotspot, it may facilitate conservation efforts. There have been numerous efforts to identify marine

Hotspot	Original extent of primary vegetation (km²)	Remaining primary vegetation (km²) (% of original extent)	Area protected (km²) (% of hotspot)	Plant species	Endemic plants (% of global plants, 300,000)	Vertebrate species	Endemic vertebrates (% of global vertebrates, 27,298)
Tropical Andes	1,258,000	314,500 (25.0)	79,687 (25.3)	45,000	20,000 (6.7%)	3,389	1,567 (5.7%)
Mesoamerica	1,155,000	231,000 (20.0)	138,437 (59.9)	24,000	5,000 1.7%)	2,859	1,159 (4.2%)
Caribbean	263,500	29,840 (11.3)	29,840 (100.0)	12,000	7,000 2.3%)	1,518	779 (2.9%)
Brazil's Atlantic Forest	1,227,600	91,930 (7.5)	33,084 (35.9)	20,000	8,000 (2.7%)	1,361	567 (2.1%)
Choc/Darien/Western Ecuador	260,600	63,000 (24.2)	16,471 (26.1)	9,000	2,250 (0.8%)	1,625	418 (1.5%)
Brazil's Cerrado	1,783,200	356,630 (20.0)	22,000 (6.2)	10,000	4,400 (1.5%)	1,268	117 (0.4%)
Central Chile	300,000	90,000 (30.0)	9,167 (10.2)	3,429	1,605 (0.5%)	335	61 (0.2%)
California Floristic Province	324,000	80,000 (24.7)	31,443 (39.3)	4,426	2,125 (0.7%)	584	71 (0.3%)
Madagascar*	594,150	59,038 (9.9)	11,548 (19.6)	12,000	9,704 (3.2%)	987	771 (2.8%)
Eastern Arc and Coastal Forests of Tanzania/Kenya	30,000	2,000 (6.7)	2,000 (100.0)	4,000	1,500 (0.5%)	1,019	121 (0.4%)
Western African Forests	1,265,000	126,500 (10.0)	20,324 (16.1)	9,000	2,250 (0.8%)	1,320	270 (1.0%)
Cape Floristic Province	74,000	18,000 (24.3)	14,060 (78.1)	8,200	5,682 (1.9%)	562	53 (0.2%)
Succulent Karoo	112,000	30,000 (26.8)	2,352 (7.8)	4,849	1,940 (0.6%)	472	45 (0.2%)
Mediterranean Basin	2,362,000	110,000 (4.7)	42,123 (38.3)	25,000	13,000 (4.3%)	770	235 (0.9%)
Caucasus	500,000	50,000 (10.0)	14,050 (28.1)	6,300	1,600 (0.5%)	632	59 (0.2%)
Sundaland	1,600,000	125,000 (7.8)	90,000 (72.0)	25,000	15,000 (5.0%)	1,800	701 (2.6%)
Wallacea	347,000	52,020 (15.0)	20,415 (39.2)	10,000	1,500 (0.5%)	1,142	529 (1.9%)
Philippines	300,800	9,023 (3.0)	3,910 (43.3)	7,620	5,832 (1.9%)	1,093	518 (1.9%)
Indo-Burma	2,060,000	100,000 (4.9)	100,000 (100.0)	13,500	7,000 (2.3%)	2,185	528 (1.9%)
South-Central China	800,000	64,000 (8.0)	16,562 (25.9)	12,000	3,500 (1.2%)	1,141	178 (0.7%)
Western Ghats/Sri Lanka	182,500	12,450 (6.8)	12,450 (100.0)	4,780	2,180 (0.7%)	1,073	355 (1.3%)
SW Australia	309,850	33,336 (10.8)	33,336 (100.0)	5,469	4,331 (1.4%)	456	100 (0.4%)
New Caledonia	18,600	5,200 (28.0)	526.7 (10.1)	3,332	2,551 (0.9%)	190	84 (0.3%)
New Zealand	270,500	59,400 (22.0)	52,068 (87.7)	2,300	1,865 (0.6%)	217	136 (0.5%)
Polynesia/Micronesia	46,000	10,024 (21.8)	4,913 (49.0)	6,557	3,334 (1.1%)	342	223 (0.8%)
Totals	17,444,300	2,122,891 (12.2)	800,767 (37.7)	†	133,149 (44%)	†	9,645 (35%)

Figure 22.29 Details of the diversity and development found in the top 25 terrestrial hotspots (data from Myers et al. 2000).

* Madagascar includes the nearby islands of Mauritius, Reunion, Seychelles and Comores.
† These totals cannot be summed owing to overlapping between hotspots.

biodiversity hotspots recently. A group of researchers from Canada, the United States, and Australia investigated the location of marine hotspots, focusing primarily on tropical reefs (Roberts et al. 2002). They found that the 10 richest hotspots contain only 16% of the world's reefs but 44%–54% of the endemic reef species. In another example from marine systems, Boris Worm, Heike Lotze, and Ransom Myers of Dalhousie University have identified the majority of biodiversity hotspots for large ocean predators such as tunas, sharks, and billfishes occur at intermediate, rather than tropical latitudes (Worm et al. 2003). These locations are generally at the intersection of the ranges of temperate and tropical prey species, and are generally concentrated around variation in ocean bottom topography (e.g., reefs, shelf breaks, etc.).

Biodiversity is not spread evenly around the globe, and efforts such as these provide critical information for conservation programs. It is up to the next generation of ecologists to find ways to protect these areas.

The failure of area to explain a significant regional diversity pattern is not unique to this example. For instance, Roger Latham and Robert Ricklefs (1993) reported a striking contrast in diversity of temperate zone trees that cannot be explained by an area effect. As we saw in chapter 2, the temperate forest biome covers approximately equal areas in Europe (1.2 million km^2), eastern Asia (1.2 million km^2), and eastern North America (1.8 million km^2). The species area relationship would lead us to predict that these three regions would support approximately equal levels of biological diversity. However, eastern Asia contains nearly three times more tree species than eastern North America and nearly six times more species of trees than Europe.

Historical and Regional Explanations

How can we explain these exceptional patterns of biological diversity? What mechanisms produced these patterns that are contrary to generalizations discussed in chapter 22 and earlier chapters? In each case, it appears that geography and history offer convincing explanations.

The Cape Floristic Region of South Africa

Pauline Bond and Peter Goldblatt (1984) attributed the unusual species richness of the Cape floristic region to several historic and geographic factors. Selection for a distinctively Mediterranean flora in southern Africa began during the late Tertiary period, about 26 million years ago. At that time, the climate became progressively cooler and drier, conditions that selected for succulence, fire resistance, and smaller, sclerophylous leaves. The initial sites for evolution of the Cape flora were likely in south-central Africa, not in the Cape region itself. At that time, Africa lay farther south and the Cape region had a cool, moist climate and supported an evergreen forest.

As Africa drifted northward, the climate of southern Africa became more arid and the ancestors of today's Cape flora gradually migrated toward the Cape region. By the time Africa neared its present latitudinal position during the late Pliocene, about three million years ago, southern Africa was very arid and the Cape region had a Mediterranean climate. Bond and Goldblatt suggest that plant speciation within this region was promoted by the highly dissected landscape, the existence of a wide variety of soil types, and repeated expansion, contraction, and isolation of plant populations during the climatic fluctuations of the Pleistocene. They suggest that extinction rates were reduced by the existence of substantial refuge areas, even during times of peak aridity.

The Diversity of Temperate Trees

How did eastern Asia, eastern North America, and Europe, three temperate regions of approximately equal area and climate, end up with such different numbers of tree species? Latham and Ricklefs offer persuasive geographic and historical reasons. They propose that we need to consider what trees in the three regions faced during the last glacial period and how those conditions may have affected extinction rates.

Refer to chapter 2 and study the distributions of temperate forest in eastern Asia, eastern North America, and Europe. Now examine the distributions of mountains in eastern Asia, eastern North America, and Europe shown in chapter 2. Notice that while there are no mountain barriers to north–south movements of organisms in eastern Asia and eastern North America, the mountains in Europe form barriers that are oriented east to west. Now imagine what happened to a tree species as glaciers began to advance during the last ice age and the climate of Europe became progressively colder. Temperate trees would have had their southward retreat largely cut off by mountain ranges running east to west.

This hypothesis proposes that the lower species richness of European trees has been at least partly a consequence of higher extinction rates during glacial periods. How would you test this hypothesis? Latham and Ricklefs searched the fossil record for extinctions in the three regions. They estimated the number of genera that have become extinct in the three regions during the last 30 to 40 million years. Their analysis showed that most of the plant genera that once lived in Europe have become extinct. A larger proportion of genera has become extinct in Europe than in either eastern Asia or eastern North America (fig. 22.30).

Now consider eastern North America. The only mountain range, the Appalachians, runs north to south. Consequently, in eastern North America, temperate trees had an avenue of retreat in the face of advancing glaciers and cooling climate. The movement of temperate tree populations in the face of climate change has been well documented by paleontologists such as Margaret Davis. There are also no mountain barriers in eastern Asia, where temperate trees can migrate even farther south than in eastern North America.

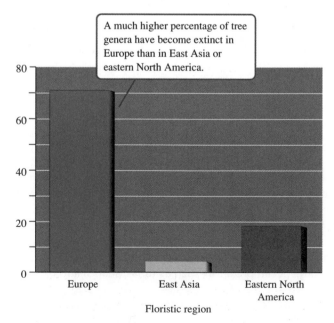

Figure 22.30 Extinctions of tree genera in Europe, East Asia, and eastern North America since the middle Tertiary period (data from Latham and Ricklefs 1993).

Higher rates of extinction during glacial periods can explain the lower diversity of trees in Europe. However, why does eastern North America include fewer tree species than eastern Asia? Latham and Ricklefs conclude that the fossil record and present-day distributions of temperate trees indicate that most temperate tree taxa originated in eastern Asia. These Asian taxa subsequently dispersed to Europe and North America. In addition, after the dispersal routes between eastern Asia and eastern North America were closed off, speciation continued in Asia, producing several endemic Asian genera. In other words, there are fewer tree species in eastern North America because most taxa originated in eastern Asia and never dispersed to North America.

Meta-communities

In chapter 10 we introduced the idea of metapopulations; subpopulations that were connected through immigration and emigration of individuals. Recently, there has been an increasing appreciation that such interconnections also occur among communities within a geographic region. Not too surprisingly, this concept has been named **meta-communities**. Research into meta-communities is just in its infancy, though it has the potential to alter the way ecologists view community boundaries and interactions. For example, Mathew Leibold and Jon Norberg (2004) suggest the meta-community model applies to planktonic systems, with frequent movement of individuals among seemingly discrete water bodies. They suggest that these connections may increase the capacity of connected systems to respond to environmental change. If such processes are common, it has significant implications in the face of global climate change.

Throughout this chapter we have shown how geographic factors can influence local species diversity. Many aspects of geographic variation in species richness can be explained by historical and regional processes, and do not necessarily rely on the processes described in section V. The ecologist interested in understanding patterns of diversity at large spatial scales must consider processes occurring over similarly large scales and over long periods of time. As we shall see in chapter 23, a large-scale, long-term perspective is also essential for understanding global ecology.

Concept 22.4 Review

1. Why should history have such a strong influence on regional diversity patterns?
2. How does the combined evidence from studies of the flora of Mediterranean regions and the diversity of trees in temperate forest regions increase confidence that historical differences can outweigh the potential influence of area on diversity?

Ecological Tools

Global Positioning Systems, Remote Sensing, and Geographic Information Systems

In 1972, Robert MacArthur defined geographic ecology as the study of patterns you can put on a map. Spatial distributions that can be put on maps are still the centre of geographic ecology, but the nature of "maps" has changed tremendously. Modern tools have revolutionized the field. Today, geographic ecologists generally record their data on geographic information systems, which are computer-based systems that store, analyze, and display geographic information. In addition, the geographic ecologists of today also have access to more information of greater accuracy because of remote sensing and global positioning systems.

Global Positioning Systems

What is the location? This is one of the most basic questions the geographer can ask. Scientists, engineers, navigators, and explorers have spent centuries devising methods to measure elevation, latitude, and longitude. Recent technological advances have improved the accuracy of these measurements.

Alexander von Humboldt, the founder of geographic ecology, would appreciate these recent technological advances. As he explored South and North America, he carefully determined the latitude, longitude, and elevation of important geographic features. For instance, Humboldt was particularly interested in verifying the existence and location of a waterway called the Casiquiare Canal. The Casiquiare reportedly connected the Orinoco River with the Rio Negro, which flows into the Amazon. A connection between two major river systems would make the Casiquiare unique, but its existence was widely doubted.

Humboldt halted his expedition at the junction of the Casiquiare and the Rio Negro so that he could record the latitude and longitude. Biting insects tormented the explorers as they waited for nightfall. Luckily, that night the clouds parted and Humboldt could see the stars well enough to take sightings and determine their position. At other times, he was not so lucky. He once waited for nearly a month for the weather to clear sufficiently to make his sightings on the stars. Today, equipped with a global positioning system, Humboldt could have determined the latitude and longitude of the junction of the Casiquiare and the Rio Negro any time he wished, regardless of weather.

A **global positioning system** determines locations on the earth's surface, including latitude, longitude, and altitude, using satellites as reference points. These satellites, which orbit the earth at a height of about 21,000 km, continuously transmit their position and the time. The satellites keep track of time with an extremely accurate atomic clock that loses or gains 1 second in about 30,000 years. A global positioning system receives the signals broadcast by these satellites. Because the system also includes an extremely accurate clock, the time required for the satellite signal to reach the receiver can be used as a measure of the distance between the two. With measurements of the distance to four satellites, a global positioning system can determine the latitude, longitude, and altitude of any point on earth with great accuracy (fig. 22.31).

While navigation satellites and global positioning systems can accurately locate places on the ground, other satellites provide a wealth of other information about those localities. These "remote sensing" satellites transmit pictures of the earth that are extremely valuable to ecologists.

Remote Sensing

Remote sensing refers to gathering information about an object without direct contact with it, mainly by gathering and processing electromagnetic radiation emitted or reflected by the object. Using this definition, the original remote sensor was the eye. However, we generally associate remote sensing with technology that extends the senses, technology ranging from binoculars and cameras to satellite-mounted sensors.

Remote sensing satellites are generally fitted with electro-optical sensors that scan several bands of the electromagnetic spectrum. These sensors convert electromagnetic radiation into electrical signals that are in turn converted to digital values by a computer. These digital values can be used to construct an image. The earliest of the *Landsat* satellites monitored four bands of electromagnetic radiation, two bands of visible light

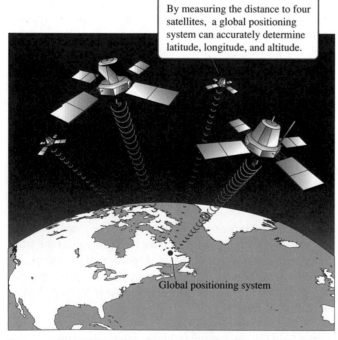

By measuring the distance to four satellites, a global positioning system can accurately determine latitude, longitude, and altitude.

Global positioning system

Figure 22.31   Global positioning systems determine latitude, longitude, and altitude by measuring the distance from several satellites.

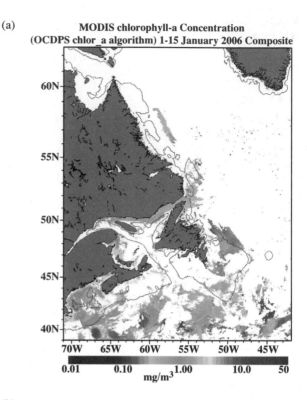

(a)   **MODIS chlorophyll-a Concentration**
(OCDPS chlor_a algorithm) 1-15 January 2006 Composite

0.01   0.10   1.00   10.0   50
mg/m³

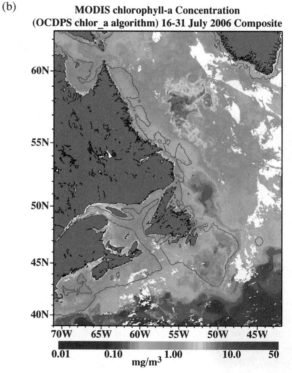

(b)   **MODIS chlorophyll-a Concentration**
(OCDPS chlor_a algorithm) 16-31 July 2006 Composite

0.01   0.10   1.00   10.0   50
mg/m³

Figure 22.32   Measures of ocean chlorophyll-a concentrations from part of Atlantic Canada in (*a*) January 2006, and (*b*) July 2006.

(0.5–0.6 μm and 0.6–0.7 μm), and two bands in the near infrared (0.7–0.8 μm and 0.8–1.1 μm). From this beginning, satellite imaging systems have gotten progressively more sophisticated both in terms of the number of wavelengths scanned and the spatial resolution.

Satellite-based remote sensing has produced detailed images of essentially every square meter of the earth's surface. You may have already seen many of these through readily available services such as Google Earth. Ecologists use a diversity of satellite-based imaging processes to monitor a variety of ecological processes, including "greenness" and primary productivity. For example, the Department of Fisheries and Oceans uses remote sensing to monitor changes in ocean productivity, often measured as chlorophyll-a concentrations (fig. 22.32). When images are taken at different points in time, it is possible to measure changes. The most obvious changes would be seasonal shifts in productivity (fig. 22.32), but could also include other factors.

Incorporating satellite imaging with a variety of methods of analysis (see next section) also allows scientists to categorize large geographic regions by the dominant vegetation. For example, using the Advanced Very High Resolution Radiometer satellite network, a team of researchers at the Canada Centre for Remote Sensing were able to develop a land cover map for all of Canada (fig. 22.33). It is important to recognize that there exists a great diversity of satellites capable of conducting remote sensing operations for ecological research. Some satellites, like those used to produce figure 22.33, are very good at imaging vast geographic regions (such as all of Canada!), but have relatively coarse resolution, such as 1 km^2. In contrast, other satellite systems can image the earth from space at a resolution of less than 1 m^2. Such detailed information is likely critical to assess change or characterize habitats within a local area (e.g., a single province), but would produce too great a volume of data to characterize larger areas (such as all of Canada).

Remote sensing allows ecologists to gather large volumes of data across a very large spatial scale—even more data than could be collected with an army of eager undergraduate assistants! However, these large quantities of data create another problem. Ecologists need a system for storing, sorting, analyzing, and displaying these large quantities of geographic information. This is the problem addressed by geographic information systems.

Geographic Information Systems

In the days of Humboldt, geographers often had too little data. Today, with new tools for gathering great quantities of information, geographers and geographic ecologists can be overwhelmed by data. **Geographic information systems (GIS)**, computer-based systems for storing, sorting, analyzing, and displaying geographic data, are designed to handle large quantities of data. Sometimes geographic information

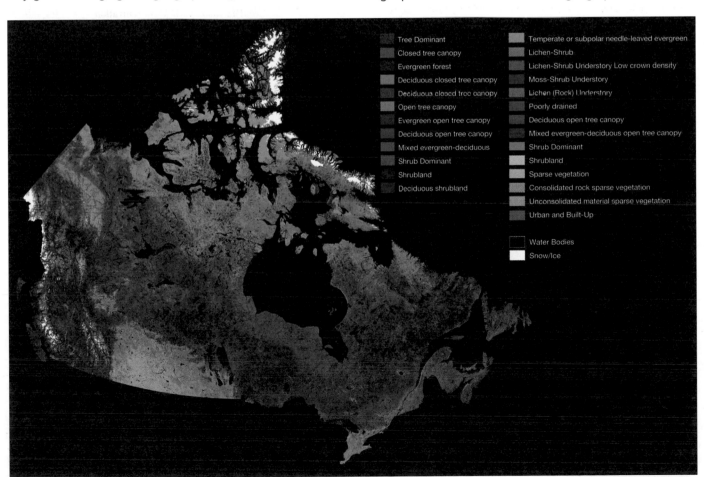

Figure 22.33 Land cover map for all of Canada, based upon satellite imaging.

systems are confused with computerized mapmaking. While these systems can produce maps, they do much more. Much of population ecology is concerned with understanding the factors controlling the distribution and abundance of organisms. However, the geographic context of populations has often been lost. Geographic information systems preserve this geographic information. Because they preserve geographic context, the systems provide ecologists with a valuable tool for exploring large-scale population responses to climate change. GIS serves as a critical tool for many studies we have already discussed, particularily in chapter 22. GIS provides a rapid method of quantifying landscape elements.

As we shall see in chapter 23, rapid global change challenges the field of ecology to continue to address large-scale environmental questions. As ecologists address these compelling questions, geographic information systems, global positioning systems, and remote sensing will be increasingly valued parts of their tool kit.

Summary

Geographic ecology focuses on large-scale patterns of the distribution and diversity of organisms and ecological processes. Research areas include island biogeography, latitudinal patterns of species diversity, and the influences of regional and historical process on diversity and function.

On islands and habitat patches on continents, species richness increases with area and decreases with isolation. Larger oceanic islands support more species of most groups of organisms than small islands. Isolated oceanic islands generally contain fewer species than islands near mainland areas. Many habitats on continents are so isolated that they can be considered as islands. Geographic isolation influences the bacterial diversity in hot springs. Lakes can also be considered as habitat islands. They are aquatic environments isolated from other aquatic environments by land. Fish species richness generally increases with lake area. Species richness is usually negatively correlated with island isolation. However, because organisms differ substantially in dispersal rates, an island that is very isolated for one group of organisms may be completely accessible to another group.

Species richness on islands can be modelled as a dynamic balance between immigration and extinction of species. The equilibrium model of island biogeography proposes that the difference between rates of immigration and extinction determines the species richness on islands. The equilibrium model of island biogeography assumes that rates of species immigration to islands are mainly determined by distance from sources of immigrants. The model assumes that rates of extinction on islands are determined mainly by island size. Species turnover is also predicated to vary as a function of isolation and island area. The predictions of the equilibrium model of island biogeography are supported by observations of species turnover on the islands and by colonization studies of mangrove islands in Florida and new islands in Lake Hjälmaren, Sweden.

Species richness generally increases from middle and high latitudes to the equator. Most groups of organisms are more species-rich in the tropics. Many factors may contribute to higher tropical species richness, including (1) time since perturbation, (2) productivity, (3) environmental heterogeneity, (4) favourableness, (5) niche breadths and interspecific interactions, and (6) differences in speciation and extinction rates. Several lines of evidence support the hypothesis that differences in surface area play a primary role in determining latitudinal gradients in species richness.

Long-term historical and regional processes significantly influence the structure of biotas and ecosystems. Much geographic variation in species richness can be explained by historical and regional processes. Regional diversity can influence the diversity of local communities through a variety of mechanisms. Some exceptional situations that seem to have resulted from unique historical and regional processes include the exceptional species richness of the Cape floristic region of South Africa, and the high species richness of temperate trees in east Asia. Dispersal among communities can result in meta-communities. These connections may buffer some effects of environmental change.

Global positioning systems, remote sensing, and geographic information systems are important tools for effective geographic ecology. A global positioning system determines locations on the earth's surface, including latitude, longitude, and altitude, using satellites as reference points. Remote sensing satellites are generally fitted with electro-optical sensors that scan several bands of the electromagnetic spectrum. These sensors convert electromagnetic radiation into electrical signals that are in turn converted to digital values by a computer. These digital values can be used to construct an image. Geographic information systems are computer-based systems that store, analyze, and display geographic information. Global positioning systems, remote sensing, and geographic information systems are increasingly valuable parts of the ecologist's tool kit. Ecologists are using these new tools to study large-scale, dynamic ecological phenomena such as interannual variation in primary production, land cover categorization, and potential responses to climate change.

Review Questions

1. The following data (Preston 1962a) give the area and number of bird species on islands in the West Indies:

Island	Area	Log10 Area	# Species	Log # Species
Cuba	43,000	4.633	124	2.093
Isle of Pines	11,000	4.041	89	1.949
Hispaniola	47,000	4.672	106	2.021
Jamaica	4,470	3.650	99	1.996
Puerto Rico	3,435	3.536	79	1.898
Bahamas	5,450	3.736	74	1.869
Virgin Islands	465	2.667	35	1.544
Guadalupe	600	2.778	37	1.568
Dominica	304	2.483	36	1.556
St. Lucia	233	2.367	35	1.544
St. Vincent	150	2.176	35	1.544
Grenada	120	2.079	29	1.462

   The numbers are expressed in two ways: as simple measurements and counts and as the logarithms of area and numbers of species. Use these data to plot your own species–area relationship. Plot area on the horizontal axis and number of species on the vertical axis. First plot the simple measurements of area and species number on one graph, and then plot the logarithms of area and species number on another graph. Which gives you the tightest relationship between area and species richness?

2. We discussed how Diamond (1969) documented immigrations and extinctions on the California Channel Islands by comparing his censuses of the birds of the islands with the birds recorded over 50 years earlier. Disregarding the numbers for San Miguel and Santa Rosa Islands, which were not well censused in 1917, Diamond showed that an average of approximately six bird species became extinct on California Channel Islands between 1917 and 1968. During the same period, an average of approximately five new bird species immigrated to the islands. Diamond suggested that his estimates of immigration and extinction were likely underestimates of the actual rates. Explain why his comparative study produced underestimates of rates of immigration and extinction.

3. Suppose you are about to study the bird communities on the islands shown on the right, which are identical in area but lie at different distances from the mainland. According to the equilibrium model of island biogeography, which of the islands should experience higher rates of immigration? What does the equilibrium model of island biogeography predict concerning relative rates of extinction on the two islands?

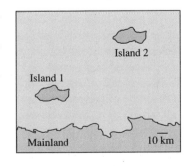

4. Now, suppose you are going to study the bird communities on the islands shown on the right, which lie equal distances from the mainland but differ in area. According to the equilibrium model of island biogeography, what should be the relative rates of immigration to the two islands? On which islands should rates of extinction be lowest? Explain.

5. Review the major hypotheses proposed to explain the higher species richness of tropical regions compared to temperate and high-latitude regions. How are each of these hypotheses related to relative rates of speciation and extinction in tropical regions and temperate and high-latitude regions?

6. Explain how speciation and extinction rates might be affected by the area of continents. What evidence is there to support your explanation? What does the influence of area on rates of extinction and speciation have to do with higher species richness in tropical regions compared to temperate and high-latitude regions?

7. Ricklefs (1987) pointed out that many large-scale contrasts in species richness and composition cannot be explained by local processes such as competition and predation. Ricklefs proposed that differences in history and geography can leave a unique stamp on regional biotas. The mammals of Australia, including kangaroos, koalas, and duck-billed platypuses, must be one of the best-known examples of a unique biota. How have history and geography, as opposed to local processes, combined to produce this unique assemblage of mammals?

8. Most examples of regional and latitudinal variation in species richness cited in chapter 22 have been terrestrial. Consider regional variation in marine biotas. Like birds on land, fish are one of the best-studied groups of marine organisms. Moyle and Cech (1982) cite the following patterns of fish species richness:

Atlantic and Gulf Coasts of North America		Pacific Coast of North America	
Area	**Species**	**Area**	**Species**
Texas	400	Gulf of California	800
South Carolina	350	California	550
Cape Cod	250	Canada	325
Gulf of Maine	225		
Labrador	61		
Greenland	34		

   As you can see, fish species richness decreases northward on both coasts. However, the Pacific coast generally supports a larger number of species. This contrast may be another situation requiring historical- and geographic-level explanations. Explore and explain this contrast in species richness using information from the fields of marine biology, oceanography, and ichthyology. Moyle and Cech (1982) and Briggs (1974) are good starting points.

9. The diversity of a local community is often linearly related to regional diversity. However, local diversity usually is lower than regional diversity. Why does local diversity not equal regional diversity? If the relationship between local and regional diversity does not saturate, does this mean that local processes such as competition are not important in structuring local communities?

10. How would you construct a map of the biodiversity hotspots for Canada? What information would you need for this to be accurate? How would you choose which taxa to include in constructing the map? Why does North America have very few biodiversity hotspots on global maps?

Suggested Readings

Bellwood, D. R. and T. P. Hughes. 2001. Regional-scale assembly rules and biodiversity of coral reefs. *Science* 292:1532–34.

An analysis of coral reef diversity that indicates that habitat area within the tropics accounts for more variation in species richness and composition than does latitude.

Brown, J. H. 1995. *Macroecology*. Chicago: University of Chicago Press.

Brown establishes a fresh framework for studies of large-scale ecology.

Brown, J. H. and M. V. Lomolino. 2000. Concluding remarks: historical perspective and the future of island biogeography theory. *Global Ecology and Biogeography* 9:87–92.

An update and historical perspective on the equilibrium theory of island biogeography from two scientists that have made major contributions to the theory.

Buzas, M. A., L. S. Collins, and S. J. Culver. 2002. Latitudinal difference in biodiversity caused by higher tropical rate of increase. *Proceedings of the National Academy of Sciences of the United States of America* 99:7841–43.

A study that uncovers evidence that rates of speciation are higher in the tropics.

Fine, P. V. A. 2001. An evaluation of the geographic area hypothesis using the latitudinal gradient in North American tree diversity. *Evolutionary Ecology Research* 3:413–28.

Detailed analysis showing that tree species richness does not increase smoothly from high latitudes to the tropics but increases gradually outside of the tropics and then increases abruptly as the tropics are entered.

Hawkins, B. A., R. Field, H. V. Cornell, D. J. Currie, J.-F. Guégan, D. M. Kaufman, J. T. Kerr, G. G. Mittelbach, T. Oberdorff, E. M. O'Brien, E. E. Porter, and J. R. G. Turner. 2003. Energy, water, and broad-scale geographic patterns of species richness. *Ecology* 84:3105–17.

The authors document a major relationship between water and energy and global patterns of species richness among plants and animals, including a latitudinal shift in the relative importance of ambient energy versus water from the poles to the equator.

Rosenzweig, M. L. 1995. *Species Diversity in Space and Time*. New York: Cambridge University Press.

Rosenzweig provides provocative analyses of one of the most stimulating subjects in ecology—spatial variation in species diversity.

Laurance, W. F. 2007. Have we overstated the tropical biodiversity crisis? *Trends in Ecology and Evolution* 22:65–70.

An interesting paper describing current controversy over the science regarding the rate of species loss in tropical forests.

Willis K. J., L. Gillson, and S. Knapp. 2007. Biodiversity hotspots through time: an introduction. *Philosophical Transaction of the Royal Society B-Biological Sciences* 362:169–74.

This paper sets the stage for a series of papers taking a longer time-scale view of biodiversity hotspots.

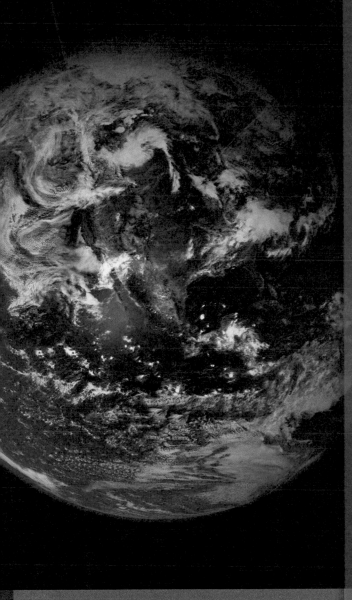

Chapter 23

Global Ecology

Outline

uring the final days of December 1968, the *Apollo 8* mission to the moon transmitted images of the earth rising above the moon's horizon. For the first time, in color, we could see how earth appears from our nearest neighbour in the solar system (fig. 23.1). The human response to the sight of the earth framed by a bleak lunar landscape is captured by the words of the *Apollo 8* astronauts: "The earth from here is a grand oasis in the … vastness of space."

That image, of earth as a shining blue ball against the blackness of space, instantaneously changed the perspective that most people held of the planet and made it easier to think of the earth as a single ecological system.

As we enter the twenty-first century, it is important that we keep that perspective alive. The rapid pace of global change challenges ecologists to study ecological phenomena at a global scale. Because many global-scale phenomena are mediated through the atmosphere, let's look briefly at the structure and origins of earth's atmospheric system.

Figure 23.1   Oasis in space: earthrise over the moon's horizon.

The Atmospheric Envelope and the Greenhouse Earth

The earth is wrapped in an atmospheric envelope that makes the biosphere a hospitable place for life as we know it. Clean, dry air at the earth's surface is approximately 78.08% nitrogen, 20.94% oxygen, 0.93% argon, 0.03% carbon dioxide, and less than 0.00005% ozone. Air also contains variable concentrations of water vapour and trace quantities of helium, hydrogen, krypton, methane, and neon. The concentrations of these gases change with altitude. The highest concentrations of atmospheric gases occur in the **troposphere,** a layer extending from the earth's surface to an altitude of 9 to 16 km. However, ozone is most concentrated in the **stratosphere,** which extends from the troposphere outward to an altitude of about 50 km. Above the troposphere are two other layers, the **mesosphere** and the **thermosphere.**

The atmosphere surrounding the earth significantly modifies earth's environment. For instance, the atmosphere reduces the amount of ultraviolet light that reaches the surface of the earth. This shielding by the atmosphere is performed principally by ozone, a trace gas with an extremely important function. The atmosphere also helps keep the surface of the earth warm, a phenomenon called the **greenhouse effect.**

How does the greenhouse effect work? The wavelengths and intensities of energy radiated by the earth into space indicate an object with a temperature of about –18°C. However, the average temperature at the earth's surface is about 15°C. This 33°C difference between predicted and actual temperature results from heat trapped near the earth's surface by the atmosphere (fig. 23.2). This heat is trapped by the greenhouse gases, which include water vapour, carbon dioxide, methane, ozone, nitrous oxide, and chlorofluorocarbons. Notice that several of these greenhouse gases are products of biological activity (chapters 19 & 20). Without the greenhouse effect, life on Earth would look quite different. To put it mildly, there wouldn't be much happening in Canada!

Let's look briefly at a budget of solar energy for the earth. About 30% of the solar energy shining on earth is reflected back into space by clouds, by particles in the atmosphere, or by the surface of the earth. Approximately 70% of the solar energy shining on the earth is absorbed either by the atmosphere or by the earth's surface. This energy is reemitted as infrared radiation. Some of the infrared radiation from the atmosphere is radiated into space, and some is radiated toward the surface of the earth. Most of the infrared radiation from the earth's surface is absorbed by greenhouse gases in the atmosphere and radiated back to the earth's surface. By radiating infrared radiation back to the earth's surface, greenhouse gases trap heat energy and raise the earth's surface temperature.

We should remember that the atmosphere is not static. The atmosphere and the oceans are in continuous motion as a consequence of the uneven heating of the earth's surface. In chapters 2 and 3 we reviewed the major patterns of atmospheric and oceanic circulation. These circulatory systems link the various regions of the globe into a single physical system by moving heat energy and materials from one part of the biosphere to another.

Biological activity is largely responsible for the current composition of earth's atmosphere, particularly the concentrations of oxygen, carbon dioxide, and methane. While the effect of life on atmospheric composition is usually associated with human activity, major biological influences on the atmosphere began about 2 billion years ago. The early atmosphere lacked oxygen and likely contained higher concentrations of carbon dioxide and hydrogen. Atmospheric oxygen began increasing about 2 billion years ago with the appearance of oxygen-producing photosynthesis.

James Walker (1986) referred to the shift in atmospheric composition that eventually produced today's aerobic atmosphere as "the most severe pollution episode in the history of the earth." Why did he refer to oxygen as a pollutant? To answer this question we need to remember what sorts of organisms inhabited the earth of 2 billion years ago. The first life-forms appeared about 3.5 billion years ago. Geological evidence indicates that the atmosphere when these early organisms lived was free of oxygen. Consequently, the earliest

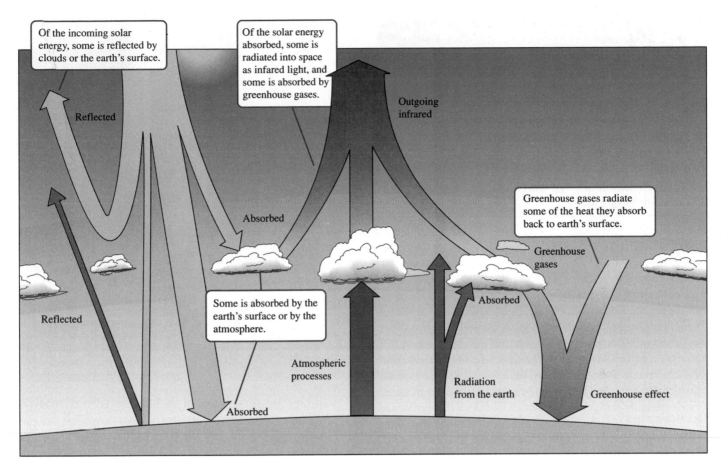

Figure 23.2 The greenhouse effect: heat trapping by earth's atmosphere.

organisms were anaerobes, for which oxygen is a deadly poison. As a result, the activity of some organisms on the planet likely caused the extinction of many others. As we shall see, the composition of the atmosphere is once again changing, this time in response to human activity.

Our discussion begins with a large-scale atmosphere-ocean system that has global effects on ecological systems. From this general discussion of climatic systems we review some key human influences on the biosphere. Michael Soulé (1991) suggests that there are six key human influences that are dramatically influencing the biosphere: (1) habitat loss, (2) habitat fragmentation, (3) overexploitation of natural populations, (4) the spread of invasive species, (5) altered

nutrient cycling and nutrient inputs, and (6) climate change. Soulé argues that these six forms of human interference can alter ecological processes and biodiversity at scales ranging from genes to ecosystems (fig. 23.3). Additionally, because the status of economic development influences the type and intensity of industrial activity, different countries throughout the globe are currently facing different sets of challenges. Because these environmental changes have already influenced global climate and biodiversity, and will likely continue to do so for generations, it is important to understand their causes and consequences. We have already discussed issues of habitat fragmentation and overexploitation in prior chapters. Here we discuss the remaining four.

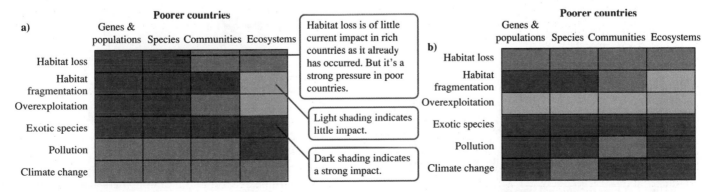

Figure 23.3 Human influences present different challenges to biodiversity as a function of ecological scale and economic status of a country (Soulé 1991).

Concepts

23.1 Large-scale atmospheric and oceanic phenomena influence ecological systems on a global scale.

23.2 Human activity has greatly increased the quantity of fixed nitrogen cycling through the biosphere.

23.3 Rapid changes in global patterns of land use threaten biological diversity.

23.4 Human activity is increasing the atmospheric concentration of CO_2, which may be increasing global temperatures.

23.1 A Global System

Large-scale atmospheric and oceanic phenomena influence ecological systems on a global scale. One of the most thoroughly studied of these systems is the *El Niño Southern Oscillation*. During an **El Niño**, a warm current appears off the west coast of Peru, generally during the Christmas season (El Niño refers to the Christ child). The term **Southern Oscillation** refers to an oscillation in atmospheric pressure that extends across the Pacific Ocean. There are other oscillations in atmospheric pressure throughout the planet, each of which influence the climate and weather of large expanses of the planet. Two that are particularly relevant for northern areas are the **North Atlantic Oscillation** and the **Northern Hemisphere Annular Mode**. Ecological understanding of the effects of El Niño is more developed than that of these other drivers of global climate, and this is where we begin.

El Niño

In 1904, a British mathematician named Gilbert Walker was appointed Director General of Observatories in India. Walker arrived in India shortly after a disastrous famine from 1899 to 1900 caused by crop failures during a drought. This tragic event led him to search for a way to predict the rainfall associated with the Asian monsoons. Walker (1924) eventually found a correspondence between barometric pressure across the Pacific Ocean and the amount of rain falling during the monsoons. He found that reduced barometric pressure in the eastern Pacific was accompanied by increased barometric pressure in the western Pacific. In a similar fashion, when the barometric pressure fell in the western Pacific, it rose in the eastern Pacific. Walker called this oscillation in barometric pressure the Southern Oscillation.

Today, meteorologists monitor the state of the Southern Oscillation with the Southern Oscillation Index. The value of the index is determined by the difference in barometric pressure between Tahiti and Darwin, Australia (fig. 23.4). Walker noticed that low values of the Southern Oscillation Index were associated with drought in Australia, Indonesia, India, and parts of Africa. Walker also suggested that winter temperatures in Canada were somehow connected to the Southern Oscillation. His studies led him to a global perspective on climate, a perspective well ahead of his time.

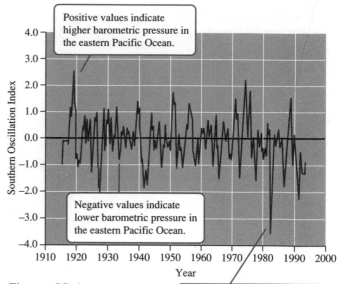

Figure 23.4 The Southern Oscillation Index shows the difference in barometric pressures between Tahiti and Darwin, Australia.

The connection between Walker's Southern Oscillation and patterns of ocean temperature during El Niños was eventually described by Jacob Bjerknes (1966, 1969). Bjerknes proposed that the gradient in sea surface temperature across the central Pacific Ocean produces a large-scale atmospheric circulation system that moves in the plane of the equator, as shown in figure 23.5. Air over the warmer western Pacific rises, flows eastward in the upper atmosphere, and then sinks over the eastern Pacific. This air mass then flows westward along with the southeast trade winds, gradually warming and

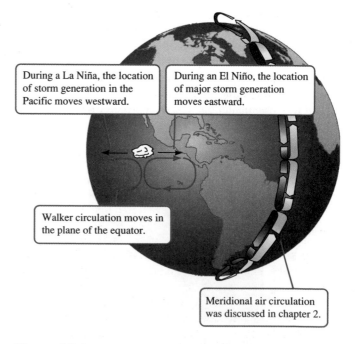

Figure 23.5 Walker circulation, El Niño, and La Niña.

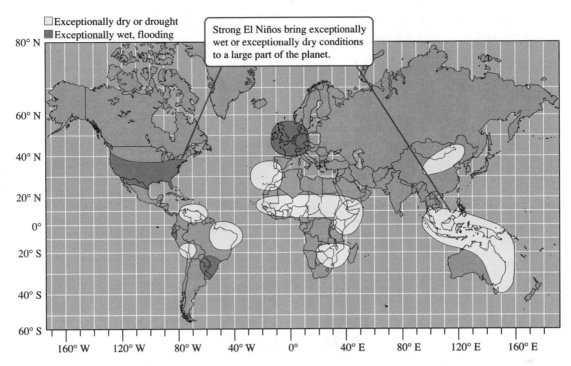

Figure 23.6 Effects of the exceptionally strong El Niño of 1982 to 1983 on patterns of global precipitation (data from Diaz and Kiladis 1992).

gathering moisture. This westward-flowing air eventually joins the rising air in the western Pacific. As this warm and moist air rises, it forms rain clouds. Bjerknes called this atmospheric system **Walker circulation** after Sir Gilbert Walker.

The El Niño Southern Oscillation affects the climate of North America, South America, Australia, southern Asia, Africa, and parts of southern Europe (fig. 23.6). This climatic variability has substantial influences on the distribution of organisms, structure of communities, and ecosystem processes.

During the mature phase of an El Niño, the sea surface in the eastern tropical Pacific Ocean is much warmer than average and the barometric pressure over the eastern Pacific is lower than average. The combination of warm sea surface temperatures and low barometric pressure promotes the formation of storms over the eastern Pacific Ocean. These storms bring increased precipitation to much of North and South America. During an El Niño, the sea surface in the western Pacific is cooler than average and the barometric pressure is higher than average. These conditions produce drought over much of the western Pacific region.

Periods of lower sea surface temperature and higher than average barometric pressure in the eastern tropical Pacific have been named **La Niñas.** La Niña brings drought to much of North and South America. During La Niñas, a pool of warm seawater moves far into the western Pacific. This warm water combined with lower barometric pressures in the western Pacific Ocean generates many storms. Consequently, La Niña brings higher than average precipitation to the western Pacific. It appears that La Niñas and El Niños represent opposite extremes in the El Niño Southern Oscillation cycle.

While often associated with the tropics, the influence of the El Niño Southern Oscillation extends well into temperate regions. During El Niños, much of the northern United States,

Canada, and Alaska are much warmer than average. During La Niñas, these regions are colder than average. As you might expect, this global climate system affects ecological systems around the globe.

El Niño and Marine Populations

Some of the most dramatic ecological responses to El Niño occur in marine populations along the west coast of South America. Long before the recent discovery of the global extent of its effects, El Niño was known to produce declines in coastal populations of anchovies and sardines and the seabirds that feed upon them. How does El Niño induce these population declines? They are produced by changes in the pattern of sea surface temperatures and coastal circulation. Figure 23.7b shows sea surface temperatures off the west coast of South America during average conditions. Notice that under average conditions, coastal waters are relatively cool along most of the west coast of South America and that a tongue of cool water extends westward toward the open Pacific Ocean. This cool water is brought to the surface by upwelling. Upwelling along the coast is driven by the southeast trade winds, while the offshore upwelling is driven by the east winds of the Walker circulation.

With the onset of an El Niño, the easterly winds slacken and the pool of warm water in the western Pacific moves eastward. Eventually this pool of warm water reaches the west coast of South America and then moves north and south along the coast (fig. 23.7a). During the mature phase of an El Niño, the warm surface water along the west coast of South America shuts off upwelling. Consequently, the supply of nutrients that upwelling usually delivers to surface waters is also shut off. A lower nutrient supply reduces primary production by phytoplankton. This decline in primary production reduces the supply of food available to consumers in the coastal food web and is followed by declines in populations of fish and their predators.

Remote sensing (chapter 22) of phytoplankton pigments in surface waters around the Galápagos Islands shows that the 1982–83 El Niño reduced average primary production and dramatically changed the location of production "hot spots." Figure 23.8 shows the concentration of phytoplankton pigments, mainly chlorophyll *a,* around the Galápagos Islands before and during the 1982–83 El Niño. The image made on

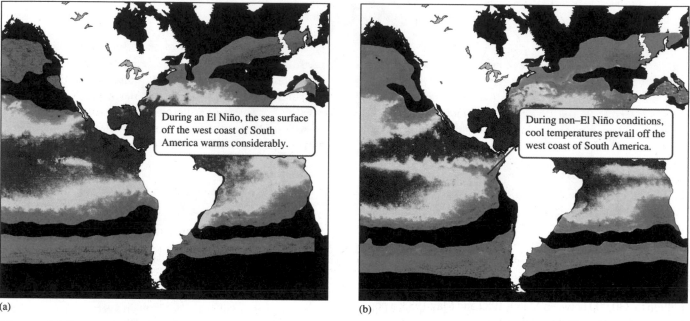

(a)   (b)

Figure 23.7   Sea surface temperature during (*a*) El Niño and (*b*) non–El Niño conditions.

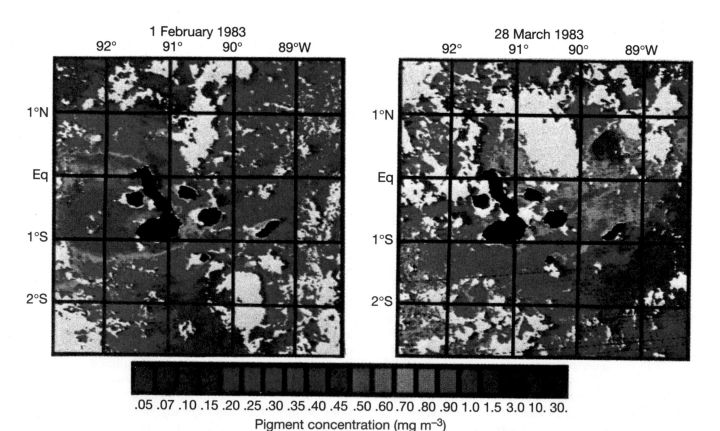

Figure 23.8   El Niño and areas of high marine primary production around the Galápagos Islands. Notice that the areas of high production were west of the islands on February 1 and east of them on March 28 (data from Feldman, Clark, and Halpern 1984).

February 1, 1983, shows the normal patterns when the southeast trade winds produce upwelling on the western sides of the islands. These upwelling areas, which are shown in red and orange, are especially apparent west of the large islands of Fernandina and Isabela. Large areas of high phytoplankton production extended for approximately 150 km west of these islands. On February 1, the mean pigment concentration for surface waters around the Galápagos archipelago was 0.30 mg per cubic meter.

A shift in wind direction reduced average phytoplankton biomass and shifted the location of high production areas. After February 1, the trade winds became progressively weaker and variable in direction. By March 28, the pigment concentration had increased back to 0.28 mg per cubic meter. However, the areas of high phytoplankton biomass had shifted far to the east.

Changes in the rate and distribution of primary production, such as those shown in figure 23.8, induced reproductive failure, migration, and widespread death among seabird populations in the Galápagos Islands and along the west coast of South America during the 1982–83 El Niño. Many seabirds abandoned their nests with the onset of this El Niño and migrated either north or south along the coast of South America. Virtually no birds reproduced and most of the migrating birds starved. Population declines were dramatic. The adult populations of three seabird species on the coast of Peru declined from 6.01 million to 330,000 between March 1982 and May 1983, a population decline of approximately 95%.

The 1982–83 El Niño also had a major impact on fur seal and sea lion populations, mainly through reductions in food supply. The main food fish for the South American fur seal, *Arctocephalus australis,* is the anchoveta, *Engraulis ringens. Engraulis* normally lives at depths of 0 to 40 m. However, during the 1982–83 El Niño, it moved away from fur seal colonies to cooler water at depths of up to 100 m.

In response, fur seals dived deeper and shifted their diets to other fishes. Both on the mainland and on the Galápagos, female fur seals increased their foraging time. Since females are away from their young while foraging, the pups in both populations did not get enough food and all died. On the Galápagos, nearly 100% of mature male fur seals died, while the mortality of adult females and nonterritorial males was approximately 30%. A large fur seal colony at Punta San Juan, Peru, declined from 6,300 to 4,200 individuals.

As the previous examples show, El Niño has well documented effects on marine populations along the coast of South America. Additional effects, on land and in sea, are found in North America and Australia, influencing a diversity of taxa and natural communities. However, northern systems appear to be more strongly influenced by two other oscillations in barometric pressure.

North Atlantic Oscillation and the Northern Hemisphere Annular Mode

The North Atlantic Oscillation (NAO) is a fluctuation in atmospheric pressure between Iceland and the Azores off the coast of Portugal (fig. 23.9). Like El Niño, the NAO has been identified for over 200 years (Saabye 1776), though only

recently has its importance in driving large-scale ecological patterns been realized (Otterson et al. 2001). A major effect of variation in NAO is a shift in the direction and speed of wind over the Atlantic ocean between 40° and 60°, particularly during winter months. When the NAO is in the positive phase, there are high atmospheric pressures below 55° and lower pressures towards the Arctic (Stenseth et al. 2003). This has the effect of moving the storms that travel across the Atlantic Ocean towards the north (the area of lower pressure), resulting in increased storm activity in southern Europe, higher temperatures over much of Europe and North America, reduced precipitation across much of the Canadian Arctic, and cool temperatures in eastern Canada. When the NAO is in the negative phase, these patterns are reversed, with the storm activity focused on southern Europe, cooler temperatures, and more precipitation in the Canadian Arctic. There is substantial

a)   Positive North Atlantic Oscillation Phase

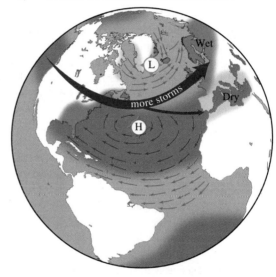

b)   Negative North Atlantic Oscillation Phase

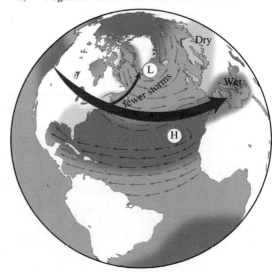

Figure 23.9 Large-scale impacts of the (*a*) positive, and (*b*) negative phases of the North Atlantic Oscillation.

variation in the strength of NAO among years (fig. 23.10), though the last few decades have been dominated primarily by strongly positive years. As a clear sign of the potential importance of the NAO on ecological communities, approximately 33% of the interannual variation in winter temperatures in the Northern Hemisphere is attributed to variation in the NAO (Hurrell 1996). Eric Post and Nils Stenseth have explored the impacts of variation in the NAO on populations of a variety of organisms (Post and Stenseth 1999).

The current condition of the NAO is measured each year, and is simply the average difference in atmospheric pressure between Stykkishomur, Iceland, and Lisbon, Portugal, through the winter. Post and Stenseth explored whether that variation was associated with changes in plant phenology or population measures of northern ungulates. As we saw in chapter 9, plant phenology is responsive to changes in temperature and is already shifting in response to global warming. Therefore it is reasonable to expect that other large-scale phenomena, such as the NAO, may also be important in determine the timing of flowering across large geographic regions. Ungulates were chosen for study because they are herbivores, and may be affected by any changes in the plant communities. Snow depth and the timing of snow can also impact large foragers, with potential impacts on population growth. Additionally, these large mammals are of great concern to indigenous communities, conservation biologists, and the general public, and thus an understanding of whether large-scale climatic variation influences their populations is critically needed.

To test whether there was a link between the NAO, plant phenology, and ungulate populations, the researchers gathered information from numerous data sets. The NAO index was available online through the National Center for Atmospheric Research in the United States. Long-term records on plant phenology were available in the literature for 43 species of flowering plants located in 37 sites across Norway. Several of the species included serve as important food sources for native ungulates. For all species, they had data on the date of first flowering in each year, and for many species they also had data for the date of first fruit set. The researchers also compiled previously published data on 16 populations of 7 ungulate species, including reindeer, moose, red deer, Soay sheep, feral goats, muskoxen, and caribou. The exact measures varied among populations and species, but often included such things as body size, fecundity, and survival of juveniles. In contrast to

the data on plant phenology, the data on ungulate populations came from sites located across the north, including Europe, North America, and Scandinavia.

In general, plants flowered earlier in Norway following a positive NAO winter, which corresponds to a warmer, wetter year. The correlations between flowering and NAO varied among species and locations, and were strongest for non-woody species, species from the more southerly latitudes within Norway, and species which typically bloom early, rather than late. For example the date of first flowering of *Anemone nemorosa* spanned a 30-day range around 57° and only a 10–20 day range around 63°. Of all the measures of ungulate populations, 72% also showed signification covariation with the NAO. There was evidence that the NAO influenced growth and fecundity in all the species studied, explaining between 40%–70% of the variation in body size and fecundity. The exact effects of positive NAO years varied among species and locations. In general, mainland populations had greater fecundity and smaller body size during positive NAO years, while maritime populations had increased body size and reduced fecundity during positive NAO winters. In total, this study provides clear evidence that the North Atlantic Oscillation can impact a diversity of populations across a broad geographic area.

Closely related to the NAO is the Northern Hemisphere Annular Mode (NAM), formerly referred to as the Arctic Oscillation. The NAM is generally of a direction opposite to the NAO such that when one is in positive phase, the other is generally in negative phase. Because of this synchrony it is not clear whether the resulting ecological effects are driven primarily by variation in NAO or the NAM. Regardless of which large-scale climatic system is driving the changes that are observed, it is very clear that these systems have impacts on ecological systems similar in scale to that of El Niño.

Concept 23.1 Review

1. How are the influences of El Niño and La Niña related to the concepts of top-down versus bottom-up control of populations, communities, and ecosystems?
2. How does a species' life history influence the effects of NOA on population dynamics?
3. Why is understanding atmospheric cycles important for ecologists?

23.2 Human Activity and the Global Nitrogen Cycle

Human activity has greatly increased the quantity of fixed nitrogen cycling through the biosphere.   When we reviewed the nitrogen cycle in chapter 20, we saw that nitrogen enters the cycle through the process of nitrogen fixation. For millions of years, the only organisms that could fix nitrogen were nitrogen-fixing bacteria and some actinomycete fungi. Then, as humans developed intensive agricultural and industrial processes that fix nitrogen, we began to manipulate the nitrogen cycle on a massive scale.

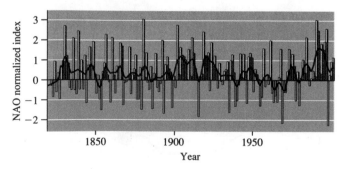

Figure 23.10 Variation in the NAO over time (Otterson et al. 2001).

How has human activity altered the nitrogen cycle? To address this question, we need to review the sources and amounts of nitrogen fixed in the absence of human manipulation. Vitousek (1994) summarized the natural background levels of nitrogen fixation as follows. The nitrogen fixed in terrestrial environments by free-living nitrogen-fixing bacteria and nitrogen-fixing plants totals approximately 100 terragrams (Tg) of nitrogen (N) per year (1 Tg = 10^{12} g). Nitrogen fixation in marine environments adds an additional 5 to 20 Tg N per year; fixation by lightning adds about 10 Tg N per year. These estimates of nonhuman sources of fixed nitrogen total approximately 130 Tg N per year.

Human additions to the nitrogen cycle now exceed historical sources of fixed nitrogen. One of the traditional ways that humans have manipulated the nitrogen cycle is by planting agricultural land with nitrogen-fixing crops. At some point, agriculturists learned that rotating legumes such as alfalfa and soybeans with grains such as oats and maize could increase crop yields. We now know that those increased grain yields are due mainly to nitrogen additions to the soil by the bacteria that are associated with legumes. Vitousek estimated that the plant–microbe mutualism that results in nitrogen-fixing crops, fix about 30 Tg N per year. Agriculturists also apply nitrogen fertilizers produced through industrial processes that fix nitrogen. The nitrogen fixed by the fertilizer industry amounts to more than 80 Tg N per year. Finally, Vitousek estimated that the internal combustion engines in cars, trucks, and other conveyances emit about 25 Tg N per year as oxides of nitrogen. V. Smil (1990) estimated the total emission of nitrogen from all combustion of fossil fuels, including coal-fired electrical generation as well as internal combustion engines, at 35 Tg N per year. The main point here is that on a global scale, nitrogen fixation resulting from human activity fixes more nitrogen (135–145 Tg N versus 130 Tg N) than all other sources of fixed nitrogen combined (fig. 23.11).

The massive human contribution to the global nitrogen cycle is a recent phenomenon. For instance, the industrial production of fertilizers dates from the early twentieth century, and Vitousek estimated that 50% of all the commercial fertilizer produced prior to 1993 was applied to land between 1982 and 1993. Figure 23.12 shows that human contributions to the global nitrogen cycle have increased exponentially.

What are some of the consequences of these human-induced alterations to the global nitrogen cycle? As we saw in chapter 20, nitrogen additions to ecosystems are associated with local reductions in plant and fungal diversity. Nitrogen enrichment appears to alter the mutualistic relationship between plants and mycorrhizal fungi. Consequently, nitrogen enrichment over large regions threatens the health and survival of entire ecosystems. The health of forests near industrial areas has been in rapid decline. By creating environmental conditions favourable to some species and unfavourable to others, large-scale nitrogen enrichment threatens biological diversity.

The impacts of large-scale nitrogen deposition have been studied by Scott Wilson and his graduate student, Martin Köchy, of the University of Regina (Köchy and Wilson 2001). The researchers were working in Elk Island National Park in Alberta, testing the effects of plant litter on nutrient dynamics. To do this, they measured the nitrogen that was mineralized beneath plant litter, and then in areas away from litter. They hypothesized that decomposition of the litter would result in higher levels of nitrogen. However, when they took their samples to the lab and analyzed them, they found the opposite pattern: areas away from litter had more nitrogen available than areas under litter. How was this possible? Köchy and Wilson hypothesized that the nitrogen they were measuring in the exposed plots was coming from the atmosphere. Because the magnitude of nitrogen deposition was so high, clearly greater then the nitrogen mineralized in litter, they decided to investigate its potential ecological effects.

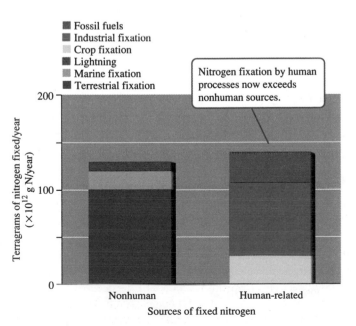

Figure 23.11   Human and nonhuman sources of fixed nitrogen (data from Vitousek 1994).

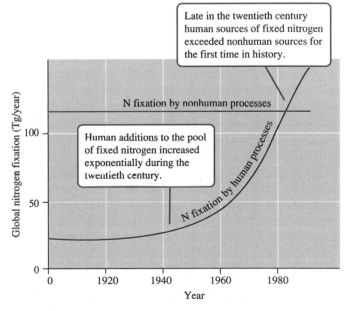

Figure 23.12   Increase in nitrogen fixation by human processes during the twentieth century (data from Vitousek 1994).

It comes as little surprise to most people that highly urbanized areas will suffer substantial nitrogen deposition. Köchy and Wilson were interested in whether there was evidence of ecological shifts due to nitrogen deposition in less densely populated areas. Additionally, nitrogen deposition is often associated with forest encroachment on grasslands. In other words, when more nitrogen is available, trees tend to competitively exclude many grasses. Köchy and Wilson realized that an ideal location for this study was in the northern region of the North American Great Plains. This area is sparsely populated, and much of the area exists as a mosaic of grasslands and forests. They decided to measure nitrogen dynamics and forest encroachment in six national parks in Manitoba, Saskatchewan, and Alberta (fig. 23.13). In each location, they measured nitrogen deposition, the amount of nitrogen available to plants in the soil, and the extent of forest invasion into land previously occupied by grasslands.

Measures of nitrogen were relatively straightforward. Within each site they collected nitrogen that was absorbed by ion-exchange resin bags. These bags are filled with small beads of a resin that absorbed nitrogen, and the amounts absorbed can be determined in the lab. Bags were placed above the soil surface to measure deposition, and below the soil surface to measure nitrogen availability to plants. Measures of forest expansion required a completely different set of methods. The researchers obtained aerial photographs of the parks ranging from 1930 to 1995. The selected a 3.5 km² area in each of the earliest photographs that contained both forest and grassland. They then measured any changes in forest and grassland cover through the subsequent photographs (chapter 21).

The results were striking. Nitrogen deposition varied among parks, and was highest in parks in areas of high population densities (Elk Island, Prince Albert) and lowest in areas of low population densities (Jasper, Wood Buffalo). High rates of nitrogen deposition were also positively associated with high levels of nitrogen availability in the soils. Over the last 50–60 years, there has been an increase in forest cover in Elk Island, Prince Albert, and Riding Mountain national parks, but not Jasper, Wood Buffalo, or Grasslands (fig. 23.14). Statistical analyses indicated these changes are positively correlated to both precipitation and nitrogen deposition rates, suggesting that both water and extra nitrogen lead to increased forest cover in the North American Great Plains. Additionally, in those parks with increased forest cover, the timing of change appears synchronized with the timing of human population growth in the prairies (fig. 23.14).

These results are just one of many examples suggesting that atmospheric nitrogen is causing shifts in the composition of natural communities. These changes have occurred over only the last several decades, and likely will continue into the foreseeable future. As we show next, changes in land use over the last several centuries has likely already been the single greatest human impact on the planet, and continued changes may represent an even greater threat to biological diversity.

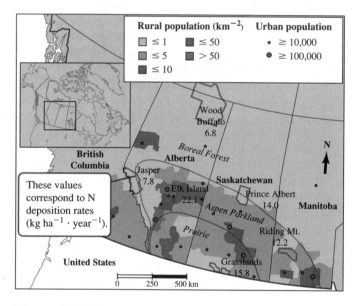

Figure 23.13 Population densities surrounding six national parks in western Canada (data from Köchy and Wilson 2001).

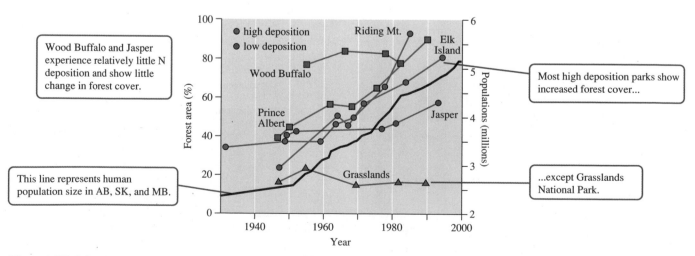

Figure 23.14 Changes in forest area and human population size throughout the prairie provinces of Canada (data from Köchy and Wilson 2001).

Concept 23.2 Review

1. Will human-induced alterations to the amount of fixed nitrogen on land influence aquatic ecosystems? Why or why not?
2. How might human-induced alterations to the global nitrogen cycle interact with other disturbances, such as fire suppression, to impact forest encroachment in grasslands?
3. In figure 23.14, Grasslands National Park in southern Saskatchewan has experience high rates of nitrogen deposition. However, forest cover has not changed. Why?

23.3 Changes in Land Cover

Rapid changes in global patterns of land use threaten biological diversity. Humans have changed the face of the earth. Human activities, mainly agriculture and urbanization, have significantly altered one-third to one-half of the ice-free land surface of the earth. Marshes have been drained and filled to build urban areas or airports. Tropical forests have been cut and converted to pasture. The courses of rivers have been changed. The Aral Sea in central Asia has been so starved for water that it is nearly dry. As shown in figure 23.3, Soulé suggested that changes in land cover pose a continued threat to biological diversity. Let's review some of the changes in land cover and the mechanisms that make landscape changes such a powerful threat to biological diversity. We will begin by taking a broad overview, and then discuss one issue of current concern.

A Global Perspective

Jonathan Foley, of the University of Wisconsin, along with other colleagues from the United States, Canada, and the United Kingdom, has recently summarized the global impact of land use (Foley et al. 2005). Humans occupy a substantial portion of the land area of the plant, and we utilize between ⅓ and ½ of global productivity (Foley et al. 2005). To date, changes in land-use due to human activity have arguably had the single greatest impact on the distribution and functioning of natural communities.

The most dominant human land uses are cropland and pastures, which together cover nearly 40% of the land surface of the planet (fig. 23.15). Associated with conversion of native grasslands and forests to croplands and rangelands has been a 700% increase in fertilizer use, and a 70% increase in irrigated croplands across the planet in the last 40 years. These two activities associated with modern agricultural practices place enormous pressures on freshwater resources. It is estimated that 85% of the freshwater used by humans goes to agriculture, and this represents 10% of the global reserves. Fertilizers routinely leach into streams and groundwater, decreasing the quality of the water and the aquatic ecosystems that surround agricultural fields.

In the last 300 years, between 7–11 million km^2 of forest have been cleared for timber and for conversion into agricultural land. Grasslands have not faired any better, with little native prairie remaining in many areas of the world, including North America (fig. 23.15). The rates of changes in land use vary across the planet. Foley and colleagues suggest that as societies develop economically, so too does their impact on the surrounding land (fig. 23.16). Much of the land base in North America and Europe has already been altered. The large expanses of land that remain relatively intact, such as the boreal forest and arctic tundra, are regions that historically were economically unviable for development. However, continued changes to the world timber markets; new technologies for processing oil sands; discovery of extensive gas fields, diamonds, and other valuable minerals; and thinning ice and snow packs are placing significant pressures for development in formerly remote areas. In other parts of the world, such as the Amazon basin and much of Africa, the rapid phase of development is just beginning. These changes present an interesting moral question: do North American and European societies have the right to suggest developing nations not develop their land, when these northern societies did exactly the same thing just a few centuries ago? Alternatively, do developed countries have a moral obligation to protect the world's biodiversity, as they may be the only countries that can afford to do so? Needless to say, there are no easy answers, even though the questions are of great importance.

The issues at stake are even greater than the direct effects of agriculture and forestry on the land base. In addition to direct impacts on vegetation cover (and thus habitat for animals and microbes), land use changes have significant impact on global climate. For example, changes in the reflectance of land cover alter albedo (chapter 2), and thus temperatures. Burning large expanses of land to clear forest for agricultural or pastureland releases large reserves of CO_2 into the atmosphere. Although historically there has been expansion of cropland and rangeland throughout the planet, of greatest current concern is the rate of deforestation of the tropical forests. These activities are of global concern due both to the speed at which they occur, and because the tropical forests are home to many of the most significant biodiversity hotspots (chapter 22). We now turn to the tropics to better understand what pressures natural communities are facing.

Tropical Deforestation

The cutting and clearing of tropical forests continues at an alarming rate. This deforestation is alarming because tropical forests support half or more of earth's species and appear to influence global climate. In the face of worldwide concern, we need accurate estimates of the state of tropical forests. However, estimates of deforestation rates vary widely.

How much tropical forest is there? How much tropical forest has been cut? What are the current rates of deforestation? David Skole and Compton Tucker (1993) provide us with answers to some of these questions. These researchers reported that tropical forest occurs in 73 countries and once covered

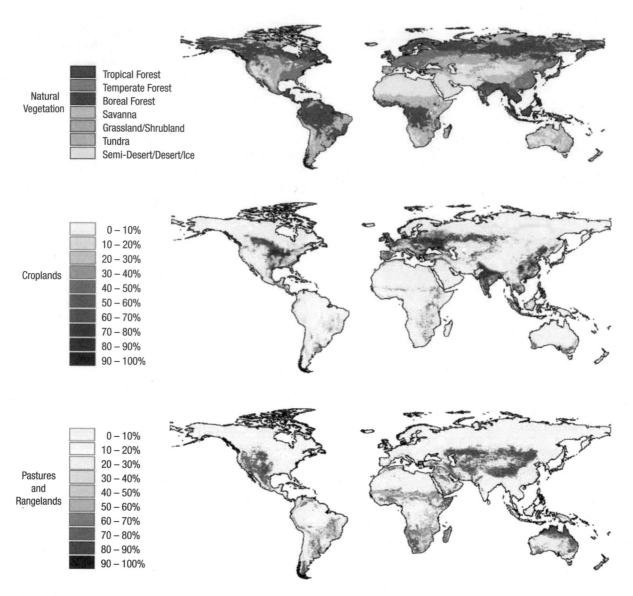

Figure 23.15   Extent of agricultural activity across the planet (data from Foley et al. 2005).

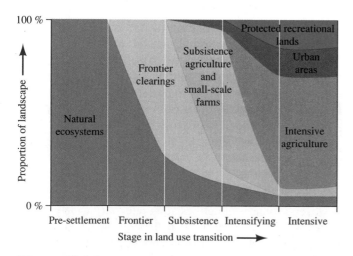

Figure 23.16   Changes in land use as societies develop (Foley et al. 2005).

11,610,350 km². However, three-fourths of the world's tropical forests occur in just 10 countries (fig. 23.17). The largest single tract of tropical forest, nearly one-third of the total, occurs in Brazil. Brazil is also the country with the highest rate of deforestation.

While there has been general agreement that rates of deforestation in Brazil are high, estimates of those rates vary widely. Skole and Tucker set out to provide an accurate estimate of deforestation rates in the Amazon Basin. They based their estimate on photographs taken by *Landsat* satellites in 1978 and 1988. The images they used, *Landsat* Thematic Mapper photos, provide high-resolution information. As you can see in figure 23.18, Thematic Mapper photos clearly show areas of deforestation, regrowth on deforested plots, and areas of isolated forest. Skole and Tucker entered these high-resolution images into a geographic information system (see chapter 22), which they used to create computerized maps of deforestation within the Amazon Basin.

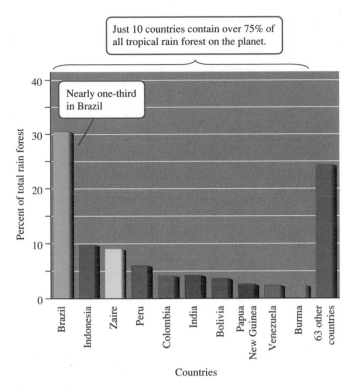

Just 10 countries contain over 75% of all tropical rain forest on the planet.

Nearly one-third in Brazil

Figure 23.17 Distribution of rain forest area by country (data from Skole and Tucker 1993).

Let's look at the maps in figure 23.19 and see what they tell us. First, notice that large areas, coloured light brown in the map, were not forested. These areas, concentrated in the southeastern Amazon Basin, have a semiarid climate and support scrubby vegetation. Some areas, shown in light violet, were covered by clouds and could not be analyzed. Skole and Tucker used the 1978 image to estimate the amount of deforestation that had occurred prior to 1978. They then compared the 1978 and 1988 photos to determine the amount of deforestation during that decade. They divided the Amazon Basin into 16 km by 16 km squares for their analysis. One of those areas is enlarged in an inset on figure 23.19. These insets show the amount of deforestation in 1978 and in 1988. Notice that the deforested area in the inset increased significantly between 1978 and 1988.

Skole and Tucker used their analyses of 16 km by 16 km areas to estimate the percentage of the land surface that had been deforested across the entire Amazon Basin. On their maps, white indicates completely forested areas, while various colours indicate increasing degrees of deforestation. At one end of their spectrum, gray indicates 0.25% to 5% deforested; at the other end, red indicates 90% to 100% deforested. Notice that the colour of the area covered by the inset is purple on the 1978 map and green on the 1988 map. Change in colour on the map of the entire basin from 1978 to 1988 reflects the increase in deforested area during that period.

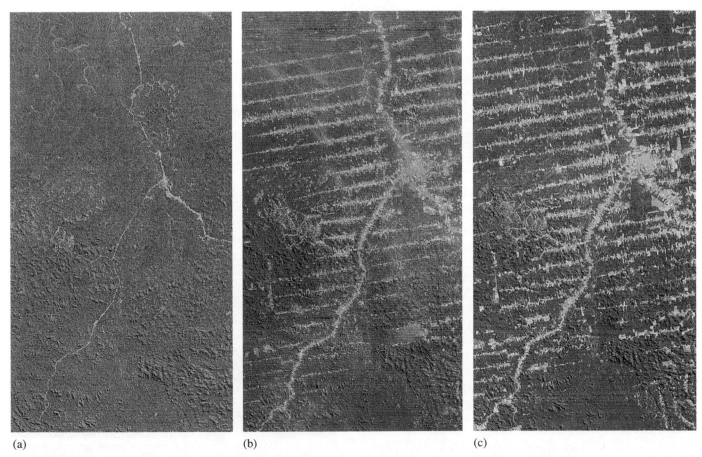

(a)   (b)   (c)

Figure 23.18 Information on tropical deforestation from satellite images: deforestation in Rondônia State, Brazil (light areas), in (*a*) 1975, (*b*) 1986, and (*c*) 1992.

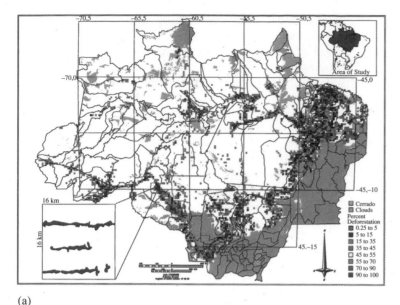

(a)

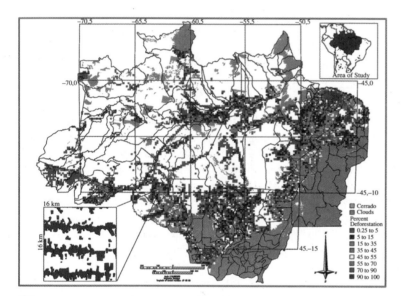

(b)

Figure 23.19   Deforestation in Amazonia between (*a*) 1978 and (*b*) 1988 (data from Skole and Tucker 1993).

How much of the Brazilian Amazon has been deforested? Skole and Tucker estimated that by 1978, 78,000 km² had been deforested. They also estimated that the annual rate of deforestation between 1978 and 1988 was about 15,000 km² per year. While this estimate indicates considerable deforestation, it is considerably lower than earlier estimates that ranged from 21,000 to 80,000 km² per year. Skole and Tucker estimated that the total area deforested by 1988 was 230,000 km². This estimate, which was slightly lower than the official estimate by the Brazilian government, is probably the most accurate estimate of deforestation within the Amazon Basin made to date.

Edge Effects and Forest Fragmentation

The area of forest removed does not give a complete picture of the ecological effects of deforestation. When a tract of forest is cut, the adjacent forest is affected by changes in the physical environment along its edges, by reduced habitat area, and by isolation. Let's look at the nature of these "edge effects" in Amazonian forest fragments.

In 1979, Brazil's National Institute for Research in Amazonia and the World Wildlife Fund began a long-term study of tropical forest fragmentation. This research project took advantage of a Brazilian law that requires that 50% of land developed in the Amazon Basin remain forested. The researchers worked with ranchers to leave forested tracts in particular areas to facilitate research on the ecological influences of forest fragment size and isolation. The fragments studied were 1, 10, 100, and 200 ha (fig. 23.20). These were compared to areas of 1, 10, 100, and 1,000 ha in undisturbed forest.

When a small fragment of forest is isolated by cutting the surrounding forest, its edge is exposed to greater amounts of solar radiation and wind. Wind and sun combine to change the physical environment within forest fragments. The physical environment along forest edges is hotter and drier and the intensity of solar radiation higher. These physical changes, in turn, affect the structure of the forest community. Tree mortality is higher along the edges of forest fragments and the forest overstory decreases while the thickness of the understory vegetation increases. Fragmentation also decreases the diversity of many animal groups, including monkeys, birds, bees, and carrion and dung beetles. Some of these reductions in animal populations may have significant impacts on key ecological processes such as pollination and decomposition.

Because edge effects, isolation, and reduced habitat area negatively affect biological diversity within tropical forest fragments, Skole and Tucker extended their analysis of deforestation in the Amazon Basin to include these effects. They assumed that edge effects extend for 1 km from the forest edge. The results of adding a 1 km

Figure 23.20   Forest fragments left by clear-cutting forest from the surrounding landscape have very different physical environments than intact forest.

Figure 23.21 Edge effect produces a greater degree of impact of deforestation than is apparent from the area of clear-cuts alone. Compare to figure 23.17*b* (data from Skole and Tucker 1993).

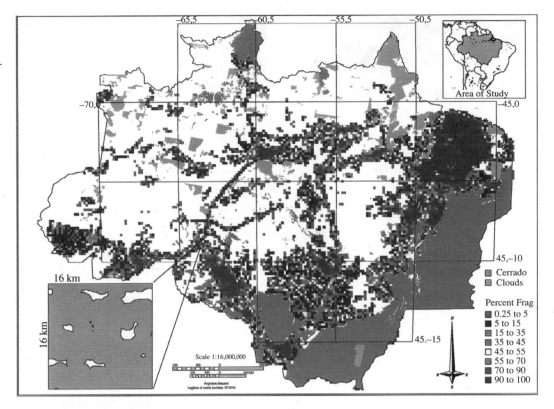

Figure 23.22 Deforestation in the forests of British Columbia.

edge effect to their deforestation analysis are shown in figure 23.21. This map is the 1988 image shown in figure 23.19, with edge effects added. As you can see, a lot more area of figure 23.21 is red, indicating 90% to 100% impact of deforestation. The inset shows the same area depicted in figure 23.19 but with edge effects added. Only tiny areas of white, indicating no effects of deforestation, remain. Edge effects increased the area of Amazonian forest affected by deforestation from 230,000 to 588,000 km².

A Global Perspective

Skole and Tucker provided a detailed picture of land cover changes in the Amazon Basin. However, what is the global rate of tropical deforestation? No one can answer this question

precisely, but the best estimates indicate that 52% to 64% of tropical deforestation occurs outside Brazil. Therefore, a conservative estimate of the global rate of deforestation from 1978 to 1988 would be approximately 30,000 km² per year.

How much land cover change is occurring outside the tropics? Though most people have focused on tropical deforestation, massive deforestation has occurred in temperate and boreal regions. As we saw in chapter 2, the temperate forest regions of Europe, eastern China, Japan, and North America support some of the densest human populations on earth. Large areas of Europe were deforested by the Middle Ages (Williams 1990), and much of the forest of eastern North America was cut by the middle 1800s (see fig. 21.21). The majority of old-growth temperate forests in northwestern North America has been cut (fig. 23.22), and the remaining old-growth forests are threatened by deforestation. In addition, vast areas of boreal forest are being cut in Russia and Canada. As you can see, deforestation is not limited to tropical regions.

Concept 23.3 Review

1. Why is reducing land cover through deforestation or agriculture a fundamental threat to biodiversity?
2. How does fragmentation of habitat as a result of human changes in land cover threaten populations?
3. Why is the ecological impact of deforestation always greater than the area of forest removed?

Ecology In Action

Invasive Species

Throughout the text we have shown examples of how the introduction of a new species to a community can have dramatic consequences for community structure and nutrient cycling. Species introductions are happening across the planet at an ever-increasing pace, and as Soulé suggests, these pose one of the most critical threats to ecological integrity and biodiversity of native communities. We begin with a definition of *biotic invaders*. According to Richard Mack and colleagues (Mack et al. 2000), these are defined as "species that establish a new range in which they proliferate, spread, and persist to the detriment of the environment." This is a generally accepted definition; in fact Mack's paper has been cited by other researchers over 500 times since it was published. This definition is critical because it differentiates "invaders" from "alien" or "exotic" species. The latter words describe species which historically were not found in a given location, but through some form of dispersal (human mediated or not), are now found in a novel area. For instance, in Canada there are about 4,200 species of vascular plants, and it is estimated that nearly ⅓ of these are exotic species. However, most exotic species are not invasive, and instead represent a relatively small fraction of the biomass and drive only a small portion of the ecosystem function. What we are concerned about here are the few species able to establish, spread, and dominate an area; the biotic invaders.

For example, smallmouth and rock bass are two invaders of Canadian lakes (fig. 23.23). A collaboration between the Ontario Ministry of Natural Resources and researchers at McGill University has demonstrated how these fish cause significant changes to the trophic structure of lakes they invade (Vander Zanden et al. 1999). These species are generally intentionally introduced to lakes well beyond their native range, in an effort to increase fishing opportunities. By using stable isotopes to understand feeding relationships (chapter 19), the research team found the introduced species caused a decline in the abundance of native prey-fish, and caused the native lake trout to feed more on zooplankton. Such shifts in trophic structure are likely to have cascading effects on phytoplankton and nutrient cycles.

As in the example of sport-fish, humans often play an important role in transporting species from one location to another. This is likely not too surprising—humans are able to travel across the planet much more efficiently than the historical dispersal vectors of plant and animals. For some species, such as these fish, Pacific oysters, a variety of horticultural plants, and a diversity of bird species, introductions are intentional. These are often when a person, or governmental organization, has decided to "improve" the use of land through new economic activities (e.g., fishing, oyster farms) or through aesthetic desires for non-native flora and fauna. Many other introductions are unintentional, such as the zebra mussel and lamprey in the Great Lakes, a variety of insect pests, and numerous agricultural weeds. These species are often introduced when ships dump ballast water near new lands, as contaminants in food shipments, and through other forms of unintentional release. Regardless of the cause of introduction, species are quickly being introduced to novel locations across the world.

We have shown many of the ecological consequences of invasion throughout this book. David Pimentel and colleagues have recently conducted an assessment of some of the economic costs of invasive species within the United States, estimating the damages and loss due to these species is nearly $120 billion ($US) per year (Pimentel et al. 2005). Although the data available for Canada are not as clear, Hugh MacIsaac and colleagues from the University of Windsor suggests costs associated with just 16 non-indigenous species can exceed $13 billion ($Cdn) annually (Colautti et al. 2006). Why are these numbers so large? To begin with, there are a lot of alien species. Pimentel and colleagues report that there are an estimated 750,000 species in the United States, with 50,000 of these being alien-invasive species. The economic costs associated with these species include attempted control programs as well as losses due to reduced agricultural production. For example, there are an estimated 25,000 alien species of plants alone in the United States. Of these alien plant species, many are major weeds in crops and Pimentel

23.4 Human Influence on Atmospheric Composition

Human activity is increasing the atmospheric concentration of CO_2, which may be increasing global temperatures. Industrial activity has increased steadily since about the year 1800. Over the same period, atmospheric CO_2 has increased steadily. The evidence discussed here shows that most of this atmospheric increase is due to the burning of fossil fuels. Soulé pointed out that recent changes in atmospheric composition are likely to affect global climate and will certainly affect the biota of all terrestrial ecosystems. The effect of human activity on atmospheric CO_2 and other gases is one of the most thoroughly studied aspects of global ecology.

Figure 23.23 Invasive species in Canada include (*a*) zebra mussels, *Dreissena polymorpha*, (*b*) sea lamprey, *Petromyzon marinus*, (*c*) Dutch elm disease, *Ophiostoma ulmi*, and (*d*) purple loosestrife, *Lythrum salicaria*.

estimates they cause $24 billion ($US) per year in reduced agricultural yield, and an additional $3 billion ($US) per year in herbicides and other control programs. Rats are estimated to cause $19 billion ($US) per year in damages due to feeding upon stored grains, fires associated with gnawing on wires, and disease transmission. The nearly 30 million feral cats in the United States (compared to the 63 million pet cats) feed upon native birds and other animals. Pimentel estimates a loss of $17 billion ($US) per year from these cats due to lost opportunities (and expenses) associated with bird watching, hunting, and other activities. Another $14 billion and $21 billion ($US) per year are associated with introduced insect and

microbial pests of crops, with another $14 billion ($US) per year for introduced livestock diseases.

The impacts of invasive species on the functioning and biological integrity of natural areas is clear. The economic costs of these species is simply enormous. Due to continued movement by people, continued desires to "improve" native lands, and continued development, we are unlikely to see any reduction in these costs in the near future. It will be up to the current and next generations of ecologists to figure out how the negative effects of these species introductions can be reduced, and maybe even how some of these species can be eliminated.

The concentration of CO_2 in the atmosphere has been dynamic over much of earth's history. Scientists have very carefully reconstructed atmospheric composition by studying air bubbles trapped in ice. As ice built up on glaciers in places such as Greenland and Antarctica, air spaces within the ice preserved a record of the ancient atmosphere. A record of atmospheric composition during the last 160,000 years was

extracted and analyzed by a joint team of scientists from France and the former Soviet Union (Lorius et al. 1985, Barnola et al. 1987). This international team studied a 2,083 m core of ice drilled by Soviet scientists and engineers near the Antarctic station of Vostok. Vostok, located in eastern Antarctica at a latitude of over 78° S, has a mean annual temperature of –55°C, ideal conditions for preserving samples of the atmosphere in ice. The Vostok research station sits on the high antarctic plateau, where the ice is about 3,700 m thick. The amazing physical feat of extracting such a long ice core in such difficult physical circumstances is equalled by the dramatic climatic record contained within the Vostok ice core.

To extract air trapped within ice, scientists place sections of an ice core into a chamber and create a vacuum, removing traces of the current atmosphere in the process. The ice, still under vacuum, is then crushed and the air it contains is released into the chamber. Sampling devices then measure the CO_2 concentration of the air released from the ice. The Barnola team made 66 measurements along the length of the Vostok ice core. At each location they were also able to estimate the air temperature at the time the ice was formed. The scientists made measurements of CO_2 every 25 m along the length of the ice core from about 850 m depth to the bottom of the core. These lower sections of the core correspond to ages from 50,000 to 160,000 years. Because there were many fractures in the core above 850 m depth, the upper portion of the core was generally sampled at intervals greater than 25 m.

Figure 23.24 shows the variation in CO_2 concentration revealed by the Vostok ice core. The core indicated two very large fluctuations in atmospheric CO_2 concentration. Overall, it shows that CO_2 concentrations have oscillated between low concentrations of approximately 190 to 200 parts per million (ppm) and high concentrations of 260 to 280 ppm. About 160,000 years ago, the atmospheric concentration of CO_2 was less than 200 ppm. This early period in the Vostok ice core corresponds to an ice age. Then, about 140,000 years ago, the atmospheric concentration of CO_2 began to rise abruptly. This rise in CO_2 corresponds to a warmer interglacial period. High

levels of CO_2 persisted until about 120,000 years ago. The concentration of CO_2 then declined and remained at relatively low concentrations until about 13,000 years ago, when atmospheric CO_2 again increased abruptly.

Notice that the fluctuations in CO_2 within the Vostok ice core correspond to variation in temperature (fig. 23.24). The periods of low CO_2 correspond to the low temperatures experienced during ice ages, while the periods of high CO_2 correspond to warmer, interglacial periods.

The most recent measurements in the Vostok ice core are about 2,000 years old. How has atmospheric CO_2 varied during the most recent 2,000 years? W. Post and colleagues (1990) assembled atmospheric CO_2 records from a number of sources to estimate atmospheric concentrations during the last 1,000 years (fig. 23.25). The first 1,000 years of the record come from the South Pole ice core, which was analyzed by Ulrich Siegenthaler and colleagues (1988) of the University of Bern, Switzerland. This record shows that the concentration of CO_2 remained relatively constant for approximately 800 years. Another study at the University of Bern provided a CO_2 record for the most recent 200 years (Friedli et al. 1986). This part of the CO_2 record comes from the Siple ice core, from Siple Station at about 75° S latitude. While the Siple ice core does not allow us to look as far back in time as the Vostok record, it provides a very detailed estimate of recent concentrations of atmospheric CO_2. H. Friedli and colleagues dated the beginning of the Siple record at about A.D. 1744. At that time, about two and a half centuries ago, the atmospheric concentration of CO_2 was about 277 ppm. This estimated concentration is almost identical to those made by the Siegenthaler team for the same time period using the South Pole ice core. Therefore, both the South Pole and Siple ice cores indicate that the CO_2 concentration in the middle 1700s was approximately the same as at the end of the Vostok record, about 2,000 years earlier.

The Siple record showed that CO_2 increased exponentially from 1744 to 1953. The Friedli team estimated the 1953 concentration of CO_2 at 315 ppm. However, the trace in CO_2 concentrations shown in figure 23.25 extends beyond 1953 and above 315 ppm. Where do these later measurements come from? These later CO_2 concentrations are direct measurements made on Mauna Loa, Hawaii, by Charles Keeling and his associates over a period of about 40 years (Keeling and Whorf 1994).

Keeling's measurements complement the ice core data from the Vostok, South Pole, and Siple stations in two ways. First, they extend the record into the present. Second, they help validate the measurements of CO_2 made from the ice cores. How do Keeling's measurements lend credence to the ice core data? Look carefully at the plot of CO_2 concentrations shown in figure 23.25. Notice that two of the measurements made from the Siple ice core overlap the period when Keeling and his team made measurements at Mauna Loa. Notice also that the two estimates made independently by Keeling at Mauna Loa and by Friedli and his colleagues from the Siple ice core are almost identical.

The data in figure 23.25 indicate that during the nineteenth and twentieth centuries the concentration of atmospheric

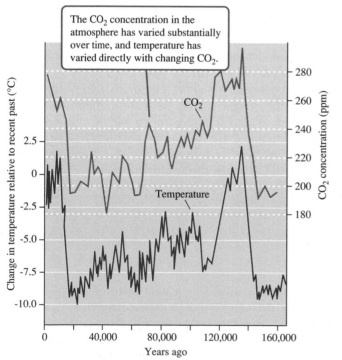

Figure 23.24 A 160,000-year record of atmospheric CO_2 concentrations and temperature change (data from Barnola et al. 1987).

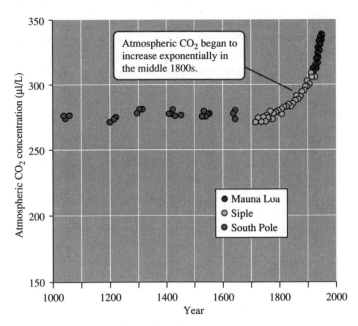

Figure 23.25 A 1,000-year atmospheric CO_2 record (data from Post et al. 1990).

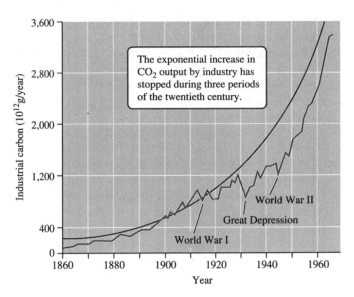

Figure 23.26 Deviations from recent exponential increases in fossil fuel burning (data from Bacastow and Keeling 1974).

CO_2 increased dramatically. This period of increase coincides with the Industrial Revolution. However, what evidence is there that human activity caused this observed increase? Vitousek provided evidence by pointing out that the annual increase in atmospheric carbon in the form of CO_2 is about 3,500 Tg (1 Tg = 10^{12} g), while the annual burning of fossil fuels releases about 5,600 Tg carbon as CO_2. So, fossil fuel burning alone produces more than enough CO_2 to account for recent increases in atmospheric concentrations.

If we look carefully at the pattern of CO_2 increase between 1860 and 1960 we find additional evidence for a human influence. Figure 23.26 shows three interruptions in the otherwise steady increase in the burning of fossil fuels. Those periods correspond to three major disruptions of global economic activity: World War I, the Great Depression, and World War II. At the end of each of these major global upheavals, the increase in atmospheric CO_2 resumed. These patterns provide circumstantial evidence that humans are responsible for the modern increase in atmospheric CO_2. However, there is also direct evidence.

Additional evidence that human industrial activity is at the heart of recent increases in atmospheric CO_2 comes from analyses of atmospheric concentrations of various carbon isotopes (see chapter 19). One of the most useful carbon isotopes for determining the contribution of fossil fuels to atmospheric CO_2 is radioactive ^{14}C. Because ^{14}C has a half-life of 5,730 years, fossil fuels, which have been buried for millions of years, contain very little of this carbon isotope. Consequently, burning fossil fuel adds CO_2 to an atmosphere that has little ^{14}C. If fossil fuel additions are a major source of increased atmospheric CO_2, then the relative concentration of ^{14}C in the atmosphere should be declining.

A recent decline in atmospheric ^{14}C was first described by Hans Suess (1955), a scientist with the U.S. Geological Survey. Suess made his discovery by analyzing the ^{14}C content of wood. He analyzed the ^{14}C content of wood laid down by single trees at various times during their growth. He found that annual growth rings laid down in the late 1800s had significantly higher concentrations of ^{14}C than those laid down in the 1950s. Suess proposed that the ^{14}C content in wood was being progressively reduced because burning of fossil fuels was reducing the atmospheric concentration of ^{14}C. Because of his pioneering work, reduced atmospheric ^{14}C as a consequence of fossil fuel burning is called the **Suess effect.**

Robert Bacastow and Charles Keeling (1974) compiled ^{14}C data from several studies of ^{14}C in trees and plotted the date when the wood was formed against the relative ^{14}C content of the wood. As figure 23.27 shows, the concentration of ^{14}C

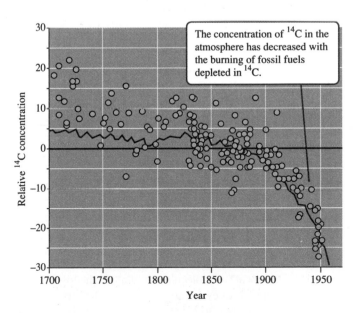

Figure 23.27 The Suess effect (data from Bacastow and Keeling 1974).

was fairly stable from A.D. 1700 until about 1850. After 1850, ^{14}C concentrations in wood declined significantly. The line shows the predictions of ^{14}C made by a model built by Bacastow and Keeling. Their model made these predictions based upon global patterns of fossil fuel burning and estimated rates of exchange of carbon between the ocean, the earth's biota, and the atmosphere.

What can we conclude from this evidence? Several things are clear. First, the concentration of CO_2 in the atmosphere has varied widely during the last 160,000 years and closely parallels variation in global temperatures. High levels of atmospheric CO_2 have corresponded to higher global temperatures. Second, the atmospheric concentration of CO_2 has increased substantially in the past two centuries. This modern increase has exceeded all levels reached during the past 160,000 years. Third, there is little doubt that the present levels of CO_2 in the atmosphere are strongly influenced by the burning of fossil fuels.

Depletion and Recovery of the Ozone Layer

In 1985, scientists of the British Antarctic Survey had discovered a major reduction in the amount of ozone, O_3, in the stratosphere over the Antarctic. Stratospheric ozone absorbs potentially harmful ultraviolet light, particularly UV-B light, or radiation. Because high-energy, UV-B radiation is capable of destroying biological molecules and damaging living tissue, the ozone layer is critical for the well-being of life on earth. The British scientific team also analyzed historical measurements of ozone, which demonstrated clearly that the total amount of ozone over the Antarctic had been declining since the 1970s. Depletion of earth's ozone layer was not the first sign of human influence on the environment. However, it was a clear and dramatic indication that human impact on the environment had achieved truly global proportions.

Though the ozone hole was centred over the Antarctic, far from most human population centres, its discovery generated widespread concern. Perhaps the greatest fear was that the breakdown of the ozone layer over the Antarctic might be a prelude to breakdown of the protective ozone layer over the entire earth, endangering humans as well as crops, wild plants, and animals. Other scientists had warned that the ozone layer was threatened by human activities. However, it was the discovery of the ozone hole that aroused world concern and stimulated international action. Attention was quickly focused on stopping the production of chlorofluorocarbons, or CFCs, organic chemicals containing carbon, chlorine, and fluorine that were widely used as refrigerants. Because CFCs are very stable molecules, their concentrations in the atmosphere gradually increased after their introduction in the 1930s. By the 1970s, the concentrations of CFCs had been increased sufficiently that they could be detected everywhere.

Chlorofluorocarbon molecules circulate in the lower atmosphere long enough to eventually move into the stratosphere, where they are exposed to a great deal more highly energetic ultraviolet light. As CFCs break down, they release chlorine, which can act as a catalyst to destroy ozone molecules. A single chlorine atom released in the stratosphere can continue to destroy ozone molecules until it is removed by some atmospheric process. Therefore, a small amount of chlorine released in the stratosphere can deplete the ozone layer substantially.

World concern over the dangers associated with ozone depletion prompted the 1987 Montreal Protocol on Substances that Deplete the Ozone Layer, which has been signed by 180 countries. The goal of the Montreal Protocol is to reduce and eventually eliminate emissions of human-generated substances that deplete ozone and may represent a model for international cooperation on a complex environmental problem. As a result of the protocol, global production of CFCs has been reduced from over one million tons annually to less than 50,000 tons in 2003.

How has the ozone hole over the Antarctic changed since its discovery in 1985? It has continued to grow larger, reaching its maximum area, so far, in 2000, when it covered nearly 29.2 million km^2. In 2002, the Antarctic ozone hole closed quickly, suggesting that the ozone layer was recovering. However, the second largest ozone hole was recorded in 2003, when it reached 28.2 million km^2 (fig. 23.28). Encouragingly, the year 2003 also saw the first reported evidence that the ozone layer is recovering, when several scientists reported (Newchurch et al. 2003) evidence for a slowdown in stratospheric ozone loss from 1997 to 2003. It appears that cooperation by the international community in the banning of CFCs has begun to reverse the process of ozone depletion. Recovery of the stratospheric ozone layer will likely take at least another half century. However, the news of ozone recovery says clearly that we not only have the capacity to seriously damage the biosphere but where we have the will, we can also act to restore it.

The Future

How will human-induced changes in atmospheric composition affect ecological systems? In 1957 Roger Revelle and Hans Suess, wrote: "Human beings are now carrying out a large

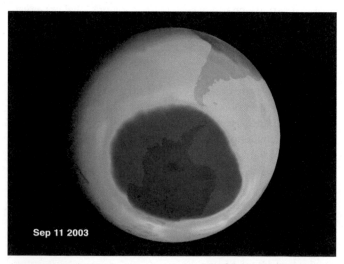

Sep 11 2003

Figure 23.28   The ozone hole in September, 2003. Even as scientists verified that the rate of ozone depletion was declining, the second largest ozone hole ever formed over Antarctica.

scale geophysical experiment of a kind that could not have happened in the past nor be reproduced in the future. Within a few centuries we are returning to the atmosphere and oceans the concentrated organic carbon stored in sedimentary rocks over hundreds of millions of years. This experiment, if adequately studied and documented, may yield a far-reaching insight into the processes determining weather and climate."

Half a century after Revelle and Suess made their prophetic statement, the results of the unprecedented experiment are being recorded around the planet. During the past century, the average global temperature has risen over 0.7°C. While there is still some debate over the extent to which natural climate cycles may be involved in the recent upswing in temperatures, there is broad agreement among scientists that increased atmospheric concentration of greenhouse gases, especially CO_2, is a major contributor to global warming. In addition, a variety of climate models predict that without reductions in the concentrations of atmospheric CO_2 and other greenhouse gases, global temperatures will increase an additional 1.5° to 5.5°C over the next century. Based on observations of responses to existing warming and modelling studies, scientists predict a wide range of environmental responses to continued warming, including:

- Increased frequency of intense hurricanes.
- Melting of glaciers, sea level rise, and inundation of coastal areas.
- More intense and more frequent heat waves in temperate regions.

- Increased summer drought in semiarid regions.
- Increased mortality of reef-building corals.
- Potential spread of insect-transmitted tropical diseases such as malaria.
- Dieback of forests due to increased incidence of disease and insect attack.
- Increased wildfires in forests and grasslands.
- Widespread extinction of plant and animal species.
- Release of CO_2 and CH_4 from arctic soils, accelerating global warming.

The overwhelming magnitude of environmental change is rallying individuals and governments everywhere to work toward reducing climate-related threats to the biosphere. In our quest to reduce and hopefully reverse human damage to the earth, ecological knowledge will play a key role. In the next section, we discuss one promising approach to studying ecological responses to global change.

Concept 23.4 Review

1. What aspects of global warming are widely supported by available evidence?
2. Are there uncertainties remaining regarding global warming?
3. Why may the history of CFCs in the atmosphere in the years following the Montreal Protocol offer encouragement as humanity strives to reverse the modern buildup of atmospheric CO_2?

Ecological Tools

Cooperative Research Networks for Global Ecology

If global climate changes rapidly, how will biological systems respond? How will such change affect individual organisms, populations, communities, ecosystems, or even whole biomes? While it is easy to ask such questions and to recognize their significance, providing adequate answers is not so easy. Responses to past climatic changes provide some clues but only for a limited number of species and biological processes.

The present possibility of rapid climate change poses a substantial challenge to the scientific community and requires the application of new tools and approaches. Some new tools, such as fractal geometry (see chapter 21), involve new conceptual or analytical methods. Other new tools will consist of high technology, such as remote sensing satellites (see chapter 22) and supercomputers to run complicated global models. New devices, often employing the most recent technological developments, are becoming more and more common in the tool kit of ecologists. However, as impressive as this hardware may be, some of the most important developments

required for global-scale ecological research may involve changes in the "culture" of science.

To effectively address the complex problems presented by global change, scientists must appreciate a variety of scientific disciplines and be capable of working effectively within multidisciplinary teams. The large scale of global change also requires that scientists work as cooperative, international teams. Such teams can conduct studies at spatial and temporal scales impossible for an individual researcher.

The U.S. Long-Term Ecological Research (LTER) network fosters large-scale ecological research. One of the central purposes of this research network is to foster cooperative, interdisciplinary research over large geographic areas. These sites include tropical forests, arctic tundra, temperate forests, grasslands, coastal ecosystems, deserts, and two cities. They extend from sea level to elevations over 4,000 m and from the Arctic to the Antarctic (fig. 23.29). This network can be used for many purposes, but, increasingly, it is being used to assess the impact that climate change may have on biological systems. Even this ambitious national effort, however, is inadequate for the task at hand. Therefore, the LTER network is forming long-term partnerships with research programs around the globe.

The first international long-term ecological research (ILTER) workshop was held in 1993 (Nottrott, Franklin, and Vande Castle 1994). Scientists from around the world met to establish active interactions and collaboration between the LTER network and long-term ecological research programs from around the globe. The geographic areas represented included North America, Central and South America, western,

central, and eastern Europe, eastern Asia, Australia, and New Zealand. Several well-developed national research programs already exist in each of these areas, and many other programs are organizing quickly. The concrete goals of the meeting were to initiate exchanges of scientists and data and to foster global-scale comparisons and modelling.

The meeting produced several recommendations:

1. Foster worldwide communication and access to information among scientists engaged in long-term ecological research.

2. Develop a global directory of long-term ecological research sites.

3. Encourage development of additional long-term ecological research sites worldwide.

4. Develop appropriate standardized sampling and study designs, paying particular attention to conducting research at scales appropriate to the question being addressed.

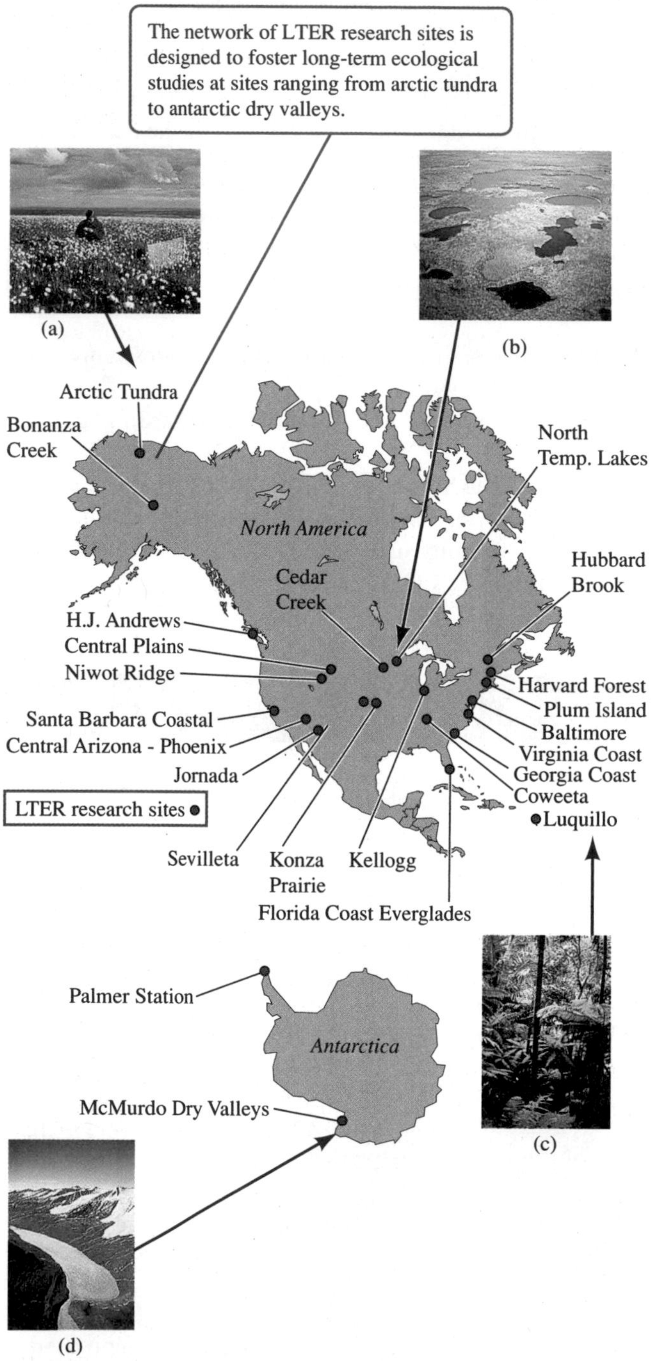

These recommendations capture what this group of scientists regarded as minimal requirements for global ecological research. By 2006, 34 countries, including Canada, were members of the ILTER.

Compared to the United States, Canada was slow to recognize the need for federal support for international research networks. Instead, long-term ecological research and environmental monitoring has been supported primarily by provincial governments. However, in the last several years there has been increased awareness of a need for a more coordinated approach to understanding global issues, and Canada has developed some programs that are tied to international networks. For example, Canada's participation in the ILTER network is centred on EMAN, the Environmental Monitoring and Assessment Network. EMAN is a loose network of organizations that form a partnership to study ecosystem changes. Members of the network record observations of plant phenology, frog abundance, ice break, and the spread of invasive earthworms among other activities. These organizations are scattered throughout Canada and include governmental organizations, individual researchers, schools, and members of the general public. Because of the varied quality and limited central coordination, EMAN has not provided the same level of ecological understanding that has emerged from the LTER. However, EMAN does serve as a starting point from which Canada can build.

A more scientifically rigorous research network, which includes substantial participation by Canadian ecologists, is FLUXNET. FLUXNET is a network of towers established in a diversity of habitat types that measure micrometeorology such as CO_2 concentrations. The goals of these measures include providing a comprehensive understanding of the relationship between climate and ecosystem productivity; and to understand long-term changes in microenvironment, including greenhouse gases. Towers are established in over 200 locations in 45 countries, including 22 sites in Canada. Hank Margolis of

The network of LTER research sites is designed to foster long-term ecological studies at sites ranging from arctic tundra to antarctic dry valleys.

Figure 23.29 The U.S. Long-Term Ecological Research (LTER) network.

the Université Laval oversees the FLUXNET-Canada network, and has recently summarized some of the findings that are beginning to emerge (Margolis et al. 2006), including (1) the forests of Canada are becoming a reduced carbon sink due to increased disturbances such as insect outbreaks and fire, (2) changes in precipitation and evapotranspiration associated with climate change will have strong effects on the carbon balance of forests and peatlands throughout Canada, and (3) recent studies indicate that root production and soil respiration play a very significant role in total ecosystem carbon fluxes, and thus more study is needed below ground.

A network of research sites can yield much more information about large-scale and long-term phenomena than can any single site. Arranging research sites into an organized array allows for synchronized measurements and provides the opportunity for observing how the ecological effects of climate change may propagate across regions or even across the entire globe. Such networks would be capable of identifying the geographic extent of a climatic event, when it began, when it ended, and the types of ecological responses that occurred in various regions. Such a network could also identify which areas are most responsive to climatic change and which are least responsive. None of this information could be determined from studies conducted at a single site.

Modern developments such as remote sensing, supercomputers, and the global network of computer communications will make an international long-term ecological network more effective. As Peter Vitousek (1994) pointed out, this is the first generation to have the tools to study ecology at the scale of the entire globe. These international networks of scientists working cooperatively on global ecological problems signal a change in the culture of science that emphasizes information sharing and an open, multidisciplinary team approach to research. These are the advancements that can make global ecological studies a reality. Ecologists increasingly recognize the urgency of the challenge posed by global change and that addressing ecological problems at a global scale requires an approach to research that is itself global.

Summary

Chapter 23 focuses on global-scale processes and phenomena, including large-scale weather systems and global change induced by humans. We are the only species that exerts global-scale influences on the environment.

The earth is wrapped in an atmospheric envelope that makes the biosphere a hospitable place for life as we know it. The earth's atmosphere reduces the amount of ultraviolet light reaching the surface. The atmosphere also helps to keep the surface of the earth warm through the *greenhouse effect*. The surface of the earth is kept warmer than it would be by the greenhouse gases, including water vapour, methane, ozone, nitrous oxide, chlorofluorocarbons, and carbon dioxide.

Large-scale atmospheric and oceanic phenomena influence ecological systems on a global scale. The El Niño Southern Oscillation is a highly dynamic, large-scale weather system that involves variation in sea surface temperature and barometric pressure across the Pacific and Indian Oceans. During the mature phase of an El Niño, the sea surface in the eastern tropical Pacific Ocean is much warmer than average and the barometric pressure over the eastern Pacific is lower than average. El Niño brings increased precipitation to much of North and parts of South America and drought to the western Pacific. Periods of lower sea surface temperature and higher than average barometric pressures in the eastern tropical Pacific have been named La Niñas. La Niña brings drought to much of North and South America and higher than average precipitation to the western Pacific. The North Atlantic Oscillation and the Northern Hemisphere Annular Mode influence the weather across more northern latitudes. The NAO is a fluctuation in pressure between Iceland and Portugal. In the positive phase there are cooler temperatures in eastern Canada, less precipitation in the Canadian Arctic, and wetter, warmer weather in northern Europe. These patterns reverse when the NAO in the negative phase. The NAM (Arctic Oscillation) is a mirror image of the NAO, also impacting global weather. The variation in weather caused by these oscillations has dramatic effects on marine and terrestrial populations around the world.

Human activity has greatly increased the quantity of fixed nitrogen cycling through the biosphere. For millions of years, the only organisms that could fix nitrogen were nitrogen-fixing bacteria and some actinomycete fungi. The total amount of nitrogen fixed by these historical sources is approximately 130 Tg N per year. The nitrogen now fixed as a consequence of human activity is about 135 to 145 Tg N per year, more than all nonhuman sources of fixed nitrogen combined. Large-scale nitrogen enrichment may threaten biological diversity by creating environmental conditions favourable to some species at the expense of others. For example, trees are encroaching into grassland in much of western Canada, likely due to increased N deposition.

Rapid changes in global patterns of land use threaten biological diversity. Human activities, mainly agriculture and urbanization, have significantly altered one-third to one-half of the ice-free land surface of the earth. Associated with these changes have been significant applications of fertilizer and water use for irrigation. These activities have placed significant pressures on aquatic systems. A widely cited example of land cover change is tropical deforestation. From 1978 to 1988, the rate of deforestation in the Amazon Basin of Brazil averaged about 15,000 km^2 per year. By 1988, the total area deforested within the Amazon Basin was 230,000 km^2. By adding in edge effects and the effects of isolation, the area of Amazonian forest affected by deforestation increases from 230,000 km^2 to 588,000 km^2. The global rate of tropical deforestation from 1978 to 1988 was about 30,000 km^2 per year. Massive deforestation has also occurred outside of the tropics. Because of the negative effect of reduced habitat area on diversity, these massive land conversions present a major threat to global biological diversity.

Human activity is increasing the atmospheric concentration of CO_2, which may be increasing global temperatures. Analyses of air trapped in ice shows that the concentration of CO_2 in the atmosphere has varied widely during the last 160,000 years and closely parallels variation in global temperatures. High levels of atmospheric CO_2 have corresponded to higher global temperatures. The buildup of atmospheric CO_2 during the past two centuries has reached levels of atmospheric CO_2 not equalled in the past 160,000 years. There is little doubt that the present level of CO_2 in the atmosphere is strongly influenced by burning of fossil fuels. Increases in atmospheric CO_2 concentration are likely to affect global climate and the structure and processes of ecological systems from populations through landscapes.

Cooperative research networks aid global ecology. The present possibility of rapid climate change poses a substantial challenge to the scientific community. Studying ecology at a global scale requires that scientists develop new tools and approaches. New devices, often employing the most recent technological developments, are becoming more and more common in the tool kit of ecologists. However, some of the most important developments required for global-scale research may involve changes in the "culture" of science. The complexity and large scale of global change requires that scientists work in multidisciplinary, national, and international teams. International networks of scientists now work on global-scale ecological problems in a research environment that emphasizes information sharing and a team approach to research.

Review Questions

1. Ecologists are now challenged to study global ecology. The apparent role played by humans in changing the global environment makes it imperative that we understand the workings of the earth as a global system. However, this study requires approaches that are significantly different from those that can be applied to traditional areas of ecological study. Historically, much of ecology focused on small areas and short-term studies. What are some of the main differences between global ecology and, for instance, the study of interspecific competition (see chapter 13) or forest succession (see chapter 18)? How will these differences affect the design of studies at the global scale?

2. Geologists, atmospheric scientists, and oceanographers have been conducting global-scale studies for some time. What role will information from these disciplines play in the study of global ecology? Why will global ecological studies generally be pursued by interdisciplinary teams? How can ecologists play a useful role in global studies?

3. What changes in sea surface temperatures and atmospheric pressures over the Pacific Ocean accompany El Niño? What physical changes accompany La Niña? How do El Niño and La Niña affect precipitation in North America, South America, and Australia?

4. Large-scale climatic processes, such as the North Atlantic Oscillation, and not amenable to experimental research. How would you design a study to determine whether the NAO impacts natural populations of plant and animals in different regions of Canada?

5. In chapter 23, we briefly discussed how humans have more than doubled the quantity of fixed nitrogen cycling through the biosphere. In chapter 15 we reviewed studies by Nancy Johnson (1993) on the effects of fertilization on the mutualistic relationship between mycorrhizal fungi and grasses. The increases in fixed nitrogen cycling through the biosphere, particularly that portion deposited by rain, are analogous to a global-scale fertilization experiment. Reasoning from the results of Johnson's study, how should increased fixed nitrogen supplies affect the relationship between mycorrhizal fungi and their plant partners? How would you test your ideas?

6. As we saw in chapters 18 and 19, nitrogen availability seems to control the rates of several ecosystem processes. How should nitrogen enrichment affect rates of primary production and decomposition in terrestrial, freshwater, and marine environments? How could you test your ideas? What role might geographic comparisons play in your studies?

7. Ecologists predict that global diversity is threatened by land use change and by the reductions in habitat area and the fragmentation that accompany land use change. What role do studies of diversity on islands and species area relationships on continents (see chapter 22) play in these predictions?

8. Deforestation poses significant risk to a number of biodiversity hotspots in the tropics. In Canada, deforestation of the boreal forest is also very high, however there are few specific areas of concentrated biodiversity in these high-latitude forests. Does this mean that rates of deforestation are not of ecological concern in the boreal? How do you balance the need for economic development with a desire to preserve large areas of undisturbed forest?

9. Review the long-term atmospheric CO_2 record as revealed by studies of air trapped in ice cores. What is the evidence that burning of fossil fuels is responsible for recent increases in atmospheric CO_2 concentrations?

10. What evidence is there that variation in atmospheric CO_2 concentration is linked to variation in global temperatures? In recent years the governments of most countries of the world have been working hard to develop international agreements to regulate CO_2 emissions. Why are these governments concerned? How might rapid changes in global temperatures lead to the extinction of large numbers of species? How might changes in global temperatures affect agriculture around the world?

Suggested Readings

Bierregaard, R. O., Jr., T. E. Lovejoy, V. Kapos, A. A. dos Santos, and R. W. Hutchings. 1992. The biological dynamics of tropical rainforest fragments. *BioScience* 42:859–66.

Malcolm, J. R. 1994. Edge effects in central Amazonian forest fragments. *Ecology* 75:2438–45.

These two papers give a solid introduction to the ecological problem of forest fragmentation in the Amazon Basin.

Clark, D. A., S. C. Piper, C. D. Keeling, and D. B. Clark. 2003. Tropical rain forest tree growth and atmospheric carbon dynamics linked to interannual temperature variation during 1984–2000. *Proceedings of the National Academy of Sciences of the United States of America* 100:5852–57.

Elevated temperatures over a 16-year period have been correlated with reduced growth by tropical rain forest trees at La Selva, Costa Rica. Thus, global warming could reduce the rate of carbon uptake by tropical forests, which would increase the rate of CO_2 accumulation in the atmosphere.

Hansen, J., L. Nazarenko, R. Ruedy, M. Sato, J. Willis, A. Del Genio, D. Koch, A. Lacis, K. Lo, S. Menon, T. Novakov, J. Perlwitz, G. Russell, G. A. Schmidt, and N. Tausnev. 2005. Earth's energy imbalance: confirmation and implications. *Science* 308:1431–35.

Precise measurements confirm that earth is aborbing more solar energy than it is emitting into space. Based on these measurements authors predict a further global warming of 0.6°C even without further increase in atmospheric concentrations of greenhouse gases.

Johnson, D., C. D. Campbell, J. A. Lee, T. V. Callaghan, and D. Gwynn-Jones. 2002. Arctic microorganisms respond more to elevated UV-B radiation than CO_2. *Nature* 416: 82–83.

This study reveals unexpected effects of UV-B radiation on soil microorganisms in the Arctic. The recorded effects, in response to simulated ozone thinning, may reduce the capacity of Arctic ecosystems to function as carbon dioxide sinks.

Keeling, C. D. and T. P. Whorf. 2005. Atmospheric CO_2 records from sites in the SIO air sampling network. In *Trends: A Compendium of Data on Global Change.* Carbon Dioxide Information Analysis Center, Oak Ridge National Laboratory, U.S. Department of Energy, Oak Ridge, TN, U.S.A. (available online).

A concise synopsis of the record of carbon dioxide rise determined from Mauna Loa, Hawaii. The online site includes the monthly data record from 1958 to 2002.

Malcolm, J. R., C. R. Liu, R. P. Neilson, L. Hansen, and L. Hannah. 2006. Global warming and extinctions of endemic species from biodiversity hotspots. *Conservation Biology* 20:538–48.

Pounds, J. A., M. R. Bustamante, L. A. Coloma, J. A. Consuegra, M. P. L. Fogden, P. N. Foster, E. La Marca, K. L. Masters, A. Merino-Viteri, R. Puschendorf, S. R. Ron, G. A. Sanchez-Azofeifa, C. J. Still, and B. E. Young. 2006. Widespread amphibian extinctions from epidemic disease driven by global warming. *Nature* 439:161–67.

Two key papers that outline the recent extinctions and the threats of future extinctions due to global warming.

Morrison, S. A. and D. T. Bolger. 2002. Variation in a sparrow's reproductive success with rainfall: food and predator-mediated processes. *Oecologia* 133:315–24.

The authors contrast reproductive output by rufous-crowned sparrows during average, El Niño, and La Niña years. Their work reveals indirect effects mediated through the effect of weather on predator activity.

Newchurch, M. J., E.-S. Yang, D. M. Cunnold, G. C. Reinsel, J. M. Zawodny, and J. M. Russell III. 2003. Evidence for slowdown in stratospheric ozone loss: first stage of ozone recovery. *Journal of Geophysical Research* 108(D16), 4507, doi:10.1029/2003JD003471, 2003 (published online).

Researchers provide the first evidence for a slowdown in the rate of depletion of earth's ozone layer.

Townsend, A. R., R. W. Howarth, F. A. Bazzaz, M. S. Booth, C. C. Cleveland, S. K. Collinge, A. P. Dobson, P. R. Epstein, E. A. Holland, D. R. Keeney, M. A. Mallin, C. A. Rogers, P. Wayne, and A. H. Wolfe. 2003. Human health effects of a changing global nitrogen cycle. *Frontiers in Ecology and the Environment* 1:240–46.

A review of the ways in which human-induced changes in the global nitrogen cycle directly impacts human health, ranging from allergies and cardiac disease to malaria and cholera.

Appendix A

Building a Statistical Toolbox

In chapter 1 we presented an overview of the scientific method, high-lighting its importance to ecologists. A central component of the scientific method is the continual testing of theory and ideas with data. Throughout this text we have provided a broad overview of the types of field and lab methods that ecologists use to collect the data needed to answer questions at a variety of temporal and spatial scales. However, data are often complex and messy, and in their raw form hard to handle. Because of the importance objective data have in the scientific method, many statistical approaches have been developed to help interpret patterns from seemingly incomprehensible pages of data. In this appendix, we provide a brief overview of the methods ecologists use to relate their collected data to their previously formed hypotheses and ideas. As a group, these critical ecological tools are referred to as statistical methods.

Describing a Group

Imagine you are an ecologist in the Yukon, conducting a study on the size of male caribou in a particular population. After learning the proper procedures for handling large mammals in the wild, you and your field crew fly across the tundra in a helicopter catching animals and weighing them. Aside from a very tired body, you bring back to your tent at base camp a rumpled notebook full of the weights of all the animals you have caught. Your professor is in camp with you and has asked you to give her an overview of the data collected. What do you do?

One of the most common and important steps in the processing of data is the production of summary statistics. In an ideal world, every individual caribou could be measured easily and cheaply. However in the real world, helicopter time is expensive, animals are evasive, and your classes start in September, and thus you have a limited summer field season. As a result, you are going to only sample a small fraction of the individuals that actually exist within the population, and you will only be able to *estimate* population measures. A statistic is a number that is used by scientists to estimate a measurable characteristic (e.g., weight) of an entire population.

Looking now at your notebook, you see you have measured 11 caribou. The average weight of these 11 animals is referred to as the **sample mean**, and this is one of the most common and useful of summary statistics. Because of its importance, it is worth describing how it is calculated. Consider the following sample of the weights of the 11 caribou measured:

Caribou Number	1	2	3	4	5	6	7	8	9	10	11
Weight (kg)	145	131	154	169	167	175	117	146	166	134	158

What is the average weight of caribou in this population? Since we did not catch all the males, we cannot know the true population mean, however, our sample of 11 males does allow us to calculate a sample mean as follows:

We calculate the sample mean by dividing the sum of measurements by the number of seedlings measured:

$$\overline{X} = \frac{\Sigma X}{n}$$

Where,

Sample mean = $\overline{X}$

n = sample size = 11

Sum of measurements = ΣX

$\Sigma X = 145 + 131 + 154 + 169 + 167 + 175 + 117 + 146 + 166 + 134 + 158 = 1,662$

$\overline{X} = 1662/11$

$\overline{X} = 151.1$ kg

So, your hard day's work is boiled down to a single number: 151.1 kg. This is the sample mean, your estimate of the true weight of the male caribou in the entire population at the time of this study. To be even more precise, we calculated the *arithmetic mean* in this example. There are other types of means used by ecologists, such as the *geometric mean* and the *harmonic mean*. However, a discussion of the uses of these other statistics is beyond the scope of this text.

While the sample mean is very useful, it is not the most appropriate statistic for some situations. One of the assumptions underlying the use of the sample mean is that the observations are drawn from a population with a normal, or bell-shaped, distribution (fig. A.1). This assumption was fine for the caribou example, but there will be many other studies in which the distribution of values within a population deviates substantially from a **normal distribution**. In those situations, it is generally better to use another estimator of the population

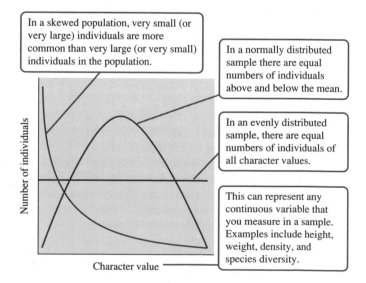

In a skewed population, very small (or very large) individuals are more common than very large (or very small) individuals in the population.

In a normally distributed sample there are equal numbers of individuals above and below the mean.

In an evenly distributed sample, there are equal numbers of individuals of all character values.

This can represent any continuous variable that you measure in a sample. Examples include height, weight, density, and species diversity.

Figure A.1 Normal, skewed, and even distributions of values of a given character (e.g., weight) among individuals within a population.

"average." One such statistic is the **sample median**. The sample median is simply the middle value when samples are ranked numerically. In our caribou example, there were 11 samples, with the middle caribou being the 6 largest (= sixth smallest), which was 154 kg. Notice that this value is very similar to the sample mean of 151.1 kg. This will be common in populations with normal distributions.

However, when the distribution of samples within a population is skewed, such that there are few very large or very small values, the sample median may give a better estimate of the typical individual within the population. Imagine you are once again back at base camp in the Yukon. Your professor wakes you up at 4 a.m. ready for a long day at work (it is light nearly 24 hours a day during the summer). Today you will be measuring the number of leaves found on individuals of *Dryas octopetala* (common name avens). The area you will be sampling has been grazed heavily by caribou, and though not a preferred food source for the caribou, many avens have been damaged by the animal's hooves. Back at camp you are again asked to provide a summary of the day's data.

Avens Number	1	2	3	4	5	6	7	8	9	10	11	12	13	14
Number of leaves	1	6	2	4	12	15	1	3	9	1	18	2	1	3

In this example there is an even number of samples, and thus the median value will be the average of the 7th and 8th largest (and smallest) individuals:

$$\text{Sample median} = \frac{3+3}{2} = 3 \text{ leaves per plant}$$

$$\text{The sample mean} = \frac{\Sigma X}{11} = \frac{78}{14} = 5.6 \text{ leaves per plant}$$

The estimate of the population mean is nearly twice that of the population median. In this case it is clear that the sample median, which represents the middle value of observations, more closely estimates the number of leaves you are likely to encounter on an individual avens plant on this day.

Being able to describe the "typical" individual in a population of samples through the use of means and medians is a critical first step, but there is much more information left behind in your data books. A second important question we can ask is how much *variation* is there around the average (fig. A.2)? This is important for several reasons. For example, two or more samples may have the same mean but quite different amounts of variation among the samples. That variation

itself may have either an ecological cause, or may influence some ecological process, and thus being able to describe variation is a critical tool for all ecologists.

Imagine now that it is the next field season and you are working on the east coast of Newfoundland, studying the diversity of invertebrate species in the rocky intertidal zones. Your basic research methods involve laying down a 50 × 50 cm quadrat (= 0.25 m²) and counting the different number of species of algae, barnacles, snails, and other macroscopic organisms you can find. You are able to finish 10 samples before lunch, and as you are eating your peanut butter and jelly sandwich (which tastes a bit salty), your professor requests a summary of the data.

Sample Number	1	2	3	4	5	6	7	8	9	10
Number of species per 0.25 m²	15	6	18	17	8	9	12	15	10	12

You quickly estimate the mean and median as 12.2 and 12 species per 0.25 m² plot. How do you quantify the variation around those numbers? The simplest index of variation is the **range**, which is the difference between the largest and smallest observations:

$$\text{Range} = 18 - 6 = 12$$

The range does not represent variation in samples very well since very different sets of observations can have the same range. A better representation of the variation in a sample is one that uses all the observations relative to the sample mean, and not just the largest and smallest samples.

The underlying distribution of the population of samples influences nearly all choices about which statistics to use. For non-normally distributed data, one common method to represent variation is to divide the samples into four equal parts, called quartiles, and use the range of measurements between the upper bound of the lowest quartile and the lower bound of the highest quartile. This representation of variation in a sample is called the **interquartile range**. For illustration, imagine you have been asked to study the recovery of mayfly nymphs following a flash flood of Tesuque Creek, New Mexico, a high mountain stream of the southern Rocky Mountains. You took samples from two forks, one disturbed and one undisturbed by the flood. Median densities are 4.5 *Baetis bicaudatus* nymphs per 0.1 m² benthic sample from the disturbed fork and 40 nymphs per 0.1 m² benthic sample in the undisturbed fork. Interquartile ranges can be seen from the data (sorted from lowest density to highest):

Sample Number	1	2	3	4	5	6	7	8	9	10	11	12
Number of nymphs, disturbed fork	2	2	2	3	3	4	5	6	6	8	10	126
Number of nymphs, undisturbed fork	12	30	32	35	37	38	42	48	52	58	71	79
Quartiles	1st			2nd			3rd			4th		

Notice that the interquartile range for the undisturbed fork is from 32 to 58; for the disturbed fork, the interquartile range is 2 to 8. Notice that 50% of the quadrat counts in each sample fall within this range.

For populations that follow the normal distribution, there exist a variety of preferred methods for estimating the variation around the mean. One commonly used index is the sample **variance**. It is calcu-

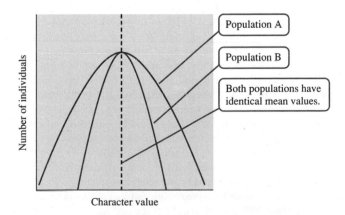

Figure A.2 Populations A and B have identical mean values for this character; however, the variation around the mean appears much greater in population A than in population B.

lated by squaring the differences between the sample mean and each of the individual observations, adding them up to produce the "sum of squares," and dividing this value by the sample size minus one:

$$\text{Sum of squares} = \Sigma(X - \overline{X})^2$$

Using our measures of intertidal diversity, the sums of squares equals:

$$\begin{aligned}
\Sigma(X - \overline{X})^2 = &(15 - 12.2)^2 + (6 - 12.2)^2 + (18 - 12.2)^2 + \\
&(17 - 12.2)^2 + (8 - 12.2)^2 + (9 - 12.2)^2 + \\
&(12 - 12.2)^2 + (15 - 12.2)^2 + (10 - 12.2)^2 + \\
&(12 - 12.2)^2 = 143.6
\end{aligned}$$

The sample variance is calculated by dividing the sum of squares by the sample size minus 1. The sample size in this case is 10 measurements.

$$\text{Sample variance} = s^2 = \frac{\Sigma(X - \overline{X})^2}{n - 1} = \frac{143.6}{10 - 1} = 15.96 \text{ (species per quadrat)}^2$$

Notice that the unit of the sample variance is the *square* of species number, not species number. Because the sample variance in expressed in squares of the original units, we generally take the square root of the variance to calculate a measure of variation called the sample **standard deviation**.

$$\text{Standard deviation} = s = \sqrt{s^2} = \sqrt{15.96} = 3.99 \text{ species per quadrat}$$

While it took a little effort to calculate it, the standard deviation of 3.99 species per quadrat provides us with a standardized index of the variation in species number found in our intertidal study. This value, in addition to the mean of 12.2 species per quadrat, helps us understand patterns in complex ecological data sets.

As you may recall, our measures of sample mean and standard deviation are only *estimates* of the true values in the system. The only way we could ever know the true values themselves is to measure every nook and cranny of the intertidal zone, a feat that would both be extraordinarily difficult and unnecessary. It is instead much more cost effective to sample only enough to have a reliable estimate of the true values. How do you know how close a given sample mean is to the true population means?

The answer to this question depends upon two factors: the variation within the population and the number of measurements in our sample of the population. Common sense suggests that we are more likely to estimate the true mean of a population that has low variability than one that has high variability. Similarly, more observations in our sample will bring us closer to the true value than few observations. Here we will build a way of representing the precision of a given estimate of a population means. Our first step will be to calculate a statistic called the **standard error** of the mean, $s_{\overline{X}}$.

$$s_{\overline{X}} = \sqrt{\frac{s^2}{n}} = \frac{s}{\sqrt{n}}$$

Where s^2 is the sample variance, s is the sample standard deviation, and n is the number of observations (sample size). Applying this formula to our intertidal example, we find:

$$s_{\overline{X}} = \frac{s}{\sqrt{n}} = \frac{3.99}{\sqrt{10}} = 1.26 \text{ species per quadrat}$$

Now let us imagine we have sampled a second intertidal region, which surprisingly has given us the same sample mean (12.2) and the same standard deviation (3.99). However, because we were feeling refreshed after lunch, we were able to take 15, rather than 10 observations. The standard error calculated for this sample is:

$$s_{\overline{X}} = \frac{s}{\sqrt{n}} = \frac{3.99}{\sqrt{15}} = 1.03 \text{ species per quadrat}$$

Notice that because there were more quadrats in the second sample the size of the standard error is reduced. In other words, our second sample mean is a more accurate estimate of the true population mean. We can further refine our estimate of the true population mean through the calculation of confidence intervals.

A **confidence interval** is a range of values within which the true population mean occurs with a particular probability. That probability is called the **level of confidence**, and is calculated as one minus the significance level, α, which is generally 0.05 (see the next section for a discussion of what "significance" represents):

$$\text{Level of confidence} = 1 - \alpha = 1 - 0.05 = 0.95$$

Using this level confidence produces the 95% confidence interval:

$$\text{Confidence interval (CI) for } \mu = \overline{X} \pm s_{\overline{X}}t$$

Where is the true population mean, $\overline{X}$ is the sample mean, $s_{\overline{X}}$ is the standard error, and t is a value from the Student's t table. The Student's t table is available in most statistics textbooks, and is available on the Online Learning Center Web site. The table summarizes the values of a statistical distribution known as the Student's t distribution. The value of t we use for calculating a confidence interval is determined by the degrees of freedom ($n - 1$) and the significance level, which in this cases is $\alpha = 0.05$.

Continuing the example of samples of diversity from two intertidal communities with identical means and standard deviations, but differing in sample size, we find:

Community 1: CI $= 12.2 \pm 1.26 \times 2.26 = 12.2 \pm 2.85$ species per quadrat

Community 2: CI $= 12.2 \pm 1.03 \times 2.14 = 12.2 \pm 2.20$ species per quadrat

With this confidence interval, we can say that there is a 95% probability that the true mean number of species per quadrat in community 1 is between 9.35 (12.2 − 2.85) and 15.05 (12.2 + 2.85). For community 2, the true mean number of species per quadrat is between 10 and 14.4. Put another way, the true population mean will fall within our confidence intervals 19 times out of 20. Although the mean and standard deviation are the same for the two communities, we have narrower confidence intervals for the community that we sampled more heavily.

Statistical Testing

Even though describing populations is important to many ecologists, this is only a very narrow component to the scientific method. Scientists use this information to formulate questions about the natural world and convert their questions into testable hypotheses. To evaluate the validity of a hypothesis it is important to know whether an observed result is different from that predicted by the hypothesis. As you will see below, the most commonly used statistical methods do not allow scientists to "prove" anything to be true, but instead are designed to test whether a hypothesis is false. For example, an ecologist may hypothesize that male elk are generally heavier than female elk. To test this, the ecologist will reword this as a null hypothesis, such as "there is no difference in mean weight between male and female elk." Data could be collected, at which point the ecologist needs to test whether the data support or reject the null hypothesis.

To determine this we need to differentiate between the variation we find in our data that would be expected due to chance from the variation between our data and predictions that are unlikely to be caused by chance alone. When we find differences that are very unlikely to occur by chance, we refer to them as *significant* differences. The critical point here is in identifying when an observed measure, such as mean weight of elk, differs significantly from some theoretical explanation, such as the mean values for males and females will be the same. That judgment is based upon the probability of being incorrect, and there are two ways we can be incorrect.

In one scenario, we could find a "significant" difference between our data and our predictions, when in fact no actual difference exists. Or to put it a more formal way, we could reject our null hypothesis (that males and female elk are the same weight) when in fact our null hypothesis is true. This type of error is a *Type I error*, and should occur at the frequency of α, which ecologists generally set as $P = 0.05$. Type I error rates are also called false positives, and if $\alpha = 0.05$, they will occur 5% of the time. A second type of error is a *Type II error*, or a false negative. In type II errors, the data fail to reject the null hypothesis when in fact it is false. The frequency of type II errors is determined by β, which is often set to $\beta = 0.20$. In other words, in a typical study, there is a 5% probability of being wrong due to a false positive, and a 20% probability of being wrong due to false negatives—not a particularly appealing reality! Why don't ecologists simply lower these values? α and β are related mathematically, such that decreasing one causes an increase in the other. As a result, we must balance these two unavoidable risks, and have historically felt reducing false positive rates was more important than reducing false negative rates, though there has recently been disagreement with this historical "decision." If ecologists can not simply reduce both of these errors by decree, what can we do? As you might imagine, the risks of errors will be associated to the variation in the data we are collecting. The larger the variance in our populations, the larger the risk of type I and II errors. Therefore, increasing sample size can reduce error rates. A second factor, though outside of our control, is **effect size**, the relative magnitude of difference between our two groups (i.e., are male elk 2% or 200% bigger than females). The larger the effect size, the lower the risk of statistical errors. In other words, for the same amount of sampling effort ecologists are more likely to detect big effects than small effects, even if both actually occur.

Type I and type II errors are hazards of all statistical tests, and are not limited to ecology. As a result, all researchers place great importance in the quality of experimental designs and the ability to replicate studies, as results repeated by others give more confidence than results found only once.

The Null Hypothesis Is:		
	True	*False*
The Data Find the Null Hypothesis to Be:		
True	**Data = Reality**	*Type II Error*
False	*Type I Error*	**Data = Reality**

Common Statistical Tests

As we discussed before, some populations of samples will be normally distributed, while others will be non-normally distributed. Different statistical tests make different assumptions about the underlying distribution of the data. In general, these can be divided into *parametric* and *nonparametric* procedures, with the former based upon normal distributions, and the latter allowing for other distributions. In the remainder of this chapter we will discuss examples where a statistical test is needed, and provide solutions based upon parametric and nonparametric procedures. In general, we will not be providing the mathematical formulae for the procedures described, and instead we suggest that you to investigate statistics courses and books for more detailed information.

Relationships Among Variables

Ecologists are often interested in the relationship between two variables, which we might call X and Y. For example, an ecologist might be interested in knowing how prey density (X) is associated with predator density (Y). One way of visualizing such relationships is with an X−Y scatterplot. There are an infinite number of possible relationships between two variables, and we present a few in figure A.3. The most basic scatterplot is one in which there is no relationship between X and Y (fig. A.3a). In contrast, figure A.3b shows a negative relationship between the variables, in which larger values of X are associated with smaller values of Y. Figure A.3c shows a positive relationship, where larger values of X are associated with larger values of Y.

Scatterplots provide a visual overview of the relationships among variables in a study; however, it is equally important to perform statistical tests on the data to determine whether these relationships are likely to have arisen by chance. Two main analyses can be used for this, **correlation** and **regression**. A simple test for correlation asks whether two continuous variables are related. A regression analysis is more formal, and requires a plausible causal link between the two variables. For example, if we measure soil N and P, we might ask whether these variables are correlated. There is no reason to think that high soil N will cause high (or low) soil P. Instead, it is likely that some other factor generates high soil fertility for all soil nutrients. Because there is no plausible causal relationship, we test for a correlation. For parametric data, a test for correlation is generally done using the *product-moment method*, which results in the index r. r can range from -1 to $+1$, with low negative values representing a strong negative correlation and high positive values representing a strong positive correlation. Correlations in nonparametric data can be tested using the *Spearman-Rank correlation*, which results in the index r_S. The main difference between the parametric and nonparametric tests is that the former uses the actual data in its calculations, while the latter tests for correlations among ranks (smallest value = 1, second smallest = 2, etc.).

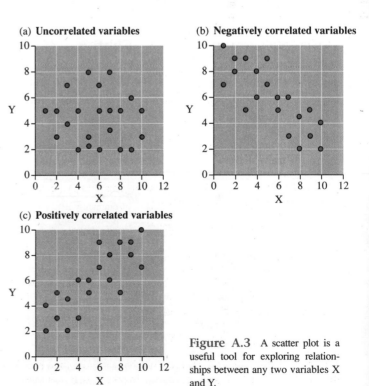

(a) Uncorrelated variables

(b) Negatively correlated variables

(c) Positively correlated variables

Figure A.3 A scatter plot is a useful tool for exploring relationships between any two variables X and Y.

Regression analysis is more formal in its treatment of the two variables, and is only conducted on normally-distributed data. In this analysis, there is a plausible causal link between the two factors, such that you believe the level of factor X (**independent variable**) determines the level of factor Y (**dependent variable**). For example, in a study of predator–prey interactions, you may believe that predators will move towards areas of high prey density, and thus there would be a positive relationship between these variables. In regression analysis we construct X-Y plots as before; however, we now also determine the equation for a line, called the **regression line**. The regression line is the line that best fits the relationship between X and Y. When this line is linear, the regression equation takes the form:

$$Y = bX + a$$

Where a is the Y-intercept and b is the slope of the line, also called the **regression coefficient**. Figure A.4 shows different possible outcomes of a regression analysis between predator and prey densities in three different communities. You can see from the figures that the slope varies among communities, suggesting different factors influence the relationship between prey and predator in these communities.

Both correlation and regression analyses can result in the *coefficient of determination*, or R^2. This value can be calculated by squaring the r value from a correlation. There are additional methods for calculating this value in regression analysis, but the principle is the same. R^2 is a very commonly used value in ecology, and it tells us how much of the variation in Y is explained by variation in X (fig. A.4). High values represent "tighter fits" of the data to the regression line. As you can see in figure A.4, in addition to variations in slopes, the communities differ in R^2, suggesting a weaker relationship between predator–prey densities in some communities than others.

Significance values (*P-values*) can be determined for both correlations and regression, again with the risks of Type I and II errors. It is important to recognize that just because you believe there to be a causal relationship between two variables does not mean that there actually is a causal relationship between the variables, even if the statistical test is "significant." The only clear way to demonstrate causality is with manipulative experiments, which is why experiments are given such prominence in science.

Differences Among Groups—Continuous Data

Correlations and regressions are very useful tools for describing relationships between two variables. However, many ecological problems involve a single variable, but multiple groups. For example, suppose you are concerned about the impacts of acid rain on the diversity of plant species in the boreal forest. You have conducted an experiment in northern Québec in which you added low pH water to ten 2 × 2 m plots, and neutral pH water to an additional ten plots over the course of several growing seasons. At the end of the experiment you measure the number of vascular plant species found in each plot:

Measurement	*1*	*2*	*3*	*4*	*5*	*6*	*7*	*8*	*9*	*10*
Low pH—Species Number	6	4	4	5	7	4	6	6	4	7
Neutral pH—Species Number	12	8	10	8	13	10	16	9	6	5

There are a variety of parametric and nonparametric methods that you can use to determine whether the mean number of plants is significantly reduced through the addition of low pH water. The first would simply to be to graph the mean values and calculate confidence intervals for each group, as we have done in figure A.5. As you can see in the figure, the average number of plant species is lower when acidified water is added to the forest. Recall from before that the true population means for each of the study populations has a 95% chance of falling somewhere within the 95% confidence intervals. Now notice that the 95% confidence intervals do not overlap. This indicates there is less than a 5% chance that the two samples were drawn from a single larger statistical population with a common mean species density. In other words, we have a basis for saying there is a statistically significant effect of adding low pH water on species diversity. There are, however, more direct ways of testing for such a difference.

As we saw in the analyses of correlation between two variables, parametric and nonparametric approaches differ in whether they use the raw data or the ranked data. We find the same difference in the analysis of groups. In our example of species diversity, we have two groups and we want to know whether the mean diversity differs between groups. The parametric procedure would be the *t*-test, and a nonparametric approach would use the *Mann-Whitney Test*. Because the *t*-test is so widely used, we present the formula here:

$$t = \frac{|\overline{X}_a - \overline{X}_n|}{s_{\overline{X}_a - \overline{X}_n}}$$

In this equation:

$\overline{X}_a$ = mean of sample from acidified water treatment = 5.3

$\overline{X}_n$ = mean of sample from neutral water control = 9.7

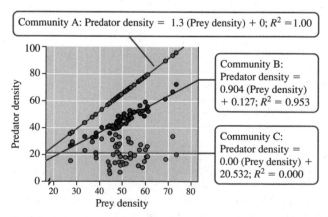

Figure A.4 Regression analysis indicates the strength and slope of the relationship between prey and predator densities in three hypothetical communities.

Community A: Predator density = 1.3 (Prey density) + 0; $R^2 = 1.00$

Community B: Predator density = 0.904 (Prey density) + 0.127; $R^2 = 0.953$

Community C: Predator density = 0.00 (Prey density) + 20.532; $R^2 = 0.000$

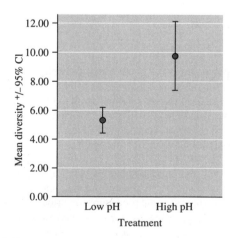

Figure A.5 Mean species diversity and 95% confidence limits for hypothetical plots treated with low and high pH water.

$s_{\overline{X}_a - \overline{X}_n}$ = the standard error of the difference between means, which is calculated as:

$$s_{\overline{X}_a - \overline{X}_n} = \sqrt{\frac{s_p^2}{n_a} + \frac{s_p^2}{n_n}}$$

Where:

n_a = number of acidified water addition plots = 10

n_n = number of neutral water addition plots = 10

s_p^2 = pooled estimate of the variance, calculated as:

$$s_p^2 = \frac{SS_a + SS_n}{DF_a + DF_n}$$

In this equation:

· SS_a = sum of squares for the samples from the acidified water addition treatment = 14.1

SS_n = sum of squares for the samples from the neutral water addition treatment = 98.1

DF_a = degrees of freedom for the acidified water addition treatment = 9

DF_n = degrees of freedom for the neutral water addition treatment = 9

Using this information, we calculate $s_p^2 = 6.23$ (species per plot)^2

We can now calculate the standard deviation of the difference between means:

$$s_{\overline{X}_a - \overline{X}_n} = \sqrt{\frac{s_p^2}{n_a} + \frac{s_p^2}{n_n}} = \sqrt{\frac{6.23}{10} + \frac{6.23}{10}} = 1.12 \text{ species per plot}$$

Now we have all the values we need to calculate t:

$$t = \frac{|\overline{X}_a - \overline{X}_n|}{s_{\overline{X}_a - \overline{X}_n}} = \frac{|5.3 \quad 9.7|}{1.12} = 3.93$$

At this point we need to compare the calculated t with the appropriate critical value. To do this, we need to know both the desired level of significance ($P < 0.05$ in this case), and the pooled degrees of freedom:

$$DF_{pooled} = DF_a + DF_n = 9 + 9 = 18$$

The Student's t for $P < 0.05$ and DF = 18 is 2.10. Since our calculated value of t, 3.93, is greater than this critical value, the probability that the population means are the same *is less than* 0.05. Therefore we reject the null hypothesis that applying acidified and neutral water have equal effects on species diversity, and instead accept the alternative hypothesis that acidification of water reduces diversity in this forest.

The t-test and Mann-Whitney tests are very useful tools for comparing differences between two groups. However, there are many ecological questions that require comparison among more than two groups, and different statistical tools are needed. For example, an ecologist may wish to know whether bluegill sunfish densities differ depending upon the species identity of the dominant predator found within the pond. To test this, one approach would be to create many artificial ponds (cattle watering tanks are often used), stocking each with a constant number of sunfish. To each pond you have added one predator species, such as large-mouth bass, northern pike, and grass pickerel. After adding the predators, you measure any changes in sunfish density. With enough replicate ponds, you can test the null hypothesis that predator species identity has no impact on sunfish density. For parametric data, the standard statistical approach for comparing among multiple groups is *ANOVA*, or the analysis of variance. The most commonly used test for comparisons of more than two groups with nonparametric data is the *Kruskal-Wallis* test. As with the other nonparametric tests we have discussed, this test is based upon a rank-sum approach.

A detailed explanation of how an ANOVA is calculated is beyond the scope of this text, and thus we provide only an overview here. The most basic ANOVA is a *one-way* ANOVA, in which there is a single *factor*, such as predator species identity. In this example, we want to know whether bluegill sunfish densities are differentially affected by three predators (bass, pike, and pickerel). You choose an experimental approach, using cattle watering tanks as experimental lakes. In each tank you place a known density of bluegills and one of the three species of predators, and after several weeks you measure bluegill densities. In this study, we have a single factor (predator species identity) with three levels (bass, pike, and pickerel). It is important to note that this experiment does not have a **control**, such as tanks without any predators. Why? The answer is due to the specific research question that is being asked: "does predator species identity impact sunfish densities." This is different from the question of whether predators alter sunfish densities. In our example, we are not interested in the density of sunfish in the absence of predators, only if sunfish obtain different densities with different predators. The details of the research question being tested will determine the appropriate experimental treatments and controls for each research project.

In the ANOVA we derive a statistic and compare it to a critical value to determine whether the differences we observe among groups are likely to have occurred by chance. If not, then we reject our null hypothesis and accept the alternative hypothesis that predator identity significantly impacts bluegill densities. A critical underlying assumption of the ANOVA is that all samples taken come from a single statistical population. This assumption is the null hypothesis, and the goal of the statistical test is to determine the likelihood that it is true. Like all populations, there will exist variation in the individual values of data around the mean. In ANOVA, significant effects of the factors are found if the amount of variation that can be attributed to the factor (between groups) is high relative to the amount of variation within a single level of a factor (within groups). In other words, if most of the overall variation in the data set is due to difference among groups, you likely will find a significant difference among groups. The test statistic used in ANOVA is the F-ratio, as it is a ratio of between-group variation:within-group variation.

ANOVAs are very flexible statistical tools, and can be expanded to allow for more than a single factor in the experimental model. For example, suppose you believe that predator identity only will impact bluegill densities if the predators are at low abundance. At high abundance, you think all predators will be very efficient at reducing prey numbers. To test this, you again use experimental ponds in which you vary species identity (Factor A, 3 levels), but you also include a second factor of predator density by stocking predators at either high or low densities (Factor B, 2 levels). In a *factorial design*, you have treatment combinations such that every level of every factor is found in combination with each other. In this example, you would have a total of six treatment combinations: (1) predator A, low density, (2) predator A, high density, (3) predator B, low density, (4) predator B, high density, (5) predator C, low density, (6) predator C, high density. ANOVA partitions the total variation in the data set into groups including predator identity (between groups), predator density (between groups), and the overall within group variation. In two-way ANOVAs (and other multi-way ANOVAs) there is an additional term which may explain some of the variation in the data, and that is the interaction between the two factors (predator identity × predator density). Interaction terms are critical to many ecological studies, as many processes are likely to be important not by themselves, but in combination with other factors. For example, in this case you have predicted that predator species identity will only impact sunfish density if predator density is low, and this can be seen in figure A.6. In more general terms, this means that the effect of one factor is dependent

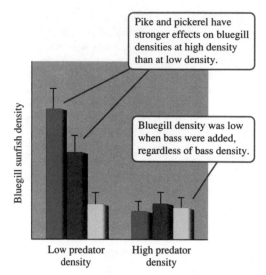

Figure A.6 Hypothetical interaction between predator species identity and predator density on bluegill sunfish densities.

upon the level of another factor. Such situations are common in ecology, and you encountered many throughout the text. It is the ability to extend beyond two levels and include more than one factor that make ANOVAs a statistical workhorse in ecology.

Differences Among Groups—Categorical Data

So far we have only discussed ecological questions that generate continuous response variables, such as number of species or elk weight. However, many types of ecological data are categorical, such as flower colour or gender. If you were interested in whether some factor influenced flower colour, *t*-tests would clearly be inappropriate: what is the average of blue and red (no, it is not purple!)? Fortunately there exists a set of statistical approaches that allow an ecologist to test whether the distributions of character states in a population differ from what would be expected by chance.

The simplest method to test hypotheses concerning the relationship between observed and hypothesized frequencies is the **chi-square** (χ^2) "goodness of fit" test. This test is used to judge how well an observed distribution of frequencies matches one "expected" from a particular hypothesis. Let's explore this test using the frequency of flower colours in a hypothetical population of *Claytonia virginica*, Spring Beauty. These plants are common in the forest understory throughout much of central and eastern North America, and different plants produce flowers that vary in colour from pure white to very dark pink. You explore a population in southern Ontario and are able to find 90 plants in flower, with individual plants displaying either white, light pink, or dark pink flowers. Let's consider this hypothetical data set and test the hypothesis that the three phenotypes are present in equal frequencies in the population.

Flower Colour	Observed Frequency (O)	Expected Frequency (E)
White	45	30
Light Pink	30	30
Dark Pink	15	30

Because our null hypothesis is that the phenotypes are present in equal proportions, and we have three possible phenotypes, our expected frequency for each phenotype is simply 1/3 the total number of samples (90) in our study population. The values of 45, 30, and 15 represent the number of individuals we encountered of each phenotype in this

hypothetical population. The question then becomes: Is 45, 30, 15 significantly different from 30, 30, 30?

The value of χ^2 is calculated as:

$$\chi^2 = \Sigma \frac{(O - E)^2}{E}$$

Where O is the observed frequency of a particular group and E is the expected frequency. For this example:

$$\chi^2 = \Sigma \frac{(O - E)^2}{E} = \frac{(45 - 30)^2}{30} + \frac{(30 - 30)^2}{30} + \frac{(15 - 30)^2}{30} = 15$$

The next step is to determine whether this value of χ^2 is greater than that expected by chance, given this number of degrees of freedom. To do this, we again consult a list of critical χ^2 values, in this case for 2 degrees of freedom and $P<0.05$. Our observed value of 15 is greater than the critical value of 5.991, and thus we can conclude that there is a significant difference in the frequencies of the three flower colour phenotypes in this population.

The χ^2 "goodness of fit" test is a powerful tool for identifying differences in frequencies among groups within a single population. However, how would you test whether some treatment (e.g., fertilization) had a significant impact on the frequency of flower colours? These questions are analogous to those we address using ANOVA and *t*-tests for continuous data, but the "goodness of fit" test is insufficient. Fortunately, there exist several statistical approaches, such as the χ^2 "test for independence" and Fisher's exact test that are well suited for this purpose. We direct you to the Online Learning Center for more information on the "test for independence."

More Complex Problems

Believe it or not, the statistics we have just described are only a basic introduction to what is a very diverse and complex set of analytical tools. Like all tools, proficiency increases with use. Also like all tools, they are generally used for a reason. In ecology, we simply are unable to answer even the most basic questions without a means to synthesize extremely complex data sets. In other words, statistical methods are just as important to ecology as is sampling natural populations, coming up with good questions, or any other part of the scientific method.

As the complexity of the scientific question increases, so too does the statistical methodology. Imagine the following ecological research questions. Many questions are centred on how whole communities, rather than individual species, respond to environmental changes. These questions are *multivariate*, rather than *univariate* in nature, which means that each species of the community represents a different dimension in the analysis. In more practical terms, this means you need a statistical method that allows for more than one *response variable*, not just more than one factor. Fortunately a variety of methods have been developed including MANOVA (multivariate analysis of variance), ordinations, and other classification methods. These latter approaches help reduce the complexity of data sets, allowing the ecologist to see underlying patterns. Although we will not discuss the details of these approaches here, results from such analyses are presented throughout the text.

Two factors that also greatly increase the complexity of ecological studies are variations in ecological patterns and processes in space and time. In other words, precipitation might strongly influence plant growth in some years but not in others. Similarly, elk may compete for forage in some locations but not in others. Understanding the contributions of spatial and temporal patterns can be critical to a holistic understanding of a natural system. Fortunately, there are advanced statistical methods to address these questions as well.

A

A horizon a biologically active soil layer consisting of a mixture of mineral materials, such as clay, silt, and sand, as well as organic material, derived from the overlying O horizon; generally characterized by leaching. *(p. 20)*

abundance the total number of individuals, or biomass, of a species present in a specified area. *(p. 262)*

abyssal zone a zone of the ocean depths between 4,000 and 6,000 m. *(p. 53)*

acclimation physiological adjustment to change in an environmental factor, such as temperature or salinity. *(p. 125)*

actual evapotranspiration (AET) the amount of water lost from an ecosystem to the atmosphere due to a combination of evaporation and transpiration by plants. *(p. 481)*

adaptation an evolutionary process that changes anatomy, physiology, or behaviour, resulting in an increased ability of a population to live in a particular environment. The term is also applied to the anatomical, physiological, or behavioural characteristics produced by this process. *(p. 89)*

adhesion-adapted a term applied to seeds with hooks, spines, or barbs that disperse by attaching to passing animals. *(p. 237)*

age distribution the distribution of individuals among age groups in a population; also called age structure. *(p. 288)*

albedo the proportion of incident radiation reflected by a surface. *(p. 119)*

allele one of the alternative forms of the same gene. *(p. 89)*

allele frequencies the proportions of alternative alleles in a population. *(p. 94)*

allochthonous inputs organic matter derived or created in a community external to the one in which they are eventually deposited. *(p. 492)*

allopatric speciation speciation that occurs when isolating mechanisms evolve among geographically separated populations. *(p. 105)*

allopolyploidy a process of speciation initiated by hybridization of two different species. *(p. 233)*

allozyme alternative form of a particular enzyme that differs structurally but not functionally from other allozymes coded for by different alleles at the same locus. *(p. 102)*

alluvial groundwater water that is derived from a surface stream in contrast to groundwater that is derived from underground streams and high water tables. *(p. 160)*

alternative stable states an ecological theory that suggests that a given location can persist as different community types depending upon disturbance regimes, nutrient inputs, and other external factors. *(p. 470)*

ammonification the conversion of organic forms of nitrogen to ammonium, generally mediated by bacteria. *(p. 503)*

anadromous fish that hatch and spawn in fresh water, but live most of their lives in salt water. *(p. 122)*

aposematic colouration bright and conspicuous colouration displayed by many toxic or distasteful potential prey species. *(p. 374)*

arbuscular mycorrhizal fungi (AMF) mycorrhizae in which the mycorrhizal fungus produces arbuscules (sites of exchange between plant and fungus), hyphae (fungal filaments), and vesicles (fungal energy storage organs within root conex cells). *(p. 394)*

arbuscule a bush-shaped organ on an endomycorrhizal fungus that acts as a site of material exchange between the fungus and its host plant. *(p. 394)*

archaea prokaryotes distinguished from bacteria on the basis of structural, physiological, and other biological features. *(p. 175)*

aril a fleshy covering of some seeds that attracts birds and other vertebrates, which act as dispersers of such seeds. *(p. 238)*

assortative mating mating among phenotypically similar (positive assortative mating), or dissimilar (negative assortative mating), individuals. *(p. 105)*

atoll a circle of low islands and coral reefs encircling a lagoon, generally formed on a submerged mountain called a seamount. *(p. 58)*

autotroph an organism that can synthesize organic molecules using inorganic molecules and energy from either sunlight (photosynthetic autotrophs) or from inorganic molecules, such as hydrogen sulphide (chemosynthetic autotrophs). *(p. 174)*

aversive conditioning repeated exposure to punishment with the intent of causing individuals to reduce the frequency of an undesired behaviour. *(p. 208)*

B

B horizon a subsoil in which materials leached from above, generally from the A horizon, accumulate. May be rich in clay, organic matter, iron, and other materials. *(p. 20)*

balanced growth cell growth in which all cell constituents, such as nitrogen, carbon, and DNA, increase at approximately the same rate. *(p. 388)*

barrier reef a long, ridgelike reef that parallels the mainland and is separated from it by a deep lagoon. *(p. 58)*

Batesian mimicry evolution of a nonnoxious species to resemble a poisonous or inedible species. *(p. 374)*

bathypelagic zone a zone within the deep ocean that extends from about 1,000 to 4,000 m. *(p. 53)*

behavioural ecology study of the relationships between organisms and environment that are mediated by behaviour. *(p. 2)*

benthic an adjective referring to the bottom of bodies of waters such as seas, lakes, or streams. *(p. 54)*

bioaccumulation the process by which toxic substances increase in concentration within a living organism due to intake rates being greater than excretion and metabolism. *(p. 305)*

biocontrol the deliberate introduction of some agent (herbivore, pathogen, etc.) that will exploit an invasive species, reducing its population size. *(p. 361)*

biological species concept a group of actually or potentially interbreeding populations, which are reproductively isolated from other such groups. *(p. 104)*

biomagnification increase in toxin levels with increased trophic position within a food web, due to predators eating contaminated prey. *(p. 305)*

biome large-scale classification of terrestrial habitats, distinguished primarily by their predominant plants and are associated with particular climates. They consist of distinctive plant formations such as the tropical rain forest biome and the desert biome. *(p. 14)*

biosphere the portions of earth that support life; also refers to the total global ecosystem. *(p. 3)*

birthrate the number of new individuals produced in a population generally expressed as births per individual or per thousand individuals in the population. *(p. 295)*

bog peat-forming wetlands with precipitation being the source of water entering the system. *(p. 80)*

boreal forest northern forests that occupy the area south of arctic tundra. Though dominated by coniferous trees they also contain aspen and birch. Also called taiga. *(p. 23)*

bottom-up control control of a community or ecosystem by physical or chemical factors such as temperature or nutrient availability. *(p. 486)*

brood parasite a species (generally birds) that lays its eggs in the nests of others, relying on the unrelated individuals to provide parental care *(p. 204)*

bundle sheath a structure, which surrounds the leaf veins of C_4 plants, made up of cells where four-carbon acids produced during carbon fixation are broken down to three-carbon acids and CO_2. *(p. 176)*

buttress roots large roots on all sides of a tree that occur above the soil surface, providing structural support rather than nutrient capture. *(p. 40)*

C

C horizon a soil layer composed of largely unaltered parent material, little affected by biological activity. *(p. 20)*

C_3 photosynthesis the photosynthetic pathway used by most plants and all algae, in which the product of the initial reaction is phosphoglyceric acid, or PGA, a three-carbon acid. *(p. 176)*

C_4 photosynthesis in C_4 photosynthesis, CO_2 is fixed in mesophyll cells by combining it with phosphoenol pyruvate, or PEP, to produce a four-carbon acid. Plants using C_4 photosynthesis are generally more drought tolerant than plants employing C_3 photosynthesis. *(p. 176)*

CAM (crassulacean acid metabolism) photosynthesis a photosynthetic pathway largely limited to succulent plants in arid and semiarid environments, in which carbon fixation takes place at night, when lower temperatures reduce the rate of water loss during CO_2 uptake. The resulting four-carbon acids are stored until daylight, when they are broken down into pyruvate and CO_2. *(p. 178)*

carnivore an organism that consumes flesh; approximately synonymous with predator. *(p. 179)*

carrying capacity (K) the maximum population of a species that a particular ecosystem can sustain. *(p. 315)*

caste a group of individuals that are physically distinctive and engage in specialized behaviour within a social unit, such as a colony. *(p. 211)*

cavitation rapid formation of air bubbles within the xylem of plants. *(p. 161)*

character displacement changes in the physical characteristics of a species' population as a consequence of natural selection for reduced interspecific competition. *(p. 346)*

chemosynthetic refers to autotrophs that use inorganic molecules as a source of carbon and energy. *(p. 174)*

chi-square (χ^2) a statistic used to measure how much a sample distribution differs from a theoretical distribution. *(p. 606)*

chronosequence a series of communities or ecosystems representing a range of ages or times since disturbance. *(p. 461)*

climate diagram a standardized form of representing average patterns of variation in temperature and precipitation that identifies several ecologically important climatic factors such as relatively moist periods and periods of drought. *(p. 16)*

climax community a community that occurs late in succession whose populations remain stable until disrupted by disturbance. *(p. 455)*

clumped distribution a pattern of distribution in a population in which individuals have a much higher probability of being found in some areas than in others; in other words, individuals are aggregated rather than dispersed. *(p. 267)*

coefficient of relationship the probability that the alleles at a given locus will be identical by descent among two individuals in the population. *(p. 205)*

coevolution a reciprocal evolutionary interaction between two or more species. *(p. 220)*

cohort a group of individuals of the same age. *(p. 288)*

cohort life table a life table based on individuals born (or beginning life in some other way) at the same time. *(p. 288)*

colonization cycle the situation in which stream populations are maintained through a dynamic interplay between downstream drift and upstream dispersal. *(p. 303)*

combined response the combined effect of functional and numerical responses by consumers on prey populations; determined by multiplying the number of prey eaten per predator times the number of predators per unit area, giving the number of prey eaten per unit area. Combined response is generally expressed as a percentage of the total number of prey. *(p. 369)*

community an association of interacting species living in a particular area; also often defined as all of the organisms living in a particular area. *(p. 409)*

community ecology The scientific study of interactions among species within a community. *(p. 3)*

community structure attributes of a community such as the number of species or the distribution of individuals among species within the community. *(p. 409)*

competition coefficient a coefficient expressing the magnitude of the negative effect of individuals of one species on individuals of a second species. *(p. 333)*

competitive exclusion principle the idea that two species with identical niches cannot coexist indefinitely. *(p. 335)*

competitive hierarchies a nested ranking of species by competitive ability. *(p. 434)*

conduction the movement of heat between objects in direct physical contact. *(p. 127)*

confidence interval a range of values within which the true population mean occurs with a particular probability called the level of confidence. *(p. 602)*

conservation threshold a level of habitat loss and/or fragmentation below which a population is sustainable, and above which the population is likely to go extinct. *(p. 543)*

constitutive defenses chemical or morphological defenses that are produced continuously, regardless of whether the organism has been previously attacked. In contrast to induced defenses. *(p. 375)*

control in an experiment, the individuals/plots/units to which the experimental treatment of interest is not applied. *(p. 605)*

convection the process of heat flow or transfer to a moving fluid, such as wind or flowing water. *(p. 127)*

Coriolis effect a phenomenon caused by the rotation of the earth, which produces a deflection of winds and water currents to the right of their direction of travel in the Northern Hemisphere and to the left of their direction of travel in the Southern Hemisphere. *(p. 16)*

correlation a statistical test to determine whether two variables are related. *(p. 603)*

corridors regions of a landscape that provide connections among habitat fragments, potentially resulting in enhanced flow or movement of individuals or genes. *(p. 533)*

D

decomposition the breakdown of organic matter accompanied by the release of carbon dioxide and other inorganic compounds; a key process in nutrient cycling. *(p. 505)*

denitrification the conversion of nitrate to gaseous nitrogen, generally mediated by bacteria. *(p. 504)*

density the number of individuals in a population per unit area. *(p. 262)*

density-dependent factor biotic factors in the environment, such as disease and competition, are often called density-dependent factors because their effects on populations may be related to, or depend upon, local population density. *(p. 318)*

density-independent factor abiotic factors in the environment, such as floods and extreme temperature, are often called density-independent factors because their effects on populations may be independent of population density. *(p. 318)*

dependent variable the variable traditionally plotted on the vertical or "Y" axis of a scatter plot. *(p. 604)*

desert an arid biome occupying approximately 20% of the land surface of the earth in which water loss due to evaporation and transpiration by plants exceeds precipitation during most of the year. *(p. 31)*

detritivore organisms that feed on nonliving organic matter. *(p. 179)*

diffusion transport of material due to the random movement of particles; net movement is from areas of high concentration to areas of low concentration. *(p. 150)*

directional selection a form of natural selection that favours an extreme phenotype over other phenotypes. *(p. 96)*

dispersal limitation the absence of a species from a community due to a lack of propagules entering the community. *(p. 565)*

disruptive selection a form of natural selection that favours two or more extreme phenotypes over the average phenotype in a population. *(p. 99)*

distribution the natural geographic range of an organism or the spatial arrangement of individuals in a local population. *(p. 262)*

disturbance Ecologists disagree on a definition of disturbance. We use that of White and Pickett (1985) who define disturbance as any relatively discrete event that disrupts ecosystem, community, or population structure and changes resources, substrate availability, or the physical environment. *(p. 248)*

DNA sequencing methods for determining the sequence of nucleic acids in DNA molecules. *(p. 111)*

drift the active or passive downstream movement of stream organisms. *(p. 303)*

drumlin a smooth hill, or series of hills, formed as a glacier cuts through a moraine. *(p. 538)*

E

ecology   study of the relationships between organisms and the environment. *(p. 2)*

ecosystem   a biological community plus all of the abiotic factors influencing that community. *(p. 5)*

ecosystem ecology   the subdiscipline of ecology that focuses on the flow of energy and nutrients among the biotic and abiotic components of an ecosystem *(p. 3)*

ecosystem engineers   species whose activity creates, or fundamentally alters, habitats. *(p. 441)*

ecosystem services   economically valuable services provided by the functioning of ecosystems, such as biomass production, water filtration, and nutrient cycling. *(p. 444)*

ecotone   a spatial transition from one type of ecosystem to another; for instance, the transition from a woodland to a grassland. *(p. 8)*

ectomycorrhizae (ECM)   an association between a fungus and plant roots in which the fungus forms a mantle around roots and a netlike structure around root cells. *(p. 394)*

ectotherm   an organism that relies mainly on external sources of energy for regulating body temperature. *(p. 128)*

effect size   statistical measurement of the magnitude of a treatment effect. *(p. 603)*

El Niño   a large-scale, coupled oceanic–atmospheric system that has major effects on climate worldwide. During an El Niño, the sea surface temperature in the eastern Pacific Ocean is higher than average and barometric pressure is lower. *(p. 578)*

elaiosome   a structure on the surface of some seeds generally containing oils attractive to ants, which act as dispersers of such seeds. *(p. 238)*

electrophoresis   an analytical technique involving the separation of molecules in an electrical field. *(p. 110)*

emigration   the movement of an organism out of a population. *(p. 298)*

endotherm   an organism that relies mainly on internal sources of energy for regulating body temperature. *(p. 127)*

energy budget   the rate at which an organism takes in energy relative to the rate at which it expends energy; gives an indication of the amount of energy available for functions such as reproduction. *(p. 139)*

epilimnion   the warm, well-lighted surface layer of lakes. *(p. 75)*

epipelagic zone   the warm, well-lighted surface layer of the oceans. *(p. 53)*

epiphyte   a plant, such as an orchid, that grows on the surface of another plant but that is not parasitic. *(p. 40)*

equilibrium   a state of balance in a system in which opposing factors cancel each other. *(p. 419)*

equilibrium model of island biogeography   a model developed by MacArthur and Wilson that predicts species diversity and rates of turnover on islands as a function of island sizes and location. *(p. 555)*

esker   a long and narrow ridge of glacial debris deposited by meltwater. *(p. 538)*

estivation   a dormant state that some animals enter during the summer; involves a reduction of metabolic rate. *(p. 142)*

estuary   the lowermost part of a river, which is under the influence of the tides and is a mixture of seawater and freshwater. *(p. 66)*

eusociality   highly specialized sociality generally including (1) individuals of more than one generation living together, (2) cooperative care of young, and (3) division of individuals into sterile, or nonreproductive, and reproductive castes. *(p. 206)*

eutrophic   a term applied to lakes, and sometimes to other ecosystems, with high nutrient content and high biological production. *(p. 77)*

eutrophication   Nutrient enrichment of a water body through natural processes or pollution, generally causing rapid algal growth and reduced dissolved oxygen levels. *(p. 5)*

evaporation   the process by which a liquid changes from liquid phase to a gas, as in the change from liquid water to water vapour. *(p. 127)*

evolution   a change in gene frequencies within a population over time *(p. 88)*

evolutionary stable strategy   a behavioural strategy that is resistant to invasion, and most likely to be maintained by natural selection. *(p. 224)*

exploitation   an interaction between species that enhances the fitness of the exploiting individual—the predator, the herbivore, etc.—while reducing the fitness of the exploited individual—the prey or host. *(p. 354)*

exploitative competition   utilization of a shared and limiting resource by two or more individuals. *(p. 332)*

exponential population growth   population growth that produces a J-shaped pattern of population increase. In exponential population growth, the change in numbers with time is the product of the per capita rate of increase, r. and population size, N. *(p. 312)*

F

facilitation model   according to the facilitation model, pioneer species modify the environment in such a way that it becomes less suitable for themselves and more suitable for species characteristic of later successional stages. *(p. 466)*

facultative mutualism   a mutualistic relationship between two species that is not required for the survival of the two species. *(p. 382)*

fecundity   the number of eggs or seeds produced by an organism. *(p. 234)*

fecundity schedule   a table of birthrates for females of different ages in a population. *(p. 295)*

female   sex that produces larger, more energetically costly gametes (eggs or ova). *(p. 215)*

fen   peat-forming wetlands that obtain water both through precipitation and groundwater. *(p. 80)*

fetch   the longest distance over which wind can blow across a body of water; directly related to the maximum size of waves that can be generated by wind. *(p. 233)*

fitness   the number of offspring contributed by an individual relative to the number of offspring produced by other members of the population. Ultimately defined as the relative genetic contribution of individuals to future generations. *(p. 88)*

flood pulse concept   a theory of river ecology identifying periodic flooding as an essential organizer of river ecosystem structure and functioning. *(p. 72)*

food web   a summary of the feeding relationships within an ecological community. *(p. 431)*

forb   herbaceous plants other than graminoids. *(p. 237)*

frequency-dependent selection   a form of selection in which the fitness of a genotype depends upon its relative abundance within a population. *(p. 294)*

fringing reef   a coral reef that forms near the shore of an island or continent. *(p. 58)*

functional response   an increase in animal feeding rate, which eventually levels off, that occurs in response to an increase in food availability. *(p. 188)*

fundamental niche   the physical conditions under which a species might live, in the absence of interactions with other species. *(p. 231)*

G

game theory   a branch of mathematics devoted to the study of strategy in which players seek to maximize their individual returns. Optimal strategies are often dependent upon the behaviour of other players. *(p. 224)*

generalist   a predator or herbivore that regularly includes a variety of prey species as part of its diet. *(p. 378)*

genetic drift   change in gene frequencies in a population due to chance or random events. *(p. 95)*

geographic ecology   the study of ecological structure and process at large geographic scales; sometimes defined as the study of ecological patterns that can be put on a map. *(p. 3)*

geographic information system (GIS)   a computer-based system that stores, analyzes, and displays geographic information, generally in the form of maps. *(p. 571)*

geometric population growth   population growth in which generations do not overlap and in which successive generations differ in size by a constant ratio. *(p. 311)*

geometric rate of increase (λ)   the ratio of the population size at two points in time: $\lambda = N_{t+1}/N_t$ where N_{t+1} is the size of the population at some future time and N_t is the size of the population at some earlier time. *(p. 296)*

germination   the sprouting of seeds. *(p. 238)*

glacial age   periods of variably cool and warm global temperatures that can last for millions of years. Within a glacial age will be a number of glaciations and interglacial periods. *(p. 538)*

glacial refugia   areas that occur within the extent of a glacial landscape that remained uncovered by glaciers. *(p. 539)*

glaciation   cold periods generally lasting between 60,000–90,000 years within a glacial age. During glaciations, glaciers increase in size across the planet. *(p. 538)*

global positioning system (GPS)   a device that determines locations on the earth's surface, including latitude, longitude, and altitude, using radio signals from satellites as references. *(p. 569)*

gonadosomatic index (GSI)   an index of reproductive effort calculated as ovary weight divided by body weight and adjusted for the number of batches of offspring produced per year. *(p. 241)*

graminoids   grasses and grasslike plants, such as sedges and rushes. *(p. 237)*

granivore   an animal that feeds chiefly on seeds. *(p. 343)*

greenhouse effect   warming of the earth's atmosphere and surface as a result of heat trapped near the earth's surface by gases in the atmosphere, especially water vapour, carbon dioxide, methane, ozone, nitrous oxide, and chlorofluorocarbons. *(p. 576)*

gross primary production   the total amount of energy fixed by all the autotrophs in an ecosystem. *(p. 480)*

group selection   selection on traits benefiting a group, even if these traits are detrimental to the individual that possesses the trait. *(p. 204)*

growth form   See *life-form.*

guild   a group of organisms that make their living in a similar way; for example, the seed-eating animals in a desert, the fruit-eating birds in a tropical rain forest, or the litter-feeding invertebrates in a stream. *(p. 409)*

gyre   a large-scale, circular oceanic current that moves to the right (clockwise) in the Northern Hemisphere and to the left (counter-clockwise) in the Southern Hemisphere. *(p. 55)*

H

hadal zone   the deepest parts of the oceans, below about 6,000 m. *(p. 53)*

haplodiploidy   sex inheritance in which males are haploid and females are diploid. *(p. 214)*

Hardy-Weinberg principle   a principle that in a population mating at random in the absence of evolutionary forces, allele frequencies will remain constant. *(p. 93)*

herbivore   a heterotrophic organism that eats plants. *(p. 179)*

herd immunity   resistance of a population to the spread of a disease due to high rates of immunity among individuals within the population. *(p. 391)*

heritability   the proportion of total phenotypic variation in a trait attributable to genetic variation; determines the potential for evolutionary change in a trait. *(p. 92)*

hermaphrodite   an individual capable of producing both sperm or pollen and eggs or ova. *(p. 215)*

heterotroph   an organism that uses organic molecules both as a source of carbon and as a source of energy. *(p. 174)*

heterozygous   having different alleles at a given locus. *(p. 93)*

hibernation   a dormant state, involving reduced metabolic rate, that occurs in some animals during the winter. *(p. 142)*

homeotherm   an organism that uses metabolic energy to maintain a relatively constant body temperature; such organisms are often called warm-blooded. *(p. 127)*

homozygous   having identical alleles at a given locus. *(p. 93)*

host race   genetically distinct subpopulations or a species that are spatially differentiated as a function of their host species. *(p. 378)*

hydrologic cycle   the sun-driven cycle of water through the biosphere through evaporation, transpiration, condensation, precipitation, and runoff. *(p. 51)*

hyperosmotic   a term describing organisms with body fluids with a lower concentration of water and higher solute concentration than the external environment. *(p. 151)*

hyphae   long, thin filaments that form the basic structural unit of fungi. *(p. 394)*

hypolimnion   the deepest layer of a lake below the epilimnion and thermocline. *(p. 75)*

hypoosmotic   a term describing organisms with body fluids with a higher concentration of water and lower solute concentration than the external environment. *(p. 151)*

hyporheic zone   a zone below the benthic zone of a stream; a zone of transition between surface, streamwater flow, and groundwater. *(p. 71)*

I

immigration   the movement of an organism into a population. *(p. 298)*

immobilization   the conversion of inorganic ions, such as nitrate, into organic compounds, such as proteins. *(p. 503)*

inbreeding   mating between close relatives. Inbreeding tends to increase levels of homozygosity in populations and often results in offspring with lower survival and reproductive rates. *(p. 103)*

inclusive fitness   overall fitness, which is determined by the survival and reproduction of an individual, plus the survival and reproduction of genetic relatives of the individual. *(p. 203)*

independent variable   the variable traditionally plotted on the horizontal or "X" axis of a scatter plot. *(p. 604)*

induced defenses   chemical or morphological defenses that are produced, or enhanced, in response to an attack by a predator or herbivore. *(p. 375)*

inhibition model   a model of succession that proposes that early occupants of an area modify the environment in a way that makes the area less suitable for both early and late successional species. *(p. 466)*

initial floristics   a model of succession in which most species are able to colonize a habitat soon after a disturbance. Species become more or less abundant over time due to shifts in limiting resources and environmental conditions. *(p. 465)*

interdisciplinary research   investigations that involve researchers from multiple disciplines working closely to produce an understanding that integrates across disciplines; may include several scientific disciplines or extend beyond the boundaries of the natural sciences into the social sciences and humanities. *(p. 525)*

interference competition   form of competition involving direct antagonistic interactions between individuals. *(p. 223)*

interglacial periods   relatively short warm periods (10,000–40,000 years) that occur between glaciations in a glacial age. During interglacials, glaciers retreat across the planet. Even without human-induced climate change, the planet is currently in an interglacial period. *(p. 538)*

interquartile range   a range of measurements that includes the middle 50% of the measurements or observations in a sample, bounded by the lowest value of the highest 25% of measurements and the highest value of the lowest 25% of measurements. *(p. 601)*

intersexual selection   sexual selection occurring when members of one sex choose mates from among the members of the opposite sex on the basis of some anatomical or behavioural trait, generally leading to the elaboration of that trait. *(p. 215)*

interspecific competition   competition between individuals of different species. *(p. 331)*

intertidal zone   See *littoral zone.*

intrasexual selection   sexual selection in which individuals of one sex compete among themselves for mates. *(p. 215)*

intraspecific competition   competition between individuals of the same species. *(p. 331)*

intrinsic rate of increase   the maximum per capita rate of population increase; may be approached under ideal environmental conditions for a species. *(p. 312)*

introduced (exotic or non-native) species   a species currently found outside its historical range. Determination of the date used to define a historical range is arbitrary. *(p. 360)*

invasive species   a species that is able to rapidly increase its population size and species range, often to the detriment of the surrounding species. Both native and introduced species have the potential to be invasive species *(p. 360)*

irradiance   the level of light intensity, often measured as photon flux density. *(p. 187)*

I_{sat}   the irradiance required to saturate the photosynthetic capacity of a photosynthetic organism. *(p. 187)*

isoclines of zero population growth   lines, in the graphical representation of the Lotka–Volterra competition model, where population growth of the species in competition is zero. *(p. 333)*

isolating mechanisms   some process that prevents the production of a viable offspring between two individuals. Isolating mechanisms are critical to the species integrity, and can occur pre- or postzygote formation. *(p. 104)*

isosmotic   a term describing organisms with body fluids containing the same concentration of water and solutes as the external environment. *(p. 151)*

isozymes all enzymes with the same biochemical function that are produced by different or the same loci. *(p. 110)*

iteroparity reproduction that involves production of an organism's offspring in two or more events, generally spaced out over the lifetime of the organism. *(p. 247)*

K

kettle a small depression on the landscape that forms when a block of glacial ice melts in place. *(p. 538)*

keystone species species that, despite low biomass, exert strong effects on the structure of the communities they inhabit. *(p. 438)*

kin selection selection in which individuals increase their inclusive fitness by helping increase the survival and reproduction of relatives (kin) that are not offspring. *(p. 204)*

L

La Niña the opposite of an El Niño. During a La Niña, the sea surface temperature in the eastern Pacific Ocean is lower than average and barometric pressure is higher. *(p. 579)*

landscape an area of land containing a patchwork of ecosystems. *(p. 525)*

landscape ecology the study of landscape structure and processes. *(p. 3)*

landscape elements the ecosystems in a landscape, which generally form a mosaic of visually distinctive patches. *(p. 525)*

landscape process the exchange of materials, energy, or organisms among the ecosystems that make up a landscape. *(p. 529)*

landscape structure the size, shape, composition, number, and position of ecosystems within a landscape. *(p. 526)*

large-scale phenomena phenomena of a geographic scale rather than a local scale. *(p. 266)*

lateritic soil soils containing high concentrations of iron and aluminum, and low concentrations of many essential plant nutrients. These soils are commonly caused through extensive weathering of the parent materials. *(p. 39)*

lentic areas of standing water. *(p. 72)*

level of confidence one minus the significance level, α, which is generally 0.05; for example, level of confidence = $1-0.05 = 0.95$. *(p. 602)*

LHF horizon the L, F, and H layers, known collectively as the LFH horizon, consist of leaves, twigs, and other organic materials. LFH horizons are found primarily in upland habitats, such as forests. *(p. 20)*

life history the adaptations of an organism that influence aspects of its biology such as the number of offspring it produces, its survival, and its size and age at reproductive maturity. *(p. 230)*

life table a table of age-specific survival and death, or mortality, rates in a population. *(p. 288)*

life-form the life-form of a plant is a combination of its structure and its growth dynamics. Plant life-forms include trees, vines, annual plants, sclerophyllous vegetation, grasses, and forbs. *(p. 237)*

light compensation point (LCP) that amount of light necessary for a plant's respiration rate to equal its photosynthetic rate. *(p. 187)*

limnetic zone the open lake beyond the littoral zone. *(p. 75)*

littoral zone the shallowest waters along a lake or ocean shore; where rooted aquatic plants may grow in lakes. *(p. 53)*

loci (plural of locus) the location along the length of a particular chromosome where a gene is located. *(p. 102)*

logistic equation $dN/dt = r_{max}N(1 - N/K)$ *(p. 316)*

logistic population growth a pattern of growth that produces a sigmoidal, or S-shaped, population growth curve; population size levels off at carrying capacity (K). *(p. 315)*

lotic areas of flowing water. *(p. 72)*

M

macroclimate the prevailing climate for a region. *(p. 117)*

male sex that produces smaller less costly gametes (sperm or pollen). *(p. 215)*

mangrove forest a forest on subtropical and tropical marine shores dominated by salt-tolerant woody plants, such as *Rhizophora* and *Avicennia*. *(p. 65)*

masting the synchronous production of large quantities of fruits by trees, such as oaks and beech. *(p. 369)*

matric force a force resulting from water's tendency to adhere to the walls of containers such as cell walls or the soil particles lining a soil pore. *(p. 152)*

matrix the landscape element within a landscape mosaic that is the most continuous spatially, for example, the forest that surrounds small isolated patches of meadow. *(p. 526)*

maximum sustainable yield (MSY) the maximum harvest of a species that can occur without reducing population growth rates. *(p. 320)*

Mediterranean woodland and shrubland a biome associated with mild, moist winter conditions and usually with dry summers. Vegetation is characterized by small, tough (sclerophyllous) leaves and adaptations to fire. This biome is found around the Mediterranean Sea and in western North America, Chile, southern Australia, and southern Africa. Also known as chaparral, garrigue, maquis, and fynbos. *(p. 29)*

mesocosm an experimental system that is intermediate between field and laboratory conditions. *(p. 341)*

mesopelagic zone a middle depth zone of the oceans, extending from about 200 to 1,000 m. *(p. 53)*

mesosphere a layer in the earth's atmosphere, extending from 64 to 80 km above the earth's surface; temperatures drop steeply with altitude in this atmospheric layer. *(p. 576)*

metabolic heat energy released within an organism during the process of cellular respiration. *(p. 127)*

metabolic water water released during oxidation of organic molecules. *(p. 155)*

meta-community a group of communities spread across a landscape that are linked through immigration and emigration of individuals and genes. *(p. 569)*

metalimnion a depth zone between the epilimnion and hypolimnion characterized by rapid decreases in temperature and increases in water density with depth. Often used synonymously with the term *thermocline*. *(p. 75)*

metapopulation a group of subpopulations living in separate locations with active exchange of individuals among subpopulations. *(p. 274)*

microbial symbiants intimate associations between microbes (e.g., bacteria) and hosts (e.g., plants) that often confer benefits to both partners. *(p. 182)*

microclimate a small-scale variation in climate caused by a distinctive substrate, location, or aspect. *(p. 117)*

microcosm small models of natural systems that allow experimental manipulation *(p. 376)*

microsatellite DNA sequence of randomly repetitive DNA, 10 to 100 base pairs long. *(p. 103)*

mineralization the breakdown of organic matter from organic to inorganic form during decomposition. *(p. 503)*

mixotroph species that are able to gain energy both from photosynthesis and from consuming organic or inorganic compounds. *(p. 185)*

moraine large piles of glacial till, typically formed along the edges of a glacier. *(p. 538)*

Müllerian mimicry comimicry among several species of noxious organisms. *(p. 374)*

mutualism interactions between individuals of different species that benefit both partners. *(p. 382)*

mycorrhizae a mutualistic association between fungi and the roots of plants. *(p. 382)*

N

natural history the description of how organisms in a particular area are influenced by factors such as climate, soils, predators, parasites, and competitors, involving field observations rather than carefully controlled experimentation or statistical analyses of patterns. *(p. 13)*

natural selection differential reproduction and survival of individuals in a population due to environmental influences on the population; proposed by Charles Darwin as the primary mechanism driving evolution. *(p. 89)*

neap tide tides occurring during the 1st and 3rd quarter phases of the moon, when tidal fluctuations are the smallest. *(p. 63)*

nectar robbers animals that visit flowers and remove nectar without providing pollination services *(p. 394)*

neritic zone a coastal zone of the oceans, extending to the margin of a continental shelf, where the ocean is about 200 m deep. *(p. 53)*

net primary production (NPP) the amount of energy left over after autotrophs have met their own energetic needs (gross primary production minus respiration by primary producers); the amount of energy available to the consumers in an ecosystem. (*p. 480*)

net reproductive rate (R_0)   the average number of offspring produced by an individual in a population. (*p. 295*)

niche   the environmental factors that influence the growth, survival, and reproduction of a species. (*p. 230*)

nitrification   the conversion of ammonia to nitrate, generally mediated by bacteria. (*p. 504*)

nitrogen use efficiency (NUE)   the magnitude of plant growth per unit nitrogen. (*p. 179*)

nonequilibrial theory   theories of ecological systems that do not assume equilibrial conditions. (*p. 69*)

nontarget effects   negative effects of a biocontrol agent on species other than the intended invasive target. (*p. 361*)

normal distribution   a bell-shaped distribution, proportioned so that predictable proportions of observations or measurements fall within one, two, or three standard deviations of the mean. (*p. 600*)

North Atlantic Oscillation (NAO)   an interannual fluctuation in atmospheric pressure between Iceland and the Azores off the coast of Portugal. Changes in the NAO are associated with altered climate and can have impacts on numerous plant and animal species. (*p. 578*)

Northern Hemisphere Annular Mode (NAM)   an interannual fluctuation in atmospheric pressure in the northern polar regions. The NAM is generally synchronized with the North Atlantic Oscillation. (*p. 578*)

nucleotide   the basic building blocks of nucleic acids, which are made up of a five-carbon sugar (deoxyribose or ribose), a phosphate group, and a nitrogenous base (guanine, cytosine, adenine, or thymine). (*p. 110*)

numerical response   change in the density of a predator population in response to increased prey density. (*p. 302*)

nunatak   a unique form of glacial refugia, in which a mountain peak was surrounded, but not covered by, continental glaciers. (*p. 539*)

nutrient   chemical substance required for the development, maintenance, and reproduction of organisms. (*p. 5*)

nutrient cycling   the use, transformation, movement, and reuse of nutrients in ecosystems. (*p. 502*)

nutrient retentiveness   the tendency of an ecosystem to retain nutrients. (*p. 512*)

nutrient spiralling   a representation of nutrient dynamics in streams, which, because of downstream displacement of organisms and materials, are better represented by a spiral than a cycle. (*p. 512*)

O

O (organic) horizon   the most superficial soil layer containing substantial amounts of organic matter, including whole leaves, twigs, other plant parts, and highly fragmented organic matter. (*p. 20*)

obligate mutualism   a mutualistic relationship in which species are so dependent upon the relationship that they cannot live in its absence. (*p. 382*)

oceanic zone   the open ocean beyond the continental shelf with water depths generally greater than 200 m. (*p. 53*)

oligotrophic   a term generally referring to lakes of low nutrient content, abundant oxygen, and low primary production. (*p. 77*)

omnivore   a heterotrophic organism that eats a wide range of food items, usually including both animal and plant matter. (*p. 185*)

optimal foraging theory   theory that attempts to model how organisms feed as an optimizing process, a process that maximizes or minimizes some quantity, such as energy intake or predation risk. (*p. 190*)

optimization   a process that maximizes or minimizes some quantity. (*p. 191*)

optimum sustainable yield (OSY)   the rate of harvest of a species which maximizes the difference between revenue and costs. (*p. 320*)

osmosis   diffusion of water down its concentration gradient. (*p. 150*)

overcompensation   increased plant growth following herbivory, compared to growth of plants that did not experience herbivory. (*p. 356*)

P

paleolimnology   the scientific discipline that uses the biological, chemical, and physical information archived in lake sediment profiles to track past environmental changes (*p. 82*)

parallel evolution   the independent evolution of similar traits in geographically separated species. (*p. 106*)

parapatric speciation   speciation that occurs when a population expands into a new habitat-type within the pre-existing range of the parent species. (*p. 105*)

parthenogenesis   the production of offspring by a female without fertilization of the egg. (*p. 246*)

patch   a relatively homogeneous area in a landscape that differs from its surroundings, for example, an area of forest surrounded by agricultural fields. (*p. 526*)

peat   partially decomposed organic matter that builds up in certain poorly drained wetland habitats. (*p. 79*)

pelagic   a term referring to marine life zones or organisms above the bottom; for instance, tuna are pelagic fish that live in the epipelagic zone of the oceans. (*p. 54*)

per capita rate of increase   usually symbolized as r, equals per capita birthrate minus per capita death rate: $r = b - d$. (*p. 297*)

permafrost   a permanently frozen layer of soil that remains frozen even during the summer months. (*p. 22*)

phenology   the study of the relationship between climate and the timing of ecological events such as the date of arrival of migratory birds on their wintering grounds, the timing of spring plankton blooms, or the onset and ending of leaf fall in a deciduous forest. (*p. 253*)

phenotypic plasticity   the ability to produce different phenotypes from a single genotype as a function of local conditions. (*p. 187*)

photic zone   the upper layers of an ocean or lake in which there is enough light to support photosynthesis. (*p. 55*)

photon flux density   the number of photons of light striking a square meter surface each second. (*p. 175*)

photorespiration   an energetically wasteful process in plants that occurs when O_2 binds to RUBISCO, leading to the release of CO_2 from the plant. (*p. 176*)

photosynthesis   process in which the photosynthetic pigments of plants, algae, or bacteria absorb light and transfer their energy to electrons; the energy carried by these electrons is used to synthesize ATP and NADPH, which in turn serve as donors of electrons and energy for the synthesis of sugars. (*p. 124*)

photosynthetic   a term describing organisms capable of photosynthesis. (*p. 174*)

photosynthetically active radiation (PAR)   wavelengths of light between 400 and 700 nm that photosynthetic organisms use as a source of energy. (*p. 175*)

phreatic zone   the region below the hyporheic zone of a stream; contains groundwater. (*p. 71*)

physiological ecology   The scientific study of how physiological limitations and adaptation influence the ability of organisms to cope with biotic and abiotic stress (*p. 2*)

phytophagous   plant-eating. (*p. 378*)

phytoplankton   microscopic photosynthetic organisms that drift with the currents in the open sea or in lakes. (*p. 55*)

pioneer community   the first community, in a successional sequence of communities, to be established following a disturbance. (*p. 454*)

pistil   female organ of a flower. (*p. 221*)

P_{max}   maximum rate of photosynthesis for a particular species of plant growing under ideal physical conditions. (*p. 187*)

poikilotherm   an organism whose body temperature varies directly with environmental temperatures; commonly called cold-blooded. (*p. 127*)

pollen vector   biotic or abiotic agents, such as wind and bees, that move pollen from an anther to a stigma. (*p. 392*)

polymorphic locus   a locus, or gene, that occurs as more than one allele, each of which synthesizes a different allozyme. (*p. 235*)

population   a group of individuals of a single species inhabiting a specific area. (*p. 261*)

population ecology   The scientific study of the structure and dynamics of populations (*p. 2*)

predator   a heterotrophic organism that kills and eats other organisms for food; usually an animal that hunts and kills other animals for food. (*p. 354*)

predator satiation   a defensive tactic in which prey reduce their individual probability of being eaten by occurring at very high densities; predators can only capture and eat so many prey and so become satiated when prey are at very high densities. (*p. 369*)

primary production   the fixation of energy by autotrophs in an ecosystem. (*p. 480*)

primary productivity a measure of plant growth rate, per unit area, per unit time. This is in contrast to standing biomass. *(p. 356)*

primary succession succession on newly exposed geological substrates, not significantly modified by organisms; for instance on newly formed volcanic lava or on substrate exposed during the retreat of a glacier. *(p. 455)*

principle of allocation the principle that if an organism allocates energy to one function, such as growth or reproduction, it reduces the amount of energy available to other functions, such as defense. *(p. 190)*

prokaryotes organisms with cells that have no membrane-bound nucleus or organelles. The prokaryotes include the bacteria and the archaea. *(p. 175)*

psychrophilic organisms that live and thrive at temperatures below 20°C. *(p. 125)*

R

radiation the transfer of heat through electromagnetic radiation, mainly infrared light. *(p. 127)*

random distribution a distribution in which individuals within a population have an equal chance of living anywhere within an area. *(p. 267)*

range of tolerance the entire set of conditions, such as air temperature or soil moisture, under which an organism is potentially able to survive. Levels outside of this range will be lethal. *(p. 121)*

range the difference between the largest and smallest values in a set of measurements or observations. *(p. 601)*

rank-abundance curve a curve that portrays the number of species in a community and their relative abundance; constructed by plotting the relative abundance of species against their rank in abundance. *(p. 413)*

rate of primary production the amount of energy fixed by the autotrophs in an ecosystem over some interval of time. *(p. 480)*

realized niche the actual niche of a species whose distribution is restricted by biotic interactions such as competition, predation, disease, and parasitism. *(p. 231)*

reciprocal altruism a mutually beneficial behaviour in which one individual helps another in expectation of a reciprocal behaviour. *(p. 206)*

regression a statistical procedure to determine whether a dependent variable is related to an independent variable. *(p. 603)*

regression coefficient the slope of a regression line. *(p. 604)*

regression line the line that best fits the relationship between two variables, X and Y. *(p. 604)*

regular distribution a distribution of individuals in a population in which individuals are uniformly spaced. *(p. 267)*

relative humidity a measure of the water content of air relative to its content at saturation; relative humidity = water vapour density/saturation water vapour density × 100. *(p. 149)*

relay floristics a model of succession in which species colonize a habitat in sequential waves. The first wave of colonizers is replaced by the second wave, and so on, until a climax community is established. *(p. 465)*

remote sensing gathering information about an object without direct contact with it, mainly by gathering and processing electromagnetic radiation emitted or reflected by the object; such measurements are typically made from remote sensing satellites. *(p. 570)*

reproductive effort the allocation of energy, time, and other resources to the production and care of offspring, generally including reduced allocation to other needs, such as maintenance and growth. *(p. 240)*

resilience the capacity to recover structure and function after disturbance; a highly resilient community or ecosystem may be completely disrupted by disturbance but quickly returns to its former state. *(p. 471)*

resistance the capacity of a community or ecosystem to maintain structure and/or function in the face of potential disturbance. *(p. 471)*

resource limitation limitation of population growth by resource availability. *(p. 331)*

restriction enzymes the enzymes produced by bacteria to cut up foreign DNA, used in DNA studies to cut DNA molecules at particular places called restriction sites. *(p. 110)*

restriction fragments the DNA fragments resulting from the cutting of a DNA molecule by a restriction enzyme. *(p. 110)*

restriction sites the particular locations where a restriction enzyme cuts a DNA molecule. *(p. 110)*

rhodopsin light-absorbing pigments found in the eyes of animals and in bacteria and archaea. *(p. 175)*

riparian vegetation vegetation growth along rivers or streams. *(p. 121)*

riparian zone the transition between the aquatic environment of a river or stream and the upland terrestrial environment, generally subject to periodic flooding and elevated groundwater table. *(p. 70)*

river continuum concept a model that predicts change in physical structure, dominant organisms, and ecosystem processes along the length of temperate rivers. *(p. 73)*

root exudates Organic compounds, such as amino acids, enzymes, and carbohydrates, that are secreted by plant roots into the surrounding soil. *(p. 20)*

ruderals plants or animals that live in highly disturbed habitats and that may depend on disturbance to persist in the face of potential competition from other species. *(p. 248)*

S

salinity the salt content of water. *(p. 55)*

salt marsh a marine shore ecosystem dominated by herbaceous vegetation, found mainly along sandy shores from temperate to high latitudes. *(p. 65)*

sample mean the average of a sample of measurements or observations; an estimate of the true population mean. *(p. 600)*

sample median the middle value in a series of measurements or observations, chosen so that there are equal numbers of measurements in the series that are larger than the median and smaller than the median. *(p. 601)*

saturation water vapour pressure the pressure exerted by the water vapour in air that is saturated with water vapour. *(p. 149)*

scatterhoarded a term applied to seeds gathered by mammals and stored in scattered caches or hoards. *(p. 238)*

secondary succession succession where disturbance has destroyed a community without destroying the soil; for instance, forest succession following a forest fire or logging. *(p. 455)*

sedimentation the deposition of suspended matter onto a surface, such as a lake bottom. *(p. 459)*

selection coefficient (s) the relative selection costs or benefits (decreased or increased fitness) associated with a particular biological trait. *(p. 401)*

self-incompatibility incapacity of a plant to fertilize itself; such plants must receive pollen from another plant to develop seeds. *(p. 221)*

self-thinning reduction in population density as a stand of plant increases in biomass, due to intraspecific competition. *(p. 337)*

self-thinning rule $\left(-\frac{3}{2}\right)$ a rule resulting from the observation that plotting the average weight of individual plants in a stand against density often produces a line with an average slope of approximately $-\frac{3}{2}$. *(p. 338)*

semelparity reproduction that involves production of all of an organism's offspring in one event, generally over a short period of time. *(p. 247)*

sex ratio the relative frequency of each sex type in a population. *(p. 294)*

sexual selection results from differences in reproductive rates among individuals as a result of differences in mating success due to intrasexual selection, intersexual selection, or a mixture of the two forms of sexual selection. *(p. 215)*

sigmoidal population growth curve an S-shaped pattern of population growth, with population size levelling off at the carrying capacity of the environment. *(p. 315)*

size-selective predation prey selection by predators based on prey size. *(p. 184)*

small-scale phenomena phenomena that take place on a local scale. *(p. 266)*

sociality group living generally involving some degree of cooperation between individuals. *(p. 206)*

soil the upper layer of the earth's land surface, consisting of organic matter and minerals. *(p. 20)*

solifluction the slow movement of tundra soils down slopes as a result of annual freezing and thawing of surface soil and the actions of water and gravity. *(p. 23)*

Southern Oscillation an oscillation in atmospheric pressure that extends across the Pacific Ocean. *(p. 578)*

spate sudden flooding in a stream. *(p. 303)*

specialist a predator or herbivore that regularly feeds upon a single, or very few, prey species. *(p. 378)*

species composition the species that occur in a given community. *(p. 418)*

species diversity a measure of diversity that increases with species evenness and species richness. *(p. 411)*

species evenness the relative abundance of species in a community or collection. *(p. 411)*

species richness   the number of species in a community or collection. *(p. 411)*

species turnover   changes in species composition on islands resulting from some species becoming extinct and others immigrating. *(p. 555)*

spiralling length   the length of stream required for an atom of a nutrient to complete a cycle from release into the water column to re-entry into the benthic ecosystem. *(p. 512)*

spring tide   tides occurring during new and full moons, when tidal fluctuations are greatest. *(p. 63)*

stability   the persistence of a community or ecosystem in the face of disturbance, usually as a consequence of a combination of resistance and resilience. *(p. 471)*

stabilizing selection   a form of natural selection that acts against extreme phenotypes; can act to impede changes in populations. *(p. 96)*

stable age distribution   a population in which the proportion of individuals in each age class is constant. *(p. 295)*

stable isotope analysis   analysis of the relative concentrations of stable isotopes, such as ^{13}C and ^{12}C, in materials; used in ecology to study the flow of energy and materials through ecosystems. *(p. 169)*

stamen   male organ of a flower. *(p. 221)*

standard deviation   the square root of the variance. *(p. 602)*

standard error   an estimate of variation among means of samples drawn from a population. *(p. 602)*

standing biomass   the amount of plant biomass found at a given location at a single point in time. This is in contrast to primary productivity. *(p. 356)*

static life table   a life table constructed by recording the age at death of a large number of individuals; the table is called static because the method involves a snapshot of survival within a population during a short interval of time. *(p. 288)*

stratosphere   a layer of earth's atmosphere that extends from about 16 km to an altitude of about 50 km. *(p. 576)*

stream order   a numerical classification of streams by where they occur in a stream drainage network. Headwater streams are first-order streams, joining of two first-order streams forms a second-order stream, joining of two second-order streams forms a third-order stream, and so forth. *(p. 71)*

stress   any strong negative environmental condition that induces physiological responses in an organism or alters the structure of functioning of an ecosystem. *(p. 248)*

Suess effect   reduced concentration of ^{14}C in the atmosphere as a result of fossil fuel burning. *(p. 593)*

succession   the gradual change in plant and animal communities in an area following disturbance or the creation of new substrate. *(p. 454)*

survivorship curve   a graphical summary of patterns of survival in a population. *(p. 289)*

sympatric speciation   speciation that occurs when isolation mechanisms evolve among populations with overlapping geographic ranges. *(p. 105)*

T

taiga   northern forests that occupy the area south of arctic tundra. Though dominated by coniferous trees they also contain aspen and birch. Also called boreal forest. *(p. 23)*

talus   rock piles pushed aside and left behind by glaciers. *(p. 538)*

temperate forest   deciduous or coniferous forests generally found between 40° and 50° of latitude, where annual precipitation averages anywhere from about 650 mm to over 3,000 mm; this biome receives more winter precipitation than temperate grasslands. *(p. 25)*

temperate grassland   grasslands growing in middle latitudes that receive between 300 and 1,000 mm of annual precipitation, with maximum precipitation usually falling during the summer months. *(p. 27)*

thermal neutral zone   the range of environmental temperatures over which the metabolic rate of a homeothermic animal does not change. *(p. 132)*

thermocline   a depth zone in a lake or ocean through which temperature changes rapidly with depth, generally about 1°C per meter of depth. *(p. 54)*

thermophilic   a term applied to organisms that tolerate or require high-temperature environments. *(p. 126)*

thermosphere   the outer layer of the earth's atmosphere beginning approximately 80 km above the earth's surface. *(p. 576)*

till   unsorted materials, such as clay, rocks, and boulders, left behind by glaciers. *(p. 538)*

tolerance model   a model of succession in which initial stages of colonization are not limited to a few pioneer species, juveniles of species dominating at climax can be present from the earliest stages of succession, and species colonizing early in succession do not facilitate colonization by species characteristic of later successional stages. Later successional species are simply those tolerant of environmental conditions early in succession. *(p. 466)*

top-down control   the control or influence of consumers on ecosystem processes. *(p. 486)*

torpor   a state of low metabolic rate and lowered body temperature. *(p. 141)*

trophic (feeding) biology   the study of the feeding biology of organisms. *(p. 174)*

trophic dynamics   the transfer of energy from one part of an ecosystem to another. *(p. 494)*

trophic level   trophic position in an ecosystem; for instance primary producer, primary consumer, secondary consumer, tertiary consumer, and so forth. *(p. 480)*

tropical dry forest   a broadleaf deciduous forest growing in tropical regions having pronounced wet and dry seasons; trees drop their leaves during the dry season. *(p. 36)*

tropical rain forest   a broadleaf evergreen forest growing in tropical regions where conditions are warm and wet year-round. *(p. 38)*

tropical savanna   a tropical grassland dotted with scattered trees; characterized by pronounced wet and dry seasons and periodic fires. *(p. 34)*

troposphere   a layer of the atmosphere extending from the earth's surface to an altitude of 9 to 16 km. *(p. 576)*

tundra   a northern biome dominated by mosses, lichens, and dwarf willows, receiving low to moderate precipitation and having a very short growing season. *(p. 21)*

type I survivorship curve   a pattern of survivorship in which there are high rates of survival among young and middle-aged individuals followed by high rates of mortality among the aged. *(p. 291)*

type II survivorship curve   a pattern of survivorship characterized by constant rates of survival throughout life. *(p. 291)*

type III survivorship curve   a pattern of survivorship in which a period of extremely high rates of mortality among the young is followed by a relatively high rate of survival. *(p. 291)*

U

upwelling   movement of deeper ocean water to the surface; occurs most commonly along the west coasts of continents and around Antarctica. *(p. 55)*

V

vapour pressure deficit (VPD)   the difference between the actual water vapour pressure and the saturation water vapour pressure at a particular temperature. *(p. 150)*

variance   a measure of variation in a population or a sample from a population. *(p. 601)*

vesicle   storage organ in vesicular-arbuscular mycorrhizal fungi. *(p. 394)*

W

Walker circulation   a large-scale atmospheric circulation system that moves in the plane of the equator. *(p. 579)*

water potential   the capacity of water to do work, which is determined by its free energy content; water flows from positions of higher to lower free energy. Increasing solute concentration decreases water potential. *(p. 151)*

water vapour pressure   the atmospheric pressure exerted by the water vapour in air; increases as the water vapour in air increases. *(p. 149)*

weed   a species that a person does not want in a certain location at a certain point in time. *(p. 347)*

Z

zonation of species   pattern of separation of species into distinctive vertical habitats or zones. *(p. 65)*

zooplankton   animals that drift in the surface waters of the oceans or lakes; most zooplankton are microscopic. *(p. 55)*

Adams, P. A. and J. E. Heath. 1964. Temperature regulation in the sphinx moth, *Celerio lineata*. *Nature* 201:20–22.

Addicott, J. F. 1986. Variation in the costs and benefits of mutualism: the interaction between yuccas and yucca moths. *Oecologia* 70:486–94.

Addicott, J. F. 1996. Cheaters in yucca/moth mutualism. *Nature* 380(6570):114–15.

Aerts, R. 2006. The freezer defrosting: global warming and litter decomposition rates in cold biomes. *Journal of Ecology* 94:713–24.

Agrawal, A. A. and P. M. Kotanen. 2003. Herbivores and the success of exotic plants: a phylogenetically controlled experiment. *Ecology Letters* 6(8):712–15.

Allen, E. B. and M. F. Allen. 1986. Water relations of xeric grasses in the field: interactions of mycorrhizae and competition. *New Phytologist* 104:559–71.

Anderson, J. M. and M. J. Swift. 1983. Decomposition in tropical forests. In S. L. Sutton, T. C. Whitmore, and A. C. Chadwick. eds. *Tropical Rain Forest: Ecology and Management*. Oxford: Blackwell Scientific Publications.

Anderson, R. M. and R. M. May. 1979. Population biology of infectious-diseases. 1. *Nature* 280(5721):361–67.

Angilletta, M. J., Jr. 2001. Thermal and physiological constraints on energy assimilation in a widespread lizard (*Sceloporus undulatus*). *Ecology* 82:3044–56.

Apps, C. D., N. J. Newhouse, and T. A. Kinley. 2002. Habitat associations of American badgers in southeastern British Columbia. *Canadian Journal of Zoology-Revue Canadienne De Zoologie* 80(7):1228–39.

Arcese, P. 1987. Age, intrusion pressure and defence against floaters by territorial male song sparrows. *Animal Behaviour* 35:773–84.

Arnemo, J. M., P. Ahlqvist, R. Andersen, F. Berntsen, G. Ericsson, J. Odden, S. Brunberg, P. Segerstrom and J. E. Swenson. 2006. Risk of capture-related mortality in large free-ranging mammals: experiences from Scandinavia. *Wildlife Biology* 12:109–13.

Arnqvist, G. and L. Rowe. 2002. Antagonistic coevolution between the sexes in a group of insects. *Nature* 415(6873):787–89.

Arrhenius, O. 1921. Species and area. *Journal of Ecology* 9:95–99.

Ashman, T. L. and D. J. Schoen. 1994. How long should flowers live. *Nature* 371(6500):788–91.

Ashman, T. L. and D. J. Schoen. 1997. The cost of floral longevity

in *Clarkia tembloriensis*: An experimental investigation. *Evolutionary Ecology* 11(3):289–300.

Atlegrim, O. 1989. Exclusion of birds from bilberry stands: impact on insect larval density and damage to the bilberry. *Oecologia* 79:136–39.

Bacastow, R. and C. D. Keeling. 1974. Atmospheric carbon dioxide and radiocarbon in the natural carbon cycle: II. Changes from AD 1700 to 2070 as deduced from a geochemical model. In G. M. Woodwell and E. V. Pecan. eds. *Carbon and the Biosphere*. BHNL/CONF 720510. Springfield, Va.: National Technical Information Service.

Bailey, N, T. J. 1952. Improvements in the interpretation of recapture data. *Journal of Animal Ecology* 21:120–27.

Bailey, N. T. J. 1951. On estimating the size of mobile populations from recapture data. *Biometrika* 38:293–306.

Baker, C. S., J. M. Straley, and A. Perry. 1992. Population characteristics of individually identified humpback whales in southeastern Alaska: summer and fall 1986. *Fishery Bulletin* 90:429–37.

Baker, M. C., L. R. Mewaldt, and R. M. Stewart. 1981. Demography of white-crowned sparrows (*Zonotrichia leucophrys nuttalli*). *Ecology* 62:636–44

Baldwin, J. and P. W. Hochachka. 1970. Functional significance of isoenzymes in thermal acclimation: acetylcholinesterase from trout brain. *Biochemical Journal* 116:883–87.

Balvanera P., A. B. Pfisterer, N. Buchmann, J. S. He, T. Nakashizuka, D. Raffaelli, and B. Schmid. 2006. Quantifying the evidence for biodiversity effects on ecosystem functioning and services. *Ecology Letters* 9:1146–56.

Barbour, C. D. and J. H. Brown. 1974. Fish species diversity in lakes. *American Naturalist* 108:473–89.

Barnes, R. S. K. and R. N. Hughes. 1988. *An Introduction to Marine Ecology*. Oxford: Blackwell Scientific Publications.

Barnola, J. M., D. Raynaud, Y. S. Korotkevich, and C. Lorius. 1987. Vostok ice core provides 160,000-year record of atmospheric CO_2. *Nature* 329:408–14.

Barrie, L. A. and 24 others. 1997. *Canadian Arctic Contaminant Assessment Report*. Ottawa, Canada: Department of Indian and Northern Affairs.

Baur, B. and A. Baur. 1993. Climatic warming due to thermal radiation from an urban area as possible cause for the local extinction of a land snail. *Journal of Applied Ecology* 30:333–40.

Béjà, O., E. N. Spudich, J. L. Spudich, M. Leclerc, and E. F. Delong. 2001.

Proteorhodopsin phototrophy in the ocean. *Nature* 411 :786–89.

Béjà, O., L. Aravind, E. V. Koonin, M. T. Suzuki, A. Hadd, L. P. Nguyen, S. B. Jovanovich, C. M. Gates, R. A. Feldman, J. L. Spudich, E. N. Spudich, and E. F. Delong. 2000. Bacterial rhodopsin: evidence for a new type of phototrophy in the sea. *Science* 289:1902–06.

Béjà, O., M. T. Suzuki, J. F. Heidelberg, W. C. Nelson, C. M. Preston, T. Hamada, J. A. Eisen, C. M. Fraser, and E. F. Delong. 2002. Unsuspected diversity among marine aerobic anoxygenic phototrophs. *Nature* 415:630–33.

Bell, G., M. J. Lechowicz, and M. J. Waterway. 2000. Environmental heterogeneity and species diversity of forest sedges. *Journal of Ecology* 88(1):67–87.

Bennett, K. D. 1983. Postglacial population expansion of forest trees in Norfolk, UK. *Nature* 303:164–67.

Ben-Shahar, Y., A. Robichon, M. B. Sokolowski, and G. E. Robinson. (2002). Influence of gene action across different time scales on behavior. *Science* 296(5568):741–44.

Bergeron, Y. 2000. Species and stand dynamics in the mixed woods of Quebec's southern boreal forest. *Ecology* 81(6):1500–16.

Berry, J. and O. Bjorkman. 1980. Photosynthetic response and adaptation to temperature in higher plants. *Annual Review of Plant Physiology* 31:491–543.

Berteaux, D., D. Reale, A. G. McAdam, and S. Boutin. 2004. Keeping pace with fast climate change: Can arctic life count on evolution? *Integrative and Comparative Biology* 44(2):140–51.

Bertschy, K. A. and M. G. Fox. 1999. The influence of age-specific survivorship on pumpkinseed sunfish life histories. *Ecology* 80:2299–313.

Bird R.D. 1930 Biotic communities of the Aspen parkland of central Canada. *Ecology* 11:356–442.

Bjerknes, J. 1966. A possible response of the atmospheric Hadley circulation to equatorial anomalies of ocean temperature. *Tellus* 18:820–29.

Bjerknes, J. 1969. Atmospheric teleconnections from the equatorial Pacific. *Monthly Weather Review* 97:163–72.

Blais, J. M., D. W. Schindler, D. C. G. Muir, L. E. Kimpe, D. B. Donald, and B. Rosenberg. 1998. Accumulation of persistent organochlorine compounds in mountains of western Canada. *Nature* 395:685–88.

Bloch, N. and D. J. Irschick. 2005. Toe-clipping dramatically reduces clinging performance in a pad-bearing

lizard (*Anolis carolinensis*). *Journal of Herpetology* 39:288–93.

Bloom, A. J., F. S. Chapin III, and H. A. Mooney. 1985. Resource limitation in plants—an economic analogy. *Annual Review of Ecology and Systematics* 16:363–92.

Boag, P. T. and P. R. Grant. 1978. Heritability of external morphology in Darwin's finches. *Nature* 274:793–94.

Boag, P. T. and P. R. Grant. 1984a. Darwin's finches on Isla Daphne Major, Galápagos: breeding and feeding ecology in a climatically variable environment. *Ecological Monographs* 54:463–89.

Boag, P. T. and P. R. Grant. 1984b. The classical case of character release: Darwin's finches (*Geospiza*) on Isla Daphne Major, Galápagos. *Biological Journal of the Linnean Society* 22:243–87.

Bogdanov, L. V. and N. G. Gagal'chii. 1986. Intraspecific variation in the Asian ladybug *Harmonia axyridis* Pall. near Vladivostok. *Soviet Journal of Ecology* 17:108–113.

Bolduc, E., C. M. Buddle, N. J. Bostanian, and C. Vincent. 2005. Ground-dwelling spider fauna (Araneae) of two vineyards in southern Quebec. *Environmental Entomology* 34(3):635–45.

Bollinger, G. 1909. *Zur Gastropodenfauna von Basel und Umgebung*. Ph.D. dissertation. University of Basel, Switzerland.

Bond, P. and P. Goldblatt. 1984. Plants of the Cape Flora. *Journal of South African Botany*. Supplementary Volume No. 13.

Bonner, J. T. 1965. *Size and Cycle: An Essay on the Structure of Biology*. Princeton, N.J.: Princeton University Press.

Bormann, F. H. and G. E. Likens. 1981. *Pattern and Process in a Forested Ecosystem*. New York: Springer-Verlag.

Bormann, F. H. and G. E. Likens. 1994. *Pattern and Process in a Forested Ecosystem*. New York: Springer-Verlag.

Bowen, G. W. and R. L. Burgess. 1981. A quantitative analysis of forest island pattern in selected Ohio landscapes. ORNL/TM 7759. Oak Ridge National Laboratory, Oak Ridge, Tenn.

Boyce, M. S. and L. L. McDonald. (1999). Relating populations to habitats using resource selection functions. *Trends in Ecology & Evolution* 14(7):268–72.

Braune, B. M., P. M. Outridge, A. T. Fisk, D. C. G. Muir, P. A. Helm, K. Hobbs, P. F. Hoekstra, Z. A. Kuzyk, M. Kwan, R. J. Letcher, W. L. Lockhart, R. J. Norstrom, G. A. Stern, and I. Stirling. 2005. Persistent organic pollutants and mercury in marine biota of the Canadian Arctic: An overview of spatial and temporal trends. *Science of the Total Environment* 351:4–56.

Briggs, J. C. 1974. *Marine Zoogeography.* New York: McGraw-Hill.

Brisson, J. and J. F. Reynolds. 1994. The effects of neighbors on root distribution in a creosote bush (*Larrea tridentata*) population. *Ecology* 75:1693–702.

Brock, T. D. 1978. *Thermophilic Microorganisms and Life at High Temperatures.* New York: Springer-Verlag.

Brown, G. P. and P. J. Weatherhead. 1999. Demography and sexual size dimorphism in northern water snakes, *Nerodia sipedon. Canadian Journal of Zoology* 77:1358–66.

Brown, J. H. 1984. On the relationship between abundance and distribution of species. *American Naturalist* 130:255–79.

Brown, J. H. 1986. Two decades of interaction between the MacArthur-Wilson model and the complexities of mammalian distributions. *Biological Journal of the Linnean Society* 28:231–51.

Brown, J. H. 1988. Species diversity. In A. A. Meyers and P. S. Giller. eds. *Analytical Biogeography.* London: Chapman and Hall.

Brown, J. H. and A. Kodric-Brown. 1977. Turnover rates in insular biogeography: effects of immigration on extinction. *Ecology* 58:445–49.

Brown, J. H. and J. C. Munger. 1985. Experimental manipulation of a desert rodent community: food addition and species removal. *Ecology* 66:1545–63.

Brown, J. H. and M. V. Lomolino. 2000. Concluding remarks: historical perspective and the future of island biogeography theory. *Global Ecology and Biogeography* 9:87–92.

Brown, J. H., D. W. Mehlman, and G. C. Stevens. 1995. Spatial variation in abundance. *Ecology* 76:2028–43.

Brown, W. L. and E. O. Wilson. 1956. Character displacement. *Systematic Zoology* 5:49–64.

Bshary, R. 2003. The cleaner wrasse, *Labroides dimidiatus*, is a key organism for reef fish diversity at Ras Mohammed National Park, Egypt. *Journal of Animal Ecology* 72:169–72.

Bush, M. B. and P. A. Colinvaux. 1994. Tropical forest disturbance: paleoecological records from Darien, Panama. *Ecology* 75:1761–68.

Bush, M. B., D. R. Piperno, and P. A. Colinvaux. 1989. A 6,000 year history of Amazonian maize cultivation. *Nature* 340:303–5.

Caddy, J. F. 1999. Fisheries management in the twenty-first century: will new paradigms apply? *Reviews in Fish Biology and Fisheries* 9(1):1–43.

Cahill, J. F., J. P. Castelli, and B. B. Casper. 2001. The herbivory uncertainty principle: visiting plants can alter herbivory. *Ecology* 82:307–12.

Calow, P. and G. E. Petts. 1992. *The Rivers Handbook.* London: Blackwell Scientific Publications.

Canada. Environment Canada. Canadian Wildlife Service. Minister's Round Table under the *Species At Risk Act.* 2006. *Conserving Wildlife Species and Recovering Species at Risk in Canada.*

Canada. Natural Resources Canada. 2007. http://www.nrcan.gc.ca/selfor/2_com_tra/new/index_e.php.

Canada. Species At Risk Act Public Registry. 2007. The Act. http://www.sararegistry.gc.ca/the_act/HTML/Part1_e.cfm.

Cardillo, M., A. Purvis, W. Sechrest, J. L. Gittleman, J. Bielby, and G. M. Mace. 2004. Human population density and extinction risk in the world's carnivores. *Plos Biology* 2(7):909–14.

Carey, F. G. 1973. Fishes with warm bodies. *Scientific American.* 228:36–44.

Cargill, S. M. and R. L. Jefferies. 1984. The effects of grazing by lesser snow geese on the vegetation of a sub-arctic salt-marsh. *Journal of Applied Ecology* 21(2):669–86.

Carpenter, F. L., M. A. Hixon, C. A. Beuchat, R. W. Russell, and D. C. Patton. 1993. Biphasic mass gain in migrant hummingbirds: body composition changes, torpor, and ecological significance. *Ecology* 74:1173–82.

Carpenter, S. R. and J. F. Kitchell. 1988. Consumer control of lake productivity. *BioScience* 38:764–69.

Carpenter, S. R. and J. F. Kitchell. 1993. *The Trophic Cascade in Lakes.* Cambridge. England: Cambridge University Press.

Carpenter, S. R., J. F. Kitchell, and J. R. Hodgson. 1985. Cascading trophic interactions and lake productivity. *BioScience* 35:634–39.

Carpenter, S. R., T. M. Frost, J. F. Kitchell, T. K. Kratz, D. W. Schindler, J. Shearer, W. G. Sprules, M. J. Vanni, and A. P. Zimmerman. 1991. Patterns of primary production and herbivory in 25 North American lake ecosystems. In J. Cole. G. Lovett. and S. F. Findlay. eds. *Comparative Analyses of Ecosystems: Patterns, Mechanisms, and Theories.* New York: Springer-Verlag.

Carroll, S. P. and C. Boyd. 1992. Host race radiation in the soapberry bug: natural history with the history. *Evolution* 46:1052–69.

Carroll, S. P., H. Dingle, and S. P. Klassen. 1997. Genetic differentiation of fitness-associated traits among rapidly evolving populations of the soapberry bug. *Evolution* 51:1182–88.

Carroll, S. P., S. P. Klassen, and H. Dingle. 1998. Rapidly evolving adaptations to host ecology and nutrition in the soapberry bug. *Evolutionary Ecology* 12:955–68.

Carruthers, R. I., T. S. Larkin, H. Firstencel, and Z. Feng. 1992. Influence of thermal ecology on the mycosis of a rangeland grasshopper. *Ecology* 73:190–204.

Case, T. J. 1976. Body size differences between populations of the chuckwalla, *Sauromalus obesus. Ecology* 57:313–23.

Caughley, G. 1977. *Analysis of Vertebrate Populations.* New York: John Wiley & Sons.

Caughley, G., J. Short, G. C. Grigg, and H. Nix. 1987. Kangaroos and climate: an analysis of distribution. *Journal of Animal Ecology* 56:751–61.

Central Intelligence Agency. 2007. *The World Factbook.* https://www.cia.gov/library/publications/the-world-factbook/index.html.

Chapin, F. S., III, L. R. Walker, C. L. Fastie, and L. C. Sharman. 1994. Mechanisms of primary succession following deglaciation at Glacier Bay, Alaska. *Ecological Monographs* 64:149–75.

Chapman, V. J. 1977. *Wet Coastal Ecosystems.* Amsterdam: Elsevier Scientific Publishing.

Charnov, E. L. 1973. *Optimal Foraging: Some Theoretical Explorations.* Ph.D. Dissertation. University of Washington. Seattle.

Charnov, E. L. 2002. Reproductive effort, offspring size and benefit-cost ratios in the classification of life histories. *Evolutionary Ecology Research* 4:1–10.

Charnov, E. L., J. Maynard Smith, and J. J. Bull. 1976. Why be a hermaphrodite? *Nature* 263:125–26.

Chetkiewicz, C. L. B., C. C. S. Clair, and M. S. Boyce. 2006. "Corridors for conservation: Integrating pattern and process." *Annual Review of Ecology Evolution and Systematics* 37:317–42.

Chiariello, N. R., C. B. Field, and H.A. Mooney. 1987. Midday wilting in a tropical pioneer tree. *Functional Ecology* 1:3–11.

Christian, C. E. 2001. Consequences of a biological invasion reveal the importance of mutualism for plant communities. *Nature* 413:635–39.

Christian, J. M. and S. D. Wilson. 1999. Long-term ecosystem impacts of an introduced grass in the northern Great Plains. *Ecology* 80:2397–3007.

Clausen, J., D. D. Keck, and W. M. Hiesey. 1940. *Experimental Studies on the Nature of Species. I. The Effect of Varied Environments on Western North American Plants.* Washington. D.C.: Carnegie Institution of Washington. Publication no. 520.

Clements, F. E. 1916. *Plant Succession: An Analysis of the Development of Vegetation.* Washington, D.C.: Carnegie Institution of Washington. Publication 242.

Clements, F. E. 1936. Nature and structure of the climax. *Journal of Ecology* 24:252–84.

Clevenger, A. P. and N. Waltho. 2005. Performance indices to identify attributes of highway crossing structures facilitating movement of large mammals. *Biological Conservation* 121(3): 453–464.

Colautti, R. I., S. A. Bailey, C. D. A. van Overdijk, K. Amundsen, and H. J. MacIsaac. 2006. Characterised and projected costs of nonindigenous species in Canada. *Biological Invasions* 8(1):45–59.

Coltman, D. W., P. O'Donoghue, J. T. Jorgenson, J. T. Hogg, C. Strobeck, and M. Festa-Bianchet. 2003. Undesirable evolutionary consequences of trophy hunting. *Nature* 426:655–58.

Connell, J. H. 1961a. The effects of competition. predation by *Thais lapillus* and other factors on natural populations of the barnacle, *Balanus balanoides. Ecological Monographs* 31:61–104.

Connell, J. H. 1961b. The influence of interspecific competition and other factors on the distribution of the barnacle *Chthamalus stellatus. Ecology* 42:710–23.

Connell, J. H. 1975. Some mechanisms producing structure in natural communities: a model and evidence from field experiments. In M. L. Cody and J. Diamond. eds. *Ecology and Evolution of Communities.* Cambridge. Mass.: Harvard University Press.

Connell, J. H. 1978. Diversity in tropical rain forests and coral reefs. *Science* 199:1302–10.

Connell, J. H. 1980. Diversity and the coevolution of competitors, or the ghost of competition past. *Oikos* 35:131–38.

Connell, J. H. 1983. On the prevalence and relative importance of interspecific competition: evidence from field experiments. *American Naturalist* 122:661–96.

Connell, J. H. and R. O. Slatyer. 1977. Mechanisms of succession in natural communities and their role in community stability and organization. *The American Naturalist* 111:1119–44.

Cooper, P. D. 1982. Water balance and osmoregulation in a free-ranging tenebrionid beetle, *Onymacris unguicularis*, of the Namib Desert. *Journal of Insect Physiology* 28:737–42.

Coppock, D. L., J. K. Delling, J. E. Ellis, and M. I. Dyer. 1983. Plant herbivore interactions in a North American mixed-grass prairie. 1. effects of black-tailed prairie dogs on intraseasonal aboveground plant biomass and nutrient dynamics and plant species diversity. *Oecologia* 56:1–9.

COSEWIC. 2006. *Canadian Species at Risk.* Committee on the Status of Endangered Wildlife in Canada.

Côte, S. D., T. P. Rooney, J. P. Tremblay, C. Dussault, and D. M. Waller. 2004. Ecological impacts of deer overabundance. *Annual Review of Ecology Evolution and Systematics* 35:113–47.

Coupland, R. T. and R. E. Johnson. 1965. Rooting characteristics of native grassland species in Saskatchewan. *Journal of Ecology* 53:475–507.

Cox, G. W. and R. E. Ricklefs. 1977. Species diversity, ecological release, and community structure in Caribbean landbird faunas. *Oikos* 29:60–66.

Culp, J. M. and G. J. Scrimgeour. 1993. Size dependent diel foraging periodicity of a mayfly grazer in streams with and without fish. *Oikos* 68:242–50.

Curtis, J. T. 1956. The modification of mid-latitude grasslands and forests by man. In W. L. Thomas. Jr. ed. *Man's Role in Changing the Face of the Earth.* Chicago: University of Chicago Press.

Damuth, J. 1981. Population density and body size in mammals. *Nature* 290:699–700.

Darwin, C. 1839. *Journal of Researches into the Geology and Natural History of the Various Countries Visited During the Voyage of H.M.S. 'Beagle' Under the Command of Captain FitzRoy, R.N., From 1832–1836.* London: Henry Colborn.

Darwin, C. 1842. *The Structure and Distribution of Coral Reefs.* London:

Smith. Elder and Company. Reprinted by the University of California Press. Berkeley. 1962.

Darwin, C. 1859. *The Origin of Species by Means of Natural Selection, or the Preservation of Favored Races in the Struggle for Life.* New York: Modern Library.

Darwin, C. 1862. On the two forms. or dimorphic condition. in the species of *Primula*, and on their remarkable sexual relations. In P. H. Barrett. ed. *The Collected Papers of Charles Darwin.* Chicago: University of Chicago Press.

Darwin, C. 1871. *The Descent of Man, and Selection in Relation to Sex.* London: John Murray.

Davis, M. B. 1981. Quaternary history and the stability of forest communities. In D. C. West, H. H. Shugart, and D. B. Botkin. eds. *Forest Succession: Concepts and Application.* New York: Springer-Verlag.

Davis, M. B. 1983. Quaternary history of deciduous forests of eastern North America and Europe. *Annals of the Missouri Botanical Garden* 70:550–63.

Davis, M. B. 1989. Retrospective studies. In G. E. Likens. ed. *Long-Term Studies in Ecology.* New York: Springer-Verlag.

Dawson, T. E., S. Mambelli, A. H. Plamboeck, P. H. Templer, and K. P. Tu. 2002. Stable isotopes in plant ecology. *Annual Review of Ecology and Systematics* 33:507–99.

Deevey, E. S. 1947. Life tables for natural populations of animals. *Quarterly Review of Biology* 22:283–314.

Demeester, L. 1993. Genotype, fish-mediated chemicals, and phototactic behavior in daphnia-magna. *Ecology* 74(5):1467–74.

Dempson, J. B., M. F. O'Connell, and N. M. Cochrane. 2001. Potential impact of climate warming on recreational fishing opportunities for Atlantic salmon, *Salmo salar* L., in Newfoundland, Canada. *Fisheries Management and Ecology* 8:69–82.

Denno, R. F. and G. K. Roderick. 1992. Density-related dispersal in planthoppers: effects of interspecific crowding. *Ecology* 73:1323–34.

Derocher, A. E., H. Wolkers, T. Colborn, M. Schlabach, T. S. Larsen, and O. Wiig. 2003. Contaminants in Svalbard polar bear samples archived since 1967 and possible population level effects. *Science of the Total Environment* 301(1-3):163–74.

Dewailly, E. A., J. P. Nantel, J. P. Weber, and F. Meyer. 1989. High levels of PCBs in breast milk of Inuit women from Arctic Quebec. *Bulletin of Environmental Contamination and Toxicology* 43:641–46.

Diamond, J. M. 1969. Avifaunal equilibria and species turnover rates on the Channel Islands of California. *Proceedings of the National Academy of Sciences* 64:57–63.

Diamond, J. M. 1984. "Normal" extinctions of isolated populations. In N.H. Nitecki. *Extinctions.* Chicago, Chicago University Press.

Diaz, H. F. and G. N. Kiladis. 1992. Atmospheric teleconnections associated with the extreme phases of the Southern Oscillation. In

H. F. Diaz and V. Markgraf. eds. *El Niño Historical and Paleoclimatic Aspects of the Southern Oscillation.* Cambridge. England: Cambridge University Press.

Diffendorfer, J. E., M. S. Gaines, and R. D. Holt. 1995. Habitat fragmentation and movements of three small mammals (*Sigmodon, Microtus*, and *Peromyscus*). *Ecology* 76:827–39.

Dillon, P. J. and F. H. Rigler. 1974. The phosphorus–chlorophyll relationship in lakes. *Limnology and Oceanography* 19:767–73.

Dillon, P. J. and F. H. Rigler. 1975. A simple method for predicting the capacity of a lake for development based on lake trophic status. *Journal of the Fisheries Research Board of Canada* 32:1519–31.

Dirzo, R. and A. Miranda. 1990. Contemporary neotropical defaunation and forest structure, function, and diversity—a sequel to John Terborgh. *Conservation Biology* 4:444–47.

Dobzhansky, T. 1937. *Genetics and the Origin of Species.* New York: Columbia University Press.

Dobzhansky, T. 1950. Evolution in the tropics. *American Scientist* 38:209–21.

Dodd, M., J. Silvertown, K. McConway, J. Potts, and M. Crawley. 1995. Community stability: a 60-year record of trends and outbreaks in the occurrence of species in the Park Grass Experiment. *Journal of Ecology* 83:277–85.

DOE. 2000. The Human Genome Project Information. http://www.ornl.gov/TechResources/Human_Genome/home.html.

Donkor, N. T. and J. M. Fryxell. 1999. Impact of beaver foraging on structure of lowland boreal forests of Algonquin Provincial Park, Ontario. *Forest Ecology and Management,* 118:83–92.

Donlan, J. et al. 2005. Re-wilding North America. *Nature* 436(7053):913–14.

Drew, M. C. 1975. Comparison of effects of a localized supply of phosphate, nitrate, ammonium and potassium on growth of seminal root system, and shoot, in barley. *New Phytologist* 75(3):479–90.

Dubois, F. D. and L. A. Giraldeau. 2005. Fighting for resources: The economics of defense and appropriation. *Ecology* 86(1):3–11.

Dyer, S. J., J. P. O'Neill, S. M. Wasel, and S. Boutin. 2002. Quantifying barrier effects of roads and seismic lines on movements of female woodland caribou in northeastern Alberta. *Canadian Journal of Zoology-Revue Canadienne De Zoologie* 80(5):839–45.

Edney, E. B. 1953. The temperature of woodlice in the sun. *Journal of Experimental Biology* 30:331–49.

Egler, F. E. 1954. Vegetation science concepts I. Initial floristic composition. A factor in old-field vegetation development. *Vegetatio* 4:412–17.

Ehleringer, J. R. 1980. Leaf morphology and reflectance in relation to water and temperature stress. In N. C. Turner and P. J. Kramer. eds. *Adaptations of Plants to Water and High*

Temperature Stress. New York: Wiley-Interscience.

Ehleringer, J. R. and C. Clark. 1988. Evolution and adaptation in *Encelia* (Asteraceae). In L. D. Gottlieb and S. K. Jain. eds. *Plant Evolutionary Biology.* London: Chapman and Hall.

Ehleringer, J. R., J. Roden, and T. E. Dawson. 2000. Assessing ecosystem-level water relations through stable isotope ratio analyses. In O. E. Sala. R. B. Jackson, H. A. Mooney. and R. W. Howarth. eds. *Methods in Ecosystem Science.* New York: Springer.

Ehleringer, J. R., S. L. Phillips, W. S. F. Schuster, and D. R. Sandquist. 1991. Differential utilization of summer rains by desert plants. *Oecologia* 88:430–34.

Elton, C. 1924. Periodic fluctuations in the numbers of animals: their causes and effects. *British Journal of Experimental Biology* 2:119–63.

Elton, C. 1927. *Animal Ecology.* London: Sidgewick & Jackson.

Endler, J. A. 1980. Natural selection on color patterns in *Poecilia reticulata. Evolution* 34:76–91.

Endler, J. A. 1995. Multiple-trait coevolution and environmental gradients in guppies. *Trends in Ecology & Evolution* 10:22-29.

Evans, M. S., D. Muir, W. L. Lockhart, G. Stern, M. Ryan, and P. Roach. 2005. Persistent organic pollutants and metals in the freshwater biota of the Canadian Subarctic and Arctic: An overview. *Science of the Total Environment* 351:94–147.

F. A. O. 1972. *Atlas of the Living Resources of the Sea.* 3d ed. Rome: F. A. O.

Fahrig, L. 1997. Relative effects of habitat loss and fragmentation on population extinction. *Journal of Wildlife Management* 61(3):603–10.

Fahrig, L. 2003. Effects of habitat fragmentation on biodiversity. *Annual Review of Ecology Evolution and Systematics* 34:487–515.

Fahrig, L. 2005. When is a landscape perspective important? In J. A. Wiens and M. R. Moss, eds. *Issues and Perspective in Landscape Ecology.* Cambridge, Cambridge University Press.

Feldman, G., D. Clark, and D. Halpern. 1984. Satellite color observations of the phytoplankton distribution in the eastern equatorial Pacific during the 1982–1983 El Niño. *Science* 226:1069–71.

Findlay, D. L. and S. E. M. Kasian. 1987. Phytoplankton community responses to nutrient addition in Lake 226, Experimental Lakes Area, northwestern Ontario. *Canadian Journal of Fisheries and Aquatic Sciences* 44(Suppl. 1):35–46.

Fisher, R. A. 1930. *The genetical theory of natural selection.* Oxford, Clarendon Press.

Fisher, S. G., L. J. Gray, N. B. Grimm, and D. E. Busch. 1982. Temporal succession in a desert stream ecosystem following flash flooding. *Ecological Monographs* 52:93–110.

Fitter, A. and R. K. M. Hay. 1987. *Environmental Physiology of Plants.* London: Academic Press.

Flessa, K. W. 1975. Area, continental drift and mammalian diversity. *Paleobiology* 1:189–94.

Flessa, K. W. 1981. The regulation of mammalian faunal similarity among continents. *Journal of Biogeography* 8:427–38.

Foley, J. A., R. DeFries, G. P. Asner, C. Barford, G. Bonan, S. R. Carpenter, F. S. Chapin, M. T. Coe, G. C. Daily, H. K. Gibbs, J. H. Helkowski, T. Holloway, E. A. Howard, C. J. Kucharik, C. Monfreda, J. A. Patz, I. C. Prentice, N. Ramankutty, and P. K. Snyder. 2005. Global consequences of land use. *Science* 309(5734):570–74.

Forbes, S. A. 1887. The lake as a microcosm. *Bulletin of the Peoria Scientific Association.* Reprinted in the Bulletin of the Illinois State Natural History Survey 15 (1925):537–50.

Forel, F. A. 1892. *Le Léman: Monograhie limnologique.* Tome I, Géographie, Hydrographie, Géologie, Climatologie, Hydrologie. Lausanne, F. Rouge. Reprinted Genève, Slatkine Reprints, 1969.

Forman, R. T. T. and L. E. Alexander. 1998. Roads and their major ecological effects. *Annual Review of Ecology and Systematics* 29:207–31.

Fortin, M. J., R. J. Olson, S. Ferson, L. Iverson, C. Hunsaker, G. Edwards, D. Levine, K. Butera, and V. Klemas. 2000. Issues related to the detection of boundaries. *Landscape Ecology,* 15:453–66.

Fortin, M. J., T. H. Keitt, B. A. Maurer, M. L. Taper, D. M. Kaufmann, and T. M. Blackburn. 2005. Species' geographic ranges and distributional limits: pattern analysis and statistical issues. *Oikos*, 108:7–17.

Frank, P. W., C. D. Boll, and R. W. Kelly. 1957. Vital statistics of laboratory cultures of *Daphnia pulex* De Geer as related to density. *Physiological Zoology* 30:287–305.

Frankham, R. and K. Ralls. 1998. Inbreeding leads to extinction. *Nature* 392:441–42.

Friedli, H., H. Lotscher, H. Oeschger, U. Siegenthaler, and B. Stauffer. 1986. Ice core record of the $^{13}C/^{12}C$ ratio of atmospheric CO_2 in the past two centuries. *Nature* 324:237–38.

Friedmann, H. 1955. The honey-guides. *Bulletin of the United States National Museum* 208:1–292.

Fu, C. H., R. Mohn, and L. P. Fanning. 2001. Why the Atlantic cod (*Gadus morhua* stock off eastern Nova Scotia has not recovered. *Canadian Journal of Fisheries and Aquatic Sciences* 58(8):1613–23.

Funk, D. J., P. Nosil, and W. J. Etges. 2006. Ecological divergence exhibits consistently positive associations with reproductive isolation across disparate taxa. *Proceedings of the National Academy of Sciences of the United States of America* 103(9):3209–13.

Gallardo, A. and J. Merino. 1993. Leaf decomposition in two Mediterranean ecosystems of southwest Spain: influence of substrate quality. *Ecology* 74:152–61.

Gamberg, M., B. Braune, E. Davey, B. Elkin, P. F. Hoekstra, D. Kennedy,

C. Macdonald, D. Muir, A. Nirwal, M. Wayland, and B. Zeeb. 2005. Spatial and temporal trends of contaminants in terrestrial biota from the Canadian Arctic. *Science of the Total Environment* 351:148–64.

Gaston, K. J. 1996. The multiple forms of the interspecific abundance-distribution relationship. *Oikos* 76:211–20.

Gaston, K. J., T. M. Blackburn, J. J. D. Greenwood, R. D. Gregory, R. M. Quinn, and J.H. Lawton. 2000. Abundance-occupancy relationships. *Journal of Applied Ecology* 37:39–59.

Gaudet, C. L. and P. A. Keddy. 1988. A comparative approach to predicted competitive ability from plant traits. *Nature* 334:242–43.

Gause, G. F. 1934. *The Struggle for Existence*. Baltimore: Williams & Wilkins. Reprinted by Hafner Publishing Company. New York. 1969.

Gause, G. F. 1935. Experimental demonstration of Volterra's periodic oscillation in the numbers of animals. *Journal of Experimental Biology* 12:44–48.

Gauslaa, Y. 1984. Heat resistance and energy budget in different Scandinavian plants. *Holarctic Ecology* 7:1–78.

Gauthier-Clerc, M., J. P. Gendner, C. A. Ribic, W. R. Fraser, E. J. Woehler, S. Descamps, C. Gilly, C. Le Bohec, and Y. Le Maho. 2004. Long-term effects of flipper bands on penguins. *Proceedings of the Royal Society of London Series B-Biological Sciences* 271:S423–26.

Gedney, N., P. M. Cox, R. A. Betts, O. Boucher, C. Huntingford, and P. A. Stott. 2006. Detection of a direct carbon dioxide effect in continental river runoff records. *Nature* 439(7078):835–38.

Gersani, M., J. S. Brown, E. E. O'Brien, G. M. Maina, and Z. Abramsky. 2001. Tragedy of the commons as a result of root competition. *Journal of Ecology* 89(4):660–69.

Getzin, S., C. Dean, F. L. He, J. A. Trofymow, K. Wiegand, and T. Wiegand. 2006. Spatial patterns and competition of tree species in a Douglas-fir chronosequence on Vancouver Island. *Ecography* 29(5):671–82.

Gibbs, H. L. and P. R. Grant. 1987. Ecological consequences of an exceptionally strong El Niño event on Darwin's finches. *Ecology* 68:1735–46.

Gibbs, R. J. 1970. Mechanisms controlling world water chemistry. *Science* 170: 1088–90.

Gillson, L. and K. J. Willis. 2004. As Earth's testimonies tell: wilderness conservation in a changing world. *Ecology Letters* 7(10):990–98.

Gjerdrum, C., A. M. J. Vallee, C. C. St Clair, D. F. Bertram, J. L. Ryder, and G. S. Blackburn. 2003. Tufted puffin reproduction reveals ocean climate variability. *Proceedings of the National Academy of Sciences of the United States of America* 100(16):9377–82.

Gleason, H. A. 1926. The individualistic concept of the plant association. *Torrey Botanical Club Bulletin* 53:7–26.

Gleason, H. A. 1939. The individualistic concept of the plant association. *American Midland Naturalist* 21:92–110.

Gobeil, J. F. and M. A. Villard. 2002. Permeability of three boreal forest landscape types to bird movements as determined from experimental translocations. *Oikos* 98(3):447–58.

Gosz, J. R., R. T. Holmes, G. E. Likens, and F. H. Bormann. 1978. The flow of energy in a forest ecosystem. *Scientific American* 238(3):92–102.

Graham, W. F. and R. A. Duce. 1979. Atmospheric pathways of the phosphorus cycle. *Geochimica et Cosmochimica Acta* 43:1195–1208.

Granéli, E., K. Wallström, U. Larsson, W. Granéli, and R. Elmgren. 1990. Nutrient limitation of primary production in the Baltic Sea area. *Ambio* 19: 142–51.

Grant, B. R. and P. R. Grant. 1989. *Evolutionary Dynamics of a Natural Population*. Chicago: University of Chicago Press.

Grant, P. R. 1986. *Ecology and Evolution of Darwin's Finches*. Princeton. N.J.: Princeton University Press.

Grassle, J. F. 1973. Variety in coral reef communities. In O. A. Jones and R. Endean. eds. *Biology and Geology of Coral Reefs*. Vol. 2. New York: Academic Press.

Grassle, J. F. 1991. Deep-sea benthic biodiversity. *BioScience* 41(7):464–69.

Grime, J. P. 1973. Competition and diversity in herbaceous vegetation. *Nature* 244:311.

Grime, J. P. 1977. Evidence for the existence of three primary strategies in plants and its relevance to ecological and evolutionary theory. *American Naturalist* 111:1169–94.

Grime, J. P. 1979. *Plant Strategies and Vegetation Processes*. New York: John Wiley & Sons.

Grimm, N. B. 1987. Nitrogen dynamics during succession in a desert stream. *Ecology* 68:1157–70.

Grimm, N. B. 1988. Role of macroinvertebrates in nitrogen dynamics of a desert stream. *Ecology* 69: 1884-93.

Grinnell, J. 1917. The niche-relationships of the California Thrasher. *Auk* 34:427–33.

Grinnell, J. 1924. Geography and evolution. *Ecology* 5:225–29.

Gross, J. E., L. A. Shipley, N. T. Hobbs, D. E. Spalinger, and B. A. Wunder. 1993. Functional response of herbivores in food-concentrated patches: tests of a mechanistic model. *Ecology* 74:778–91.

Grutter, A. S. 1999. Cleaner fish really do clean. *Nature* 398:672–73.

Guénette, J. S. and M. A. Villard. 2005. Thresholds in forest bird response to habitat alteration as quantitative targets for conservation. *Conservation Biology* 19(4):1168–80.

Gumel, A. B., S. G. Ruan, T. Day, J. Watmough, F. Brauer, P. van den Driessche, D. Gabrielson, C. Bowman, M. E. Alexander, S. Ardal, J. H. Wu, and B. M. Sahai. 2004. Modelling strategies for controlling SARS outbreaks. *Proceedings of the Royal Society of London Series B-Biological Sciences* 271(1554):2223–32.

Gunderson, D. R. 1997. Trade-off between reproductive effort and adult survival in oviparous and viviparous fishes. *Canadian Journal of Fisheries and Aquatic Sciences* 54:990–98.

Gurevitch, J., L. L. Morrow, A. Wallace, and J. S. Walsh. 1992. A meta-analysis of competition in field experiments. *American Naturalist* 140:539–72.

Hadley, N. F. and T. D. Schultz. 1987. Water loss in three species of tiger beetles (*Cicindela*): correlations with epicuticular hydrocarbons. *Journal of Insect Physiology* 33:677–82.

Hamilton, W. D. 1964. The genetical evolution of social behaviour, I and II. *Journal of Theoretical Biology* 7:1–52.

Handford, P., G. Bell, and T. Reimchen. 1977. A gillnet fishery considered as an experiment in artificial selection. *Journal of Fisheries Research Board of Canada* 34:954–61.

Hanski, I. 1982. Dynamics of regional distribution: the core and satellite hypothesis. *Oikos* 38:210–21.

Hanski, I., M. Kuussaari, and M. Nieminen. 1994. Metapopulation structure and migration in the butterfly *Melitaea cinxia*. *Ecology* 75:747–62.

Hardie, K. 1985. The effect of removal of extraradical hyphae on water uptake by vesicular-arbuscular mycorrhizal plants. *New Phytologist* 101:677–84.

Hardin, G. 1960. The competitive exclusion principle. *Science* 131:1292–97.

Hardy, G. H. 1908. Mendelian proportions in a mixed population. *Science* 28:49–50.

Harper, J. L., P. H. Lovell, and K. G. Moore. 1970. The shapes and sizes of seeds. *Annual Review of Ecology and Systematics* 1:327–56.

Haukioja, E., K. Kapiainen, P. Niemelä, and J. Tuomi. 1983. Plant availability hypothesis and other explanations of herbivore cycles: complementary or exclusive alternatives? *Oikos* 40:419–32.

Hawkes, C. V. and J. J. Sullivan. 2001. The impact of herbivory on plants in different resource conditions: A meta-analysis. *Ecology* 82(7):2045–58.

Heath, J. E. and P. J. Wilkin. 1970. Temperature responses of the desert cicada, *Diceroprocta apache* (Homoptera, Cicadidae). *Physiological Zoology* 43:145–54.

Hebert, P. D. N., A. Cywinska, S. L. Ball, and J. R. DeWaard. 2003. Biological identifications through DNA barcodes. *Proceedings of the Royal Society of London Series B-Biological Sciences* 270(1512):313–21.

Hedin, L. O., P. M. Vitousek, and P. A. Matson. 2003. Nutrient losses over four million years of tropical forest development. *Ecology* 84:2231–55.

Hegazy, A. K. 1990. Population ecology and implications for conservation of *Cleome droserifolia*: a threatened xerophyte. *Journal of Arid Environments* 19:269–82.

Heinrich, B. 1979. *Bumblebee Economics*. Cambridge, Mass.: Harvard University Press.

Heinrich, B. 1984. Strategies of thermoregulation and foraging in two vespid wasps, *Dolichovespula maculata* and *Vespula vulgaris*. *Journal of Comparative Physiology* B154:175–80.

Heinrich, B. 1993. *The Hot-Blooded Insects*. Cambridge, Mass.: Harvard University Press.

Heisenberg, W. 1927. Über den anschaulichen Inhalt der quantentheoretischen Kinematik und Mechanik, *Zeitschrift für Physik*, 43:172–98. English translation: J. A. Wheeler and H. Zurek. 1983. *Quantum Theory and Measurement*. Princeton Univ. Press, 62–84.

Hengeveld, R. 1988. Mechanisms of biological invasions. *Journal of Biogeography* 15:819–28.

Heske, E. J., J. H. Brown, and S. Mistry. 1994. Long-term experimental study of a Chihuahuan Desert rodent community: 13 years of competition. *Ecology* 75:438–45.

Hik, D. S. and R. L. Jefferies. 1990. Increases in the net aboveground primary production of a salt-marsh forage grass—a test of the predictions of the herbivore-optimization model. *Journal of Ecology* 78(1):180–95.

Hillis, D. M., B. K. Mable, A. Larson, S. K. Davis, and E. A. Zimmer. 1996. Nucleic acids IV: sequencing and cloning. In D. M. Hillis, C. Moritz, and B. K. Mable. eds. *Molecular Systematics*. Sunderland, Mass.: Sinauer Associates, Inc.

Hobbie, S. E., J. P. Schimel, S. E. Trumbore, and J. R. Randerson. 2000. Controls over carbon storage and turnover in high-latitude soils. *Global Change Biology* 6:196–210.

Hobbs, R. J. and L. F. Huenneke. 1992. Disturbance, diversity, and invasion—implications for conservations. *Conservation Biology* 6(3):324–37.

Hogetsu, K. and S. Ichimura. 1954. Studies on the biological production of Lake Suwa. 6. The ecological studies in the production of phytoplankton. *Japanese Journal of Botany* 14:280–303.

Hölldobler, B. and E. O. Wilson. 1990. *The Ants*. Cambridge, Mass.: The Belknap Press of Harvard University Press.

Holling, C. S. 1959. The components of predation as revealed by a study of small mammal predation of the European pine sawfly. *The Canadian Entomologist* 91:293–320.

Houde, A. E. 1997. *Sex, Color, and Mate Choice in Guppies*. Princeton, N.J.: Princeton University Press.

Houghton, J. 2001. The science of global warming. *Interdisciplinary Science Reviews* 26(4):247–57.

Howe, W. H. and F. L. Knopf. 1991. On the imminent decline of the Rio Grande cottonwoods in central New Mexico. *Southwestern Naturalist* 36:218–24.

Huang, H. T. and P. Yang. 1987. The ancient cultured citrus ant. *BioScience* 37:665–67.

Hudson, P. J., A. P. Dobson, and D. Newborn. 1992. Do parasites make prey vulnerable to predation? *Journal of Animal Ecology* 61:681–92.

Huffaker, C. B. 1958. Experimental studies on predation: dispersion factors and predator-prey oscillations. *Hilgardia* 27:343–83.

Hughes, T. P. 1996. Demographic approaches to community dynamics: a coral reef example. *Ecology* 77:2256–60.

Hulshoff, R. M. 1995. Landscape indices describing a Dutch landscape. *Landscape Ecology* 10:101–11.

Huntly, N. and R. Inouye. 1988. Pocket gophers in ecosystems: patterns and mechanisms. *BioScience* 38:786–93.

Hurrell, J. W. 1996. Influence of variations in extratropical wintertime teleconnections on Northern Hemisphere temperature. *Geophysical Research Letters* 23(6):665–68.

Huston, M. 1994b. *Biological Diversity*. New York: Cambridge University Press.

Hutchings, J. A. 1996. Spatial and temporal variation in the density of northern cod and a review of hypotheses for the stock's collapse. *Canadian Journal of Fisheries and Aquatic Sciences* 53(5):943–62.

Hutchinson, G. E. 1957. Concluding remarks. *Cold Spring Symposia on Quantitative Biology* 22:415–27.

Hutchinson, G. E. 1959. Homage to Santa Rosalia or why are there so many kinds of animals? *American Naturalist* 93:145–59.

Hutchinson, G. E. 1961. The paradox of the plankton. *American Naturalist* 95:137–45.

Hutchinson, G. E. 1978. *An Introduction to Population Ecology*. New Haven, Conn.: Yale University Press.

Ichimura, S. 1956. On the standing crop and productive structure of phytoplankton community in some lakes of central Japan. *Japanese Botany Magazine Tokyo* 69:7–16.

Innes, D. J. and P. D. N. Hebert. 1988. The origin and genetic-basis of obligate parthenogenesis in *daphnia-pulex*. *Evolution* 42(5):1024–35.

Innes, D. J. and R. L. Dunbrack. 1993. Sex allocation variation in *Daphnia-pulex*. *Journal of Evolutionary Biology* 6(4):559–75.

Iriarte, J. A., W. L. Franklin, W. E. Johnson, and K. H. Redford. 1990. Biogeographic variation of food habits and body size of the American puma. *Oecologia* 85:185–90.

Isack, H. A. and H.-V. Reyer. 1989. Honeyguides and honey gatherers: interspecific communication in a symbiotic relationship. *Science* 243:1343–46.

Ishii, K. and K. Marumo. 2002. Microbial diversity in hydrothermal systems and their influence on geological environments. *Resource Geology* 52:135–46.

Jaenike, J. 1991. Mass extinction of European fungi. *TREE* 6:174–75.

Jakobsson, A. and O. Eriksson. 2000. A comparative study of seed number, seed size, seedling size and recruitment in grassland plants. *Oikos* 88:494–502.

Janzen, D. H. 1966. Coevolution of mutualism between ants and acacias in Central America. *Evolution* 20:249–75.

Janzen, D. H. 1967. Why mountain passes are higher in the tropics. *American Naturalist* 101:233–49.

Janzen, D. H. 1967a. Fire, vegetation structure, and the ant x acacia

interaction in Central America. *Ecology* 48:26–35.

Janzen, D. H. 1967b. Interaction of the bull's-horn acacia (*Acacia cornigera* L.) with an ant inhabitant (*Pseudomyrmex ferruginea* F. Smith) in eastern Mexico. *The University of Kansas Science Bulletin* 47:315–558.

Janzen, D. H. 1978. Seeding patterns of tropical trees. In P. B. Tomlinson and M. H. Zimmermann. eds. *Tropical Trees as Living Systems*. Cambridge, England: Cambridge University Press.

Janzen, D. H. 1981. The peak in North American ichneumonid species richness lies between 38° and 42°. *Ecology* 62:532–37.

Janzen, D. H. 1981a. Guanacaste tree seed-swallowing by Costa Rican range horses. *Ecology* 62:587–92.

Janzen, D. H. 1981b. *Enterolobium cyclocarpum* seed passage rate and survival in horses, Costa Rican Pleistocene seed dispersal agents. *Ecology* 62:593–601.

Janzen, D. H. 1985. Natural history of mutualisms. In D. H. Boucher. ed. *The Biology of Mutualism: Ecology and Evolution*. London: Croom Helm.

Jarvis, J. U. M. 1981. Eusociality in a mammal: cooperative breeding in naked mole-rat colonies. *Science* 212:571–73.

Jenny, H. 1980. *The Soil Resource*. New York: Springer Verlag.

Johnson, N. C. 1993. Can fertilization of soil select less mutualistic mycorrhizae. *Ecological Applications* 3:749–57.

Jones, C. G., J. H. Lawton, and M. Shachak. 1994. Organisms as Ecosystem Engineers. *Oikos* 69:373–86.

Jonsen, I. D. and P. D. Taylor. 2000. Fine-scale movement behaviors of calopterygid damselflies are influenced by landscape structure: an experimental manipulation. *Oikos* 88(3):553–62.

Jordan, C. F. 1985. Soils of the Amazon rain forest. In G. T. Prance and T. E. Lovejoy. eds. *Amazonia*. Oxford: Pergamon Press.

Kairiukstis, L. A. 1967. In J. L. Tselniker (ed.) Svetovoi rezhim fotosintez i produktiwnost lesa. (Light regime, photosynthesis and forest productivity) Nauka, Moscow.

Kallio, P. and L. Karenlampi. 1975. Photosynthesis in mosses and lichens. In J. P. Cooper. ed. *Photosynthesis and Productivity in Different Environments*. Cambridge, England: Cambridge University Press.

Kalmar, A. and D. J. Currie. 2006. A global model of island biogeography. *Global Ecology and Biogeography* 15(1):72–81.

Karlson, R. H., H. V. Cornell, and T. P. Hughes. 2004. Coral communities are regionally enriched along an oceanic biodiversity gradient. *Nature* 429(6994):867–70.

Kaser, S. A. and J. Hastings. 1981. Thermal physiology of the cicada, *Tibicen duryi*. *American Zoologist* 21:1016.

Katona, S. K. 1989. Getting to know you. *Oceanus* 32:37–44.

Keddy, P. A. and B. Shipley. 1989. Competitive Hierarchies In

Herbaceous Plant-Communities. *Oikos* 54:234–41.

Keeler, K. H. 1981. A model of selection for facultative nonsymbiotic mutualism. *American Naturalist* 118:488–98.

Keeler, K. H. 1985. Benefit models of mutualism. In D. H. Boucher. ed. *The Biology of Mutualism: Ecology and Evolution*. London: Croom Helm.

Keeling, C. D. and T. P. Whorf. 1994. Atmospheric CO_2 records from sites in the SIO air sampling network. In T. A. Boden, D. P. Kaiser, R. J. Sepanski, and F. W. Stoss. eds. *Trends '93: A Compendium of Data on Global Change*. ORNL/CDIAC-65, Oak Ridge, Tenn.: Carbon Dioxide Information Analysis Center, Oak Ridge National Laboratory.

Keith, L. B. 1963. *Wildlife's Ten-year Cycle*. Madison, Wis.: University of Wisconsin Press.

Keith, L. B. 1983. Role of food in hare population cycles. *Oikos* 40:385–95.

Keith, L. B., J. R. Cary, O. J. Rongstad, and M. C. Brittingham. 1984. Demography and ecology of a declining snowshoe hare population. *Wildlife Monographs* 90:1–43.

Kembel, S. K. and J. F. Cahill, Jr. 2005. Plant phenotypic plasticity belowground: a phylogenetic perspective on root foraging tradeoffs. *American Naturalist* 166:216–30.

Kerr, J. T. 1997. Species richness, endemism, and the choice of areas for conservation. *Conservation Biology* 11(5):1094–100.

Kevan, P. G. 1975. Sun-tracking solar furnaces in high arctic flowers: significance for pollination and insects. *Science* 189:723–26.

Kidron, G. J., E. Barzilay, and E. Sachs. 2000. Microclimate control upon sand microbiotic crusts, western Negev Desert, Israel. *Geomorphology* 36:1–18.

Killingbeck, K. T. and W. G. Whitford. 1996. High foliar nitrogen in desert shrubs: an important ecosystem trait or defective desert doctrine? *Ecology* 77:1728–37.

Klemmedson, J. O. 1975. Nitrogen and carbon regimes in an ecosystem of young dense ponderosa pine in Arizona. *Forest Science* 21:163–68.

Klironomos, J. N. 2003. Variation in plant response to native and exotic arbuscular mycorrhizal fungi. *Ecology* 84(9): 2292–2301.

Klironomos, J. N. and M. M. Hart. 2001. Food-web dynamics—Animal nitrogen swap for plant carbon. *Nature* 410(6829):651–52.

Kloppers, E. L., C. C. St. Clair, and T. E. Hurd. 2005. Predator-resembling aversive conditioning for managing habituated wildlife. *Ecology and Society* 10(1):31. http://www.ecology andsociety.org/vol10/iss1/art31/.

Knutson, R. M. 1974. Heat production and temperature regulation in eastern skunk cabbage. *Science* 186:746–47.

Knutson, R. M. 1979. Plants in heat. *Natural History* 88:42–47.

Köchy, M. and S. D. Wilson. 2001. Nitrogen deposition and forest expansion in the northern Great Plains. *Journal of Ecology* 89(5):807–17.

Kodric-Brown, A. 1993. Female choice of multiple male criteria in guppies: interacting effects of dominance, coloration and courtship. *Behavioral Ecology and Sociobiology* 32:415–20.

Koh, L. P., R. R. Dunn, N. S. Sodhi, R. K. Colwell, H. C. Proctor, and V. S. Smith. 2004. Species coextinctions and the biodiversity crisis. *Science* 305(5690):1632–34.

Kolber, Z. S., C. L. Van Dover, R. A. Niederman, and P. G. Falkowski. 2000. Bacterial photosynthesis in surface waters of the open ocean. *Nature* 407:177–79.

Komai, T. and Y. Hosino. 1951. Contributions to the evolutionary genetics of the lady-beetle, *Harmonia*. II Microgeographic variations. *Genetics* 36:382–390.

Korpimäki, E. 1988. Factors promoting polygyny in European birds of prey— a hypothesis. *Oecologia* 77:278–85.

Korpimäki, E. and K. Norrdahl. 1991. Numerical and functional responses of kestrels, short-eared owls, and long-eared owls to vole densities. *Ecology* 72:814–26.

Kotanen, P. M. and R. L. Jefferies. 1997. Long-term destruction of sub-arctic wetland vegetation by lesser snow geese. *Ecoscience* 4(2):179–82.

Krawchuk, M. A., S. G. Cumming, M. D. Flannigan, and R. W. Wein. 2006. Biotic and abiotic regulation of lightning fire initiation in the mixedwood boreal forest. *Ecology* 87(2):458–68.

Krebs, C. J. 2006. Ecology after 100 years: Progress and pseudo-progress. *New Zealand Journal of Ecology* 30(1):3–11.

Krebs, C. J., R. Boonstra, S. Boutin, and A. R. E. Sinclair. 2001. What drives the 10-year cycle of snowshoe hares? *BioScience* 51:25–36.

Krebs, C. J., S. Boutin, R. Boonstra, A. R. E. Sinclair, J. N. M. Smith, M. R. T. Dale, K. Martin, and R. Turkington. 1995. Impact of food and predation on the snowshoe hare cycle. *Science* 269:1112–15.

Krebs, C.J., S. Boutin, and R. Boonstra (eds.). 2001. *Ecosystem Dynamics of the Boreal Forest: The Kluane Project*. Oxford, Oxford University Press.

Kubien, D. S., S. von Cammerer, R. T. Furbank, and R. F. Sage. 2003. C-4 photosynthesis at low temperature. A study using transgenic plants with reduced amounts of Rubisco. *Plant Physiology* 132(3):1577–85.

Laird, R. A. and B. S. Schamp. 2006. Competitive intransitivity promotes species coexistence. *American Naturalist* 168:182–93.

Lamb, E. G., A. U. Mallik, and R. W. Mackereth. 2003. The early impact of adjacent clearcutting and forest fire on riparian zone vegetation in northwestern Ontario. *Forest Ecology and Management* 177(1–3):529–38.

Lamberti, G. A. and V. H. Resh. 1983. Stream periphyton and insect herbivores: an experimental study of grazing by a caddisfly population. *Ecology* 64:1124–35.

Landhausser, S. M. and V. J. Lieffers. 2001. Photosynthesis and carbon allocation of six boreal tree species grown in understory and open conditions. *Tree Physiology* 21(4):243–50.

Larcher, W. 1995. *Physiological Plant Ecology*. 3d ed. Berlin: Springer.

Latham, R. E. and R. E. Ricklefs. 1993. Continental comparisons of temperate-zone tree species diversity. In R. E. Ricklefs and D. Schluter. eds. *Species Diversity in Ecological Communities*. Chicago: University of Chicago Press.

Lebo, M. E., J. E. Reuter, C. R. Goldman, C. L. Rhodes, N. Vucinich, and D. Mosely. 1993, Spatial variations in nutrient and particulate matter concentrations in Pyramid Lake. Nevada. USA, during a dry period. *Canadian Journal of Fisheries and Aquatic Science* 50:1045–54.

Lechowicz, M. J. and G. Bell. 1991. The ecology and genetics of fitness in forest plants .2. Microspatial heterogeneity of the edaphic environment. *Journal of Ecology* 79(3):687–96.

Ledig, F. T., V. Jacob-Cervantes, P. D. Hodgskiss, and T. Eguiluz-Piedra. 1997. Recent evolution and divergence among populations of a rare Mexican endemic, Chihuahua spruce, following Holocene climatic warming. *Evolution* 51:1815–27.

Leibold, M. A. and J. Norberg. 2004. Biodiversity in metacommunities: Plankton as complex adaptive systems? *Limnology and Oceanography* 49(4):1278–89.

Lemon, W. C. 1993. Heritability of selectively advantageous foraging behavior in a small passerine. *Evolutionary Ecology* 7(4):421–28.

Levang-Brilz, N. and M. E. Biondini. 2002. Growth rate, root development and nutrient uptake of 55 plant species from the Great Plains Grasslands, USA. *Plant Ecology* 165: 117-44.

Leverich, W. J.and D.A. Levin. 1979. Age-specific survivorship and reproduction in *Phlox drummondii*. *American Naturalist* 113:881–903.

Lie, E., H. J. S. Larsen, S. Larsen, G. M. Johansen, A. E. Derocher, N. J. Lunn, R. J. Norstrom, O. Wiig, and J. U. Skaare. 2005. Does high organochlorine (OC) exposure impair the resistance to infection in polar bears (*Ursus maritimus*)? Part II: Possible effect of OCs on mitogen- and antigen-induced lymphocyte proliferation. *Journal of Toxicology and Environmental Health-Part a-Current Issues* 68(6):457–84.

Lie, E., H. J. S. Larsen, S. Larsen, G. M. Johnsen, A. E. Derocher, N. J. Lunn, R. J. Norstrom, O. Wiig, and J. U. Skaare. 2004. Does high organochlorine (OC) exposure impair the resistance to infection in polar bears (*Ursus maritimus*)? Part 1: effect of OCs on the humoral immunity. *Journal of Toxicology and Environmental Health-Part a-Current Issues* 67(7):555–82.

Liebig, J. 1840. *Chemistry in its Application to Agriculture and Physiology*. London: Taylor and Walton.

Ligon, D. 1999. *The Evolution of Avian Mating Systems*. Oxford: Oxford University Press.

Likens, G. E. and F. H. Bormann. 1995. *Biogeochemistry of a Forested Ecosystem*. 2d ed. New York: Springer-Verlag.

Likens, G. E., F. H. Bormann, N. M. Johnson, D. W. Fisher, and R. S. Pierce. 1970. Effects of forest cutting and herbicide treatment on nutrient budgets in the Hubbard Brook watershed-ecosystem. *Ecological Monographs* 40:23–47.

Likens, G. E., F. H. Bormann, R. S. Pierce, and W. A. Reiners. 1978. Recovery of a deforested ecosystem. Science 199:492–96.

Lindeman, R. L. 1942. The trophic-dynamic aspect of ecology. *Ecology* 23:399–418.

Liu J., J. M. Chen, J. Cihlar, and W. Chen W. 2002. Net primary productivity mapped for Canada at 1-km resolution. *Global Ecology and Biogeography* 11:115–29.

Lomolino, M. V. 1990. The target hypothesis—the influence of island area on immigration rates of non-volant mammals. *Oikos* 57:297–300.

Lomolino, M. V., J. H. Brown, and R. Davis. 1989. Island biogeography of montane forest mammals in the American Southwest. *Ecology* 70:180–94.

Long, S. P. and C. F. Mason. 1983. *Saltmarsh Ecology*. Glasgow: Blackie.

Lorius, C., J. Jouzel, C. Ritz, L. Merlivat, N.I. Barkov, Y. S. Korotkevich, and V. M. Kotlyakov. 1985. A 150,000-year climatic record from antarctic ice. *Nature* 316:591–96.

Lotka, A. J. 1925. *Elements of Physical Biology*. Baltimore, Md.: Williams and Wilkins.

Lotka, A. J. 1932a. Contribution to the mathematical theory of capture. I. Conditions for capture. *Proceedings of the National Academy of Science* 18:172–200.

Lotka, A. J. 1932b. The growth of mixed populations: two species competing for a common food supply. *Journal of the Washington Academy of Sciences* 22:461–69.

Louda, S. M., R. W. Pemberton, M. T. Johnson, and P. A. Follett. 2003. Nontarget effects—The Achilles' Heel of biological control? Retrospective analyses to reduce risk associated with biocontrol introductions. *Annual Review of Entomology* 48:365–96.

MacArthur, R. H. 1958. Population ecology of some warblers of northeastern coniferous forests. *Ecology* 39:599–619.

MacArthur, R. H. 1972. *Geographical Ecology*. New York: Harper & Row.

MacArthur, R. H. and E. O. Wilson. 1963. An equilibrium theory of insular zoogeography, *Evolution* 17:373–87.

MacArthur, R. H. and E. O. Wilson. 1967. *The Theory of Island Biogeography*. Princeton, N.J.: Princeton University Press.

MacArthur, R. H. and E. R. Pianka. 1966. On optimal use of a patchy environment. *American Naturalist* 100:603–9.

MacArthur, R. H. and J. W. MacArthur. 1961. On bird species diversity. *Ecology* 42:594–98.

Macdonald, J. S., E. A. MacIsaac, and H. E. Herunter. 2003. The effect of variable-retention riparian buffer zones on water temperatures in small headwater streams in sub-boreal forest ecosystems of British Columbia. *Canadian Journal of Forest Research* 33:1371–82.

Mack, R. N., D. Simberloff, W. M. Lonsdale, H. Evans, M. Clout, and F. A. Bazzaz. 2000. Biotic invasions: Causes, epidemiology, global consequences, and control. *Ecological Applications* 10(3):689–710.

MacLachlan, A. 1983. Sandy beach ecology-a review. In A. Mclachlan and T. Erasmus. eds. *Sandy Beaches as Ecosystems*. The Hague: Dr. W. Junk Publishers.

MacLulich, D. A. 1937. Fluctuation in the numbers of the varying hare (*Lepus americanus*). *University of Toronto Studies in Biology Series No. 43.*

Mandelbrot, B. 1982. *The Fractal Geometry of Nature*. New York: W. H. Freeman.

Mao, J. S., M. S. Boyce, D. W. Smith, F. J. Singer, D. J. Vales, J. M. Vore, and E. H. Merrill. 2005. Habitat selection by elk before and after wolf reintroduction in Yellowstone National Park. *Journal of Wildlife Management* 69:1691–1707.

Marchand, P. J. 1996. *Life in the cold*. Hanover, NH, University Press of New England.

Margolis, H. A., L. B. Flanagan, and B. D. Amiro. 2006. The Fluxnet-Canada Research Network: Influence of climate and disturbance on carbon cycling in forests and peatlands. *Agricultural and Forest Meteorology* 140(1-4):1–5.

Margulis, L. and R. Fester. 1991. *Symbiosis as a Source of Evolutionary Innovation: Speciation and Morphogenesis* Cambridge. Mass.: MIT Press.

Maron, J. L. and E. Crone. 2006. Herbivory: effects on plant abundance, distribution and population growth. *Proceedings of the Royal Society B-Biological Sciences* 273(1601):2575–84.

Marquis, R. J. and C. J. Whelan. 1994. Insectivorous birds increase growth of white oak through consumption of leaf-chewing insects. *Ecology* 75:2007–14.

Marshall, D. L. 1990. Non-random mating in a wild radish, *Raphanus sativus*. *Plant Species Biology* 5:143–56.

Marshall, D. L. and M. W. Folsom. 1991. Mate choice in plants: an anatomical to population perspective. *Annual Review of Ecology and Systematics* 22:37–63.

Marshall, D. L. and M. W. Folsom. 1992. Mechanisms of nonrandom mating in wild radish. In R. Wyatt. ed. *Ecology and Evolution of Plant Reproduction: New Approaches*. New York: Chapman and Hall.

Marshall, D. L. and O. S. Fuller. 1994. Does nonrandom mating among wild radish plants occur in the field as well as in the greenhouse? *American Journal of Botany* 81:439–45.

Marshall, D. L., M. W. Folsom, C. Hatfield, and T. Bennett. 1996. Does interference competition among

pollen grains occur in wild radish? *Evolution* 50:1842–48.

Mathewson, D. D., M. D. Hocking, and T. E. Reimchen. 2003. Nitrogen uptake in riparian plant communities across a sharp ecological boundary of salmon density. *BMC Ecology* 3:4.

May, R. M. 1975. Patterns of species abundance and diversity. In M. L. Cody and J. M. Diamond. eds. *Ecology and Evolution of Communities*. Cambridge, Mass.: Harvard University Press.

May, R. M. 1989. Honeyguides and humans. *Nature* 338:707–8.

Maynard Smith, J. 1964. Group selection and kin selection. *Nature* 201:1145–47.

Maynard Smith, J. 1982. *Evolution and the Theory of Games*. Cambridge, Cambridge University Press.

Mayr, E. 1942. *Systematics and the Origin of Species*. New York: Columbia University Press.

Mazerolle, M. J. and M. A. Villard. 1999. Patch characteristics and landscape context as predictors of species presence and abundance: A review. *Ecoscience* 6(1):117–24.

McCullough, D. A. 1999. A review and synthesis of effects of alterations to the water temperature regime on freshwater life stages of salmonids, with special reference to chinook salmon. Environmental Protection Agency. EPA 910-R-99-010.

McKinnon, J. S., S. Mori, B. K. Blackman, L. David, D. M. Kingsley, L. Jamieson, J. Chou, and D. Schluter. 2004. Evidence for ecology's role in speciation. *Nature* 429(6989):294–98.

McNaughton, S. J. 1976. Serengeti migratory wildebeest: facilitation of energy flow by grazing. *Science* 191:92–94.

McNaughton, S. J. 1985. Ecology of a grazing ecosystem: the Serengeti. *Ecological Monographs* 55:259–94.

McNaughton, S. J., R. W. Ruess, and S. W. Seagle. 1988. Large mammals and process dynamics in African ecosystems. *BioScience* 38:794–800.

Meentemeyer, V. 1978. An approach to the biometeorology of decomposer organisms. *International Journal of Biometeorology* 22:94–102.

Melillo, J. M., J. D. Aber, and J. F. Muratore. 1982. Nitrogen and lignin control of hardwood leaf litter decomposition dynamics. *Ecology* 63:621–26.

Mertz, D. B. 1972. The *Tribolium* model and the mathematics of population growth. *Annual Review of Ecology and Systematics* 3:51–106.

Messier, F. 1994. Ungulate population models with predation: a case study with the North American moose. *Ecology* 75:478–88.

Meybeck, M. 1982. Carbon, nitrogen, and phosphorus transport by world rivers. *American Journal of Science* 282:401–50.

Meyer, J. L. and G. E. Likens. 1979. Transport and transformation of phosphorus in a forest stream ecosystem. *Ecology* 60:1255–69.

Meyer, J. R., S. P. Ellner, N. G. Hairston, L. E. Jones, and T. Yoshida. 2006. Prey evolution on the time scale of predator-prey dynamics revealed by allele-specific quantitative PCR. *Proceedings of the National Academy of Sciences of the United States of America* 103(28):10690–95.

Miller, R. B. 1923. First report on a forestry survey of Illinois. *Illinois Natural History Bulletin* 14:291–377.

Mills, E. L.. J, H. Leach, J. T. Carlton, and C. L. Secor. 1994. Exotic species and the integrity of the Great Lakes. *BioScience* 44:666–76.

Mills, K. H. and D. W. Schindler. 1987. Preface. *Canadian Journal of Fisheries and Aquatic Sciences* 44(Suppl. 1):3–5.

Milne, B. T. 1993. Pattern analysis for landscape evaluation and characterization. In M. E. Jensen and P. S. Bourgeron. eds. *Ecosystem Management: Principles and Applications.* Gen. Tech. Report PNW-GTR-318. Portland, Ore.: U.S. Department of Agriculture Forest Service, Pacific Northwest Research Station.

Minnich, R. A. 1983. Fire mosaics in southern California and northern Baja California. *Science* 219:1287–94.

Molles, M. C., Jr. 1978. Fish species diversity on model and natural reef patches: experimental insular biogeography. *Ecological Monographs* 48:289–305.

Mooers, A. O., L. R. Prugh, M. Festa-Bianchet, and J. A. Hutchings. 2007. Biases in legal listings under Canadian endangered species legislation. *Conservation Biology* 21:572–75.

Moore, D. R. J., P. A. Keddy, C. L. Gaudet, and I. C. Wisheu. 1989. Conservation of Wetlands—Do Infertile Wetlands Deserve a Higher Priority. *Biological Conservation* 47:203–17.

Moore, J. 1983. Responses of an avian predator and its isopod prey to an acanthocephalan parasite. *Ecology* 64:1000–15.

Moore, J. 1984a. Altered behavioral responses in intermediate hosts—an acanthocephalan parasite strategy. *American Naturalist* 123:572–77.

Moore, J. 1984b. Parasites that change the behavior of their host. *Scientific American* 250:108–15.

Moore, J. A. H. and T. J. Roper. 2003. Temperature and humidity in badger *Meles meles* setts. *Mammal Review* 33:308–13.

Mooring, M. S. and W. M. Samuel. 1999. Premature loss of winter hair in free-ranging moose (*Alces alces*) infested with winter ticks (*Dermacentor albipictus*) is correlated with grooming rate. *Canadian Journal of Zoology-Revue Canadienne De Zoologie* 77(1):148–56.

Moran, P. A. P. 1949. The statistical analysis of the sunspot and lynx cycles. *Journal of Animal Ecology* 18:115–16.

Morita, R. Y. 1975. Psychrophilic bacteria. *Bacteriological Reviews* 39:144–67.

Moritz, R. E., C. M. Bitz, and E. J. Steig. 2002. Dynamics of recent climate change in the Arctic. *Science* 297:1497–502.

Morse, D. H. 1980. Foraging and coexistence of spruce woods warblers. *Living Bird* 18:7–25.

Morse, D. H. 1989. *American Warblers.* Cambridge, Mass.: Harvard University Press.

Mosser, J. L., A. G. Mosser, and T. D. Brock. 1974. Population ecology of *Sulfolobus acidocaldarius.* I. Temperature strains. *Archives for Microbiology* 97:169–79.

Moyle, P. B. and J. J. Cech Jr. 1982. *Fishes and Introduction to Ichthyology.* Englewood Cliffs. N.J.: Prentice Hall.

Muir, J. 1915. *Travels in Alaska.* Boston: Houghton Mifflin.

Müller, K. 1954. Investigations on the organic drift in north Swedish streams. *Reports of the Institute of Freshwater Research of Drottningholm* 35:133–48.

Müller, K. 1974. Stream drift as a chronobiological phenomenon in running water ecosystems. *Annual Review of Ecology and Systematics* 5:309–23.

Mullon, C., P. Freon, and P. Cury. 2005. The dynamics of collapse in world fisheries. *Fish and Fisheries* 6(2):111–20.

Munger, J. C. and J. H. Brown. 1981. Competition in desert rodents: an experiment with semipermeable exclosures. *Science* 211:510–12.

Murie, A. 1944. The wolves of Mount McKinley. *Fauna of the National Parks of the U.S.. Fauna Series No.5.* Washington, D.C.: U.S. Department of the Interior, National Park Service.

Murphy, P. G. and A. E. Lugo. 1986. Ecology of tropical dry forest. *Annual Review of Ecology and Systematics* 17:67–88.

Murphy-Klassen, H. M., T. J. Underwood, S. G. Sealy, and A. A. Czyrnyj. 2005. Long-term trends in spring arrival dates of migrant birds at Delta Marsh, Manitoba, in relation to climate change. *Auk* 122(4):1130–48.

Muscatine, L. and C. F. D'Elia. 1978. The uptake. retention, and release of ammonium by reef corals. *Limnology and Oceanography* 23:725–34.

Myers, N., R. A. Mittermeier, C. G. Mittermeier, G. A. B. da Fonseca, and J. Kent. 2000. Biodiversity hotspots for conservation priorities. *Nature* 403(6772):853–58.

Naiman, R. J., G. Pinay, C. A. Johnston, and J. Pastor. 1994. Beaver influences on the long-term biogeochemical characteristics of boreal forest drainage networks. *Ecology* 75:905–21.

National Audubon Society. 2002. The Christmas Bird Count Historical Results. http://www.audubon.org/bird/cbc.

Neilson, R. P. 1995. A model for predicting continental-scale vegetation distribution and water balance. *Ecological Applications* 5:362–85.

Neilson, R. P., G. A. King, and G. Koeper. 1992. Toward a rule-based biome model. *Landscape Ecology* 7:135–47.

Newbold, J. D., J. W. Elwood, R. V. O'Neill, and A. L. Sheldon. 1983. Phosphorus dynamics in a woodland stream ecosystem: a study of nutrient spiraling. *Ecology* 64:1249–65.

Newchurch, M. J., E.-S. Yang, D. M. Cunnold, G. C. Reinsel, J. M. Zawodny, and J. M. Russell III. 2003. Evidence for slowdown in stratospheric ozone loss: first stage of ozonerecovery. *Journal of Geophysical Research* 108(DI6). 4507,doi:10.1029/2003JD003471, 2003 (published online).

Newman, E. I. 1973. Competition and diversity in herbaceous vegetation. *Nature* 244:310–11.

Nilsson, S. G., J. Bengtsson, and S. Ås. 1988. Habitat diversity or area *per se*? Species richness of woody plants. carabid beetles and land snails on islands. *Journal of Animal Ecology* 57:685–704.

Nottrott, R. W., J. F. Franklin, and J. R. Vande Castle. 1994. *International Networking in Long-Term Ecological Research.* Seattle: U.S. LTER Network Office, University of Washington.

Ødegaard, F. 2000. How many species of arthropods? Erwin's estimate revised. *Biological Journal of the Linnean Society* 71(4):583–97.

O'Donoghue, M., S. Boutin, C. J. Krebs, and E. J. Hofer. 1997. Numerical responses of coyotes and lynx to the snowshoe bare cycle. *Oikos* 80:150–62.

O'Donoghue, M., S. Boutin, C. J. Krebs, G. Zuleta, D. L. Murray, and E. J. Hofer. 1998. Functional responses of coyotes and lynx to the snowshoe hare cycle. *Ecology* 79:1193–208.

O'Dowd, D. J. and A. M. Glll. 1984. Predator satiation and site alteration following fire: mass reproduction of alpine ash (*Eucalyptus delegatensis*) in southeastern Australia. *Ecology* 65:1052–66.

Olff, H. and M. E. Ritchie. 1998. Effects of herbivores on grassland plant diversity. *Trends in Ecology & Evolution* 13(7):261–65.

Olsen, E. M., M. Heino, G. R. Lilly, M. J. Morgan, J. Brattey, B. Ernande, and U. Dieckmann. 2004. Maturation trends indicative of rapid evolution preceded the collapse of northern cod. *Nature* 428:932–35.

Olsen, G. H., M. Mauritzen, A. E. Derocher, E. G. Sormo, J. U. Skaare, O. Wiig, and B. M. Jenssen. 2003. Space-use strategy is an important determinant of PCB concentrations in female polar bears in the Barents sea. *Environmental Science & Technology* 37(21):4919–24.

Osawa, N. and T. Nishida. 1992. Seasonal variation in elytral colour polymorphism in *Harmonia axyridis* (the ladybird beetle): the role of non-random mating. *Heredity* 69:297–307.

Ottersen, G., B. Planque, A. Belgrano, E. Post, P. C. Reid, and N. C. Stenseth. 2001. Ecological effects of the North Atlantic Oscillation. *Oecologia* 128(1):1–14.

Packer, C. and A. E. Pusey. 1982. Cooperation and competition within coalitions of male lions: kin selection or game-theory? *Nature* 296:740–42.

Packer, C. and A. E. Pusey. 1983. Cooperation and competition in lions: reply. *Nature* 302:356.

Packer, C. and A. E. Pusey. 1997. Divided we fall: cooperation among lions. *Scientific American* 276(5):52–59.

Packer, C., D. A. Gilbert, A. E. Pusey, and S. J. O'Brien. 1991. A molecular genetic analysis of kinship and cooperation in African lions. *Nature* 351:562–65.

Packer, L. 1991. The evolution of social-behavior and nest architecture in sweat bees of the subgenus evylaeus (Hymenoptera, halictidae)—a phylogenetic approach. *Behavioral Ecology and Sociobiology* 29(3):153–60.

Paine, R. T. 1966. Food web complexity and species diversity. *American Naturalist* 100:65–75.

Paine, R. T. 1969. A note on trophic complexity and community stability. *American Naturalist* 103:91–93.

Paine, R. T. 1976. Size-limited predation: an observational and experimental approach with the *Mytilus-Pisaster* interaction. *Ecology* 57:858–73.

Palumbi, S. R. 2001. Humans as the world's greatest evolutionary force. *Science* 293:1786–90.

Papke, R. T., N. B. Ramsing, M. M. Bateson, and D. M. Ward. 2003. Geographical isolation in hot spring cyanobacteria. *Environmental Microbiology* 5(8):650–59.

Pappers, S. M., G. van der Velde, N. J. Ouborg, and J. M. van Groenendael. 2002. Genetically based polymorphisms in morphology and life history associated with putative host races of the water lily leaf beetle *Galerucella nymphaeae.* *Evolution* 56:1610–21.

Park, T. 1948. Experimental studies of interspecific competition. I. Competition between populations of flour beetles *Tribolium confusum* Duval and *Tribolium castaneum* Herbst. *Ecological Monographs* 18:267–307.

Park, T. 1954. Experimental studies of interspecific competition. II. Temperature, humidity and competition in two species of *Tribolium. Physiological Zoology* 27:177–238.

Park, T., D. B. Mertz, W. Grodzinski, and T. Prus. 1965. Cannibalistic predation in populations of flour beetles. *Physiological Zoology* 38:289–321.

Park, Y. M. 1990. Effects of drought on two grass species with different distribution around coastal sand dunes. *Functional Ecology* 4:735–41.

Parmenter, R. R. and V.A. Lamarra. 1991. Nutrient cycling in a freshwater marsh: the decomposition of fish and waterfowl carrion. *Limnology and Oceanography* 36:976–87.

Parmenter, R. R., C. A. Parmenter, and C. D. Cheney. 1989. Factors influencing microhabitat partitioning among coexisting species of arid-land darkling beetles (Tenebrionidae): behavioural responses to vegetation architecture. *The Southwestern Naturalist* 34:319–29.

Parmesan, C. and G. Yohe. 2003. A globally coherent fingerprint of climate change impacts across natural systems. *Nature* 421(6918):37–42.

Partel, M. and S. D. Wilson. 2002. Root dynamics and spatial pattern in prairie and forest. *Ecology* 83(5):1199–203.

Pauly, D., V. Christensen, J. Dalsgaard, R. Froese, and F. Torres. 1998. Fishing down marine food webs. *Science* 279(5352):860–63.

Pearcy, R. W. 1977. Acclimation of photosynthetic and respiratory carbon dioxide exchange to growth temperature in *Atriplex lentiformis* (Torr.) Wats. *Plant Physiology* 59:795–99.

Pearcy, R. W. and A. T. Harrison. 1974. Comparative photosynthetic and respiratory gas exchange characteristics of *Atriplex lentiformis* (Torr.) Wats. in coastal and desert habitats. *Ecology* 55:1104–11.

Pearson, O. P. 1954. Habits of the lizard *Liolaemus multiformis multiformis* at high altitudes in southern Peru. *Copeia* 1954:111–16.

Peckarsky, B. L. 1980. Behavioural interactions between stoneflies and mayflies: behavioural observations. *Ecology* 61:932–43.

Peckarsky, B. L. 1982. Aquatic insect predator-prey relations. *BioScience* 32:261–66.

Peierls, B. L., N. F. Caraco, M. L. Pace, and J. J. Cole. 1991. Human influence on river nitrogen. *Nature* 350:386–87.

Peters, R. H. 1991. *A Critique for Ecology.* Cambridge, England: Cambridge University Press.

Peters, R. H. and K. Wassenberg. 1983. The effect of body size on animal abundance. *Oecologia* 60:89–96.

Peters, V. S., S. E. Macdonald, and M. R. T. Dale. 2006. Patterns of initial versus delayed regeneration of white spruce in boreal mixed wood succession. *Canadian Journal of Forest Research-Revue Canadienne de Recherche Forestière* 36(6):1597–1609.

Peterson, B. J., R. W. Howarth, and R. H. Garritt. 1985. Multiple stable isotopes used to trace the flow of organic matter in estuarine food webs. *Science* 227:1361–63.

Pianka, E. R. 1970. On r and K selection. *American Naturalist* 102:592–97.

Pianka, E. R. 1972. r and K selection or b and d selection. *American Naturalist* 106:581–88.

Pielou, E. C. 1966. Measurement of diversity in different types of biological collections. *Journal of Theoretical Biology* 13:131–44.

Pielou, E. C. 1977. *Mathematical Ecology.* New York: Wiley.

Pielou, E. C. 1991. *After the ice age: the return of life to glaciated North America.* University of Chicago Press. 5–38.

Pimentel, D., R. Zuniga, and D. Morrison. 2005. Update on the environmental and economic costs associated with alien-invasive species in the United States. *Ecological Economics* 52(3):273–88.

Polischuk, S. C., R. J. Norstrom, and M. A. Ramsay. 2002. Body burdens and tissue concentrations of organochlorines in polar bears (*Ursus maritimus*) vary during seasonal fasts. *Environmental Pollution* 118(1):29–39.

Post, E. and N. C. Stenseth. 1999. Climatic variability, plant phenology, and northern ungulates. *Ecology* 80(4):1322–39.

Post, W. M., T.-H. Peng, W. R. Emanuel, A. W. King, V. H. Dale, and D. L. DeAngelis. 1990. The global carbon cycle. *American Scientist* 78:310–26.

Poulin, R. and W. L. Vickery. 1995. Cleaning symbiosis as an evolutionary game—to cheat or not to cheat. *Journal of Theoretical Biology* 175(1):63–70.

Power, M. E. 1990. Effects of fish on river food webs. *Science* 250:811–14.

Power, M. E., D. Tilman, J. A. Estes, B. A. Menge, W. J. Bond, L. S. Mills, G. Daily, J. C. Castilla, J. Lubchenco, and R. T. Paine. 1996. Challenges in the quest for keystones. *BioScience* 46:609–20.

Preston, F. W. 1948. The commonness, and rarity, of species. *Ecology* 29:254–83.

Preston, F. W. 1962a. The canonical distribution of commonness and rarity: part I. *Ecology* 43:185–215.

Preston, F. W. 1962b. The canonical distribution of commonness and rarity: part II. *Ecology* 43:410–32.

Purvis, A., J. L. Gittleman, G. Cowlishaw, and G. M. Mace. 2000. Predicting extinction risk in declining species. *Proceedings of the Royal Society of London Series B-Biological Sciences* 267(1456):1947–52.

Rabinowitz, D. 1981. Seven forms of rarity. In H. Synge. ed. *The Biological Aspects of Rare Plant Conservation.* New York: John Wiley & Sons.

Ralph, C. J. 1985. Habitat association patterns of forest and steppe birds of northern Patagonia, Argentina. *The Condor* 87:471–83.

Reader, R. J., S. D. Wilson, J. W. Belcher, I. Wisheu, P. A. Keddy, D. Tilman, E. C. Morris, J. B. Grace, J. B. McGraw, H. Olff, R. Turkington, Y. Klein, B. Leung, B. Shipley, R. Van Hulst, E. Johansson, C. Nilsson, J. Gurevitch, K. Grigulis, and B. E. Beisner. 1994. Plant competition in relation to neighbor biomass: An intercontinental study with *Poa pratensis. Ecology* 75(6):1753–60.

Réale, D., A. G. McAdam, S. Boutin, and D. Berteaux. 2003. Genetic and plastic responses of a northern mammal to climate change. *Proceedings of the Royal Society of London Series B-Biological Sciences* 270(1515):591–96.

Reckhow, K. H. and J. T. Simpson. 1980. A procedure using modeling and error analysis for the prediction of lake phosphorus concentration from land use information. *Canadian Journal of Fisheries and Aquatic Science* 37:1439–48.

Redford, K. H. 1992. The empty forest. *BioScience* 42:412–22.

Reid, W. V. and K. R. Miller. 1989. *Keeping Options Alive: The Scientific Basis for Conserving Biodiversity.* Washington, D.C.: World Resources Institute.

Reiners, W. A., I. A. Worley, and D. B. Lawrence. 1971. Plant diversity in a chronosequence at Glacier Bay, Alaska. *Ecology* 52:55–69.

Revelle, R. and H. E. Suess. 1957. Carbon dioxide exchange between atmosphere and ocean and the question of an increase of atmospheric CO_2 during the past decades. *Tellus* 9:18–27.

Reynolds, H. L. and C. D'Antonio. 1996. The ecological significance of plasticity in root weight ratio in response to nitrogen: Opinion. *Plant and Soil* 185:75–97.

Reynolds, J. D. 2003. Life histories and extinction risk. In T. M. Blackburn and K. J. Gaston. *Macroecology.* Oxford: Blackwell Publishing.

Reysenbach, A. L., M. Ehringer, and K. Hershberger. 2000. Microbial diversity at 83°C in Calcite Springs, Yellowstone National Park: another environment where the Aquificales and "Korarchaeota" coexist. *Extremophiles* 4:61–67.

Richey, J. E. 1983. The phosphorus cycle. In B. Bolin and R. B. Cook. eds. *The Major Biogeochemical Cycles and Their Interaction.* New York: John Wiley & Sons.

Ricklefs, R. E. 1987. Community diversity: relative roles of local and regional processes. *Science* 235:167–71.

Ripple, W. J., and R. L. Beschta. 2006. Linking wolves to willows via risk-sensitive foraging by ungulates in the northern Yellowstone ecosystem. *Forest Ecology and Management* 230:96–106.

Risch, S. J. and C. R. Carroll. 1982. Effect of a keystone predaceous ant, *Solenopsis geminata*, on arthropods in a tropical agroecosystem. *Ecology* 63:1979–83.

Roberts, C. M., C. J. McClean, J. E. N. Veron, J. P. Hawkins, G. R. Allen, D. E. McAllister, C. G. Mittermeier, F. W. Schueler, M. Spalding, F. Wells, C. Vynne, and T. B. Werner. 2002. Marine biodiversity hotspots and conservation priorities for tropical reefs. *Science* 295(5558):1280–84.

Robertson, G. P., M. A. Huston, F. C. Evans, and J. M. Tiedje. 1988. Spatial variability in a successional plant community: patterns of nitrogen availability. *Ecology* 69:1517–24.

Rochefort, L. 2000. New frontiers in bryology and lichenology—*Sphagnum*—A keystone genus in habitat restoration. *Bryologist* 103:503–08.

Roland, J., N. Keyghobadi, and S. Fownes. 2000. Alpine Parnassius butterfly dispersal: effects of landscape and population size. *Ecology* 81:1642–53.

Rood, S. B., G. M. Samuelson, J. H. Braatne, C. R. Gourley, F. M. R. Hughes, and J. M. Mahoney. 2005. Managing river flows to restore floodplain forests. *Frontiers in Ecology and the Environment* 3(4):193–201.

Rood, S. B., G. M. Samuelson, J. K. Weber, and K. A. Wywrot. 2005. Twentieth-century decline in streamflows from the hydrographic apex of North America. *Journal of Hydrology* 306(1-4): 215–33.

Rood, S. B., J. H. Braatne, and F. M. R. Hughes. 2003. Ecophysiology of riparian cottonwoods: stream flow dependency, water relations and restoration. *Tree Physiology* 23(16):1113–24.

Root, T. 1988. *Atlas of Wintering North American Birds.* Chicago: University of Chicago Press.

Root, T. L., J. T. Price, K. R. Hall, S. H. Schneider, C. Rosenzweig, and J. A. Pounds. 2003. Fingerprints of global warming on wild animals and plants. *Nature* 421(6918):57–60.

Rosell, F., O. Bozser, P. Collen, and H. Parker. 2005. Ecological impact of beavers *Castor fiber* and *Castor canadensis* and their ability to modify ecosystems. *Mammal Review* 35:248–76.

Rosemond, A. D., C. M. Pringle, A. Ramirez, M. J. Paul, and J. L. Meyer. 2002. Landscape variation in phosphorus concentration and effects on detritus-based tropical streams. *Limnology and Oceanography* 47:278–89.

Rosenzweig, M. L. 1968. Net primary productivity of terrestrial environments: predictions from climatological data. *American Naturalist* 102:67–84.

Rosenzweig, M. L. 1992. Species diversity gradients: we know more and less than we thought. *Journal of Mammalogy* 73:715–30.

Roth J.D. 2002 Temporal variability in arctic fox diet as reflected in stable-carbon isotopes; the importance of sea ice. *Oecologia* 133:70–77.

Rowe, L., G. Arnqvist, A. Sih, and J. Krupa. 1994. Sexual conflict and the evolutionary ecology of mating patterns—water striders as a model system. *Trends in Ecology & Evolution* 9(8):289–93.

Rydin, H. and S-O. Borgegård. 1988. Plant species richness on islands over a century of primary succession: Lake Hjälmaren. *Ecology* 69:916–27.

Ryer, C. H., A. Lawton, R. J. Lopez, and B. L. Olla. 2002. A comparison of the functional ecology of visual vs. nonvisual foraging in two planktivorous marine fishes. *Canadian Journal of Fisheries and Aquatic Sciences* 59:1305–14.

Ryther, J. H. 1969. Photosynthesis and fish production in the sea. *Science* 166:72–76.

Saabye, H. E. 1776. Fragments of a diary kept in Greenland during the years 1770–1779. In H. Osterman (ed.). 1942. *Reports from Greenland.*

Saccheri, I., M. Kuussaari, M. Kankare, P. Vikman, W. Fortelius, I. Hanski. 1998. Inbreeding and extinction in a butterfly metapopulation. *Nature* 392:491–94.

Sage, R. F. 1999. Why C_4 photosynthesis? In R. F. Sage and R. K. Monson, *C4 Plant Biology.* San Diego: Academic Press.

Sage, R. F. 2004. The evolution of C-4 photosynthesis. *New Phytologist* 161(2):341–70.

Sage, R. F. and D. S. Kubien. 2003. Quo vadis C-4? An ecophysiological perspective on global change and the future of C4 plants. *Photosynthesis Research* 77(2-3):209–25.

Sakai, A. and C. J. Weiser. 1973. Freezing resistance of trees in North

America with reference to tree regions. *Ecology* 54(1):118–26.

Sakamoto, M. 1966. Primary production by phytoplankton community in some Japanese lakes and its dependence on lake depth. *Archive für Hydrobiologie* 62:1–28.

Sala, O. E., W. J. Parton, L. A. Joyce, and W. K. Laurenroth. 1988. Primary production of the central grassland regions of the United States. *Ecology* 69:40–45.

Samuel, B. 2004. *White as a Ghost: Winter Ticks and Moose*. Edmonton, Federation of Alberta Naturalists.

Schenk, H. J. 2006. Root competition: beyond resource depletion. *Journal of Ecology* 94(4):725–39.

Schenk, H. J. and R. B. Jackson. 2002. The global biogeography of roots. *Ecological Monographs* 72:311–28.

Schimel, D. S. 1995. Terrestrial ecosystems and the carbon cycle. *Global change biology* 1:77–91.

Schindler, D. W. 1974. Eutrophication and recovery in experimental lakes: Implications for lake management. *Science*, 184:897–99.

Schindler, D. W. 1977. Evolution of phosphorus limitation in lakes. *Science*, 195:260–62.

Schindler, D. W. 1987. Detecting ecosystem responses to anthropogenic stress. *Canadian Journal of Fisheries and Aquatic Sciences* 44:6–25.

Schindler, D. W. 1990. Experimental perturbations of whole lakes as tests of hypotheses concerning ecosystem structure and function. *Oikos* 57:25–41.

Schindler, D. W., K. G. Beaty, E. J. Fee, D. R. Cruikshank, E. R. Debruyn, d. L. Findlay, G. A. Linsey, J. A. Shearer, M. P. Stainton, and M. A. Turner. 1990. Effects of Climatic Warming on Lakes of the Central Boreal Forest. *Science*, 250:967–70.

Schindler, D. W., K. H. Mills, D. F. Malley, D. L. Findlay, J. A. Shearer, I. J. Davies, M. A. Turner, G. A. Linsey, and D. R. Cruikshank. 1985. Long-Term Ecosystem Stress—The Effects of Years of Experimental Acidification on a Small Lake. *Science*, 228:1395–1401.

Schlesinger, W. H. 1991. *Biogeochemistry: An Analysis of Global Change*. New York: Academic Press.

Schluter, D. 1994. Experimental evidence that competition promotes divergence in adaptive radiation. *Science* 266:798–800.

Schluter, D. and J. D. McPhail. 1992. Ecological character displacement and speciation in sticklebacks. *The American Naturalist* 140:85–108.

Schmidt-Nielsen, K. 1964. *Desert Animals: Physiological Problems of Heat and Water*. Oxford: Clarendon Press.

Schmidt-Nielsen, K. 1969. The neglected interface. The biology of water as a liquid-gas system. *Quarterly Review of Biophysics* 2:283–304.

Schmidt-Nielsen, K. 1983. *Animal Physiology: Adaptation and Environment*. 3d ed. Cambridge, England: Cambridge University Press.

Schmiegelow, F. K. A., C. S. Machtans, and S. J. Hannon. 1997. Are boreal birds resilient to forest fragmentation?

An experimental study of short-term community responses. *Ecology* 78(6):1914–32.

Schmitt, J., A. C. McCormac, and H. Smith. 1995. A test of the adaptive plasticity hypothesis using transgenic and mutant plants disabled in phytochrome-mediated elongation responses to neighbors. *American Naturalist* 146(6):937–53.

Schoener, T. W. 1983. Field experiments on interspecific competition. *American Naturalist* 122:240–85.

Scholander, P. F., R. Hock, V. Walters, F. Johnson, and L. Irving. 1950. Heat regulation in some arctic and tropical mammals and birds. *Biological Bulletin* 99:237–58.

Schultz, T. D., M. C. Quinlan, and N. F. Hadley. 1992. Preferred body temperature, metabolic physiology, and water balance of adult *Cicindela longilabris*: a comparison of populations from boreal habitats and climatic refugia. *Physiological Zoology* 65:226–42.

Schumacher, H. 1976. *Korallenriff*. Munich: BLV Verlagsgesellschaft mbH.

Seiwa, K. and K. Kikuzawa. 1991. Phenology of tree seedlings in relation to seed size. *Canadian Journal of Botany* 69:532–38.

Serreze, M. C., J. E. Walsh, F. S. Chapin, T. Osterkamp, M. Dyurgerov, V. Romanovsky, W. C. Oechel, J. Morison, T. Zhang, and R. G. Barry. 2000. Observational evidence of recent change in the northern high-latitude environment. *Climatic Change* 46:159–207.

Shaver, G. R. and F. S. Chapin III. 1986. Effect of fertilizer on production and biomass of tussock tundra, Alaska, U.S.A. *Arctic and Alpine Research* 18:261–68.

Shaver, G. R., A. E. Giblin, K. J. Nadelhoffer, K. K. Thieler, M. R. Downs, J. A. Laundre, and E. B. Rastetter. 2006. Carbon turnover in Alaskan tundra soils: effects of organic matter quality, temperature, moisture and fertilizer. *Journal of Ecology* 94:740–53.

Sherman, P. W. 1977. Nepotism and evolution of alarm calls. *Science* 197(4310):1246–53.

Sherman, P.W., J. U. M. Jarvis, and S. H. Braude. 1992. Naked mole rats. *Scientific American* 257(8):72–78.

Shine, R. and E. L. Charnov. 1992. Patterns of survival, growth, and maturation in snakes and lizards. *American Naturalist* 139:1257–69.

Shipley B. 1993. A Null Model For Competitive Hierarchies In Competition Matrices. *Ecology* 74:1693–99.

Shurin, J. B., D. S. Gruner, and H. Hillebrand. 2006. All wet or dried up? Real differences between aquatic and terrestrial food webs. *Proceedings of the Royal Society B-Biological Sciences* 273:1–9.

Shurin, J. B., J. E. Havel, M. A. Leibold, and B. Pinel-Alloul. 2000. Local and regional zooplankton species richness: A scale-independent test for saturation. *Ecology* 81(11):3062–73.

Siegenthaler, U., H. Friedli, H. Loetscher, E. Moor, A. Neftel, H. Oeschger, and B. Stauffer. 1988. Stable-isotope ratios and

concentrations of CO_2 in air from polar ice cores. *Annals of Glaciology* 10:151–56.

Silvertown, J. 1987. Ecological stability: a test case. *American Naturalist* 130:807–10.

Simard, S. W., D. A. Perry, M. D. Jones, D. D. Myrold, D. M. Durall, and R. Molina. 1997. Net transfer of carbon between ectomycorrhizal tree species in the field. *Nature* 388(6642):579–82.

Simberloff, D. S. 1976. Experimental zoogeography of islands: effects of island size. *Ecology* 57:629–48.

Simberloff, D. S. 1998. Flagships, umbrellas, and keystones: Is single-species management passe in the landscape era? *Biological Conservation* 83:247–57.

Simberloff, D. S. and E. O. Wilson. 1969. Experimental zoogeography of islands: the colonization of empty islands. *Ecology* 50:278–96.

Sinclair, A. R. E. 1977. *The African Buffalo*. Chicago: University of Chicago Press.

Sinclair, A.R.E. 2003. Mammal population regulation, keystone processes and ecosystem dynamics. *Philosophical Transactions of the Royal Society of London Series B-Biological Sciences* 358:1729–40.

Singer, M. C. and P. Wedlake. 1981. Capture does affect probability of recapture in a butterfly species. *Ecological Entomology* 6:215–16.

Skole, D. and C. Tucker. 1993. Tropical deforestation and habitat fragmentation in the Amazon: satellite data from 1978 to 1988. *Science* 260:1905–10.

Smil, V. 1990. Nitrogen and phosphorus. In B. L. Turner II. W. C. Clark, R. W. Kates. J. F. Richards. J. T. Mathews. and W. B. Meyer. eds. *The Earth as Transformed by Human Action*. Cambridge, England: Cambridge University Press.

Smith, C. L. and J. C. Tyler. 1972. Space resource sharing in a coral reef fish community. Natural History Museum of Los Angeles County. *Science Bulletin* 14:125–70.

Smith, J. N. M. and P. Arcese. 1994. Brown-headed cowbirds and an island population of song sparrows—a 16-year study. *Condor* 96(4):916-34.

Smith, V. H. 1979. Nutrient dependence of primary productivity in lakes. *Limnology and Oceanography* 24:1051–64.

Smol, J. P., A. P. Wolfe, H. J. B. Birks, M. S. V. Douglas, V. J. Jones, A. Korhola, R. Pienitz, K. Ruhland, S. Sorvari, D. Antoniades, S. J. Brooks, M. A. Fallu, M. Hughes, B. E. Keatley, T. E. Laing, N. Michelutti, L. Nazarova, M. Nyman, A. M. Paterson, B. Perren, R. Quinlan, M. Rautio, E. Saulnier-Talbot, S. Siitonen, N. Solovieva and J. Weckstrom. 2005. Climate-driven regime shifts in the biological communities of arctic lakes. *Proceedings of the National Acadamy of Sciences* 102:4397–402.

Snelgrove, P. V. R. 1999. Getting to the bottom of marine biodiversity: Sedimentary habitats. *Bioscience* 49:129–38.

Snelgrove, P. V. R. 2000. Linking biodiversity above and below the marine sediment-water interface. *Bioscience* 50:1076–88.

Söderlund, R. and T. Rosswall. 1982. The nitrogen cycles. In O. Hutzinger. ed. *The Handbook of Environmental Chemistry*, vol. I, part B. *The Natural Environment and the Biogeochemical Cycles*. New York: Springer-Verlag.

Soulé, M. E. 1991. Conservation—Tactics for a Constant Crisis. *Science* 253(5021):744–50.

Sousa, W. P. 1979a. Disturbance in marine intertidal boulder fields: the nonequilibrium maintenance of species diversity. *Ecology* 60:1225–39.

Sousa, W. P. 1979b. Experimental investigations of disturbance and ecological succession in a rocky intertidal algal community. *Ecological Monographs* 49:227–54.

Sousa, W. P. 1984. The role of disturbance in natural communities. *Annual Review of Ecology and Systematics* 15:353–91.

Spector, W. S. 1956. *Handbook of Biological Data*. Philadelphia: W. B. Saunders.

Stastny, M., U. Schaffner, and E. Elle. 2005. Do vigour of introduced populations and escape from specialist herbivores contribute to invasiveness? *Journal of Ecology* 93(1):27–37.

Stearns, S. C. 1976. Life-history tactics—review of ideas. *Quarterly Review of Biology* 51(1):3–47.

Stenseth, N. C., G. Ottersen, J. W. Hurrell, A. Mysterud, M. Lima, K. S. Chan, N. G. Yoccoz, and B. Adlandsvik. 2003. Studying climate effects on ecology through the use of climate indices: the North Atlantic Oscillation, El Niño, Southern Oscillation and beyond. *Proceedings of the Royal Society of London Series B-Biological Sciences* 270(1529):2087–96.

Stevens E. D., J. W. Kanwisher, and F. G. Carey. 2000. Muscle temperature in free-swimming giant Atlantic bluefin tuna (*Thunnus thynnus* L.). *Journal of Thermal Biology* 25:419–23.

Stevens, G. C. 1989. The latitudinal gradient in geographical range: how so many species coexist in the tropics. *American Naturalist* 133:240–56.

Stevens, O. A. 1932. The number and weight of seeds produced by weeds. *American Journal of Botany* 19:784–94.

Stireman, J. O., J. D. Nason, and S. B. Heard. 2005. Host-associated genetic differentiation in phytophagous insects: General phenomenon or isolated exceptions? Evidence from a goldenrod-insect community. *Evolution* 59(12):2573–87.

Stireman, J. O., J. D. Nason, S. B. Heard, and J. M. Seehawer. 2006. Cascading host-associated genetic differentiation in parasitoids of phytophagous insects. *Proceedings of the Royal Society B-Biological Sciences* 273(1586):523–30.

Storey, K. B. and J. M. Storey. 1992. Natural freeze tolerance in ectothermic vertebrates. *Annual Review of Physiology* 54:619–37.

Strahler, A. N. 1952. Dynamic Basis of Geomorphology. *Geological Society of America Bulletin* 63(9): 923–38.

Strong, D. R. 1992. Are trophic cascades all wet? Differentiation and donor-control in speciose ecosystems. *Ecology* 73:747–54.

Suberkropp, K. and E. Chauvet. 1995. Regulation of leaf breakdown by fungi in streams: influences of water chemistry. *Ecology* 76:1433–45.

Suess, H. E. 1955. Radiocarbon concentration in modern wood. *Science* 122:415–17.

Sugihara, G. 1980. Minimal community structure: an explanation of species abundance patterns. *American Naturalist* 116:770–87.

Summerhayes, V. S. and C. S. Elton. 1923. Contribution to the ecology of Spitsbergen and Bear Island. *Journal of Ecology* 11:214–86.

Swift, M., O. Heal, and J. Anderson. 1979. *Decomposition in terrestrial ecosystems.* Oxford, UK: Blackwell Scientific Publications.

Takyu, M., S.-I Aiba, and K. Kitayama. 2003. Changes in biomass, productivity and decomposition along topographical gradients under different geological conditions in tropical lower montane forests on Mount Kinabalu, Borneo. *Oecologia* 134:397–404.

Tan, C. C. 1946. Mosaic dominance in the inheritance of color patterns in the lady-bird beetle, *Harmonia axyridis. Genetics* 31:195–210.

Tan, C. C. and J. C. Li. 1934. Inheritance of the elytral color patterns of the lady-bird beetle, *Harmonia axyridis* Pallas. *American Naturalist* 68:252–65.

Tansley, A. G. 1917. On competition between *Galium saxatile* L. (*G. hercynicum* Weig.) and *Galium sylvestre* Poll. (*G. asperum* Schreb.) on different types of soil. *Journal of Ecology* 5:173–79.

Tansley, A. G. 1935. The use and abuse of vegetational concepts and terms. *Ecology* 16:284–307.

Terborgh, J. 1973. On the notion of favorableness in plant ecology. *American Naturalist* 107:481–501.

Terborgh, J. 1988. The big things that run the world: a sequel to E. O. Wilson. *Conservation Biology* 2:402–403.

Thompson, J. N. 1994. *The Coevolutionary Process.* Chicago, University of Chicago Press.

Thomson, D. A. and C. E. Lehner. 1976. Resilience of a rocky intertidal fish community in a physically unstable environment. *Journal of Experimental Marine Biology and Ecology* 22: 1–29.

Thoreau, H. D. 1854. *Walden.* G. S. Haight ed. Reprinted 1942. New York: W. J. Black.

Tilman, D. 1977. Resource competition between planktonic algae: an experimental and theoretical approach. *Ecology* 58:338–48.

Tilman, D. 1987. The importance of the mechanisms of interspecific competition. *The American Naturalist* 129(5):767–74.

Tilman, D. 1994. Competition and biodiversity in spatially structured habitats. *Ecology* 75:2–16.

Todd, A. W. and L. B. Keith. 1983. Coyote demography during a snowshoe hare decline in Alberta. *Journal of Wildlife Management* 47:394–404.

Tonn, W. M. and J. J. Magnuson. 1982. Patterns in the species composition and richness of fish assemblages in northern Wisconsin lakes. *Ecology* 63:1149–66.

Toolson, E. C. 1987. Water profligacy as an adaptation to hot deserts: water loss rates and evaporative cooling in the Sonoran Desert cicada, *Diceroprocta apache* (Homoptera, Cicadidae). *Physiological Zoology* 60:379–85.

Toolson, E. C. and N. F. Hadley. 1987. Energy-dependent facilitation of transcuticular water flux contributes to evaporative cooling in the Sonoran Desert cicada. *Diceroprocta apache* (Homoptera, Cicadidae). *Journal of Experimental Biology* 131:439–44.

Tosi, J. and R. F. Voertman. 1964. Some environmental factors in the economic development of the tropics. *Economic Geography* 40:189–205.

Tourney, J. W. and R. Kienholz. 1931. Trenched plots under forest canopies. *Yale University School of Forestry Bulletin* 30:1–31.

Tracy, C. R. 1999. Differences in body size among chuckwalla (*Sauromalus obesus*) populations. *Ecology* 80:259–71.

Tracy, R. L. and G. E. Walsberg. 2000. Prevalence of cutaneous evaporation in Merriam's kangaroo rat and its adaptive variation at the subspecific level. *Journal of Experimental Biology* 203:773–81.

Tracy, R. L. and G. E. Walsberg. 2001. Intraspecific variation in water loss in a desert rodent, *Dipodomys merriami. Ecology* 82:1130–37.

Tracy, R. L. and G. E. Walsberg. 2002. Kangaroo rats revisited: re-evaluating a classic case of desert survival. *Oecologia* 133:449–57.

Tress, G., B. Tress, and G. Fry. 2005. Clarifying integrative research concepts in landscape ecology. *Landscape Ecology* 20:479–93.

Troll, C. 1939. Luftbildplan und olologische bodenforschung. *Zeitschrift der Gesellschaft fur Erdkunde Zu Berlin,* pp. 241–98.

Turkington R., E. John, C. J. Krebs, M. R. T. Dale, V. O. Nams, R. Boonstra, S. Boutin, K. Martin, A. R. E. Sinclair, and J. N. M. Smith. 1998. The effects of NPK fertilization for nine years on boreal forest vegetation in northwestern Canada. *Journal of Vegetation Science* 9:333–46.

Turner, R. M. 1990. Long-term vegetation change at a fully protected Sonoran Desert site. *Ecology* 71:464–77.

Turner, T. 1983. Facilitation as a successional mechanism in a rocky intertidal community. *The American Naturalist* 121:729–38.

Turner, T. F. and J. C. Trexler. 1998. Ecological and historical associations of gene flow in darters (Teleostei: Percidae). *Evolution* 52:1781–801.

U.S. Bureau of the Census, International Data Base. http://www.census.gov/pub/ipc/www/idbnew.html.

Ueno, H., Y. Sato, and K. Tsuchida. 1998. Colour-associated mating success in a polymorphic ladybird beetle, *Harmonia axyridis. Functional Ecology* 12:757-61.

Underwood, T. J. and S. G. Sealy. 2006. Influence of shape on egg discrimination in American robins and gray catbirds. *Ethology* 112(2):164–73.

United Nations Population Information Network. http://www.un.org/popin/.

Urton, E. J. M. and K. A. Hobson. 2005. Intrapopulation variation in gray wolf isotope (delta N-15 and delta C-13) profiles: implications for the ecology of individuals. *Oecologia* 145(2):317–26.

USGS. 1995. The cranes: status survey and conservation action plan, whooping crane (*Grus americana*). http://www.npsc.nbs.gov.

Utida, S. 1957. Cyclic fluctuations of population density intrinsic to the host-parasite system. *Ecology* 38:442–49.

Valett, H. M., S. G. Fisher, N. B. Grimm, and P. Camill. 1994. Vertical hydrologic exchange and ecological stability of a desert stream ecosystem. *Ecology* 75:548–60.

van Valen, L. 1973. A new evolutionary law. *Evolutionary Theory* 1:1–30.

Vancouver, G. and J. D. Vancouver. 1798. *A Voyage of Discovery to the North Pacific Ocean.* London: G. G. and J. Robinson.

Vander Zanden, M. J., J. M. Casselman, and J. B. Rasmussen. 1999. Stable isotope evidence for the food web consequences of species invasions in lakes. *Nature* 401(6752):464–67.

Vannote, R. L., G. W. Minshall, K. W. Cummins, J. R. Sedell, and C. E. Cushing. 1980. The river continuum. *Canadian Journal of Fisheries and Aquatic Sciences* 37:130–37.

Verhulst, P. F. and A. Quetelet. 1838. Notice sur la loi que la population suit dans son accroissement. *Correspance in Mathematics and Physics* 10:113–21.

Verreault, J., D. C. G. Muir, R. J. Norstrom, I. Stirling, A. T. Fisk, G. W. Gabrielsen, A. E. Derocher, T. J. Evans, R. Dietz, C. Sonne, G. M. Sandala, W. Gebbink, F. F. Riget, E. W. Born, M. K. Taylor, J. Nagy, and R. J. Letcher. 2005. Chlorinated hydrocarbon contaminants and metabolites in polar bears (*Ursus maritimus*) from Alaska, Canada, East Greenland, and Svalbard: 1996-2002. *Science of the Total Environment* 351:369–90.

Vitousek, P. M. 1994. Beyond global warming: ecology and global change. *Ecology* 75: 1861–76.

Vitousek, P. M., J. R. Gosz, C. C. Grier, J. M. Melillo, and W. A. Reiners. 1982. A comparative analysis of potential nitrification and nitrate mobility in forest ecosystems. *Ecological Monographs* 52:155–77.

Vitousek, P. M., J. R. Gosz, C. C. Grier, J. M. Melillo, W. A. Reiners, and R. L. Todd. 1979. Nitrate losses from disturbed ecosystems. *Science* 204:469–74.

Volterra, V. 1926. Variations and fluctuations of the number of individuals in animal species living together. Reprinted 1931. In R. Chapman. *Animal Ecology.* New York: McGraw-Hill.

Wade, M. J. 1977. Experimental-study of group selection. *Evolution* 31(1):134–53.

Wagner, R. G., K. M. Little, B. Richardson, and K. McNabb. 2006. The role of vegetation management for enhancing productivity of the world's forests. *Forestry* 79:57–79.

Walker, J. C. G. 1986. *Earth History: The Several Ages of the Earth.* Boston: Jones and Bartlett Publishers.

Walker, G. T. 1924. Correlation in seasonal variations of weather. no. 9: a further study of world weather. *Memoirs of the Indian Meteorology Society* 24:275–332.

Wall, D. H., A. H. Fitter, and E. A. Paul. 2005. Developing new perspectives from advances in soil biodiversity research. In R. D. Bardgett, M. B. Usher, and D. W. Hopkins. *Biological diversity and function in soils.* Cambridge: Cambridge University Press.

Walter, H. 1985. *Vegetation of the Earth.* 3d ed. New York: Springer-Verlag.

Wan, C. S. M. and R. F. Sage. 2001. Climate and the distribution of C-4 grasses along the Atlantic and Pacific coasts of North America. *Canadian Journal of Botany-Revue Canadienne De Botanique* 79(4):474–86.

Ward, J. V. 1985. Thermal characteristics of running waters. *Hydrobiologia* 125:31–46.

Watwood, M. E. and C. N. Dahm. 1992. Effects of aquifer environmental factors on biodegradation of organic contaminants. In *Proceedings of the International Topical Meeting on Nuclear and Hazardous Waste Management Spectrum '92.* La Grange Park. III.: American Nuclear Society.

Webster, J. R. 1975. Analysis of potassium and calcium dynamics in stream ecosystems on three southern Appalachian watersheds of contrasting vegetation. Ph.D. thesis, University of Georgia. Athens.

Webster, J. R. and E. F. Benfield. 1986. Vascular plant breakdown in freshwater ecosystems. *Annual Review of Ecology and Systematics* 17:567–94.

Webster, K. E., T. K. Kratz, C. J. Bowser, J. J. Magnuson, W. J. Rose. 1996. The influence of landscape position on lake chemical responses to drought in northern Wisconsin. *Limnology and Oceanography* 41:977–84.

Weiser, C. J. 1970. Cold resistance and injury in woody plants. *Science* 169(3952):1269–1278.

Werner, E. E. and G. G. Mittelbach. 1981. Optimal foraging: field tests of diet choice and habitat switching. *American Zoologist* 21:813–29.

Westoby, M. 1984. The self-thinning rule. *Advances in Ecological Research* 14:167–255.

Westoby, M., M. Leishman, and J. Lord. 1996. Comparative ecology of seed size and dispersal. *Philosophical Transactions of the Royal Society of London Series B* 351:1309–18.

Wetzel, R.G. 1975. *Limnology*. Philadelphia: W. B. Saunders.

Whicker, A. D. and J. K. Detling. 1988. Ecological consequences of prairie dog disturbances. *BioScience* 38:778–85.

White, C. S. and J. T. Markwiese. 1994. Assessment of the potential for *in sutu* bioremediation of cyanide and nitrate contamination at a heap leach mine in central New Mexico. *Journal of Soil Contamination* 3:271–83.

White, J. 1985. The thinning rule and its application to mixtures of plant populations. In J. White. ed. *Studies in Plant Demography*. New York: Academic Press.

White, J. and J. L. Harper. 1970. Correlated changes in plant size and number in plant populations. *Journal of Ecology* 58:467–85.

White, P. S. and S. T. A. Pickett. 1985. Natural disturbance and patch dynamics: an introduction. In S. T. A. Pickell and P. S. White. eds. *The Ecology of Natural Disturbance and Patch Dynamics*. New York: Academic Press.

Whittaker, R. H. 1956. Vegetation of the Great Smoky Mountains. *Ecological Monographs* 26:1–80.

Whittaker, R. H. 1965. Dominance and diversity in land plant communities. *Science* 147:250–60.

Whittaker, R. H. and G. E. Likens. 1973. The primary production of the biosphere. *Human Ecology* 1:299–369.

Whittaker, R. H. and G. E. Likens. 1975. The biosphere and man. In *Primary Productivity of the Biosphere*. New York: Springer-Verlag.

Whittaker, R. H. and W. A. Niering. 1965. Vegetation of the Santa Catalina Mountains. Arizona: a gradient analysis of the south slope. *Ecology* 46:429–52.

Wiebe, H. H., R. W. Brown, T. W. Daniel, and E. Campbell. 1970. Water potential measurement in trees. *BioScience* 20:225–26.

Wiens, J.A., R.L. Schooley, and R.D. Weeks. 1997. Patchy landscapes and animal movements: do beetles percolate? *Oikos* 78:257–64.

Williams, G. C. 1966. *Adaptation and Natural Selection*. Princeton, N.J.: Princeton University Press.

Williams, G. C. and R. M. Nesse. 1991. The dawn of Darwinian medicine. *Quarterly Review of Biology* 66(1):1–22.

Williams, K. S., K. G. Smith, and F. M. Stephen. 1993. Emergence of 13-yr periodical cicadas (Cicadidae, *Magicicada*): phenology, mortality, and predator satiation. *Ecology* 74:1143–52.

Williams, M. 1990. Forests. In B. L. Turner II, W. C. Clark. R. W. Kates. J. F. Richards. J. T. Mathews. and W. B. Meyer. eds. *The Earth as Transformed by Human Action*. Cambridge, England: Cambridge University Press.

Williamson, M. 1981. *Island Populations*. Oxford: Oxford University Press.

Willis, C. K. R., J. E. Lane, E. T. Liknes, D. L. Swanson, and R. M. Brigham. 2005. Thermal energetics of female big brown bats (*Eptesicus fuscus*). *Canadian Journal of Zoology-Revue Canadienne De Zoologie* 83(6):871–79.

Wilmers, C. C. and W. M. Getz. 2005. Gray wolves as climate change buffers in Yellowstone. *Plos Biology* 3:571–76.

Wilmers, C. C., R. L. Crabtree, D. W. Smith, K. M. Murphy, and W. M. Getz. 2003. Trophic facilitation by introduced top predators: grey wolf subsidies to scavengers in Yellowstone National Park. *Journal of Animal Ecology* 72:909–16.

Wilson, D. R. and J. F. Hare. 2004. Ground squirrel uses ultrasonic alarms. *Nature* 430(6999):523.

Wilson, E. O. 1980. Caste and division of labor in leafcutter ants (Hymenoptera: Formicidae: *Atta*), I: The overall pattern in *A. sexdens*. *Behavioral Ecology and Sociobiology* 7:143–56.

Wilson, E. O. and D. S. Simberloff. 1969. Experimental zoogeography of islands: defaunation and monitoring techniques. *Ecology* 50:267–78.

Wilson, R. P. and C. R. McMahon. 2006. Measuring devices on wild animals: what constitutes acceptable practice? *Frontiers in Ecology and the Environment* 4(3):147–54.

Wilson, R. P., W. S. Grant, and D. C. Duffy. 1986. Recording devices on free-ranging marine animals: does measurement affect foraging performance? *Ecology* 67:1091–93.

Winemiller, K. O. 1992. Life history strategies and the effectiveness of sexual selection. *Oikos* 63:318–27.

Winemiller, K. O. 1995. Fish ecology. pp. 49–65 In Vol. 2 *Encyclopedia of Environmental Biology*. New York: Academic Press. Inc.

Winemiller, K. O. and K. A. Rose. 1992. Patterns of life-history diversification in North American fishes: implications for population regulation. *Canadian Journal of Fisheries and Aquatic Sciences* 49:2196–218.

Winston, M. L. 1992. Biology and management of Africanized bees. *Annual Review of Entomology* 37:173–93.

Wisheu, I. C. and P. A. Keddy. 1992. Competition and Centrifugal Organization of Plant-Communities—Theory and Tests. *Journal of Vegetation Science* 3:147–56.

Worm, B., H. K. Lotze, and R. A. Myers. 2003. Predator diversity hotspots in the blue ocean. *Proceedings of the National Academy of Sciences of the United States of America* 100(17):9884–88.

Wu, J. and R. Hobbs. 2007. Landscape ecology: the state of the science. Topic 15, pp. 271–287. In J. Wu and R. Hobbs, eds. *Key Topics in Landscape Ecology*. Cambridge, UK: Cambridge University Press.

Wynne-Edwards, V. C. 1962. *Animal Dispersion in Relation to Social Behavior*. London, Oliver & Boyd.

Yoda, K., T. Kira, H. Ogawa, and K. Hozumi. 1963. Intraspecific competition among higher plants. XI. Self-thinning in overcrowded pure stands under cultivated and natural conditions. *Journal of Biology Osaka City University* 14:107–29.

Credits

from *Plant Biology*, Vol. 1, Sage, R.F. and Monson, R.K., "The Biogeography of C4," pages 316-317, 1999. With permission from Elsevier; 7.26: Adapted from Wan and Sage (2001), *Canadian Journal of Botany*, Figure 3b, p. 79:474-486.

Chapter 8: Figure 8.1: © Gregory G. Dimijian/Photo Researchers; 8.2: Courtesy of David Hik (ground squirrel), Gustaf Samelius (arctic fox and caribou), and Krista Bush; 8.4a-b: Figure 1 from Underwood 2006, *Ethology* 112-164-173, Blackwell Publishing; 8.5: Table from Underwood 2006, *Ethology* 112-164-173, Blackwell Publishing; 8.6: © Mitsuaki Iwago/Minden Pictures; 8.7a-c: Elsabe Kloppers; 8.8: Figures 2 and 5 from Kloppers et al. (2005), *Ecology and Society* 10:31; 8.11: © Mark W. Moffett/Minden Pictures; 8.12: © Raymond A. Mendez/ Animals, Animals; 8.16: © Dr. Paul A. Zahl/ Photo Researchers; 8.22: Chris MacQuarrie; 8.23: © Richard Parker/Photo Researchers.

Chapter 9: Figure 9.1: © Donald Specker/ Animals, Animals; 9.7: Courtesy, Mark McCorry, University College Dublin; 9.9: © David M. Schleser/Photo Researchers; 9.13: © Frans Lanting/Minden Pictures; 9.21: © Breck P. Kent/Animals, Animals; 9.26: gorilla photo copyright Bruce J. Hayward, courtesy of University of Alaska Museum; peregrine falcon photo by Dr. Gordon Court; snow leopard photo by Pasi Laaksonen; caribou photo by John A. Nagy; shark photo by Kaus Jost (www.jostimages.com); labelled photo by Heather Proctor, Rainer Ehnsberger, and Jacek Dabert; 9.27: David Innes; 9.29a: © David Schleser/Photo Researchers; 9.29b: Corbis Digital Stock; 9.35: Adapted by permission from Macmillan Publishers Ltd., *Nature*, Root et al., "Fingerprints of global warming on wild animals and plants." (2003); 9.36: American Ornithologists' Union and the Auk. Data from Murphy-Klassen et al., Figure 4, *Auk*, 122:1130-1148 (2005); 9.37: Colleen Cassady St. Clair; 9.38a-b: Adapted from Gjerdrum et al. (2003), *PNAS*, 100:9377-9382. Copyright 2003 National Academy of Sciences, U.S.A.; 9.39: Figure 1b from Reale et al. 2003. "Genetic and plastic responses of a northern mammal to climate change." *Proceedings of the Royal Society*, 270: 591-596.

Chapter 10: Figure 10.1a: Mark K. Peck; 10.1b: Gustaf Samelius; 10.11: J.A. Trofymow, Canadian Forest Service; 10.12: From Getzin et al., "Spatial patterns and competition of tree species in a douglas-fir chronosequence on Vancouver Island," *Ecography* (2006), Blackwell Publishing Ltd.; 10.14a: Photo by Gordon Court; 10.14b: Andrew Fyson; 10.14c: Ed Snucins; 10.14d: Joyce Gould; 10.15a-b: © Birdsource, a joint project of the National Audubon Society and the Cornell Laboratory of Ornithology; 10.20: © Natalie Fobes; 10.26: Pasi Laaksonen; 10.27: © Michio Hoshino/ Minden Pictures; 10.28a-b: © Tom Fernald, College of the Atlantic, Bar Harbor, Maine.

Chapter 11: Figure 11.1: © Leonard Lee Rue III/ Photo Researchers; 11.11a-b: Douglas Dix; 11.19: David Beaune; 11.23a-b: Courtesy, Daniel W. Schneider and John Lyons; 11.24: Ian Stirling.

Chapter 12: Figure 12.1a: © M.I. Walker/ Science Source/Photo Researchers; 12.1b: © James Bell/Science Source/Photo Researchers; 12.6: Brian Johns; 12.18a-b: © Peter R. Grant, Princeton University; 12.22: From Figure 2b of Mullon et al. 2005. *Fish and Fisheries*, 6:11-120, Blackwell Publishing; 12.24: © Peter R. Grant, Princeton University.

Chapter 13: Figure 13.1: © Jodi Jacobson/ Peter Arnold; 13.2: © George Haling/Photo Researchers; 13.12: Reprinted from *Animal Behaviour*, 35, Arcese, P., "Age, intrusion pressure, and defence," p. 776, copyright 1987. With permission from Elsevier; 13.14: Figure 2b, Reader et al. (1994) *Ecology*, 75: 1753-1760. Reproduced with permission from The Ecological Society of America; 13.15: © Heather Angel; 13.19: © Dr. James H. Brown; 13.20a-b: © Dr. James H. Brown; 13.23: Photo by Brett Purdy; 13.24: Figure 3 reprinted from Schluter & McPhail (1992), "Ecological Character Displacement and Speciation..." *American Naturalist*, 140. Reprinted with permission of University of Chicago Press; 13.25: Reprinted with permission from Schluter and Dolph, *Science*, 266:798-801 (Fig. 1), copyright 1994 AAAS; 13.26: Reprinted by permission from Macmillan Publishers Ltd: *Nature*, Gaudet, Connie L. and Paul A. Keddy, "A comparative approach to predicting competitive ability from plant traits," copyright 1988.

Chapter 14: Figure 14.1: © Mark Newman/Photo Researchers; 14.2a-b: David Hik; 14.3: Cargill and Jeffries. (1984). "The effects of grazing by lesser snow geese on the vegetation of a sub-arctic salt marsh." *Journal of Applied Ecology*, 21:669-686. Figure 2b and 3b reprinted with permission of Blackwell Publishing; 14.4: Bob Jefferies; 14.8a-b: Courtesy, Dr. Gary A. Lamberti; 14.9: Reproduced with permission from the Ecological Society of America; 14.10a-b: Urs Schaffner; 14.22: © Gregory G. Dimijian/Photo Researchers; 14.26a: © Runk/Schoenberger/Grant Heilman Photography; 14.26b: © John Colwell/Grant Heilman Photography; 14.27: © Mitsuaki Iwago/Minden Pictures; 14.28: Photo by T. Yoshida and R.O. Wayne; 14.29: Meyer et al. (2006). "Prey evolution on the time scale of predator-prey dynamics revealed by allele-specific quantitative PCR." *Proceedings of the National Academy of Sciences*, 103: 10690-10695. Page 10692, Figure 3. Copyright 2006, National Academy of Sciences, U. S.A.; 14.30a-c: Courtesy of Graham Cox, Stephen Heard, and Chris Kolaczan.

Chapter 15: Figure 15.1: © Anthony Mercieca/Photo Researchers; 15.3a-d: Bill Samuel; 15.4: Bill Samuel; 15.6: © Robert & Linda Mitchell; 15.11: Reprinted by permission from Macmillan Publishers Ltd: Nature, Anderson and May (1979), "Population biology of infectious diseases: Part I." Copyright 1979; 15.12: Gumel et al. (2004). "Modelling strategies for controlling SARS outbreaks," *Proceedings of the Royal Society of London*. B. 271: 2223-2232. Figure 1 (appearing on page 2224) and Figure 5 (appearing on page 2230) reprinted with permission; 15.13: Gumel et al. (2004). "Modelling strategies for controlling SARS outbreaks," *Proceedings of the Royal Society of London*. B. 271: 2223-2232. Figure 1 (appearing on page 2224) and Figure 5 (appearing on page 2230) reprinted with permission; 15.14: Reprinted from *The Lancet*, Vol. 335, Anderson and May, "Immunization and Herd Immunity," 641-645, copyright 1990, with permission from Elsevier; 15.15: Sandra Gillsepie; 15.17a-b: John Addicott; 15.18a: © Dr. Nancy Collins Johnson; 15.18b: Courtesy, Randy Molina/U. S. Forest Service; 15.23: Barbara Zimonick; 15.24: Reprinted by permission from Macmillan Publishers Ltd: Nature, Simard et al. (1997). "Net transfer of carbon between ectomycorrhizal tree species in the field." 388: 579-582. Copyright 1997; 15.25: Figure 6 from Klironomos (2003), *Ecology* 84:2292-2301. Reprinted with permission; 15.26: © Nigel Dennis/Photo Researchers.

Chapter 16: Figure 16.1: © Charlie Ott/ Photo Researchers; 16.2: © Carr Clifton/ Minden Pictures (appears with caption); 16.15: Martin Duval; 16.16: Bell et al. (2000). "Environmental heterogeneity and species diversity of forest sedges." *Journal of Ecology*. Reprinted with permission of Blackwell Publishing; 16.17: Bell et al. (2000). "Environmental heterogeneity and species diversity of forest sedges," *Journal of Ecology*. Reprinted with permission of Blackwell Publishing; 16.24: Bolduc et al. (2005). "Ground-dwelling spider fauna (Araneae) of two vineyards in south Quebec." *Environmental Entomology*. 34:635-645. Reprinted with permission.

Chapter 17: Figure 17.1: © Francois Gohier/Photo Researchers; 17.4: Figures 1, 4, 9, 12, and 14 from Bird (1930), Ecology 11:356-442. Reprinted with permission; 17.5: Figures 1, 4, 9, 12, and 14 from Bird (1930), *Ecology* 11:356-442. Reprinted with permission; 17.7a-b: Paul Keddy; 17.8: Wisheu and Keddy. (1992). *Journal of Vegetation Science*. 3:147-156. Figures 1 and 4 reprinted with permission.; 17.9: Wisheu and Keddy. (1992). *Journal of Vegetation Science*. 3:147-156. Figures 1 and 4 reprinted with permission. Original source for 17.9, as adapted by Wisheu and Keddy: Reprinted from *Biological Conservation*, 47, Moore et al., "Conservation of Wetlands....," 203-217, copyright 1989, with permission from Elsevier; 17.11a-b: Courtesy, Mary E. Power, UC Berkeley; 17.15: PhotoLink/Getty Images; 17.16: Reprinted from *Forest Ecology and Management*, 118, Donkor and Fryxell, "Impact of beaver foraging...," 83-92, copyright 1999. With permission from Elsevier; 17.18: NPS photo; 17.22: © Mark Moffett/Minden Pictures.

Chapter 18: Figure 18.1: © Carr Clifton/ Minden Pictures; 18.4a-d: Danielle Charron; 18.5: From Bergeron et al. (2000). *Ecology*. 81:1500-1516, Figures 1 and 2. Reprinted with permission; 18.6: © Jim Zipp/Photo Researchers 18.21a-b: Reprinted from Egler. (1954). "Vegetation science concepts I." *Plant Ecology*. 4:412-417. With kind permission from Springer Science and Business Media; 18.26: From Krawchuk et al. (2006). *Ecology*. 87:458-468, Figure 1. Reprinted with permission; 18.32: Dave Smith, Parks Canada; 18.33a: © D.T. MacDougal; 18.33b-c: © J.R. Hastings; 18.33d: © R.M. Turner; 18.34a: © J.R. Hastings; 18.34b-c: © R.M. Turner.

Chapter 19: Figure 19.1: Jason Sanders; 19.2: Liu et al. (2002). "Net primary productivity mapped for Canada at 1-km resolution." *Global Ecology and Biogeography*. Reprinted with permission of Blackwell Publishing; 19.6: Table 7 from Turkington et al. (1998). *Journal of Vegetation Science*. 9:333-346. Reprinted with permission; 19.17a-b: G. David Tilman; 19.18: From Balvanera et al. (2006). "Quantifying the evidence for biodiversity effects on ecosystem functioning and services." *Ecology Letters*. Reprinted with permission of Blackwell Publishing; 19.19a: Dan Klinka; 19.19b: Katie Christie; 19.23: From Roth. (2002). "Temporal variability in arctic fox diet as reflected in stable-carbon isotopes: The importance of sea ice." *Oecologia*. 133:70-77. With kind permission from Springer Science and Business Media.

Chapter 20: Figure 20.11: Greg Henry; 20.12: From Aerts. (2006). "The freezer defrosting: Global warming and litter decomposition rates in cold biomes." *Journal of Ecology*. Reprinted by permission of Blackwell Publishers; 20.20: Scott Wilson; 20.21: Figures 3 and 5 from Christian and Wilson. (1999). *Ecology*. 80:2397-2407. Reprinted with permission.

Chapter 21: Figure 21.1: © Owen Franken/ Corbis; 21.2: © Keren Su/Corbis Images; 21.7: Wiens, J.A. and Moss, M.R. "Issues and perspectives in landscape ecology." Figures 1.1 and 1.2 from Fahrig (2005), "When is a landscape perspective important?" Chapter 1, page 4. Reprinted with the permission of Cambridge University Press; 21.10: Schmiegelow et al. (1997). *Ecology*. 78:1914-1932. Reprinted with permission; 21.11: Figures 1, 2, and 3 from Schmiegelow et al. (1997). Ecology. 78:1914-1932. Reprinted with permission; 21.13: Johnson and Taylor. (2000). "Fine-scale movement behaviors of calopterygid damselflies are influenced by landscape structure: An experimental manipulation." *Oikos*. Reprinted by permission of Blackwell Publishing; 21.15: Nicole McCutchen; 21.16: Tony Clevenger; 21.17: Pielou. (1991). After the Ice Age. Chicago, IL: University of Chicago Press. Figure 1: "The present extent of perennial ice in northern North America." Reprinted with permission; 21.18a: Alasdair Veitch; 21.18b: Reproduced with the permission of the Minister of Public Works and Government Services Canada, 2007, and courtesy of Natural Resources Canada, Geological Survey of Canada. Photographer: Lynda Dredge; 21.18c: Reproduced with the permission of the Minister of Public Works and Government Services Canada, 2007, and courtesy of Natural Resources Canada, Geological Survey of Canada. Photographer: Jean Veillette; 21.18d: Reproduced with the permission of the Minister of Public Works and Government Services Canada, 2007, and courtesy of Natural Resources Canada, Geological Survey of Canada. Photographer: Lynda Dredge; 21.19: Robin Karpan; 21.22 © Steve Starr/ Stock Boston; 21.24: Figure 8 from Fahrig. (2003). "Annual review of Ecology, Evolution and Systematics." 34:487-515. Reprinted with permission from *The Annual Review of Ecology, Evolution, and Systematics*, Volume 34. © 2003 by Annual Reviews: www.annualreviews.org; 21.25: Guenette and Villard. (2005). "Thresholds in Forest Bird Response to Habitat Alteration as Quantitative Targets for Conservation." *Conservation Biology*. Reprinted with permission of Blackwell Publishing; 21.26: Guenette and Villard. (2005). "Thresholds in Forest Bird Response to Habitat Alteration as Quantitative Targets for Conservation." *Conservation Biology*. Reprinted with permission of Blackwell Publishing; 21.27a: Figure 3 from Apps et al. (2002). *Canadian Journal of Zoology*. 80:1228-1239. Reprinted with permission; 21.27b: Figure 1b from Chetkiewicz et al. (2006). "Annual Review of Ecology, Evolution, and Systematics." 37:317-342. Reprinted with permission from *The Annual Review of Ecology, Evolution, and Systematics*. Volume 37. © 2006 by Annual Reviews: www.annualreviews.org.

Chapter 22: Figure 22.1: © Norman Owen Tomalin/Bruce Coleman; 22.2a-b: Kalmar and Currie. (2006). "A global model of island biogeography." *Global Ecology & Biogeography*. Reprinted with permission of Blackwell Publishing; 22.7a-b: Dave Ward; 22.12: © H.W. Kitchen/Photo Researchers; 22.24: Robert Semple; 22.25: Reprinted by permission from Macmillan Publishers, Ltd: Nature, Karlson et al. "Coral communities are regionally enriched along an oceanic biodiversity gradient," copyright 2004; 22.26: Reprinted by permission from Macmillan Publishers, Ltd: *Nature*, Karlson et al. "Coral communities are regionally enriched along an oceanic biodiversity gradient," copyright 2004; 22.28: Reprinted by permission from Macmillan Publishers, Ltd: Nature 403: 853-858, Myers et al. (2000). "Biodiversity hotspots for conservation priorities," copyright 2000; 22.29: Reprinted by permission from Macmillan Publishers, Ltd: *Nature* 403:853-858, Myers et al. (2000). "Biodiversity hotspots for conservation priorities," copyright 2000; 22.32a-b: MODIS chlorophyll-a concentration maps for January and July 2006, from Fisheries and Oceans Canada. Reproduced with permission of Her Majesty the Queen in Right of Canada, 2007; 22.33: Land Cover of Canada, 2005, Natural Resources Canada, 2006. Reproduced with the permission of the Minister of Public Works and Government Services Canada, courtesy of Natural Resources Canada, 2007.

Chapter 23: Figure 23.1: © NASA; 23.3a-b: Fig. 2 from Soulé, *Science* 253:744-750 (1991). Reprinted with permission from AAAS; 23.8 (both): Gene Feldman et al. Nov 30, 1984. "Satellite color observations of the phytoplankton distribution in the eastern equatorial Pacific during the 1982-1983 El Nino." *Science*, 226:1069-1071. Fig. 2A. © 1984 American Association for the Advancement of Science; 23.10: Ottersen et al. (2001). "Ecological effects of the North Atlantic Oscillation." *Oecologia*. 128:1-14. With kind permission from Springer Science and Business Media; 23.13: Kochy and Wilson. (2001). "Nitrogen deposition and forest expansion in the northern Great Plains." *Journal of Ecology*. Reprinted with permission of Blackwell Publishing; 23.14: Kochy and Wilson. (2001). "Nitrogen deposition and forest expansion in the northern Great Plains." *Journal of Ecology*. Reprinted with permission of Blackwell Publishing.; 23.15: Figures 1 and 2 from Foley et al., Science 309:570-574 (2005). Reprinted with permission from AAAS; 23.16: Figures 1 and 2 from Foley et al., *Science* 309:570-574 (2005). Reprinted with permission from AAAS; 23.18a-c: USGS/ EROS; 23.20: © Richard O. Bierregaard, Jr./ University of North Carolina, Biology Department; 23.21: From Skole, D. and Tucker, C. June 25, 1993. "Tropical deforestation and habitat fragmentation on the Amazon." *Science* 260:1908. © 1993 American Association for the Advancement of Science. Map courtesy Walter Chomentowski; 23.22: Anina Hundsdörfer; 23.23a: Randy Westbrooks, U.S. Geological Survey, Bugwood.org; 23.23b: U.S. Fish and Wildlife Service Archive, U.S. Fish and Wildlife Service, Bugwood.org; 23.23c: R. Scott Cameron, International Paper, Bugwood.org; 23.23d: Randy Westbrooks, U.S. Geological Survey, Bugwood.org; 23.28: © NASA, Goddard Space Flight Center; 23.29a, c, d: Courtesy of the U.S. Long-Term Ecological Research Network; 23.29b: Courtesy, John J. Magnuson.